MATERIALS PROPERTIES LOCATOR

Table No.	Page	Material Type	Data Listed
2.2	37	Whiskers, fibers, wires	E, σ_u
3.1	49	Metals, alloys	T_m, ρ, E
3.9	70	Polymers	T_g, T_m
3.10	77	Ceramics, glasses	$T_m, \rho, E, \sigma_u, \sigma_{uc}$
3.13	88	Representative	E, σ_o or σ_u, ρ, cost
4.2	120	Metals	$E, \sigma_o, \sigma_u, 100\varepsilon_f, \%RA$
4.3	121	Polymers	$E, \sigma_o, \sigma_f, 100\varepsilon_f$, Izod energy, T_d
4.4	122	SiC in Al composite	$E, \sigma_o, \sigma_u, 100\varepsilon_f$
4.6	134	Metals	$\tilde{\sigma}_{fB}, \tilde{\varepsilon}_f, H, n, HB$
4.7	143	Ceramics, glasses	E, σ_{fb}, HV
5.2	184	Metals, polymers, ceramics	E, ν
5.3	200	Fibers, epoxy, composites	E, G, ν, ρ
7.1	287	Rock, concrete, gray iron	σ_u, σ_{uc}, C-M fitting constants
8.1	322	Metals	K_{Ic}; also $\sigma_o, \sigma_u, 100\varepsilon_f, \%RA$
8.2	323	Polymers, ceramics	K_{Ic}
9.1	406	Metals	σ_a-N_f constants; also $\sigma_o, \sigma_u, \tilde{\sigma}_{fB}$
10.1	487	Metals	Fatigue limit estimates
10.2	504	Metals	S-N curve estimates at 10^3 cycles
11.1	549	Steels by class	da/dN-ΔK constants
11.2	560	Steels, aluminums	da/dN-ΔK constants (Walker); also K_{Ic}, σ_o
11.3	564	Metals	da/dN-ΔK constants (Forman); also K_{Ic}, σ_o
12.1	647	Steels, aluminums	E, H', n'; also σ_o, σ_u
14.1	733	Metals	ε_a-N_f constants; E, H', n'; $\sigma_o, \sigma_u, \tilde{\sigma}_{fB}, \%RA$
15.2	806	Metals	Q for S-D parameter
15.3	809	Metals	L-M parameter constants
15.4	823	Metals	σ-ε-t nonlinear creep constants
B.5	888	Metals, rock, concrete	K_{Ic} and statistics; also σ_o or σ_{uc}

Explanation of Symbols for Materials Properties

E	Elastic modulus	T_g	Glass transition temperature
G	Shear modulus	T_m	Melting temperature
H, n	Monotonic σ-ε constants (Ramberg–Osgood)	$100\varepsilon_f$	Percent elongation
		$\tilde{\varepsilon}_f$	True fracture strain
H', n'	Cyclic σ-ε constants (Ramberg–Osgood)	ν	Poisson's ratio
		ρ	Density
HB	Brinell hardness	σ_f	Engineering fracture strength
HV	Vickers hardness	$\tilde{\sigma}_{fB}$	True fracture strength
K_{Ic}	Plane strain fracture toughness	σ_{fb}	Bend strength
Q	Activation energy	σ_o	Yield strength
$\%RA$	Percent reduction in area	σ_u	Ultimate tensile strength
T_d	Heat deflection temperature	σ_{uc}	Ultimate compressive strength

UNITS AND CONVERSION FACTORS

Quantity	SI Unit	U.S. Unit	SI Equivalent to U.S. Unit
Length	meter (m)	inch (in)	0.0254 m
	millimeter (mm)	inch (in)	25.4 mm
Force	newton (N)	pound (lb)	4.448 N
	kilonewton (kN)	kilopound (kip)	4.448 kN
Moment or Torque	N·m	lb·in	0.1130 N·m
Energy	joule (J) $=$ N·m	in·lb	0.1130 J
		ft·lb	1.356 J
		calorie (cal)	4.184 J
Energy per Unit Volume	J/m^3	$in·lb/in^3$	$6895 \ J/m^3$
Stress or Pressure	pascal (Pa) $= N/m^2$	psi $= lb/in^2$	6895 Pa
	$MPa = MN/m^2 = N/mm^2$	ksi $= kip/in^2$	6.895 MPa
Stress Intensity K of Fracture Mechanics	$MPa\sqrt{m}$	$ksi\sqrt{in}$	$1.099 \ MPa\sqrt{m}$

Notes:

(1) Under standard gravity on earth, a 1 kilogram (kg) mass has a weight force of 9.807 N, or 2.205 lb. Also, for stress, $(\sigma, \ kg/mm^2) \times 9.807 = (\sigma, \ MPa)$.

(2) Time is given in units of seconds (s), minutes (min), or hours (h).

(3) Temperature is given in degrees Celsius (°C), on the absolute scale of kelvins (K), or in degrees Fahrenheit (°F). Conversions are

$$T(K) = T(°C) + 273.15, \qquad T(°C) = \frac{T(°F) - 32}{1.8}$$

(4) Prefixes indicating changes in the order of magnitude of the basic units, such as 10^3 N $=$ kN, are as follows:

Prefix	giga	mega	kilo	centi	milli	micro	nano
Symbol	G	M	k	c	m	μ	n
Factor	10^9	10^6	10^3	10^{-2}	10^{-3}	10^{-6}	10^{-9}

Mechanical Behavior of Materials

Mechanical Behavior of Materials

Engineering Methods for Deformation, Fracture, and Fatigue

Fourth Edition

Norman E. Dowling

Frank Maher Professor of Engineering
Engineering Science and Mechanics Department, and
Materials Science and Engineering Department
Virginia Polytechnic Institute and State University
Blacksburg, Virginia

International Edition contributions by

Katakam Siva Prasad

Assistant Professor
Department of Metallurgical and Materials Engineering
National Institute of Technology
Tiruchirappalli

R. Narayanasamy

Professor
Department of Production Engineering
National Institute of Technology
Tiruchirappalli

PEARSON

Boston Columbus Indianapolis New York San Francisco Upper Saddle River
Amsterdam Cape Town Dubai London Madrid Milan Munich Paris
Montréal Toronto Delhi Mexico City São Paulo Sydney Hong Kong Seoul
Singapore Taipei Tokyo

VP/Editorial Director, Engineering/Computer Science: Marcia J. Horton
Executive Editor: Holly Stark
Senior Marketing Manager: Tim Galligan
Marketing Assistant: Jon Bryant
Senior Managing Editor: Scott Disanno
Project Manager: Greg Dulles
Publisher, International Edition: Angshuman Chakraborty
Acquisitions Editor, International Edition: Somnath Basu
Publishing Assistant, International Edition: Shokhi Shah
Print and Media Editor, International Edition: Ashwitha Jayakumar
Project Editor, International Edition: Jayashree Arunachalam
Operations Specialist: Lisa McDowell
Senior Art Director: Jayne Conte
Media Editor: Daniel Sandin
Full-Service Project Management: Integra Software Services Pvt. Ltd.
Cover Printer: Lehigh-Phoenix Color/Hagerstown

Pearson Education Limited
Edinburgh Gate
Harlow
Essex CM20 2JE
England

and Associated Companies throughout the world

Visit us on the World Wide Web at:
www.pearsoninternationaleditions.com

ISBN 10: 0-273-76455-1
ISBN 13: 978-0-273-76455-7

British Library Cataloguing-in-Publication Data
A catalogue record for this book is available from the British Library

10 9 8 7 6 5 4 3 2 1
14 13 12

Typeset in Times-Roman by Integra Software Services Pvt. Ltd.
Printed and bound by Courier/Westford in The United States of America

The publisher's policy is to use paper manufactured from sustainable forests.

Contents

13 Stress–Strain Analysis of Plastically Deforming Members   693

14 Strain-Based Approach to Fatigue   745

15 Time-Dependent Behavior: Creep and Damping   802

Appendix A   Review of Selected Topics from Mechanics of Materials   880

Preface

Designing machines, vehicles, and structures that are safe, reliable, and economical requires both efficient use of materials and assurance that structural failure will not occur. It is therefore appropriate for undergraduate engineering majors to study the mechanical behavior of materials, specifically such topics as deformation, fracture, and fatigue.

This book may be used as a text for courses on mechanical behavior of materials at the junior or senior undergraduate level, and it may also be employed at the first-year graduate level by emphasizing the later chapters. The coverage includes traditional topics in the area, such as materials testing, yielding and plasticity, stress-based fatigue analysis, and creep. The relatively new methods of fracture mechanics and strain-based fatigue analysis are also considered and are, in fact, treated in some detail. For a practicing engineer with a bachelor's degree, this book provides an understandable reference source on the topics covered.

Emphasis is placed on analytical and predictive methods that are useful to the engineering designer in avoiding structural failure. These methods are developed from an engineering mechanics viewpoint, and the resistance of materials to failure is quantified by properties such as yield strength, fracture toughness, and stress–life curves for fatigue or creep. The intelligent use of materials property data requires some understanding of how the data are obtained, so their limitations and significance are clear. Thus, the materials tests used in various areas are generally discussed prior to considering the analytical and predictive methods.

In many of the areas covered, the existing technology is more highly developed for metals than for nonmetals. Nevertheless, data and examples for nonmetals, such as polymers and ceramics, are included where appropriate. Highly anisotropic materials, such as continuous fiber composites, are also considered, but only to a limited extent. Detailed treatment of these complex materials is not attempted here.

The remainder of the Preface first highlights the changes made for this new edition. Then comments follow that are intended to aid users of this book, including students, instructors, and practicing engineers.

WHAT IS NEW IN THIS EDITION?

Relative to the third edition, this fourth edition features improvements and updates throughout. Areas that received particular attention in the revisions include the following:

- The end-of-chapter problems and questions are extensively revised, with 35% being new or significantly changed, and with the overall number increased by 54 to be 659. In each chapter, at least 33% of the problems and questions are new or changed, and these revisions emphasize the more basic topics where instructors are most likely to concentrate.
- New to this edition, answers are given near the end of the book for approximately half of the Problems and Questions where a numerical value or the development of a new equation is requested.
- The end-of-chapter reference lists are reworked and updated to include recent publications, including databases of materials properties.
- Treatment of the methodology for estimating S-N curves in Chapter 10 is revised, and also updated to reflect changes in widely used mechanical design textbooks.
- In Chapter 12, the example problem on fitting stress–strain curves is improved.
- Also in Chapter 12, the discussion of multiaxial stress is refined, and a new example is added.
- The topic of mean stress effects for strain-life curves in Chapter 14 is given revised and updated coverage.
- The section on creep rupture under multiaxial stress is moved to an earlier point in Chapter 15, where it can be covered along with time-temperature parameters.

PREREQUISITES

Elementary mechanics of materials, also called strength of materials or mechanics of deformable bodies, provides an introduction to the subject of analyzing stresses and strains in engineering components, such as beams and shafts, for linear-elastic behavior. Completion of a standard (typically sophomore) course of this type is an essential prerequisite to the treatment provided here. Some useful review and reference material in this area is given in Appendix A, along with a treatment of fully plastic yielding analysis.

Many engineering curricula include an introductory (again, typically sophomore) course in materials science, including such subjects as crystalline and noncrystalline structure, dislocations and other imperfections, deformation mechanisms, processing of materials, and naming systems for materials. Prior exposure to this area of study is also recommended. However, as such a prerequisite may be missing, limited introductory coverage is given in Chapters 2 and 3.

Mathematics through elementary calculus is also needed. A number of the worked examples and student problems involve basic numerical analysis, such as least-squares curve fitting, iterative solution of equations, and numerical integration. Hence, some background in these areas is useful, as is an ability to perform plotting and numerical analysis on a personal computer. The numerical analysis needed is described in most introductory textbooks on the subject, such as Chapra (2010), which is listed at the end of this Preface.

REFERENCES AND BIBLIOGRAPHY

Each chapter contains a list of *References* near the end that identifies sources of additional reading and information. These lists are in some cases divided into categories such as general references, sources of materials properties, and useful handbooks. Where a reference is mentioned in the text, the first author's name and the year of publication are given, allowing the reference to be quickly found in the list at the end of that chapter.

Where specific data or illustrations from other publications are used, these sources are identified by information in brackets, such as [Richards 61] or [ASM 88], where the two-digit numbers indicate the year of publication. All such *Bibliography* items are listed in a single section near the end of the book.

PRESENTATION OF MATERIALS PROPERTIES

Experimental data for specific materials are presented throughout the book in numerous illustrations, tables, examples, and problems. These are always real laboratory data. However, the intent is only to present typical data, not to give comprehensive information on materials properties. For actual engineering work, additional sources of materials properties, such as those listed at the ends of various chapters, should be consulted as needed. Also, materials property values are subject to statistical variation, as discussed in Appendix B, so typical values from this book, or from any other source, need to be used with appropriate caution.

Where materials data are presented, any external source is identified as a bibliography item. If no source is given, then such data are either from the author's research or from test results obtained in laboratory courses at Virginia Tech.

UNITS

The International System of Units (SI) is emphasized, but U.S. Customary Units are also included in most tables of data. On graphs, the scales are either SI or dual, except for a few cases of other units where an illustration from another publication is used in its original form. Only SI units are given in most exercises and where values are given in the text, as the use of dual units in these situations invites confusion.

The SI unit of force is the newton (N), and the U.S. unit is the pound (lb). It is often convenient to employ thousands of newtons (kilonewtons, kN) or thousands of pounds (kilopounds, kip). Stresses and pressures in SI units are thus presented in newtons per square meter, N/m^2, which in the SI system is given the special name of pascal (Pa). Millions of pascals (megapascals, MPa) are generally appropriate for our use. We have

$$1 \, MPa = 1 \, \frac{MN}{m^2} = 1 \, \frac{N}{mm^2}$$

where the latter equivalent form that uses millimeters (mm) is sometimes convenient. In U.S. units, stresses are generally given in kilopounds per square inch (ksi).

These units and others frequently used are listed, along with conversion factors, inside the front cover. As an illustrative use of this listing, let us convert a stress of 20 ksi to MPa. Since 1 ksi is equivalent to 6.895 MPa, we have

$$20.0 \, ksi = 20.0 \, ksi \left(6.895 \, \frac{MPa}{ksi} \right) = 137.9 \, MPa$$

Conversion in the opposite direction involves dividing by the equivalence value.

$$137.9\,\text{MPa} = \frac{137.9\,\text{MPa}}{\left(6.895\,\dfrac{\text{MPa}}{\text{ksi}}\right)} = 20.0\,\text{ksi}$$

It is also useful to note that strains are dimensionless quantities, so no units are necessary. Strains are most commonly given as straightforward ratios of length change to length, but percentages are sometimes used, $\varepsilon_\% = 100\varepsilon$.

MATHEMATICAL CONVENTIONS

Standard practice is followed in most cases. The function *log* is understood to indicate logarithms to the base 10, and the function *ln* to indicate logarithms to the base $e = 2.718\ldots$ (that is, natural logarithms). To indicate selection of the largest of several values, the function MAX( ) is employed.

NOMENCLATURE

In journal articles and in other books, and in various test standards and design codes, a wide variety of different symbols are used for certain variables that are needed. This situation is handled by using a consistent set of symbols throughout, while following the most common conventions wherever possible. However, a few exceptions or modifications to common practice are necessary to avoid confusion.

For example, K is used for the stress intensity of fracture mechanics, but not for stress concentration factor, which is designated k. Also, H is used instead of K or k for the strength coefficient describing certain stress–strain curves. The symbol S is used for nominal or average stress, whereas σ is the stress at a point and also the stress in a uniformly stressed member. Dual use of symbols is avoided except where the different usages occur in separate portions of the book. A list of the more commonly used symbols is given inside the back cover. More detailed lists are given near the end of each chapter in a section on *New Terms and Symbols*.

USE AS A TEXT

The various chapters are constituted so that considerable latitude is possible in choosing topics for study. A semester-length course could include at least portions of all chapters through 11, and also portions of Chapter 15. This covers the introductory and review topics in Chapters 1 to 6, followed by yield and fracture criteria for uncracked material in Chapter 7. Fracture mechanics is applied to static fracture in Chapter 8, and to fatigue crack growth in Chapter 11. Also, Chapters 9 and 10 cover the stress-based approach to fatigue, and Chapter 15 covers creep. If time permits, some topics on plastic deformation could be added from Chapters 12 and 13, and also from Chapter 14 on the strain-based approach to fatigue. If the students' background in materials science is such that Chapters 2 and 3 are not needed, then Section 3.8 on materials selection may still be useful.

Particular portions of certain chapters are not strongly required as preparation for the remainder of that chapter, nor are they crucial for later chapters. Thus, although the topics involved are important in their own right, they may be omitted or delayed, if desired, without serious loss of continuity. These include Sections 4.5, 4.6 to 4.9, 5.4, 7.7 to 7.9, 8.7 to 8.9, 10.7, 11.7, 11.9, and 13.3.

After completion of Chapter 8 on fracture mechanics, one option is to proceed directly to Chapter 11, which extends the topic to fatigue crack growth. This can be done by passing over all of Chapters 9 and 10 except Sections 9.1 to 9.3. Also, various options exist for limited, but still coherent, coverage of the relatively advanced topics in Chapters 12 through 15. For example, it might be useful to include some material from Chapter 14 on strain-based fatigue, in which case some portions of Chapters 12 and 13 may be needed as prerequisite material. In Chapter 15, Sections 15.1 to 15.4 provide a reasonable introduction to the topic of creep that does not depend heavily on any other material beyond Chapter 4.

SUPPLEMENTS FOR INSTRUCTORS

For classroom instructors, as at academic institutions, four supplements are available: (1) a set of printable, downloadable files of the illustrations, (2) digital files of Microsoft Excel solutions for all but the simplest example problems worked in the text, (3) a manual containing solutions to approximately half of the end-of-chapter problems for which calculation or a difficult derivation is required, and (4) answers to all problems and questions that involve numerical calculation or developing a new equation. These items are posted on a secure website available only to documented instructors.

Instructor resources for the International Edition are available at www.pearsoninternationaleditions.com/dowling.

REFERENCES

ASTM. 2010. "American National Standard for Use of the International System of Units (SI): The Modern Metric System," *Annual Book of ASTM Standards,* Vol. 14.04, No. SI10, ASTM International, West Conshohocken, PA.

CHAPRA, S. C. and R. P. CANALE. 2010. *Numerical Methods for Engineers*, 6th ed., McGraw-Hill, New York.

Acknowledgments

I am indebted to numerous colleagues who have aided me with this book in a variety of ways. Those whose contributions are specific to the revisions for this edition include: Masahiro Endo (Fukuoka University, Japan), Maureen Julian (Virginia Tech), Milo Kral (University of Canterbury, New Zealand), Kevin Kwiatkowski (Pratt & Miller Engineering), John Landes (University of Tennessee), Yung-Li Lee (Chrysler Group LLC), Marshal McCord III (Virginia Tech), George Vander Voort (Vander Voort Consulting), and William Wright (Virginia Tech). As listed in the acknowledgments for previous editions, many others have also provided valuable aid. I thank these individuals again and note that their contributions continue to enhance the present edition.

The several years since the previous edition of this book have been marked by the passing of three valued colleagues and mentors, who influenced my career, and who had considerable input into the development of the technology described herein: JoDean Morrow, Louis Coffin, and Gary Halford.

Encouragement and support were provided by Virginia Tech in several forms. I especially thank David Clark, head of the Materials Science and Engineering Department, and Ishwar Puri, head of the Engineering Science and Mechanics Department. (The author is jointly appointed in these departments.) Also, I am grateful to Norma Guynn and Daniel Reed, two staff members in ESM who were helpful in a variety of ways.

The photographs for the front and back covers were provided by Pratt & Miller Engineering, New Hudson, Michigan. Their generosity in doing so is appreciated.

I thank those at Prentice Hall who worked on the editing and production of this edition, especially Gregory Dulles, Scott Disanno, and Jane Bonnell, with whom I had considerable and most helpful personal interaction.

I also thank Shiny Rajesh of Integra Software Services, and others working with her, for their care and diligence in assuring the accuracy and quality of the book composition.

Finally, I thank my wife Nancy and family for their encouragement, patience, and support during this work.

The publishers would like to thank Professor Manoj Kumar Mitra of the Department of Metallurgical and Material Engineering, Jadavpur University, Kolkata, for reviewing the content of the International Edition.

1

Introduction

OBJECTIVES

- Gain an overview of the types of material failure that affect mechanical and structural design.
- Understand in general how the limitations on strength and ductility of materials are dealt with in engineering design.
- Develop an appreciation of how the development of new technology requires new materials and new methods of evaluating the mechanical behavior of materials.
- Learn of the surprisingly large costs of fracture to the economy.

1.1 INTRODUCTION

Designers of machines, vehicles, and structures must achieve acceptable levels of performance and economy, while at the same time striving to guarantee that the item is both safe and durable. To assure performance, safety, and durability, it is necessary to avoid excess *deformation*—that is, bending, twisting, or stretching—of the components (parts) of the machine, vehicle, or structure. In addition, cracking in components must be avoided entirely, or strictly limited, so that it does not progress to the point of complete *fracture*.

The study of deformation and fracture in materials is called *mechanical behavior of materials*. Knowledge of this area provides the basis for avoiding these types of failure in engineering applications. One aspect of the subject is the physical testing of samples of materials by applying forces and deformations. Once the behavior of a given material is quantitatively known from testing, or from published test data, its chances of success in a particular engineering design can be evaluated.

The most basic concern in design to avoid structural failure is that the *stress* in a component must not exceed the *strength* of the material, where the strength is simply the stress that causes a deformation or fracture failure. Additional complexities or particular causes of failure often require further analysis, such as the following:

1. Stresses are often present that act in more than one direction; that is, the state of stress is biaxial or triaxial.
2. Real components may contain flaws or even cracks that must be specifically considered.
3. Stresses may be applied for long periods of time.
4. Stresses may be repeatedly applied and removed, or the direction of stress repeatedly reversed.

In the remainder of this introductory chapter, we will define and briefly discuss various types of material failure, and we will consider the relationships of mechanical behavior of materials to engineering design, to new technology, and to the economy.

1.2 TYPES OF MATERIAL FAILURE

A *deformation failure* is a change in the physical dimensions or shape of a component that is sufficient for its function to be lost or impaired. Cracking to the extent that a component is separated into two or more pieces is termed *fracture*. *Corrosion* is the loss of material due to chemical action, and *wear* is surface removal due to abrasion or sticking between solid surfaces that touch. If wear is caused by a fluid (gas or liquid), it is called *erosion*, which is especially likely if the fluid contains hard particles. Although corrosion and wear are also of great importance, this book primarily considers deformation and fracture.

The basic types of material failure that are classified as either deformation or fracture are indicated in Fig. 1.1. Since several different causes exist, it is important to correctly identify the ones that may apply to a given design, so that the appropriate analysis methods can be chosen to predict the behavior. With such a need for classification in mind, the various types of deformation and fracture are defined and briefly described next.

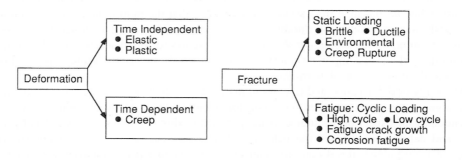

Figure 1.1   Basic types of deformation and fracture.

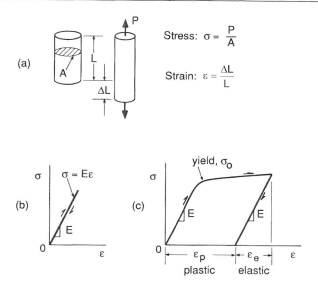

Figure 1.2   Axial member (a) subject to loading and unloading, showing elastic deformation (b) and both elastic and plastic deformation (c).

1.2.1 Elastic and Plastic Deformation

Deformations are quantified in terms of normal and shear strain in elementary mechanics of materials. The cumulative effect of the strains in a component is a deformation, such as a bend, twist, or stretch. Deformations are sometimes essential for function, as in a spring. Excessive deformation, especially if permanent, is often harmful.

Deformation that appears quickly upon loading can be classed as either elastic deformation or plastic deformation, as illustrated in Fig. 1.2. *Elastic deformation* is recovered immediately upon unloading. Where this is the only deformation present, stress and strain are usually proportional. For axial loading, the constant of proportionality is the *modulus of elasticity*, E, as defined in Fig. 1.2(b). An example of failure by elastic deformation is a tall building that sways in the wind and causes discomfort to the occupants, although there may be only remote chance of collapse. Elastic deformations are analyzed by the methods of elementary mechanics of materials and extensions of this general approach, as in books on theory of elasticity and structural analysis.

Plastic deformation is not recovered upon unloading and is therefore permanent. The difference between elastic and plastic deformation is illustrated in Fig. 1.2(c). Once plastic deformation begins, only a small increase in stress usually causes a relatively large additional deformation. This process of relatively easy further deformation is called *yielding*, and the value of stress where this behavior begins to be important for a given material is called the *yield strength*, σ_o.

Materials capable of sustaining large amounts of plastic deformation are said to behave in a *ductile* manner, and those that fracture without very much plastic deformation behave in a *brittle* manner. Ductile behavior occurs for many metals, such as low-strength steels, copper, and lead, and for some plastics, such as polyethylene. Brittle behavior occurs for glass, stone, acrylic plastic,

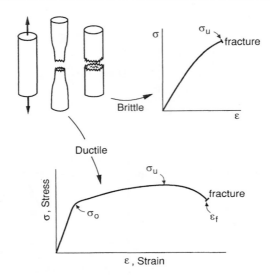

Figure 1.3 Tension test showing brittle and ductile behavior. There is little plastic deformation for brittle behavior, but a considerable amount for ductile behavior.

and some metals, such as the high-strength steel used to make a file. (Note that the word *plastic* is used both as the common name for polymeric materials and in identifying plastic deformation, which can occur in any type of material.)

Tension tests are often employed to assess the strength and ductility of materials, as illustrated in Fig. 1.3. Such a test is done by slowly stretching a bar of the material in tension until it breaks (fractures). The *ultimate tensile strength*, σ_u, which is the highest stress reached before fracture, is obtained along with the yield strength and the strain at fracture, ε_f. The latter is a measure of ductility and is usually expressed as a percentage, then being called the *percent elongation*. Materials having high values of both σ_u and ε_f are said to be *tough*, and tough materials are generally desirable for use in design.

Large plastic deformations virtually always constitute failure. For example, collapse of a steel bridge or building during an earthquake could occur due to plastic deformation. However, plastic deformation can be relatively small, but still cause malfunction of a component. For example, in a rotating shaft, a slight permanent bend results in unbalanced rotation, which in turn may cause vibration and perhaps early failure of the bearings supporting the shaft.

Buckling is deformation due to compressive stress that causes large changes in alignment of columns or plates, perhaps to the extent of folding or collapse. Either elastic or plastic deformation, or a combination of both, can dominate the behavior. Buckling is generally considered in books on elementary mechanics of materials and structural analysis.

1.2.2 Creep Deformation

Creep is deformation that accumulates with time. Depending on the magnitude of the applied stress and its duration, the deformation may become so large that a component can no longer perform its

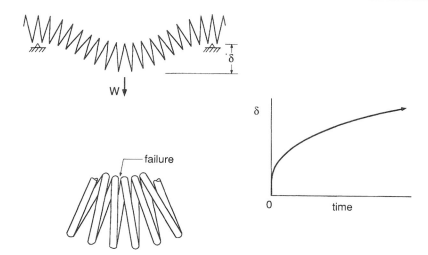

Figure 1.4   A tungsten lightbulb filament sagging under its own weight. The deflection increases with time due to creep and can lead to touching of adjacent coils, which causes bulb failure.

function. Plastics and low-melting-temperature metals may creep at room temperature, and virtually any material will creep upon approaching its melting temperature. Creep is thus often an important problem where high temperature is encountered, as in gas-turbine aircraft engines. Buckling can occur in a time-dependent manner due to creep deformation.

An example of an application involving creep deformation is the design of tungsten lightbulb filaments. The situation is illustrated in Fig. 1.4. Sagging of the filament coil between its supports increases with time due to creep deformation caused by the weight of the filament itself. If too much deformation occurs, the adjacent turns of the coil touch one another, causing an electrical short and local overheating, which quickly leads to failure of the filament. The coil geometry and supports are therefore designed to limit the stresses caused by the weight of the filament, and a special tungsten alloy that creeps less than pure tungsten is used.

1.2.3 Fracture under Static and Impact Loading

Rapid fracture can occur under loading that does not vary with time or that changes only slowly, called *static loading*. If such a fracture is accompanied by little plastic deformation, it is called a *brittle fracture*. This is the normal mode of failure of glass and other materials that are resistant to plastic deformation. If the loading is applied very rapidly, called *impact loading*, brittle fracture is more likely to occur.

If a crack or other sharp flaw is present, brittle fracture can occur even in ductile steels or aluminum alloys, or in other materials that are normally capable of deforming plastically by large amounts. Such situations are analyzed by the special technology called *fracture mechanics*, which is the study of cracks in solids. Resistance to brittle fracture in the presence of a crack is measured by a material property called the *fracture toughness*, K_{Ic}, as illustrated in Fig. 1.5. Materials with high

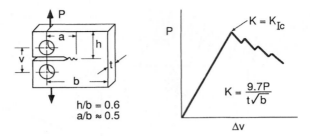

Figure 1.5   Fracture toughness test. *K* is a measure of the severity of the combination of crack size, geometry, and load. K_{Ic} is the particular value, called the *fracture toughness*, where the material fails.

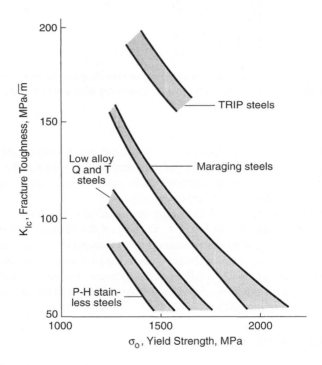

Figure 1.6   Decreased fracture toughness, as yield strength is increased by heat treatment, for various classes of high-strength steel. (Adapted from [Knott 79]; used with permission.)

strength generally have low fracture toughness, and vice versa. This trend is illustrated for several classes of high-strength steel in Fig. 1.6.

   Ductile fracture can also occur. This type of fracture is accompanied by significant plastic deformation and is sometimes a gradual tearing process. Fracture mechanics and brittle or ductile fracture are especially important in the design of pressure vessels and large welded structures, such as bridges and ships. Fracture may occur as a result of a combination of stress and chemical

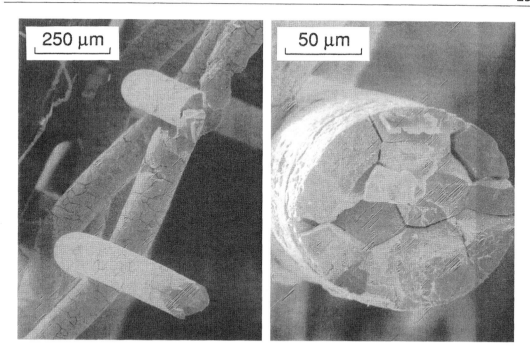

Figure 1.7 Stainless steel wires broken as a result of environmental attack. These were employed in a filter exposed at 300°C to a complex organic environment that included molten nylon. Cracking occurred along the boundaries of the crystal grains of the material. (Photos by W. G. Halley; courtesy of R. E. Swanson.)

effects, and this is called *environmental cracking*. Problems of this type are a particular concern in the chemical industry, but also occur widely elsewhere. For example, some low-strength steels are susceptible to cracking in caustic (basic or high pH) chemicals such as NaOH, and high-strength steels may crack in the presence of hydrogen or hydrogen sulfide gas. The term *stress-corrosion cracking* is also used to describe such behavior. This latter term is especially appropriate where material removal by corrosive action is also involved, which is not the case for all types of environmental cracking. Photographs of cracking caused by a hostile environment are shown in Fig. 1.7. Creep deformation may proceed to the point that separation into two pieces occurs. This is called *creep rupture* and is similar to ductile fracture, except that the process is time dependent.

1.2.4 Fatigue under Cyclic Loading

A common cause of fracture is *fatigue*, which is failure due to repeated loading. In general, one or more tiny cracks start in the material, and these grow until complete failure occurs. A simple example is breaking a piece of wire by bending it back and forth a number of times. Crack growth during fatigue is illustrated in Fig. 1.8, and a fatigue fracture is shown in Fig. 1.9.

Prevention of fatigue fracture is a vital aspect of design for machines, vehicles, and structures that are subjected to repeated loading or vibration. For example, trucks passing over bridges cause

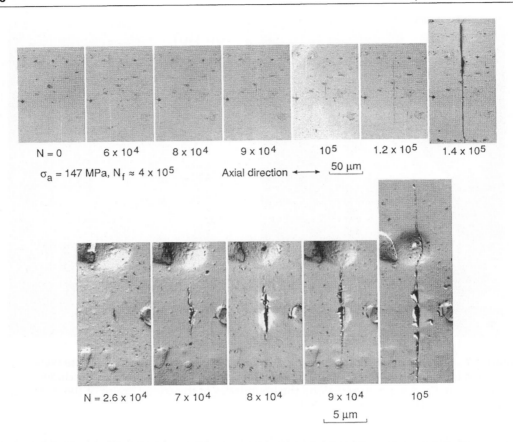

Figure 1.8   Development of a fatigue crack during rotating bending of a precipitation-hardened aluminum alloy. Photographs at various numbers of cycles are shown for a test requiring 400,000 cycles for failure. The sequence in the bottom row of photographs shows more detail of the middle portion of the sequence in the top row. (Photos courtesy of Prof. H. Nisitani, Kyushu Sangyo University, Fukuoka, Japan. Published in [Nisitani 81]; reprinted with permission from *Engineering Fracture Mechanics*, Pergamon Press, Oxford, UK.)

fatigue in the bridge, and sailboat rudders and bicycle pedals can fail in fatigue. Vehicles of all types, including automobiles, tractors, helicopters, and airplanes, are subject to this problem and must be extensively analyzed and tested to avoid it. For example, some of the parts of a helicopter that require careful design to avoid fatigue problems are shown in Fig. 1.10.

If the number of repetitions (cycles) of the load is large, say, millions, then the situation is termed *high-cycle fatigue*. Conversely, *low-cycle fatigue* is caused by a relatively small number of cycles, say, tens, hundreds, or thousands. Low-cycle fatigue is generally accompanied by significant amounts of plastic deformation, whereas high-cycle fatigue is associated with relatively small deformations that are primarily elastic. Repeated heating and cooling can cause a cyclic stress due to differential thermal expansion and contraction, resulting in *thermal fatigue*.

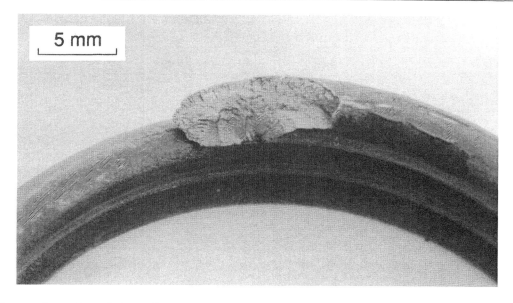

Figure 1.9   Fatigue failure of a garage door spring that occurred after 15 years of service. (Photo by R. A. Simonds; sample contributed by R. S. Alvarez, Blacksburg, VA.)

Cracks may be initially present in a component from manufacture, or they may start early in the service life. Emphasis must then be placed on the possible growth of these cracks by fatigue, as this can lead to a brittle or ductile fracture once the cracks are sufficiently large. Such situations are identified by the term *fatigue crack growth* and may also be analyzed by the previously mentioned technology of fracture mechanics. For example, analysis of fatigue crack growth is used to schedule inspection and repair of large aircraft, in which cracks are commonly present.

Such analysis is useful in preventing problems similar to the fuselage (main body) failure in 1988 of a passenger jet, as shown in Fig. 1.11. The problem in this case started with fatigue cracks at rivet holes in the aluminum structure. These cracks gradually grew during use of the airplane, joining together and forming a large crack that caused a major fracture, resulting in separation of a large section of the structure. The failure could have been avoided by more frequent inspection and repair of cracks before they grew to a dangerous extent.

1.2.5 Combined Effects

Two or more of the previously described types of failure may act together to cause effects greater than would be expected by their separate action; that is, there is a *synergistic effect*. Creep and fatigue may produce such an enhanced effect where there is cyclic loading at high temperature. This may occur in steam turbines in electric power plants and in gas-turbine aircraft engines.

Wear due to small motions between fitted parts may combine with cyclic loading to produce surface damage followed by cracking, which is called *fretting fatigue*. This may cause failure at surprisingly low stress levels for certain combinations of materials. For example, fretting fatigue

Figure 1.10 Main mast region of a helicopter, showing inboard ends of blades, their attachment, and the linkages and mechanism that control the pitch angles of the rotating blades. The cylinder above the rotors is not ordinarily present, but is part of instrumentation used to monitor strains in the rotor blades for experimental purposes. (Photo courtesy of Bell Helicopter Textron, Inc., Ft. Worth, TX.)

could occur where a gear is fastened on a shaft by shrink fitting or press fitting. Similarly, *corrosion fatigue* is the combination of cyclic loading and corrosion. It is often a problem in cyclically loaded components of steel that must operate in seawater, such as the structural members of offshore oil well platforms.

Material properties may degrade with time due to various environmental effects. For example, the ultraviolet content of sunlight causes some plastics to become brittle, and wood decreases in strength with time, especially if exposed to moisture. As a further example, steels become brittle if exposed to neutron radiation over long periods of time, and this affects the retirement life of nuclear reactors.

1.3 DESIGN AND MATERIALS SELECTION

Design is the process of choosing the geometric shape, materials, manufacturing method, and other details needed to completely describe a machine, vehicle, structure, or other engineered item. This

Figure 1.11   Fuselage failure in a passenger jet that occurred in 1988. (Photo courtesy of J. F. Wildey II, National Transportation Safety Board, Washington, DC; see [NTSB 89] for more detail.)

process involves a wide range of activities and objectives. It is first necessary to assure that the item is capable of performing its intended function. For example, an automobile should be capable of the necessary speeds and maneuvers while carrying up to a certain number of passengers and additional weight, and the refueling and maintenance requirements should be reasonable as to frequency and cost.

However, any engineered item must meet additional requirements: The design must be such that it is physically possible and economical to manufacture the item. Certain standards must be met as to esthetics and convenience of use. Environmental pollution needs to be minimized, and, hopefully, the materials and type of construction are chosen so that eventual recycling of the materials used is possible. Finally, the item must be safe and durable.

Safety is affected not only by design features such as seat belts in automobiles, but also by avoiding structural failure. For example, excessive deformation or fracture of an automobile axle or steering component can cause a serious accident. *Durability* is the capacity of an item to survive its intended use for a suitably long period of time, so that good durability minimizes the cost of maintaining and replacing the item. For example, more durable automobiles cost less to drive than otherwise similar ones that experience more repairs and shorter life due to such gradually occurring processes as fatigue, creep, wear, and corrosion. In addition, durability is important to safety, as poor durability can lead to a structural failure or malfunction that can cause an accident. Moreover, more durable items require less frequent replacement, thus reducing the environmental impact of manufacturing new items, including pollution, greenhouse gas emissions, energy use, depletion of natural resources, and disposal and recycling needs.

1.3.1 Iterative and Stepwise Nature of Design

A flow chart showing some of the steps necessary to complete a mechanical design is shown in Fig. 1.12. The logic loops shown by arrows indicate that the design process is fundamentally iterative in nature. In other words, there is a strong element of trial and error where an initial design is done and then analyzed, tested, and subjected to trial production. Changes may be made at any stage of the process to satisfy requirements not previously considered or problems just discovered. Changes may in turn require further analysis or testing. All of this must be done while observing constraints on time and cost.

Each step involves a *synthesis* process in which all of the various concerns and requirements are considered together. Compromises between conflicting requirements are usually necessary, and continual effort is needed to maintain simplicity, practicability, and economy. For example, the cargo weight limit of an aircraft cannot be made too large without causing unacceptable limits on the weight of fuel that can be carried, and therefore also on flight distance. Prior individual or organizational experience may have important influences on the design. Also, certain design codes and standards may be used as an aid, and sometimes they are required by law. These are generally developed and published by either professional societies or governmental units, and one of their main purposes is to assure safety and durability. An example is the *Bridge Design Specifications* published by the American Association of State Highway and Transportation Officials.

One difficult and sometimes tricky step in design is estimation of the applied loads (forces or combinations of forces). Even rough estimates are often difficult to make, especially for vibratory loads resulting from such sources as road roughness or air turbulence. It is sometimes possible to use measurements from a similar item that is already in service, but this is clearly impossible if the item being designed is unique. Once at least rough estimates (or assumptions) are made of the loads, then stresses in components can be calculated.

The initial design is often made on the basis of avoiding stresses that exceed the yield strength of the material. Then the design is checked by more refined analysis, and changes are made as necessary to avoid more subtle modes of material failure, such as fatigue, brittle fracture, and creep. The geometric shape or size may be changed to lower the magnitude or alter the distribution of stresses and strains to avoid one of these problems, or the material may be changed to one more suitable to resist a particular failure mode.

1.3.2 Safety Factors

In making design decisions that involve safety and durability, the concept of a *safety factor* is often used. The safety factor in stress is the ratio of the stress that causes failure to the stress expected to occur in the actual service of the component. That is,

$$X_1 = \frac{\text{stress causing failure}}{\text{stress in service}} \tag{1.1}$$

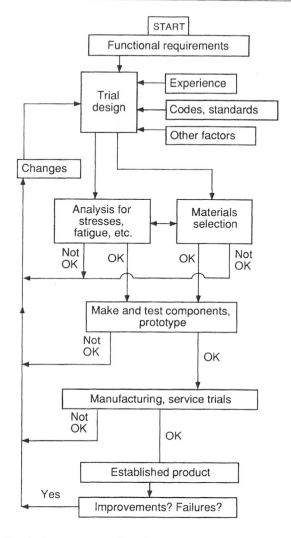

Figure 1.12   Steps in the design process related to avoiding structural failure. (Adapted from [Dowling 87]; used with permission; © Society of Automotive Engineers.)

For example, if $X_1 = 2.0$, the stress necessary to cause failure is twice as high as the highest stress expected in service. Safety factors provide a degree of assurance that unexpected events in service do not cause failure. They also allow some latitude for the usual lack of complete input information for the design process and for the approximations and assumptions that are often necessary. Safety factors must be larger where there are greater uncertainties or where the consequences of failure are severe.

Values for safety factors in the range $X_1 = 1.5$ to 3.0 are common. If the magnitude of the loading is well known, and if there are few uncertainties from other sources, values near the lower end of this range may be appropriate. For example, in the allowable stress design method of the American Institute of Steel Construction, used for buildings and similar applications, safety factors for design against yielding under static loading are generally in the range 1.5 to 2.0, with 1.5 applying for bending stress in the most favorable situations. Elsewhere, safety factors even as low as 1.2 are sometimes used, but this should be contemplated only for situations where there is quite thorough engineering analysis and few uncertainties, and also where failure has economic consequences only.

For the basic requirement of avoiding excessive deformation due to yielding, the failure stress is the yield strength of the material, σ_o, and the service stress is the largest stress in the component, calculated for the conditions expected in actual service. For ductile materials, the service stress employed is simply the net section nominal stress, S, as defined for typical cases in Appendix A, Figs. A.11 and A.12. However, the localized effects of stress raisers do need to be included in the service stress for brittle materials, and also for fatigue of even ductile materials. Where several causes of failure are possible, it is necessary to calculate a safety factor for each cause, and the lowest of these is the final safety factor. For example, safety factors might be calculated not only for yielding, but also for fatigue or creep. If cracks or sharp flaws are possible, a safety factor for brittle fracture is needed as well.

Safety factors in stress are sometimes supplemented or replaced by safety factors in life. This safety factor is the ratio of the expected life to failure to the desired service life. Life is measured by time or by events such as the number of flights of an aircraft:

$$X_2 = \frac{\text{failure life}}{\text{desired service life}} \tag{1.2}$$

For example, if a helicopter part is expected to fail after 10 years of service, and if it is to be replaced after 2 years, there is a safety factor of 5 on life. Safety factors in life are used where deformation or cracking progresses gradually with time, as for creep or fatigue. As the life is generally quite sensitive to small changes in stress, values of this factor must be relatively large, typically in the range $X_2 = 5$ to 20.

The use of safety factors as in Eq. 1.1 is termed *allowable stress design*. An alternative is *load factor design*. In this case, the loads (forces, moments, torques, etc.) expected in service are multiplied by a *load factor*, Y. The analysis done with these multiplied loads corresponds to the failure condition, not to the service condition.

$$(\text{load in service}) \times Y = \text{load causing failure} \tag{1.3}$$

The two approaches give generally similar results, depending on the details of how they are applied. In some cases, they are equivalent, so that $X_1 = Y$. The load factor approach has the advantage that it can be easily expanded to allow different load factors to be employed for different sources of loading, reflecting different uncertainties in how well each is known.

1.3.3 Prototype and Component Testing

Even though mechanical behavior of materials considerations may be involved in the design process from its early stages, testing is still often necessary to verify safety and durability. This arises because of the assumptions and imperfect knowledge reflected in many engineering estimates of strength or life.

A *prototype*, or trial model, is often made and subjected to *simulated service testing* to demonstrate whether or not a machine or vehicle functions properly. For example, a prototype automobile is generally run on a test course that includes rough roads, bumps, quick turns, etc. Loads may be measured during simulated service testing, and these are used to improve the initial design, as the early estimate of loads may have been quite uncertain. A prototype may also be subjected to simulated service testing until either a mechanical failure occurs, perhaps by fatigue, creep, wear, or corrosion, or the design is proven to be reliable. This is called *durability testing* and is commonly done for new models of automobiles, tractors, and other vehicles. A photograph of an automobile set up for such a test is shown in Fig. 1.13.

For very large items, and especially for one-of-a-kind items, it may be impractical or uneconomical to test a prototype of the entire item. A part of the item, that is, a *component*, may then be tested. For example, wings, tail sections, and fuselages of large aircraft are separately tested to destruction under repeated loads that cause fatigue cracking in a manner similar to actual service. Individual joints and members of offshore oil well structures are similarly tested. Component testing may also be done as a prelude to testing of a full prototype. An example of this is the testing of a new design of an automobile axle prior to manufacture and the subsequent testing of the first prototype of the entire automobile.

Various sources of loading and vibration in machines, vehicles, and structures can be simulated by the use of digital computers, as can the resulting deformation and fracture of the material.

Figure 1.13   Road simulation test of an automobile, with loads applied at all four wheels and the bumper mounts. (Photo courtesy of MTS Systems Corp., Eden Prairie, MN.)

This technology is now being used to reduce the need for prototype and component testing, thus accelerating the design process. However, computer simulations are only as good as the simplifying assumptions used in analysis, and the limitations on input data, which are always present. Thus, some physical testing will continue to be frequently needed, at least as a final check on the design process.

1.3.4 Service Experience

Design changes may also be made as a result of experience with a limited production run of a new product. Purchasers of the product may use it in a way not anticipated by the designer, resulting in failures that necessitate design changes. For example, early models of surgical implants, such as hip joints and pin supports for broken bones, experienced failure problems that led to changes in both geometry and material.

The design process often continues even after a product is established and widely distributed. Long-term usage may uncover additional problems that need to be corrected in new items. If the problem is severe—perhaps safety related—changes may be needed in items already in service. Recalls of automobiles are an example of this, and a portion of these involve problems of deformation or fracture.

1.4 TECHNOLOGICAL CHALLENGE

In recent history, technology has advanced and changed at a rapid rate to meet human needs. Some of the advances from 1500 A.D. to the present are charted in the first column of Table 1.1. The second column shows the improved materials, and the third the materials testing capabilities that were necessary to support these advances. Representative technological failures involving deformation or fracture are also shown. These and other types of failure further stimulated improvements in materials, and in testing and analysis capability, by having a feedback effect. Such interactions among technological advances, materials, testing, and failures are still under way today and will continue into the foreseeable future.

As a particular example, consider improvements in engines. Steam engines, as used in the mid-1800s for water and rail transportation, operated at little more than the boiling point of water, 100°C, and employed simple materials, mainly cast iron. Around the turn of the century, the internal combustion engine had been invented and was being improved for use in automobiles and aircraft. Gas-turbine engines became practical for propulsion during World War II, when they were used in the first jet aircraft. Higher operating temperatures in engines provide greater efficiency, with temperatures increasing over the years. At present, materials in jet engines must withstand temperatures around 1800°C. To resist the higher temperatures, improved low-alloy steels and then stainless steels were developed, followed by increasingly sophisticated metal alloys based on nickel and cobalt. However, failures due to such causes as creep, fatigue, and corrosion still occurred and had major influences on engine development. Further increases in operating temperatures and efficiency are now being pursued through the use of advanced ceramic and ceramic composite materials. These materials have superior temperature and corrosion resistance. But their inherent brittleness must be managed by improving the materials as much as possible,

Table 1.1   Some Major Technological Advances from 1500 A.D., the Parallel Developments in Materials and Materials Testing, and Failures Related to Behavior of Materials

Years	Technological Advance	New Materials Introduced	Materials Testing Advances	Failures
1500's 1600's	Dikes Canals Pumps Telescope	(Stone, brick, wood, copper, bronze, and cast and wrought iron in use)	Tension (L. da Vinci) Tension, bending (Galileo) Pressure burst (Mariotte) Elasticity (Hooke)	
1700's	Steam engine Cast iron bridge	Malleable cast iron	Shear, torsion (Coulomb)	
1800's	Railroad industry Suspension bridge Internal combustion engine	Portland cement Vulcanized rubber Bessemer steel	Fatigue (Wöhler) Plasticity (Tresca) Universal testing machines	Steam boilers Railroad axles Iron bridges
1900's 1910's	Electric power Powered flight Vacuum tube	Alloy steels Aluminum alloys Synthetic plastics	Hardness (Brinell) Impact (Izod, Charpy) Creep (Andrade)	Quebec bridge Boston molasses tank
1920's 1930's	Gas-turbine engine Strain gage	Stainless steel Tungsten carbide	Fracture (Griffith)	Railroad wheels, rails Automotive parts
1940's 1950's	Controlled fission Jet aircraft Transistor; computer Sputnik	Ni-base alloys Ti-base alloys Fiberglass	Electronic testing machine Low-cycle fatigue (Coffin, Manson) Fracture mechanics (Irwin)	Liberty ships Comet airliner Turbine generators
1960's 1970's	Laser Microprocessor Moon landing	HSLA steels High-performance composites	Closed-loop testing machine Fatigue crack growth (Paris) Computer control	F-111 aircraft DC-10 aircraft Highway bridges
1980's 1990's	Space station Magnetic levitation	Tough ceramics Al-Li alloys	Multiaxial testing Direct digital control	Alex. Kielland rig Surgical implants
2000's 2010's	Sustainable energy Extreme fossil fuel extraction	Nanomaterials Bio-inspired materials	User-friendly test software	Space Shuttle tiles Deepwater Horizon offshore oil rig

Source: [Herring 89], [Landgraf 80], [Timoshenko 83], [Whyte 75], *Encyclopedia Britannica*, news reports.

while designing hardware in a manner that accommodates their still relatively low fracture toughness.

In general, the challenges of advancing technology require not only improved materials, but also more careful analysis in design and more detailed information on materials behavior than before. Furthermore, there has recently been a desirable increased awareness of safety and warranty issues. Manufacturers of machines, vehicles, and structures now find it appropriate not just to maintain current levels of safety and durability, but to improve these at the same time that the other technological challenges are being met.

1.5 ECONOMIC IMPORTANCE OF FRACTURE

A division of the U.S. Department of Commerce, the National Institute of Standards and Technology (formerly the National Bureau of Standards), completed a study in 1983 of the economic effects of fracture of materials in the United States. The total costs per year were large—specifically, $119 billion in 1982 dollars. This was 4% of the gross national product (GNP), therefore representing a significant use of resources and manpower. The definition of fracture used for the study was quite broad, including not only fracture in the sense of cracking, but also deformation and related problems such as delamination. Wear and corrosion were not included. Separate studies indicated that adding these to obtain the total cost for materials durability would increase the total to roughly 10% of the GNP. A study of fracture costs in Europe reported in 1991 also yielded an overall cost of 4% of the GNP, and a similar value is likely to continue to apply to all industrial nations. (See the paper by Milne, 1994, in the References.)

In the U.S. fracture study, the costs were considered to include the extra costs of designing machines, vehicles, and structures, beyond the requirements of resisting simple yielding failure of the material. Note that resistance to fracture necessitates the use of more raw materials, or of more expensive materials or processing, to give components the necessary strength. Also, additional analysis and testing are needed in the design process. The extra use of materials and other activities all involve additional costs for manpower and facilities. There are also significant expenses associated with fracture for repair, maintenance, and replacement parts. Inspection of newly manufactured parts for flaws and of parts in service for developing cracks involves considerable cost. There are also costs such as recalls, litigation, insurance, etc., collectively called *product liability costs*, that add to the total.

The costs of fracture are spread rather unevenly over various sectors of the economy. In the U.S. study, the sectors involving the largest fracture costs were motor vehicles and parts, with around 10% of the total, aircraft and parts with 6%, residential construction with 5%, and building construction with 3%. Other sectors with costs in the range of 2 to 3% of the total were food and related products, fabricated structural products, nonferrous metal products, petroleum refining, structural metal, and tires and inner tubes. Note that fatigue cracking is the major cause of fracture for motor vehicles and for aircraft, the two sectors with the highest fracture costs. However, brittle and ductile fracture, environmental cracking, and creep are also important for these and other sectors.

The study further found that roughly one-third of this $119 billion annual cost could be eliminated through better use of then-current technology. Another third could perhaps be eliminated over a longer time period through research and development—that is, by obtaining new knowledge and developing ways to put this knowledge to work. And the final roughly one-third would be difficult to eliminate without major research breakthroughs. Hence, noting that two-thirds of these costs could be eliminated by improved use of currently available technology, or by technology that could be developed in a reasonable time, there is a definite economic incentive for learning about deformation and fracture. Engineers with knowledge in this area can help the companies they work for avoid costs due to structural failures and help make the design process more efficient—hence more economical and faster—by early attention to such potential problems. Benefits to society result, such as lower costs to the consumer and improved safety and durability.

1.6 SUMMARY

Mechanical behavior of materials is the study of the deformation and fracture of materials. Materials tests are used to evaluate the behavior of a material, such as its resistance to failure in terms of the yield strength or fracture toughness. The material's strength is compared with the stresses expected for a component in service to assure that the design is adequate.

Different methods of testing materials and of analyzing trial engineering designs are needed for different types of material failure. These failure types include elastic, plastic, and creep deformation. Elastic deformation is recovered immediately upon unloading, whereas plastic deformation is permanent. Creep is deformation that accumulates with time. Other types of material failure involve cracking, such as brittle or ductile fracture, environmental cracking, creep rupture, and fatigue. Brittle fracture can occur due to static loads and involves little deformation, whereas ductile fracture involves considerable deformation. Environmental cracking is caused by a hostile chemical environment, and creep rupture is a time-dependent and usually ductile fracture. Fatigue is failure due to repeated loading and involves the gradual development and growth of cracks. A special method called fracture mechanics is used to specifically analyze cracks in engineering components.

Engineering design is the process of choosing all details necessary to describe a machine, vehicle, or structure. Design is fundamentally an iterative (trial and error) process, and it is necessary at each step to perform a synthesis in which all concerns and requirements are considered together, with compromises and adjustments made as necessary. Prototype and component testing and monitoring of service experience are often important in the later stages of design. Deformation and fracture may need to be analyzed in one or more stages of the synthesis, testing, and actual service of an engineered item.

Advancing and changing technology continually introduces new challenges to the engineering designer, demanding more efficient use of materials and improved materials. Thus, the historical and continuing trend is that improved methods of testing and analysis have developed along with materials that are more resistant to failure.

Deformation and fracture are issues of major economic importance, especially in the motor vehicle and aircraft sectors. The costs involved in avoiding fracture and in paying for its consequences in all sectors of the economy are on the order of 4% of the GNP.

NEW TERMS AND SYMBOLS

allowable stress design
brittle fracture
component testing
creep
deformation
ductile fracture
durability; durability testing
elastic deformation
environmental cracking
fatigue
fatigue crack growth
fracture
fracture mechanics
fracture toughness, K_{Ic}
high-cycle fatigue

load factor, Y
load factor design
low-cycle fatigue
modulus of elasticity, E
percent elongation, $100\varepsilon_f$
plastic deformation
prototype
safety factor, X
simulated service testing
static loading
synergistic effect
synthesis
thermal fatigue
ultimate tensile strength, σ_u
yield strength, σ_o

REFERENCES

AASHTO. 2010. *AASHTO LRFD Bridge Design Specifications*, 5th ed., Am. Assoc. of State Highway and Transportation Officials, Washington, DC.

AISC. 2006. *Steel Construction Manual,* 13th ed., Am. Institute of Steel Construction, Chicago, IL.

HERRING, S. D. 1989. *From the Titanic to the Challenger: An Annotated Bibliography on Technological Failures of the Twentieth Century*, Garland Publishing, Inc., New York.

MILNE, I. 1994. "The Importance of the Management of Structural Integrity," *Engineering Failure Analysis*, vol. 1, no. 3, pp. 171–181.

REED, R. P., J. H. SMITH, and B. W. CHRIST. 1983. "The Economic Effects of Fracture in the United States: Part 1," Special Pub. No. 647-1, U.S. Dept. of Commerce, National Bureau of Standards, U.S. Government Printing Office, Washington, DC.

SCHMIDT, L. C., and G. E. DIETER. 2009. *Engineering Design: A Materials and Processing Approach*, 4th ed., McGraw-Hill, New York, NY.

WHYTE, R. R., ed. 1975. *Engineering Progress Through Trouble*, The Institution of Mechanical Engineers, London.

WULPI, D. J. 1999. *Understanding How Components Fail*, 2d ed., ASM International, Materials Park, OH.

PROBLEMS AND QUESTIONS

Section 1.2

1.1 Classify each of the following failures by identifying its category in Fig. 1.1, and explain the reasons for each choice in one or two sentences:

  (a) The plastic frames on eyeglasses gradually spread and become loose.

  (b) A glass bowl with a small crack breaks into two pieces when it is immersed, while still hot, into cold water.

  (c) Plastic scissors develop a small crack just in front of one of the finger rings.
  (d) A copper water pipe freezes and develops a lengthwise split that causes a leak.
  (e) The steel radiator fan blades in an automobile develop small cracks near the base of the blades.

1.2 Repeat Prob. 1.1 for the following failures:
  (a) A child's plastic tricycle, used in rough play to make skidding turns, develops cracks where the handlebars join the frame.
  (b) An aluminum baseball bat develops a crack.
  (c) A large steel artillery tube (barrel), which previously had cracks emanating from the rifling, suddenly bursts into pieces. Classify both the cracks and the final fracture.
  (d) The fuselage (body) of a passenger airliner breaks into two pieces, with the fracture starting from cracks that had previously initiated at the corners of window cutouts in the aluminum-alloy material. Classify both the cracks and the final fracture.
  (e) The nickel-alloy blades in an aircraft turbine engine lengthen during service and rub the casing.

1.3 Think of four deformation or fracture failures that have actually occurred, either from your personal experience or from items that you have read about in newspapers, magazines, or books. Classify each according to a category in Fig. 1.1, and briefly explain the reason for your classification.

Section 1.3

1.4 As an engineer, you work for a company that makes mountain bicycles. Some bicycles that have been in use for several years have had handlebars that failed by completely breaking off where the handlebar is clamped into the stem that connects it to the rest of the bicycle. What is the most likely cause of these failures? Describe some of the steps that you might take to redesign this part and to verify that your new design will solve this problem.

1.5 Repeat Prob. 1.4 for failures in the cast aluminum bracket used to attach the rudder of a small recreational sailboat.

1.6 Repeat Prob. 1.4 for failures of leaf springs in small boat trailers.

1.7 A plate with a width change is subjected to a tension load as in Fig. A.11(c). The tension load is $P = 3800$ N, and the dimensions are $w_2 = 30$, $w_1 = 14$, and $t = 6$ mm. It is made of a polycarbonate plastic with yield strength $\sigma_o = 65$ MPa. In a tension test, as in Fig. 1.3, this material exhibits quite ductile behavior, finally breaking at a strain around $\varepsilon_f = 110$ to 150%. What is the safety factor against large amounts of deformation occurring in the plate due to yielding? Does the value seem adequate? (Comment: Note that the stress units MPa $= \text{N/mm}^2$.)

1.8 A shaft with a circumferential groove is subjected to bending, as in Fig. A.12(c). The bending moment is $M = 150$ N·m, and the dimensions are $d_2 = 22$, $d_1 = 14$, and $\rho = 3$ mm. It is made of a titanium alloy with yield strength $\sigma_o = 900$ MPa. In a tension test, as in Fig. 1.3, this material exhibits reasonably ductile behavior, finally breaking at a strain around $\varepsilon_f = 14\%$. What is the safety factor against large amounts of deformation occurring in the shaft due to yielding? Does the value seem adequate? (Comment: Note that the stress units MPa $= \text{N/mm}^2$.)

2

Structure and Deformation in Materials

OBJECTIVES

- Review chemical bonding and crystal structures in solid materials at a basic level, and relate these to differences in mechanical behavior among various classes of material.
- Understand the physical basis of elastic deformation, and employ this to estimate the theoretical strength of solids due to their chemical bonding.
- Understand the basic mechanisms of inelastic deformations due to plasticity and creep.
- Learn why actual strengths of materials fall far below the theoretical strength to break chemical bonds.

2.1 INTRODUCTION

A wide variety of materials are used in applications where resistance to mechanical loading is necessary. These are collectively called *engineering materials* and can be broadly classified as metals and alloys, polymers, ceramics and glasses, and composites. Some typical members of each class are given in Table 2.1.

Differences among the classes of materials as to chemical bonding and microstructure affect mechanical behavior, giving rise to relative advantages and disadvantages among the classes. The situation is summarized by Fig. 2.1. For example, the strong chemical bonding in ceramics and glasses imparts mechanical strength and stiffness (high E), and also temperature and corrosion resistance, but causes brittle behavior. In contrast, many polymers are relatively weakly bonded between the chain molecules, in which case the material has low strength and stiffness and is susceptible to creep deformation.

Table 2.1   Classes and Examples of Engineering Materials

Metals and Alloys	Ceramics and Glasses
Irons and steels	Clay products
Aluminum alloys	Concrete
Titanium alloys	Alumina (Al_2O_3)
Copper alloys; brasses, bronzes	Tungsten carbide (WC)
Magnesium alloys	Titanium aluminide (Ti_3Al)
Nickel-base superalloys	Silica (SiO_2) glasses

Polymers	Composites
Polyethylene (PE)	Plywood
Polyvinyl chloride (PVC)	Cemented carbides
Polystyrene (PS)	Fiberglass
Nylons	Graphite-epoxy
Epoxies	SiC-aluminum
Rubbers	Aramid-aluminum laminate (ARALL)

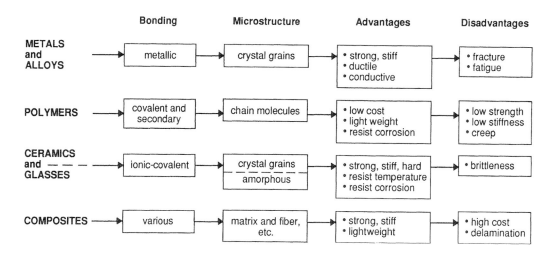

Figure 2.1   General characteristics of the major classes of engineering materials.

Starting from the size scale of primary interest in engineering, roughly one meter, there is a span of 10 orders of magnitude in size down to the scale of the atom, which is around 10^{-10} m. This situation and various intermediate size scales of interest are indicated in Fig. 2.2. At any given size scale, an understanding of the behavior can be sought by looking at what happens at a smaller scale: The behavior of a machine, vehicle, or structure is explained by the behavior of its component parts, and the behavior of these can in turn be explained by the use of small (10^{-1} to 10^{-2} m) test specimens of the material. Similarly, the macroscopic behavior of the material is explained by the behavior of crystal grains, defects in crystals, polymer chains, and other microstructural features

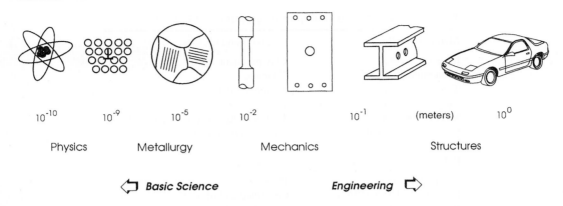

$$10^{-10} \qquad 10^{-9} \qquad 10^{-5} \qquad 10^{-2} \qquad\qquad 10^{-1} \qquad \text{(meters)} \qquad 10^{0}$$

Physics   Metallurgy   Mechanics   Structures

◁┐ *Basic Science*   *Engineering* ┌▷

Figure 2.2   Size scales and disciplines involved in the study and use of engineering materials. (Illustration courtesy of R. W. Landgraf, Howell, MI.)

that exist in the size range of 10^{-3} to 10^{-9} m. Thus, knowledge of behavior over the entire range of sizes from 1 m down to 10^{-10} m contributes to understanding and predicting the performance of machines, vehicles, and structures.

This chapter reviews some of the fundamentals needed to understand mechanical behavior of materials. We will start at the lower end of the size scale in Fig. 2.2 and progress upward. The individual topics include chemical bonding, crystal structures, defects in crystals, and the physical causes of elastic, plastic, and creep deformation. The next chapter will then apply these concepts in discussing each of the classes of engineering materials in more detail.

2.2 BONDING IN SOLIDS

There are several types of chemical bonds that hold atoms and molecules together in solids. Three types of bonds—*ionic*, *covalent*, and *metallic*—are collectively termed *primary* bonds. Primary bonds are strong and stiff and do not easily melt with increasing temperature. They are responsible for the bonding of metals and ceramics, and they provide the relatively high elastic modulus (E) in these materials. *Van der Waals* and *hydrogen* bonds, which are relatively weak, are called *secondary* bonds. These are important in determining the behavior of liquids and as bonds between the carbon-chain molecules in polymers.

2.2.1 Primary Chemical Bonds

The three types of primary bonds are illustrated in Fig. 2.3. Ionic bonding involves the transfer of one or more electrons between atoms of different types. Note that the outer shell of electrons surrounding an atom is stable if it contains eight electrons (except that the stable number is two for the single shell of hydrogen or helium). Hence, an atom of the metal sodium, with only one electron in its outer shell, can donate an electron to an atom of chlorine, which has an outer shell with seven electrons. After the reaction, the sodium atom has an empty outer shell and the chlorine atom has a stable outer shell of eight electrons. The atoms become charged ions, such as Na^+ and Cl^-,

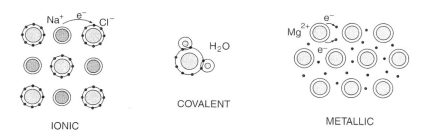

Figure 2.3   The three types of primary chemical bond. Electrons are transferred in ionic bonding, as in NaCl; shared in covalent bonding, as in water; and given up to a common "cloud" in metallic bonding, as in magnesium metal.

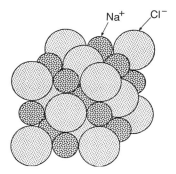

Figure 2.4   Three-dimensional crystal structure of NaCl, consisting of two interpenetrating FCC structures.

which attract one another and form a chemical bond due to their opposite electrostatic charges. A collection of such charged ions, equal numbers of each in this case, forms an electrically neutral solid by arrangement into a regular crystalline array, as shown in Fig. 2.4.

The number of electrons transferred may differ from one. For example, in the salt $MgCl_2$ and in the oxide MgO, two electrons are transferred to form an Mg^{2+} ion. Electrons in the next-to-last shell may also be transferred. For example, iron has two outer shell electrons, but may form either Fe^{2+} or Fe^{3+} ions. Many common salts, oxides, and other solids have bonds that are mostly or partially ionic. These materials tend to be hard and brittle.

Covalent bonding involves the sharing of electrons and occurs where the outer shells are half full or more than half full. The shared electrons can be thought of as allowing both atoms involved to have stable outer shells of eight (or two) electrons. For example, two hydrogen atoms each share an electron with an oxygen atom to make water, H_2O, or two chlorine atoms share one electron to form the diatomic molecule Cl_2. The tight covalent bonds make such simple molecules relatively independent of one another, so that collections of them tend to form liquids or gases at ambient temperatures.

Metallic bonding is responsible for the usually solid form of metals and alloys. For metals, the outer shell of electrons is in most cases less than half full; each atom donates its outer shell electrons

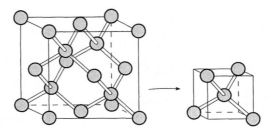

Figure 2.5   Diamond cubic crystal structure of carbon. As a result of the strong and directional covalent bonds, diamond has the highest melting temperature, the highest hardness, and the highest elastic modulus E, of all known solids.

to a "cloud" of electrons. These electrons are shared in common by all of the metal atoms, which have become positively charged ions as a result of giving up electrons. The metal ions are thus held together by their mutual attraction to the electron cloud.

2.2.2 Discussion of Primary Bonds

Covalent bonds have the property—not shared by the other two types of primary bonds—of being strongly directional. This arises from covalent bonds being dependent on the sharing of electrons with specific neighboring atoms, whereas ionic and metallic solids are held together by electrostatic attraction involving all neighboring ions.

A continuous arrangement of covalent bonds can form a three-dimensional network to make a solid. An example is carbon in the form of diamond, in which each carbon atom shares an electron with four adjacent ones. These atoms are arranged at equal angles to one another in three-dimensional space, as illustrated in Fig. 2.5. As a result of the strong and directional bonds, the crystal is very hard and stiff. Another important continuous arrangement of covalent bonds is the carbon chain. For example, in the gas *ethylene*, C_2H_4, each molecule is formed by covalent bonds, as shown in Fig. 2.6. However, if the double bond between the carbon atoms is replaced by a single bond to each of two adjacent carbon atoms, then a long chain molecule can form. The result is the polymer called *polyethylene*.

Many solids, such as SiO_2 and other ceramics, have chemical bonds that have a mixed ionic–covalent character. The examples given previously of NaCl for ionic bonding and of diamond for covalent bonding do represent cases of nearly pure bonding of these types, but mixed bonding is more common.

Metals of more than one type may be melted together to form an *alloy*. Metallic bonding is the dominant type in such cases. However, *intermetallic compounds* may form within alloys, often as hard particles. These compounds have a definite chemical formula, such as $TiAl_3$ or Mg_2Ni, and their bonding is generally a combination of the metallic and ionic or covalent types.

2.2.3 Secondary Bonds

Secondary bonds occur due to the presence of an electrostatic dipole, which can be induced by a primary bond. For example, in water, the side of a hydrogen atom away from the covalent bond to

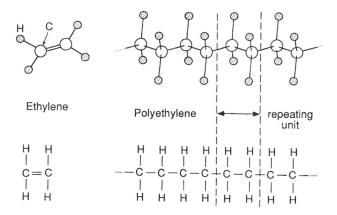

H H		H H H H	H H	H H
C = C		C — C — C — C + C — C + C — C —

Figure 2.6   Molecular structures of ethylene gas (C_2H_4) and polyethylene polymer. The double bond in ethylene is replaced by two single bonds in polyethylene, permitting formation of the chain molecule.

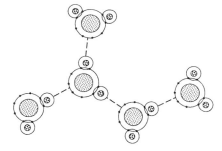

Figure 2.7   Oxygen-to-hydrogen secondary bonds between water (H_2O) molecules.

the oxygen atom has a positive charge, due to the sole electron being predominantly on the side toward the oxygen atom. Conservation of charge over the entire molecule then requires a negative charge on the exposed portion of the oxygen atom. The dipoles formed cause an attraction between adjacent molecules, as illustrated in Fig. 2.7.

Such bonds, termed *permanent dipole bonds*, occur between various molecules. They are relatively weak, but are nevertheless sometimes sufficient to bind materials into solids, water ice being an example. Where the secondary bond involves hydrogen, as in the case of water, it is stronger than other dipole bonds and is called a *hydrogen bond*.

Van der Waals bonds arise from the fluctuating positions of electrons relative to an atom's nucleus. The uneven distribution of electric charge that thus occurs causes a weak attraction between atoms or molecules. This type of bond can also be called a *fluctuating dipole bond*—distinguished from a permanent dipole bond because the dipole is not fixed in direction as it is in a water molecule. Bonds of this type allow the inert gases to form solids at low temperature.

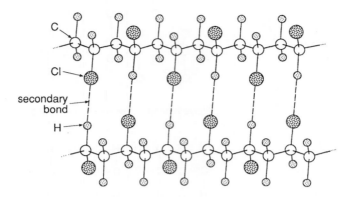

Figure 2.8   Hydrogen-to-chlorine secondary bonds between chain molecules in polyvinyl chloride.

In polymers, covalent bonds form the chain molecules and attach hydrogen and other atoms to the carbon backbone. Hydrogen bonds and other secondary bonds occur between the chain molecules and tend to prevent them from sliding past one another. This is illustrated in Fig. 2.8 for polyvinyl chloride. The relative weakness of the secondary bonds accounts for the low melting temperatures, and the low strengths and stiffnesses, of these materials.

2.3 STRUCTURE IN CRYSTALLINE MATERIALS

Metals and ceramics are composed of aggregations of small grains, each of which is an individual crystal. In contrast, glasses have an amorphous or noncrystalline structure. Polymers are composed of chainlike molecules, which are sometimes arranged in regular arrays in a crystalline manner.

2.3.1 Basic Crystal Structures

The arrangement of atoms (or ions) in crystals can be described in terms of the smallest grouping that can be considered to be a building block for a perfect crystal. Such a grouping, called a *unit cell*, can be classified according to the lengths and angles involved. There are seven basic types of unit cell, three of which are shown in Fig. 2.9. If all three angles are 90° and all distances are the same, the crystal is classed as *cubic*. But if one distance is not equal to the other two, the crystal is *tetragonal*. If, in addition, one angle is 120° while the other two remain at 90°, the crystal is *hexagonal*. The four additional types are orthorhombic, rhombohedral, monoclinic, and triclinic.

For a given type of unit cell, various arrangements of atoms are possible; each such arrangement is called a *crystal structure*. Three crystal structures having a cubic unit cell are the *primitive cubic* (PC), *body-centered cubic* (BCC), and *face-centered cubic* (FCC) structures. These are illustrated in Fig. 2.10. Note that the PC structure has atoms only at the corners of the cube, whereas the BCC structure also has one in the center of the cube. The FCC structure has atoms at the cube corners and in the center of each surface. The PC structure occurs only rarely, but the BCC structure is found in a number of common metals, such as chromium, iron, molybdenum, sodium, and

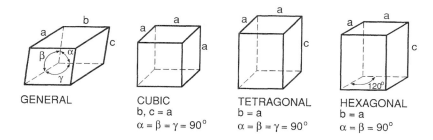

Figure 2.9   The general case of a unit cell in a crystal and three of the seven basic types.

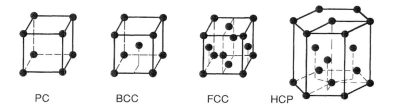

Figure 2.10   Four crystal structures: primitive cubic (PC), body-centered cubic (BCC), face-centered cubic (FCC), and hexagonal close-packed (HCP) structures.

tungsten. Similarly, the FCC structure is common for metals, as in silver, aluminum, lead, copper, and nickel.

The *hexagonal close-packed* (HCP) crystal structure is also common in metals. Although the unit cell is the one shown in Fig. 2.9, it is useful to illustrate this structure by using a larger grouping that forms a hexagonal prism, as shown in Fig. 2.10. Two parallel planes, called basal planes, have atoms at the corners and center of a hexagon, and there are three additional atoms halfway between these planes, as shown. Some common metals having this structure are beryllium, magnesium, titanium, and zinc.

A given metal or other material may change its crystal structure with temperature or pressure, or with the addition of alloying elements. For example, the BCC structure of iron changes to FCC above 910°C, and back to BCC above 1390°C. These phases are often called, respectively, alpha iron, gamma iron, and delta iron, denoted α-Fe, γ-Fe, and δ-Fe. Also, the addition of about 10% nickel or manganese changes the crystal structure to FCC, even at room temperature. Similarly, HCP titanium is called α-Ti, whereas β-Ti has a BCC structure and occurs above 885°C, although it can also exist at room temperature as a result of alloying and processing.

2.3.2 More Complex Crystal Structures

Compounds formed by ionic or covalent bonding, such as ionic salts and ceramics, have more complex crystal structures than elemental materials. This is due to the necessity of accommodating more than one type of atom and to the directional aspect of even partially covalent bonds. However,

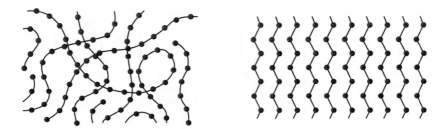

Figure 2.11   Two-dimensional schematics of amorphous structure (left) and crystalline structure (right) in a polymer.

the structure can often be thought of as an elaboration of one of the basic crystal structures. For example, NaCl is an FCC arrangement of Cl^- ions with Na^+ ions at intermediate positions, so these also form an FCC structure that is merged with the one for the Cl^- ions. See Fig. 2.4. Many important ionic salts and ceramics have this structure, including oxides such as MgO and FeO, and carbides such as TiC and ZrC.

In the *diamond cubic* structure of carbon, half of the atoms form an FCC structure, and the other half lie at intermediate positions, as required by the tetragonal bonding geometry, also forming an FCC structure. (See Fig. 2.5.) Another solid with a diamond cubic structure is SiC, in which Si and C atoms occupy alternate sites in the same structure as in Fig. 2.5. The ceramic Al_2O_3 has a crystal structure with a hexagonal unit cell, with aluminum atoms occurring in two-thirds of the spaces available between the oxygen atoms. Many ceramics have even more complex crystal structures than these examples. Intermetallic compounds also have crystal structures that range from fairly simple to quite complex. An example of one of the simpler ones is Ni_3Al, which has an FCC structure, with aluminum atoms at the cube corners and nickel atoms at the face centers.

Polymers may be amorphous, in that the structure is an irregular tangle of chain molecules. Alternatively, portions or even most of the material may have the chains arranged in a regular manner under the influence of the secondary bonds between the chains. Such regions are said to have a crystalline structure. This is illustrated in Fig. 2.11.

2.3.3 Defects in Crystals

Ceramics and metals in the form used for engineering applications are composed of crystalline *grains* that are separated by *grain boundaries*. This is shown for a metal in Fig. 2.12, and also in Fig. 1.7. Materials with such a structure are said to be *polycrystalline* materials. Grain sizes vary widely, from as small as $1\ \mu m$ to as large as $10\ mm$, depending on the material and its processing. Even within grains, the crystals are not perfect, with defects occurring that can be classed as *point defects*, *line defects*, or *surface defects*. Both grain boundaries and crystal defects within grains can have large effects on mechanical behavior. In discussing these, it is useful to use the term *lattice plane* to describe the regular parallel planes of atoms in a perfect crystal, and the term *lattice site* to describe the position of one atom.

Some types of point defects are illustrated in Fig. 2.13. A *substitutional impurity* occupies a normal lattice site, but is an atom of a different element than the bulk material. A *vacancy* is the

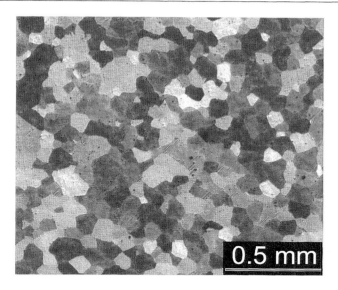

Figure 2.12   Crystal grain structure in a magnesium alloy containing 12 wt% lithium. This cast metal was prepared in a high-frequency induction melting furnace under an argon atmosphere. (Photo courtesy of Milo Kral, University of Canterbury, Christchurch, New Zealand; used with permission.)

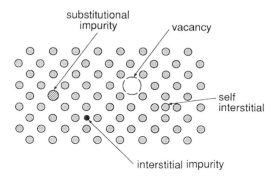

Figure 2.13   Four types of point defect in a crystalline solid.

absence of an atom at a normally occupied lattice site, and an *interstitial* is an atom occupying a position between normal lattice sites. If the interstitial is of the same type as the bulk material, it is called a *self interstitial*; and if it is of another kind, it is called an *interstitial impurity*.

Relatively small impurity atoms often occupy interstitial sites in materials with larger atoms. An example is carbon in solid solution in iron. If the impurity atoms are of similar size to those of the bulk material, they are more likely to appear as substitutional impurities. This is the normal situation where two metals are alloyed—that is, melted together. An example is the addition of 10 to 20% chromium to iron (and in some cases also of 10 to 20% nickel) to make stainless steel.

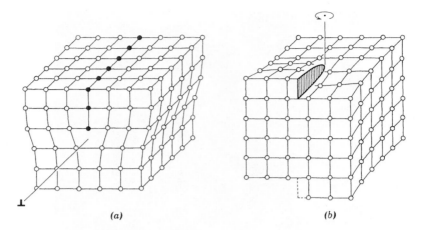

(a)   *(b)*

Figure 2.14   The two basic types of dislocations: (a) edge dislocation, and (b) screw dislocation. (From [Hayden 65] p. 63; used with permission.)

Line defects are called *dislocations* and are the edges of surfaces where there is a relative displacement of lattice planes. One type is an *edge dislocation*, and the other is a *screw dislocation*, both of which are illustrated in Fig. 2.14. The edge dislocation can be thought of as the border of an extra plane of atoms, as shown in (a). The *dislocation line* shown identifies the edge of the extra plane, and the special symbol indicated is sometimes used.

The screw dislocation can be explained by assuming that a perfect crystal is cut as shown in Fig. 2.14(b). The crystal is then displaced parallel to the cut and finally reconnected into the configuration shown. The dislocation line is the edge of the cut and hence also the border of the displaced region. Dislocations in solids generally have a combined edge and screw character and form curves and loops. Where many are present, complex tangles of dislocation lines may form.

Grain boundaries can be thought of as a class of surface defect where the lattice planes change orientation by a large angle. Within a grain, there may also be *low-angle boundaries*. An array of edge dislocations can form such a boundary, as shown in Fig. 2.15. Several low-angle boundaries may exist within a grain, separating regions of slightly different lattice orientation, which are called *subgrains*.

There are additional types of surface defects. A *twin boundary* separates two regions of a crystal where the lattice planes are a mirror image of one another. If the lattice planes are not in the proper sequence for a perfect crystal, a *stacking fault* is said to exist.

2.4 ELASTIC DEFORMATION AND THEORETICAL STRENGTH

The discussion of bonding and structure in solids can be extended to a consideration of the physical mechanisms of deformation, as viewed at the size scales of atoms, dislocations, and grains. Recall from Chapter 1 that there are three basic types of deformation: elastic, plastic, and

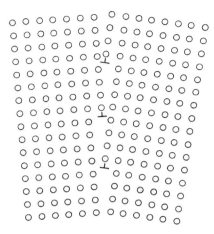

Figure 2.15 Low-angle boundary in a crystal formed by an array of edge dislocations. (From [Boyer 85] p. 2.15; used with permission.)

creep deformation. Elastic deformation is discussed next, and this leads to some rough theoretical estimates of strength for solids.

2.4.1 Elastic Deformation

Elastic deformation is associated with stretching, but not breaking, the chemical bonds between the atoms in a solid. If an external stress is applied to a material, the distance between the atoms changes by a small amount that depends on the material and the details of its structure and bonding. These distance changes, when accumulated over a piece of material of macroscopic size, are called elastic deformations.

  If the atoms in a solid were very far apart, there would be no forces between them. As the distance x between atoms is decreased, they begin to attract one another according to the type of bonding that applies to the particular case. This is illustrated by the upper curve in Fig. 2.16. A repulsive force also acts that is associated with resistance to overlapping of the electron shells of the two atoms. This repulsive force is smaller than the attractive force at relatively large distances, but it increases more rapidly, becoming larger at short distances. The total force is thus attractive at large distances, repulsive at short distances, and zero at one particular distance x_e, which is the equilibrium atomic spacing. This is also the point of minimum potential energy.

  Elastic deformations of engineering interest usually represent only a small perturbation about the equilibrium spacing, typically less than 1% strain. The slope of the total force curve over this small region is approximately constant. Let us express force on a unit area basis as stress, $\sigma = P/A$, where A is the cross-sectional area of material per atom. Also, note that strain is the ratio of the change in x to the equilibrium distance x_e.

$$\sigma = \frac{P}{A}, \qquad \varepsilon = \frac{x - x_e}{x_e} \tag{2.1}$$

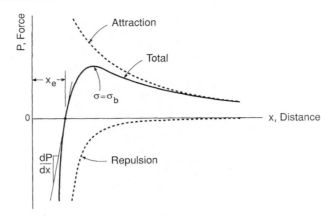

Figure 2.16 Variation with distance of the attractive, repulsive, and total forces between atoms. The slope dP/dx at the equilibrium spacing x_e is proportional to the elastic modulus E; the stress σ_b, corresponding to the peak in total force, is the theoretical cohesive strength.

Since the elastic modulus E is the slope of the stress–strain relationship, we have

$$E = \left.\frac{d\sigma}{d\varepsilon}\right|_{x=x_e} = \left.\frac{x_e}{A}\frac{dP}{dx}\right|_{x=x_e} \qquad (2.2)$$

Hence, E is fixed by the slope of the total force curve at $x = x_e$, which is illustrated in Fig. 2.16.

2.4.2 Trends in Elastic Modulus Values

Strong primary chemical bonds are resistant to stretching and so result in a high value of E. For example, the strong covalent bonds in diamond yield a value around $E = 1000$ GPa, whereas the weaker metallic bonds in metals give values generally within a factor of three of $E = 100$ GPa. In polymers, E is determined by the combination of covalent bonding along the carbon chains and the much weaker secondary bonding between chains. At relatively low temperatures, many polymers exist in a glassy or crystalline state. The modulus is then on the order of $E = 3$ GPa, but it varies considerably above and below this level, depending on the chain-molecule structure and other details. If the temperature is increased, thermal activation provides increased *free volume* between chain molecules, permitting motion of increased lengths of chain. A point is reached where large scale motions become possible, causing the elastic modulus to decrease, often dramatically. This trend is shown for polystyrene in Fig. 2.17.

The temperature where the rapid decrease in E occurs varies for different polymers and is called the *glass transition temperature*, T_g. Melting does not occur until the polymer reaches a somewhat higher temperature, T_m, provided that chemical decomposition does not occur first. Above T_g, the elastic modulus may be as low as $E = 1$ MPa. Viscous flow is now prevented only by tangling of the long chain molecules and by the secondary bonds in any crystalline regions of the polymer.

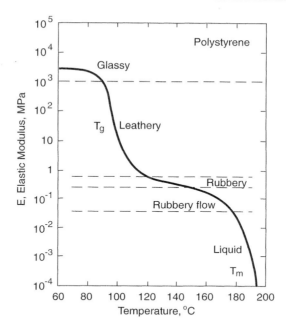

Figure 2.17   Variation of elastic modulus with temperature for polystyrene. (Data from [Tobolsky 65].)

A polymer has a leathery or rubbery character above its T_g, as do vulcanized natural rubber and synthetic rubbers at room temperature.

For single crystals, E varies with the direction relative to the crystal structure; that is, crystals are more resistant to elastic deformation in some directions than in others. But in a polycrystalline aggregate of randomly oriented grains, an averaging effect occurs, so that E is the same in all directions. This latter situation is at least approximated for most engineering metals and ceramics.

2.4.3 Theoretical Strength

A value for the *theoretical cohesive strength* of a solid can be obtained by using solid-state physics to estimate the tensile stress necessary to break primary chemical bonds, which is the stress σ_b corresponding to the peak value of force in Fig. 2.16. These values are on the order of $\sigma_b = E/10$ for various materials. Hence, for diamond, $\sigma_b \approx 100\,\text{GPa}$, and for a typical metal, $\sigma_b \approx 10\,\text{GPa}$.

Rather than the bonds being simply pulled apart in tension, another possibility is shear failure. A simple calculation can be done to obtain an estimate of the *theoretical shear strength*. Consider two planes of atoms being forced to move slowly past one another, as in Fig. 2.18. The shear stress τ required first increases rapidly with displacement x, then decreases and passes through zero as the atoms pass opposite one another at the unstable equilibrium position $x = b/2$. The stress

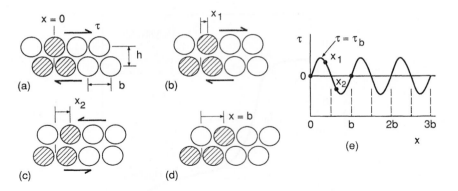

Figure 2.18 Basis of estimates of theoretical shear strength, where it is assumed that entire planes of atoms shift simultaneously, relative to one another.

changes direction beyond this as the atoms try to snap into a second stable configuration at $x = b$. A reasonable estimate is a sinusoidal variation

$$\tau = \tau_b \sin \frac{2\pi x}{b} \tag{2.3}$$

where τ_b is the maximum value as τ varies with x; hence, it is the theoretical shear strength.

The initial slope of the stress–strain relationship must be the shear modulus, G, in a manner analogous to E for the tension case previously discussed. Noting that the shear strain for small values of displacement is $\gamma = x/h$, we have

$$G = \frac{d\tau}{d\gamma}\bigg|_{x=0} = h\frac{d\tau}{dx}\bigg|_{x=0} \tag{2.4}$$

Obtaining $d\tau/dx$ from Eq. 2.3 and substituting its value at $x = 0$ gives τ_b:

$$\tau_b = \frac{Gb}{2\pi h} \tag{2.5}$$

The ratio b/h varies with the crystal structure and is generally around 0.5 to 1, so this estimate is on the order of $G/10$.

In a tension test, the maximum shear stress occurs on a plane $45°$ to the direction of uniaxial stress and is half as large. Thus, a theoretical estimate of shear failure in a tension test is

$$\sigma_b = 2\tau_b = \frac{Gb}{\pi h} \tag{2.6}$$

Since G is in the range $E/2$ to $E/3$, this estimate gives a value similar to the previously mentioned $\sigma_b = E/10$ estimate based on the tensile breaking of bonds. Estimates of theoretical strength are discussed in more detail in the first chapter of Kelly (1986).

Table 2.2   Elastic Modulus and Strength of Single-Crystal Whiskers and Strong Fibers and Wires

Material	Elastic Modulus E, GPa (10^3 ksi)		Tensile Strength σ_u, GPa (ksi)		Ratio E/σ_u
(a) Whiskers					
SiC	700	(102)	21.0	(3050)	33
Graphite	686	(99.5)	19.6	(2840)	35
Al_2O_3	420	(60.9)	22.3	(3230)	19
α-Fe	196	(28.4)	12.6	(1830)	16
Si	163	(23.6)	7.6	(1100)	21
NaCl	42	(6.09)	1.1	(160)	38
(b) Fibers and wires					
SiC	616	(89.3)	8.3	(1200)	74
Tungsten (0.26 μm diameter)	405	(58.7)	24.0	(3500)	17
Tungsten (25 μm diameter)	405	(58.7)	3.9	(570)	104
Al_2O_3	379	(55.0)	2.1	(300)	180
Graphite	256	(37.1)	5.5	(800)	47
Iron	220	(31.9)	9.7	(1400)	23
Linear polyethylene	160	(23.2)	4.6	(670)	35
Drawn silica glass	73.5	(10.7)	10.0	(1450)	7.4

Source: Data in [Kelly 86].

Theoretical tensile strengths around $\sigma_b = E/10$ are larger than the actual strengths of solids by a large amount, typically by a factor of 10 to 100. This discrepancy is thought to be due mainly to the imperfections present in most crystals, which decrease the strength. However, small whiskers can be made that are nearly perfect single crystals. Also, thin fibers and wires may have a crystal structure such that strong chemical bonds are aligned with the length direction. Tensile strengths in such cases are indeed much higher than for larger and more imperfect samples of material. Strengths in the range from $E/100$ to $E/20$, corresponding to one-tenth to one-half of the theoretical strength, have been achieved in this way, lending credence to the estimates. Some representative data are given in Table 2.2.

2.5 INELASTIC DEFORMATION

As discussed in the previous section, elastic deformation involves the stretching of chemical bonds. When the stress is removed, the deformation disappears. More drastic events can occur which have the effect of rearranging the atoms so that they have new neighbors after the deformation is complete. This causes an inelastic deformation that does not disappear when the stress is removed. Inelastic deformation that occurs almost instantaneously as the stress is applied is called *plastic* deformation, as distinguished from *creep* deformation, which occurs only after passage of time under stress.

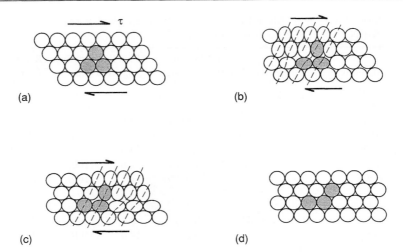

Figure 2.19   Shear deformation occurring in an incremental manner due to dislocation motion. (Adapted from [Van Vlack 89] p. 265, © 1989 by Addison-Wesley Publishing Co., Inc., by permission of Pearson Education, Inc., Upper Saddle River, NJ, and by permission of the Department of Materials Science and Engineering, University of Michigan, Ann Arbor, MI.)

2.5.1 Plastic Deformation by Dislocation Motion

Single crystals of pure metals that are macroscopic in size and which contain only a few dislocations are observed to yield in shear at very low stresses. For example, for iron and other BCC metals, this occurs around $\tau_o = G/3000$, that is, about $\tau_o = 30\,\text{MPa}$. For FCC and HCP metals, even lower values are obtained around $\tau_o = G/100,000$, or typically $\tau_o = 0.5\,\text{MPa}$. Thus, shear strengths for imperfect crystals of pure metals can be lower than the theoretical value for a perfect crystal of $\tau_b = G/10$ by at least a factor of 300 and sometimes by as much as a factor of 10,000.

This large discrepancy can be explained by the fact that plastic deformation occurs by motion of dislocations under the influence of a shear stress, as illustrated in Fig. 2.19. As a dislocation moves through the crystal, plastic deformation is, in effect, proceeding one atom at a time, rather than occurring simultaneously over an entire plane, as implied by Fig. 2.18. This incremental process can occur much more easily than simultaneous breaking of all the bonds, as assumed in the theoretical shear strength calculation for a perfect crystal.

The deformation resulting from dislocation motion proceeds for edge and screw dislocations, as illustrated in Fig. 2.20 and Fig. 2.21, respectively. The plane in which the dislocation line moves is called the *slip plane*, and where the slip plane intersects a free surface, a *slip step* is formed. Since dislocations in real crystals are usually curved and thus have both edge and screw character, plastic deformation actually occurs by a combination of the two types of dislocation motion.

Plastic deformation is often concentrated in bands called *slip bands*. These are regions where the slip planes of numerous dislocations are concentrated; hence, they are regions of intense plastic shear deformation separated by regions of little shear. Where slip bands intersect a free surface, steps are formed as a result of the combined slip steps of numerous dislocations. (See Fig. 2.22.)

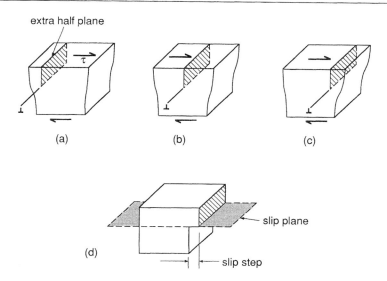

Figure 2.20   Slip caused by the motion of an edge dislocation.

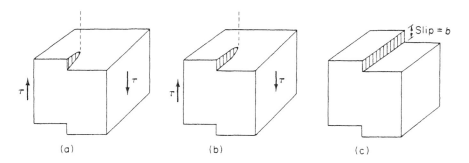

Figure 2.21   Slip caused by the motion of a screw dislocation. (From [Felbeck 96] p. 114; © 1996 by Prentice Hall, Upper Saddle River, NJ; reprinted with permission.)

For a given crystal structure, such as BCC, FCC, or HCP, slip is easier on certain planes, and within these planes in certain directions. For metals, the most common planes and directions are shown in Fig. 2.23. The preferred planes are those on which the atoms are relatively close together, called *close-packed planes*, such as the basal plane for the HCP crystal. Similarly, the preferred slip directions within a given plane are the *close-packed directions* in which the distances between atoms is smallest. This is the case because a dislocation can more easily move if the distance to the next atom is smaller. Also, atoms in adjacent planes project less into the spaces between atoms in the close-packed planes than in other planes, so there is less interference with slip displacement.

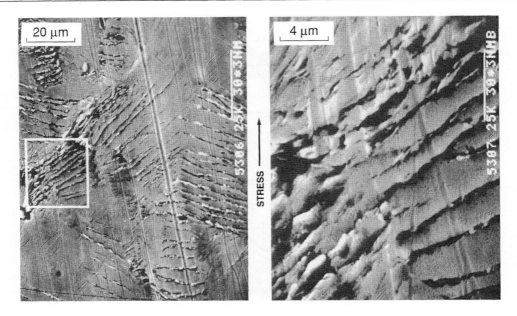

Figure 2.22   Slip bands and slip steps caused by the motion of many dislocations resulting from cyclic loading of AISI 1010 steel. (Photos courtesy of R. W. Landgraf, Howell, MI.)

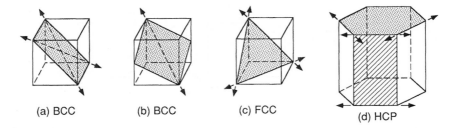

Figure 2.23   Some slip planes and directions frequently observed for BCC, FCC, and HCP crystal structures. Considering symmetry, there are additional combinations of slip plane and direction similar to each of these, giving a total of twelve slip systems similar to each of (a), (b), and (c), and three for each of the two cases in (d). (Adapted from [Hayden 65] p. 100; used with permission.)

2.5.2 Discussion of Plastic Deformation

The result of plastic deformation (yielding) is that atoms change neighbors and return to a stable configuration with new neighbors after the dislocation has passed. Note that this is a fundamentally different process than elastic deformation, which is merely the stretching of chemical bonds. Elastic deformation occurs as an essentially independent process along with plastic deformation. When

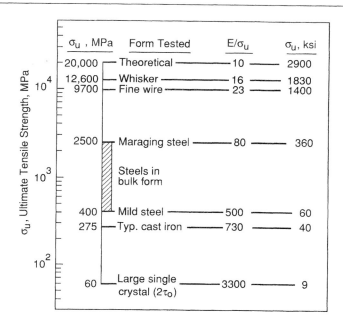

Figure 2.24 Ultimate tensile strengths for irons and steels in various forms. Note that steels are mostly composed of iron and contain small to moderate amounts of other elements. (Data from [Boyer 85], [Hayden 65], and [Kelly 86].)

a stress that causes yielding is removed, the elastic strain is recovered just as if there had been no yielding, but the plastic strain is permanent. (See Fig. 1.2.)

Metals used in load-resisting applications have strengths considerably above the very low values observed in crystals of pure metals with some defects, but not nearly as high as the very high theoretical value for a perfect crystal. This is illustrated in Fig. 2.24 for irons and steels, which are composed mostly of iron. If there are obstacles that impede dislocation motion, the strength may be increased by a factor of 10 or more above the low value for a pure metal crystal. Grain boundaries have this effect, as does a second phase of hard particles dispersed in the metal. Alloying also increases strength, as the different-sized atoms make dislocation motion more difficult. If a large number of dislocations are present, these interfere with one another, forming dense tangles and blocking free movement.

In nonmetals and compounds where the chemical bonding is covalent or partially covalent, the directional nature of the bonds makes dislocation motion difficult. Materials in this class include the crystals of carbon, boron, and silicon, and also intermetallic compounds and compounds formed between metals and nonmetals, such as metal carbides, borides, nitrides, oxides, and other ceramics. At ambient temperatures, these materials are hard and brittle and do not generally fail by yielding due to dislocation motion. Instead, the strength falls below the high theoretical value for a perfect crystal mainly because of the weakening effect of small cracks and pores that are present in the material. However, some dislocation motion does occur, especially for temperatures above about half of the (usually high) melting temperature, where T_m is measured relative to absolute zero.

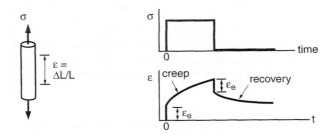

Figure 2.25   Accumulation of creep strain with time under constant stress, and partial recovery after removal of the stress.

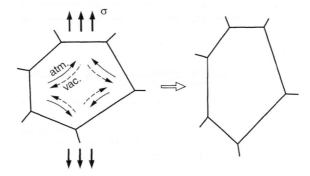

Figure 2.26   Mechanism of creep by diffusion of vacancies within a crystal grain.

2.5.3 Creep Deformation

In addition to elastic and plastic deformation as already described, materials deform by mechanisms that result in markedly time-dependent behavior, called *creep*. Under constant stress, the strain varies with time, as shown in Fig. 2.25. There is an initial elastic deformation ε_e, and following this, the strain slowly increases as long as the stress is maintained. If the stress is removed, the elastic strain is quickly recovered, and a portion of the creep strain may be recovered slowly with time; the rest remains as permanent deformation.

In crystalline materials—that is, in metals and ceramics—one important mechanism of creep is *diffusional flow* of vacancies. Spontaneous formation of vacancies is favored near grain boundaries that are approximately normal to the applied stress and is disfavored for parallel ones. This results in an uneven distribution of vacancies and in vacancies diffusing, or moving, from regions of high concentration to regions of low concentration, as illustrated in Fig. 2.26. As indicated, movement of a vacancy in one direction is equivalent to movement of an atom in the opposite direction. The overall effect is a change in the shape of the grain, contributing to a macroscopic creep strain.

Some other creep mechanisms that operate in crystalline materials include special dislocation motions that can circumvent obstacles in a time-dependent manner. There may also be sliding of grain boundaries and the formation of cavities along grain boundaries. Creep behavior in crystalline materials is strongly temperature dependent, typically becoming an important engineering consideration around 0.3 to $0.6T_m$, where T_m is the absolute melting temperature.

Different creep mechanisms operate in amorphous (noncrystalline) glasses and in polymers. One of these is viscous flow in the manner of a very thick liquid. This occurs in polymers at temperatures substantially above the glass transition temperature T_g and approaching T_m. The chainlike molecules simply slide past one another in a time-dependent manner. Around and below T_g, more complex behavior involving segments of chains and obstacles to chain sliding become important. In this case, much of the creep deformation may disappear slowly (recover) with time after removal of an applied stress, as illustrated in Fig. 2.25. Creep is a major limitation on the engineering application of any polymer above its T_g, which is generally in the range -100 to $200°C$ for common polymers.

Additional discussion on mechanisms of creep deformation is given in Chapter 15.

2.6 SUMMARY

Atoms and molecules in solids are held together by primary chemical bonds of three kinds: ionic, covalent, and metallic. Secondary bonds, especially hydrogen bonds, also influence the behavior. Covalent bonds are strong and directional and therefore resist deformation. This contributes to the high strength and brittleness of ceramics and glasses, as these materials are bound by covalent or mixed ionic–covalent bonds. Metallic bonds in metals do not have such a directionality and therefore deform more easily. Polymers are composed of carbon-chain molecules formed by covalent bonds. However, they may deform easily by relative sliding between the chain molecules where this is prevented only by secondary bonds.

A variety of crystal structures exist in solid materials. Three of particular importance for metals are the body-centered cubic (BCC), face-centered cubic (FCC), and hexagonal close-packed (HCP) structures. The crystal structures of ceramics are often elaborations of these simple structures, but greater complexity exists due to the necessity in these compounds of accommodating more than one type of atom. Crystalline materials (metals and ceramics) are composed of aggregations of small crystal grains. Numerous defects, such as vacancies, interstitials, and dislocations are usually present in these grains.

Elastic deformation, caused by the stretching of chemical bonds, disappears if the stress is removed. The elastic modulus E is therefore higher if the bonding is stronger and is highest in covalent solids such as diamond. Metals have a value of E about 10 times lower than that for highly covalent solids, and polymers have a value of E that is generally lower by an additional factor of 10 or more, due to the influence of the chain-molecule structure and secondary bonds. Above the glass-transition temperature for a given polymer, E is further lowered by a large amount, then becoming smaller than for diamond by as much as a factor of 10^6.

Estimates of the theoretical tensile strength to break chemical bonds in perfect crystals give values on the order of $E/10$. However, strengths approaching such a high value are realized only in tiny, perfect single crystals and in fine wires with an aligned structure. Strengths in large samples of material are much lower, as these are weakened by defects. In ceramics, the defects of importance are small cracks and pores that contribute to brittle behavior.

In metals, the defects that lower the strength are primarily dislocations. These move under the influence of applied stresses and cause yielding behavior. In large single crystals containing a few dislocations, yielding occurs at very low stresses that are lower than the theoretical value by a factor of 300 or more. Strengths are increased above this value if there are obstacles to dislocation motion, such as grain boundaries, hard second-phase particles, alloying elements, and dislocation entanglements. The resulting strength for engineering metals in bulk form may be as high as one-tenth of the theoretical value of $E/10$, that is, around $E/100$.

Materials are also subject to time-dependent deformation called creep. Such deformation is especially likely at temperatures approaching melting. Physical mechanisms vary with material and temperature. Examples include diffusion of vacancies in metals and ceramics and sliding of chain molecules in polymers.

The necessarily brief treatment given in this chapter on structure and deformation in materials represents only a minimal introduction to the topic. More detail is given in a number of excellent books, a few of which are listed as references at the end of this chapter.

NEW TERMS AND SYMBOLS

body-centered cubic (BCC) structure

close-packed planes, directions

covalent bond

diamond cubic structure

edge dislocation

face-centered cubic (FCC) structure

glass transition temperature, T_g

grain boundary

hexagonal close-packed (HCP) structure

interstitial

ionic bond

lattice plane; lattice site

melting temperature, T_m

metallic bond

polycrystalline material

screw dislocation

secondary (hydrogen) bond

slip plane

slip step

substitutional impurity

theoretical cohesive strength, $\sigma_b \approx E/10$

theoretical shear strength, $\tau_b \approx G/10$

unit cell

vacancy

REFERENCES

CALLISTER, W. D., Jr., and D. G. RETHWISCH. 2010. *Materials Science and Engineering: An Introduction*, 8th ed., John Wiley, Hoboken, NJ.

COURTNEY, T. H. 2000. *Mechanical Behavior of Materials*, McGraw-Hill, New York.

DAVIS, J. R., ed. 1998. *Metals Handbook: Desk Edition*, 2d ed., ASM International, Materials Park, OH.

HAYDEN, H. W., W. G. MOFFATT, and J. WULFF. 1965. *The Structure and Properties of Materials, Vol. III: Mechanical Behavior*, John Wiley, New York.

HOSFORD, W. H. 2010. *Mechanical Behavior of Materials*, 2nd ed., Cambridge University Press, New York.

KELLY, A., and N. H. MACMILLAN. 1986. *Strong Solids*, 3d ed., Clarendon Press, Oxford, UK.

MOFFATT, W. G., G. W. PEARSALL, and J. WULFF. 1964. *The Structure and Properties of Materials, Vol. I: Structure*, John Wiley, New York.

SHACKELFORD, J. F. 2009. *Introduction to Materials Science for Engineers*, 7th ed., Prentice Hall, Upper Saddle River, NJ.

PROBLEMS AND QUESTIONS

Section 2.4

2.1 Table 2.2(b) gives a value of $E = 160\,\text{GPa}$ for a fiber of linear polyethylene, in which the polymer chains are aligned with the fiber axis. Why is this value so much higher than the typical $E = 3\,\text{GPa}$ mentioned for polymers—in fact almost as high as the value for iron and steel?

2.2 Consider Fig. 2.16, and assume that it is possible to make accurate measurements of the elastic modulus E for high stresses in both tension and compression. Describe the expected variation of E with stress.

2.3 Consider Fig. 2.16 and two atoms that are initially an infinite distance apart, $x = \infty$, at which point the potential energy of the system is $U = 0$. If they are brought together to $x = x_1$, the potential energy is related to the total force P by

$$\frac{dU}{dx}\bigg|_{x=x_1} = P$$

Given this, qualitatively sketch the variation of U with x. What happens at $x = x_e$? What is the significance of $x = x_e$ in terms of the potential energy?

2.4 Using Table 2.2, compare the strengths of Al_2O_3 whiskers versus Al_2O_3 fibers, and also compare the two diameters of tungsten wire with each other. Can you explain the large differences observed?

2.5 Consult Callister (2010) or Shackelford (2009) in the References, or another materials science or chemistry text, and study the crystal structure of carbon in the form of graphite. How does the structure differ from that of diamond? Why is graphite in bulk form usually soft and weak? And how could a whisker of such a material have the high strength and elastic modulus indicated in Table 2.2(a)?

Section 2.5

2.6 Explain why slip in a crystal is easiest in close-packed planes, and within these planes, in close-packed directions.

2.7 Explain why polycrystalline metals with an HCP crystal structure are generally more brittle than polycrystalline BCC metals.

2.8 With a proper sequence of thermal processing, aluminum alloyed with 4% copper can be caused to contain a large number of very small particles of the hard intermetallic compound $CuAl_2$. How would you expect the yield strength of such a processed alloy to differ from that for pure aluminum? Answer the same question for the percent elongation? Why?

2.9 Cold working a metal by rolling it to a lesser thickness or hammering it introduces a large number of dislocations into the crystal structure. Would you expect the yield strength to be affected by this; and if so, should it increase or decrease, and why? Also, answer the same question for the elastic modulus.

2.10 In metals, grain size d is observed to be related to yield strength by

$$\sigma_o = A + Bd^{-1/2}$$

where A and B are constants for a given material. Does this trend make physical sense? Can you explain qualitatively why this equation is reasonable? What physical interpretation can you make of the constant A?

2.11 An important group of polymers called thermosetting plastics forms a network structure by means of covalent bonds between the chain molecules. How would you expect these to differ from other polymers as to the value of the elastic modulus and the resistance to creep deformation, and why?

2.12 Consider creep by diffusion of vacancies in a polycrystalline metal or ceramic, as illustrated in Fig. 2.26. Would you expect the resulting creep strain to vary with the crystal grain size of the material? Do larger grains result in more rapid accumulation of creep strain, or in slower accumulation of creep strain? Why?

3

A Survey of Engineering Materials

OBJECTIVES

- Become familiar with the four major classes of materials used to resist mechanical loading: metals and alloys, polymers, ceramics and glasses, and composites.
- For each major class, gain a general knowledge of their characteristics, internal structure, behavior, and processing methods.
- Learn typical materials, naming systems, and common uses, and develop an appreciation for how uses of materials are related to their properties.
- Apply a general method for selecting a material for a given engineering component.

3.1 INTRODUCTION

Materials used for resistance to mechanical loading, which are here termed *engineering materials*, can belong to any of four major classes: metals and alloys, polymers, ceramics and glasses, and composites. The first three of these categories have already been discussed to an extent in the previous chapter from the viewpoint of structure and deformation mechanisms. Examples of members of each class are given in Table 2.1, and their general characteristics are illustrated in Fig. 2.1.

In this chapter, each major class of materials is considered in more detail. Groups of related materials within each major class are identified, the effects of processing variables are summarized, and the systems used for naming various materials are described. Metals and alloys are the dominant engineering materials in current use in many applications, so more space is devoted to these than to the others. However, polymers, ceramics and glasses, and composites are also of major importance. Recent improvements in nonmetallic and composite materials have resulted in a trend toward these replacing metals in some applications.

An essential part of the process of engineering design is the selection of suitable materials from which to make engineering components. This requires at least a general knowledge of the composition, structure, and characteristics of materials, as summarized in this chapter. For a particular engineering component, the choice among candidate materials may sometimes be aided by systematic analysis, for example, to minimize mass or cost. Such analysis is introduced near the end of this chapter. Materials selection is also aided by specific prediction of strength, life, or amount of deformation, as described in later chapters related to yielding, fracture, fatigue, and creep.

3.2 ALLOYING AND PROCESSING OF METALS

Approximately 80% of the one-hundred-plus elements in the periodic table can be classed as metals. A number of these possess combinations of availability and properties that lead to their use as *engineering metals* where mechanical strength is needed. The most widely used engineering metal is iron, which is the main constituent of the iron-based alloys termed steels. Some other structural metals that are widely used are aluminum, copper, titanium, magnesium, nickel, and cobalt. Additional common metals, such as zinc, lead, tin, and silver, are used where the stresses are quite low, as in various low-strength cast parts and solder joints. The *refractory metals*, notably molybdenum, niobium, tantalum, tungsten, and zirconium, have melting temperatures somewhat or even substantially above that of iron (1538°C). Relatively small quantities of these are used as engineering metals for specialized applications, particularly where high strength is needed at a very high temperature. Some properties and uses for selected engineering metals are given in Table 3.1.

A metal alloy is usually a melted-together combination of two or more chemical elements, where the bulk of the material consists of one or more metals. A wide variety of metallic and nonmetallic chemical elements are used in alloying the principal engineering metals. Some of the more common ones are boron, carbon, magnesium, silicon, vanadium, chromium, manganese, nickel, copper, zinc, molybdenum, and tin. The amounts and combinations of alloying elements used with various metals have major effects on their strength, ductility, temperature resistance, corrosion resistance, and other properties.

For a given alloy composition, the properties are further affected by the particular processing used. Processing includes *heat treatment*, *deformation*, and *casting*. In heat treatment, a metal or alloy is subjected to a particular schedule of heating, holding at temperature, and cooling that causes desirable physical or chemical changes. Deformation is the process of forcing a piece of material to change its thickness or shape. Some of the means of doing so are *forging, rolling, extruding*, and *drawing*, as illustrated in Fig. 3.1. Casting is simply the pouring of melted metal into a mold so that it conforms to the shape of the mold when it solidifies. Heat treatment and deformation or casting may be used in combination, and particular alloying elements are often added because they

Table 3.1   Properties and Uses for Selected Engineering Metals and their Alloys

Metal	Melting Temp.	Density	Elastic Modulus	Typical Strength	Uses; Comments
	T_m °C (°F)	ρ g/cm^3 (lb/ft^3)	E GPa (10^3 ksi)	σ_u MPa (ksi)	
Iron (Fe) and steel	1538 (2800)	7.87 (491)	212 (30.7)	200 to 2500 (30 to 360)	Diverse: structures, machine and vehicle parts, tools. Most widely used engineering metal.
Aluminum (Al)	660 (1220)	2.70 (168)	70 (10.2)	140 to 550 (20 to 80)	Aircraft and other lightweight structure and parts.
Titanium (Ti)	1670 (3040)	4.51 (281)	120 (17.4)	340 to 1200 (50 to 170)	Aircraft structure and engines; industrial machine parts; surgical implants.
Copper (Cu)	1085 (1985)	8.93 (557)	130 (18.8)	170 to 1400 (25 to 200)	Electrical conductors; corrosion-resistant parts, valves, pipes. Alloyed to make bronze and brass.
Magnesium (Mg)	650 (1200)	1.74 (108)	45 (6.5)	170 to 340 (25 to 50)	Parts for high-speed machinery; aerospace parts.
Nickel (Ni)	1455 (2650)	8.90 (556)	210 (30.5)	340 to 1400 (50 to 200)	Jet engine parts; alloying addition for steels.
Cobalt (Co)	1495 (2720)	8.83 (551)	211 (30.6)	650 to 2000 (95 to 300)	Jet engine parts; wear resistant coatings; surgical implants.
Tungsten (W)	3422 (6190)	19.3 (1200)	411 (59.6)	120 to 650 (17 to 94)	Electrodes, light bulb filaments, flywheels, gyroscopes.
Lead (Pb)	328 (620)	11.3 (708)	16 (2.3)	12 to 80 (2 to 12)	Corrosion resistant piping; weights, shot. Alloyed with tin in solders.

Notes: The values of T_m, ρ, and E are only moderately sensitive to alloying. Ranges for σ_u and uses include alloys based on these metals. Properties ρ, E, and σ_u are at room temperature, except σ_u is at 1650°C for tungsten.
Source: Data in [Davis 98] and [Boyer 85].

influence such processing in a desirable way. Metals that are subjected to deformation as the final processing step are termed *wrought metals* to distinguish them as a group from cast metals.

The details of alloying and processing are chosen so that the material has appropriate temperature resistance, corrosion resistance, strength, ductility, and other required characteristics for its intended use. Recalling that plastic deformation is due to the motion of dislocations, the yield strength of a metal or alloy can usually be increased by introducing obstacles to dislocation motion. Such obstacles can be tangles of dislocations, grain boundaries, distorted crystal structure due to impurity atoms, or small particles dispersed in the crystal structure. Some of the principal processing methods used for strengthening metals are listed, along with the type of obstacle, in Table 3.2. We will now discuss each of these methods.

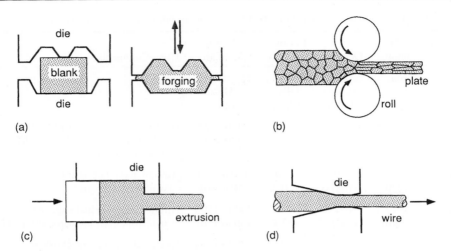

Figure 3.1   Some methods of forming metals into useful shapes are (a) forging, which employs compression or hammering; (b) rolling; (c) extrusion; and (d) drawing.

Table 3.2   Strengthening Methods for Metals and Alloys

Method	Features That Impede Dislocation Motion
Cold work	High dislocation density causing tangles
Grain refinement	Changes in crystal orientation and other irregularities at grain boundaries
Solid solution strengthening	Interstitial or substitutional impurities distorting the crystal lattice
Precipitation hardening	Fine particles of a hard material precipitating out of solution upon cooling
Multiple phases	Discontinuities in crystal structure at phase boundaries
Quenching and tempering	Multiphase structure of martensite and Fe_3C precipitates in BCC iron

3.2.1 Cold Work and Annealing

Cold work is the severe deforming of a metal at ambient temperature, often by rolling or drawing. This causes a dense array of dislocations and disorders the crystal structure, resulting in an increase in yield strength and a decrease in ductility. Strengthening occurs because the large number of dislocations form dense tangles that act as obstacles to further deformation. Hence, controlled amounts of cold work can be used to vary the properties. For example, this is done for copper and its alloys.

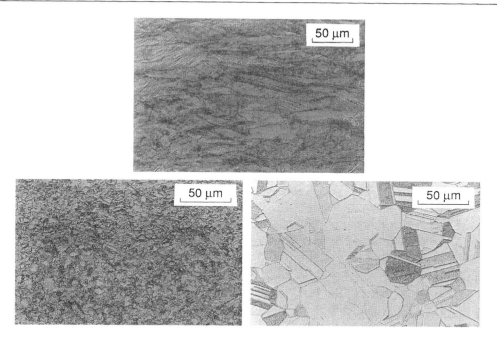

Figure 3.2   Microstructures of 70% Cu, 30% Zn brass in three conditions: cold worked (top); annealed one hour at 375°C (bottom left); and annealed one hour at 500°C (bottom right). (Photos courtesy of Olin Corp., New Haven, CT.)

The effects of cold work can be partially or completely reversed by heating the metal to such a high temperature that new crystals form within the solid material, a process called *annealing*. If this is done following severe cold work, the recrystallized grains are at first quite small. Cooling the material at this stage creates a situation where strengthening is said to be due to *grain refinement*, because the grain boundaries impede dislocation motion. A long annealing time, or annealing at a higher temperature, causes the grains to coalesce into larger sizes, resulting in a loss of strength, but a gain in ductility. The microstructural changes involved in cold working and annealing are illustrated in Fig. 3.2.

3.2.2 Solid Solution Strengthening

Solid solution strengthening occurs as a result of impurity atoms distorting the crystal lattice and thus making dislocation motion more difficult. Note that alloying elements are said to form a solid solution with the major constituent if their atoms are incorporated into the crystal structure in an orderly manner. The atoms providing the strengthening may be located at either interstitial or substitutional lattice positions. Atoms of much smaller size than those of the major constituent usually form interstitial alloys, as for hydrogen, boron, carbon, nitrogen, and oxygen in metals. Substitutional alloys may be formed by combinations of two or more metals, especially if the atomic sizes are similar and the preferred crystal structures are the same.

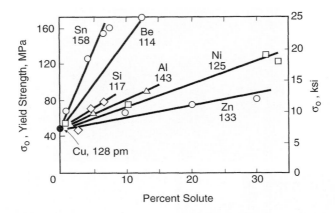

Figure 3.3   Effect of alloying on the yield strength of copper. Atomic sizes are given in picometers (10^{-12} m), and yield strengths correspond to 1% strain. (Adapted from [French 50]; used with permission.)

As might be expected, the effect of a substitutional impurity is greater if the atomic size differs more from that of the major constituent. This is illustrated by the effects of various percentages of alloying elements in copper in Fig. 3.3. Zinc and nickel have atomic sizes that do not differ very much from that of copper, so that the strengthening effect is small. But the small atoms of beryllium and the large ones of tin have a dramatic effect.

3.2.3 Precipitation Hardening and Other Multiple Phase Effects

The solubility of a particular impurity species in a given metal may be quite limited if the two elements have dissimilar chemical and physical properties, but this limited solubility usually increases with temperature. Such a situation may provide an opportunity for strengthening due to *precipitation hardening*. Consider an impurity that exists as a solid solution while the metal is held at a relatively high temperature, but also assume that the amount present exceeds the solubility limit for room temperature. Upon cooling, the impurity tends to precipitate out of solution, sometimes forming a chemical compound in the process. The precipitate is said to constitute a *second phase* as the chemical composition differs from that of the surrounding material. The yield strength may be increased substantially if the second phase has a hard crystal structure that resists deformation, and particularly if it exists as very small particles that are distributed fairly uniformly. Also, it is desirable for the precipitate particles to be *coherent* with the parent metal, meaning that the crystal planes are continuous across the precipitate particle boundary. This causes distortion of the crystal structure of the parent metal over some distance beyond the particle, enhancing its effect in making dislocation motion more difficult.

For example, aluminum with around 4% copper forms strengthening precipitates of the intermetallic compound $CuAl_2$. The means of achieving this is illustrated in Fig. 3.4. Slow cooling allows the impurity atoms to move relatively long distances, and the precipitate forms along the grain boundaries where it has little benefit. However, substantial benefit can be achieved by rapid cooling to form a supersaturated solution and then reheating to an intermediate temperature for a limited time. The reduced movement of the impurities at the intermediate temperature causes

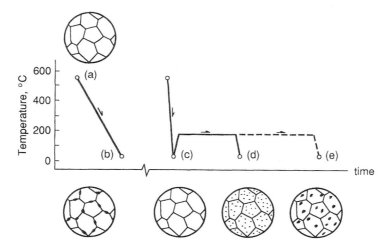

Figure 3.4   Precipitation hardening of aluminum alloyed with 4% Cu. Slow cooling from a solid solution (a) produces grain boundary precipitates (b). Rapid cooling to obtain a supersaturated solution (c) can be followed by aging at a moderate temperature to obtain fine precipitates within grains (d), but overaging gives coarse precipitates (e).

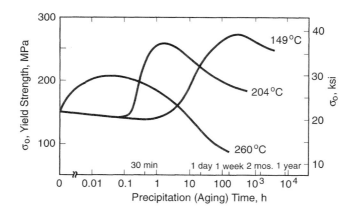

Figure 3.5   Effects of precipitation (aging) time and temperature on the resulting yield strength in aluminum alloy 6061. (Adapted from [Boyer 85] p. 6.7; used with permission.)

the precipitate to form as fairly uniformly scattered small particles. However, if the intermediate temperature is too high, or the holding time too long, the particles coalesce into larger ones and some of the benefit is lost, the particles being too far apart to effectively impede dislocation motion. Thus, for a given temperature, there is a precipitation (aging) time that gives the maximum effect. The resulting trends in strength are illustrated for a commercial aluminum alloy, where similar precipitation hardening occurs, in Fig. 3.5.

    If an alloy contains interspersed regions of more than one chemical composition, as for precipitate particles, as just discussed, a *multiple phase* situation is said to exist. Other multiple phase situations involve needlelike or layered microstructural features, or crystal grains of more than one type. For example, some titanium alloys have a two-phase structure involving grains of both alpha (HCP) and beta (BCC) crystal structures. Multiple phases increase strength, because the discontinuities in the crystal structure at the phase boundaries make dislocation motion more difficult, and also because one phase may be resistant to deformation. The two-phase (alpha–beta) structure just mentioned for titanium provides a portion of the strengthening for the highest strength titanium alloys. Also, the processing of steels by *quenching and tempering*, which will be discussed in the next section, owes its benefits to multiple phase effects.

3.3 IRONS AND STEELS

Iron-based alloys, also called *ferrous* alloys, include cast irons and steels and are the most widely used structural metals. *Steels* consist primarily of iron and contain some carbon and manganese, and often additional alloying elements. They are distinguished from nearly pure iron, which is called *ingot iron*, and also from *cast irons*, which contain carbon in excess of 2% and from 1 to 3% silicon. Irons and steels can be divided into various classes, depending on their alloy compositions and other characteristics, as indicated in Table 3.3. Some examples of particular irons or steels and their alloy compositions are given in Table 3.4.

A wide variation in properties exists for various steels, as illustrated in Fig. 3.6. Pure iron is quite weak, but is strengthened considerably by the addition of small amounts of carbon. Additional alloying with small amounts of niobium, vanadium, copper, or other elements permits strengthening by grain refinement, precipitation, or solid solution effects. If sufficient carbon is

Table 3.3   Commonly Encountered Classes of Irons and Steels

Class	Distinguishing Features	Typical Uses	Source of Strengthening
Cast iron	More than 2% C and 1 to 3% Si	Pipes, valves, gears, engine blocks	Ferrite-pearlite structure as affected by free graphite
Plain-carbon steel	Principal alloying element is carbon up to 1%	Structural and machine parts	Ferrite-pearlite structure if low carbon; quenching and tempering if medium to high carbon
Low-alloy steel	Metallic elements totaling up to 5%	High-strength structural and machine parts	Grain refinement, precipitation, and solid solution if low carbon; otherwise quenching and tempering
Stainless steel	At least 10% Cr; does not rust	Corrosion resistant piping and nuts and bolts; turbine blades	Quenching and tempering if < 15% Cr and low Ni; otherwise cold work or precipitation
Tool steel	Heat treatable to high hardness and wear resistance	Cutters, drill bits, dies	Quenching and tempering, etc.

Table 3.4 Some Typical Irons and Steels

Description	Identification	UNS No.	Principal Alloying Elements, Typical % by Weight							
			C	Cr	Mn	Mo	Ni	Si	V	Other
Ductile cast iron	ASTM A395	F32800	3.5	—	—	—	—	2	—	—
Low-carbon steel	AISI 1020	G10200	0.2	—	0.45	—	—	0.2	—	—
Medium-carbon steel	AISI 1045	G10450	0.45	—	0.75	—	—	0.2	—	—
High-carbon steel	AISI 1095	G10950	0.95	—	0.4	—	—	0.2	—	—
Low-alloy steel	AISI 4340	G43400	0.40	0.8	0.7	0.25	1.8	0.2	—	—
HSLA steel	ASTM A588-A	K11430	0.15	0.5	1.1	—	—	0.2	0.05	0.3 Cu
Martensitic stainless steel	AISI 403	S40300	0.15	12	1.0	—	0.6	0.5	—	—
Austenitic stainless steel	AISI 310	S31000	0.25	25	2.0	—	20	1.5	—	—
Precipitation hardening stainless steel	17-4 PH	S17400	0.07	17	1.0	—	4	1.0	—	4 Cu 0.3 (Nb + Ta)
Tungsten high-speed tool steel	AISI T1	T12001	0.75	3.8	0.25	—	0.2	0.3	1.1	18 W
18 Ni maraging steel	ASTM A538-C	K93120	0.01	—	—	5	18	—	—	9 Co, 0.7 Ti

added for quenching and tempering to be effective, a major increase in strength is possible. Additional alloying and special processing can be combined with quenching and tempering and/or precipitation hardening to achieve even higher strengths.

3.3.1 Naming Systems for Irons and Steels

A number of different organizations have developed naming systems and specifications for various irons and steels that give the required alloy composition and sometimes required mechanical properties. These include the American Iron and Steel Institute (AISI), the Society of Automotive Engineers (SAE International), and the American Society for Testing and Materials (ASTM International). In addition, SAE and ASTM have cooperated to develop a new Unified Numbering System (UNS) that gives designations not only for irons and steels, but also for all other metal alloys. See the *Metals Handbook: Desk Edition* (Davis, 1998) for an introduction to various naming

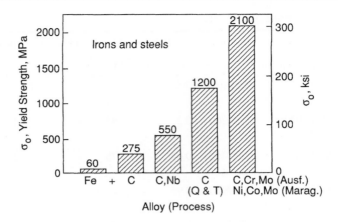

Figure 3.6   Effects of alloying additions and processing (*x*-axis) on the yield strength of steel. Alloying iron with carbon and other elements provides substantial strengthening, but even higher strengths can be achieved by heat treating with quenching and tempering. The highest strengths are obtained by combining alloying with special processing, such as ausforming or maraging. (Adapted from an illustration courtesy of R. W. Landgraf, Howell, MI.)

systems, and the current publication on the UNS System (SAE, 2008) for a description of those designations and their equivalence with other specifications.

The AISI and SAE designations for various steels are coordinated between the two organizations and are nearly identical. Details for common carbon and low-alloy steels are given in Table 3.5. Note that in this case there is usually a four-digit number. The first two digits specify the alloy content other than carbon, and the second two give the carbon content in hundredths of a percent. For example, AISI 1340 (or SAE 1340) contains 0.40% carbon with 1.75% manganese as the only other alloying element. (Percentages of alloys are given on the basis of weight.)

The UNS system has a letter followed by a five-digit number. The letter indicates the category of alloy, such as *F* for cast irons, *G* for carbon and low-alloy steels in the AISI–SAE naming system, *K* for various special-purpose steels, *S* for stainless steels, and *T* for tool steels. For carbon and low-alloy steels, the number is in most cases the same as that used by AISI and SAE, except that a zero is added at the end. Thus, AISI 1340 is the same steel as UNS G13400.

Some particular classes of irons and steels will now be considered.

3.3.2 Cast Irons

Cast irons in various forms have been used for more than two thousand years and continue to be relatively inexpensive and useful materials. The iron is not highly refined subsequent to extraction from ore or scrap, and it is formed into useful shapes by melting and pouring into molds. The temperature required to melt iron in a furnace is difficult to achieve. As a result, prior to the modern industrial era, there was also considerable use of *wrought iron*, which is heated and forged into useful shapes, but never melted in processing. Several different types of cast iron exist. All contain large amounts of carbon, typically 2 to 4% by weight, and also 1 to 3% silicon. The large amount

Table 3.5 Summary of the AISI–SAE Designations for Common Carbon and Low-Alloy Steels

Designation[1]	Approx. Alloy Content, %	Designation	Approx. Alloy Content, %
Carbon steels		*Nickel–molybdenum steels*	
10XX	Plain carbon	46XX	Ni 0.85 or 1.82; Mo 0.25
11XX	Resulfurized	48XX	Ni 3.50; Mo 0.25
12XX	Resulfurized and rephosphorized		
15XX	Mn 1.00 to 1.65		
Manganese steels		*Chromium steels*	
13XX	Mn 1.75	50XX(X)	Cr 0.27 to 0.65
		51XX(X)	Cr 0.80 to 1.05
		52XXX	Cr 1.45
Molybdenum steels		*Chromium–vanadium steels*	
40XX	Mo 0.25	61XX	Cr 0.6 to 0.95; V 0.15
44XX	Mo 0.40 or 0.52		
Chromium–molybdenum steels		*Silicon–manganese steels*	
41XX	Cr 0.50 to 0.95; Mo 0.12 to 0.30	92XX	Si 1.40 or 2.00; Mn 0.70 to 0.87; Cr 0 or 0.70
Nickel–chromium–molybdenum steels		*Boron steels*[2]	
43XX	Ni 1.82; Cr 0.50 or 0.80; Mo 0.25	YYBXX	B 0.0005 to 0.003
47XX	Ni 1.45; Cr 0.45; Mo 0.20 or 0.35		
81XX	Ni 0.30; Cr 0.40; Mo 0.12		
86XX	Ni 0.55; Cr 0.50; Mo 0.20		
87XX	Ni 0.55; Cr 0.50; Mo 0.25		
94XX	Ni 0.45; Cr 0.40; Mo 0.12		

Notes: [1]Replace "XX" or "XXX" with carbon content in hundredths of a percent, such as AISI 1045 having 0.45% C, or 52100 having 1.00% C. [2]Replace "YY" with any two digits from earlier in table to indicate the additional alloy content.

of carbon present exceeds the 2% that can be held in solid solution at elevated temperature, and in most cast irons the excess is present in the form of graphite.

Gray iron contains graphite in the form of flakes, as seen in Fig. 3.7 (left). These flakes easily develop into cracks under tensile stress, so that gray iron is relatively weak and brittle in tension. In compression, the strength and ductility are both considerably higher than for tension. *Ductile iron*, also called *nodular iron*, contains graphite in the more nearly spherical form of nodules, as seen in Fig. 3.7 (right). This is achieved by careful control of impurities and by adding small amounts of magnesium or other elements that aid in nodule formation. As a result of the different form of the graphite, ductile iron has considerably greater strength and ductility in tension than gray iron.

White iron is formed by rapid cooling of a melt that would otherwise form gray iron. The excess carbon is in the form of a multiphase network involving large amounts of iron carbide,

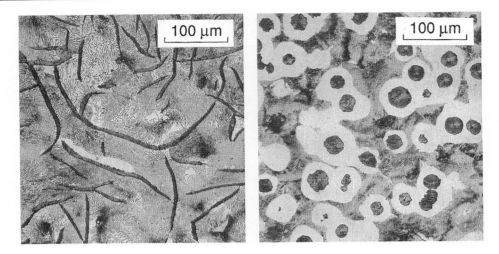

Figure 3.7   Microstructures of gray cast iron (left) and ductile (nodular) cast iron (right). The graphite flakes on the left are the heavy dark bands, and the graphite nodules on the right are the dark shapes. In gray iron (left), the fine lines are a pearlitic structure similar to that in mild steel. (Photos courtesy of Deere and Co., Moline, IL.)

Fe_3C, also called *cementite*. This very hard and brittle phase results in the bulk material also being hard and brittle. For *malleable* iron, special heat treatment of white iron is used to obtain a result similar to ductile iron. In addition, various alloying elements are used in making special-purpose cast irons that have improved response to processing or desirable properties, such as resistance to heat or corrosion.

3.3.3 Carbon Steels

Plain-carbon steels contain carbon, in amounts usually less than 1%, as the alloying element that controls the properties. They also contain limited amounts of manganese and (generally undesirable) impurities, such as sulfur and phosphorus. The more specific terms *low-carbon steel* and *mild steel* are often used to indicate a carbon content of less than 0.25%, such as AISI 1020 steel. These steels have relatively low strength, but excellent ductility. The structure is a combination of BCC iron, also called α-iron or *ferrite*, and *pearlite*. Pearlite is a layered two-phase structure of ferrite and cementite (Fe_3C), as seen in Fig. 3.8 (left). Low-carbon steels can be strengthened somewhat by cold working, but only minor strengthening is possible by heat treatment. Uses include structural steel for buildings and bridges, and sheet metal applications, such as automobile bodies.

    Medium-carbon steels, with carbon content around 0.3 to 0.6%, and *high-carbon steels*, with carbon content around 0.7 to 1% and greater, have higher strengths than low-carbon steels, as a result of the presence of more carbon. In addition, the strength can be increased significantly by heat treatment using the quenching and tempering process, increasingly so for higher carbon contents. However, high strengths are accompanied by loss of ductility—that is, by more brittle behavior. Medium-carbon steels have a wide range of uses as shafts and other components of machines and

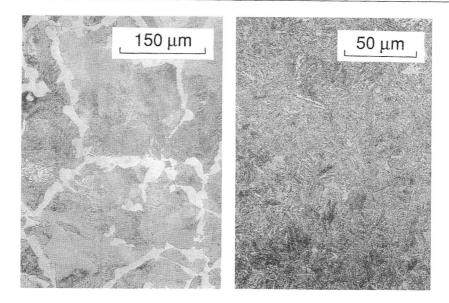

Figure 3.8   Steel microstructures: ferrite-pearlite structure in normalized AISI 1045 steel (left), with ferrite being the light-colored areas, and pearlite the striated regions; quenched and tempered structure in AISI 4340 steel (right). (Left photo courtesy of Deere and Co., Moline, IL.)

vehicles. High-carbon steels are limited to uses where their high hardness is beneficial and the low ductility is not a serious disadvantage, as in cutting tools and springs.

In *quenching and tempering*, the steel is first heated to about 850°C so that the iron changes to the FCC phase known as γ-iron or *austenite*, with carbon being in solid solution. A supersaturated solution of carbon in BCC iron is then formed by rapid cooling, called *quenching*, which can be accomplished by immersing the hot metal into water or oil. After quenching, a structure called *martensite* is present, which has a BCC lattice distorted by interstitial carbon atoms. The martensite exists either as groupings of parallel thin crystals (laths) or as more randomly oriented thin plates, surrounded by regions of austenite.

As-quenched steel is very hard and brittle due to the two phases present, the distorted crystal structure, and a high dislocation density. To obtain a useful material, it must be subjected to a second stage of heat treatment at a lower temperature, called *tempering*. This causes removal of some of the carbon from the martensite and the formation of dispersed particles of Fe_3C. Tempering lowers the strength, but increases the ductility. The effect is greater for higher tempering temperatures and varies with carbon content and alloying, as illustrated in Fig. 3.9. The microstructure of a quenched and tempered steel is shown in Fig. 3.8 (right).

3.3.4 Low-Alloy Steels

In *low-alloy steels*, also often called simply *alloy steels*, small amounts of alloying elements totaling no more than about 5% are added to improve various properties or the response to processing. Percentages of the principal alloying elements are given for some of these in Table 3.5. As examples

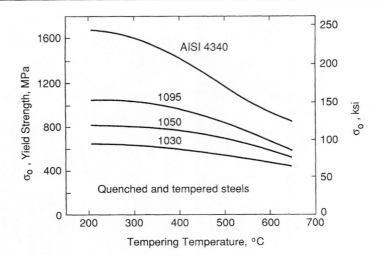

Figure 3.9   Effect of tempering temperature on the yield strength for several steels. These data are for 13 mm diameter samples machined from material heat treated as 25 mm diameter bars. (Data from [Boyer 85] p. 4.21.)

of the effects of alloying, sulfur improves machineability, and molybdenum and vanadium promote grain refinement. The combination of alloys used in the steel AISI 4340 gives improved strength and toughness—that is, resistance to failure due to a crack or sharp flaw. In this steel, the metallurgical changes during quenching proceed at a relatively slow rate so that quenching and tempering is effective in components as thick as 100 mm. Note that the corresponding plain-carbon steel, AISI 1040, requires very rapid quenching that cannot be achieved except within about 5 mm of the surface.

Various special-purpose low-alloy steels are used that may not fit any of the standard AISI–SAE designations. Many of these are described in the *ASTM Standards*, where requirements are placed on mechanical properties in addition to alloy content. Some of these are classified as *high-strength low-alloy* (HSLA) steels, which have a low carbon content and a ferritic-pearlitic structure, with small amounts of alloying resulting in higher strengths than in other low-carbon steels. Examples include structural steels as used in buildings and bridges, such as ASTM A242, A441, A572, and A588. Note that use of the term "high-strength" here can be somewhat misleading, as the strengths are high for a low-carbon steel, but not nearly as high as for many quenched and tempered steels. The low-alloy steels used for pressure vessels, such as ASTM A302, A517, and A533, constitute an additional group of special-purpose steels.

3.3.5 Stainless Steels

Steels containing at least 10% chromium are called *stainless steels* because they have good corrosion resistance; that is, they do not rust. These alloys also frequently have improved resistance to high temperature. A separate system of AISI designations employs a three-digit number, such as AISI 316 and AISI 403, with the first digit indicating a particular class of stainless steels. The corresponding UNS designations often use the same digits, such as S31600 and S40300 for the two just listed.

The 400-series stainless steels have carbon in various percentages and small amounts of metallic alloying elements in addition to the chromium. If the chromium content is less than about 15%, as in types 403, 410, and 422, the steel in most cases can be heat treated by quenching and tempering to have a martensitic structure, so that it is called a *martensitic stainless steel*. Uses include tools and blades in steam turbines. However, if the chromium content is higher, typically 17 to 25%, the result is a *ferritic stainless steel* that can be strengthened only by cold work, and then only modestly. These are used where high strength is not as essential as high corrosion resistance, as in architectural use.

The 300-series stainless steels, such as types 304, 310, 316, and 347, contain around 10 to 20% nickel in addition to 17 to 25% chromium. Nickel further enhances corrosion resistance and results in the FCC crystal structure being stable even at low temperatures. These are termed *austenitic stainless steels*. They either are used in the annealed condition or are strengthened by cold work, and they have excellent ductility and toughness. Uses include nuts and bolts, pressure vessels and piping, and medical bone screws and plates.

Another group is the *precipitation-hardening stainless steels*. These are strengthened as the name implies, and they are used in various high-stress applications where resistance to corrosion and high temperature are required, as in heat-exchanger tubes and turbine blades. An example is 17-4 PH stainless steel (UNS S17400), which contains 17% chromium and 4% nickel—hence its name—and also 4% copper and smaller amounts of other elements.

3.3.6 Tool Steels and Other Special Steels

Tool steels are specially alloyed and processed to have high hardness and wear resistance for use in cutting tools and special components of machinery. Most contain several percent chromium, some have quite high carbon contents in the 1 to 2% range, and some contain fairly high percentages of molybdenum and/or tungsten. Strengthening generally involves quenching and tempering or related heat treatments. The AISI designations are in the form of a letter followed by a one- or two-digit number. For example, tool steels M1, M2, etc., contain 5 to 10% molybdenum and smaller amounts of tungsten and vanadium; and tool steels T1, T2, etc., contain substantial amounts of tungsten, typically 18%.

The tool steel H11, containing 0.4% carbon, 5% chromium, and modest amounts of other elements, is used in various high-stress applications. It can be fully strengthened in thick sections up to 150 mm and retains moderate ductility and toughness even at very high yield strengths around 2100 MPa and above. This is achieved by the *ausforming* process, which involves deforming the steel at a high temperature within the range where the austenite (FCC) crystal structure exists. An extremely high dislocation density and a very fine precipitate are introduced, which combine to provide additional strengthening that is added to the usual martensite strengthening due to quenching and tempering. Ausformed H11 is one of the strongest steels that has reasonable ductility and toughness.

Various additional specialized high-strength steels have names that are nonstandard trade names. Examples include 300 M, which is AISI 4340 modified with 1.6% silicon and some vanadium, and D-6a steel used in aerospace applications. Maraging steels contain 18% nickel and other alloying elements, and they have high strength and toughness due to a combination of a martensitic structure and precipitation hardening.

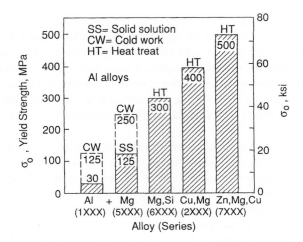

Figure 3.10   Effects of alloying additions and processing (*x*-axis) on the yield strength of aluminum alloys. Pure aluminum can be strengthened by cold work, and alloying increases strength due to solid-solution hardening. The higher strength alloys are heat treated to produce precipitation hardening. (Adapted from an illustration courtesy of R. W. Landgraf, Howell, MI.)

3.4 NONFERROUS METALS

Quenching and tempering to produce a martensitic structure is the most effective means of strengthening steels. In the common nonferrous metals, martensite may not occur; and where it does occur, the effect is not as large as in steels. Hence, the other methods of strengthening, which are generally less effective, must be used. The higher strength nonferrous metals often employ precipitation hardening.

For example, consider the strength levels achievable in aluminum alloys, as illustrated by Fig. 3.10. Annealed pure aluminum is very weak and can be strengthened only by cold work. Adding magnesium provides solid-solution strengthening, and the resulting alloy can be cold worked. Further strengthening is possible by precipitation hardening, which is achieved by various combinations of alloying elements and aging treatments. However, the highest strength available is only about 25% of that for the highest strength steel. Aluminum is nevertheless widely used, as in aerospace applications, where its light weight and corrosion resistance are major advantages that offset the disadvantage of lower strength than some steels.

We will now discuss the nonferrous metals that are commonly used in structural applications.

3.4.1 Aluminum Alloys

For aluminum alloys produced in wrought form, as by rolling or extruding, the naming system involves a four-digit number. The first digit specifies the major alloying elements as listed in Table 3.6. Subsequent digits are then assigned to indicate specific alloys, with some examples being given in Table 3.7. The UNS numbers for wrought alloys are similar, except that A9 precedes the

Table 3.6   Naming System for Common Wrought Aluminum Alloys

Series	Major Additions	Other Frequent Additions	Heat Treatable
1XXX	None	None	No
2XXX	Cu	Mg, Mn, Si, Li	Yes
3XXX	Mn	Mg, Cu	No
4XXX	Si	None	Most no
5XXX	Mg	Mn, Cr	No
6XXX	Mg, Si	Cu, Mn	Yes
7XXX	Zn	Mg, Cu, Cr	Yes

Processing Designations		Common TX Treatments	
-F	As fabricated	-T3	Cold worked, then naturally aged
-O	Annealed	-T4	Naturally aged
-H1X	Cold worked	-T6	Artificially aged
-H2X	Cold worked, then partially annealed	-T8	Cold worked, then artificially aged
-H3X	Cold worked, then stabilized	-TX51	Stress relieved by stretching
-TX	Solution heat treated, then aged		

four-digit number. Following the four-digit number, a processing code is used, as in 2024-T4, as detailed in Table 3.6.

For codes involving cold work, HXX, the first number indicates whether only cold work is used (H1X), or whether cold work is followed by partial annealing (H2X) or by a stabilizing heat treatment (H3X). The latter is a low-temperature heat treatment that prevents subsequent gradual changes in the properties. The second digit indicates the degree of cold work, HX8 for the maximum effect of cold work on strength, and HX2, HX4, and HX6 for one-fourth, one-half, and three-fourths as much effect, respectively.

Processing codes of the form TX all involve a *solution heat treatment* at a high temperature to create a solid solution of alloying elements. This may or may not be followed by cold work, but the material is always subsequently *aged*, during which precipitation hardening occurs. *Natural aging* occurs at room temperature, whereas *artificial aging* involves a second stage of heat treatment, as in Fig. 3.4. Additional digits following HXX or TX describe additional variations in processing, such as T651 for a T6 treatment in which the material is also stretched up to 3% in length to relieve residual (locked-in) stresses.

Table 3.7 Some Typical Wrought Aluminum Alloys

Identification	UNS No.	Principal Alloying Elements, Typical % by Weight					
		Cu	Cr	Mg	Mn	Si	Other
1100-O	A91100	0.12	—	—	—	—	—
2014-T6	A92014	4.4	—	0.5	0.8	0.8	—
2024-T4	A92024	4.4	—	1.5	0.6	—	—
2219-T851	A92219	6.3	—	—	0.3	—	0.1 V, 0.18 Zr
3003-H14	A93003	0.12	—	—	1.2	—	—
4032-T6	A94032	0.9	—	1.0	—	12.2	0.9 Ni
5052-H38	A95052	—	0.25	2.5	—	—	—
6061-T6	A96061	0.28	0.2	1.0	—	0.6	—
7075-T651	A97075	1.6	0.23	2.5	—	—	5.6 Zn

The alloy content determines the response to processing. Alloys in the 1XXX, 3XXX, and 5XXX series, and most of those in the 4XXX series, do not respond to precipitation-hardening heat treatment. These alloys achieve some of their strength from solid-solution effects, and all can be strengthened beyond the annealed condition by cold work. The alloys capable of the highest strengths are those that do respond to precipitation hardening, namely the 2XXX, 6XXX, and 7XXX series, with the exact response to this processing being affected by the alloy content. For example, 2024 can be precipitation hardened by natural aging, but 7075 and similar alloys require artificial aging.

Aluminum alloys produced in cast form have a similar, but separate, naming system. A four-digit number with a decimal point is used, such as 356.0-T6. Corresponding UNS numbers have A0 preceding the four-digit number and no decimal point, such as A03560.

3.4.2 Titanium Alloys

The density of titanium is considerably greater than that of aluminum, but still only about 60% of that of steel. In addition, the melting temperature is somewhat greater than for steel and far greater than for aluminum. In aerospace applications, the strength-to-weight ratio is important, and in this respect the highest strength titanium alloys are comparable to the highest strength steels. These characteristics and good corrosion resistance have led to an increase in the application of titanium alloys since commercial development of the material began in the 1940s.

Because only about 30 different titanium alloys are in common use, it is sufficient to identify these by simply giving the weight percentages of alloying elements, such as Ti-6Al-4V or Ti-10V-2Fe-3Al. Three categories exist: the alpha and near alpha alloys, the beta alloys, and the alpha–beta alloys. Although the alpha (HCP) crystal structure is stable at room temperature in pure titanium, certain combinations of alloying elements, such as chromium along with vanadium, cause the beta (BCC) structure to be stable, or they result in a mixed structure. Small percentages of molybdenum or nickel improve corrosion resistance; and aluminum, tin, and zirconium improve creep resistance of the alpha phase.

Alpha alloys are strengthened mainly by solid-solution effects and do not respond to heat treatment. The other alloys can be strengthened by heat treatment. As in steels, a martensitic transformation occurs upon quenching, but the effect is less. Precipitation hardening and the effects of complex multiple phases are the principal means of strengthening alpha–beta and beta alloys.

3.4.3 Other Nonferrous Metals

A wide range of copper alloys are employed in diverse applications as a result of their electrical conductivity, corrosion resistance, and attractiveness. Copper is easily alloyed with various other metals, and copper alloys are generally easy to deform or to cast into useful shapes. Strengths are typically lower than for the metals already discussed, but still sufficiently high that copper alloys are often useful as engineering metals.

Percentages of alloying elements range from relatively small to quite substantial, such as 35% zinc in common yellow brass. Copper with approximately 10% tin is called bronze, although this term is also used to describe various alloys with aluminum, silicon, zinc, and other elements. Copper alloys with zinc, aluminum, or nickel are strengthened by solid-solution effects. Beryllium additions permit precipitation hardening and produce the highest strength copper alloys. Cold work is also frequently used for strengthening, often in combination with the other methods. A variety of common names are in use for various copper alloys, such as *beryllium copper*, *naval brass*, and *aluminum bronze*. The UNS numbering system with a prefix letter C is used for copper alloys.

Magnesium has a melting temperature near that of aluminum, but a density only 65% as great, making it only 22% as dense as steel and the lightest engineering metal. This silvery-white metal is most commonly produced in cast form, but is also extruded, forged, and rolled. Alloying elements do not generally exceed 10% total for all additions, the most common being aluminum, manganese, zinc, and zirconium. Strengthening methods are roughly similar to those for aluminum alloys. The highest strengths are about 60% as large, resulting in comparable strength-to-weight ratios. The naming system in common use is generally similar to that for aluminum alloys, but differs as to the details. A combination of letters and numbers that identifies the specific alloy is followed by a processing designation, such as AZ91C-T6.

Superalloys are special heat-resisting alloys that are used primarily above 550°C. The major constituent is either nickel or cobalt, or a combination of iron and nickel, and percentages of alloying elements are often quite large. For example, the Ni-base alloy Udimet 500 contains 48% Ni, 19% Cr, and 19% Co, and the Co-base alloy Haynes 188 has 37% Co, 22% Cr, 22% Ni, and 14% W, with both also containing small percentages of other elements. Nonstandard combinations of trade names and letters and numerals are commonly used to identify the relatively small number of superalloys that are in common use. Some examples, in addition to the two just described, are Waspaloy, MAR-M302, A286, and Inconel 718.

Although nickel and cobalt have melting temperatures just below that of iron, superalloys have superior resistance to corrosion, oxidation, and creep compared with steels. Many have substantial strengths even above 750°C, which is beyond the useful range for low-alloy and stainless steels.

This accounts for their use in high-temperature applications, despite the high cost due to the relative scarcity of nickel, chromium, and cobalt. Superalloys are often produced in wrought form, and Ni-base and Co-base alloys are also often cast. Strengthening is primarily by solid-solution effects and by various heat treatments, resulting in precipitation of intermetallic compounds or metal carbides.

3.5 POLYMERS

Polymers are materials consisting of long-chain molecules formed primarily by carbon-to-carbon bonds. Examples include all materials commonly referred to as plastics, most familiar natural and synthetic fibers, rubbers, and cellulose and lignin in wood. Polymers that are produced or modified by man for use as engineering materials can be classified into three groups: thermoplastics, thermosetting plastics, and elastomers.

When heated, a *thermoplastic* softens and usually melts; then, if cooled, it returns to its original solid condition. The process can be repeated a number of times. However, a *thermosetting plastic* changes chemically during processing, which is often done at elevated temperature. It will not melt upon reheating, but will instead decompose, as by charring or burning. *Elastomers* are distinguished from plastics by being capable of rubbery behavior. In particular, they can be deformed by large amounts, say 100% to 200% strain or more, with most of this deformation being recovered after removal of the stress. Examples of polymers in each of these groups are listed, along with typical uses, in Table 3.8.

After chemical synthesis based primarily on petroleum products, polymers are made into useful shapes by various molding and extrusion processes, two of which are illustrated in Fig. 3.11. For thermosetting plastics and elastomers that behave in a similar manner, the final stage of chemical reaction is often accomplished by the application of temperature and/or pressure, and this must occur while the material is being molded into its final shape.

Polymers are named according to the conventions of organic chemistry. These sometimes lengthy names are often abbreviated by acronyms, such as PMMA for polymethyl methacrylate. In addition, various trade names and popular names, such as Plexiglas, Teflon, and nylon, are often used in addition to, or in place of, the chemical names.

An important characteristic of polymers is their light weight. Most have a mass density similar to that of water, around $\rho = 1 \, \text{g/cm}^3$, and few exceed $\rho = 2 \, \text{g/cm}^3$. Hence, polymers are typically half as heavy as aluminum ($\rho = 2.7 \, \text{g/cm}^3$) and much lighter than steel ($\rho \approx 7.9 \, \text{g/cm}^3$). Most polymers in unmodified form are relatively weak, with ultimate tensile strengths typically in the range 10 to 200 MPa.

In the discussion that follows, we first consider the basic molecular structure of typical polymers in each group. This provides the background for later discussion of how the details of molecular structure affect the mechanical properties.

3.5.1 Molecular Structure of Thermoplastics

Many thermoplastics have a molecular structure related to that of the hydrocarbon gas ethylene, C_2H_4. In particular, the *repeating unit* in the chain molecule is similar to an ethylene molecule, except that the carbon-to-carbon bond is rearranged as illustrated previously in Fig. 2.6. The

Table 3.8   Classes, Examples, and Uses of Representative Polymers

Polymer	Typical Uses
(a) Thermoplastics: ethylene structure	
Polyethylene (PE)	Packaging, bottles, piping
Polyvinyl chloride (PVC)	Upholstery, tubing, electrical insulation
Polypropylene (PP)	Hinges, boxes, ropes
Polystyrene (PS)	Toys, appliance housings, foams
Polymethyl methacrylate (PMMA, Plexiglas, acrylic)	Windows, lenses, clear shields, bone cement
Polytetrafluoroethylene (PTFE, Teflon)	Tubing, bottles, seals
Acrylonitrile butadiene styrene (ABS)	Telephone and appliance housings, toys
(b) Thermoplastics: others	
Nylon	Gears, tire cords, tool housings
Aramids (Kevlar, Nomex)	High-strength fibers
Polyoxymethylene (POM, acetal)	Gears, fan blades, pipe fittings
Polyetheretherketone (PEEK)	Coatings, fans, impellers
Polycarbonate (PC)	Safety helmets and lenses
(c) Thermosetting plastics	
Phenol formaldehyde (phenolic, Bakelite)	Electrical plugs and switches, pot handles
Melamine formaldehyde	Plastic dishes, tabletops
Urea formaldehyde	Buttons, bottle caps, toilet seats
Epoxies	Matrix for composites
Unsaturated polyesters	Fiberglass resin
(d) Elastomers	
Natural rubber; cis-polyisoprene	Shock absorbers, tires
Styrene-butadiene rubber (SBR)	Tires, hoses, belts
Polyurethane elastomers	Shoe soles, electrical insulation
Nitrile rubber	O-rings, oil seals, hoses
Polychloroprene (Neoprene)	Wet suits, gaskets

molecular structures of some of the simpler polymers of this type are illustrated by giving their repeating unit structures in Fig. 3.12.

Polyethylene (PE) is the simplest case, in that the only modification to the ethylene molecule is the rearranged carbon-to-carbon bond. In polyvinyl chloride (PVC), one of the hydrogen atoms is replaced by a chlorine atom, whereas polypropylene (PP) has a similar substitution of a methyl (CH_3) group. Polystyrene (PS) has a substitution of an entire benzene ring, and PMMA is based on two substitutions, as shown. Polytetrafluoroethylene (PTFE), also known as Teflon, has four

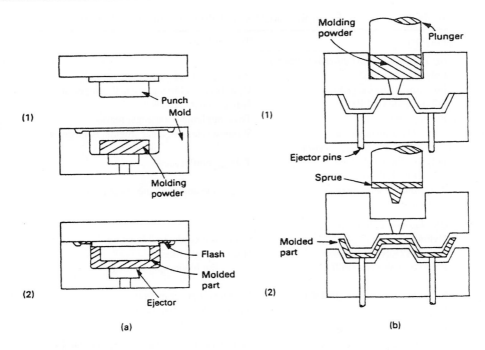

Figure 3.11   Forming of plastics by (a) compression molding and (b) transfer molding. (From [Farag 89] p. 91; used with permission.)

fluorine substitutions. Ethylene-based thermoplastics are by far the most widely used plastics, with PE, PVC, PP, and PS accounting for more than half the weight of plastics usage.

However, other classes of thermoplastics that are used in smaller quantities are more suitable for engineering applications where high strength is needed. The *engineering plastics* include the nylons, the aramids such as Kevlar, polyoxymethylene (POM), polyethylene terephthalate (PET), polyphenylene oxide (PPO), and polycarbonate (PC). Their molecular structures are generally more complex than those of the ethylene-based thermoplastics. The repeating unit structures of two of these, nylon 6 and polycarbonate, are shown as examples in Fig. 3.12. Other nylons, such as nylon 66 and nylon 12, have more complex structures than nylon 6. Kevlar belongs to the polyamide group, along with the nylons, and has a related structure involving benzene rings, so that it is classed as an aromatic polyamide, that is, an *aramid.*

3.5.2 Crystalline Versus Amorphous Thermoplastics

Some thermoplastics are composed partially or mostly of material where the polymer chains are arranged into an orderly crystalline structure. Examples of such *crystalline polymers* include PE, PP, PTFE, nylon, Kevlar, POM, and PEEK. A photograph of crystal structure in polyethylene is shown as Fig. 3.13.

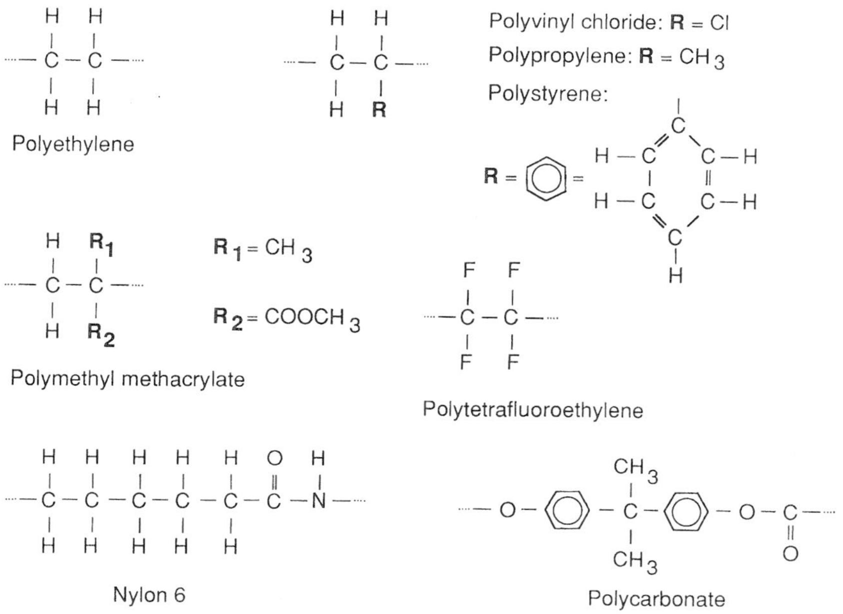

Polyethylene

Polyvinyl chloride: **R** = Cl
Polypropylene: **R** = CH₃
Polystyrene:

$$R = \bigcirc$$

R_1 = CH₃

R_2 = COOCH₃

Polymethyl methacrylate

Polytetrafluoroethylene

Nylon 6

Polycarbonate

Figure 3.12   Molecular structure of several linear polymers. All but the last two are related to the polyethylene structure by simple substitutions, *R*, *R₁* and *R₂*, or *F*.

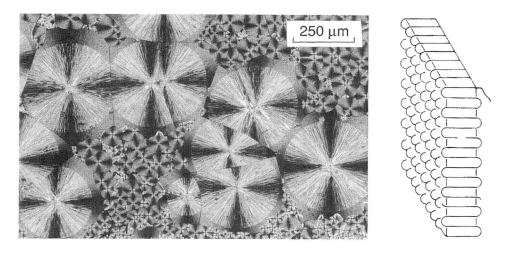

Figure 3.13   Crystal structure of polyethylene. Layers similar to that shown in the diagram are seen edge-on in the photo, being arranged in a radiating pattern to form the prominent crystalline features called *spherulites*. (Photo courtesy of A. S. Holik, General Electric Co., Schenectady, NY. Diagram reprinted with permission from [Geil 65]; © 1965 by the American Chemical Society.)

Table 3.9 Typical Values of Glass Transition and Melting Temperatures for Various Thermoplastics and Elastomers

Polymer	Transition $T_g, °C$	Melting $T_m, °C$
(a) Amorphous thermoplastics		
Polyvinyl chloride (PVC)	87	212
Polystyrene (atactic)	100	≈ 180
Polycarbonate (PC)	150	265
(b) Primarily crystalline thermoplastics		
Low-density polyethylene (LDPE)	−110	115
High-density polyethylene (HDPE)	−90	137
Polyoxymethylene (POM)	−85	175
Polypropylene (PP)	−10	176
Nylon 6	50	215
Polystyrene (isotactic)	100	240
Polyetheretherketone (PEEK)	143	334
Aramid	375	640
(c) Elastomers		
Silicone rubber	−123	−54
Cis-polyisoprene	−73	28
Polychloroprene	−50	80

Source: Data in [ASM 88] pp. 50–54.

If the chain molecules are instead arranged in a random manner, the polymer is said to be *amorphous*. Examples of amorphous polymers include PVC, PMMA, and PC. Polystyrene (PS) is amorphous in its *atactic* form where the benzene ring substitution is randomly located within each repeating unit of the molecule, but is crystalline in the *isotactic* form where the substitution occurs at the same location in each repeating unit. This same situation occurs for other polymers as well, due to the regular structure of the isotactic form promoting crystallinity. If the side groups alternate their positions in a regular manner, the polymer is said to be *syndiotactic*, with a crystalline structure being likely in this case also.

Amorphous polymers are generally used around and below their respective glass transition temperatures T_g, some values of which are listed in Table 3.9. Above T_g, the elastic modulus decreases rapidly, and time-dependent deformation (creep) effects become pronounced, limiting the usefulness of these materials in load-resisting applications. Their behavior below T_g tends to be glassy and brittle, with the elastic modulus being on the order of $E = 3$ GPa. Amorphous polymers composed of single-strand molecules are said to be *linear polymers*. Another possibility is that there is some degree of *branching*, as shown in Fig. 3.14.

Crystalline polymers tend to be less brittle than amorphous polymers, and the stiffness and strength do not drop as dramatically beyond T_g. For example, such differences occur between the amorphous and crystalline forms of PS, as illustrated in Fig. 3.15. As a result of this behavior, many crystalline polymers can be used above their T_g values. Crystalline polymers tend to be opaque to light, whereas amorphous polymers are transparent.

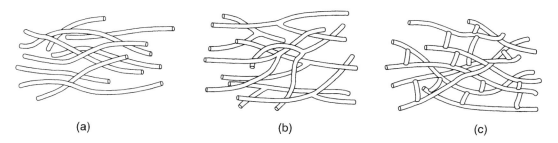

Figure 3.14   Polymer chain structures that are (a) linear, (b) branched, or (c) cross-linked. (From [Budinski 96] pp. 63–64; © 1996 by Prentice Hall, Upper Saddle River, NJ; reprinted with permission.)

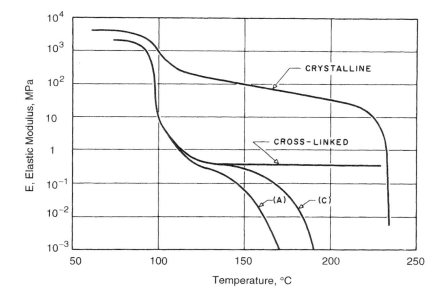

Figure 3.15   Elastic modulus versus temperature for amorphous, lightly cross-linked, and crystalline polystyrene. For amorphous samples (A) and (C), the chain lengths correspond to average molecular weights of 2.1×10^5 and 3.3×10^5, respectively. (Adapted from [Tobolsky 65] p. 75; reprinted by permission of John Wiley & Sons, Inc.; copyright © 1965 by John Wiley & Sons, Inc.)

3.5.3 Thermosetting Plastics

The molecular structure of a thermosetting plastic consists of a three-dimensional network. Such a network may be formed by frequent strong covalent bonds between chains, called *cross-links*, as illustrated in Fig. 3.14(c). In some cases, most repeating units have three carbon–carbon bonds to other units, so that the cross-linking is maximized. This is the case for phenol formaldehyde

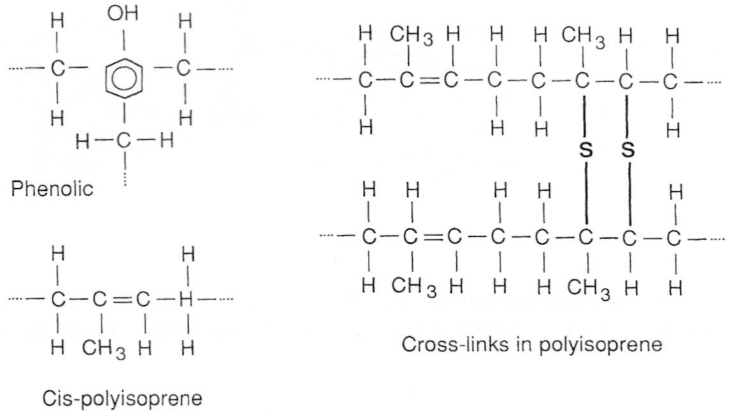

Figure 3.16 Molecular structures of a phenolic thermosetting plastic and of a synthetic similar to natural rubber, cis-polyisoprene. In the phenolics, carbon–carbon bonds form cross-links, whereas in polyisoprene cross-links are formed by sulfur atoms.

(phenolic), the structure of which is shown in Fig. 3.16. The common plastic Bakelite is a phenolic. Some other common thermosetting polymers are the epoxy adhesives and polyester resins used for fiberglass.

The cross-linking (thermosetting) chemical reaction occurs during the final stage of processing, which is typically compression molding at elevated temperature. Following this reaction, the resulting solid will neither soften nor melt upon heating, but will usually decompose or burn instead. The network structure results in a rigid and strong, but brittle, solid.

Recall that thermal expansion and the resulting increased free volume produces the glass transition temperature (T_g) effect in thermoplastics, above which deformation may occur by relative sliding between chain molecules. This situation contrasts with that for a thermosetting plastic where relative motion between the molecules is prevented by strong and temperature-resistant covalent bonds. As a result, there is no distinct T_g effect in highly cross-linked thermosetting plastics.

3.5.4 Elastomers

Elastomers are typified by natural rubber, but also include a variety of synthetic polymers with similar mechanical behavior. Some elastomers, such as the polyurethane elastomers, behave in a thermoplastic manner, but others are thermosetting materials. For example, polyisoprene is a synthetic rubber with the same basic structure as natural rubber, but lacking various impurities found in natural rubber. This structure is shown in Fig. 3.16. Adding sulfur and subjecting the rubber to pressure and a temperature around 160°C causes sulfur cross-links to form, as shown. A greater degree of cross-linking results in a harder rubber. This particular thermosetting process is called *vulcanization*.

Although cross-linking results in the rigid network structure of thermosetting plastics, typical elastomers behave in a very different manner because the cross-links occur much less frequently along the chains, specifically at intervals on the order of hundreds of carbon atoms. Also, the

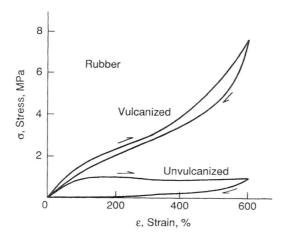

Figure 3.17 Stress–strain curves for unvulcanized and vulcanized natural rubber. (Data from [Hock 26].)

cross-links and the main chains themselves are flexible in elastomers, rather than stiff as in the thermosetting plastics. This flexibility exists because the geometry at the carbon-to-carbon double bond causes a bend in the chain, which has a cumulative effect over long lengths of chain, such that the chain is coiled between cross-link points. Upon loading, these coils unwind between the cross-link attachment points, and after removal of the stress, the coils recover, resulting in the macroscopic effect of recovery of most of the deformation. Typical deformation response is shown in Fig. 3.17.

The initial elastic modulus is very low, as it is associated only with uncoiling the chains, resulting in a value on the order of $E = 1$ MPa. Some stiffening occurs as the chains straighten. This low value of E contrasts with that for a glassy polymer below its T_g, where elastic deformation is associated with stretching the combination of covalent and secondary chemical bonds involved, resulting in a value of E on the order of 1000 times higher.

3.5.5 Strengthening Effects

The molecular structures of polymers are affected by the details of their chemical synthesis, such as the pressure, temperature, reaction time, presence and amount of catalysts, and cooling rate. These are often varied to produce a wide range of properties for a given polymer. Any molecular structure that tends to retard relative sliding between the chainlike molecules increases the stiffness and strength. Longer chain molecules—that is, those with a greater molecular weight—have this effect, as longer chains are more prone to becoming entangled with one another. Stiffness and strength are similarly increased by more branching in an amorphous polymer, by greater crystallinity, and by causing some cross-linking to occur in normally thermoplastic polymers. All of these effects are most pronounced above T_g, where relative sliding between chain molecules is possible.

For example, one variant of polyethylene, called low-density polyethylene (LDPE), has a significant degree of chain branching. These irregular branches interfere with the formation of an

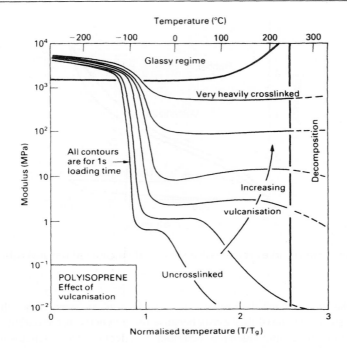

Figure 3.18   Effect of degree of cross-linking on the elastic modulus E of a synthetic similar to natural rubber. (From [Ashby 06] p. 272; reprinted with permission of Elsevier, Oxford, UK; © 2006 M. F. Ashby and D. R. H. Jones.)

orderly crystalline structure, so that the degree of crystallinity is limited to about 65%. In contrast, the high-density variant HDPE has less branching, and the degree of crystallinity can reach 90%. As a result of the structural differences, LDPE is quite flexible, whereas HDPE is stronger and stiffer.

An extreme variation in the properties of rubber is possible by varying the amount of vulcanization, resulting in different degrees of cross-linking. The effect on the elastic modulus (stiffness) of the synthetic rubber polyisoprene is shown in Fig. 3.18. Unvulcanized rubber is soft and flows in a viscous manner. Cross-linking by sulfur at about 5% of the possible sites yields a rubber that is useful in a variety of applications, such as automobile tires. A high degree of cross-linking yields a hard and tough material called *ebonite* that is capable of only limited deformation.

3.5.6 Combining and Modifying Polymers

Polymers are seldom used in pure form, often being combined with one another or with other substances in various ways. *Alloying*, also called *blending*, involves melting two or more polymers together so that the resulting material contains a mixture of two or more chain types. This mixture may be fairly uniform, or the components may separate themselves into a multiphase structure. For example, PVC and PMMA are blended to make a tough plastic with good flame and chemical resistance.

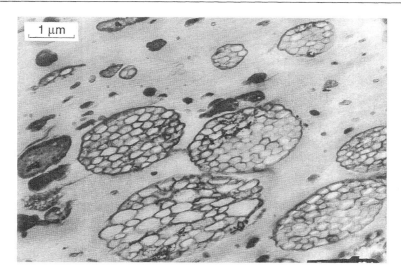

Figure 3.19 Microstructure of rubber modified polystyrene, in which the dark-colored particles and networks are rubber, and all light-colored areas inside and outside of particles are polystyrene. The originally equiaxial particles were elongated somewhat when cut to prepare the surface. (Photo courtesy of R. P. Kambour, General Electric Co., Schenectady, NY.)

Copolymerization is another means of combining two polymers, in which the ingredients and other details of the chemical synthesis are chosen so that the individual chains are composed of two types of repeating units. For example, styrene–butadiene rubber is a copolymer of three parts butadiene and one part styrene, both of which occur in most individual chain molecules. ABS plastic is a combination of three polymers, called a *terpolymer*. In particular, the acrylonitrile–styrene copolymer chain has side branches of butadiene polymer.

Among the nonpolymer substances added to modify the properties of polymers are *plasticizers*. These generally have the objective of increasing toughness and flexibility, while often decreasing strength in the process. Plasticizers are usually high-boiling-point organic liquids, the molecules of which distribute themselves through the polymer structure. The plasticizer molecules tend to separate the polymer chains and allow easier relative motion between them—that is, easier deformation. For example, plasticizers are added to PVC to make flexible vinyl, which is used as imitation leather.

Polymers are often *modified* or *filled* by adding other materials in the form of particles of fibers. For example, carbon black, which is similar to soot, is usually added to rubber, increasing its stiffness and strength, in addition to the effects of vulcanization. Also, rubber particles are added to polystyrene to reduce its brittleness, with the resulting material being called high-impact polystyrene (HIPS). The microstructure of a HIPS material is shown in Fig. 3.19. If the added substance has the specific purpose of increasing strength, it is called a *reinforcement*. For example, chopped glass fibers are added as reinforcement to various thermoplastics to increase strength and stiffness.

Reinforcement may also take the form of long fibers or woven cloth made of high-strength fibers, such as glass, carbon in the form of graphite, or Kevlar. These are often used in a matrix of a thermosetting plastic. For example, fiberglass contains glass fibers in the form of mats or woven cloth, and these are embedded in a matrix of unsaturated polyester. Such a combination is a *composite material*, which topic is considered further in a separate section near the end of this chapter.

3.6 CERAMICS AND GLASSES

Ceramics and glasses are solids that are neither metallic nor organic (carbon-chain based) materials. Ceramics thus include clay products, such as porcelain, china, and brick, and also natural stone and concrete. Ceramics used in high-stress applications, called *engineering ceramics*, are often relatively simple compounds of metals, or the metalloids silicon or boron, with nonmetals such as oxygen, carbon, or nitrogen. Carbon in its graphite or diamond forms is also considered to be a ceramic. Ceramics are predominantly crystalline, whereas glasses are amorphous. Most glass is produced by melting silica (SiO_2), which is ordinary sand, along with other metal oxides, such as CaO, Na_2O, B_2O_3, and PbO. In contrast, ceramics are usually processed not by melting, but by some other means of binding the particles of a fine powder into a solid. Specific examples of ceramics and glasses and some of their properties are given in Table 3.10. The microstructure of a polycrystalline ceramic is shown in Fig. 3.20.

Engineering ceramics have a number of important advantages compared with metals. They are highly resistant to corrosion and wear, and melting temperatures are typically quite high. These characteristics all arise from the strong covalent or ionic–covalent chemical bonding of these compounds. Ceramics are also relatively stiff (high E) and light in weight. In addition, they are often inexpensive, as the ingredients for their manufacture are typically abundant in nature.

As discussed in the previous chapter in connection with plastic deformation, slip of crystal planes does not occur readily in ceramics, due to the strength and directional nature of even partially covalent bonding and the relatively complex crystal structures. This results in ceramics being inherently brittle, and glasses are similarly affected by covalent bonding. In ceramics, the brittleness is further enhanced by the fact that grain boundaries in these crystalline compounds are relatively weaker than in metals. This arises from disrupted chemical bonds, where the lattice planes are discontinuous at grain boundaries, and also from the existence of regions where ions of the same charge are in proximity. In addition, there is often an appreciable degree of porosity in ceramics, and both ceramics and glasses usually contain microscopic cracks. These discontinuities promote macroscopic cracking and thus also contribute to brittle behavior.

The processing and uses of ceramics are strongly influenced by their brittleness. As a consequence, recent efforts aimed at developing improved ceramics for engineering use involve various means of reducing brittleness. Noting the advantages of ceramics, as just listed, success in this area would be of major importance, as it would allow increased use of ceramics in applications such as automobile and jet engines, where lighter weights and operation at higher temperatures both result in greater fuel efficiency.

Various classes of ceramics will now be discussed separately as to their processing and uses.

3.6.1 Clay Products, Natural Stone, and Concrete

Clays consist of various silicate minerals that have a sheetlike crystal structure, an important example being kaolin, Al_2O_3–$2SiO_2$–$2H_2O$. In processing, the clay is first mixed with water to

Table 3.10 Properties and Uses for Selected Engineering and Other Ceramics

Ceramic	Melting Temp.	Density	Elastic Modulus	Typical Strength		Uses
	T_m °C	ρ g/cm³	E GPa	σ_u, MPa (ksi)		
	(°F)	(lb/ft³)	(10³ ksi)	Tension	Compression	
Soda-lime glass	730 (1350)	2.48 (155)	74 (10.7)	≈ 50 (7)	1000 (145)	Windows, containers
Type S glass (fibers)	970 (1780)	2.49 (155)	85.5 (12.4)	4480 (650)	—	Fibers in aerospace composites
Zircon porcelain	1567 (2850)	3.60 (225)	147 (21.3)	56 (8.1)	560 (81)	High-voltage electrical insulators
Magnesia, MgO	2850 (5160)	3.60 (225)	280 (40.6)	140 (20.3)	840 (122)	Refractory brick, wear parts
Alumina, Al_2O_3 (99.5% dense)	2050 (3720)	3.89 (243)	372 (54)	262 (38)	2620 (380)	Spark plug insulators, cutting tool inserts, fibers for composites
Zirconia, ZrO_2	2570 (4660)	5.80 (362)	210 (30.4)	147 (21.3)	2100 (304)	High-temperature crucibles, refractory brick, engine parts
Silicon carbide, SiC (reaction bonded)	2837 (5140)	3.10 (194)	393 (57)	307 (44.5)	2500 (362)	Engine parts, abrasives, fibers for composites
Boron carbide, B_4C	2350 (4260)	2.51 (157)	290 (42)	155 (22.5)	2900 (420)	Bearings, armor, abrasives
Silicon nitride, Si_3N_4 (hot pressed)	1900 (3450)	3.18 (199)	310 (45)	450 (65)	3450 (500)	Turbine blades, fibers for composites, cutting tool inserts
Dolomitic limestone (Hokie stone)	—	2.79 (174)	69.0 (10.0)	19.2 (2.79)	283 (41.0)	Building stone, monuments
Westerly granite	—	2.64 (165)	49.6 (7.20)	9.58 (1.39)	233 (33.8)	Building stone, monuments

Notes: Data are for materials in bulk form except for type S glass. Temperatures given for the two forms of glass correspond to softening, with complete melting occurring above this.
Source: Data in [Farag 89] p. 510, [Ashby 06] p. 180, [Coors 89], [Gauthier 95] p. 104, [Karfakis 90], [Musikant 90] p. 24, and [Schwartz 92] p. 2.75.

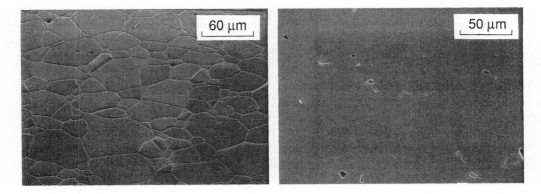

Figure 3.20   Surface (left) of near-maximum-density Al_2O_3, with grain boundaries visible. In a polished section (right), grain boundaries cannot be seen, but pores are visible as black areas. (Left photo same as in [Venkateswaran 88]; reprinted by permission of the American Ceramic Society. Right photo courtesy of D. P. H. Hasselman, Virginia Tech, Blacksburg, VA.)

the consistency of a thick paste and then formed into a cup, dish, brick, or other useful shape. Firing at a temperature in the range 800 to 1200°C then drives off the water and melts some of the SiO_2 to form a glass that binds the Al_2O_3 and the remaining SiO_2 into a solid. The presence or addition of small amounts of minerals containing sodium or potassium enhances formation of the glass by permitting a lower firing temperature.

Natural stone is of course used without processing other than cutting it into useful shapes. The prior processing done by nature varies greatly. For example, limestone is principally crystalline calcium carbonate ($CaCO_3$) that has precipitated out of ocean water, and marble is the same mineral that has been recrystallized (metamorphosed) under the influence of temperature and pressure. Sandstone consists of particles of silica sand (SiO_2) bound together by additional SiO_2, or by $CaCO_3$, which is present due to precipitation from water solution. In contrast, igneous rocks such as granite have been melted and are multiphase alloys of various crystalline minerals.

Concrete is a combination of crushed stone, sand, and a cement paste that binds the other components into a solid. The modern cement paste, called Portland cement, is made by firing a mixture of limestone and clay at 1500°C. This forms a mixture of fine particles involving primarily lime (CaO), silica (SiO_2), and alumina (Al_2O_3), where these are in the form of tricalcium silicate ($3CaO–SiO_2$), dicalcium silicate ($2CaO–SiO_2$), and tricalcium aluminate ($3CaO–Al_2O_3$). When water is added, a *hydration* reaction starts during which water is chemically bound to these minerals by being incorporated into their crystal structures. During hydration, interlocking needle-like crystals form that bind the cement particles to each other and to the stone and sand. The reaction is rapid at first and slows with time. Even after long times, some residual water remains in small pores, between layers of the crystal structure, and chemically adsorbed to the surface of hydrated paste.

Clay products, natural stone, and concrete are used in great quantities for familiar purposes, including their major use in buildings, bridges, and other large stationary structures. All are quite brittle and have poor strength in tension, but reasonable strength in compression. Concrete is very economical to use in construction and has the important advantage that it can be poured as a slurry into forms and hardened in place into complex shapes. Improved concretes continue to be developed, including some exotic varieties with quite high strength achieved by minimizing the porosity or by adding substances such as metal or glass particles or fibers.

3.6.2 Engineering Ceramics

The processing of engineering ceramics composed of simple chemical compounds involves first obtaining the compound. For example, alumina (Al_2O_3) is made from the mineral bauxite (Al_2O_3–$2H_2O$) by heating to remove the hydrated water. Other engineering ceramics, such as ZrO_2, are also obtainable directly from naturally available minerals. But some, such as WC, SiC, and Si_3N_4, must be produced by appropriate chemical reactions, starting from constituents that are available in nature. After the compound is obtained, it is ground to a fine powder if it is not already in this form. The powder is then compacted into a useful shape, typically by cold or hot pressing. A binding agent, such as a plastic, may be used to prevent the consolidated powder from crumbling. The ceramic at this stage is said to be in a *green* state and has little strength. Green ceramics are sometimes machined to obtain flat surfaces, holes, threads, etc., that would otherwise be difficult to achieve.

The next and final step in processing is *sintering*, which involves heating the green ceramic, typically to around 70% of its absolute melting temperature. This causes the particles to fuse and form a solid that contains some degree of porosity. Improved properties result from minimizing the porosity—that is, the volume percentage of voids. This can be done by using a gradation of particle sizes or by applying pressure during sintering. Small percentages of other ceramics may be added to the powder to improve response to processing. Also, small to medium percentages of other ceramics may be mixed with a given compound to tailor the properties of the final product.

One variation on the sintering process that aids in minimizing voids is *hot isostatic pressing*. This involves enclosing the ceramic in a sheet metal enclosure and placing this in a vessel that is pressurized with a hot gas. Some additional methods of processing that are sometimes used are *chemical vapor deposition* and *reaction bonding*. The former process involves chemical reactions among hot gases that result in a solid deposit of ceramic material onto the surface of another material. Reaction bonding combines the chemical reaction that forms the ceramic compound with the sintering process.

Engineering ceramics typically have high stiffness, light weight, and very high strength in compression. Although all are relatively brittle, their strength in tension and fracture toughness may be sufficiently high that their use in high-stress structural applications is not precluded if the limitations of the material are considered in the details of the component design. Increased use of ceramics in the future is likely, due to their high-temperature capability.

3.6.3 Cermets; Cemented Carbides

A *cermet* is made from powders of a ceramic and a metal by sintering them together. The metal surrounds the ceramic particles and binds them together, with the ceramic constituent providing high hardness and wear resistance. *Cemented carbides*, as made into cutting tools, are the most important cermets. In this case, tungsten carbide (WC) is sintered with cobalt metal in amounts

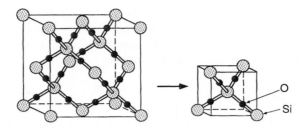

Figure 3.21   Diamond cubic crystal structure of silica, SiO_2, in its high-temperature cristobalite form. The crystal structure at ambient temperatures is a more complex arrangement of the basic tetrahedral unit shown on the right.

ranging from 3 to 25%. Other carbides are also used in the same manner, namely, TiC, TaC, and Cr_3C_2, typically in combination with WC. The most frequent binder metal is cobalt, but nickel and steel are also employed.

The metal matrix of cemented carbides provides useful toughness, but limits resistance to temperature and oxidation. Ordinary ceramics, such as alumina (Al_2O_3) and boron nitride (BN), are also used for cutting tools and have advantages, compared with cemented carbides, of greater hardness, lighter weight, and greater resistance to temperature and oxidation. But the extra care needed in working with brittle ceramics leads to the prevalence of cemented carbides, except where ceramics cannot be avoided. Some of the advantages of ceramics can be obtained by chemical vapor deposition of a coating of a ceramic onto a cemented carbide tool. Ceramics used in this manner include TiC, Al_2O_3, and TiN.

3.6.4 Glasses

Pure silica (SiO_2) in crystalline form is a quartz mineral, the crystal structure of one of which is illustrated in Fig. 3.21. However, when silica is solidified from a molten state, an amorphous solid results. This occurs because the molten glass has a high viscosity due to a chainlike molecular structure, which limits the molecular mobility to the extent that perfect crystals do not form upon solidification. The three-dimensional crystal structure in Fig. 3.21 is depicted in a simplified two-dimensional form in Fig. 3.22. A perfect crystal, as formed from solution in nature, is represented by (a). Glass formed from molten silica has a network structure that is similar, but highly imperfect, as in (b).

In processing, glasses are sometimes heated until they melt and are then poured into molds and cast into useful shapes. Alternatively, they may be heated only until soft and then formed by rolling (as for plate glass) or by blowing (as for bottles). Forming is made easier by the fact that the viscosity of glass varies gradually with temperature, so that the temperature can be adjusted to obtain a consistency that is appropriate to the particular method of forming. However, for pure silica, the temperatures involved are around 1800°C, which is inconveniently high. The temperature for forming can be lowered to around 800 to 1000°C by adding Na_2O, K_2O, or CaO. These oxides are called *network modifiers*, because the metal ions involved tend to form nondirectional ionic bonds with oxygen atoms, resulting in terminal ends in the structure, as illustrated by Fig. 3.22(c).

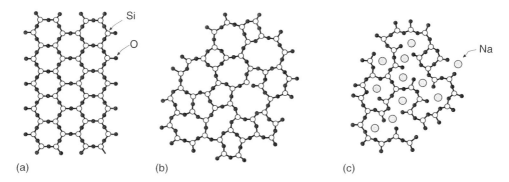

Figure 3.22   Simplified two-dimensional diagram of the structure of silica in the form of (a) quartz crystal, (b) glass, and (c) glass with a network modifier. (Part (b) adapted from [Zachariasen 32]; published 1932 by the American Chemical Society. Part (c) adapted from [Warren 38]; reprinted by permission of the American Ceramic Society.)

Table 3.11   Typical Compositions and Uses of Representative Silica Glasses

Glass	Major Components, % by Weight							Uses; Comment
	SiO_2	Al_2O_3	CaO	Na_2O	B_2O_3	MgO	PbO	
Fused silica	99	—	—	—	—	—	—	Furnace windows
Borosilicate (Pyrex)	81	2	—	4	12	—	—	Cookware, laboratory ware
Soda-lime	72	1	9	14	—	3	—	Windows, containers
Leaded	66	1	1	6	1	—	15	Tableware; also contains 9% K_2O
Type E	54	14	16	1	10	4	—	Fibers in fiberglass
Type S	65	25	—	—	—	10	—	Fibers for aerospace composites

Source: Data in [Lyle 74] and [Schwartz 92] p. 2.56.

This change in the molecular structure also causes the glass to be less brittle than pure silica glass. Commercial glasses contain varying amounts of the network modifiers, as indicated by typical compositions in Table 3.11.

Other oxides are added to modify the optical or electrical properties, color, or other characteristics of glass. Some oxides, such as B_2O_3, can form a glass themselves and may result in a two-phase structure. Leaded glass contains PbO, in which the lead participates in the chain structure. This modifies the glass to increase its resistivity and also gives a high index of refraction, which contributes to the brilliance of fine crystal. The addition of Al_2O_3 increases the strength and stiffness of the glass fibers used in fiberglass and other composite materials.

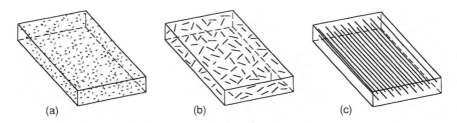

Figure 3.23   Composites reinforced by (a) particles, (b) chopped fibers or whiskers, and (c) continuous fibers. (Adapted from [Budinski 96] p. 121; © 1996 by Prentice Hall, Upper Saddle River, NJ; reprinted with permission.)

3.7 COMPOSITE MATERIALS

A *composite material* is made by combining two or more materials that are mutually insoluble by mixing or bonding them in such a way that each maintains its integrity. Some composites have already been discussed, namely, plastics modified by adding rubber particles, plastics reinforced by chopped glass fibers, cemented carbides, and concrete. These and many other composite materials consist of a matrix of one material that surrounds particles or fibers of a second material, as shown in Fig. 3.23. Some composites involve layers of different materials, and the individual layers may themselves be composites. Materials that are melted (alloyed) together are not considered composites, even if a two-phase structure results, nor are solid solutions or precipitate structures arising from solid solutions. Some representative types and examples of composite materials and their uses are listed in Table 3.12.

Materials of biological origin are usually composites. Wood contains *cellulose* fibers surrounded by *lignin* and *hemicellulose*, all of which are polymers. Bone is composed of the fibrous protein *collagen* in a ceramic-like matrix of the crystalline mineral *hydroxylapatite*, $Ca_5(PO_4)_3OH$.

Composite materials have a wide range of uses, and their use is rapidly increasing. Man-made composites can be tailored to meet special needs such as high strength and stiffness combined with light weight. The resulting high-performance (and expensive) materials are increasingly being used in aircraft, space, and defense applications, and also for high-grade sports equipment, as in golf club shafts and fishing rods. More economical composites, such as glass-reinforced plastics, are continually finding new uses in a wide range of products, such as automotive components, boat hulls, sports equipment, and furniture. Wood and concrete, of course, continue to be major construction materials, and new composites involving these and other materials have also come into recent use in the construction industry.

Various classes of composite materials will now be discussed.

3.7.1 Particulate Composites

Particles can have various effects on a matrix material, depending on the properties of the two constituents. Ductile particles added to a brittle matrix increase the toughness, as cracks have difficulty passing through the particles. An example is rubber-modified polystyrene, the

Table 3.12   Representative Types and Examples of Composite Materials

Reinforcing Type	Matrix Type	Example	Typical Use
(a) Particulate composites			
Ductile polymer or elastomer	Brittle polymer	Rubber in polystyrene	Toys, cameras
Ceramic	Ductile metal	WC with Co metal binder	Cutting tools
Ceramic	Ceramic	Granite, stone, and silica sand in Portland cement	Bridges, buildings
(b) Short-fiber, whisker composites			
Strong fiber	Thermosetting plastic	Chopped glass in polyester resin	Auto body panels
Ceramic	Ductile metal	SiC whiskers in Al alloy	Aircraft structural panels
(c) Continuous-fiber composites			
Ceramic	Thermosetting plastic	Graphite in epoxy	Aircraft wing flaps
Ceramic	Ductile metal	Boron in Al alloy	Aircraft structure
Ceramic	Ceramic	SiC in Si_3N_4	Engine parts
(d) Laminated composites			
Stiff sheet	Foamed polymer	PVC and ABS sheets over ABS foam core	Canoes
Composite	Metal	Kevlar in epoxy between Al alloy layers (ARALL)	Aircraft structure

microstructure of which has already been illustrated in Fig. 3.19. Another ductile particle composite made from two polymers is shown broken open in Fig. 3.24.

Particles of a hard and stiff (high E) material added to a ductile matrix increase its strength and stiffness. An example is carbon black added to rubber. As might be expected, hard particles generally decrease the fracture toughness of a ductile matrix, and this limits the usefulness of some composites of this type. However, the composite may still be useful if it has other desirable properties that outweigh the disadvantages of limited toughness, such as the high hardness and wear resistance of cemented carbides.

If the hard particles in a ductile matrix are quite small and limited in quantity, the reduction in toughness is modest. In a metal matrix, a desirable strengthening effect similar to that of precipitation hardening can be achieved by sintering the metal in powder form with ceramic particles of size on the order of $0.1 \ \mu$m. This is called *dispersion hardening*. The volume fraction of particles seldom exceeds 15%, and the amount may be as small as 1%. Aluminum reinforced in this manner with Al_2O_3 has improved creep resistance. Tungsten is similarly dispersion hardened with small

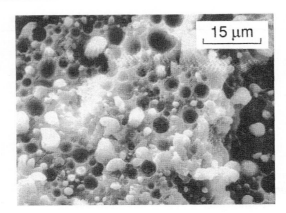

Figure 3.24   Fracture surface of polyphenylene oxide (PPO) modified with high-impact polystyrene particles. (Photo courtesy of General Electric Co., Pittsfield, MA.)

amounts of oxide ceramics, such as ThO_2, Al_2O_3, SiO_2, and K_2O, so that it has sufficient creep resistance for use in lightbulb filaments. Note that particles introduced in this manner will not have a coherent crystal structure with the parent material.

3.7.2 Fibrous Composites

Strong and stiff fibers can be made from ceramic materials that are difficult to use as structural materials in bulk form, such as glass, graphite (carbon), boron, and silicon carbide (SiC). When these are embedded in a matrix of a ductile material, such as a polymer or a metal, the resulting composite can be strong, stiff, and tough. The fibers carry most of the stress, whereas the matrix holds them in place. Fibers and matrix can be seen in the photograph of a broken open composite material in Fig. 3.25. Good adhesion between fibers and matrix is important, as this allows the matrix to carry the stress from one fiber to another where a fiber breaks or where one simply ends because of its limited length. Fiber diameters are typically in the size range 1 to $100\,\mu$m.

Fibers are used in composites in a variety of different configurations, two of which are shown in Fig. 3.23. Short, randomly oriented fibers result in a composite that has similar properties in all directions. Chopped glass fibers used to reinforce thermoplastics are of this type. *Whiskers* are a special class of short fiber that consist of tiny, elongated, single crystals that are very strong because they are dislocation free. Diameters are 1 to $10\,\mu$m or smaller, and lengths are 10 to 100 times larger than the diameter. For example, randomly oriented SiC whiskers can be used to strengthen and stiffen aluminum alloys.

Long fibers can be woven into a cloth or made into a mat of intertwined strands. Glass fibers in both of these configurations are used with polyester resins to make common fiberglass. High-performance composites are often made by using long, straight, continuous fibers. Continuous fibers all oriented in a single direction provide maximum strength and stiffness parallel to the fibers. Since such a material is weak if stressed in the transverse direction, several thin layers with different fiber orientations are usually stacked into a *laminate*, as shown in Fig. 3.26. For example, composites with a thermosetting plastic matrix, often epoxy, are assembled in this manner by using partially

Figure 3.25   Fracture surface showing broken fibers for a composite of Nicalon-type SiC fibers in a CAS glass–ceramic matrix. (Photo by S. S. Lee; material manufactured by Corning.)

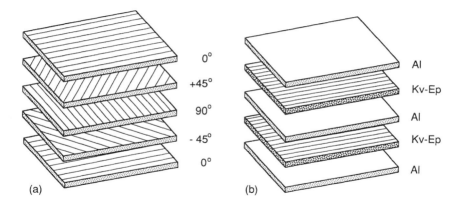

Figure 3.26   Laminated composites. Sheets having various fiber directions, as shown in (a), may be bonded together. The ARALL laminate (b) is constructed with aluminum sheets bonded to sheets of composite, with the latter being made of Kevlar fibers in an epoxy matrix.

cured sheets, which are called *prepregs* because they have been previously impregnated with the epoxy resin. Appropriate heat and pressure are applied to complete the cross-linking reaction, while at the same time bonding the layers into a solid laminate. Fibers commonly used in this manner with an epoxy matrix include glass, graphite, boron, and the aramid polymer Kevlar. The microstructure of a laminated composite can be seen in Fig. 3.27.

For polymer matrix fibrous composites, strengths comparable to those of structural metals are obtained, as shown in Fig. 3.28(a). The values for ordinary polyester matrix fiberglass and the lower strength structural metals are similar. But for epoxy reinforced with long fibers of S-glass or graphite, the strength rivals that of the stronger steels. Values of stiffness (E) for high-performance laminates are comparable to those for aluminum, but less than for steel. However, in considering materials for weight-critical applications such as aircraft structure, it is more relevant to consider the

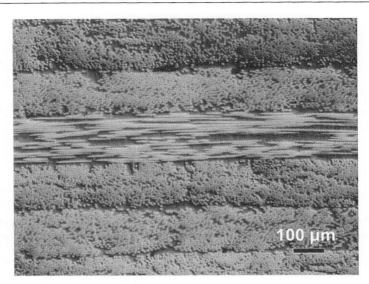

Figure 3.27 Microstructure of a graphite reinforced polymer composite, showing fibers normal to the sectioned surface, and others approximately parallel, as imaged by the Nomarski DIC technique. The matrix is a thermosetting polymer with a toughening agent. (Photo courtesy of George F. Vander Voort, Vander Voort Consulting, Wadsworth, IL; used with permission.)

strength-to-weight ratio and the stiffness-to-weight ratio. On this basis, high-performance fibrous composites are superior to structural metals in both strength and stiffness. This is illustrated for strength by Fig. 3.28(b).

Due to the limitations of the matrix, polymer matrix composites have limited resistance to high temperature. Composites with an aluminum or titanium matrix have reasonable temperature resistance. These metals are sometimes used with continuous straight fibers of silicon carbide of fairly large diameter, around $140 \, \mu$m. Other fiber types and configurations are also used.

For high-temperature applications, ceramic matrix composites have been developed. These materials have a matrix that is already strong and stiff, but which is brittle and has a low fracture toughness. Whiskers or fibers of another ceramic can act to retard cracking by bridging across small cracks that exist and holding them closed so that their growth is retarded. For example, whiskers of SiC in a matrix of Al_2O_3 are used in this manner. Continuous fibers can also be used, such as SiC fibers in a matrix of Si_3N_4. Some intermetallic compounds, such as Ti_3Al and NiAl, have ceramic-like properties, but also a helpful degree of ductility at high temperature that encourages their use as matrix materials for temperature-resistant composites.

3.7.3 Laminated Composites

A material made by combining layers is called a *laminate*. The layers may differ as to the fiber orientation, or they may consist of different materials. Plywood is a familiar example of a laminate, the layers differing as to grain direction and perhaps also as to type of wood. As already noted, unidirectional composite sheets are frequently laminated, as in Fig. 3.26(a). Aramid–aluminum

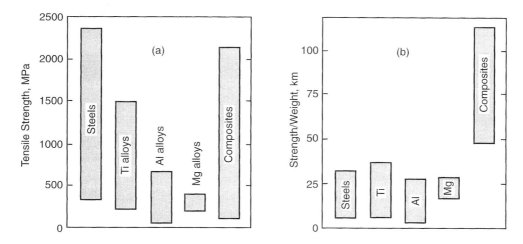

Figure 3.28   Comparison of strength for various classes of structural metals and polymer matrix composites, showing ranges for (a) tensile strength, and (b) tensile strength per unit weight. (Data from [Farag 89] pp. 174–176.)

laminate (ARALL) has layers of an aluminum alloy and a composite with unidirectional Kevlar fibers in an epoxy matrix. See Fig. 3.26(b).

Where stiffness in bending is needed along with light weight, layers of a strong and stiff material may be placed on either side of a lightweight core. Such *sandwich* materials include aluminum or fibrous composite sheets bonded on each side of a core that is made of a stiff foam. Another possibility is a core made of a honeycomb of aluminum or other material.

3.8 MATERIALS SELECTION FOR ENGINEERING COMPONENTS

An engineering component, such as a beam, shaft, tension member, column, or machine part, must not deform excessively or fail by fracture or collapse. At the same time, the cost and often the weight must not be excessive. The most basic consideration in avoiding excessive deformation is to limit the deflection due to elastic strain. For a given component geometry and applied load, the resistance to elastic deflection—that is, the *stiffness*—is determined by the *elastic modulus E* of the material. As to *strength*, the most basic requirement is to avoid having the stress exceed the failure strength of the material, such as the *yield strength σ_o* from a tension test.

Consider the general situation in which an engineering component must meet one or more requirements related to its performance, such as a maximum permissible deflection and/or a given safety factor against yielding in the material. Further, assume that any of several candidate materials may be chosen. It is often possible in such situations to perform a systematic analysis that will provide a ranking of materials for each performance requirement, thus providing an organized framework for making the final choice. Such methodology will be introduced in this section.

Before we proceed, note that materials properties such as the elastic modulus and yield strength will be considered in detail in the next chapter from the viewpoint of obtaining their values from

Table 3.13   Selected Typical Materials for Selection Examples and Problems

Material Type	Example	Elastic Modulus E, GPa	Strength σ_c, MPa	Density ρ, g/cm^3	Relative Cost, C_m
Structural (mild) steel	AISI 1020 steel	203	260[1]	7.9	1
Low alloy steel	AISI 4340 steel	207	1103[1]	7.9	3
High strength aluminum alloy	7075-T6 Al	71	469[1]	2.7	6
Titanium alloy	Ti-6Al-4V	117	1185[1]	4.5	45
Engineering polymer	Polycarbonate (PC)	2.4	62[1]	1.2	5
Wood	Loblolly pine	12.3[2]	88[2]	0.51	1.5
Economical composite	Glass cloth in epoxy (GFRP)	21	380[3]	2.0	10
High-performance composite	Graphite fiber in epoxy laminate (CFRP)	76	930[3]	1.6	200

Notes: [1]Yield strengths σ_o in tension are listed for metals and polymers. [2]Elastic modulus and ultimate strength in bending are given for loblolly pine. [3]Ultimate tensile strength σ_u is provided for composites.
Sources: Tables 4.2, 4.3, and 14.1; author's synthesis of miscellaneous data.

laboratory tests. However, for our present purposes, it will be sufficient to employ the simple definitions given in Section 1.2.1. The elastic modulus E is specifically a measure of the stiffness of the material under axial loading. For shear stress and strain, which are important for torsional loading, it is replaced by the similarly defined *shear modulus G*. The yield strength σ_o is mainly relevant to ductile materials, where this stress characterizes the beginning of relatively easy further deformation. For brittle materials, there is no clear yielding behavior, and the most important strength property is the *ultimate tensile strength* σ_u. (See Fig. 1.3.) In addition, we will need to employ some results from elementary mechanics of materials, specifically equations for stresses and deflections for simple component geometries. Such equations for selected cases are given in Appendix A at the end of this book, especially in Figs. A.1, A.4, and A.7.

A few representative structural engineering materials from various classes and some of their properties are listed in Table 3.13. We will use this list in examples and problems related to materials selection. There are, of course, many thousands of engineering materials or variations of a given material. Hence, selections from this list should be regarded only as a rough indication of what class or classes of material might be considered in more detail for a given situation.

3.8.1 Selection Procedure

Consider the case of a cantilever beam having a circular cross section and a load at the end, as in Fig. 3.29. Assume that the function of the beam requires that it have a particular length L and be capable of carrying a particular load P. Further, let it be required that the maximum stress be below the failure strength of the material, $\sigma_c = \sigma_o$ or σ_u, by a safety factor X, which might be on

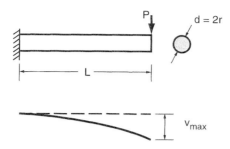

Figure 3.29   Cantilever beam.

the order of 2 or 3. Weight is critical, so the mass m of the beam must be minimized. Finally, the diameter, $d = 2r$, of the cross section may be varied to allow the material chosen to meet the various requirements just noted.

A systematic procedure can be followed that allows the optimum material to be chosen in this and other analogous cases. To start, classify the variables that enter the problem into categories as follows: (1) requirements, (2) geometry that may vary, (3) materials properties, and (4) quantity to be minimized or maximized. For the beam example, with ρ being the mass density, these are

1. Requirements: L, P, X
2. Geometry variable: r
3. Material properties: ρ, σ_c
4. Quantity to minimize: m

Next, express the quantity Q to be minimized or maximized as a mathematical function of the requirements and the material properties, in which the geometry variable does not appear:

$$Q = f_1 \text{ (Requirements) } f_2 \text{ (Material)} \tag{3.1}$$

For the beam example, Q is the mass m, so that the functional dependencies needed are

$$m = f_1(L, P, X) f_2(\rho, \sigma_c) \tag{3.2}$$

with the beam radius r not appearing. Note that all the quantities in f_1 are constants for a given design, whereas those in f_2 vary with material.

For the procedure to work, the equation for Q must be expressed as the product of two separate functions f_1 and f_2, as indicated. Fortunately, this is usually possible. The geometry variable cannot appear, as its different values for each material are not known at this stage of the procedure. However, it can be calculated later for any desired values of the requirements. Once the desired $Q = f_1 f_2$ is obtained, it may be applied to each candidate material, and the one with smallest or largest value of Q chosen, depending on the situation.

Example 3.1

For the beam of Fig. 3.29 and the materials of Table 3.13, proceed as follows:

    (a) Perform the materials selection for minimum mass.
    (b) Calculate the beam radius r that is required for each material. Assume values of
        $P = 200$ N, $L = 100$ mm, and $X = 2$.

Solution   **(a)** To obtain the specific mathematical expression for Eq. 3.2, start by expressing the mass as the product of the beam volume and the mass density:

$$m = (\pi r^2 L)\rho$$

The beam radius r needs to be eliminated and the other variables brought into the equation. This can be accomplished by noting that the maximum stress in the beam is

$$\sigma = \frac{M_{max} c_1}{I_z}$$

where this is the standard expression for stress due to bending, as obtained from Fig. A.1(b) in Appendix A.

    For a circular cross section, the distance $c_1 = r$. The area moment of inertia from Fig. A.2(b) and the maximum bending moment from Fig. A.4(c) are

$$I_z = \frac{\pi r^4}{4}, \qquad M_{max} = PL$$

Substituting for M_{max}, c_1, and I_z in the equation for stress σ gives

$$\sigma = \frac{(PL)(r)}{(\pi r^4 / 4)} = \frac{4PL}{\pi r^3}$$

The highest permissible stress is the materials failure strength divided by the safety factor:

$$\sigma = \frac{\sigma_c}{X}$$

Combining the last two equations and solving for r then gives

$$r = \left(\frac{4PLX}{\pi \sigma_c} \right)^{1/3}$$

Finally, substituting this expression for r into the equation for m gives

$$m = \pi L \rho \left(\frac{4PLX}{\pi \sigma_c} \right)^{2/3}, \qquad m = [f_1][f_2] = \left[\pi \left(\frac{4PX}{\pi} \right)^{2/3} L^{5/3} \right] \left[\frac{\rho}{\sigma_c^{2/3}} \right]$$

Table E3.1

Material	$\dfrac{\rho}{\sigma_c^{2/3}}$	Rank for Min. Mass	Radius r, mm	$\dfrac{C_m \rho}{\sigma_c^{2/3}}$	Rank for Min. Cost
Structural steel	0.194	8	5.81	0.194	2
Low-alloy steel	0.0740	6	3.59	0.222	3
Aluminum alloy	0.0447	5	4.77	0.268	4
Titanium alloy	0.0402	4	3.50	1.81	7
Polymer	0.0766	7	9.37	0.383	6
Wood	0.0258	2	8.33	0.0387	1
Glass–epoxy	0.0381	3	5.12	0.381	5
Graphite–epoxy	0.0168	1	3.80	3.36	8

Notes: Units are g/cm^3 for ρ and MPa for σ_c. The strength σ_c is the yield strength for metals, and the ultimate strength for wood, glass, and composites. Ranks are 1 = best, etc., for minimum mass or cost.

where the second form has been manipulated to obtain the desired separate f_1 and f_2, as set off by brackets.

Since all of the quantities in f_1 have fixed values, the mass will be minimized if the f_2 expression is minimized. For example, for AISI 1020 steel,

$$f_2 = \frac{\rho}{\sigma_c^{2/3}} = \frac{7.9 \,\text{g/cm}^3}{(260 \,\text{MPa})^{2/3}} = 0.194$$

The similarly calculated values for the other materials are listed in the first column of Table E3.1.

The ranking of materials as to mass (1 = best, etc.) is given in the second column. On this basis, the graphite–epoxy composite is the best choice and wood the second best.

(b) Values of the required beam radius r may be calculated from the equation just developed with the given values of P, L, and X, along with σ_c for each material. For AISI 1020 steel, this gives

$$r = \left(\frac{4PLX}{\pi \sigma_c}\right)^{1/3} = \left[\frac{4(200\,\text{N})(100\,\text{mm})(2)}{\pi(260\,\text{N/mm}^2)}\right]^{1/3} = 5.81\,\text{mm}$$

The similarly calculated values for the other materials are listed in the third column of Table E3.1.

3.8.2 Discussion

In selecting a material, there may be additional requirements or more than one quantity that needs to be maximized or minimized. For example, for the preceding beam example, there might be a maximum permissible deflection. Application of the selection procedure to this situation gives a new $f_2 = f_2(\rho, E)$ and a different ranking of materials. Hence, a compromise choice that considers both sets of rankings may be needed.

Cost is almost always an important consideration, and the foregoing selection procedure can be applied, with Q being the cost. Since costs of materials vary with time and market conditions, current information from materials suppliers is needed for an exact comparison of costs. Some rough values of relative cost are listed for the materials in Table 3.13. These relative costs are obtained by rationing the cost to that of ordinary low-carbon structural steel (mild steel). Values are given in terms of relative cost per unit mass, C_m. The material ranking in terms of cost will seldom agree with that based on performance, so compromise is usually required in making the final selection.

Other factors besides stiffness, strength, weight, and cost usually also affect the selection of a material. Examples include the cost and practicality of manufacturing the component from the material, space requirements that limit the permissible values of the geometry variable, and sensitivity to hostile chemical and thermal environments. Concerning the latter, particular materials are subject to degradation in particular environments, and these combinations should be avoided. Information on environmental sensitivity is included in materials handbooks, such as those listed at the end of this chapter.

In addition to deflections due to elastic strain, there are situations in which it is important to consider deflections, or even collapse, due to plastic strain or creep strain. Also, fracture may occur by means other than the stress simply exceeding the materials yield or ultimate strength. For example, flaws may cause brittle fracture, or cyclic loading may lead to fatigue cracking at relatively low stresses. Materials selection must consider such additional possible causes of component failure. Note that plasticity, creep, fracture, and fatigue are covered in later chapters in this book, starting with Chapter 8.

The general type of systematic materials selection procedure considered in this section is developed in detail in the book by Ashby (2011), and it is also employed in the *CES Selector 2009* materials database.

Example 3.2

For the beam problem of Ex. 3.1, extend the analysis to a consideration of cost.

Solution   This can be accomplished by minimizing the quantity

$$Q = C_m m$$

where C_m is the relative cost per unit mass from Table 3.13. Using the expression obtained for mass m near the end of Ex. 3.1, we find that this Q is

$$Q = [f_1(L, P, X)] \left[\frac{C_m \rho}{\sigma_c^{2/3}} \right]$$

where f_1 is the same as before, and the quantity to be minimized is the expression in the second brackets. Values of this new f_2 are added to Table E3.1, along with a new ranking.

If cost is indeed important, the previous choice of graphite–epoxy composite would probably have to be eliminated as it is the most costly. Wood is now the highest ranking material, and mild steel is the second highest. If both light weight and cost are important, then wood is the clear choice. If wood is unsuitable for some reason, then either glass–epoxy composite or an aluminum alloy might be chosen as representing a reasonable compromise.

3.9 SUMMARY

A number of metals have combinations of properties and availability that result in their use as load-resisting engineering materials. These include irons and steels, and aluminum, titanium, copper, and magnesium. Pure metals in bulk form yield at quite low stresses, but useful levels of strength can be obtained by introducing obstacles to dislocation motion through such means as cold work, solid-solution strengthening, precipitation hardening, and the introduction of multiple phases. Alloying with various amounts of one or more additional metals or nonmetals is usually needed to achieve this strengthening and to otherwise tailor the properties to obtain a useful engineering metal.

In steels, small amounts of carbon and other elements in solid solution provide some strengthening without heat treatment. For carbon contents above about 0.3%, substantially greater strengthening can be obtained from heat treating by the quenching and tempering process. Small percentages of alloying elements, such as Ni, Cr, and Mo, enhance the strengthening effect. Special steels, such as stainless steels and tool steels, typically include fairly substantial percentages of various alloying elements.

Considering aluminum alloys, the highest strengths in this lightweight metal are obtained by alloying and heat treatment that causes precipitation hardening (aging) to be effective. Magnesium is strengthened in a similar manner and is noteworthy as being the lightest engineering metal. Titanium alloys are somewhat heavier than aluminum, but have greater temperature resistance. They are strengthened by a combination of the various methods, including multiple phase effects in the alpha–beta alloys. Superalloys are corrosion- and temperature-resistant metals that have large percentages of two or more of the metals nickel, cobalt, and iron.

Polymers have long chainlike molecules, or a network structure, based on carbon. Compared to metals, they lack strength, stiffness, and temperature resistance. However, these disadvantages are offset to an extent by light weight and corrosion resistance, leading to their use in numerous low-stress applications. Polymers are classified as thermoplastics if they can be repeatedly melted and solidified. Some examples of thermoplastics are polyethylene, polymethyl methacrylate, and nylon. Contrasting behavior occurs for thermosetting plastics, which change chemically during processing and thereafter cannot be melted. Examples include phenolics and epoxies. Elastomers, such as natural and synthetic rubbers, are distinguished by being capable of deformations of at least 100% to 200%, and of then recovering most of this deformation after removal of the stress.

A given thermoplastic is usually glassy and brittle below its glass transition temperature, T_g. Above the T_g of a given polymer, the stiffness (E) is likely to be very low unless the material has a substantially crystalline structure. Stiffness and strength in polymers is also enhanced by longer lengths of the chain molecules, by chain branching in amorphous polymers, and by cross-linking between chains. Thermosetting plastics have a molecular structure that causes a large number of cross-links, or a network structure, to form during processing. Once these covalent bonds are formed, the material cannot later be melted—this explains the thermosetting behavior. Vulcanizing of rubber is also a thermosetting process, in which case sulfur atoms form bonds that link chain molecules.

Ceramics are nonmetallic and inorganic crystalline solids that are generally chemical compounds. Clay products, porcelain, natural stone, and concrete are fairly complex combinations of crystalline phases, primarily silica (SiO_2) and metal oxides, and $CaCO_3$ in the case of some natural stones, bound together by various means. High-strength engineering ceramics tend to be fairly simple chemical compounds, such as metal oxides, carbides, or nitrides. Cermets, such as cemented carbides, are ceramic materials sintered with a metal phase that acts as a binder. Glasses are amorphous (noncrystalline) materials consisting of SiO_2 combined with varying amounts of metal oxides.

All ceramics and glasses tend to be brittle, compared with metals. However, many have advantages, such as light weight, high stiffness, high compressive strength, and temperature resistance, that cause them to be the most suitable materials in certain situations.

Composites are combinations of two or more materials, with one generally acting as a matrix and the other as reinforcement. The reinforcement may be in the form of particles, short fibers, or continuous fibers. Composites include many common man-made materials, such as concrete, cemented carbides, and fiberglass, and other reinforced plastics, as well as biological materials, notably wood and bone. High-performance composites, as used in aerospace applications, generally employ high-strength fibers in a ductile matrix. The fibers are often a ceramic or glass, and the matrix is typically a polymer or a lightweight metal. However, even a ceramic matrix is made stronger and less brittle by the presence of reinforcing fibers.

It is often useful to combine layers to make a laminated composite. The layers may differ as to fiber direction, or they may consist of more than one type of material, or both. High-performance composite laminates may be advantageous for use in situations such as aerospace structure, as their strength and stiffness are both quite high compared with those of metals on a unit-weight basis.

Materials selection for engineering design requires an understanding of materials and their behavior, and also detailed information as found in handbooks or provided by materials suppliers. Systematic analysis as described in Section 3.8 may be useful.

The survey of engineering materials given in this chapter should be considered to be only a summary. Numerous sources of more detailed information exist, some of which are given in the References section of this chapter. Companies that supply materials are also often a useful source of information on their particular products.

NEW TERMS AND SYMBOLS

alpha–beta titanium alloy   ceramic
annealing   cermet
austenite   coherent precipitate
casting   cold work
cast iron   composite material
cemented carbide   copolymer
cementite, Fe_3C cross-linking

deformation processing
dispersion hardening
ductile (nodular) iron
elastomer
ferrite
fibrous composite
glass
grain refinement
gray iron
heat treatment
intermetallic compound
laminate
low-alloy steel
martensite
materials selection
network modifier
particulate composite
pearlite

plain-carbon steel
plasticizer
precipitation hardening
quenching and tempering
reinforced plastic
second phase
sintering
solid-solution strengthening
stainless steel
steel
superalloy
thermoplastic
thermosetting plastic
tool steel
vulcanization
whisker
wrought metals

REFERENCES

(a) General References

ASHBY, M. F. 2011. *Materials Selection in Mechanical Design*, 4th ed., Butterworth-Heinemann, Oxford, UK.

ASHBY, M., H. SHERCLIFF and D. CEBON. 2010. *Materials: Engineering, Science, Processing and Design*, 2nd ed., Butterworth-Heinemann, Oxford, UK.

ASTM. 2010. *Annual Book of ASTM Standards, Section 1: Iron and Steel Products*, Vols. 01.01 to 01.08, ASTM International, West Conshohocken, PA.

BUDINSKI, K. G., and M. K. BUDINSKI. 2010. *Engineering Materials: Properties and Selection*, 9th ed., Prentice Hall, Upper Saddle River, NJ.

KINGERY, W. D., H. K. BOWEN, and D. R. UHLMANN. 1976. *Introduction to Ceramics*, 2d ed., John Wiley, New York.

MALLICK, P. K. 2008. *Fiber-Reinforced Composites: Materials, Manufacturing, and Design*, 3rd ed., CRC Press, Boca Raton, FL.

SAE. 2008. *Metals and Alloys in the Unified Numbering System*, 11th ed., Pub. No. SAE HS-1086, SAE International, Warrendale, PA; also Pub. No. ASTM DS56J, ASTM International, West Conshohocken, PA.

SPERLING, L. H. 2006. *Introduction to Physical Polymer Science*, 4th ed., John Wiley, Hoboken, NJ.

(b) Materials Handbooks and Databases

ASM. 2001. *ASM Handbook: Vol. 1, Properties and Selection: Irons, Steels, and High Performance Alloys; Vol. 2, Properties and Selection: Nonferrous Alloys and Special-Purpose Materials;* and *Vol. 21, Composites*, pub. 1990, 1990, and 2001, respectively, ASM International, Materials Park, OH.

ASM. 1991. *Engineered Materials Handbook: Vol. 2, Engineering Plastics; Vol. 3, Adhesives and Sealants;* and *Vol. 4, Ceramics and Glasses*, pub. 1988, 1990 and 1991, respectively, ASM International, Materials Park, OH.

CES. 2009. *CES Selector 2009*, database of materials and processes, Granta Design Ltd, Cambridge, UK. (See *http://www.grantadesign.com.*)

DAVIS, J. R., ed. 1998. *Metals Handbook: Desk Edition*, 2d ed., ASM International, Materials Park, OH.

DAVIS, J. R., ed. 2003. *Handbook of Materials for Medical Devices*, ASM International, Materials Park, OH.

GAUTHIER, M. M., vol. chair. 1995. *Engineered Materials Handbook, Desk Edition*, ASM International, Materials Park, OH.

HARPER, C. A., ed. 2006. *Handbook of Plastics Technologies*, McGraw-Hill, New York.

SOMIYA, S., et al., eds. 2003. *Handbook of Advanced Ceramics*, vols. 1 and 2, Elsevier Academic Press, London, UK.

PROBLEMS AND QUESTIONS

Sections 3.2 to 3.4

3.1 Examine several small metal tools or parts. Try to determine whether each was formed by forging, rolling, extrusion, drawing, or casting. Consider the overall shape of the object, any surface features that exist, and even words that are marked on the part.

3.2 Nickel and copper are mutually soluble in all percentages as substitutional alloys with an FCC crystal structure. The effect of up to 30% nickel on the yield strength of copper is shown in Fig. 3.3. Draw a qualitative graph showing how you expect the yield strength of otherwise pure Cu-Ni alloys to vary as the nickel content is varied from zero to 100%.

3.3 Briefly explain why austenitic stainless steels cannot be strengthened by quenching and tempering.

3.4 In the development of human technology, the stone age was followed by a bronze age, which in turn was followed by an iron age. Why not a brass age? (Note that copper alloyed with 35% zinc gives a typical brass. Also, copper alloyed with 10% tin gives a typical bronze.) Why did the iron age not occur immediately after the stone age?

3.5 Explain why beryllium metal is a good choice for the hexagonal sections of the primary mirror for the James Webb Space Telescope, scheduled by NASA to be launched in 2014. Start by finding values of some of the basic properties of beryllium, such as its melting temperature T_m, density ρ, elastic modulus E, and coefficient of thermal expansion α, as well as general information about this telescope.

Section 3.5

3.6 In your own words, explain why thermosetting plastics do not have a pronounced decrease in the elastic modulus, E, at a glass transition temperature, T_g.

3.7 For the polymers in Table 3.9, plot T_g versus T_m after converting both to absolute temperature. Use a different plotting symbol for each class of polymers. Does there appear to be a correlation between T_g and T_m? Are there different trends for the different classes of polymers?

3.8 Engineering plastics in bulk form typically have elastic moduli in the range $E = 2$ to 3 GPa. However, for Kevlar fibers, the value can be as high as 120 GPa. Explain how this is possible.

3.9 Ultrahigh molecular weight polyethylene (UHMWPE) is used for bearing surfaces in joint replacement surgery. Consult one or more references, and/or do an Internet search, on this subject. Determine in more detail how and where UHMWPE is used in the human body, and identify its special characteristics that make it suitable for such use. Then write a few paragraphs summarizing what you have found.

Section 3.6

3.10 For S-glass in Table 3.11, explain why some oxides commonly used in glass are not included and why the percentage of Al_2O_3 is high. How would you expect the strength of S-glass fibers to compare with those of E-glass?

3.11 Consider the data for strength of Al_2O_3, SiC, and glass in both bulk and fiber form in Tables 3.10 and 2.2(b), respectively. Explain the large differences between the strengths in tension and compression for these materials in bulk form, and also explain why the strengths of fibers in tension are so much greater than for bulk material.

3.12 The ancient Romans employed a volcanic ash called *pozzolana* to make a material somewhat similar to the modern Portland cement concrete. Consult sources beyond this textbook and write two or three paragraphs about how this material differed from modern concrete, and how it was similar, and the Roman's degree of success in using it as a building material.

Section 3.7

3.13 Compute strength-to-density and stiffness-to-density ratios, σ_u/ρ and E/ρ, for the first five metals in Table 3.1 and for the SiC and Al_2O_3 whiskers and fibers in Table 2.2(a) and (b). Use the upper limits of strength for the metals. For SiC and Al_2O_3, use densities from Table 3.10 as approximate values. Plot σ_u/ρ versus E/ρ, using different plotting symbols for metals, fibers, and whiskers. What trends do you observe? Discuss the significance of these trends in view of the possibility of making metal matrix composites containing, say, 50% fibers or whiskers by volume.

3.14 Concisely discuss the differences between precipitation hardening and dispersion hardening.

Section 3.8

3.15 Consider the beam of circular cross section of Fig. 3.29 and Ex. 3.1. As before, the radius r of the cross section may vary with material, and the beam is required to have length L and carry load P. However, in this case, the strength requirement is replaced by a requirement that the deflection not exceed a particular value v_{max}.

    (a) Select a material from Table 3.13 such that the mass is minimized.

    (b) Repeat the selection with cost being minimized.

    (c) Briefly discuss your results, and suggest one or more materials that represent a reasonable choice, where both light weight and cost are important.

3.16 Consider a tension member that is part of the structure of a personal aircraft. For a preliminary materials selection, assume that the member has a square cross section of side h that may vary with material choice. The length L is fixed. There are two functional requirements. First, a force P must be resisted such that there is a safety factor X against the material exceeding its failure strength. Second, the deflection due to force P must not exceed a given length change ΔL. Make a compromise choice among the materials of Table 3.13 that considers these requirements, light weight, cost, and any other considerations that you believe are important. Briefly justify your choice.

3.17 A column is a structural member that resists a compressive force. If a column fails, it does so by buckling—that is, by suddenly deflecting sideways. For relatively long, thin columns, this occurs at a critical load of

$$P_{cr} = \frac{\pi^2 E I}{L^2}$$

where E is the elastic modulus of the column material and I is the moment of inertia of the cross-sectional area. Assume that the cross section is a thin-walled tube of wall thickness t and inner radius r_1, with the proportions $t = 0.2r_1$ being maintained, as the section size is allowed to vary with material choice. The column must have a particular length L and resist a load P that is lower than P_{cr} by a safety factor X. Noting that the relative importance of light weight and cost may vary with the application, make a preliminary selection of column materials from Table 3.13 for the following:

(a) A structural compression member in a space station.

(b) A support for the second floor above the garage in a private residence.

3.18 A spherical pressure vessel that must hold compressed air is to be designed with a given inner radius r_1, and the wall thickness t may vary with material choice. The vessel must resist a pressure p such that there is a safety factor X against the material exceeding its failure strength.

(a) Considering weight and cost, and any other factors that you believe to be important, make a preliminary materials selection from Table 3.13 for this application.

(b) Calculate the vessel thickness required for each material. Assume a vessel inner radius of $r_1 = 2$ m, a pressure of $p = 0.7$ MPa, and a safety factor on the material strength of $X = 3$. Comment on the values obtained. Why are some much larger than others?

3.19 A leaf spring in the suspension system of an experimental vehicle is a beam of length $L = 0.5$ m, with a rectangular cross section, as shown in Fig. P3.19. This part, as currently designed with a low-alloy steel, has a width $t = 60$ mm and a depth $h = 5$ mm. However, if possible, it is desirable to replace this steel with another material to reduce the weight of the component. To avoid redesigning other related parts, the t dimension should not be changed, but h can be varied, as long as it does not exceed 12 mm. The spring stiffness must be $k = P/v = 50$ kN/m. Also, the spring hits a limit to its motion at $v_{max} = 30$ mm, at which point the stress should not be so large that the safety factor against material failure is less than $X = 1.4$.

(a) First, considering only the $k = 50$ kN/m requirement, determine which materials in Table 3.13 would provide a lighter weight component.

(b) Next, for each material, calculate the h necessary to meet the $k = 50$ kN/m requirement, and also the safety factor relative to σ_c at $v_{max} = 30$ mm. Eliminate any materials that do not meet $h \leq 12$ mm and $X \geq 1.4$.

(c) Finally, compare the alloy steel design with the use of each of the remaining candidates, considering cost and any other factors that you believe to be important.

3.20 A beam is simply supported at its ends, has a length $L = 1.50$ m, and is subjected to a uniformly distributed load $w = 2.00$ kN/m, as in Fig. A.4(b). The beam is a hollow box section, as in Fig. A.2(d), with proportions $b_2 = h_2$ and $b_1 = h_1 = 0.70h_2$. There are two design requirements: The safety factor against yielding or other failure of the material must be at least $X = 3.0$, and the midspan deflection must not exceed 25 mm. Using properties from

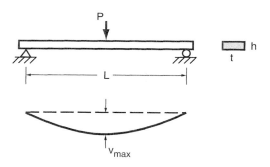

Figure P3.19

Table 3.13, consider making the beam from one of three materials, AISI 4340 steel, 7075-T6 Al, or glass–epoxy composite.

    (a) What beam size h_2 is required for each material to meet the $X = 3$ requirement?

    (b) What size h_2 is required for each material to avoid a deflection greater than 25 mm?

    (c) Considering both requirements, what is the required size h_2 for each choice of material?

    (d) Which choice of material is the most economical? The lightest weight?

Section 3.9

3.21 Examine a bicycle and attempt to identify the materials used for six different parts. How is each material appropriate for use in the part where it is found? (You may wish to visit a bicycle shop or consult a book on bicycling.)

3.22 Look at one or more catalogs that include toys, sports equipment, tools, or appliances. Make a list of the materials named, and guess at a more precise identification where trade names or abbreviated names are used. Are any composite materials identified?

4

Mechanical Testing: Tension Test and Other Basic Tests

OBJECTIVES

- Become familiar with the basic types of mechanical tests, including tests in tension, compression, indentation hardness, notch impact, bending, and torsion.
- Analyze data from tension tests to determine materials properties, including both engineering properties and true stress–strain properties.
- Understand the significance of the properties obtained from basic mechanical tests, and explore some of the major trends in behavior that are seen in these tests.

4.1 INTRODUCTION

Samples of engineering materials are subjected to a wide variety of mechanical tests to measure their strength or other properties of interest. Such samples, called *specimens*, are often broken or grossly deformed in testing. Some of the common forms of test specimen and loading situation are shown in Fig. 4.1. The most basic test is simply to break the sample by applying a tensile force, as in (a). Compression tests (b) are also common. In engineering, hardness is usually defined in terms of resistance of the material to penetration by a hard ball or point, as in (c). Various forms of bending test are also often used, as is torsion of cylindrical rods or tubes.

The simplest test specimens are smooth (unnotched) ones, as illustrated in Fig. 4.2(a). More complex geometries can be used to produce conditions resembling those in actual engineering

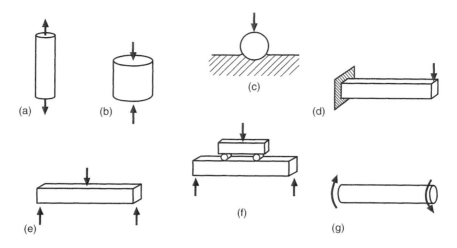

Figure 4.1   Geometry and loading situations commonly employed in mechanical testing of materials: (a) tension, (b) compression, (c) indentation hardness, (d) cantilever bending, (e) three-point bending, (f) four-point bending, and (g) torsion.

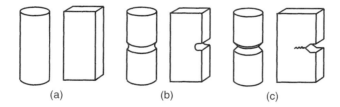

Figure 4.2   Three classes of test specimen: (a) smooth or unnotched, (b) notched, and (c) precracked.

components. Notches that have a definite radius at the end may be machined into test specimens, as in (b). (The term *notch* is used here in a generic manner to indicate any notch, hole, groove, slot, etc., that has the effect of a stress raiser.) Sharp notches that behave similar to cracks are also used, as well as actual cracks that are introduced into the specimen prior to testing, as in (c).

To understand mechanical testing, it is first necessary to briefly consider materials testing equipment and standard test methods. We will then discuss tests involving tension, compression, indentation, notch impact, bending, and torsion. Various more specialized tests are discussed in later chapters in connection with such topics as brittle fracture, fatigue, and creep.

4.1.1 Test Equipment

Equipment of a variety of types is used for applying forces to test specimens. Test equipment ranges from very simple devices to complex systems that are controlled by digital computer.

Two common configurations of relatively simple devices *called universal testing machines* are shown in Fig. 4.3. These general types of testing machine first became widely used from 1900 to

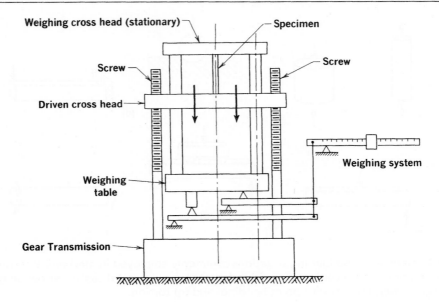

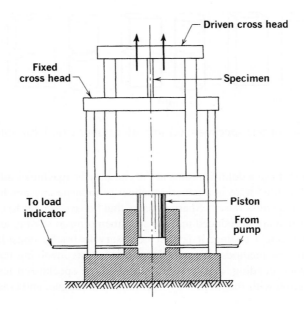

Figure 4.3 Schematics of two relatively simple testing machine designs, called universal testing machines. The mechanical system (top) drives two large screws to apply the force, and the hydraulic system (bottom) uses the pressure of oil in a piston. (From [Richards 61] p. 114; reprinted by permission of PWS-Kent Publishing Co., Boston, MA.)

1920, and they are still frequently employed today. In the mechanical-screw-driven machine (top diagram), rotation of two large threaded posts (screws) moves a crosshead that applies a force to the specimen. A simple balance system is used to measure the magnitude of the force applied. Forces may also be applied by using the pressure of oil pumped into a hydraulic piston (bottom diagram). In this case, the oil pressure provides a simple means of measuring the force applied. Testing machines of these types can be used for tension, compression, or bending, and torsion machines based on a similar level of technology are also available.

The introduction of the Instron Corp. testing machine in 1946 represented a major step, in that rather sophisticated electronics, based initially on vacuum tube technology, came into use. This is also a screw-driven machine with a moving crosshead, but the electronics, used both in controlling the machine and in measuring forces and displacements, makes the test system much more versatile than its predecessors.

Around 1958, transistor technology and closed-loop automation concepts were employed by the forerunner of the present MTS Systems Corp. to develop a high-rate test system that used a double-action hydraulic piston, as illustrated in Fig. 4.4. The result is called a *closed-loop servohydraulic test system*. Desired variations of force, strain, or testing machine motion (stroke) can be enforced

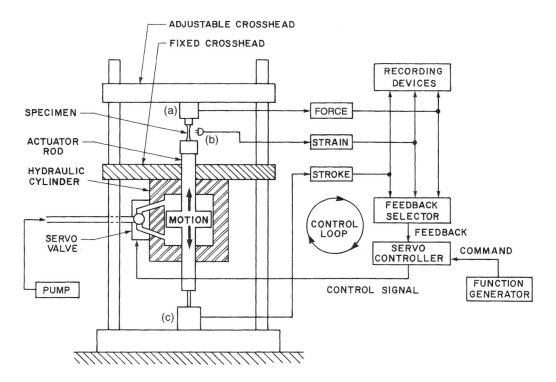

Figure 4.4 Modern closed-loop servohydraulic testing system. Three sensors are employed: (a) load cell, (b) extensometer, and (c) LVDT. (Adapted from [Richards 70]; used with permission.)

upon a test specimen. Note that the only active motion is that of the actuator rod and piston combination. Hence, the stroke of this actuator replaces the crosshead motion in the older types of testing machines.

The closed-loop servohydraulic concept is the basis of the most advanced test systems in use today. Integrated electronic circuitry has increased the sophistication of these systems. Also, digital computer control and monitoring of such test systems has steadily developed since its introduction around 1965.

Sensors for measuring forces and displacements by means of electrical signals are important features of testing machines. *Linear variable differential transformers* (LVDTs) were used in this manner relatively early for measuring displacements, which in turn give strains in test specimens. Wire *strain gages* were developed in 1937, and the wire elements were replaced by thin foil elements, starting around 1952. Strain gages change their resistance when the material to which they are bonded is deformed, and this change can be converted to an electrical voltage that is proportional to the strain. They can be used to construct *load cells* for measuring applied force and *extensometers* for measuring displacements on test specimens. The Instron and closed-loop servohydraulic testing machines require electrical signals from such sensors. Strain gages are the type of transducer primarily used at present, but LVDTs are also often employed.

Besides the general-purpose test equipment just described, various types of special-purpose test equipment are also available. Some of these will be discussed in later chapters as appropriate.

4.1.2 Standard Test Methods

The results of materials tests are used for a variety of purposes. One important use is to obtain values of materials properties, such as the strength in tension, for use in engineering design. Another use is quality control of material that is produced, such as plates of steel or batches of concrete, to be sure that they meet established requirements.

Such application of measured values of materials properties requires that everyone who makes these measurements does so in a consistent way. Otherwise, users and producers of materials will not agree as to standards of quality, and much confusion and inefficiency could occur. Perhaps even more important, the safety and reliability of engineered items requires that materials properties be well-defined quantities.

Therefore, materials producers and users and other involved parties, such as practicing engineers, governmental agencies, and research organizations, have worked together to develop *standard test methods*. This activity is often organized by professional societies, with the American Society for Testing and Materials (ASTM International) being the most active organization in this area in the United States. Many of the major industrial nations have similar organizations, such as the British Standards Institution (BSI). The International Organization for Standardization (ISO) coordinates and publishes standards on a worldwide basis, and the European Union (EU) publishes European Standards that are generally consistent with those of ISO.

A wide variety of standard methods have been developed for various materials tests, including all of the basic types discussed in this chapter and other, more specialized, tests considered in later chapters. The *Annual Book of ASTM Standards* is published yearly and consists of more than 80 volumes, a number of which include standards for mechanical tests. The details of the test methods differ, depending on the general class of material involved, such as metals, concrete, plastics, rubber,

Table 4.1   Volumes in the ASTM Standards
Containing Basic Mechanical Test Methods

Class of Material or Item	Volume(s)
Iron and steel	01.01 to 01.08
Aluminum and magnesium alloys	02.02
Metals test methods	03.01
Concrete	04.02
Stone and rock	04.07 to 04.09
Wood and plywood	04.10
Plastics	08.01 to 08.03
Rubber	09.01 to 09.02
Medical devices	13.01
Ceramics, glass, and composites	15.01 to 15.03

and glass. The ASTM standards are organized according to such classes of material, with Table 4.1 identifying the volumes that contain standards for mechanical testing.

Volume 03.01 contains numerous test standards for metals, including a variety of basic mechanical tests. Other mechanical testing standards are included in the volumes for more specific classes of material, along with standards of other types. For each class of material, there are one or more standard methods for tests in tension, compression, and bending, and also often for hardness, impact, and torsion. Volume 13.01 contains standards for materials and devices used in medicine, such as mechanical tests for bone cement, bone screws, fixation devices, and components of artificial joints. The various national organizations, the EU, and ISO have standards that parallel those of ASTM in many areas, with the details for a given test sometimes differing among these.

Test standards give the procedures to be followed in detail, but the theoretical basis of the test and background discussion are not generally given. Hence, one purpose of this book is to provide the basic understanding needed to apply materials test standards and to make intelligent use of the results.

Measured values of any property of a given material, such as its elastic modulus, yield strength, or hardness, are subject to statistical variation. This issue is often addressed in test standards, and it is discussed in Appendix B of this book. Note that multiple measurements of a given property are needed to obtain an average value and to characterize the statistical scatter about this average.

4.2 INTRODUCTION TO TENSION TEST

A tension test consists of slowly pulling a sample of material with an axial force, as in Fig. 4.1(a), until it breaks. This section of the chapter provides an introduction to the methodology for tension tests, as well as some additional comments. Sections that follow discuss tension testing in more detail, after which other types of test are considered.

4.2.1 Test Methodology

The test specimen used may have either a circular or a rectangular cross section, and its ends are usually enlarged to provide extra area for gripping and to avoid having the sample break where it is

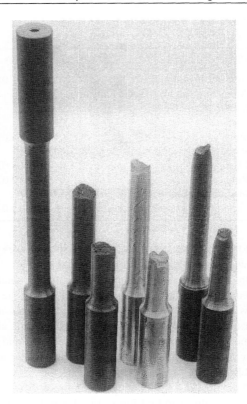

Figure 4.5 Tensile specimens of metals (left to right): untested specimen with 9 mm diameter test section, and broken specimens of gray cast iron, aluminum alloy 7075-T651, and hot-rolled AISI 1020 steel. (Photo by R. A. Simonds.)

being gripped. Specimens both before and after testing are shown for several metals and polymers in Figs. 4.5 and 4.6.

Methods of gripping the ends vary with specimen geometry. A typical arrangement for threaded-end specimens is shown in Fig. 4.7. Note that spherical bearings are used at each end to provide a pure tensile force, with no undesirable bending. The usual manner of conducting the test is to deform the specimen at a constant speed. For example, in the universal testing machines of Fig. 4.3, the motion between the fixed and moving crossheads can be controlled at a constant speed. Hence, distance h in Fig. 4.7 is varied so that

$$\frac{dh}{dt} = \dot{h} = \text{constant}$$

The axial force that must be applied to achieve this displacement rate varies as the test proceeds. This force P may be divided by the cross-sectional area A_i to obtain the stress in the specimen at

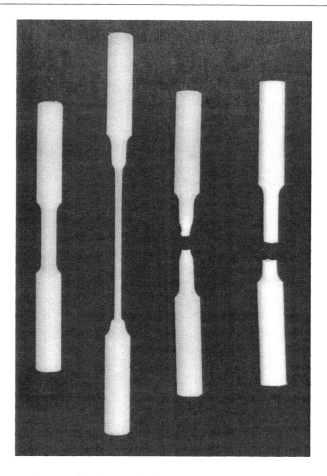

Figure 4.6   Tensile specimens of polymers (left to right): untested specimen with a 7.6 mm diameter test section, a partially tested specimen of high-density polyethylene (HDPE), and broken specimens of nylon 101 and Teflon (PTFE). (Photo by R. A. Simonds.)

any time during the test:

$$\sigma = \frac{P}{A_i} \tag{4.1}$$

Displacements in the specimen are measured within a straight central portion of constant cross section over a *gage length* L_i, as indicated in Fig. 4.7. Strain ε may be computed from the change in this length, ΔL:

$$\varepsilon = \frac{\Delta L}{L_i} \tag{4.2}$$

Stress and strain, based on the initial (undeformed) dimensions, A_i and L_i, as just presented, are called *engineering stress and strain*.

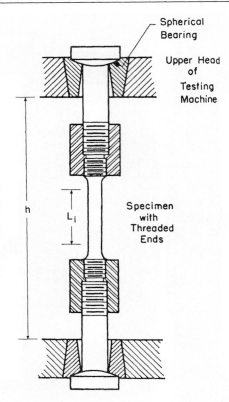

Figure 4.7 Typical grips for a tension test in a universal testing machine. (Adapted from [ASTM 97] Std. E8; copyright © ASTM; reprinted with permission.)

It is sometimes reasonable to assume that all of the grip parts and the specimen ends are nearly rigid. In this case, most of the change in crosshead motion is due to deformation within the straight section of the test specimen, so that ΔL is approximately the same as Δh, the change in h. Strain may therefore be estimated as $\varepsilon = \Delta h / L_i$. However, actual measurement of ΔL is preferable, as use of Δh may cause considerable error in the measured strain values.

Strain ε as calculated from Eq. 4.2 is dimensionless. As a convenience, strains are sometimes given as percentages, where $\varepsilon_\% = 100\varepsilon$. Strains may also be expressed in millionths, called *microstrain*, where $\varepsilon_\mu = 10^6 \varepsilon$. If strains are given as percentages or as microstrain, then, prior to using the value for most calculations, it is necessary to convert to the dimensionless form ε.

The principal result obtained from a tension test is a graph of engineering stress versus engineering strain for the entire test, called a *stress–strain curve*. With the use of digital computers in the laboratory, the form of the data is a list of numerical values of stress and strain, as sampled at short time intervals during the test. Stress–strain curves vary widely for different materials. *Brittle* behavior in a tension test is failure without extensive deformation. Gray cast iron, glass, and some polymers, such as PMMA (acrylic), are examples of materials with such behavior. A stress–strain curve for gray iron is shown in Fig. 4.8. Other materials exhibit *ductile behavior*, failing in tension

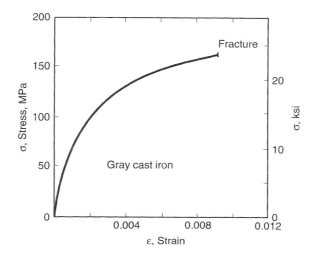

Figure 4.8 Stress–strain curve for gray cast iron in tension, showing brittle behavior.

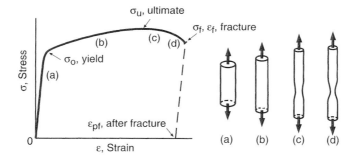

Figure 4.9 Schematic of the engineering stress–strain curve of a typical ductile metal that exhibits necking behavior. Necking begins at the ultimate stress point.

only after extensive deformation. Stress–strain curves for ductile behavior in engineering metals and some polymers are similar to Figs. 4.9 and 4.10, respectively.

4.2.2 Additional Comments

One might ask why we describe tension test results in terms of stress and strain, σ and ε, rather than simply force and length change, P and ΔL. Note that samples of a given material with different cross-sectional areas A_i will fail at higher forces for larger areas. By calculating the force per unit area, or stress, this effect of sample size is removed. Hence, a given material is expected to have the same yield, ultimate, and fracture stress for any cross-sectional area A_i, while the corresponding forces P vary with A_i. (An actual experimental comparison for different A_i will be affected by minor variations in properties with location in the parent batch of material, lack of absolute precision

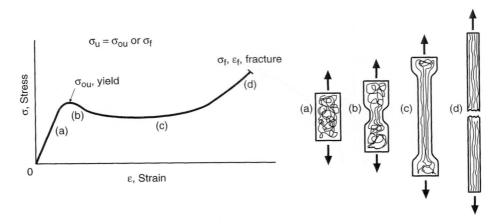

Figure 4.10   Engineering stress–strain curve and geometry of deformation typical of some polymers.

in the laboratory measurements, and other such statistical errors.) The use of strain ε similarly removes the effect of sample length. For a given stress, specimens with greater length L will exhibit a proportionately larger length change ΔL, but the strain ε corresponding to the yield, ultimate, and fracture points is expected to be the same for any length of sample. Hence, the stress–strain curve is considered to give a fundamental characterization of the behavior of the material.

4.3 ENGINEERING STRESS–STRAIN PROPERTIES

Various quantities obtained from the results of tension tests are defined as materials properties. Those obtained from engineering stress and strain will now be described. In a later portion of this chapter, additional properties obtained on the basis of different definitions of stress and strain, called true stress and strain, will be considered.

4.3.1 Elastic Constants

Initial portions of stress–strain curves from tension tests exhibit a variety of different behaviors for different materials as shown in Fig. 4.11. There may be a well-defined initial straight line, as for many engineering metals, where the deformation is predominantly elastic. The *elastic modulus*, E, also called *Young's modulus*, may then be obtained from the stresses and strains at two points on this line, such as A and B in (a):

$$E = \frac{\sigma_B - \sigma_A}{\varepsilon_B - \varepsilon_A} \tag{4.3}$$

For accuracy, the two points should be as far apart as possible, and it may be convenient to locate them on an extrapolation of the straight-line portion. Where laboratory stress–strain data are recorded at short intervals with the use of a digital computer, values judged to be on the linear portion may be fitted to a least-squares line to obtain the slope E.

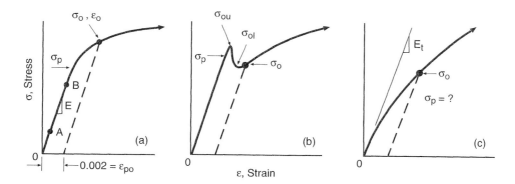

Figure 4.11   Initial portions of stress–strain curves: (a) many metals and alloys, (b) material with yield drop, and (c) material with no linear region.

If there is no well-defined linear region, a *tangent modulus*, E_t, may be employed, which is the slope of a straight line that is tangent to the stress–strain curve at the origin, as shown in Fig. 4.11(c). As a practical matter, obtaining E_t often involves the use of considerable judgment, so this is not a very well-defined property.

Poisson's ratio ν can also be obtained from a tension test by measuring transverse strains during elastic behavior. Diameter measurements or a strain gage can be used for this purpose. (See the next chapter, Section 5.3, for detailed discussion of Poisson's ratio.)

4.3.2 Engineering Measures of Strength

The *ultimate tensile strength*, σ_u, also called simply the *tensile strength*, is the highest engineering stress reached prior to fracture. If the behavior is brittle, as for gray cast iron in Fig. 4.8, the highest stress occurs at the point of fracture. However, in ductile metals, the force, and hence the engineering stress, reaches a maximum and then decreases prior to fracture, as in Fig. 4.9. In either case, the highest force reached at any point during the test, $P_{\max}$, is used to obtain the ultimate tensile strength by dividing by the original cross-sectional area:

$$\sigma_u = \frac{P_{\max}}{A_i} \tag{4.4}$$

The *engineering fracture strength*, σ_f, is obtained from the force at fracture, P_f, even if this is not the highest force reached:

$$\sigma_f = \frac{P_f}{A_i} \tag{4.5}$$

Hence, for brittle materials, $\sigma_u = \sigma_f$, whereas for ductile materials, σ_u often exceeds σ_f.

The departure from linear-elastic behavior, as in Fig. 4.11, is called *yielding* and is of considerable interest. This is simply because stresses that cause yielding result in rapidly increasing deformation due to the contribution of plastic strain. As discussed in Section 1.2 and illustrated by Fig. 1.2, any strain in excess of the elastic strain σ/E is plastic strain and is not recovered on unloading. Hence, plastic strains result in permanent deformation. Such deformation in an engineering member changes its dimensions and/or shape, which is almost always undesirable. Thus, the first step in engineering design is usually to assure that stresses are sufficiently small that yielding does not occur, except perhaps in very small regions of a component.

The yielding event can be characterized by several methods. The simplest is to identify the stress where the first departure from linearity occurs. This is called the *proportional limit*, σ_p, and is illustrated in Fig. 4.11. Some materials, as in (c), may exhibit a stress–strain curve with a gradually decreasing slope and no proportional limit. Even where there is a definite linear region, it is difficult to precisely locate where this ends. Hence, the value of the proportional limit depends on judgment, so that this is a poorly defined quantity. Another quantity sometimes defined is the *elastic limit*, which is the highest stress that does not cause permanent (i.e., plastic) deformation. Determination of this quantity is difficult, as periodic unloading to check for permanent deformation is necessary.

A third approach is the *offset method*, which is illustrated by dashed lines in Fig. 4.11. A straight line is drawn parallel to the elastic slope, E or E_t, but offset by an arbitrary amount. The intersection of this line with the engineering stress–strain curve is a well-defined point that is not affected by judgment, except in cases where E_t is difficult to establish. This is called the *offset yield strength*, σ_o. The most widely used and standardized offset for engineering metals is a strain of 0.002, that is, 0.2%, although other values are also used. Note that the offset strain is a plastic strain, such as $\varepsilon_{po} = 0.002$, as unloading from σ_o would follow a dashed line in Fig. 4.11, and this ε_{po} would be the unrecovered strain.

In some engineering metals, notably in low-carbon steels, there is very little nonlinearity prior to a dramatic drop in load, as illustrated in Fig. 4.11(b). In such cases, one can identify an *upper yield point*, σ_{ou}, and a *lower yield point*, σ_{ol}. The former is the highest stress reached prior to the decrease, and the latter is the lowest stress prior to a subsequent increase. Values of the upper yield point in metals are sensitive to testing rate and to inadvertent small amounts of bending, so that reported values for a given material vary considerably. The lower yield point is generally similar to the 0.2% offset yield strength, with the latter having the advantage of being applicable to other types of stress–strain curve as well. Thus, the offset yield strength is generally the most satisfactory means of defining the yielding event for engineering metals.

For polymers, offset yield strengths are also used. However, it is more common for polymers to define a yield point only if there is an early relative maximum (upper yield point) or flat region in the curve, in which case σ_o is the stress where $d\sigma/d\varepsilon = 0$ first occurs. In polymers with an upper yield point, σ_{ou}, this stress may exceed that at fracture, σ_f, but in other cases, it does not. (See Fig. 4.10.) Hence, the ultimate tensile strength σ_u is the higher of either σ_{ou} or σ_f. The two situations are distinguished by describing the value as either the *tensile strength at yield* or the *tensile strength at break*.

In most materials, the proportional limit, elastic limit, and offset yield strength can be considered to be alternative measures of the beginning of permanent deformation. However, for a nonlinear elastic material such as rubber, the first two of these measure distinctly different events, and the offset yield strength loses its significance. (See Fig. 3.17.)

4.3.3 Engineering Measures of Ductility

Ductility is the ability of a material to accommodate inelastic deformation without breaking. In the case of tension loading, this means the ability to stretch by plastic strain, but with creep strain also sometimes contributing.

The *engineering strain at fracture*, ε_f, is one measure of ductility. This is usually expressed as a percentage and is then termed the *percent elongation at fracture*, which we will denote as $100\varepsilon_f$. This value corresponds to the fracture point on the stress–strain curve, as identified in Figs. 4.9 and 4.10. The ASTM standard for tension testing of polymers includes this property, and it is given as an option in the standard for tension testing of metals. For this measurement, test standards specify the gage length as a multiple of the test section diameter or width. For example, for specimens with round cross sections, a ratio of gage length to diameter of $L_i/d_i = 4$ is specified by ASTM for use in the United States. But international standards generally employ $L_i/d_i = 5$.

Another method of determining the elongation that is sometimes used for metals is to employ marks on the test section. The distance L_i between these marks before testing is subtracted from the distance L_f measured after fracture. The resulting length change provides a strain value, which gives the *percent elongation after fracture*.

$$\varepsilon_{pf} = \frac{L_f - L_i}{L_i}, \quad \% \text{ elongation after fracture} = 100\varepsilon_{pf} \tag{4.6}$$

Note that the elastic strain is lost when the stress drops to zero after fracture, so this quantity is a plastic strain, as identified in Fig. 4.9.

For metals with considerable ductility, the difference between $100\varepsilon_f$ and $100\varepsilon_{pf}$ is small, so that the distinction between these two quantities is not of great importance. However, for metals of limited ductility, the elastic strain recovered after fracture may constitute a significant fraction of ε_f. Moreover, the elongation may be so small as to be difficult to measure directly from marks on the sample. It may then be useful to determine ε_{pf} from a value of ε_f taken from the fracture point on the stress–strain record, specifically, by subtracting the elastic strain that is estimated to be lost:

$$\varepsilon_{pf} = \varepsilon_f - \frac{\sigma_f}{E}, \quad \% \text{ elongation after fracture} = 100\varepsilon_{pf} \tag{4.7}$$

This gives an estimated after-fracture result consistent with a measurement made on a broken specimen.

Another measure of ductility is the *percent reduction in area*, called *%RA*, which is obtained by comparing the cross-sectional area after fracture, A_f, with the original area:

$$\%RA = 100\frac{A_i - A_f}{A_i}, \quad \%RA = 100\frac{d_i^2 - d_f^2}{d_i^2} \quad \text{(a, b)} \tag{4.8}$$

Here, form (b) is derived from (a) as a convenience for round cross sections of initial diameter d_i and final diameter d_f. As for the elongation, a discrepancy may exist between the area after fracture and the area that existed at fracture. This presents little problem for ductile metals, but caution is needed in interpreting area reductions after fracture for polymers.

4.3.4 Discussion of Necking Behavior and Ductility

If the behavior in a tension test is ductile, a phenomenon called *necking* usually occurs, as illustrated in Fig. 4.12. The deformation is uniform along the gage length early in the test, as in (a) and (b), but later begins to concentrate in one region, resulting in the diameter there decreasing more than

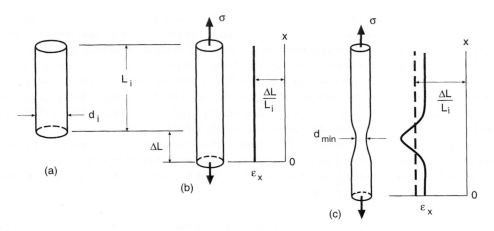

Figure 4.12 Deformation in a tension test of a ductile metal: (a) unstrained, (b) after uniform elongation, and (c) during necking.

elsewhere, as in (c). In ductile metals, necking begins at the maximum force (ultimate strength) point, and the decrease in force beyond this is a consequence of the cross-sectional area rapidly decreasing. Once necking begins, the longitudinal strain becomes nonuniform, as illustrated in (c).

Examine the metal samples of Fig. 4.5. Necking occurred in the steel, and to an extent in the aluminum alloy, but not in the brittle cast iron. Enlarged views show the steel and cast iron fractures in more detail in Fig. 4.13.

The percent reduction in area is based on the minimum diameter at the fracture point and so is a measure of the highest strain along the gage length. In contrast, the percent elongation at fracture is an average over an arbitrarily chosen length. Its value varies with the ratio of gage length to diameter, L_i/d_i, increasing for smaller values of this ratio. As a consequence, it is necessary to standardize the gage lengths used, such as the $L_i/d_i = 4$ commonly used in the United States for specimens with round cross sections, and the $L_i/d_i = 5$ specified in international standards. The reduction in area is not affected by such arbitrariness and is thus a more fundamental measure of ductility than is the elongation.

4.3.5 Engineering Measures of Energy Capacity

In a tension test, let the applied force be P, and let the displacement over gage length L_i be $\Delta L = x$. The amount of work done in deforming the specimen to a value of $x = x'$ is then

$$U = \int_0^{x'} P \, dx \tag{4.9}$$

The volume of material in the gage length is $A_i L_i$. Dividing both sides of the equation by this volume, and using the definitions of engineering stress and strain, Eqs. 4.1 and 4.2, gives

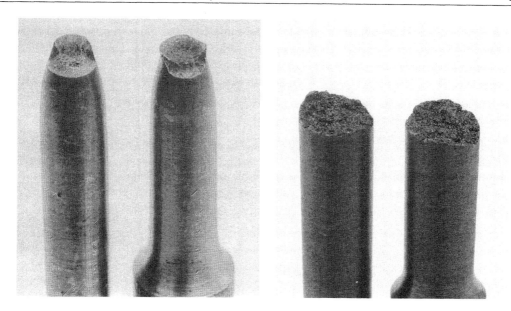

Figure 4.13   Fractures from tension tests on 9 mm diameter specimens of hot-rolled AISI 1020 steel (left) and gray cast iron (right). (Photos by R. A. Simonds.)

$$u = \frac{U}{A_i L_i} = \int_0^{x'} \frac{P}{A_i} \, d\left(\frac{x}{L_i}\right) = \int_0^{\varepsilon'} \sigma \, d\varepsilon \tag{4.10}$$

Hence, u is the work done per unit volume of material to reach a strain ε', and it is equal to the area under the stress–strain curve up to ε'. The work done is equal to the energy absorbed by the material.

The area under the entire engineering stress–strain curve up to fracture is called the *tensile toughness*, u_f. This is a measure of the ability of the material to absorb energy without fracture. Where there is considerable plastic strain beyond yielding, as for many engineering metals, some of the energy is stored in the microstructure of the material, but most of it is dissipated as heat.

If the stress–strain curve is relatively flat beyond yielding, then u_f may be approximated as the area of a rectangle. The height is equal to the average of the yield and ultimate, and the width is equal to the fracture strain:

$$u_f \approx \varepsilon_f \left(\frac{\sigma_o + \sigma_u}{2}\right) \tag{4.11}$$

For materials that behave in a brittle manner, the gradually curving stress–strain response may be similar to a parabolic curve with vertex at the origin, in which case $u_f \approx 2\sigma_f \varepsilon_f / 3$.

Brittle materials have low tensile toughness, despite perhaps high strength, due to low ductility. In low-strength ductile materials, the converse occurs, and the tensile toughness is also low. To have a high tensile toughness, both the strength and the ductility must be reasonably high, so that a high tensile toughness indicates a "well rounded" material.

Tensile toughness, as just defined, should not be confused with *fracture toughness*, which is the resistance to failure in the presence of a crack, as explored in Chapter 8. The tensile toughness is a useful means of comparing materials, but the fracture toughness should be considered to be the primary measure of toughness for engineering purposes.

4.3.6 Strain Hardening

The rise in the stress–strain curve following yielding is described by the term *strain hardening*, as the material is increasing its resistance with increasing strain. A measure of the degree of strain hardening is the ratio of the ultimate tensile strength to the yield strength. Hence, we define the *strain hardening ratio* $= \sigma_u/\sigma_o$. Values of this ratio above about 1.4 are considered relatively high for metals, and those below 1.2 relatively low.

Example 4.1

A tension test was conducted on a specimen of AISI 1020 hot-rolled steel having an initial diameter of 9.11 mm. Representative test data are given in Table E4.1(a) in the form of force and engineering strain. For strain, the extensometer gage length was $L_i = 50.8$ mm. In addition, minimum diameters were measured manually with a micrometer in the necked region at several

Table E4.1 Data and Analysis for a Tension Test on AISI 1020 Hot-Rolled Steel

(a) Test Data			(b) Calculated Values				
Force P, kN	Engr. Strain ε	Diam. d, mm	Engr. Stress σ, MPa	True Strain $\tilde{\varepsilon}$	Raw True Stress $\tilde{\sigma}$, MPa	Corrected True Stress $\tilde{\sigma}_B$, MPa	True Plastic Strain $\tilde{\varepsilon}_p$
0	0	9.11	0	0	0	0	0
6.67	0.00050	—	102.3	0.00050	102.3	102.3	0
13.34	0.00102	—	204.7	0.00102	204.7	204.7	0
19.13	0.00146	—	293.5	0.00146	293.5	293.5	0
17.79	0.00230	—	272.9	0.00230	272.9	272.9	0
17.21	0.00310	—	264.0	0.00310	264.0	264.0	0.00178
17.53	0.00500	—	268.9	0.00499	268.9	268.9	0.00365
17.44	0.00700	—	267.6	0.00698	269.4	269.4	0.00564
17.21	0.01000	—	264.0	0.00995	266.7	266.7	0.00862
20.77	0.0490	8.89[4]	318.6	0.0478	334.3	334.3	0.0462
24.25	0.1250	—	372.0	0.1178	418.5	418.5	0.1157
25.71	0.2180	8.26[4]	394.4	0.1972	480.4	465.3	0.1949
25.75[1]	0.2340	—	395.0	0.2103	487.5	469.8	0.2079
25.04	0.3060	7.62	384.2	0.3572	549.1	505.0	0.3547
23.49	0.3300	6.99	360.4	0.5298	612.1	540.9	0.5271
21.35	0.3480	6.35	327.5	0.7218	674.2	576.2	0.7190
18.90	0.3600	5.72	290.0	0.9308	735.5	611.5	0.9278
17.39[2]	0.3660	5.28[3]	266.8	1.0909	794.2	649.1	1.0877

Notes: [1]Ultimate. [2]Fracture. [3]Measured from broken specimen. [4]Not used in calculations.

points during the test. After fracture, the broken halves were reassembled, and the following measurements were made: (1) Marks originally 25.4 mm apart and on opposite sides of the necked region were 38.6 mm apart due to the lengthwise stretching in the specimen. (2) Similar marks originally 50.8 mm apart were 70.9 mm apart. (3) The final minimum diameter in the necked region was 5.28 mm.

   (a) Determine the following materials properties: elastic modulus, 0.2% offset yield strength, ultimate tensile strength, percent elongation, and percent reduction in area.
   (b) Assume that the test was interrupted upon reaching a strain $\varepsilon = 0.0070$, and the specimen unloaded to zero force. Estimate the elastic strain recovered and the plastic strain remaining. Also, what would be the new length of the original 50.8 mm gage section?

Solution   (a) For each force value, engineering stresses are first calculated from Eq. 4.1, as given in the first column of Table E4.1(b). For example, for the first force value above zero,

$$\sigma = \frac{P}{A_i} = \frac{P}{\pi d_i^2 / 4} = \frac{4(6670\,\text{N})}{\pi (9.11\,\text{mm})^2} = 102.3\,\frac{\text{N}}{\text{mm}^2} = 102.3\,\text{MPa}$$

Plotting these versus the corresponding engineering strains gives Fig. E4.1(a). However, on this graph, the yield region is too crowded to see the needed detail, so the data for the beginning of the test are plotted with a sensitive strain scale in Fig. E4.1(b). The first four data points appear to lie on a straight line in Fig. E4.1(b), so that a least squares line of the form $y = mx$ is fitted to these, giving the elastic modulus as $E = 201{,}200\,\text{MPa}$ (**Ans.**). A line is drawn on Fig. E4.1(b) parallel to the slope E and through the plastic strain offset of $\varepsilon_{po} = 0.002$. The intersection of this with the stress–strain curve gives the yield strength as $\sigma_o = 264\,\text{MPa}$ (**Ans.**). From Fig. E4.1(a), or from the numerical values in Table E4.1(b), it is evident that the highest stress reached, and hence the ultimate tensile strength, is $\sigma_u = 395\,\text{MPa}$ (**Ans.**).

   Noting that the last line of Table E4.1 corresponds to fracture, the stress and strain at fracture are $\sigma_f = 266.8\,\text{MPa}$ and $\varepsilon_f = 0.366$. The latter gives a percent elongation *at* fracture of $\varepsilon_{f\%} = 100\varepsilon_f = 36.6\%$ (**Ans.**). The corresponding elongation *after* fracture can then be estimated from Eq. 4.7:

$$\varepsilon_{pf} = \varepsilon_f - \frac{\sigma_f}{E} = 0.366 - \frac{266.8\,\text{MPa}}{201{,}200\,\text{MPa}} = 0.365, \qquad \varepsilon_{pf\%} = 36.5\% \qquad \textbf{Ans.}$$

The length measurements made from the broken specimen give additional values for the elongation after fracture:

$$\varepsilon_{pf} = \frac{L_f - L_i}{L_i} = \frac{(38.6 - 25.4)\,\text{mm}}{25.4\,\text{mm}} = 0.520, \qquad \varepsilon_{pf\%} = 52.0\% \qquad (\text{over } 25.4\,\text{mm})$$

$$\varepsilon_{pf} = \frac{L_f - L_i}{L_i} = \frac{(70.9 - 50.8)\,\text{mm}}{50.8\,\text{mm}} = 0.396, \qquad \varepsilon_{pf\%} = 39.6\% \qquad (\text{over } 50.8\,\text{mm})$$

$$\textbf{Ans.}$$

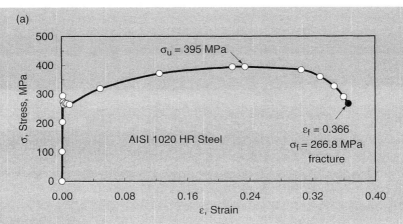

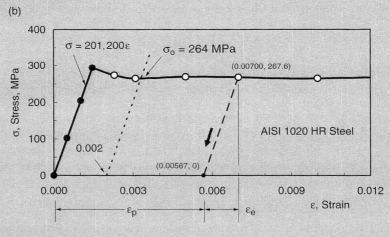

Figure E4.1

Also, the reduction in area from Eq. 4.8(b) is

$$\%RA = 100\frac{d_i^2 - d_f^2}{d_i^2} = 100\frac{(9.11^2 - 5.28^2)\,\text{mm}^2}{(9.11\,\text{mm})^2} = 66.4\% \qquad \textbf{Ans.}$$

Discussion   The elongation from extensometer measurements, $\varepsilon_{pf\%} = 36.5\%$, is only roughly equal to the value of 39.6% from the broken specimen for the same gage length of 50.8 mm. Exact agreement should not be expected, as measurements from a broken specimen are not precise, and the two gage lengths were very likely shifted relative to one another along the specimen length. The elongation of 52% over 25.4 mm is higher than the other values, due to this being the average strain over a shorter gage length spanning the necked region, so that the value is more strongly affected by the concentrated deformation in the neck.

(b) If the test were interrupted at $\varepsilon = 0.0070$, the stress–strain path during unloading would be expected to approximately follow the elastic modulus slope E, as shown in Fig. E4.1(b). Noting from Table E4.1(b) that the stress value corresponding to this strain is $\sigma = 267.6\,\text{MPa}$, the elastic strain ε_e recovered, and the plastic strain ε_p remaining, are estimated to be

$$\varepsilon_e = \frac{\sigma}{E} = \frac{267.6\,\text{MPa}}{201{,}200\,\text{MPa}} = 0.00133, \qquad \varepsilon_p = \varepsilon - \varepsilon_e = 0.00700 - 0.00133 = 0.00567 \quad \textbf{Ans.}$$

The original gage length of 50.8 mm would be permanently stretched by a ΔL corresponding to the plastic strain, where $\varepsilon_p = \Delta L / L_i$, so that the new length is

$$L = L_i + \Delta L = L_i + \varepsilon_p L_i = 50.8\,\text{mm} + 0.00567(50.8\,\text{mm}) = 51.09\,\text{mm} \qquad \textbf{Ans.}$$

4.4 TRENDS IN TENSILE BEHAVIOR

A wide variety of tensile behaviors occur for different materials. Even for a given chemical composition of a material, the prior processing of the material may have substantial effects on the tensile properties, as may the temperature and strain rate of the test.

4.4.1 Trends for Different Materials

Engineering metals vary widely as to their strength and ductility. This is evident from Table 4.2, where engineering properties from tension tests are given for a number of metals. Relatively high strength polymers in bulk form are typically only 10% as strong as engineering metals, and their elastic moduli are typically only 3% as large. Their ductilities vary quite widely, some being quite brittle and others quite ductile. Properties of some commercial polymers are given in Table 4.3 to illustrate these trends.

Rubber and rubber-like polymers (elastomers) have very low elastic moduli and relatively low strengths, and they often have extreme ductility. Ceramics and glasses represent the opposite case, as their behavior is generally so brittle that measures of ductility have little meaning. Strengths in tension are generally lower than for metals, but higher than for polymers. The elastic moduli of ceramics are relatively high, often higher than for many metals. Some typical values of ultimate tensile strength and elastic modulus have already been given in Table 3.10.

The tensile behavior of composite materials is, of course, strongly affected by the details of the reinforcement. For example, hard particles in a ductile matrix increase stiffness and strength, but decrease ductility, more so for larger volume percentages of reinforcement. Long fibers have qualitatively similar effects, with the increase in strength and stiffness being especially large for loading directions parallel to large numbers of fibers. Whiskers and short chopped fibers generally produce effects intermediate between those of particles and long fibers. Some of these trends are evident in Table 4.4, where data are given for various SiC reinforcements of an aluminum alloy.

Table 4.2 Tensile Properties for Some Engineering Metals

Material	Elastic Modulus E	0.2% Yield Strength σ_o	Ultimate Strength σ_u	Elongation[1] $100\varepsilon_f$	Reduction in Area %RA
	GPa (10^3 ksi)	MPa (ksi)	MPa (ksi)	%	%
Ductile cast iron A536 (65-45-12)	159 (23)	334 (49)	448 (65)	15	19.8
AISI 1020 steel as rolled	203 (29.4)	260 (37.7)	441 (64)	36	61
ASTM A514, T1 structural steel	208 (30.2)	724 (105)	807 (117)	20	66
AISI 4142 steel as quenched	200 (29)	1619 (235)	2450 (355)	6	6
AISI 4142 steel 205°C temper	207 (30)	1688 (245)	2240 (325)	8	27
AISI 4142 steel 370°C temper	207 (30)	1584 (230)	1757 (255)	11	42
AISI 4142 steel 450°C temper	207 (30)	1378 (200)	1413 (205)	14	48
18 Ni maraging steel (250)	186 (27)	1791 (260)	1860 (270)	8	56
SAE 308 cast aluminum	70 (10.2)	169 (25)	229 (33)	0.9	1.5
2024-T4 aluminum	73.1 (10.6)	303 (44)	476 (69)	20	35
7075-T6 aluminum	71 (10.3)	469 (68)	578 (84)	11	33
AZ91C-T6 cast magnesium	40 (5.87)	113 (16)	137 (20)	0.4	0.4

Note: [1]Typical values from [Boyer 85] are listed in most cases.
Sources: Data in [Conle 84] and [SAE 89].

Some stress–strain curves from tension tests of engineering metals are shown in Figs. 4.14 and 4.15. The former gives curves for three steels with contrasting behavior, and the latter gives curves for three aluminum alloys. Tensile stress–strain curves for low-ductility metals have only limited curvature and no drop in stress prior to fracture, as for gray cast iron in Fig. 4.8 and also for the as-quenched steel in Fig. 4.14.

Stress–strain curves from tension tests on three ductile polymers are shown in Fig. 4.16. These are, in fact, the curves for the test specimens shown in Fig. 4.6. An early relative maximum in stress is common for polymers, and this is associated with the distinctive necking behavior evident for

Table 4.3   Mechanical Properties for Polymers at Room Temperature[1]

Material	Tensile properties[2]				Izod Energy[3]	Heat Defl. Temp.
	Modulus E	Yield σ_o	Fracture σ_f	Elong. $100\varepsilon_f$		
	GPa (10^3 ksi)	MPa (ksi)	MPa (ksi)	%	J/m (ft·lb/in)	°C
ABS, medium impact	2.1–2.8 (0.3–0.4)	34–50 (5–7.2)	38–52 (5.5–7.5)	5–60	160–510 (3–9.6)	90–104
ABS, 30% glass fibers	6.9–8.3 (1–1.2)	—	90–110 (13–16)	1.5–1.8	64–69 (1.2–1.3)	102–110
Acrylic, PMMA	2.3–3.2 (0.33–0.47)	54–73 (7.8–10.6)	48–72 (7–10.5)	2–5.5	11–21 (0.2–0.4)	68–100
Epoxy, cast	2.4 (0.35)	—	28–90 (4–13)	3–6	11–53 (0.2–1)	46–290
Phenolic, cast	2.8–4.8 (0.4–0.7)	—	34–62 (5–9)	1.5–2	13–21 (0.24–0.4)	74–79
Nylon 6, dry	2.6–3.2 (0.38–0.46)	90 (13)	41–165 (6–24)	30–100	32–120 (0.6–2.2)	68–85
Nylon 6, 33% glass fibers	8.6–11 (1.25–1.6)	—	165–193 (24–28)	2.2–3.6	110–180 (2.1–3.4)	200–215
Polycarbonate PC	2.4 (0.345)	62 (9)	63–72 (9.1–10.5)	110–150	110–960 (2–18)	121–132
Polyethylene LDPE	0.17–0.28 (0.025–0.041)	9–14.5 (1.3–2.1)	8.3–32 (1.2–4.6)	100–650	No break	40–44
Polyethylene HDPE	1.08 (0.157)	26–33 (3.8–4.8)	22–31 (3.2–4.5)	10–1200	21–210 (0.4–4)	79–91
Polystyrene PS	2.3–3.3 (0.33–0.48)	—	36–52 (5.2–7.5)	1.2–2.5	19–24 (0.35–0.45)	76–94
Polystyrene HIPS	1.1–2.6 (0.16–0.37)	14.5–41 (2.1–6)	13–43 (1.9–6.2)	20–65	53–370 (1–7)	77–96
Rigid PVC	2.4–4.1 (0.35–0.6)	41–45 (5.9–6.5)	41–52 (5.9–7.5)	40–80	21–1200 (0.4–22)	60–77

Notes: [1]Properties vary considerably; values are ranges from *Modern Plastics Encyclopedia* [Kaplan 95] pp. B-146 to 206. [2]The ultimate strength σ_u is the higher of σ_o or σ_f. [3]Energy per unit thickness is tabulated.

HDPE in Fig. 4.6. Necking begins when the stress reaches the early relative maximum, and then it spreads along the specimen length, but with the diameter in the neck remaining approximately constant once the process starts, as illustrated in Fig. 4.10. This behavior is due to the chainlike molecules being drawn out of their original amorphous or crystalline structure into an approximately linear and parallel arrangement.

Table 4.4 Tensile Properties for Various SiC Reinforcements in a
6061-T6 Aluminum Matrix

Reinforcement[1]	Modulus E GPa (10^3 ksi)	0.2% Yield σ_o MPa (ksi)	Ultimate σ_u MPa (ksi)	Elongation $100\varepsilon_f$ %
None	69 (10)	275 (40)	310 (45)	12
Particles, 20%	103 (15)	414 (60)	496 (72)	5.5
Particles, 40%	145 (21)	448 (65)	586 (85)	2
Whiskers, 20%	110 (16)	382 (55)	504 (73)	5
Fibers, 47%, 0°	204 (29.6)	—	1460 (212)	0.9
Fibers, 47%, 90°	118 (17.1)	—	86.2 (12.5)	0.1
Fibers, 47%, 0°/90°	137 (19.8)	—	673 (98)	0.9
Fibers, 47%, 0°/ ± 45°/90°	127 (18.4)	—	572 (83)	1.0

Note: [1]Volume percentage is given. For fibers, angles are orientations relative
to the tensile axis. For the last two cases, there are equal numbers of fibers at
each angle given. Fiber properties are $E = 400$ GPa and $\sigma_u = 3950$ MPa.
Source: Data in [ASM 87] pp. 858–901.

   Other polymers, such as Nylon 101, neck in a manner more similar to metals. An additional type
of behavior is seen for Teflon (PTFE). This material deformed a considerable amount by developing
a large number of small tears bridged by filaments of material, a process called *crazing*, followed by
failure without necking. Some polymers, such as acrylic (PMMA), behave in a brittle manner and
have stress–strain curves that are nearly linear up to the point of fracture.

   Ceramics and glass have stress–strain curves with limited curvature, as for low ductility metals,
with the curve often being reduced to essentially a straight line terminating at the fracture point.

4.4.2 Effects of Temperature and Strain Rate

If a material is tested in a temperature range where creep occurs—that is, where there is time-
dependent deformation—strains from this source will contribute to the inelastic deformation in the
test. Moreover, the creep strain that occurs is greater if the speed of the test is slower, as a slower test
provides more time for the creep strain to accumulate. Under such circumstances, it is important to
run the test at a constant value of strain rate, $\dot{\varepsilon} = d\varepsilon/dt$, and to report this value along with the test
results.

   For polymers, recall from Chapters 2 and 3 that creep effects are especially large above the
particular polymer's glass transition temperature, T_g. As T_g values around and below room temperature are common, large creep effects occur for many polymers. Tension tests on these materials
thus require care concerning the effects of strain rate, and it is often useful to evaluate the tensile
behavior at more than one rate.

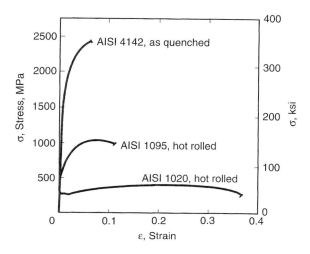

Figure 4.14   Engineering stress–strain curves from tension tests on three steels.

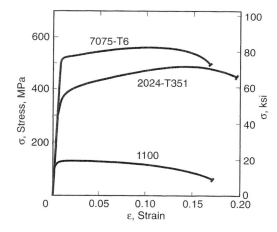

Figure 4.15   Engineering stress–strain curves from tension tests on three aluminum alloys.

For metals and ceramics, creep effects become significant around 0.3 to $0.6T_m$, where T_m is the absolute melting temperature. Thus, creep strains are a factor at room temperature for metals with low melting temperatures. Strain rate may also affect the tensile behavior of ceramics at room temperature, but for an entirely different reason unrelated to creep, namely, time-dependent cracking due to the detrimental effects of moisture.

For engineering metals at room temperature, strain-rate effects due to creep exist, but are not dramatic. For example, some data for copper are given in Fig. 4.17. In this case, for an increase in strain rate of a factor of 10,000, the ultimate tensile strength at room temperature increases about 14%. Larger relative effects occur at higher temperatures as creep effects become more

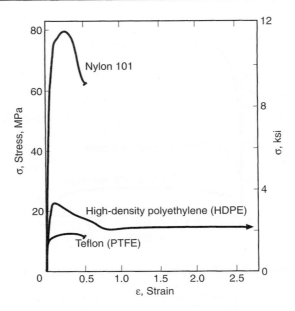

Figure 4.16   Engineering stress–strain curves from tension tests on three polymers.

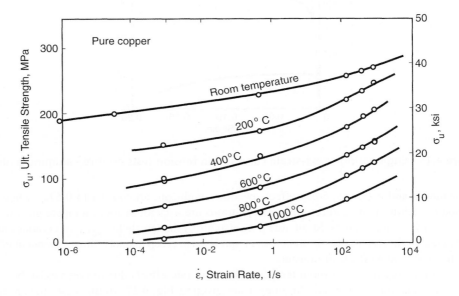

Figure 4.17   Effect of strain rate on the ultimate tensile strength of copper for tests at various temperatures. (Adapted from [Nadai 41]; used with permission of ASME.)

important. Also, note that the strength is drastically lowered by increased temperature, especially as $T_m = 1085°C$ is approached.

The following generalizations usually apply to the tensile properties of a given material in a temperature range where creep-related strain-rate effects occur: (1) At a given temperature, increasing the strain rate increases the strength, but decreases the ductility. (2) For a given strain rate, decreasing the temperature has the same qualitative effects, specifically, increasing the strength, but decreasing the ductility.

4.5 TRUE STRESS–STRAIN INTERPRETATION OF TENSION TEST

In analyzing the results of tension tests, and in certain other situations, it is useful to work with *true stresses and strains*. Note that engineering stress and strain are most appropriate for small strains where the changes in specimen dimensions are small. True stresses and strains differ in that finite changes in area and length are specifically considered. For a ductile material, plotting true stress and strain from a tension test gives a curve that differs markedly from the engineering stress–strain curve. An example is shown in Fig. 4.18.

4.5.1 Definitions of True Stress and Strain

True stress is simply the axial force P divided by the current cross-sectional area A, rather than the original area A_i. Hence, given A, true stress $\tilde{\sigma}$ may be calculated from force P or from engineering stress σ:

$$\tilde{\sigma} = \frac{P}{A}, \qquad \tilde{\sigma} = \sigma \frac{A_i}{A} \qquad \text{(a, b)} \tag{4.12}$$

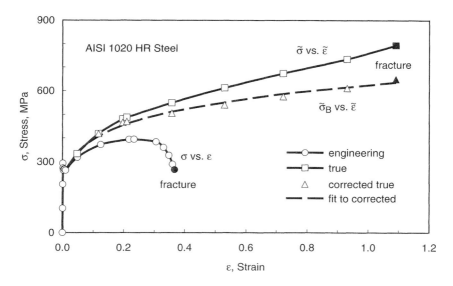

Figure 4.18   Engineering and true stress–strain curves from a tension test on hot-rolled AISI 1020 steel.

Since the area A decreases as a tension test proceeds, true stresses increasingly rise above the corresponding engineering stresses. Also, there is no drop in stress beyond an ultimate point, which is expected, as this behavior in the engineering stress–strain curve is due to the rapid decrease in cross-sectional area during necking. These trends are evident in Fig. 4.18.

For true strain, let the length change be measured in small increments, ΔL_1, ΔL_2, ΔL_3, etc., and let the new gage length, L_1, L_2, L_3, etc., be used to compute the strain for each increment. The total strain is thus

$$\tilde{\varepsilon} = \frac{\Delta L_1}{L_1} + \frac{\Delta L_2}{L_2} + \frac{\Delta L_3}{L_3} + \cdots = \sum \frac{\Delta L_j}{L_j} \tag{4.13}$$

where ΔL is the sum of these ΔL_j. If the ΔL_j are assumed to be infinitesimal—that is, if ΔL is measured in very small steps—the preceding summation is equivalent to an integral that defines true strain:

$$\tilde{\varepsilon} = \int_{L_i}^{L} \frac{dL}{L} = \ln \frac{L}{L_i} \tag{4.14}$$

Here, $L = L_i + \Delta L$ is the final length. Note that $\varepsilon = \Delta L / L_i$ is the engineering strain, leading to the following relationship between ε and $\tilde{\varepsilon}$:

$$\tilde{\varepsilon} = \ln \frac{L_i + \Delta L}{L_i} = \ln \left(1 + \frac{\Delta L}{L_i} \right) = \ln (1 + \varepsilon) \tag{4.15}$$

4.5.2 Constant Volume Assumption

For materials that behave in a ductile manner, once the strains have increased substantially beyond the yield region, most of the strain that has accumulated is inelastic strain. Since neither plastic strain nor creep strain contributes to volume change, the volume change in a tension test is limited to the small amount associated with elastic strain. Thus, it is reasonable to approximate the volume as constant:

$$A_i L_i = A L \tag{4.16}$$

This gives

$$\frac{A_i}{A} = \frac{L}{L_i} = \frac{L_i + \Delta L}{L_i} = 1 + \varepsilon \tag{4.17}$$

Substitution into Eqs. 4.12(b) and 4.14 then gives two additional equations relating true and engineering stress and strain:

$$\tilde{\sigma} = \sigma (1 + \varepsilon) \tag{4.18}$$

$$\tilde{\varepsilon} = \ln \frac{A_i}{A} \tag{4.19}$$

For members with round cross sections of original diameter d_i and final diameter d, the last equation may be used in the form

$$\tilde{\varepsilon} = \ln \frac{\pi d_i^2/4}{\pi d^2/4} = 2\ln \frac{d_i}{d} \qquad (4.20)$$

It should be remembered that Eqs. 4.17 through 4.20 depend on the constant volume assumption and may be inaccurate unless the inelastic (plastic plus creep) strain is large compared with the elastic strain.

True strains from Eq. 4.15 are somewhat smaller than the corresponding engineering strains. But once necking starts and Eq. 4.19 is employed with the rapidly decreasing values of A, the true strain may increase substantially beyond the engineering strain, as seen in Fig. 4.18.

4.5.3 Limitations on True Stress–Strain Equations

The ranges of applicability of the various equations for calculating engineering and true stresses and strains are summarized by Fig. 4.19. First, note that engineering stress and strain may always be determined from their definitions, Eqs. 4.1 and 4.2. True stress may always be obtained from Eq. 4.12 if areas are directly measured, as from diameters in round cross sections.

Once necking starts at the engineering ultimate stress point, the engineering strain becomes merely an average over a region of nonuniform deformation. Hence, it does not represent the maximum strain and becomes unsuitable for calculating true stresses and strains. This situation requires that Eqs. 4.15 and 4.18 not be used beyond the ultimate point. Beyond this, true stresses and strains can be calculated only if the varying minimum cross-sectional area in the necked region is measured, as by measuring diameters for round specimens. Hence, only Eqs. 4.12 and 4.19 are available beyond the ultimate point where necking starts.

In addition, Eq. 4.18 is limited by the constant volume assumption. Hence, this conversion to true stress is inaccurate at small strains, such as those below and around the yield stress. An

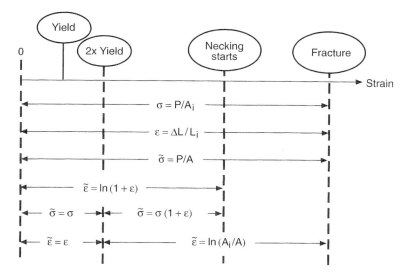

Figure 4.19   Use and limitations of various equations for stresses and strains from a tension test.

arbitrary lower limit of twice the strain that accompanies the offset yield strength, $2\varepsilon_o$, is suggested in Fig. 4.19. (Note that ε_o is defined in Fig. 4.11(a).) Below this limit, the difference between true and engineering stress is generally so small that it can be neglected, so that no conversion is needed. A similar limitation is encountered by Eqs. 4.19 and 4.20, which are otherwise valid at any strain.

4.5.4 Bridgman Correction for Hoop Stress

A complication exists in interpreting tensile results near the end of a test where there is a large amount of necking. As pointed out by P. W. Bridgman in 1944, large amounts of necking result in a tensile hoop stress being generated around the circumference in the necked region. Thus, the state of stress is no longer uniaxial as assumed, and the behavior of the material is affected. In particular, the axial stress is increased above what it would otherwise be. (This is caused by plastic deformation; see Chapter 12.)

A correction for steel can be made on the basis of the empirical curve developed by Bridgman, which is shown in Fig. 4.20. The curve is entered with the true strain based on area, and it gives a value of the correction factor, B, which is used as follows:

$$\tilde{\sigma}_B = B\tilde{\sigma} \tag{4.21}$$

Here, $\tilde{\sigma}$ is true stress simply computed from area by using Eq. 4.12, and $\tilde{\sigma}_B$ is the corrected value of true stress. Values of B for steels may be estimated from the following equation that closely approximates the curve of Fig. 4.20:

$$B = 0.0684x^3 + 0.0461x^2 - 0.205x + 0.825, \qquad \text{where } x = \log_{10}\tilde{\varepsilon} \qquad (0.12 \le \tilde{\varepsilon} \le 3) \tag{4.22}$$

The correction is not needed for $\tilde{\varepsilon} < 0.12$. Note that a 10% correction ($B = 0.9$) corresponds to a true strain of $\tilde{\varepsilon} = 0.44$. By Eq. 4.20, this gives a ratio of initial to necked diameter of 1.25. Hence, fairly large strains must occur for the correction to be significant.

Similar correction curves are not generally available for other metals, but a correction can still be done if the radius of the neck profile is measured. For details, see the references Bridgman (1952)

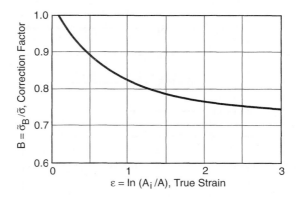

Figure 4.20   Curve of [Bridgman 44] giving correction factors on true stress for the effect of hoop stress due to necking in steels.

and Marshal (1952) given at the end of this chapter. The one for steel should not be applied to other metals except as a rough approximation.

Example 4.2

For the data of Table E4.1 for a tension test on AISI hot-rolled steel,

  (a) Calculate true stresses and strains, and plot the true stress–strain curve.
  (b) Calculate corrected values of true stress, and plot the resulting stress–strain curve.

Solution   **(a)** The requested values are given as the second and third columns in Table E4.1(b), and plotting these gives the curve labeled $\tilde{\sigma}$ versus $\tilde{\varepsilon}$ in Fig. 4.18. With reference to Fig. 4.19, true strain is given by Eq. 4.15 from the beginning of the test to the start of necking at the ultimate strength point, including all points above the lower horizontal line in Table E4.1. Also, true stress may be taken as equal to engineering stress where the strain is less than twice the yield strain. From Fig. E4.1(b), the yield strain can be read at the σ_o point to be $\varepsilon_o = 0.0033$. Hence, for $\varepsilon < 2\varepsilon_o = 0.0066$, no adjustment is made, which points correspond to those above the first horizontal line in Table E4.1. Beyond twice the yield strain, and to and including the ultimate strength point, Eq. 4.18 is employed. For example, for the line in the table with $P = 24.25\,\text{kN}$, we have

$$\tilde{\varepsilon} = \ln(1 + \varepsilon) = \ln(1 + 0.1250) = 0.1178, \quad \tilde{\sigma} = \sigma(1 + \varepsilon) = 372.0(1 + 0.1250) = 418.5\,\text{MPa}$$

Beyond the ultimate point (that is, below the lower horizontal line in Table E4.1), we must use only the equations that employ measurements of the varying diameter. Hence, we now need Eq. 4.12(a) or (b) for true stress, and Eq. 4.19 or 4.20 for true strain. For example, for the line in the table with $P = 21.35\,\text{kN}$, we have

$$\tilde{\varepsilon} = 2\ln\frac{d_i}{d} = 2\ln\frac{9.11\,\text{mm}}{6.35\,\text{mm}} = 0.7218, \quad \tilde{\sigma} = \frac{P}{A} = \frac{P}{\pi d^2/4} = \frac{4(21{,}350\,\text{N})}{\pi(6.35\,\text{mm})^2} = 674.2\,\text{MPa}$$

Similar calculations give the remaining $\tilde{\sigma}$ and $\tilde{\varepsilon}$ values in Table E4.1.
  (b) The corrected values of true stress $\tilde{\sigma}_B$ from Eqs. 4.21 and 4.22 are given in the fourth column of Table E4.1(b), and plotting these gives the curve labeled $\tilde{\sigma}_B$ versus $\tilde{\varepsilon}$ in Fig. 4.18. For $\tilde{\varepsilon} < 0.12$, no correction is needed, so that $\tilde{\sigma}_B = \tilde{\sigma}$, and in effect $B = 1$. For the line in the table with $P = 25.71\,\text{kN}$, and below this in the table, a correction is required. For example, for the line with $P = 21.35\,\text{kN}$, we have

$$x = \log_{10}\tilde{\varepsilon} = \log_{10}0.7218 = -0.1416, \quad B = 0.0684x^3 + 0.0461x^2 - 0.205x + 0.825$$

$$B = 0.0684(-0.1416)^3 + 0.0461(-0.1416)^2 - 0.205(-0.1416) + 0.825 = 0.855$$

$$\tilde{\sigma}_B = B\tilde{\sigma} = 0.855(674.2\,\text{MPa}) = 576.2\,\text{MPa}$$

Similar calculations give the remaining $\tilde{\sigma}_B$ values in Table E4.1. The corrected true stresses are seen to be always smaller than the raw values.

4.5.5 True Stress–Strain Curves

For true stress–strain curves of metals in the region beyond yielding, the stress versus plastic strain behavior often fits a power relationship:

$$\tilde{\sigma} = H\,\tilde{\varepsilon}_p^n \tag{4.23}$$

If stress versus plastic strain is plotted on log–log coordinates, this equation gives a straight line. The slope is n, which is called the *strain hardening exponent*. The quantity H, which is called the *strength coefficient*, is the intercept at $\tilde{\varepsilon}_p = 1$. At large strains during the advanced stages of necking, Eq. 4.23 should be used with true stresses that have been corrected by means of the Bridgman factor:

$$\tilde{\sigma}_B = H\,\tilde{\varepsilon}_p^n \tag{4.24}$$

A log–log plot of true stress versus true plastic strain for the test on AISI 1020 steel of Ex. 4.1 and 4.2 is shown in Fig. 4.21. Note that the $\tilde{\sigma}$ versus $\tilde{\varepsilon}_p$ data curve upward at the higher strains, but the $\tilde{\sigma}_B$ versus $\tilde{\varepsilon}_p$ (corrected) data do lie along an apparent straight line trend, to which a power relationship of the form of Eq. 4.24 has been fitted as shown.

   Since the total strain is the sum of its elastic and plastic parts, Eq. 4.24 can be solved for plastic strain, and this can be added to the elastic strain, $\tilde{\varepsilon}_e = \tilde{\sigma}_B/E$, to obtain a relationship between true stress and the total true strain $\tilde{\varepsilon}$:

$$\tilde{\varepsilon} = \tilde{\varepsilon}_e + \tilde{\varepsilon}_p, \qquad \tilde{\varepsilon} = \frac{\tilde{\sigma}_B}{E} + \left(\frac{\tilde{\sigma}_B}{H}\right)^{1/n} \tag{4.25}$$

This form is called the Ramberg–Osgood relationship, as considered in more detail in Chapter 12. Using the constants for the example AISI 1020 steel to plot Eq. 4.25, we obtain the dashed curve

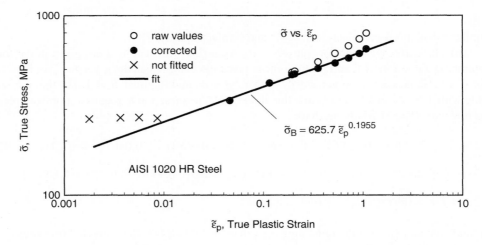

Figure 4.21   Log–log plot of true stress versus true plastic strain for AISI 1020 hot-rolled steel.

in Fig. 4.18. This is seen to represent the corrected data very well over all strains that are beyond the anomalous upper/lower yield region of this material. Where the stress–strain curve exhibits a smooth, gradual yielding behavior, Eq. 4.25 may provide a good fit for all strains. For some materials, Eq. 4.25 does not fit very well, and some cases of this type can be handled by two power laws that fit different portions of the stress–strain curve.

If cross-sectional area (diameter) measurements are not available for a tension test, then Eq. 4.25 may still be employed, but the fit is restricted to data that are not beyond the engineering ultimate stress point. The Bridgman correction then becomes unnecessary, so that Eq. 4.23 applies, and $\tilde{\sigma}_B$ in Eq. 4.25 is replaced by the uncorrected $\tilde{\sigma}$. Also, since the ultimate point is not exceeded, $\tilde{\sigma}$ and $\tilde{\varepsilon}$ may be calculated simply from Eqs. 4.18 and 4.15.

4.5.6 True Stress–Strain Properties

Additional materials properties obtained from tension tests may be defined on the basis of true stress and strain. The *true fracture strength*, $\tilde{\sigma}_f$, is obtained simply from the load at fracture and the final area, or from the engineering stress at fracture:

$$\tilde{\sigma}_f = \frac{P_f}{A_f} = \sigma_f \left(\frac{A_i}{A_f} \right) \tag{4.26}$$

Since the Bridgman correction is generally needed, the value obtained should be converted to $\tilde{\sigma}_{fB}$ by using Eq. 4.21, but note the limitation of Eq. 4.22 to steels.

The *true fracture strain*, $\tilde{\varepsilon}_f$, may be obtained from the final area or from the percent reduction in area:

$$\tilde{\varepsilon}_f = \ln \frac{A_i}{A_f}, \qquad \tilde{\varepsilon}_f = \ln \frac{100}{100 - \%RA} \qquad \text{(a, b)} \tag{4.27}$$

The second equation follows readily from the first. Note that $\tilde{\varepsilon}_f$ cannot be computed if only the engineering strain at fracture (percent elongation) is available.

The *true toughness*, $\tilde{u}_f$, is the area under the true stress–strain curve up to fracture. Assume that the material is quite ductile, so that the elastic strains are small, compared with the plastic strains, over most of the stress–strain curve. Hence, let the plastic and total strains be taken as equivalent, $\tilde{\varepsilon}_p \approx \tilde{\varepsilon}$, and consequently replace Eq. 4.24 with $\tilde{\sigma}_B = H \tilde{\varepsilon}^n$. On this basis, the true toughness is

$$\tilde{u}_f = \int_0^{\tilde{\varepsilon}_f} \tilde{\sigma}_B \, d\tilde{\varepsilon} = H \int_0^{\tilde{\varepsilon}_f} \tilde{\varepsilon}^n d\tilde{\varepsilon} = \frac{H \tilde{\varepsilon}_f^{n+1}}{n+1} = \frac{\tilde{\sigma}_{fB} \tilde{\varepsilon}_f}{n+1} \tag{4.28}$$

The various engineering and true stress–strain properties from tension tests are summarized by the categorized listing of Table 4.5. Note that the engineering fracture strain ε_f and the percent elongation are only different ways of stating the same quantity. Also, the $\%RA$ and $\tilde{\varepsilon}_f$ can each be calculated from the other by using Eq. 4.27(b). The strength coefficient H determines the magnitude of the true stress in the large strain region of the stress–strain curve, so it is included as a measure of strength. The strain hardening exponent n is a measure of the rate of strain hardening for the true

Table 4.5   Materials Properties Obtainable from Tension Tests

Category	Engineering Property	True Stress–Strain Property
Elastic constants	Elastic modulus, E, E_t Poisson's ratio, ν	—
Strength	Proportional limit, σ_p Yield strength, σ_o Ultimate tensile strength, σ_u Engineering fracture strength, σ_f	True fracture strength, $\tilde{\sigma}_{fB}$ Strength coefficient, H
Ductility	Percent elongation, $100\varepsilon_f$ Reduction in area, $\%RA$	True fracture strain, $\tilde{\varepsilon}_f$
Energy capacity	Tensile toughness, u_f	True toughness, $\tilde{u}_f$

Strain hardening	Strain hardening
	      ratio, σ_u/σ_o
		Strain hardening
		      exponent, n

stress–strain curve. For engineering metals, values above $n = 0.2$ are considered relatively high, and those below 0.1 are considered relatively low.

True stress–strain properties are listed for several engineering metals in Table 4.6. These are the same metals for which engineering properties have already been given in Table 4.2.

Example 4.3 _____

Using the stresses and strains in Table E4.1 for the tension test on AISI 1020 steel, determine the constants H and n for Eq. 4.24, and also the true fracture stress and strain, $\tilde{\sigma}_{fB}$ and $\tilde{\varepsilon}_f$.

Solution   First, we need to calculate true plastic strains $\tilde{\varepsilon}_p$ for the data in Table E4.1. This is done by subtracting elastic strains from total strains. For example, for the line in Table E4.1 with $P = 25.71$ kN, the calculation is

$$\tilde{\varepsilon}_p = \tilde{\varepsilon} - \frac{\tilde{\sigma}_B}{E}, \qquad \tilde{\varepsilon}_p = 0.1972 - \frac{465.3\,\text{MPa}}{201{,}200\,\text{MPa}} = 0.1949$$

where $E = 201{,}200$ MPa from Ex. 4.1. To find H and n, note that Eq. 4.24 can be written

$$\log \tilde{\sigma}_B = n \log \tilde{\varepsilon}_p + \log H$$

which is a straight line $y = mx + b$ on a log–log plot, where $y = \log \tilde{\sigma}_B$ (dependent variable) and $x = \log \tilde{\varepsilon}_p$ (independent variable). Hence, n and H are readily obtained from the fitting parameters m and b.

$$n = m, \qquad b = \log H, \qquad H = 10^b$$

Thus, if $\tilde{\sigma}_B$ is plotted versus $\tilde{\varepsilon}_p$ on log–log coordinates, a straight line should be formed of slope n and intercept at $\tilde{\varepsilon}_p = 1$ of $\tilde{\sigma}_B = H$. This is shown in Fig. 4.21. A least squares fit gives

$$m = n = 0.1955 \qquad \textbf{Ans.}$$

$$b = 2.79634, \qquad H = 10^b = 625.7 \qquad \textbf{Ans.}$$

Hence, the equation is $\tilde{\sigma}_B = 625.7 \, \tilde{\varepsilon}_p^{0.1955}$ MPa.

The foregoing fit is based on the last nine data points in Table E4.1. The first four plastic strain values in Table E4.1 for nonzero force are very small values judged to be meaningless, as arising from subtracting two nearly equal quantities that include experimental error. The next four did not appear to lie on the straight line trend in Fig. 4.21 and so were also excluded.

The true fracture stress and strain are simply the values from the last line of Table E4.1, as this corresponds to the fracture point:

$$\tilde{\sigma}_{fB} = 649 \text{ MPa}, \qquad \tilde{\varepsilon}_f = 1.091 \qquad \textbf{Ans.}$$

4.6 COMPRESSION TEST

Some materials have dramatically different behavior in compression than in tension, and in some cases these materials are used primarily to resist compressive stresses. Examples include concrete and building stone. Data from compression tests are therefore often needed for engineering applications. Compression tests have many similarities to tension tests in the manner of conducting the test and in the analysis and interpretation of the results. Since tension tests have already been considered in detail, the discussion here will focus on areas where these two types of tests differ.

4.6.1 Test Methods for Compression

A typical arrangement for a compression test is shown in Fig. 4.22. Uniform displacement rates in compression are applied in a manner similar to a tension test, except, of course, for the direction of loading. The specimen is most commonly a simple cylinder having a ratio of length to diameter, L/d, in the range 1 to 3. However, values of L/d up to 10 are sometimes used where the primary objective is to accurately determine the elastic modulus in compression. Specimens with square or rectangular cross sections may also be tested.

The choice of a specimen length represents a compromise. Buckling may occur if the L/d ratio is relatively large. If this happens, the test result is meaningless as a measure of the fundamental compressive behavior of the material. Buckling is affected by the unavoidable small imperfections in the geometry of the test specimen and its alignment with respect to the testing machine. For example, the ends of the specimen can be almost parallel, but never perfectly so.

Conversely, if L/d is small, the test result is affected by the details of the conditions at the end. In particular, as the specimen is compressed, the diameter increases due to the Poisson effect, but friction retards this motion at the ends, resulting in deformation into a barrel shape. This effect can be minimized by proper lubrication of the ends. In materials that are capable of large amounts of deformation in compression, the choice of too small of an L/d ratio may result in a situation where

Table 4.6 True Stress–Strain Tensile Properties for Some Engineering Metals, and Also Hardness

Material	True Fracture		Strength Coefficient H	Strain Hardening Exponent n	Brinell Hardness[1] HB
	Strength $\tilde{\sigma}_{fB}$	Strain $\tilde{\varepsilon}_f$			
	MPa (ksi)		MPa (ksi)		
Ductile cast iron A536 (65-45-12)	524 (76)	0.222	456 (66.1)	0.0455	167
AISI 1020 steel as rolled	713 (103)	0.96	737 (107)	0.19	107
ASTM A514, T1 structural steel	1213 (176)	1.08	1103 (160)	0.088	256
AISI 4142 steel as quenched	2580 (375)	0.060	—	0.136	670
AISI 4142 steel 205°C temper	2650 (385)	0.310	—	0.091	560
AISI 4142 steel 370°C temper	1998 (290)	0.540	—	0.043	450
AISI 4142 steel 450°C temper	1826 (265)	0.660	—	0.051	380
18 Ni maraging steel (250)	2136 (310)	0.82	—	0.02	460
SAE 308 cast aluminum	232 (33.6)	0.009	567 (82.2)	0.196	80
2024-T4 aluminum	631 (91.5)	0.43	806 (117)	0.20	120
7075-T6 aluminum	744 (108)	0.41	827 (120)	0.113	150
AZ91C-T6 cast magnesium	137 (20)	0.004	653 (94.7)	0.282	61

Note: [1]Load 3000 kg for irons and steels, 500 kg otherwise; typical values from [Boyer 85] are listed in some cases.

Sources: Data in [Conle 84] and [SAE 89].

the behavior of the specimen is dominated by the end effects, so that the test does not measure the fundamental compressive behavior of the material.

Considering both the desirability of small L/d to avoid buckling and large L/d to avoid end effects, a reasonable compromise is $L/d = 3$ for ductile materials. Values of $L/d = 1.5$ or 2 are suitable for brittle materials, where end effects are small.

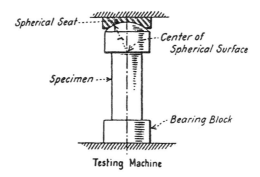

Figure 4.22 Compression test in a universal testing machine that uses a spherical-seated bearing block. (From [ASTM 97] Std. E9; copyright © ASTM; reprinted with permission.)

Figure 4.23 Compression specimens of metals (left to right): untested specimen, and tested specimens of gray cast iron, aluminum alloy 7075-T651, and hot-rolled AISI 1020 steel. Diameters before testing were approximately 25 mm, and lengths were 76 mm. (Photo by R. A. Simonds.)

Some examples of compression specimens of various materials both before and after testing are shown in Figs. 4.23 and 4.24. Mild steel shows typical ductile behavior, specifically large deformation without fracture ever occurring. The gray cast iron and concrete behaved in a brittle manner, and the aluminum alloy deformed considerably, but then also fractured. Fracture in compression usually occurs on an inclined plane or on a conical surface.

4.6.2 Materials Properties in Compression

The initial portions of compressive stress–strain curves have the same general nature as those in tension. Thus, various materials properties may be defined from the initial portion in the same manner as for tension, such as the elastic modulus E, the proportional limit σ_p, and the yield strength σ_o.

Figure 4.24   Untested and tested 150 mm diameter compression specimens of concrete with Hokie limestone aggregate. (Photo by R. A. Simonds.)

The ultimate strength behavior in compression differs in a qualitative way from that in tension. Note that the decrease in force prior to final fracture in tension is associated with the phenomenon of necking. This, of course, does not occur in compression. In fact, an opposite effect occurs, in that the increasing cross-sectional area causes the stress–strain curve to rise rapidly rather than showing a maximum. As a result, there is no force maximum in compression prior to fracture, and the engineering ultimate strength is the same as the engineering fracture strength. Brittle and moderately ductile materials will fracture in compression. But many ductile metals and polymers simply never fracture. Instead, the specimen deforms into an increasingly larger and thinner pancake shape until the force required for further deformation becomes so large that the test must be suspended.

Ductility measurements for compression are analogous to those for tension. Such measures include percentage changes in length and area, as well as engineering and true fracture strain. The same measures of energy capacity may also be employed, as can constants for true stress–strain curves of the form of Eq. 4.23.

4.6.3 Trends in Compressive Behavior

Ductile engineering metals often have nearly identical initial portions of stress–strain curves in tension and compression; an example of this is shown in Fig. 4.25. After large amounts of deformation, the curves may still agree if true stresses and strains are plotted.

Many materials that are brittle in tension have this behavior because they contain cracks or pores that grow and combine to cause failures along planes of maximum tension—that is, perpendicular to the specimen axis. Examples are the graphite flakes in gray cast iron, cracks at the aggregate boundaries in concrete, and porosity in sintered ceramics. Such flaws have much less effect in compression, so materials that behave in a brittle manner in tension usually have considerably higher compressive strengths. For example, compare the strengths in tension and compression given for various ceramics in Table 3.10. Quite ductile behavior can occur even for materials that are brittle in tension, as for the polymer in Fig. 4.26.

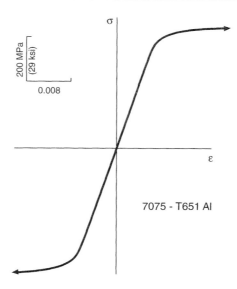

Figure 4.25   Initial portions of stress–strain curves in tension and compression for 7075-T651 aluminum.

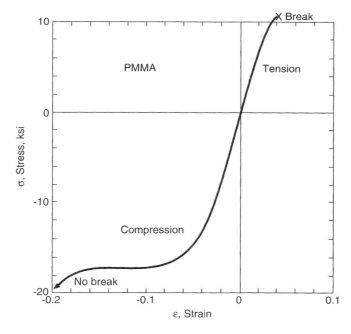

Figure 4.26   Stress–strain curves for plexiglass (acrylic, PMMA) in both tension and compression. (Adapted from [Richards 61] p. 153; reprinted by permission of PWS-Kent Publishing Co., Boston.)

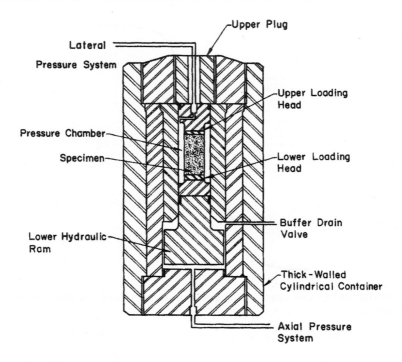

Figure 4.27   System for testing brittle materials such as concrete and stone in compression with lateral pressure. This system was in use at the U.S. Bureau of Reclamation Laboratories, Denver, CO, in the 1960s. Lateral pressures up to 860 MPa (125 ksi) could be applied by using kerosene as the hydraulic fluid, which did not contact the specimen, due to the use of a neoprene sheath. (From [Hilsdorf 73] as adapted from [Chinn 65]; used with permission.)

Where compressive failure does occur, it is generally associated with a shear stress, so the fracture is inclined relative to the specimen axis. This type of fracture is evident for gray cast iron, an aluminum alloy, and concrete in Figs. 4.23 and 4.24. Compare the cast iron fracture plane with that for tension in Fig. 4.13. The tension fracture plane is oriented normal to the applied tension stress, which is typical of brittle behavior in all materials.

For brittle materials such as concrete and stone, some engineering applications involve multiaxial compressive stresses, as in foundations for buildings, bridges, and dams. A testing arrangement that simulates such conditions by employing hydraulic pressure for multiaxial testing is shown in Fig. 4.27. The *axial pressure system* provides a compressive force in the vertical direction, as for a simple compression test. And the *lateral pressure system* compresses the specimen laterally on all sides. The compressive strength of concrete or stone in the axial direction is affected by such lateral pressure; and for large values of lateral pressure, the compressive strength is substantially higher than in an ordinary compression test. (This behavior is addressed in some detail later in Sections 7.7 and 7.8, where methods of predicting strength of brittle materials under multiaxial stress are considered.)

4.7 HARDNESS TESTS

In engineering, hardness is most commonly defined as the resistance of a material to *indentation*. Indentation is the pressing of a hard round ball or point against the material sample with a known force so that a depression is made. The depression, or indentation, results from plastic deformation beneath the indenter, as shown in Fig. 4.28. Some specific characteristic of the indentation, such as its size or depth, is then taken as a measure of hardness.

Other principles are also used to measure hardness. For example, the *Scleroscope hardness test* is a rebound test that employs a hammer with a rounded diamond tip. This hammer is dropped from a fixed height onto the surface of the material being tested. The hardness number is proportional to the height of rebound of the hammer, with the scale for metals being set so that fully hardened tool steel has a value of 100. A modified version of this test is also used for polymers.

In mineralogy, the *Mohs hardness scale* is used. Diamond, the hardest known material, is assigned a value of 10. Decreasing values are assigned to other minerals, down to 1 for the soft mineral talc. Decimal fractions, such as 9.7 for tungsten carbide, are used for materials intermediate between the standard ones. Where a material lies on the Mohs scale is determined by a simple manual scratch test. If two materials are compared, the harder one is capable of scratching the softer one, but not vice versa. This allows materials to be ranked as to hardness, and decimal values between the standard ones are assigned as a matter of judgment.

Very hard steels have a Mohs hardness around 7, and lower strength steels and other relatively hard metal alloys are generally in the range 4 to 5. Soft metals may be below 1, so their Mohs hardness is difficult to specify. Various materials are compared as to their Mohs hardness in Fig. 4.29. Also shown are values for two of the indentation hardness scales that will be discussed shortly.

Indentation hardness has an advantage over Mohs hardness in that the values obtained are less a matter of interpretation and judgment. There are a number of different standard indentation hardness tests. They differ from one another as to the geometry of the indenter, the amount of force used, etc. As time-dependent deformations may occur that affect the indentation, loading rates and/or times of application are fixed for each standard test.

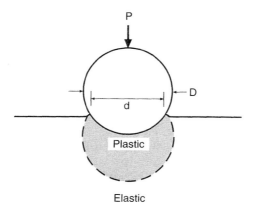

Figure 4.28   Plastic deformation under a Brinell hardness indenter.

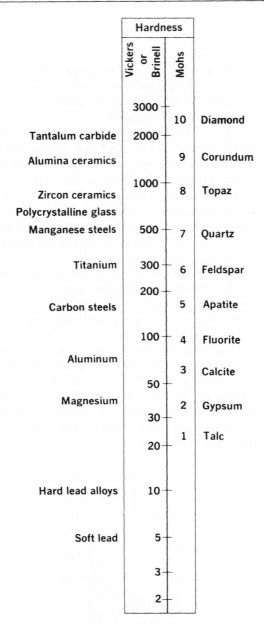

Figure 4.29 Approximate relative hardness of various metals and ceramics. (From [Richards 61] p. 402, as based on data from [Zwikker 54] p. 261; reprinted by permission of PWS-Kent Publishing Co., Boston.)

Figure 4.30 Brinell hardness tester (left), and indenter being applied to a sample (right). (Photographs courtesy of Tinius Olsen Testing Machine Co., Inc., Willow Grove, PA.)

Test apparatus for the *Brinell* hardness test is shown in Fig. 4.30. Some of the resulting indentations are shown, along with those for *Rockwell* type tests, in Fig. 4.31. These two and the *Vickers* test are commonly used for engineering purposes.

4.7.1 Brinell Hardness Test

In this test, a large steel ball—specifically, 10 mm in diameter—is used with a relatively high force. The force used is 3000 kg for fairly hard materials, such as steels and cast irons, and 500 kg for softer materials, such as copper and aluminum alloys. For very hard materials, the standard steel ball will deform excessively, and a tungsten carbide ball is used.

The Brinell hardness number, designated *HB*, is obtained by dividing the applied force *P*, in kilograms, by the curved surface area of the indentation, which is a segment of a sphere. This gives

$$HB = \frac{2P}{\pi D \left[D - (D^2 - d^2)^{0.5} \right]}$$

(4.29)

where D is the diameter of the ball and d is the diameter of the indentation, both in millimeters, as illustrated in Fig. 4.28. Brinell hardness numbers are listed for the metals in Table 4.6.

Figure 4.31   Brinell and Rockwell hardness indentations. On the left, in hot-rolled AISI 1020 steel, the larger Brinell indentation has a diameter of 5.4 mm, giving $HB = 121$, and the smaller Rockwell B indentation gave $HRB = 72$. On the right, a higher strength steel has indentations corresponding to $HB = 241$ and $HRC = 20$. (Photo by R. A. Simonds.)

4.7.2 Vickers Hardness Test

The Vickers hardness test is based on the same general principles as the Brinell test. It differs primarily in that the indenter is a diamond point in the shape of a pyramid with a square base. The angle between the faces of the pyramid is $\alpha = 136°$, as shown in Fig. 4.32. This shape results in the depth of penetration, h, being one-seventh of the indentation size, d, measured on the diagonal. The Vickers hardness number HV is obtained by dividing the applied force P by the surface area of the pyramidal depression. This yields

$$HV = \frac{2P}{d^2} \sin \frac{\alpha}{2} \tag{4.30}$$

where d is in millimeters and P in kilograms.

Note that the standard pyramidal shape causes the indentations to be geometrically similar, regardless of their size. For reasons derived from plasticity theory and which are beyond the scope of the present discussion, this geometric similarity is expected to result in a Vickers hardness value that is independent of the magnitude of the force used. Hence, a wide range of standard forces usually between 1 and 120 kg are used, so that essentially all solid materials can be included in a single wide-ranging hardness scale.

Approximate Vickers hardness numbers are given for various classes of materials in Fig. 4.29. Also, values for some ceramics are given in Table 4.7. Within the more limited range where the Brinell test can be used, there is approximate agreement with the Vickers scale. This approximate agreement is shown, by average curves for steels of various strengths, in Fig. 4.33.

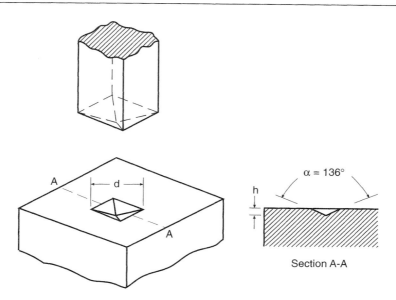

Figure 4.32   Vickers hardness indentation.

Table 4.7   Vickers Hardness and Bending Strength for Some Ceramics and Glasses

Material	Hardness HV, 0.1 kg	Bend Strength MPa (ksi)	Elastic Modulus GPa (10^3 ksi)
Soda-lime glass	600	65 (9.4)	74 (10.7)
Fused silica glass	650	70 (10.1)	70 (10.1)
Aluminous porcelain	≈ 800	120 (17.4)	120 (17.4)
Silicon nitride Si_3N_4, hot pressed	1700	600 (87)	400 (58)
Alumina, Al_2O_3 99.5% dense	1750	400 (58)	400 (58)
Silicon carbide SiC, hot pressed	2600	600 (87)	400 (58)
Boron carbide, B_4C hot pressed	3200	400 (58)	475 (69)

Source: Data in [Creyke 82] p. 38.

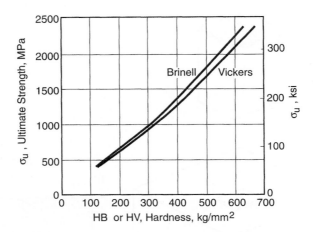

Figure 4.33 Approximate relationship between ultimate tensile strength and Brinell and Vickers hardness of carbon and alloy steels. (Data from [Boyer 85] p. 1.61.)

Another hardness test that is somewhat similar to the Vickers test is the Knoop test. It differs in that the pyramidal indenter has a diamond-shaped base and in the use of the projected area to calculate hardness.

4.7.3 Rockwell Hardness Test

In the Rockwell test, a diamond point or a steel ball is employed as the indenter. The diamond point, called a Brale indenter, is a cone with an included angle of 120° and a slightly rounded end. Balls of sizes ranging between 1.6 mm and 12.7 mm are also used. Various combinations of indenter and force are applied in the *regular Rockwell test* to accommodate a wide range of materials, as listed in Table 4.8. In addition, there is a *superficial Rockwell hardness test* that uses smaller forces and causes smaller indentations.

Rockwell tests differ from other hardness tests in that the depth of the indentation is measured, rather than the size. A small initial force called the *minor load* is first applied to establish a reference position for the depth measurement and to penetrate through any surface scale or foreign particles. A minor load of 10 kg is used for the regular test. The *major load* is then applied, and the additional penetration due to the major load is measured. This is illustrated by the difference between h_2 and h_1 in Fig. 4.34.

Each Rockwell hardness scale has a maximum useful value around 100. An increase of one unit of regular Rockwell hardness represents a decrease in penetration of 0.002 mm. Hence, the hardness number is

$$HRX = M - \frac{\Delta h}{0.002} \tag{4.31}$$

where $\Delta h = h_2 - h_1$ is in millimeters and M is the upper limit of the scale. For regular Rockwell hardness, $M = 100$ for all scales using the diamond point (*A*, *C*, and *D* scales), and $M = 130$ for all

Table 4.8 Commonly Used Rockwell Hardness Scales

Symbol, HRX X =	Penetrator Diameter if Ball, mm (in)	Force kg	Typical Application
A	Diamond point	60	Tool materials
D	Diamond point	100	Cast irons, sheet steels
C	Diamond point	150	Steels, hard cast irons, Ti alloys
B	1.588 (0.0625)	100	Soft steels, Cu and Al alloys
E	3.175 (0.125)	100	Al and Mg alloys, other soft metals; reinforced polymers
M	6.35 (0.250)	100	Very soft metals; high-modulus polymers
R	12.70 (0.500)	60	Very soft metals; low-modulus polymers

scales using ball indenters (B, E, M, R, etc., scales). The hardness numbers are designated *HRX*, where X indicates the scale involved, such as 60 HRC for 60 points on the C scale. Note that a Rockwell hardness number is meaningless unless the scale is specified. In practice, the hardness numbers are read directly from a dial on the hardness tester, rather than being calculated.

4.7.4 Hardness Correlations and Conversions

The deformations caused by a hardness indenter are of similar magnitude to those occurring at the ultimate tensile strength in a tension test. However, an important difference is that the material cannot freely flow outward, so that a complex triaxial state of stress exists under the indenter. Nevertheless, empirical correlations can be established between hardness and tensile properties, primarily the ultimate tensile strength σ_u. For example, for low- and medium-strength carbon and alloy steels, σ_u can be estimated from Brinell hardness as

$$\sigma_u = 3.45(HB) \text{ MPa}, \qquad \sigma_u = 0.50(HB) \text{ ksi} \qquad (4.32)$$

where HB is assumed to be in units of kg/mm^2. Note that we may also express hardness in units of MPa by applying the conversion factor 1 kg/mm^2 = 9.807 MPa. If the same units (such as MPa) are used for both HB and σ_u, Eq. 4.32 becomes $\sigma_u = 0.35(HB)$.

Observe that Eq. 4.32 approximates the curve shown in Fig. 4.33. However, there is considerable scatter in actual data, so this relationship should be considered to provide rough estimates only. For other classes of material, the empirical constant will differ, and the relationship may even become nonlinear. Similarly, the relationship will change for a different type of hardness test. Rockwell hardness correlates well with σ_u and with other types of hardness test, but the relationships are usually nonlinear. This situation results from the unique indentation-depth basis of this test. For

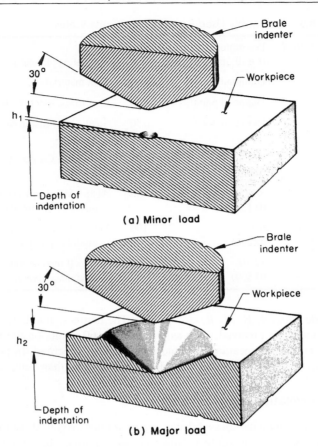

Figure 4.34   Rockwell hardness indentation made by application of (a) the minor load, and (b) the major load, on a diamond Brale indenter. (Adapted from [Boyer 85] p. 34.6; used with permission.)

carbon and alloy steels, a conversion chart for estimating various types of hardness from one another, and also ultimate tensile strength, is given as Table 4.9. More detailed conversion charts for steels and other metals are given in ASTM Standard No. E140, in various handbooks, and in information provided by manufacturers of hardness testing equipment.

4.8 NOTCH-IMPACT TESTS

Notch-impact tests provide information on the resistance of a material to sudden fracture where a sharp stress raiser or flaw is present. In addition to providing information not available from any other simple mechanical test, these tests are quick and inexpensive, so they are frequently employed.

Table 4.9 Approximate Equivalent Hardness Numbers and Ultimate Tensile Strengths for Carbon and Alloy Steels

Brinell	Vickers	Rockwell		Ultimate, σ_u	
HB	*HV*	*HRB*	*HRC*	MPa	ksi
627	667	—	58.7	2393	347
578	615	—	56.0	2158	313
534	569	—	53.5	1986	288
495	528	—	51.0	1813	263
461	491	—	48.5	1669	242
429	455	—	45.7	1517	220
401	425	—	43.1	1393	202
375	396	—	40.4	1267	184
341	360	—	36.6	1131	164
311	328	—	33.1	1027	149
277	292	—	28.8	924	134
241	253	100	22.8	800	116
217	228	96.4	—	724	105
197	207	92.8	—	655	95
179	188	89.0	—	600	87
159	167	83.9	—	538	78
143	150	78.6	—	490	71
131	137	74.2	—	448	65
116	122	67.6	—	400	58

Note: Force 3000 kg for *HB*. Both *HB* and *HV* are assumed to be in units of kg/mm^2.
Source: Values in [Boyer 85] p. 1.61.

4.8.1 Types of Test

In various standard impact tests, notched beams are broken by a swinging pendulum or a falling weight. The most common tests of this type are the *Charpy V-notch* and the *Izod tests*. Specimens and loading configurations for these are shown in Fig. 4.35. A swinging pendulum arrangement is used for applying the impact load in both cases; a device for Charpy tests is shown in Fig. 4.36. The energy required to break the sample is determined from an indicator that measures how high the pendulum swings after breaking the sample. Some broken Charpy specimens are shown in Fig. 4.37. The impact resistance of polymers (plastics) is often evaluated with the use of the Izod test. Some representative data are included in Table 4.3.

Another test that is used fairly often is the *dynamic tear test*. Specimens for this test have a center notch, as for the Charpy specimen, and they are impacted in three-point bending, but by a falling weight. These specimens are quite large, 180 mm long, 40 mm wide, and 16 mm thick. An even larger size, 430 mm long, 120 mm wide, and 25 mm thick, is also used.

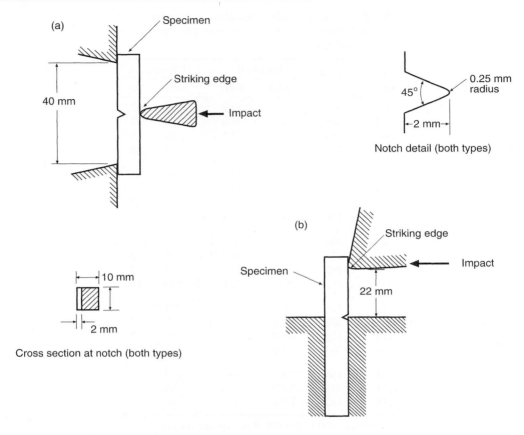

Figure 4.35   Specimens and loading configurations for (a) Charpy *V*-notch, and (b) Izod tests. (Adapted from [ASTM 97] Std. E23; copyright © ASTM; reprinted with permission.)

In notch-impact tests, the energies obtained depend on the details of the specimen size and geometry, including the notch-tip radius. The support and loading configuration used are also important, as are the mass and velocity of the pendulum or weight. Hence, results from one type of test cannot be directly compared with those from another. In addition, all such details of the test must be kept constant, as specified in the published standards, such as those of ASTM.

4.8.2 Trends in Impact Behavior, and Discussion

Polymers, metals, and other materials with low notch-impact energy are generally prone to brittle behavior and typically have low ductility and low toughness in a tension test. However, the correlation with tensile properties is only a general trend, as the results of impact fracture tests are special due to both the high rate of loading and the presence of a notch.

Many materials exhibit marked changes in impact energy with temperature. For example, for plain carbon steels of various carbon contents, Charpy energy is plotted versus temperature in

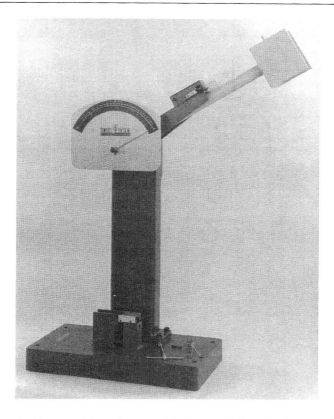

Figure 4.36   Charpy testing machine, shown with the pendulum in the raised position prior to its release to impact a specimen. (Photo courtesy of Tinius Olsen Testing Machine Co., Inc., Willow Grove, PA.)

Figure 4.37   Broken Charpy specimens, left to right, of gray cast iron, AISI 4140 steel tempered to $\sigma_u \approx 1550\,\mathrm{MPa}$, and the same steel at $\sigma_u \approx 950\,\mathrm{MPa}$. The specimens are 10 mm in both width and thickness. (Photo by R. A. Simonds.)

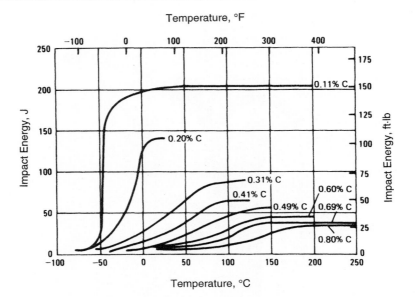

Figure 4.38 Variation in Charpy *V*-notch impact energy with temperature for normalized plain carbon steels of various carbon contents. (From [Boyer 85] p. 4.85; used with permission.)

Fig. 4.38. However, even for the same carbon content, and for heat treatment to the same hardness (ultimate strength), there are still differences in the impact behavior of steels due to the influence of different percentages of minor alloying elements. This behavior is illustrated by Fig. 4.39.

In Figs. 4.38 and 4.39, there tends to be a region of temperatures over which the impact energy increases rapidly from a lower level that may be relatively constant to an upper level that may also be relatively constant. Such a *temperature-transition* behavior is common in various materials. The fracture surfaces for low-energy (brittle) impact failures are generally relatively smooth, and in metals have a crystalline appearance. But those for high-energy (ductile) fractures have regions of shear where the fracture surface is inclined about 45° to the tensile stress, and they have, in general, a rougher, more highly deformed appearance, called fibrous fracture. These differences can be seen in Fig. 4.37.

The temperature-transition behavior is of some engineering significance, as it aids in comparing materials for use at various temperatures. In general, a material should not be severely loaded at temperatures where it has a low impact energy. However, some caution is needed in attaching too much significance to the exact position of the temperature transition. This is because the transition shifts even for different types of impact tests, as discussed in the book by Barsom (1999). Notch-impact test results can be quantitatively related to engineering situations of interest only in an indirect manner through empirical correlations, with this situation applying both to the energies and to the temperature transition.

By the use of fracture mechanics (as described later in Chapter 8), materials containing cracks and sharp notches can be analyzed in a more specific way. In particular, the *fracture toughness* can be quantitatively related to the behavior of an engineering component, and loading-rate effects can

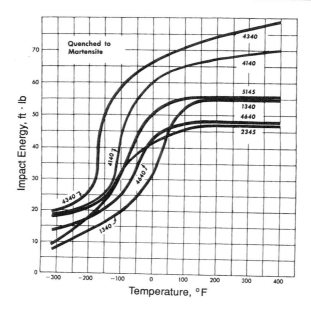

Figure 4.39   Temperature dependence of Charpy *V*-notch impact resistance for different alloy steels of similar carbon content, all quenched and tempered to HRC 34. (Adapted from [French 56]; used with permission.)

be included in the analysis. However, these advantages are achieved at the sacrifice of simplicity and economy. Notch-impact tests have thus remained popular despite their shortcomings, as they serve a useful purpose in quickly comparing materials and obtaining general information on their behavior.

4.9 BENDING AND TORSION TESTS

Various bending and torsion tests are widely used for evaluating the elastic modulus, strength, shear modulus, shear strength, and other properties of materials. These tests differ in a critical way from tension and compression tests, in that the stresses and strains are not uniform over the cross section of the test specimen. The only useful exception is the case of torsion of thin-walled circular tubes, where the shear stress and strain are approximately uniform if the wall is sufficiently thin. In other cases of bending and torsion, the nonuniform stresses and strains create a situation where a stress–strain curve cannot be determined directly from the test data.

A procedure does exist for obtaining a stress–strain curve by numerically analyzing slopes on a moment versus curvature plot for rectangular cross sections in bending. And there is a similar procedure for analyzing torque versus twist angle data for solid round shafts in torsion. These procedures are not covered here, but for torsion can be found in the books by Dieter (1986) and Hill (1998), and for both bending and torsion in the book by Nadai (1950). The opposite problem, that of determining the moment or torque given the material's stress–strain curve, will be considered

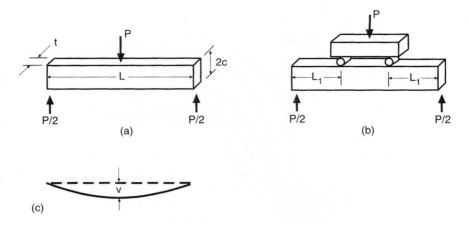

Figure 4.40   Loading configuration for (a) three-point bending and (b) four-point bending. The deflection of the centerline of either beam is similar to (c).

in detail in Chapter 13. Note that the simple equations commonly employed to calculate stresses for bending and torsion, as in Fig. A.1(b) and (c), are based on linear-elastic behavior and so do not apply if the stress–strain behavior is nonlinear due to yielding.

4.9.1 Bending (Flexure) Tests

Bending tests on smooth (unnotched) bars of material are commonly used, as in various ASTM standard test methods for flat metal spring material, and for concrete, natural stone, wood, plastics, glass, and ceramics. Bending tests, also called *flexure tests*, are especially needed to evaluate tensile strengths of brittle materials, as such materials are difficult to test in simple uniaxial tension due to cracking in the grips. (Think of trying to grab a piece of glass in the jaw-like grips often used for testing flat pieces of metal.) The specimens often have rectangular cross sections and may be loaded in either three-point bending or four-point bending, as illustrated in Fig. 4.40.

In bending, note that the stress varies through the depth of the beam in such a way that yielding first occurs in a thin surface layer. This results in the load versus deflection curve not being sensitive to the very beginning of yielding. Also, if the stress–strain curve is not linear, as after yielding, the simple elastic bending analysis is not valid. Hence, bending tests are most meaningful for brittle materials that have approximately linear stress–strain behavior up to the point of fracture.

For materials that do have approximately linear behavior, the fracture stress may be estimated from the failure load in the bending test by simple linear elastic beam analysis:

$$\sigma = \frac{Mc}{I} \tag{4.33}$$

Here, M is the bending moment. For a rectangular cross section of depth $2c$ and width t, as in Fig. 4.40, the area moment of inertia about the neutral axis is $I = 2tc^3/3$. Consider three-point bending of a beam of length L due to a force P at midspan, as in Fig. 4.40(a). In this case, the highest bending moment occurs at midspan and is $M = PL/4$. Equation 4.33 then gives

$$\sigma_{fb} = \frac{3L}{8tc^2} P_f \tag{4.34}$$

where P_f is the fracture force in the bending test and σ_{fb} is the calculated fracture stress. This is usually identified as the bend strength or the *flexural strength*, with the quaint term *modulus of rupture in bending* also being used. Values for some ceramics are given in Table 4.7.

Such values of σ_{fb} should always be identified as being from a bending test. This is because they may not agree precisely with values from tension tests, primarily due to departure of the stress–strain curve from linearity. Note that brittle materials are usually stronger in compression than in tension, so the maximum tension stress is the cause of failure in the beam. Corrections for nonlinearity in the stress–strain curve could be made on the basis of methods presented later in Chapter 13, but this is virtually never done.

Yield strengths in bending are also sometimes evaluated. Equation 4.34 is used, but with P_f replaced by a load P_i, corresponding to a strain offset or other means of identifying the beginning of yielding. Such σ_o values are less likely than σ_{fb} to be affected by nonlinear stress–strain behavior, but agreement with values from tension tests is affected by the previously noted insensitivity of the test to the beginning of yielding.

The elastic modulus may also be obtained from a bending test. For example, for three-point bending, as in Fig. 4.40(a), linear-elastic analysis gives the maximum deflection at midspan. From Fig. A.4(a), this is

$$v = \frac{PL^3}{48EI} \tag{4.35}$$

The value of E may then be calculated from the slope dP/dv of the initial linear portion of the load versus deflection curve:

$$E = \frac{L^3}{48I} \left(\frac{dP}{dv} \right) = \frac{L^3}{32tc^3} \left(\frac{dP}{dv} \right) \tag{4.36}$$

Elastic moduli derived from bending are generally reasonably close to those from tension or compression tests of the same material, but several possible causes of discrepancy exist: (1) Local elastic or plastic deformations at the supports and/or points of load application may not be small compared with the beam deflection. (2) In relatively short beams, significant deformations due to shear stress may occur that are not considered by the ideal beam theory used. (3) The material may have differing elastic moduli in tension and compression, so that an intermediate value is obtained from the bending test. Hence, values of E from bending need to be identified as such.

For four-point bending, or for other modes of loading or shapes of cross section, Eqs. 4.34 to 4.36 need to be replaced by the analogous relationships from Appendix A that apply.

4.9.2 Heat-Deflection Test

In this test used for polymers, small beams having rectangular cross sections are loaded in three-point bending with the use of a special apparatus described in ASTM Standard No. D648. Beams $2c = 13$ mm deep, and $t = 3$ to 13 mm thick, are loaded over a span of $L = 100$ mm. A force is applied such that the maximum bending stress, calculated by assuming elastic behavior, is either 0.455 MPa or 1.82 MPa. The temperature is then increased at a rate of 2°C per minute until the deflection of the beam exceeds 0.25 mm, at which point the temperature is noted. This *heat-deflection temperature* is used as an index to compare the resistance of polymers to excessive softening and deformation as a result of heat. It also gives an indication of the temperature range where the material loses its usefulness. Some values are given in Table 4.3.

4.9.3 Torsion Test

Tests of round bars loaded in simple torsion are relatively easy to conduct, and unlike tension tests, they are not complicated by the necking phenomenon. The state of stress and strain in a torsion test on a round bar corresponds to pure shear, as illustrated in Fig. 4.41, where T is torque, τ is shear stress, and γ is shear strain. The same state of stress and strain also applies if the bar is hollow, such as a thin-walled circular tube. Note that with a 45° rotation of the coordinate axes, the pure shear stress and strain are equivalent to normal stresses and strains, as shown.

Fractures from torsion tests are shown in Fig. 4.42. The gray cast iron (top) behaves in a brittle manner, with fracture on planes of maximum tension stress, 45° to the specimen axis, consistent with Fig. 4.41. As the fracture wraps around the circumference, maintaining 45° to the specimen axis causes the helical fracture pattern shown. In contrast, ductile behavior occurs for the aluminum alloy (bottom), where fracture occurs on a plane of maximum shear stress transverse to the bar axis.

For linear-elastic behavior, the shear stress τ_f at fracture can be related to the torque T_f by applying Figs. A.1(c) and A.2(c). We obtain

$$\tau_f = \frac{T_f r_2}{J}, \qquad \tau_f = \frac{2\,T_f r_2}{\pi\left(r_2^4 - r_1^4\right)} \qquad \text{(a, b)} \qquad\qquad (4.37)$$

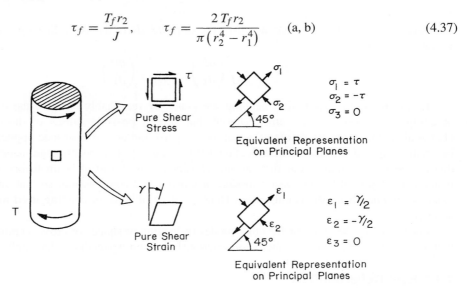

Figure 4.41 A round bar in torsion and the resulting state of pure shear stress and strain. The equivalent normal stresses and strains for a 45° rotation of the coordinate axes are also shown.

Figure 4.42   Typical torsion failures, showing brittle behavior (top) in gray cast iron, and ductile behavior (bottom) in aluminum alloy 2024-T351. (Photo by R. A. Simonds.)

where J is the polar moment of inertia of the cross-sectional area and r_2 is the outer radius. Form (b) is obtained from (a) by evaluating J for a hollow bar or tube with inner radius r_1. A solid bar is included by letting $r_1 = 0$. However, as a result of Eq. 4.37 being derived from linear-elastic behavior, τ_f values so calculated are inaccurate if there is nonlinear deformation (yielding), a situation similar to that for bending tests. However, this limitation can be largely overcome by testing thin-walled tubes, as discussed in the next section.

In a torsion test, the torque T is usually plotted versus the angle of twist θ. The shear modulus G can be evaluated from the slope $dT/d\theta$ of the initial linear portion of such a plot. Noting the equation for θ in Fig. A.1(c), we see that the desired G is given by

$$G = \frac{L}{J}\left(\frac{dT}{d\theta}\right), \qquad G = \frac{2L}{\pi\left(r_2^4 - r_1^4\right)}\left(\frac{dT}{d\theta}\right) \qquad \text{(a, b)} \qquad (4.38)$$

where L is the bar length and J, r_2, and r_1 are the same as before, with $r_1 = 0$ for a solid bar.

Torsion tests on solid bars are often conducted as a means of comparing the strength and ductility of different materials or variations of a given material. This is valid, as long as it is noted that stresses from Eq. 4.37 may be fictitious values, as they do not include the effects of yielding. (See Chapter 13.)

4.9.4 Testing of Thin-Walled Tubes in Torsion

If it is desired to investigate significant nonlinear deformation in torsion, the most straightforward approach is to test thin-walled tubes, as illustrated in Fig. 4.43. The approximately uniform shear

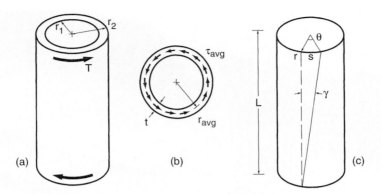

Figure 4.43 Thin-walled tube in torsion (a). The approximately uniform shear stress τ_{avg} on the cross section is shown in (b), and the geometry for an angle of twist θ in (c).

stress and strain through the wall thickness can be obtained from

$$\tau_{avg} = \frac{T}{2\pi r_{avg}^2 t}, \qquad \gamma_{avg} = \frac{r_{avg}\theta}{L}, \qquad \text{where } r_{avg} = \frac{r_2 + r_1}{2} \qquad \text{(a, b, c)} \qquad (4.39)$$

The wall thickness is $t = r_2 - r_1$, and r_{avg} is the radius to the middle of the wall thickness. The subscripts *avg* for shear stress and strain indicate averages for these quantities that vary somewhat through the wall thickness.

By the use of Eq. 4.39, the shear stress–strain curve, τ versus γ, can be obtained directly and simply from T versus θ data. This gives us a testing and data analysis situation that is analogous to the use of Eqs. 4.1 and 4.2 to obtain σ versus ε curves from P versus ΔL data from tension tests. The choice of a wall thickness for test specimens involves a compromise, with ratios in the range $t/r_1 = 0.10$ to 0.25 being reasonable. The former gives only a 10% variation in strain through the wall, but is thin enough that buckling could be a problem. The latter value gives more resistance to buckling, but with a 25% variation in strain.

Equation 4.39 can be derived with the aid of Fig. 4.43(b). The shear stress τ_{avg} is treated as constant through the wall thickness. Multiplying this by the cross-sectional area gives the total annular force, which has a torque arm r_{avg}, and which must equilibrate the torque T:

$$T = (\text{stress})(\text{area})(\text{distance}) = (\tau_{avg})(2\pi r_{avg}t)(r_{avg}) = 2\pi \tau_{avg} r_{avg}^2 t \qquad (4.40)$$

Solving for τ_{avg} then gives Eq. 4.39(a). Now consider a cylinder of any radius r that is twisted by an angle θ, as shown in Fig. 4.43(c). Noting that the shear strain is the distortion angle γ, which is assumed to be small compared with unity, the arc length $s = r\theta = L\gamma$, so that $\gamma = r\theta/L$. Applying this for r_{avg} gives Eq. 4.39(b). Also, applying the same relationship to compare γ for the inner and outer walls gives

$$\gamma_2 = \frac{r_2\theta}{L}, \qquad \gamma_1 = \frac{r_1\theta}{L}, \qquad \frac{\gamma_2}{\gamma_1} = \frac{r_2}{r_1} = 1 + \frac{t}{r_1} \qquad (4.41)$$

Hence, for $t/r_1 = 0.1$, we have $\gamma_2/\gamma_1 = 1.10$, or a 10% variation, as stated earlier, and similarly a 25% variation for $t/r_1 = 0.25$.

The testing of thin-walled tubes in torsion is not nearly as prevalent as tension testing. But it nevertheless provides a viable alternative for characterizing the fundamental stress–strain behavior of materials.

4.10 SUMMARY

A variety of relatively simple mechanical tests are used to evaluate materials properties. The results are used in engineering design and as a basis for comparing and selecting materials. These include tests involving tension, compression, indentation, impact, bending, and torsion.

Tension tests are frequently used to evaluate stiffness, strength, ductility, and other character-istics of materials, as summarized in Table 4.5. One property of interest is the elastic modulus E, a measure of stiffness and a fundamental elastic constant of the material. Poisson's ratio ν can also be obtained if transverse strains are measured. The yield strength σ_o characterizes resistance to the beginning of plastic deformation, and the ultimate tensile strength σ_u is the highest engineering stress the material can withstand.

Ductility is the ability to resist deformation without fracture. In a tension test, this is characterized by the percent elongation at fracture, $100\varepsilon_f$, and by the percent reduction in area. Also, detailed analysis of test results can be done by using true stresses and strains, which consider the finite changes in gage length and cross-sectional area that may occur. Additional properties can then be obtained, notably, the strain hardening exponent n and the true fracture stress and strain, $\tilde{\sigma}_{fB}$ and $\tilde{\varepsilon}_f$.

If a material is tested under conditions where significant creep strain occurs during the tension test, then the results are sensitive to strain rate. At a given temperature, increasing the strain rate usually increases the strength, but decreases the ductility. Qualitatively similar effects occur for a given strain rate if the temperature is decreased. These effects are important for most engineering metals only at elevated temperature, but they are significant in many polymers at room temperature.

Compression tests can be used to measure similar properties as tension tests. These tests are especially valuable for materials used primarily in compression, such as concrete and building stone, and for other materials that behave in a brittle manner in tension, such as ceramics and glass. In these materials, the strength and ductility are generally greater in compression than in tension, sometimes dramatically so.

Hardness in engineering is usually measured by using one of several standard tests that measure resistance to indentation by a ball or sharp point. The Brinell test uses a 10 mm ball, and the Vickers test a pyramidal point. Both evaluate hardness as the average stress in kg/mm^2 on the surface area of the indentation. The values obtained are similar, but the Vickers test is useful for a wider range of materials. Rockwell hardness is based on the depth of indentation by a ball or conical diamond point. There are several Rockwell hardness scales to accommodate various materials.

Notch-impact tests evaluate the ability of a material to resist rapid loading where a sharp notch is present. The impact load is applied by a swinging pendulum or a falling weight. Details of specimen size and shape and the manner of loading differ for various standard tests, which include the Charpy, Izod, and dynamic tear tests.

Impact energies often exhibit a temperature transition, below which the behavior is brittle. Thus, impact energy versus temperature curves are useful in comparing the behavior of different materials. However, too much significance should not be attached to the exact position of the temperature transition, as this is sensitive to the details of the test and will not in general correspond to the engineering situation of interest.

Bending tests on unnotched bars are useful for evaluating the elastic modulus and strength of brittle materials. Since linear-elastic behavior is assumed in data analysis, strengths will differ from those in tension tests, if significant nonlinear stress–strain behavior occurs prior to fracture. A special bending test called the heat-deflection test is used to identify the limits of usefulness of polymers with respect to temperature. Torsion tests permit direct evaluation of the shear modulus, G, and also can be used to determine strength and ductility in shear. Thin-walled tubes tested in torsion have nearly constant stress and strain through the wall thickness, so such tests may be employed to obtain stress–strain curves in shear.

NEW TERMS AND SYMBOLS

bending (flexure) test

bend strength, σ_{fb}

Brinell hardness, HB

Charpy V-notch test

compression test

corrected true stress, $\tilde{\sigma}_B$

elastic limit

engineering strain, ε

engineering stress, σ

heat-deflection temperature

indentation hardness

Izod test

necking

notch-impact test

offset yield strength, σ_o

percent elongation, $100\varepsilon_f$

percent reduction in area, $\%RA$

proportional limit, σ_p

Rockwell hardness, HRC, etc.

strain hardening exponent, n

strength coefficient, H

tangent modulus, E_t

tensile toughness, u_f

torsion test

true fracture strain, $\tilde{\varepsilon}_f$

true fracture strength, $\tilde{\sigma}_f$, $\tilde{\sigma}_{fB}$

true strain, $\tilde{\varepsilon}$

true stress, $\tilde{\sigma}$

true toughness, $\tilde{u}_f$

ultimate tensile strength, σ_u

Vickers hardness, HV

yielding

REFERENCES

(a) General References

ASTM. 2010. *Annual Book of ASTM Standards*, ASTM International, West Conshohocken, PA. (Multiple volume set published annually.)

BARSOM, J. M., and S. T. ROLFE. 1999. *Fracture and Fatigue Control in Structures*, 3d ed., ASTM International, West Conshohocken, PA.

BRIDGMAN, P. W. 1952. *Studies in Large Plastic Flow and Fracture*, McGraw-Hill, New York.

DAVIS, J. R., ed. 1998. *Metals Handbook: Desk Edition*, 2d ed., ASM International, Materials Park, OH.

DIETER, G. E., Jr. 1986. *Mechanical Metallurgy*, 3d ed., McGraw-Hill, New York.

GAUTHIER, M. M., vol. chair. 1995. *Engineered Materials Handbook, Desk Edition*, ASM International, Materials Park, OH.

HILL, R. 1998. *The Mathematical Theory of Plasticity*, Oxford University Press, Oxford, UK.

KUHN, H., and D. MEDLIN, eds. 2000. *ASM Handbook: Vol. 8, Mechanical Testing and Evaluation*, ASM International, Materials Park, OH.

MARSHALL, E. R., and M. C. SHAW. 1952. "The Determination of Flow Stress From a Tensile Specimen," *Trans. of the Am. Soc. for Metals*, vol. 44, pp. 705–725.

NADAI, A. 1950. *Theory of Flow and Fracture of Solids*, 2nd ed., McGraw-Hill, New York.

RICHARDS, C. W. 1961. *Engineering Materials Science*, Wadsworth, Belmont, CA.

(b) Sources of Materials Properties and Databases

BAUCCIO, M. L., ed. 1993. *ASM Metals Reference Book*, 3d ed., ASM International, Materials Park, OH.

CES. 2009. *CES Selector 2009*, database of materials and processes, Granta Design Ltd, Cambridge, UK. (See *http://www.grantadesign.com.*)

CINDAS. 2010. *Aerospace Structural Metals Database (ASMD)*, CINDAS LLC, West Lafayette, IN. (See *https://cindasdata.com.*)

HOLT, J. M., H. MINDLIN, and C. Y. HO, eds. 1996. *Structural Alloys Handbook*, CINDAS LLC, West Lafayette, IN. (See *https://cindasdata.com.*)

MMPDS. 2010. *Metallic Materials Properties Development and Standardization Handbook*, MMPDS-05, U.S. Federal Aviation Administration; distributed by Battelle Memorial Institute, Columbus, OH. (See *http://projects.battelle.org/mmpds*; replaces MIL-HDBK-5.)

PROBLEMS AND QUESTIONS

Section 4.3[1]

4.1 Define the following concepts in your own words: (a) stiffness, (b) strength, (c) ductility, (d) yielding, (e) toughness, and (f) strain hardening.

4.2 Define the following adjectives that might be used to describe the behavior of a material: (a) brittle, (b) ductile, (c) tough, (d) stiff, and (e) strong.

4.3 The offset yield stress and the proportional limit stress are both used to characterize the beginning of nonlinear behavior in a tension test. Why is the offset method generally preferable? Can you think of any disadvantages of the offset method?

4.4 Force and length change data are given in Table P4.4 for the initial portion of a tension test on AISI 4140 steel tempered at 538°C (1000°F). The diameter before testing was 10 mm, and the gage length L_i for the length change measurement was 50 mm.

  (a) Calculate corresponding values of engineering stress and strain and display these values on a stress–strain plot. (Your graph should agree with Fig. P4.5.)

  (b) Determine the yield strength for a plastic strain offset of 0.002, that is, 0.2%.

  (c) What tensile load is required to cause yielding in a bar of the same material but with a diameter of 25 mm? How does this value compare with the load at yielding in the 10 mm diameter test specimen? Why do the two values differ?

---

[1]Numerical values given in tables are representative actual data from a large number of samples recorded in each test.

Table P4.4

Force P, kN	Length Change ΔL, mm	Force P, kN	Length Change ΔL, mm
0	0	67.16	0.3944
19.04	0.0794	67.75	0.6573
38.53	0.1600	68.63	1.0951
58.81	0.2505	69.43	1.5156
65.63	0.2815	70.02	1.9534
67.60	0.2952		

4.5   Stress–strain data are plotted in Fig. P4.5 for the initial portion of a tension test on AISI 4140 steel tempered at 538°C (1000°F). Note that data points A and B are labeled with their stress–strain coordinates.

    (a) Determine the elastic modulus E.

    (b) If a bar of this material 100 mm long is strained to point A and then unloaded, what is its length at point A and also after unloading?

    (c) If a sample of this material is strained to point B and then unloaded, what is the plastic (permanent) strain that remains after unloading?

    (d) Repeat (b) where the bar is instead loaded to point B and then unloaded.

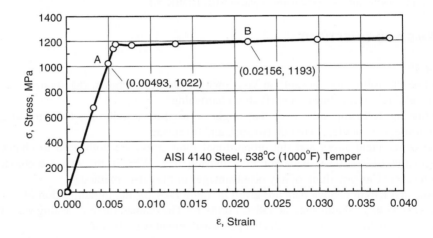

Figure P4.5

4.6   Engineering stress–strain data from a tension test on 6061-T6 aluminum are plotted in Fig. P4.6, and representative data points are listed in Table P4.6. Curve 1 shows the initial part of the data plotted at a sensitive strain scale, and Curve 2 shows all of the data to fracture. The diameter before testing was 10 mm, and after fracture the minimum diameter in the necked region was 8 mm. Determine the following: elastic modulus, 0.2% offset yield strength, ultimate tensile strength, percent elongation, and percent reduction in area.

Table P4.6

σ, MPa	ε, %	σ, MPa	ε, %
0	0	309	2.00
50	0.069	315	3.51
100	0.138	319	5.02
151	0.210	322	6.51
199	0.280	323	7.44
242	0.343	320	8.48
268	0.384	311	9.52
290	0.438	293	10.90
298	0.493	267	12.51
302	0.651	246	13.63
305	0.992	223	14.59

(Final point is fracture.)

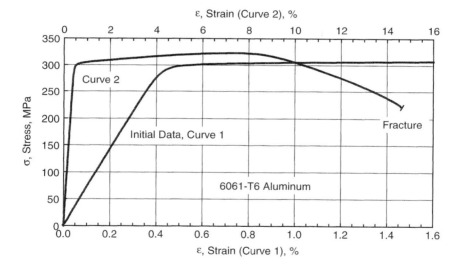

Figure P4.6

4.7 Engineering stress–strain data from a tension test on gray cast iron are given in Table P4.7. The diameter before testing was 10 mm, and after fracture it was 9.5 mm.

(a) Determine the following: tangent modulus, 0.2% offset yield strength, ultimate tensile strength, percent elongation, and percent reduction in area.

(b) How do these properties differ from the corresponding values for ductile cast iron in Table 4.2? Referring to Section 3.3, explain why these two cast irons have contrasting tensile behavior.

Table P4.7

σ, MPa	ε, %	σ, MPa	ε, %
0	0	182.4	0.402
19.45	0.0199	196.9	0.503
39.2	0.0443	208	0.601
60.0	0.0717	217	0.701
88.6	0.1168	224	0.804
110.1	0.1560	230	0.903
131.0	0.203	236	1.035
149.6	0.257	240	1.173
169.1	0.333		

(Final point is fracture.)

4.8   Engineering stress–strain data from a tension test on AISI 4140 steel tempered at 649°C (1200°F) are listed in Table P4.8. The diameter before testing was 10 mm, and after fracture the minimum diameter in the necked region was 6 mm. Determine the following: elastic modulus, 0.2% offset yield strength, ultimate tensile strength, percent elongation, and percent reduction in area.

Table P4.8

σ, MPa	ε, %	σ, MPa	ε, %
0	0	897	4.51
202	0.099	912	5.96
403	0.195	918	8.07
587	0.283	915	9.94
785	0.382	899	12.04
822	0.405	871	13.53
836	0.423	831	15.03
832	0.451	772	16.70
829	0.887	689	18.52
828	1.988	574	20.35
864	2.94		

(Final point is fracture.)

4.9   Engineering stress–strain data from a tension test on AISI 4140 steel tempered at 204°C (400°F) are listed in Table P4.9. The diameter before testing was 9.61 mm, and after fracture the minimum diameter in the necked region was 9 mm. Determine the following: elastic modulus, 0.2% offset yield strength, ultimate tensile strength, percent elongation, and percent reduction in area.

4.10 Engineering stress–strain data from a tension test on 7075-T651 aluminum are given in Table P4.10. The diameter before testing was 10 mm, and after fracture the minimum diameter in the necked region was 8 mm. Determine the following: elastic modulus, 0.2% offset yield strength, ultimate tensile strength, percent elongation, and percent reduction in area.

Table P4.9

σ, MPa	ε, %	σ, MPa	ε, %
0	0	1803	1.751
276	0.135	1889	2.24
553	0.276	1970	3.00
829	0.421	2013	3.76
1102	0.573	2037	4.50
1303	0.706	2047	5.24
1406	0.799	2039	5.99
1522	0.951	2006	6.73
1600	1.099	1958	7.46
1683	1.308	1893	8.22
1742	1.497		

(Final point is fracture.)

Table P4.10

σ, MPa	ε, %	σ, MPa	ε, %
0	0	557	1.819
112	0.165	563	2.30
222	0.322	577	4.02
326	0.474	587	5.98
415	0.605	593	8.02
473	0.703	596	9.52
505	0.797	597	10.97
527	0.953	597	12.50
542	1.209	591	13.90
551	1.498	571	15.33

(Final point is fracture.)

4.11 Engineering stress–strain data from a tension test on a near-γ titanium aluminide, Ti-48Al-2V-2Mn (atomic percentages), are given in Table P4.11. Determine the following: elastic modulus, 0.2% offset yield strength, ultimate tensile strength, percent elongation at fracture, and percent elongation after fracture. (Data courtesy of S. L. Kampe; see [Kampe 94].)

Table P4.11

σ, MPa	ε, %	σ, MPa	ε, %
0	0	431	0.607
85	0.060	446	0.717
169	0.119	457	0.825
254	0.181	467	0.932
313	0.236	478	1.080
355	0.303	483	1.125
383	0.373	482	1.313
412	0.493	480	1.45

(Final point is fracture.)

4.12 Engineering stress–strain data from a tension test on PVC polymer are plotted in Fig. P4.12 and listed in Table P4.12. Curve 1 shows the initial part of the data plotted at a sensitive strain scale, and Curve 2 shows all of the data until the extensometer had to be removed as the measurement was approaching its 50% strain capacity. The specimen had a rectangular cross section with original dimensions width 14.5 and thickness 4.02 mm. After fracture, these dimensions were width 9.5 and thickness 2.02 mm. Gage marks originally 50 mm apart had stretched to 82.5 mm after fracture, which occurred at a load of 1.319 kN. Determine the following: elastic modulus, yield strength, ultimate tensile strength, percent elongation, and percent reduction in area.

Table P4.12

σ, MPa	ε, %	σ, MPa	ε, %
0	0	50.4	6.14
11.57	0.328	44.9	8.92
19.94	0.582	39.5	11.84
28.2	0.880	37.7	13.48
39.5	1.365	35.9	16.11
51.1	2.10	35.0	19.19
54.7	2.57	34.8	24.7
55.6	2.87	33.4	36.4
55.9	3.21	32.4	48.0
55.5	3.61		

(Extensometer removed after final point.)

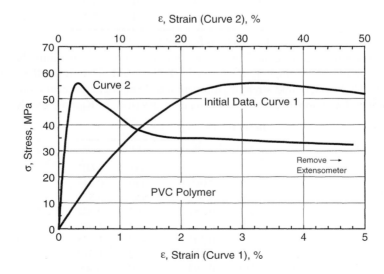

Figure P4.12

4.13 Engineering stress–strain data from a tension test on polycarbonate are given in Table P4.13. Data acquisition was terminated when the extensometer had to be removed as the measurement was approaching its 50% strain capacity. The specimen had a rectangular cross section with original dimensions width 14.5 and thickness 2.45 mm. After fracture, these dimensions were width 10.6 and thickness 1.4 mm. Gage marks originally 50 mm apart had stretched to 82.5 mm after fracture, which occurred at a force of 1.319 kN. Determine the following: elastic modulus, yield strength, ultimate tensile strength, percent elongation, and percent reduction in area.

Table P4.13

σ, MPa	ε, %	σ, MPa	ε, %
0	0	60.8	8.44
10.81	0.427	56.3	9.80
21.8	0.906	49.7	10.98
31.5	1.388	48.2	12.22
39.8	1.895	47.5	13.32
48.8	2.63	46.8	14.91
55.7	3.47	47.2	19.88
60.3	4.40	48.1	28.8
62.5	5.23	48.8	38.6
63.3	6.21	49.2	48.5
63.0	7.00		

(Extensometer removed after final point.)

4.14 Engineering stress–strain data from a tension test on PMMA polymer are given in Table P4.14. The specimen had a rectangular cross section with original dimensions width 12.61 and thickness 2.92 mm. After fracture, these dimensions were the same within the repeatability of the measurement. Determine the following: elastic modulus, yield strength, ultimate tensile strength, percent elongation, and percent reduction in area.

Table P4.14

σ, MPa	ε, %	σ, MPa	ε, %
0	0	49.5	1.729
9.00	0.241	53.7	1.960
17.20	0.490	57.7	2.23
24.8	0.733	60.6	2.46
32.3	0.995	63.3	2.75
38.7	1.239	64.9	2.95
44.6	1.487	66.3	3.19

(Final point is fracture.)

Section 4.4

4.15 Using Tables 3.10, 4.2, and 4.3, write a paragraph that discusses in general terms the differences among engineering metals, polymers, ceramics, and silica glasses as to their tensile strength, ductility, and stiffness.

4.16 Using the data for various steels in Tables 4.2 and 14.1, plot ultimate tensile strength versus percent reduction in area. Use linear coordinates. Also, use two different plotting symbols, one for the steels that are not strengthened by heat treating, which are 1020, 1015, Man-Ten, and 1045 (HR), and one for all of the others (which are strengthened by heat treatment). Then comment on any general trends that are apparent and any exceptions to these trends.

4.17 On the basis of the data for SiC reinforced aluminum in Table 4.4, write a paragraph discussing the effects of various types and orientations of reinforcement on the stiffness, strength, and ductility. Also, estimate the tensile toughness u_f for each case, and include this in your discussion.

Section 4.5[2]

4.18 Explain in your own words, without using equations, the difference between engineering stress and true stress and the difference between engineering strain and true strain.

4.19 Consider the tension test of Prob. 4.9 for AISI 4140 steel tempered at 204°C (400°F).

    (a) Calculate true stresses and strains for the data up to the ultimate tensile strength. Plot these values and compare the resulting true stress–strain curve with the engineering one from the original data.

    (b) For the points from (a) that are beyond yielding, calculate true *plastic* strains, and fit these with the true stresses to Eq. 4.23 to obtain values of H and n. Show data and fit on a log–log plot.

    (c) Calculate the true fracture strength and the true fracture strain, including the Bridgman correction for the former. Also calculate the true *plastic* strain at fracture, and add the corresponding point to your log–log plot from (b). If your fitted line is extended, is it consistent with the fracture point?

4.20 Consider the tension test of Prob. 4.6 for 6061-T6 aluminum. Analyze these data in terms of true stresses and strains by following the same procedure as in Prob. 4.19(a) and (b).

4.21 Consider the tension test of Prob. 4.10 for 7075-T651 aluminum. Analyze these data in terms of true stresses and strains by following the same procedure as in Prob. 4.19(a) and (b).

4.22 For a number of points during a tension test on Man-Ten steel, engineering stress and strain data are given in Table P4.22. Also given are minimum diameters measured in the necked region in the latter portions of the test. The initial diameter was 6.32 mm.

    (a) Evaluate the following engineering stress–strain properties: elastic modulus, yield strength, ultimate tensile strength, and percent reduction in area.

---

[2]Where fitting of Eq. 4.23 is requested, do not include data points with plastic strain values smaller than about 0.001, as needed to obtain a good linear trend on a log–log plot similar to Fig. 4.21.

(b) Determine true stresses and strains, and plot the true stress–strain curve, showing both raw and corrected values of true stress. Also evaluate the true fracture stress and strain.

(c) Calculate true plastic strains for the data beyond yielding to fracture. Then fit Eq. 4.24 to these values and the corresponding corrected stresses, determining H and n.

Table P4.22

Engr. Stress σ, MPa	Engr. Strain ε	Diameter d, mm
0	0	6.32
125	0.0006	—
257	0.0012	—
359	0.0017	—
317	0.0035	—
333	0.0070	—
357	0.0100	—
397	0.0170	—
458	0.0300	—
507	0.0500	—
541	0.0790	5.99
576	—	5.72
558	—	5.33
531	—	5.08
476	—	4.45
379	—	3.50

(Final point is fracture.)

4.23 Several values of the strength coefficient H are missing from Table 4.6. Estimate these values.

4.24 Assume that a material is quite ductile, so that elastic strains are small compared with plastic strains over most of the stress–strain curve. Plastic and total strains can then be taken as equivalent, $\tilde{\varepsilon}_p \approx \tilde{\varepsilon}$, and Eq. 4.23 becomes $\tilde{\sigma} = H \tilde{\varepsilon}^n$.

(a) Show that the strain hardening exponent n is then expected to be equal to the true strain $\tilde{\varepsilon}_u$ at the engineering ultimate strength point—that is, $n \approx \tilde{\varepsilon}_u$. (Suggestion: Start by making substitutions into $\tilde{\sigma} = H \tilde{\varepsilon}^n$ from Sections 4.5.1 and 4.5.2, to obtain an equation $\sigma = f(\tilde{\varepsilon}, H, n)$ that gives engineering stress.)

(b) How closely is this expectation realized for the tension test on AISI 1020 steel of Ex. 4.1, 4.2, and 4.3? (See Table E4.1 and Fig. 4.21.)

(c) From your derivation for (a), write an equation for estimating the ultimate tensile strength σ_u from H and n. How well does this estimate work for the AISI 1020 steel of Ex. 4.1, 4.2, and 4.3?

4.25 On the basis of the data in Tables 4.2 and 4.6 for 2024-T4 aluminum, draw the entire engineering stress–strain curve up to the point of fracture on linear graph paper. Accurately plot the initial elastic slope and the points corresponding to yield, ultimate, and fracture, and approximately sketch the remainder of the curve. How does your result compare with the curve for similar material in Fig. 4.15?

4.26 Proceed as in Prob. 4.25, except draw the true stress–strain curve, and also calculate several additional $(\tilde{\sigma}, \tilde{\varepsilon})$ points along the curve to aid in plotting.

Section 4.6

4.27 Engineering stress–strain data from a compression test on a cylinder of gray cast iron are given in Table P4.27. Strain measurements up to 4.5% are from an extensometer with a 12.70 mm gage length, and beyond this strains are approximated from crosshead displacements. The diameter before testing was 12.75 mm, and after fracture it was 14.68 mm. Also, the length before testing was 38.12 mm, and after fracture it was 33.20 mm. The fracture occurred on an inclined plane similar to the gray cast iron sample in Fig. 4.23.

   (a) Determine the following: elastic modulus, 0.2% offset yield strength, ultimate compressive strength, percent deformation at fracture, and percent change in area.

   (b) Compare the results of this test to the tension test on material from the same batch of cast iron in Prob. 4.7, in which the fracture occurred normal to the specimen axis. Explain why the fracture plane differs and why the strength and ductility differ.

Table P4.27

σ, MPa	ε, %	σ, MPa	ε, %
0	0	617	2.88
60.3	0.059	671	4.01
114.1	0.114	719	5.50
159.4	0.158	751	7.03
218	0.225	773	8.49
289	0.326	790	10.00
350	0.445	801	11.49
397	0.604	804	12.80
448	0.900	802	13.49
497	1.326	795	14.00
565	2.096		

(Final point is fracture)

4.28 How would you expect the stress–strain curves for concrete to differ between tension and compression? Give physical reasons for the expected differences.

4.29 Consider the data in Table 3.10 where strengths are given for both tension and compression for a number of glasses and ceramics. Plot the tensile strengths σ_{ut} versus the corresponding compressive strengths σ_{uc}. What general trend is seen in this comparison? Try to provide a physical explanation for this trend.

Section 4.7

4.30 Explain why the Brinell and Vickers hardness tests give generally similar results, as in Fig. 4.33.

4.31 Using the hardness conversion chart of Table 4.9, plot both Rockwell B and C hardness versus ultimate tensile strength for steel. Comment on the trends observed. Is the relationship approximately linear as for Brinell hardness?

4.32 Consider the typical hardness values for steels in Table 4.9.

    (a) Plot the ultimate tensile strength σ_u as a function of the Brinell hardness values HB. Show the estimate of Eq. 4.32 on the same graph, and comment on the success of this relationship for estimating σ_u from HB.

    (b) Develop an improved relationship for estimating σ_u from Brinell hardness.

    (c) Plot σ_u as a function of the Vickers hardness values HV, and develop a relationship for estimating σ_u from HV.

4.33 Vickers hardness and tensile data are listed in Table P4.33 for AISI 4140 steel that has been heat treated to various strength levels by varying the tempering temperature. Plot the hardness and the various tensile properties all as a function of tempering temperature. Then discuss the trends observed. How do the various tensile properties vary with hardness?

Table P4.33

Temper, °C	205	315	425	540	650
Hardness, HV	619	535	468	399	300
Ultimate, σ_u, MPa	2053	1789	1491	1216	963
Yield, σ_o, MPa	1583	1560	1399	1158	872
Red. in Area, $\%RA$	7	33	38	48	55

Section 4.8

4.34 Explain in your own words why notch-impact fracture tests are widely used, and why caution is needed in applying the results to real engineering situations.

Section 4.9

4.35 For both three-point bending and four-point bending, as illustrated in Fig. 4.40, look at the shear and moment diagrams of Figs. A.4 and A.5. Then use these diagrams to discuss the differences between the two types of test. Can you think of any relative advantages and disadvantages of the two types?

4.36 Equations 4.34 and 4.36 give values of fracture strength and elastic modulus from bending tests, but they apply only to the case of three-point bending. Derive analogous equations for the case of four-point bending with a rectangular cross section, as illustrated in Fig. 4.40(b).

4.37 The load-displacement record for a three-point bending test on alumina (Al_2O_3) ceramic is shown in Fig. P4.37. The final fracture occurred at a force of 192 N and a displacement of 0.091 mm. With reference to Fig. 4.40(a), the distance between supports was $L = 40$ mm, and the cross-sectional dimensions were width $t = 4.01$ mm and depth $2c = 3.01$ mm. Determine the bend strength σ_{fb} and the elastic modulus E. Note that the nonlinearity in the record just above zero should be ignored, as it includes displacement associated with developing full contact between the specimen and the loading fixtures.

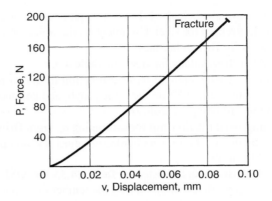

Figure P4.37

4.38 Bend strengths from Eq. 4.34 are given below for 100 three-point bending tests on alumina (Al_2O_3) ceramic. The specimens were approximately 3.12 mm square, and the distance between supports was 40.0 mm. These data are from tests conducted by students in a laboratory course during a three-year period from 2006 to 2009.

    (a) Using equations from Appendix B, calculate the sample mean, standard deviation, and coefficient of variation. Also plot a histogram analogous to Fig. B.1 of numbers of samples versus the bend strength.

    (b) Write a paragraph concisely discussing the statistical variation in these data. Does the variation seem relatively small or relatively large? What do you think are the major causes of the variation?

Table P4.38

σ_{fb}, Bend Strength, MPa									
443	358	328	398	438	457	345	475	445	387
437	446	389	373	459	422	383	409	442	521
477	437	454	422	472	385	368	391	449	527
433	324	302	406	335	415	364	398	445	473
416	386	405	397	410	424	417	471	442	348
524	437	392	471	425	428	429	463	454	379
360	477	426	458	452	362	417	426	458	387
419	329	451	376	441	355	447	431	369	359
464	350	426	426	435	429	442	505	443	403
333	431	404	382	426	457	425	449	471	404

Section 4.10

4.39 What characteristics are needed for the steel cable that supports and moves a ski lift? What materials tests would be important in judging the suitability of a given steel for this use?

4.40 You are an engineer designing pressure vessels to hold liquid nitrogen. What general characteristics should the material to be used have? Of the various types of materials tests described in this chapter, which would you employ to aid in selecting among candidate materials? Explain the reason you need each type of test chosen.

4.41 Answer the questions of Prob. 4.40, where you are instead designing plastic motorcycle helmets.

4.42 Answer the questions of Prob. 4.40, where you are designing the femoral stem part of a hip prosthesis. Note that the lower end of the stem projects into the bone, and the upper end holds the metal femoral head (ball).

5

Stress–Strain Relationships and Behavior

5.1 INTRODUCTION
5.2 MODELS FOR DEFORMATION BEHAVIOR
5.3 ELASTIC DEFORMATION
5.4 ANISOTROPIC MATERIALS
5.5 SUMMARY

OBJECTIVES

- Become familiar with the elastic, plastic, steady creep, and transient creep types of strain, as well as simple rheological models for representing the stress–strain–time behavior for each.
- Explore three-dimensional stress–strain relationships for linear-elastic deformation in isotropic materials, analyzing the interdependence of stresses or strains imposed in more than one direction.
- Extend the knowledge of elastic behavior to basic cases of anisotropy, including sheets of matrix-and-fiber composite material.

5.1 INTRODUCTION

The three major types of deformation that occur in engineering materials are elastic, plastic, and creep deformation. These have already been discussed in Chapter 2 from the viewpoint of physical mechanisms and general trends in behavior for metals, polymers, and ceramics. Recall that *elastic* deformation is associated with the stretching, but not breaking, of chemical bonds. In contrast, the two types of inelastic deformation involve processes where atoms change their relative positions, such as slip of crystal planes or sliding of chain molecules. If the inelastic deformation is time dependent, it is classed as *creep*, as distinguished from *plastic* deformation, which is not time dependent.

In engineering design and analysis, equations describing stress–strain behavior, called stress–strain relationships, or *constitutive equations*, are frequently needed. For example, in

190

elementary mechanics of materials, elastic behavior with a linear stress–strain relationship is assumed and used in calculating stresses and deflections in simple components such as beams and shafts. More complex situations of geometry and loading can be analyzed by employing the same basic assumptions in the form of *theory of elasticity*. This is now often accomplished by using the numerical technique called *finite element analysis* with a digital computer.

Stress–strain relationships need to consider behavior in three dimensions. In addition to elastic strains, the equations may also need to include plastic strains and creep strains. Treatment of creep strain requires the introduction of time as an additional variable. Regardless of the method used, analysis to determine stresses and deflections always requires appropriate stress–strain relationships for the particular material involved.

For calculations involving stress and strain, we express strain as a dimensionless quantity, as derived from length change, $\varepsilon = \Delta L / L$. Hence, strains given as percentages need to be converted to the dimensionless form, $\varepsilon = \varepsilon_\% / 100$, as do strains given as microstrain, $\varepsilon = \varepsilon_\mu / 10^6$.

In this chapter, we will first consider one-dimensional stress–strain behavior and some corresponding simple physical models for elastic, plastic, and creep deformation. The discussion of elastic deformation will then be extended to three dimensions, starting with *isotropic* behavior, where the elastic properties are the same in all directions. We will also consider simple cases of *anisotropy*, where the elastic properties vary with direction, as in composite materials. However, discussion of three-dimensional plastic and creep deformation behavior will be postponed to Chapters 12 and 15, respectively.

5.2 MODELS FOR DEFORMATION BEHAVIOR

Simple mechanical devices, such as linear springs, frictional sliders, and viscous dashpots, can be used as an aid to understanding the various types of deformation. Four such models and their responses to an applied force are illustrated in Fig. 5.1. Such devices and combinations of them are called *rheological models*.

Elastic deformation, Fig. 5.1(a), is similar to the behavior of a simple linear spring characterized by its constant k. The deformation is always proportional to the force, $x = P/k$, and it is recovered instantly upon unloading. Plastic deformation, Fig. 5.1(b), is similar to the movement of a block of mass m on a horizontal plane. The static and kinetic coefficients of friction μ are assumed to be equal, so that there is a critical force for motion $P_o = \mu m g$, where g is the acceleration of gravity. If a constant applied force P' is less than the critical value, $P' < P_o$, no motion occurs. However, if it is greater, $P' > P_o$, the block moves with an acceleration

$$a = \frac{P' - P_o}{m} \tag{5.1}$$

When the force is removed at time t, the block has moved a distance $x = at^2/2$, and it remains at this new location. Hence, the model behavior produces a permanent deformation, x_p.

Creep deformation can be subdivided into two types. *Steady-state creep*, Fig. 5.1(c), proceeds at a constant rate under constant force. Such behavior occurs in a linear dashpot, which is an element where the velocity, $\dot{x} = dx/dt$, is proportional to the force. The constant of proportionality is the

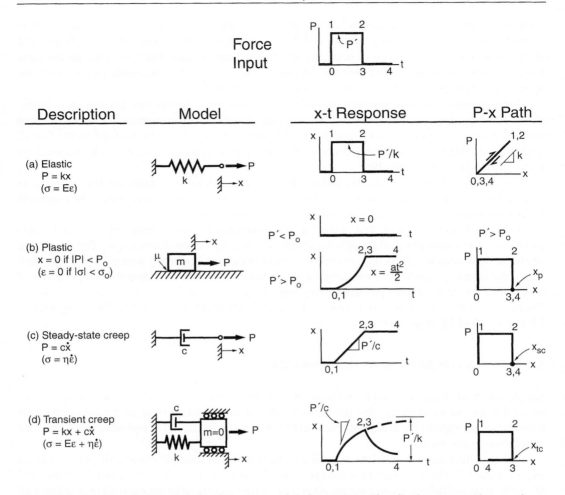

Figure 5.1 Mechanical models for four types of deformation. The displacement–time and force–displacement responses are also shown for step inputs of force P, which is analogous to stress σ. Displacement x is analogous to strain ε.

dashpot constant c, so that a constant value of force P' gives a constant velocity, $\dot{x} = P'/c$, resulting in a linear displacement versus time behavior. When the force is removed, the motion stops, so that the deformation is permanent—that is, not recovered. A dashpot could be physically constructed by placing a piston in a cylinder filled with a viscous liquid, such as a heavy oil. When a force is applied, small amounts of oil leak past the piston, allowing the piston to move. The velocity of motion will be approximately proportional to the magnitude of the force, and the displacement will remain after all force is removed.

The second type of creep, called *transient creep*, Fig. 5.1(d), slows down as time passes. Such behavior occurs in a spring mounted parallel to a dashpot. If a constant force P' is applied, the

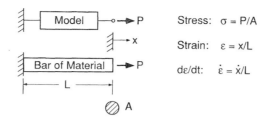

Figure 5.2   Relationship of models to stress, strain, and strain rate, in a bar of material.

deformation increases with time. But an increasing fraction of the applied force is needed to pull against the spring as x increases, so that less force is available to the dashpot, and the rate of deformation decreases. The deformation approaches the value P'/k if the force is maintained for a long period of time. If the applied force is removed, the spring, having been extended, now pulls against the dashpot. This results in all of the deformation being recovered at infinite time.

Rheological models may be used to represent stress and strain in a bar of material under axial loading, as shown in Fig. 5.2. The model constants are related to material constants that are independent of the bar length L or area A. For elastic deformation, the constant of proportionality between stress and strain is the *elastic modulus*, also called *Young's modulus*, given by

$$E = \frac{\sigma}{\varepsilon} \tag{5.2}$$

Substituting the definitions of stress and strain, and also employing $P = kx$, yields the relationship between E and k:

$$E = \frac{kL}{A} \tag{5.3}$$

For the plastic deformation model, the yield strength of the material is simply

$$\sigma_o = \frac{P_o}{A} \tag{5.4}$$

For the steady-state creep model, the material constant analogous to the dashpot constant c is called the *coefficient of tensile viscosity*[1] and is given by

$$\eta = \frac{\sigma}{\dot{\varepsilon}} \tag{5.5}$$

---

[1]In fluid mechanics, viscosities are defined in terms of shear stresses and strains, $\eta_\tau = \tau/\dot{\gamma}$, where $\eta = 3\eta_\tau$ relates values of tensile and shear viscosity for an ideal incompressible material.

where $\dot{\varepsilon} = d\varepsilon/dt$ is the strain rate. Substitution from Fig. 5.2 and $P = c\dot{x}$ yields the relationship between η and c:

$$\eta = \frac{cL}{A} \tag{5.6}$$

Equations 5.3 and 5.6 also apply to the spring and dashpot elements in the transient creep model.

Before proceeding to the detailed discussion of elastic deformation, it is useful to further discuss plastic and creep deformation models.

5.2.1 Plastic Deformation Models

As discussed in Chapter 2, the principal physical mechanism causing plastic deformation in metals and ceramics is sliding (slip) between planes of atoms in the crystal grains of the material, occurring in an incremental manner due to dislocation motion. The material's resistance to plastic deformation is roughly analogous to the friction of a block on a plane, as in the rheological model of Fig. 5.1(b).

For modeling stress–strain behavior, the block of mass m can be replaced by a massless frictional slider, which is similar to a spring clip, as shown in Fig. 5.3(a). Two additional models, which are combinations of linear springs and frictional sliders, are shown in (b) and (c). These give improved representation of the behavior of real materials, by including a spring in series with the slider, so that they exhibit elastic behavior prior to yielding at the slider yield strength σ_o. In addition, model (c) has a second linear spring connected parallel to the slider, so that its resistance increases as deformation proceeds. Model (a) is said to have rigid, perfectly plastic behavior; model (b) elastic, perfectly plastic behavior; and model (c) elastic, linear-hardening behavior.

Figure 5.3 gives each model's response to three different strain inputs. The first of these is simple *monotonic* straining—that is, straining in a single direction. For this situation, for models (a) and (b), the stress remains at σ_o beyond yielding.

For monotonic loading of model (c), the strain ε is the sum of strain ε_1 in spring E_1 and strain ε_2 in the (E_2, σ_o) parallel combination:

$$\varepsilon = \varepsilon_1 + \varepsilon_2, \qquad \varepsilon_1 = \frac{\sigma}{E_1} \tag{5.7}$$

The vertical bar is assumed not to rotate, so that both spring E_2 and slider σ_o have the same strain. Prior to yielding, the slider prevents motion, so that strain ε_2 is zero:

$$\varepsilon_2 = 0, \qquad \varepsilon = \frac{\sigma}{E_1} \qquad (\sigma \le \sigma_o) \tag{5.8}$$

Since there is no deflection in spring E_2, its stress is zero, and all of the stress is carried by the slider. Beyond yielding, the slider has a constant stress σ_o, so that the stress in spring E_2 is $(\sigma - \sigma_o)$. Hence, the strain ε_2 and the overall strain ε are

$$\varepsilon_2 = \frac{\sigma - \sigma_o}{E_2}, \qquad \varepsilon = \frac{\sigma}{E_1} + \frac{\sigma - \sigma_o}{E_2} \qquad (\sigma \ge \sigma_o) \tag{5.9}$$

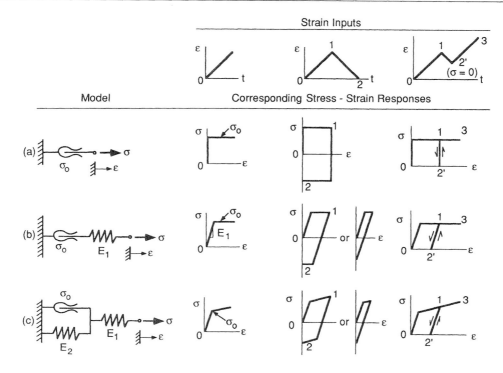

Figure 5.3 Rheological models for plastic deformation and their responses to three different strain inputs. Model (a) has behavior that is rigid, perfectly plastic; (b) elastic, perfectly plastic; and (c) elastic, linear hardening.

From the second equation, the slope of the stress–strain curve is seen to be

$$\frac{d\sigma}{d\varepsilon} = E_e = \frac{E_1 E_2}{E_1 + E_2} \tag{5.10}$$

which is the equivalent stiffness E_e, lower than both E_1 and E_2, corresponding to E_1 and E_2 in series.

Figure 5.3 also gives the model responses where strain is increased beyond yielding and then decreased to zero. In all three cases, there is no additional motion in the slider until the stress has changed by an amount $2\sigma_o$ in the negative direction. For models (b) and (c), this gives an elastic unloading of the same slope E_1 as the initial loading. Consider the point during unloading where the stress passes through zero, as shown in Fig. 5.4 (a) or (b). The elastic strain, ε_e, that is recovered corresponds to the relaxation of spring E_1. The permanent or plastic strain ε_p corresponds to the motion of the slider up to the point of maximum strain. Real materials generally have nonlinear hardening stress–strain curves as in (c), but with elastic unloading behavior similar to that of the rheological models.

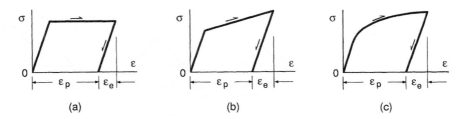

Figure 5.4 Loading and unloading behavior of (a) an elastic, perfectly plastic model, (b) an elastic, linear-hardening model, and (c) a material with nonlinear hardening.

Now consider the response of each model to the situation of the last column in Fig. 5.3, where the model is reloaded after elastic unloading to $\sigma = 0$. In all cases, yielding occurs a second time when the strain again reaches the value ε_1 from which unloading occurred. It is obvious that the two perfectly plastic models will again yield at $\sigma = \sigma_o$. But the linear-hardening model now yields at a value $\sigma = \sigma_1$, which is higher than the initial yield stress. Furthermore, σ_1 is the same value of stress that was present at $\varepsilon = \varepsilon_1$, when the unloading first began. For all three models, the interpretation may be made that the model possesses a *memory* of the point of previous unloading. In particular, yielding again occurs at the same σ-ε point from which unloading occurred, and the subsequent response is the same as if there had never been any unloading. Real materials that deform plastically exhibit a similar memory effect.

We will return to spring and slider models of plastic deformation in Chapter 12, where they will be considered in more detail and extended to nonlinear hardening cases.

5.2.2 Creep Deformation Models

Significant time-dependent deformation occurs in engineering metals and ceramics at elevated temperature. This also occurs at room temperature in low-melting-temperature metals, such as lead, and in many other materials, such as glass, polymers, and concrete. A variety of physical mechanisms are involved, as discussed to an extent in Chapter 2 and considered again in Chapter 15.

The creep models of Fig. 5.1(c) and (d) are shown in Fig. 5.5, with springs E_1 added to simulate elastic strain, as in real materials. Note that in (b) the vertical bar is assumed not to rotate, so that the parallel spring and dashpot are subjected to the same strain. Also, these models are expressed in terms of stress and strain, so that springs deform according to $\varepsilon = \sigma/E$ and dashpots according to $\dot{\varepsilon} = \sigma/\eta$. If a constant stress σ' is applied to either model, an elastic strain $\varepsilon_e = \sigma'/E_1$ appears instantly (0–1) and then later disappears (2–3) when the stress is removed.

The use of constant viscosities η in these models results in all strain rates and strains being proportional to the applied stress, a situation described by the term *linear viscoelasticity*. Such idealized linear behavior is sometimes a reasonable approximation for real materials, as for some polymers, and also for metals and ceramics at high temperature, but low stress. However, for metals and ceramics at high stress, strain rate is proportional not to the first power of stress, but to a higher power on the order of five. In such cases, models or equations involving more complex

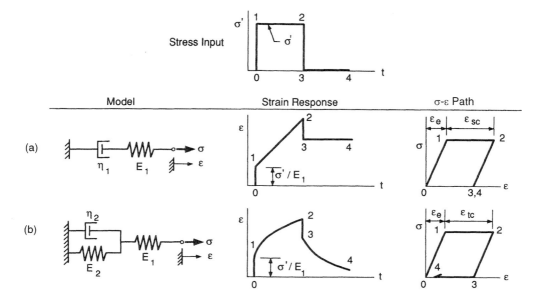

Figure 5.5 Rheological models having time-dependent behavior and their responses to a stress–time step. Both strain–time and stress–strain responses are shown. Model (a) exhibits steady-state creep with elastic strain added, and model (b) transient creep with elastic strain added.

stress dependence can be used, as described later in Chapter 15. However, the simple linear models will suffice here to illustrate some of the gross features of creep behavior.

For the model of Fig. 5.5(a), the response during 1–2 is given by adding the elastic and creep components of the strain:

$$\varepsilon = \varepsilon_e + \varepsilon_c = \frac{\sigma'}{E_1} + \varepsilon_c \tag{5.11}$$

The rate of creep strain is related to the stress by the dashpot constant:

$$\dot{\varepsilon}_c = \frac{d\varepsilon_c}{dt} = \frac{\sigma'}{\eta_1} \tag{5.12}$$

This represents a very simple differential equation that can be solved for ε_c by integration, and combined with Eq. 5.11 to give the strain–time response:

$$\varepsilon = \frac{\sigma'}{E_1} + \frac{\sigma't}{\eta_1} \tag{5.13}$$

This is the equation of the linear ε-t response during 1–2 as shown in Fig. 5.5(a). After removal of the stress, the elastic strain disappears, but the creep strain accumulated during 1–2 remains as a permanent strain.

In the transient creep model of Fig. 5.5(b), while the stress is applied during 1–2, the elastic strain in spring E_1 is added to the creep strain in the (η_2, E_2) parallel combination. Hence, Eq. 5.11 again applies. The creep strain can be analyzed by noting that the stress in the (η_2, E_2) stage is the sum of the separate stresses in the spring and the dashpot:

$$\sigma = E_2 \varepsilon_c + \eta_2 \dot{\varepsilon}_c \tag{5.14}$$

This gives

$$\dot{\varepsilon}_c = \frac{d\varepsilon_c}{dt} = \frac{\sigma - E_2 \varepsilon_c}{\eta_2} \tag{5.15}$$

Solving this differential equation for the case of a constant stress σ' gives the creep strain versus time response:

$$\varepsilon_c = \frac{\sigma'}{E_2}\left(1 - e^{-E_2 t/\eta_2}\right) \tag{5.16}$$

Finally, adding the elastic strain gives the total strain:

$$\varepsilon = \frac{\sigma'}{E_1} + \frac{\sigma'}{E_2}\left(1 - e^{-E_2 t/\eta_2}\right) \tag{5.17}$$

Study of this equation shows that the strain rate decreases with time, as shown in Fig. 5.5(b). Moreover, the creep strain asymptotically approaches the limit σ'/E_2. This occurs as a result of stress being transferred from the dashpot to the spring as time passes, until the spring must resist all of the stress at infinite time.

After removal of the stress, the strain in the transient creep model varies as shown by 3–4 in Fig. 5.5(b). In particular, it decreases toward zero at infinite time due to the spring in the parallel arrangement pulling on the dashpot. Equations for this *recovery* response may also be obtained by solving the differential equations involved.

5.2.3 Relaxation Behavior

So far, we have considered two types of time-dependent behavior. These are *creep*, which is the accumulation of strain with time, as under constant stress, and *recovery*, which is the gradual disappearance of creep strain that sometimes occurs after removal of the stress. A third type of behavior is *relaxation*, which is the decrease in stress when a material is held at constant strain.

Relaxation is illustrated for the steady-state creep plus elastic strain model in Fig. 5.6. Since the strain ε' is suddenly applied, all of this strain is absorbed by the spring as a result of the fact that the dashpot requires a finite time to respond. With time, motion occurs in the dashpot, and the strain in the spring decreases, as it must, due to the total strain being held constant. We have

$$\varepsilon' = \varepsilon_e + \varepsilon_c \tag{5.18}$$

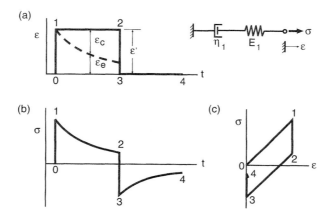

Figure 5.6 Relaxation under constant strain for a model with steady-state creep and elastic behavior. The step in strain (a) causes stress–time behavior as in (b), and stress–strain behavior as in (c).

where ε' is the constant total strain and ε_c is the creep strain. Hence, elastic strain is being replaced by creep strain.

The stress necessary to maintain the constant strain is related to the elastic strain by

$$\sigma = E_1\varepsilon_e \tag{5.19}$$

Since ε_e is decreasing, this requires that σ must also decrease. The rate of creep strain is related to the value of σ at any time by

$$\dot{\varepsilon}_c = \frac{d\varepsilon_c}{dt} = \frac{\sigma}{\eta_1} \tag{5.20}$$

Combining these equations and solving the resulting differential equation gives the variation of σ as it decreases:

$$\sigma = E_1\varepsilon'e^{-E_1 t/\eta_1} \tag{5.21}$$

This corresponds to a σ-t response that decays—that is, relaxes—with time, as illustrated by curve 1–2 in Fig. 5.6(b).

Relaxation is the same phenomenon as creep, differing only in that it is observed under constant strain rather than constant stress. Real engineering materials that exhibit creep will also show relaxation behavior.

In Fig. 5.6, if the strain is returned to zero after a period of relaxation, the stress is forced into compression. Additional relaxation then occurs, but in the opposite direction, as the relaxation always proceeds toward zero stress.

Creep and relaxation, and models of the types just discussed, are considered in more detail in Chapter 15.

Example 5.1 _____

Derive Eq. 5.21, which describes stress relaxation in the elastic, steady-state creep model, as illustrated by 1–2 in Fig. 5.6(b). Base this on the other equations given just prior to Eq. 5.21.

Solution   Differentiate both sides of Eqs. 5.18 and 5.19 with respect to time, noting that $d\varepsilon'/dt = 0$ as ε' is held constant:

$$0 = \dot{\varepsilon}_e + \dot{\varepsilon}_c, \qquad \frac{d\sigma}{dt} = \dot{\sigma} = E_1\dot{\varepsilon}_e$$

Substitute $\dot{\varepsilon}_e$ from the second equation, and also $\dot{\varepsilon}_c$ from Eq. 5.20, into the first equation to obtain

$$\frac{1}{E_1}\frac{d\sigma}{dt} + \frac{\sigma}{\eta_1} = 0$$

Separate the variables σ and t and integrate both sides of the equation, resulting in

$$\ln\sigma = -\frac{E_1}{\eta_1}t + C$$

where C is a constant of integration that can be evaluated by noting that the creep strain is initially zero, so that $\sigma = E_1\varepsilon'$ at $t = 0$. This gives $C = \ln E_1\varepsilon'$. Substituting for C and solving for σ then produces the desired result:

$$\sigma = E_1\varepsilon' e^{-E_1 t/\eta_1} \qquad\qquad \textbf{Ans.}$$

5.2.4 Discussion

We have discussed models of three major types of deformation, namely, elastic, plastic, and creep deformation. These are characterized in Table 5.1. Elastic strain is the result of stretching of chemical bonds. It is not considered to be time dependent and is recovered immediately on unloading. Plastic strain is also not considered to be dependent on time and is permanent, due to its being caused by the relative sliding of crystal planes through the incremental process of dislocation motion. Note that perfectly plastic behavior, as in the models of Fig. 5.3(a) and (b), will result in unstable rapid deformation if a stress above σ_o is maintained. However, some degree of strain hardening usually occurs in real materials.

Creep strain may be divided into steady-state and transient types, according to whether the rate is constant or decreases with time. In the ideal model of Fig. 5.5(b), all transient strain is recovered. However, a portion of this may be permanent in real materials. The recovered portion of the creep strain may be quite large in polymers due to chain molecules interfering with one another in such a way that they slowly reestablish their original configuration after removal of the stress, causing the strain to slowly disappear. For example, creep strains as large as 100% in flexible vinyl (plasticized PVC) may be mostly recovered after unloading. In metals and ceramics, large creep strains can

Table 5.1   Characteristics of the Various Types of Deformation

Type of Deformation	Time Dependent?	Additional Distinguishing Characteristics
Elastic	No	Recovered instantly
Plastic	No	Not recovered
Steady-state creep	Yes	Constant rate; not recovered
Transient creep	Yes	Decreasing rate; may be recovered

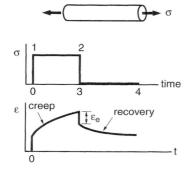 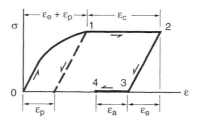

Figure 5.7   Stress–time step applied to a material exhibiting strain response that includes elastic, plastic, and creep components.

occur above about $0.5T_m$, due to motion of lattice vacancies or dislocations, grain boundary sliding, etc. Relatively little recovery occurs for such strains.

Creep strain that is recovered is often termed *anelastic strain*, which distinction is useful for real materials where only a portion of the transient strain is recovered. Recovery should not be confused with relaxation, as in Fig. 5.6, which is the result of creep deformation while the strain is held constant.

Deformation in real materials may be dominated by one type of strain, or more than one type may occur, depending on the material, temperature, loading rate, and stress level. For a case where all four types from Table 5.1 occur, the behavior for a suddenly applied and then constant stress would be similar to Fig. 5.7. The instantaneous deformation that occurs is a combination of elastic and plastic strain. The plastic portion ε_p could be isolated by immediate unloading, as illustrated by the dashed line. If the stress is instead maintained, creep deformation ε_c may occur that is a combination of the transient and steady-state types.

Removal of the stress causes the elastic strain ε_e to be instantly recovered. Some of the creep strain may be recovered after a period of time, as indicated by 3–4. This recovered or anelastic portion is labeled ε_a in Fig. 5.7.

5.3 ELASTIC DEFORMATION

From the discussion in Chapter 2, elastic deformation is associated with stretching the bonds between the atoms in a solid. As a result, the value of the elastic modulus, E, is quite high for

Table 5.2 Elastic Constants for Various Materials at Ambient Temperature

Material	Elastic Modulus E, GPa (10^3 ksi)		Poisson's Ratio ν
(a) Metals			
Aluminum	70.3	(10.2)	0.345
Brass, 70Cu-30Zn	101	(14.6)	0.350
Copper	130	(18.8)	0.343
Iron; mild steel	212	(30.7)	0.293
Lead	16.1	(2.34)	0.44
Magnesium	44.7	(6.48)	0.291
Stainless steel, 2Ni-18Cr	215	(31.2)	0.283
Titanium	120	(17.4)	0.361
Tungsten	411	(59.6)	0.280
(b) Polymers			
ABS, medium impact	2.4	(0.35)	0.35
Acrylic, PMMA	2.7	(0.40)	0.35
Epoxy	3.5	(0.51)	0.33
Nylon 66, dry	2.7	(0.39)	0.41
Nylon 66, 33% glass fibers	9.5	(1.38)	0.39
Polycarbonate	2.4	(0.345)	0.38
Polyethylene, HDPE	1.08	(0.157)	0.42
(c) Ceramics and glasses			
Alumina, Al_2O_3	400	(58.0)	0.22
Diamond	960	(139)	0.20
Magnesia, MgO	300	(43.5)	0.18
Silicon carbide, SiC	396	(57.4)	0.22
Fused silica glass	70	(10.2)	0.18
Soda-lime glass	69	(10.0)	0.20
Type E glass	72.4	(10.5)	0.22
Dolomitic limestone	69.0	(10.0)	0.281
Westerly granite	49.6	(7.20)	0.213

Sources: Data in [Boyer 85] p. 216, [Creyke 82] p. 222, [Kaplan 95] pp. B-146 to B-206, [Karfakis 90], [Kelly 86] pp. 376, 392, [Kelly 94] p. 285, [Morrell 85] Pt. 1, p. 96, [PDL 91] Vol. I-B, pp. 133–136, and [Schwartz 92] p. 2.75.

strongly bound covalent solids. Metals have intermediate values, and polymers generally have low values due to the effect of secondary bonds between chain molecules. Some representative values for various materials are given in Table 5.2.

5.3.1 Elastic Constants

A material that has the same properties at all points within the solid is said to be *homogeneous*, and if the properties are the same in all directions, the material is *isotropic*. When viewed at macroscopic

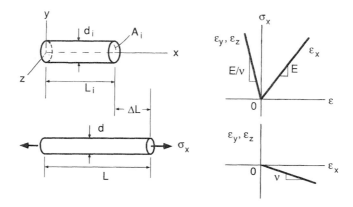

Figure 5.8 Longitudinal extension and lateral contraction used to obtain constants for a linear-elastic material that is isotropic and homogeneous.

size scales, real materials obey these idealizations if they are composed of tiny, randomly oriented crystal grains. This is at least approximately true for many metals and ceramics. Amorphous materials, such as glass and some polymers, may also be approximately isotropic and homogeneous. Hence, for the present, we will proceed with these simplifying assumptions.

Let a bar of a homogeneous and isotropic material be subjected to an axial stress σ_x, as in Fig. 5.8. The strain in the direction of the stress is

$$\varepsilon_x = \frac{L - L_i}{L_i} = \frac{\Delta L}{L_i} \tag{5.22}$$

where L is the deformed length, L_i the initial length, and ΔL the change. In a similar manner, we obtain the strain in any direction perpendicular to the stress—that is, along any diameter of the bar:

$$\varepsilon_y = \varepsilon_z = \frac{d - d_i}{d_i} = \frac{\Delta d}{d_i} \tag{5.23}$$

This transverse strain is negative for tensile σ_x, as the bar becomes thinner when stretched in the length direction. Conversely, ε_y is positive for compressive σ_x.

The material is said to be *linear elastic* if the stress is linearly related to these strains, and if the strains return immediately to zero after unloading, in the manner of a simple linear spring. In this situation, two elastic constants are needed to characterize the material. One is the *elastic modulus*, $E = \sigma_x/\varepsilon_x$, which is the slope of the σ_x versus ε_x line in Fig. 5.8. The second constant is *Poisson's ratio*,

$$\nu = -\frac{\text{transverse strain}}{\text{longitudinal strain}} = -\frac{\varepsilon_y}{\varepsilon_x} \tag{5.24}$$

Since ε_y is of opposite sign to ε_x, positive ν is obtained. Hence, as also shown, the slope of a plot of ε_y versus ε_x is $-\nu$. Substituting ε_x from Eq. 5.24 into $E = \sigma_x/\varepsilon_x$ gives

$$\varepsilon_y = -\frac{\nu}{E}\sigma_x \tag{5.25}$$

This linear relationship is also shown in Fig. 5.8. The same situation also occurs along any other diameter, such as the z-direction.

5.3.2 Discussion

Values of the elastic modulus vary widely for different materials. Poisson's ratio is often around 0.3 and does not vary outside the range 0 to 0.5, except under very unusual circumstances. Note that negative values of ν imply lateral expansion during axial tension, which is unlikely. As will be seen subsequently, $\nu = 0.5$ implies constant volume, and values larger than 0.5 imply a decrease in volume for tensile loading, which is also unlikely. Values of ν for various materials are included in Table 5.2.

It should be noted that no material has perfectly linear or perfectly elastic behavior. Use of elastic constants such as E and ν should therefore be regarded as a useful approximation, or model, that often gives reasonably accurate answers. For example, most engineering metals can be modeled in this way at relatively low stresses below the yield strength, beyond which the behavior becomes nonlinear and inelastic. Also, original dimensions and cross-sectional areas are used in the present discussion to determine stresses and strains. Such an approach is appropriate for many situations of practical engineering interest, where dimensional changes are small. Except where otherwise indicated, this assumption, called *small-strain theory*, will be used.

If a given metal is alloyed (melted together) with relatively small percentages of one or more other metals, the effect on the elastic constants E and ν is small. Hence, where specific values of these elastic constants are not available for a given alloy, they can be approximated as being the same as the corresponding pure metal values, as from Table 5.2. For example, this applies for all common aluminum alloys and titanium alloys, where the total alloying is in most cases less than 10%. But a contrary example is 70Cu-30Zn brass, where the 30% zinc causes the values to differ significantly from those for pure copper. For low-alloy steels, which are iron with total alloying less than 5%, the values are close to those for pure iron. However, for some high-alloy steels, such as stainless steels, which contain at least 12% chromium and also other alloying, the values may be affected to a modest degree. Materials handbooks, such as those listed in the references for Chapters 3 and 4, can be consulted to obtain E and ν for specific alloys. For polymers and ceramics, there may be significant batch-to-batch variation in the elastic constants, as the values are affected by processing.

5.3.3 Hooke's Law for Three Dimensions

Consider the general state of stress at a point, as illustrated in Fig. 5.9. A complete description consists of normal stresses in three directions, σ_x, σ_y, and σ_z, and shear stresses on three planes, τ_{xy}, τ_{yz}, and τ_{zx}. Considering normal stresses first, and assuming that small-strain theory applies, the strains caused by each component of stress can simply be added together. A stress in the x-direction causes a strain in the x-direction of σ_x/E. This σ_x also causes a strain in the y-direction, from Eq. 5.25, of $-\nu\sigma_x/E$, and the same strain in the z-direction. Similarly, normal stresses in the y- and z-directions each cause strains in all three directions.

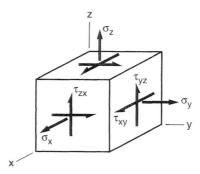

Figure 5.9   The six components needed to completely describe the state of stress at a point.

The situation can be summarized by the following table:

	Resulting Strain Each Direction		
Stress	x	y	z
σ_x	$\dfrac{\sigma_x}{E}$	$-\dfrac{\nu\sigma_x}{E}$	$-\dfrac{\nu\sigma_x}{E}$
σ_y	$-\dfrac{\nu\sigma_y}{E}$	$\dfrac{\sigma_y}{E}$	$-\dfrac{\nu\sigma_y}{E}$
σ_z	$-\dfrac{\nu\sigma_z}{E}$	$-\dfrac{\nu\sigma_z}{E}$	$\dfrac{\sigma_z}{E}$

Adding the columns in this table to obtain the total strain in each direction gives the following equations:

$$\varepsilon_x = \frac{1}{E}\left[\sigma_x - \nu\left(\sigma_y + \sigma_z\right)\right] \qquad \text{(a)}$$

$$\varepsilon_y = \frac{1}{E}\left[\sigma_y - \nu\left(\sigma_x + \sigma_z\right)\right] \qquad \text{(b)} \qquad\qquad (5.26)$$

$$\varepsilon_z = \frac{1}{E}\left[\sigma_z - \nu\left(\sigma_x + \sigma_y\right)\right] \qquad \text{(c)}$$

The shear strains that occur on the orthogonal planes are each related to the corresponding shear stress by a constant called the *shear modulus*, G:

$$\gamma_{xy} = \frac{\tau_{xy}}{G}, \qquad \gamma_{yz} = \frac{\tau_{yz}}{G}, \qquad \gamma_{zx} = \frac{\tau_{zx}}{G} \qquad\qquad (5.27)$$

Note that the shear strain on a given plane is unaffected by the shear stresses on other planes. Hence, for shear strains, there is no effect analogous to Poisson contraction. Equations 5.26 and 5.27, taken together, are often called the *generalized Hooke's law*.

Only two independent elastic constants are needed for an isotropic material, so that one of E, G, and v can be considered redundant. The following equation allows any one of these to be calculated from the other two:

$$G = \frac{E}{2\,(1+v)} \tag{5.28}$$

This equation can be derived by considering a state of pure shear stress, as in a round bar under torsion in Fig. 4.41. Recall from elementary mechanics of materials that the state of shear stress, τ, can be equivalently represented by principal normal stresses on planes rotated 45° with respect to the planes of pure shear. Similarly, the shear strain is equivalent to normal strains as shown in Fig. 4.41, also on 45° planes. Let the (x, y, z) directions for Eq. 5.26 correspond to the principal $(1, 2, 3)$ directions. The following substitutions can then be made in Eq. 5.26(a):

$$\sigma_x = \tau, \qquad \sigma_y = -\tau, \qquad \sigma_z = 0, \qquad \varepsilon_x = \frac{\gamma}{2} \tag{5.29}$$

This yields

$$\gamma = \frac{2\,(1+v)}{E}\tau \tag{5.30}$$

From the definition of G, the constant of proportionality is $G = \tau/\gamma$, so that Eq. 5.28 is confirmed.

Measured values of the three constants E, G, and v for real materials will not generally obey Eq. 5.28 perfectly. This situation is mainly due to the material not being perfectly isotropic.

Example 5.2

A cylindrical pressure vessel 10 m long has closed ends, a wall thickness of 5 mm, and an inner diameter of 3 m. If the vessel is filled with air to a pressure of 2 MPa, how much do the length, diameter, and wall thickness change, and in each case is the change an increase or a decrease? The vessel is made of a steel having elastic modulus $E = 200{,}000$ MPa and Poisson's ratio $v = 0.3$. Neglect any effects associated with the details of how the ends are attached.

Solution   Attach a coordinate system to the surface of the pressure vessel, as shown in Fig. E5.2, such that the z-axis is normal to the surface.

The ratio of radius to thickness, r/t, is such that it is reasonable to employ the thin-walled tube assumption and the resulting stress equations, given in Fig. A.7(a) in Appendix A. Denoting the pressure as p, we have

$$\sigma_x = \frac{pr}{2t} = \frac{(2\text{ MPa})\,(1500\text{ mm})}{2\,(5\text{ mm})} = 300\text{ MPa}$$

$$\sigma_y = \frac{pr}{t} = \frac{(2\text{ MPa})\,(1500\text{ mm})}{5\text{ mm}} = 600\text{ MPa}$$

The value of σ_z varies from $-p$ on the inside wall to zero on the outside, so its value for the present case is everywhere sufficiently small that $\sigma_z \approx 0$ can be used. Substitute these stresses and the known E and v into Hooke's law, Eq. 5.26, which gives

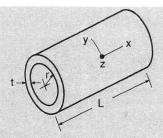

Figure E5.2

$$\varepsilon_x = 600 \times 10^{-6}, \qquad \varepsilon_y = 2550 \times 10^{-6}, \qquad \varepsilon_z = -1350 \times 10^{-6}$$

These strains are related to the changes in length ΔL, circumference $\Delta(\pi d)$, diameter Δd, and thickness Δt, as follows:

$$\varepsilon_x = \frac{\Delta L}{L}, \qquad \varepsilon_y = \frac{\Delta(\pi d)}{\pi d} = \frac{\Delta d}{d}, \qquad \varepsilon_z = \frac{\Delta t}{t}$$

Substituting the strains and the known dimensions gives

$$\Delta L = 6.00 \,\text{mm}, \qquad \Delta d = 7.65 \,\text{mm}, \qquad \Delta t = -6.75 \times 10^{-3} \,\text{mm} \qquad \textbf{Ans.}$$

Thus, there are small increases in length and diameter, and a tiny decrease in the wall thickness.

Example 5.3

A sample of material subjected to a compressive stress σ_z is confined so that it cannot deform in the y-direction, as shown in Fig. E5.3. Assume that there is no friction against the die, so that deformation can freely occur in the x-direction. Assume further that the material is isotropic and exhibits linear-elastic behavior.

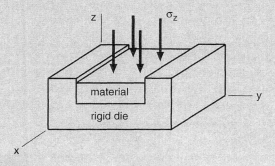

Figure E5.3

Determine the following in terms of σ_z and the elastic constants of the material:

(a) The stress that develops in the y-direction.
(b) The strain in the z-direction.
(c) The strain in the x-direction.
(d) The stiffness $E' = \sigma_z / \varepsilon_z$ in the z-direction. Is this apparent modulus equal to the elastic modulus E from a uniaxial test on the material? Why or why not?
(e) Assume that the compressive stress in the z-direction has a magnitude of 75 MPa and that the block is made of a copper alloy, and then calculate σ_y, ε_z, ε_x, and E'.

Solution   Hooke's law for the three-dimensional case, Eq. 5.26, is needed. The situation posed requires substituting $\varepsilon_y = 0$ and $\sigma_x = 0$, and also treating σ_z as a known quantity.

(a) The stress in the y-direction is obtained from Eq. 5.26(b):

$$0 = \frac{1}{E}\left[\sigma_y - \nu\left(0 + \sigma_z\right)\right], \qquad \sigma_y = \nu\sigma_z \qquad \textbf{Ans.}$$

(b) The strain in the z-direction is given by substituting this σ_y into Eq. 5.26(c):

$$\varepsilon_z = \frac{1}{E}\left[\sigma_z - \nu\left(0 + \nu\sigma_z\right)\right], \qquad \varepsilon_z = \frac{1 - \nu^2}{E}\sigma_z \qquad \textbf{Ans.}$$

(c) The strain in the x-direction is given by Eq. 5.26(a) with σ_y from part (a) substituted:

$$\varepsilon_x = \frac{1}{E}\left[0 - \nu\left(\nu\sigma_z + \sigma_z\right)\right], \qquad \varepsilon_x = -\frac{\nu\left(1 + \nu\right)}{E}\sigma_z \qquad \textbf{Ans.}$$

(d) The apparent stiffness in the z-direction is obtained immediately from the equation for ε_z:

$$E' = \frac{\sigma_z}{\varepsilon_z} = \frac{E}{1 - \nu^2} \qquad \textbf{Ans.}$$

(e) For the copper alloy, Table 5.2 provides constants, $E = 130\text{ GPa} = 130{,}000\text{ MPa}$, and $\nu = 0.343$. The compressive stress requires that a negative sign be applied, so that $\sigma_z = -75\text{ MPa}$. Substituting these quantities into the equations previously derived gives

$$\sigma_y = \nu\sigma_z = (0.343)(-75\text{ MPa}) = -25.7\text{ MPa} \qquad \textbf{Ans.}$$

$$\varepsilon_z = \frac{1 - \nu^2}{E}\sigma_z = \frac{1 - 0.343^2}{130{,}000\text{ MPa}}(-75\text{ MPa}) = -509 \times 10^{-6} \qquad \textbf{Ans.}$$

$$\varepsilon_x = -\frac{\nu(1+\nu)}{E}\sigma_z = -\frac{0.343(1+0.343)}{130{,}000 \text{ MPa}}(-75 \text{ MPa}) = 266 \times 10^{-6} \qquad \textbf{Ans.}$$

$$E' = \frac{E}{1-\nu^2} = \frac{130{,}000 \text{ MPa}}{1-0.343^2} = 147{,}300 \text{ MPa} \qquad \textbf{Ans.}$$

Discussion   The compressive σ_z results in negative (that is, compressive) values for σ_y and ε_z, but positive ε_x, as expected from the physical situation. The apparent elastic modulus E' is larger than the elastic modulus E, differing by the ratio $E'/E = 1/(1-\nu^2)$; specifically, $E'/E = 1.133$ in this case. This is explained by noting that E is the ratio of stress to strain only for the uniaxial case, and ratios of stress to strain for other states of stress and strain are determined by behavior obeying the three-dimensional form of Hooke's law.

5.3.4 Volumetric Strain and Hydrostatic Stress

In stressed bodies, small volume changes occur that are associated with normal strains. Shear strains are not involved, as they cause no volume change, only distortion. Consider a rectangular solid, as in Fig. 5.10, where there are normal strains in three directions. The dimensions L, W, and H change by infinitesimal amounts, dL, dW, and dH, respectively, so that the normal strains are

$$\varepsilon_x = \frac{dL}{L}, \qquad \varepsilon_y = \frac{dW}{W}, \qquad \varepsilon_z = \frac{dH}{H} \qquad (5.31)$$

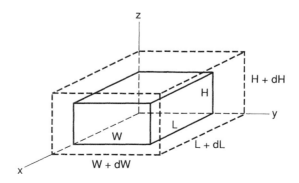

Figure 5.10   Volume change due to normal strains.

The volume, $V = LWH$, changes by an amount dV that can be evaluated from differential calculus, where V is considered to be a function of the three independent variables L, W, and H:

$$dV = \frac{\partial V}{\partial L} dL + \frac{\partial V}{\partial W} dW + \frac{\partial V}{\partial H} dH \tag{5.32}$$

Evaluating the partial derivatives and dividing both sides by $V = LWH$ gives

$$\frac{dV}{V} = \frac{dL}{L} + \frac{dW}{W} + \frac{dH}{H} \tag{5.33}$$

This ratio of the change in volume to the original volume is called the *volumetric strain*, or *dilatation*, ε_v. By substituting Eq. 5.31, the volumetric strain is seen to be simply the sum of the normal strains:

$$\varepsilon_v = \frac{dV}{V} = \varepsilon_x + \varepsilon_y + \varepsilon_z \tag{5.34}$$

For an isotropic material, the volumetric strain can be expressed in terms of stresses by substituting the generalized Hooke's law, specifically Eq. 5.26, into Eq. 5.34. The following is obtained after collecting terms:

$$\varepsilon_v = \frac{1 - 2v}{E} \left(\sigma_x + \sigma_y + \sigma_z \right) \tag{5.35}$$

Note from this that $v = 0.5$ causes the change in volume to be zero, $\varepsilon_v = 0$, even in the presence of nonzero stresses. Also, a value of v exceeding 0.5 would imply negative ε_v for tensile stresses—that is, a decrease in volume. This would be highly unusual, so that 0.5 appears to be an upper limit on v that is seldom exceeded for real materials.

The average normal stress is called the *hydrostatic stress* and is given by

$$\sigma_h = \frac{\sigma_x + \sigma_y + \sigma_z}{3} \tag{5.36}$$

Substituting this into Eq. 5.35 yields

$$\varepsilon_v = \frac{3 (1 - 2v)}{E} \sigma_h \tag{5.37}$$

Hence, the volumetric strain is proportional to the hydrostatic stress. The constant of proportionality relating these is called the *bulk modulus*, given by

$$B = \frac{\sigma_h}{\varepsilon_v} = \frac{E}{3 (1 - 2v)} \tag{5.38}$$

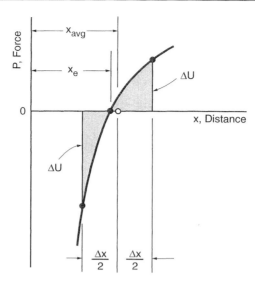

Figure 5.11   Force vs. distance between atoms. A thermal oscillation of equal potential energies about the equilibrium position x_e gives an average distance x_{avg} greater than x_e.

Note that ε_v and σ_h are classed as *invariant* quantities. This means that they will always have the same values, regardless of the choice of coordinate system. In other words, a different choice of x-y-z axes at a particular point in a material will cause the various stress and strain components to have different values, but the sum of the normal strains and the sum of the normal stresses will have the same value for any coordinate system.

5.3.5 Thermal Strains

Thermal strain is a special class of elastic strain that results from expansion with increasing temperature, or contraction with decreasing temperature. Increased temperature causes the atoms in a solid to vibrate by a larger amount. The vibrations follow the force versus distance (P-x) curve between the atoms, as in Fig. 2.16, which curve results from chemical bonding, as discussed in Section 2.4. In particular, the vibration causes equal potential energy changes ΔU about the equilibrium position x_e, corresponding to equal areas under the P-x curve. The shape of the P-x curve in this region is such that the average position, x_{avg}, is greater than x_e, as illustrated in Fig. 5.11. Such larger average atomic spacings accumulate over a macroscopic distance in the material to produce a dimensional increase. Similarly, decreasing the temperature causes the average spacing to decrease and approach x_e.

In isotropic materials, the effect is the same in all directions. Over a limited range of temperatures, the thermal strains at a given temperature T can be assumed to be proportional to the temperature change, ΔT. That is,

$$\varepsilon = \alpha \left(T - T_0 \right) = \alpha \left(\Delta T \right) \tag{5.39}$$

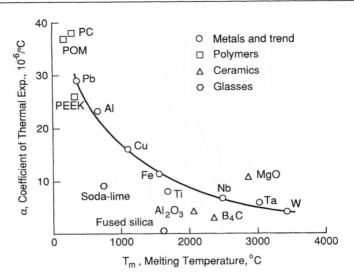

Figure 5.12   Coefficients of thermal expansion at room temperature versus melting temperature for various materials. (Data from [Boyer 85] p. 1.44, [Creyke 82] p. 50, and [ASM 88] p. 69.)

where T_0 is a reference temperature where the strains are taken to be zero. The *coefficient of thermal expansion*, α, is seen to be in units of $1/°C$, where strain is dimensionless.

Thermal effects are generally greater at higher temperatures; that is, α increases with temperature. Hence, it may be necessary to allow for variation in α if ΔT is large. Thermal strains, and therefore values of α, are smaller where the chemical bonding is stronger. If values of α at room temperature for various materials are compared, this leads to a trend of decreasing α with increasing melting temperature, as the chemical bonding is stronger at temperatures more remote from the melting temperature. Figure 5.12 shows this trend for various materials.

In an isotropic material, since uniform thermal strains occur in all directions, Hooke's law for three dimensions from Eq. 5.26 can be generalized to include thermal effects:

$$\varepsilon_x = \frac{1}{E}\left[\sigma_x - \nu\left(\sigma_y + \sigma_z\right)\right] + \alpha(\Delta T) \qquad \text{(a)}$$

$$\varepsilon_y = \frac{1}{E}\left[\sigma_y - \nu\left(\sigma_x + \sigma_z\right)\right] + \alpha(\Delta T) \qquad \text{(b)} \qquad (5.40)$$

$$\varepsilon_z = \frac{1}{E}\left[\sigma_z - \nu\left(\sigma_x + \sigma_y\right)\right] + \alpha(\Delta T) \qquad \text{(c)}$$

If free thermal expansion is prevented by geometric constraint, a sufficient ΔT will cause large stresses to develop that may be of engineering significance.

For example, consider the case of a smooth piece of material at temperature T_i that is suddenly immersed in a liquid or gas having a temperature T_f. A thin surface layer will reach T_f quickly, but strain in the $(x\text{-}y)$ plane of the surface will be prevented due to the material below not having had time to adjust its temperature. Hence, we have $\varepsilon_x = \varepsilon_y = 0$, and also $\sigma_z = 0$ due to the free surface. Applying this situation to Eqs. 5.40(a) and (b) gives

$$\sigma_x = \sigma_y = -\frac{E\alpha(\Delta T)}{1-\nu} \tag{5.41}$$

where $\Delta T = T_f - T_i$, so that the stresses are compressive for a temperature increase, and tensile for a decrease.

5.3.6 Comparison with Plastic and Creep Deformations

Elastic deformation, which is the stretching of chemical bonds, usually involves volume change, as reflected in a Poisson's ratio less than 0.5. However, plastic deformation and creep deformation involve atoms changing neighbors by various mechanisms and so do not ordinarily result in significant volume change. Consider the two-dimensional schematic of plastic deformation in Fig. 2.19. The areas (a) before and (d) after slip are the same, implying constant volume. Similarly, the movement of vacancies in creep does not cause volume change. (See Fig. 2.26.)

Let transverse strain measurements in a tension test be extended beyond yielding, as shown in Fig. 5.13. Prior to yielding, the slope of $-\varepsilon_y$ versus ε_x is simply Poisson's ratio. However, after yielding, the slope increases and approaches 0.5, as plastic strains dominate the behavior. To describe such behavior in a general three-dimensional way, Hooke's law, Eq. 5.26, is needed, in addition to analogous relationships for plastic strain. These are considered later in Chapter 12, specifically as Eq. 12.24. Note that the form is the same as Eq. 5.26, but with ν replaced by 0.5 for constant volume, and the elastic modulus E replaced by a variable E_p.

For creep, the equations analogous to Hooke's law are relationships between stress and strain rate $\dot{\varepsilon}$. These are considered in Chapter 15 as Eq. 15.64. Note that Poisson's ratio ν is replaced by 0.5, and the elastic modulus E by the tensile viscosity η.

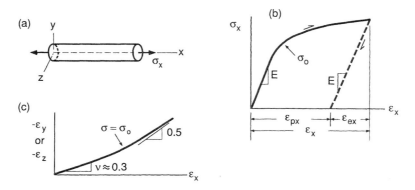

Figure 5.13 Elastic and plastic components of total strain, and the effect of plastic deformation on Poisson's ratio.

5.4 ANISOTROPIC MATERIALS

Real materials are never perfectly isotropic. In some cases, the differences in properties for different directions are so large that analysis assuming isotropic behavior is no longer a reasonable approximation. Some examples of anisotropic materials are shown in Fig. 5.14.

Due to the presence of stiff fibers in particular directions, composite materials can be highly anisotropic, and engineering design and analysis for these materials requires the use of a more general version of Hooke's law than was presented previously. In what follows, we will first discuss Hooke's law for anisotropic cases in general, and then we will apply it to in-plane loading of composite materials. Anisotropic plasticity is not considered in this chapter or even in later chapters. This advanced topic is important in some cases, but note that many composite materials fail prior to the occurrence of large amounts of inelastic strain.

5.4.1 Anisotropic Hooke's Law

In the general three-dimensional case, there are six components of stress: σ_x, σ_y, σ_z, τ_{xy}, τ_{yz}, and τ_{zx}, as illustrated in Fig. 5.9. There are also six corresponding components of strain: ε_x, ε_y, ε_z, γ_{xy}, γ_{yz}, and γ_{zx}. In highly anisotropic materials, any one component of stress can cause strains in all six components. The general anisotropic form of Hooke's law is given by the following six equations, here written with the coefficients shown as a matrix:

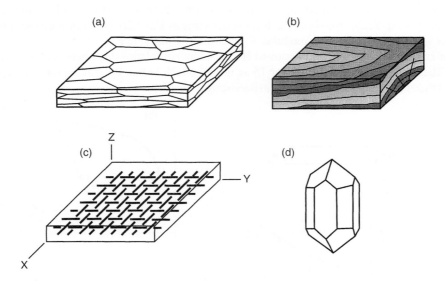

Figure 5.14   Anisotropic materials: (a) metal plate with oriented grain structure due to rolling, (b) wood, (c) glass-fiber cloth in an epoxy matrix, and (d) a single crystal.

$$
\begin{Bmatrix} \varepsilon_x \\ \varepsilon_y \\ \varepsilon_z \\ \gamma_{yz} \\ \gamma_{zx} \\ \gamma_{xy} \end{Bmatrix} =
\begin{bmatrix}
S_{11} & S_{12} & S_{13} & S_{14} & S_{15} & S_{16} \\
S_{12} & S_{22} & S_{23} & S_{24} & S_{25} & S_{26} \\
S_{13} & S_{23} & S_{33} & S_{34} & S_{35} & S_{36} \\
S_{14} & S_{24} & S_{34} & S_{44} & S_{45} & S_{46} \\
S_{15} & S_{25} & S_{35} & S_{45} & S_{55} & S_{56} \\
S_{16} & S_{26} & S_{36} & S_{46} & S_{56} & S_{66}
\end{bmatrix}
\begin{Bmatrix} \sigma_x \\ \sigma_y \\ \sigma_z \\ \tau_{yz} \\ \tau_{zx} \\ \tau_{xy} \end{Bmatrix}
\tag{5.42}
$$

General anisotropy is considerably more complex than the isotropic case. Not only are there a large number of different materials constants S_{ij}, but their values also change if the orientation of the x-y-z coordinate system is changed.

In the isotropic case, the constants do not depend on the orientation of the coordinate axes, and most of the constants are either zero or have the same values as other ones. For example, $\gamma_{xy} = \tau_{xy}/G$, so that all of the S_{ij} in the γ_{xy} row of the matrix are zero except $S_{66} = 1/G$. This contrasts with the situation for highly anisotropic materials, where γ_{xy} is the sum of contributions due to all six stress components. The matrix of S_{ij} coefficients, specialized to the isotropic case as given by Eq. 5.26, is

$$
[S_{ij}] =
\begin{bmatrix}
\dfrac{1}{E} & -\dfrac{\nu}{E} & -\dfrac{\nu}{E} & 0 & 0 & 0 \\[6pt]
-\dfrac{\nu}{E} & \dfrac{1}{E} & -\dfrac{\nu}{E} & 0 & 0 & 0 \\[6pt]
-\dfrac{\nu}{E} & -\dfrac{\nu}{E} & \dfrac{1}{E} & 0 & 0 & 0 \\[6pt]
0 & 0 & 0 & \dfrac{1}{G} & 0 & 0 \\[6pt]
0 & 0 & 0 & 0 & \dfrac{1}{G} & 0 \\[6pt]
0 & 0 & 0 & 0 & 0 & \dfrac{1}{G}
\end{bmatrix}
\tag{5.43}
$$

where G is given by Eq. 5.28, so that there are only two independent constants.

In the most general form of anisotropy, each unique S_{ij} in Eq. 5.42 has a different nonzero value. The matrix is symmetrical about its diagonal in such a way that there are two occurrences of each S_{ij}, where $i \neq j$, so that there are 21 independent constants. An example of a situation with this degree of complexity is the most general form of a single crystal, called a triclinic crystal, where $a \neq b \neq c$ and $\alpha \neq \beta \neq \gamma$, these being the distances and angles defined in Fig. 2.9.

5.4.2 Orthotropic Materials; Other Special Cases

If the material possesses symmetry about three orthogonal planes—that is, about planes oriented $90°$ to each other—then a special case called an *orthotropic material* exists. In this case, Hooke's law has a form of intermediate complexity between the isotropic and the general anisotropic cases.

To deal with the situation of the S_{ij} values changing with the orientation of the x-y-z coordinate system, it is convenient to define the values for the directions parallel to the planes of symmetry in the material. This special coordinate system will here be identified by capital letters (X, Y, Z), as indicated for one case in Fig. 5.14. The coefficients for Hooke's law for an orthotropic material are

$$
[S_{ij}] =
\begin{bmatrix}
\dfrac{1}{E_X} & -\dfrac{\nu_{YX}}{E_Y} & -\dfrac{\nu_{ZX}}{E_Z} & 0 & 0 & 0 \\[2mm]
-\dfrac{\nu_{XY}}{E_X} & \dfrac{1}{E_Y} & -\dfrac{\nu_{ZY}}{E_Z} & 0 & 0 & 0 \\[2mm]
-\dfrac{\nu_{XZ}}{E_X} & -\dfrac{\nu_{YZ}}{E_Y} & \dfrac{1}{E_Z} & 0 & 0 & 0 \\[2mm]
0 & 0 & 0 & \dfrac{1}{G_{YZ}} & 0 & 0 \\[2mm]
0 & 0 & 0 & 0 & \dfrac{1}{G_{ZX}} & 0 \\[2mm]
0 & 0 & 0 & 0 & 0 & \dfrac{1}{G_{XY}}
\end{bmatrix}
\tag{5.44}
$$

Examples include an orthorhombic single crystal, where $\alpha = \beta = \gamma = 90°$, but $a \neq b \neq c$, and fibrous composite materials with fibers in directions such that there are three orthogonal planes of symmetry.

In Eq. 5.44, there are three moduli E_X, E_Y, and E_Z for the three different directions in the material. These in general have different values. There are also three different shear moduli G_{XY}, G_{YZ}, and G_{ZX} corresponding to three planes. The constants ν_{ij} are Poisson's ratio constants; thus,

$$
\nu_{ij} = -\frac{\varepsilon_j}{\varepsilon_i}
\tag{5.45}
$$

giving the transverse strain in the j-direction due to a stress in the i-direction. Because of the symmetry of S_{ij} values about the matrix diagonal,

$$
\frac{\nu_{ij}}{E_i} = \frac{\nu_{ji}}{E_j}
\tag{5.46}
$$

where $i \neq j$ and $i, j = X, Y$, or Z. These relationships reduce the number of independent Poisson's ratios to three for a total of nine independent constants. It is important to remember that these constants apply only for the special X-Y-Z coordinate system.

If the material has the same properties in the X-, Y-, and Z-directions, then it is called a *cubic material*. In this case, all three E_i have the same value E_X, all three G_{ij} have the same value G_{XY}, and all six Poisson's ratios have the same value ν_{XY}. Thus, there are three independent constants. Examples of such a case include all single crystals with a cubic structure, such as BCC, FCC, and diamond cubic crystals. Note that there is still one more independent constant than for the isotropic case, and the elastic constants still apply only for the special X-Y-Z coordinate system.

For example, for a single crystal of alpha (BCC) iron, $E_X = 129\,\text{GPa}$. However, consider the direction that is a body diagonal of the cubic unit cell—that is, along the direction of one of the arrows in Fig. 2.23(a). The elastic modulus in this direction is $E_{[111]} = 276\,\text{GPa}$, which is about twice as large as E_X. Considering E values for all possible directions, these two are the largest and smallest that occur. Polycrystalline iron is isotropic, and the value of $E \approx 210\,\text{GPa}$ that applies is the result of an averaging from randomly oriented single crystals. As expected, this E is between the extreme values E_X and $E_{[111]}$ for single crystals.

Another special case is a *transversely isotropic* material, where the properties are the same for all directions in a plane, such as the X-Y plane, but different for the third (Z) direction. Here there are five independent elastic constants: E_X and ν_{XY} for the X-Y plane, with Eq. 5.28 giving the corresponding shear modulus G_{XY}, and also E_Z, ν_{XZ}, and G_{ZX}. An example is a composite sheet material made from a mat of randomly oriented and intertwined long fibers.

5.4.3 Fibrous Composites

Many applications of composite materials involve thin sheets or plates that have symmetry corresponding to the orthotropic case, such as simple unidirectional or woven arrangements of fibers, as in Fig. 5.14(c). Also, most laminates (Fig. 3.26) have overall behavior that is orthotropic.

For plates or sheets, the stresses that do not lie in the X-Y plane of the sheet are usually small, so that plane stress with $\sigma_Z = \tau_{YZ} = \tau_{ZX} = 0$ is a reasonable assumption. Although strains ε_Z still occur, these are not of particular interest, so Hooke's law can be used in the following reduced form derived from Eq. 5.44:

$$
\begin{Bmatrix} \varepsilon_X \\ \varepsilon_Y \\ \gamma_{XY} \end{Bmatrix} =
\begin{bmatrix} \dfrac{1}{E_X} & -\dfrac{\nu_{YX}}{E_Y} & 0 \\[2mm] -\dfrac{\nu_{XY}}{E_X} & \dfrac{1}{E_Y} & 0 \\[2mm] 0 & 0 & \dfrac{1}{G_{XY}} \end{bmatrix}
\begin{Bmatrix} \sigma_X \\ \sigma_Y \\ \tau_{XY} \end{Bmatrix}
\tag{5.47}
$$

Here, capital letters still indicate that the stresses, strains, and elastic constants are expressed only for directions parallel to the planes of symmetry of the material. (Stresses and strains in other directions can be found by using transformation equations or Mohr's circle, as discussed later in Chapter 6, or in textbooks on mechanics of materials.) Equation 5.46 applies, so that

$$
\frac{\nu_{YX}}{E_Y} = \frac{\nu_{XY}}{E_X}
\tag{5.48}
$$

with the result that four independent elastic constants are being employed out of the total of nine. Values for some composite materials with unidirectional fibers are given in Table 5.3.

Values of these constants can be obtained from laboratory measurements, but they are also commonly estimated from the separate (and generally known) properties of the reinforcement and matrix materials. The topic of so estimating elastic constants is rather complex and is considered in detail in books on composite materials, such as Gibson (2004). In the discussion that follows, we will consider only the simple case of unidirectional fibers in a matrix.

Table 5.3   Elastic Constants and Density for Fiber-Reinforced Epoxy with 60% Unidirectional Fibers by Volume

(a) Reinforcement			(b) Composite, $V_r = 0.60$				
Type	E_r	ν_r	E_X	E_Y	G_{XY}	ν_{XY}	ρ
	GPa (10^3 ksi)		GPa (10^3 ksi)				g/cm^3
E-glass	72.3 (10.5)	0.22	45 (6.5)	12 (1.7)	4.4 (0.64)	0.25	1.94
Kevlar 49	124 (18.0)	0.35	76 (11.0)	5.5 (0.8)	2.1 (0.3)	0.34	1.30
Graphite (T-300)	218 (31.6)	0.20	132 (19.2)	10.3 (1.5)	6.5 (0.95)	0.25	1.47
Graphite (GY-70)	531 (77.0)	0.20	320 (46.4)	5.5 (0.8)	4.1 (0.6)	0.25	1.61

Note: For approximate matrix properties, use $E_m = 3.5$ GPa (510 ksi) and $\nu_m = 0.33$.
Sources: Data in [ASM 87] pp. 175–178, and [Kelly 94] p. 285.

Example 5.4

A plate of the epoxy reinforced with unidirectional Kevlar 49 fibers in Table 5.3 is subject to stresses as follows: $\sigma_X = 400$, $\sigma_Y = 12$, and $\tau_{XY} = 15$ MPa, where the coordinate system is that of Fig. 5.15(a). Determine the in-plane strains ε_X, ε_Y, and γ_{XY}.

Solution   Equation 5.47 applies directly.

$$\varepsilon_X = \frac{\sigma_X}{E_X} - \frac{\nu_{YX}}{E_Y}\sigma_Y, \qquad \varepsilon_Y = -\frac{\nu_{XY}}{E_X}\sigma_X + \frac{\sigma_Y}{E_Y}, \qquad \gamma_{XY} = \frac{\tau_{XY}}{G_{XY}}$$

Since ν_{YX} is not given in the table, it is convenient to employ Eq. 5.48.

$$\frac{\nu_{YX}}{E_Y} = \frac{\nu_{XY}}{E_X} = \frac{0.34}{76,000} = 4.474 \times 10^{-6} \ 1/\text{MPa}$$

Substituting this quantity and the given stresses, with E_X, E_Y, and G_{XY} from Table 5.3, converted to MPa, gives the strains:

$$\varepsilon_X = \frac{400}{76,000} - \left(4.474 \times 10^{-6}\right)(12) = 0.00521 \qquad \textbf{Ans.}$$

$$\varepsilon_Y = -\left(4.474 \times 10^{-6}\right)(400) + \frac{12}{5500} = 0.00039 \qquad \textbf{Ans.}$$

$$\gamma_{XY} = \frac{15}{2100} = 0.00714 \qquad \textbf{Ans.}$$

5.4.4 Elastic Modulus Parallel to Fibers

Consider a uniaxial stress σ_x parallel to fibers aligned in the X-direction, as shown in Fig. 5.15(a). Let the fibers (reinforcement) be an isotropic material with elastic constants E_r, v_r, and G_r, and let the matrix be another isotropic material, E_m, v_m, G_m. Assume that the fibers are perfectly bonded to the matrix so that fibers and matrix deform as a unit, resulting in the same strain ε_X in both. Further, let the total cross-sectional area be A, and let the areas occupied by fibers and by matrix be A_r and A_m, respectively. Then

$$A = A_r + A_m \tag{5.49}$$

Since the applied force must be the sum of contributions from fibers and matrix, we have

$$\sigma_X A = \sigma_r A_r + \sigma_m A_m \tag{5.50}$$

where σ_r, σ_m are the differing stresses in fibers and matrix, respectively. The definitions of the various elastic moduli require that

$$\sigma_X = E_X \varepsilon_X, \qquad \sigma_r = E_r \varepsilon_r, \qquad \sigma_m = E_m \varepsilon_m \tag{5.51}$$

Note that the strain in the composite is the same as that in both fibers and matrix:

$$\varepsilon_X = \varepsilon_r = \varepsilon_m \tag{5.52}$$

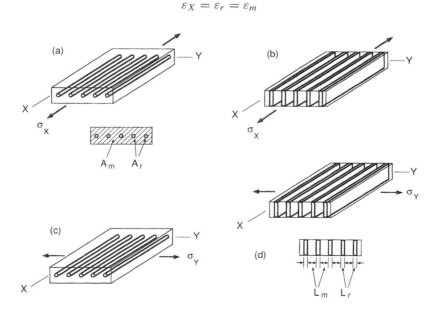

Figure 5.15 Composite materials with various combinations of stress direction and unidirectional reinforcement. In (a) the stress is parallel to fibers, and in (b) to sheets of reinforcement, whereas in (c) and (d) the stresses are normal to similar reinforcement.

Substitution of Eq. 5.51 into Eq. 5.50, and also applying Eq. 5.52, yields the desired modulus of the composite material:

$$E_X = \frac{E_r A_r + E_m A_m}{A} \tag{5.53}$$

The ratios A_r/A and A_m/A are also the *volume fractions* of fiber and matrix, respectively, denoted V_r and V_m:

$$V_r = \frac{A_r}{A}, \qquad V_m = 1 - V_r = \frac{A_m}{A} \tag{5.54}$$

Thus, Eq. 5.53 can also be written

$$E_X = V_r E_r + V_m E_m \tag{5.55}$$

This result confirms that, in this case, a simple *rule of mixtures* applies. Note that the same relationship is also valid for a case where the reinforcement is in the form of well-bonded layers, as in Fig. 5.15(b).

5.4.5 Elastic Modulus Transverse to Fibers

Now consider uniaxial loading in the other orthogonal in-plane direction, specifically, a stress σ_Y as shown in Fig. 5.15(c). An exact analysis of this case is more difficult, but analysis of a transversely loaded layered composite as shown in (d) is a useful approximation. In fact, the E_Y so obtained can be shown by detailed analysis to provide a lower bound on the correct value for case (c). Therefore, let us proceed to analyze case (d).

The stresses in reinforcement and matrix must now be the same and equal to the applied stress:

$$\sigma_Y = \sigma_r = \sigma_m \tag{5.56}$$

As before, we can use the definitions of the various elastic moduli:

$$\sigma_Y = E_Y \varepsilon_Y, \qquad \sigma_r = E_r \varepsilon_r, \qquad \sigma_m = E_m \varepsilon_m \tag{5.57}$$

The total length in the Y-direction is the sum of contributions from the layers of reinforcement and the layers of matrix:

$$L = L_r + L_m \tag{5.58}$$

Also, the changes in these lengths give the strains in the overall composite material and in the reinforcement and matrix portions. That is,

$$\varepsilon_Y = \frac{\Delta L}{L}, \qquad \varepsilon_r = \frac{\Delta L_r}{L_r}, \qquad \varepsilon_m = \frac{\Delta L_m}{L_m} \tag{5.59}$$

where

$$\Delta L = \Delta L_r + \Delta L_m \tag{5.60}$$

Substituting for each ΔL in this equation from Eq. 5.59 yields

$$\varepsilon_Y = \frac{\varepsilon_r L_r + \varepsilon_m L_m}{L} \tag{5.61}$$

Next, substitute for the strains, using Eq. 5.57, and also note that all of the stresses are equal, to obtain

$$\frac{1}{E_Y} = \frac{1}{E_r}\frac{L_r}{L} + \frac{1}{E_m}\frac{L_m}{L} \tag{5.62}$$

The length ratios are equivalent to volume fractions:

$$V_r = \frac{L_r}{L}, \qquad V_m = 1 - V_r = \frac{L_m}{L} \tag{5.63}$$

Thus, we finally obtain

$$\frac{1}{E_Y} = \frac{V_r}{E_r} + \frac{V_m}{E_m}, \qquad E_Y = \frac{E_r E_m}{V_r E_m + V_m E_r} \qquad \text{(a, b)} \tag{5.64}$$

where (b) is obtained from (a) by solving for E_Y.

5.4.6 Other Elastic Constants, and Discussion

Similar logic also leads to an estimate of ν_{XY}, the larger of the two Poisson's ratios, called the *major Poisson's ratio*, and also an estimate of the shear modulus:

$$\nu_{XY} = V_r \nu_r + V_m \nu_m \tag{5.65}$$

$$G_{XY} = \frac{G_r G_m}{V_r G_m + V_m G_r} \tag{5.66}$$

The estimates of composite elastic constants just described are all approximations. Actual values of E_X are usually reasonably close to the estimate. Since E_Y from Eq. 5.64 is a lower bound for the case of fibers, actual values are somewhat higher. Books on composite materials contain more accurate, but considerably more complex, derivations and equations. In addition, fibers may occur in two directions, and laminated materials are often employed that consist of several layers of unidirectional or woven composite. Estimates for these more complex cases can also be made.

In a laminate, if equal numbers of fibers occur in several directions, such as the $0°$, $90°$, $+45°$, and $-45°$ directions, the elastic constants may be approximately the same for any direction in the X-Y plane, but different in the Z-direction. Such a material is said to be *quasi-isotropic*, and it may be approximated as an isotropic material for in-plane loading, or as a transversely isotropic material for general three-dimensional analysis.

Example 5.5

A composite material is to be made of tungsten wire aligned in a single direction in a copper matrix. The elastic modulus parallel to the fibers must be at least 250 GPa, and the elastic modulus perpendicular to the fibers must be at least 200 GPa.

   (a) What is the smallest volume fraction of wire that can be used?
   (b) For the volume fraction of wire chosen in (a), what are the major Poisson's ratio and the shear modulus of the composite material?

Solution   (a) We need to determine the volume fractions of fibers V_r needed to meet each requirement. The larger of the two different V_r values obtained is then chosen as meeting or exceeding both requirements. The matrix and reinforcement properties are:

$$\text{Tungsten reinforcement:} \quad E = 411 \text{ GPa}, \quad v = 0.280, \quad G = 160.5 \text{ GPa}$$
$$\text{Copper matrix:} \quad E = 130 \text{ GPa}, \quad v = 0.343, \quad G = 48.4 \text{ GPa}$$

where E and v are from Table 5.2, and each G is calculated from Eq. 5.28 under the assumption that each material is isotropic.

First consider the $E_X = 250$ GPa requirement, where X is the fiber direction. Equation 5.55 can be solved to obtain the needed V_r. Substituting the appropriate preceding values and solving for V_r gives

$$E_X = V_r E_r + V_m E_m, \qquad V_m = 1 - V_r$$

$$250 \text{ GPa} = V_r(411 \text{ GPa}) + (1 - V_r)(130 \text{ GPa}), \qquad V_r = 0.427$$

Then, similarly, consider the $E_Y = 200$ GPa requirement, and employ Eq. 5.64 to obtain

$$\frac{1}{E_Y} = \frac{V_r}{E_r} + \frac{V_m}{E_m}, \qquad V_m = 1 - V_r$$

$$\frac{1}{200 \text{ GPa}} = \frac{V_r}{411 \text{ GPa}} + \frac{1 - V_r}{130 \text{ GPa}}, \qquad V_r = 0.512$$

Hence, the required volume fraction is the larger value, $V_r = 0.512$.   **Ans.**

   (b) The major Poisson's ratio and the shear modulus for the composite material with $V_r = 0.512$ can be estimated from Eqs. 5.65 and 5.66:

$$v_{XY} = V_r v_r + V_m v_m = 0.512(0.280) + (1 - 0.512)(0.343) = 0.311 \qquad \textbf{Ans.}$$

$$G_{XY} = \frac{G_r G_m}{V_r G_m + V_m G_r} = \frac{(160.5 \text{ GPa})(48.4 \text{ GPa})}{0.512(48.4 \text{ GPa}) + (1 - 0.512)(160.5 \text{ GPa})} = 75.3 \text{ GPa} \quad \textbf{Ans.}$$

> **Discussion**   In (a), note that choosing the smaller value, $V_r = 0.427$, gives $E_Y = 183.6$ GPa from Eq. 5.64. Hence, this choice fails the $E_Y = 200$ GPa requirement. But the $V_r = 0.512$ choice gives $E_X = 273.8$ GPa from Eq. 5.55, so that the $E_X = 250$ GPa requirement is exceeded, and this choice is suitable.

5.5 SUMMARY

Deformations may be classified according to physical mechanisms and analogies with rheological models as elastic, plastic, or creep deformations. The latter category may be further subdivided into steady-state creep and transient creep. The simplest rheological models for each are shown in Fig. 5.1.

Elastic deformation is associated with stretching the chemical bonds in solids so that the distances between atoms increases. The deformation is not time dependent and is recovered immediately upon unloading. Stress–strain curves for metals, especially, but also for many other materials, exhibit a distinct elastic region where the stress–strain behavior is linear.

Plastic deformation is associated with the relative movement of planes of atoms, or of chainlike molecules, and is not strongly time dependent. Rheological models containing frictional sliders have behavior analogous to plastic deformation, sharing the following characteristics with plastically deforming materials: (1) Departure from linear behavior occurs that results in permanent deformation if the load is removed. (2) Compressive stressing is required to achieve a return to zero strain after yielding. (3) There is a memory effect on reloading after elastic unloading, in that yielding occurs at the same stress and strain from which unloading occurred.

Creep is time-dependent deformation that may or may not be recovered after unloading. The physical mechanisms include vacancy and dislocation motions, grain boundary sliding, and flow as a viscous fluid. Such mechanisms acting in metals, ceramics, and glasses produce creep deformations that are mostly not recovered after unloading. However, considerable recovery of creep deformation may occur in polymers as a result of interactions among the long carbon-chain molecules. Rheological models built up of springs and dashpots can be used to study creep behavior. In the simplest form of such models, strain rates are proportional to applied stresses, a situation termed *linear viscoelasticity*. If a strain is applied and held constant, creep behavior in the material causes the stress to decrease, a phenomenon termed *relaxation*.

Elastic deformation occurs in all materials at all temperatures. Plastic deformation is important in strengthened metal alloys at room temperature, whereas creep effects are small. Significant creep occurs at room temperature in low-melting-temperature metals, and in many polymers. At sufficiently high temperature, creep becomes an important factor for strengthened metal alloys and even for ceramics.

If a material is both isotropic and homogeneous, the elastic strains for the general three-dimensional case are related to stresses by the generalized Hooke's law:

$$\varepsilon_x = \frac{1}{E}\left[\sigma_x - \nu\left(\sigma_y + \sigma_z\right)\right], \qquad \gamma_{xy} = \frac{\tau_{xy}}{G} \tag{5.67}$$

and similarly for the y- and z-directions and the yz and zx planes. There are two independent elastic constants: the elastic modulus E, and Poisson's ratio ν. The shear modulus G is related to these by

$$G = \frac{E}{2(1 + \nu)} \tag{5.68}$$

The volumetric strain is the sum of the normal strains, $\varepsilon_v = \varepsilon_x + \varepsilon_y + \varepsilon_z$. For the isotropic, homogeneous case, volumetric strain is related to the applied stresses by

$$\varepsilon_v = \frac{1 - 2\nu}{E} \left(\sigma_x + \sigma_y + \sigma_z \right) \tag{5.69}$$

This equation indicates that the volume change is zero for $\nu = 0.5$. Values for virtually all materials lie within the limits $\nu = 0$ and 0.5, usually between $\nu = 0.2$ and 0.4.

Some materials, notably fibrous composites, are significantly anisotropic. A particular case of anisotropy that is often encountered is orthotropy, in which the material has symmetry about three orthogonal planes. Such a material has nine independent elastic constants. There is a different value of the elastic modulus for each orthogonal direction, E_X, E_Y, and E_Z, and also three independent values of Poisson's ratio and of shear modulus, ν_{XY}, G_{XY}, etc., corresponding to the three orthogonal planes. These constants are defined only on the special X-Y-Z coordinate axes that are parallel to the planes of symmetry in the material. If the orientation of the coordinate axes change, the elastic constants change.

For in-plane loading of sheets and plates of composite materials with unidirectional fibers, the elastic constants can be estimated from those of the reinforcement and matrix materials:

$$E_X = V_r E_r + V_m E_m, \qquad E_Y = \frac{E_r E_m}{V_r E_m + V_m E_r} \tag{5.70}$$

In this case, X is the fiber (reinforcement) direction, Y is the transverse direction, and V_r, V_m are the volume fractions of reinforcement and matrix, respectively.

NEW TERMS AND SYMBOLS

(a) Terms

anelastic strain	perfectly plastic
bulk modulus, B	Poisson's ratio, ν
elastic (Young's) modulus, E	recovery
generalized Hooke's law	relaxation
homogeneous	rheological model
hydrostatic stress, σ_h	shear modulus, G
isotropic	steady-state creep
linear elasticity	tensile viscosity, η
linear hardening	thermal expansion coefficient, α
linear viscoelasticity	transient creep
orthotropic	volumetric strain, ε_v

(b) Nomenclature for Stresses and Strains

x, y, z	Coordinate axes identifying directions for stresses and strains
$\gamma_{xy}, \gamma_{yz}, \gamma_{zx}$	Shear strains
$\varepsilon_x, \varepsilon_y, \varepsilon_z$	Normal strains
ε_c	Creep strain
ε_e	Elastic strain
ε_p	Plastic strain
$\varepsilon_{sc}, \varepsilon_{tc}$	Steady-state and transient creep strains, respectively
$\sigma_x, \sigma_y, \sigma_z$	Normal stresses
$\tau_{xy}, \tau_{yz}, \tau_{zx}$	Shear stresses

(c) Nomenclature for Orthotropic and Composite Materials

X, Y, Z	The particular x-y-z coordinate axes that are aligned with the planes of material symmetry.
E_X, E_Y, E_Z	Elastic moduli in the X-, Y- and Z-directions.
G_{XY}, G_{YZ}, G_{ZX}	Shear moduli in X-Y, etc., planes.
m, r	Subscripts indicating matrix and reinforcement materials, respectively.
V_m, V_r	Volume fractions for matrix and reinforcement materials, respectively.
ν_{XY}, etc.	Poisson's ratio giving the transverse strain in the Y-direction due to a stress in the X-direction; others similarly.

REFERENCES

BRINSON, H. F., and L. C. BRINSON. 2008. *Polymer Engineering Science and Viscoelasticity: An Introduction*, Springer, New York.

GIBSON, R. F. 2004. *Principles of Composite Material Mechanics*, 2d ed., McGraw-Hill, New York.

MCCLINTOCK, F. A., and A. S. ARGON, eds. 1966. *Mechanical Behavior of Materials*, Addison-Wesley, Reading, MA.

RÖSLER, J., H. HARDERS, and M. BÄKER. 2007. *Mechanical Behavior of Engineering Materials*, Springer, Berlin.

TIMOSHENKO, S. P., and J. N. GOODIER. 1970. *Theory of Elasticity*, 3d ed., McGraw-Hill, New York.

PROBLEMS AND QUESTIONS

Section 5.2

5.1 Define the following terms in your own words: (a) elastic strain, (b) plastic strain, (c) creep strain, (d) tensile viscosity, (e) recovery, and (f) relaxation.

5.2 An aluminum alloy is represented by the elastic, perfectly plastic model of Fig. 5.3(b), with constants $E_1 = 80$ GPa and $\sigma_o = 250$ MPa.

    (a) Plot the stress–strain response for loading to a strain of $\varepsilon = 0.010$. Of this total strain, how much is elastic, and how much is plastic?

    (b) Also plot the response following (a) if the strain now decreases until it reaches zero.

5.3 For the elastic, linear-hardening rheological model of Fig. 5.3(c), how is the behavior affected by changing E_2 while E_1 remains constant? You may wish to enhance your discussion by including a sketch showing how the σ-ε path varies with E_2.

5.4 A brass alloy is represented by the elastic, linear hardening model of Fig. 5.3(c), with constants of $E_1 = 100$ GPa, $E_2 = 3$ GPa, and $\sigma_o = 500$ MPa. Plot the stress–strain response for loading to a strain of $\varepsilon = 0.025$. Of this total strain, how much is elastic, and how much is plastic?

5.5 At 500°C, a material has an elastic modulus of $E = 70$ GPa and a tensile viscosity of $\eta = 1200$ GPa-s. Assuming that the elastic, steady-state creep model of Fig. 5.5(a) applies, determine the response to a stress of 50 MPa maintained for 5 minutes and then removed. Plot both the strain versus time and stress versus strain for a total time of interval of 10 minutes.

5.6 Consider the strain in a transient creep model, as during the time span 0–1–2 in Fig. 5.5(b). Starting from Eq. 5.15, derive Eq. 5.17 that gives the strain at time 2.

5.7 A polymer has constants for the elastic, transient creep model of Fig. 5.5(b) of $E_1 = 2$ GPa, $E_2 = 4$ GPa, and $\eta = 10^5$ GPa-s. Determine and plot the strain versus time response for a stress of 50 MPa applied for one day.

5.8 Consider relaxation under constant strain ε' of a model with a spring and dashpot in series, as in Fig. 5.6, but let the dashpot behave according to the nonlinear equation $\dot{\varepsilon} = B\sigma^m$, where B and m are material constants, with m being typically in the range 3 to 7. Derive an equation for σ as a function of ε', time t, and the various model constants.

5.9 A polymer is used for shrink-on banding to keep cardboard boxes from popping open during shipment of merchandise. The tension in the banding is observed to have dropped to 90% of its initial value after three months. Estimate how long it will take for the tension to drop to 50% of its original value. The polymer may be assumed to behave according to an elastic, steady-state creep model, as in Fig. 5.6.

Section 5.3[2]

5.10 Consider a material of length 300 mm, with a rectangular cross section, 40 mm wide by 3 mm thick. When subjected to a tensile load of 3000 N, assume that the length is found to increase by 3 mm and the width to decrease by 0.15 mm. Also assume that, upon removal of the load, the length and width are measured again and are found to have returned to approximately their original values. Determine the following: (a) stress in the length direction, (b) strain in the length direction, (c) strain in the width direction, (d) elastic modulus, (e) Poisson's ratio, and (f) shear modulus.

5.11 A bar of brass alloy is 200 mm long and has a circular cross section of diameter 50 mm. It is subjected to a tensile load of 500 kN, which gives a stress well below the material's yield

---

[2]For metal alloys, where specific values are not available, the elastic constants E and ν may generally be approximated as being the same as for the corresponding pure metal, as from Table 5.2. See the discussion in Section 5.3.2.

strength. Determine the following: (a) stress in the length direction, (b) strain in the length direction, (c) strain in the transverse direction, (d) length while under load, and (e) diameter while under load.

5.12 Employ Eq. 5.26(a) and (b) as follows:

    (a) Obtain an expression for the ratio $\varepsilon_y / \varepsilon_x$ as a function of stresses and the elastic constants for the material. Under what conditions is the negative of this ratio equal to Poisson's ratio ν?

    (b) Obtain an expression for the ratio σ_x / ε_x as a function of stresses and the elastic constants for the material. Under what conditions is this ratio equal to the elastic modulus E?

5.13 For the special case of plane stress, $\sigma_z = \tau_{yz} = \tau_{zx} = 0$, proceed as follows:

    (a) Write the resulting simplified version of Hooke's law, Eqs. 5.26 and 5.27.

    (b) Then invert the simplified forms of Eq. 5.26(a) and (b) to obtain relationships that give the stresses σ_x and σ_y, each as a function of strains and materials constants only.

    (c) Also derive the equation that gives ε_z as a function of the other two strains and materials constants.

5.14 Strains are measured on the surface of a brass alloy part as follows: $\varepsilon_x = 1600 \times 10^{-6}$, $\varepsilon_y = 1300 \times 10^{-6}$, and $\gamma_{xy} = 1500 \times 10^{-6}$. Estimate the in-plane stresses σ_x, σ_y, and τ_{xy}, and also the strain ε_z normal to the surface. (Assume that the gages were bonded to the metal when there was no load on the part, that there has been no yielding, and that no loading is applied directly to the surface, so that $\sigma_z = \tau_{yz} = \tau_{zx} = 0$.)

5.15 Strains are measured on the surface of a polycarbonate plastic part as follows: $\varepsilon_x = 0.022$, $\varepsilon_y = -0.0158$, and $\gamma_{xy} = 0.0096$. Estimate in-plane stresses σ_x, σ_y, and τ_{xy}, and also the strain ε_z normal to the surface. (The same assumptions apply as for Prob. 5.14.)

5.16 Strains are measured on the surface of a low alloy steel part as follows: $\varepsilon_x = -1750 \times 10^{-6}$, $\varepsilon_y = 900 \times 10^{-6}$, and $\gamma_{xy} = 600 \times 10^{-6}$. Estimate in-plane stresses σ_x, σ_y, and τ_{xy}, and also the strain ε_z normal to the surface. (The same assumptions apply as for Prob. 5.14.)

5.17 Strains are measured on the surface of a mild steel part as follows: $\varepsilon_x = 250 \times 10^{-6}$, $\varepsilon_y = -950 \times 10^{-6}$, and $\gamma_{xy} = 400 \times 10^{-6}$. Estimate in-plane stresses σ_x, σ_y, and τ_{xy}, and also the strain ε_z normal to the surface. (The same assumptions apply as for Prob. 5.14.)

5.18 Strains are measured on the surface of a titanium alloy part as follows: $\varepsilon_x = 3300 \times 10^{-6}$, $\varepsilon_y = 110 \times 10^{-6}$, and $\gamma_{xy} = 650 \times 10^{-6}$. Estimate the in-plane stresses σ_x, σ_y, and τ_{xy}, and also the strain ε_z normal to the surface. (The same assumptions apply as for Prob. 5.14.)

5.19 A plate of metal is subjected to stresses $\sigma_x = 186 \text{ MPa}$ and $\sigma_y = 152 \text{ MPa}$. The strains that occur as a result of these stresses are measured to be $\varepsilon_x = 1900 \times 10^{-6}$ and $\varepsilon_y = 1250 \times 10^{-6}$. No yielding occurs in the plate, that is, the behavior is elastic. Estimate the elastic modulus E and Poisson's ratio ν for the metal. What type of metal is it?

5.20 A thin-walled *spherical* vessel contains a pressure p and has inner radius r and wall thickness t. It is made of an isotropic material that behaves in a linear-elastic manner. Determine the each of following as a function of the pressure, geometric dimensions, and material constants involved: (a) change in radius, Δr, and (b) change in wall thickness, Δt.

5.21 Consider a pressure vessel that is a thin-walled tube with closed ends and wall thickness t. The volume *enclosed* by the vessel is determined from the inner diameter D and length L by $V_e = \pi D^2 L / 4$. The ratio of a small change in the enclosed volume to the original volume can be found by obtaining the differential dV_e and then dividing by V_e, which gives

$$\frac{dV_e}{V_e} = 2\frac{dD}{D} + \frac{dL}{L}$$

Verify this expression. Then derive an equation for dV_e/V_e as a function of the pressure p in the vessel, the vessel dimensions, and elastic constants of the isotropic material. Assume that L is large compared with D, so that the details of the behavior of the ends are not important.

5.22 Consider a thin-walled *spherical* pressure vessel of inner diameter D and wall thickness t. Derive an equation for the ratio dV_e/V_e, where V_e is the volume *enclosed* by the vessel, and dV_e is the change in V_e when the vessel is pressurized. Express the result as a function of pressure p, vessel dimensions, and elastic constants of the isotropic material.

5.23 A block of isotropic material is stressed in the x- and y-directions as shown in Fig. P5.23. The ratio of the magnitudes of the two stresses is a constant, so that $\sigma_y = \lambda\sigma_x$.

   (a) Determine the stiffness in the x-direction, $E' = \sigma_x/\varepsilon_x$, as a function of only λ and the elastic constants E and ν of the material.

   (b) Compare this apparent modulus E' with the elastic constant E as obtained from a uniaxial test, and comment on the comparison. (Suggestion: Assume that $\nu = 0.3$ and consider λ values of -1, 0, and $+1$.)

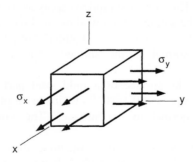

Figure P5.23

5.24 A sample of isotropic material is subjected to a compressive stress σ_z and is confined so that it cannot deform in either the x- or y-directions, as shown in Fig. P5.24.

   (a) Do stresses occur in the material in the x- and y-directions? If so, obtain equations for σ_x and for σ_y, each as functions of only σ_z and the elastic constant ν for the material.

   (b) Determine the stiffness $E' = \sigma_z/\varepsilon_z$ in the direction of the applied stress σ_z in terms of only the elastic constants E and ν for the material. Is E' equal to the elastic modulus E as obtained from a uniaxial test? Why or why not?

   (c) What happens if Poisson's ratio for the material approaches 0.5?

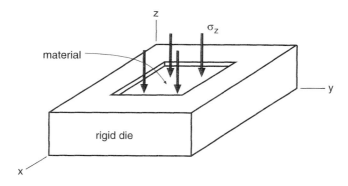

Figure P5.24

5.25 A block of isotropic material is stressed in the x- and y-directions, but rigid walls prevent deformation in the z-direction, as shown in Fig. P5.25. The ratio of the two applied stresses is a constant, so that $\sigma_y = \lambda \sigma_x$.

    (a) Does a stress develop in the z-direction? If so, obtain an equation for σ_z as a function of σ_x, λ , and the elastic constant ν for the material.

    (b) Determine the stiffness $E' = \sigma_x / \varepsilon_x$ for the x-direction as a function of only λ and the elastic constants E and ν for the material.

    (c) Compare this apparent modulus E' with the elastic modulus E as obtained from a uniaxial test. (Suggestion: Assume that $\nu = 0.3$ and consider λ values of $-1, 0$, and 1.)

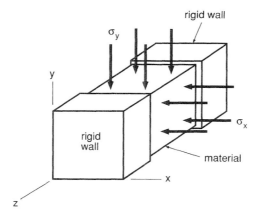

Figure P5.25

5.26 For the situation of Fig. P5.24, where a rigid die prevents deformation in either the x- or y-directions, the material is a polycarbonate plastic, and the stress in the z-direction is 30 MPa compression.

    (a) Determine the stresses in the x- and y-directions, the strain in the z-direction, and the volumetric strain.

    (b) Evaluate the ratio of stress to strain for the z-direction, $E' = \sigma_2 / \varepsilon_z$, and comment on the value obtained.

5.27 A block of material is confined by a rigid die as shown in Fig. P5.24, so that it cannot deform in either the x- or y-directions. A compressive stress is applied in the z-direction. Assume that there is no friction along the walls and that no yielding occurs in the metal. What is the largest value of the compressive stress σ_z that can be applied without the strain in the z-direction exceeding $0.2\% = 0.002$?

5.28 For the solution of Fig. P5.25, the material is brass (70% Cu, 30% Zn), and the compressive stresses applied in x- and y-directions are 80 and 120 MPa, respectively. What stress develops in the z-direction, and what are the strains in the x- and y-directions?

5.29 For the situation of Fig. P5.25, where a rigid die prevents deformation in the z-direction, the material is an aluminum alloy, and equal compressive stresses of 150 MPa are applied in the x- and y-directions.

    (a) Determine the stress in the z-direction, the strains in the x- and y-directions, and the volumetric strain.

    (b) Evaluate the ratio of stress to strain for the x-direction and comment on the value obtained.

5.30 Equation 5.41 is sometimes used as a basis for making a preliminary comparison of the *thermal shock* resistance of ceramic materials by calculating the maximum ΔT that can occur without the material reaching its ultimate strength. The compressive ultimate σ_{uc} applies for a temperature increase (upward shock), and the tensile ultimate σ_{ut} applies for a temperature decrease (downward shock). Coefficients of thermal expansion, α, and Poisson's ratio, ν, for some of the ceramic materials of Table 3.10 are given in Table P5.30.

    (a) Calculate ΔT_{max} for each ceramic for both upward shock and downward shock.

    (b) Briefly discuss the trends observed. Include your opinion and supporting logic as to which of these materials might be the best choice for high temperature engine parts, such as turbine blades, where rapid temperature changes occur.

Table P5.30

Material	α, $10^{-6}/°C$	ν
MgO	13.5	0.18
Al_2O_3	8.0	0.22
ZrO_2	10.2	0.30
SiC	4.5	0.22
Si_3N_4	2.9	0.27

Sources: Table 5.2 and [Gauthier 95]
pp. 103, 935, 961, 964, and 979.

5.31 A plate of aluminum alloy is subjected to in-plane stresses of $\sigma_x = 100$, $\sigma_y = -40$, and $\tau_{xy} = 60$ MPa, with other stresses components being zero. The coefficient of thermal expansion for the alloy is $23.6 \times 10^{-6}/°C$.

(a) Determine all nonzero strain components if the temperature remains constant.

(b) Determine all nonzero strain components if the temperature decreases by 25°C while the given stresses are present.

(c) Compare the strain values from (a) and (b), and comment on the trends in the values.

5.32 A plate of magnesium alloy is subjected to in-plane stresses of $\sigma_x = 80$, $\sigma_y = 30$, and $\tau_{xy} = 50$ MPa, with the other stress components being zero. The coefficient of thermal expansion for the alloy is $26 \times 10^{-6}/°C$. Proceed as in Prob. 5.31(a), (b), and (c).

5.33 For the situation of Example 5.3(e), consider the possibility of a temperature change ΔT in addition to the stress $\sigma_z = -75$ MPa being applied.

(a) For a temperature increase, how would you expect the value of σ_y to qualitatively change, as to its magnitude becoming larger or smaller? For a temperature decrease?

(b) Calculate the temperature change that would cause the copper alloy block to be on the verge of losing contact with the walls in the y-direction. The coefficient of thermal expansion for the alloy is $16.5 \times 10^{-6} \ 1/°C$.

Section 5.4[3]

5.34 Name two materials that fit into each of the following categories: (a) isotropic, (b) transversely isotropic, and (c) orthotropic. Try to think of your own examples rather than using those from the text.

5.35 A composite material is made with a titanium alloy matrix and 35%, by volume, of unidirectional SiC fibers. Estimate the elastic constants E_X, E_Y, G_{XY}, ν_{XY}, and ν_{YX}.

5.36 A composite material is to be made by extruding 50% by volume of unidirectional type E-glass fibers in an epoxy matrix.

(a) Estimate the composite properties E_X, E_Y, G_{XY}, ν_{XY}, and ν_{XY}, where X is the fiber direction. Fiber (reinforcement) and the matrix properties are given in Table 5.3(a) and in the note below the table.

(b) Compare your values with the data given in Table 5.3(b) for a similar composite with 60% unidirectional fibers. Are the differences qualitatively what you would expect from the different fiber volumes?

5.37 For the epoxy reinforced with 60% unidirectional E-glass fibers in Table 5.3, use the reinforcement and matrix properties given in Table 5.3(a), and in the note below the table, to estimate the composite properties E_X, E_Y, G_{XY}, ν_{XY}, and ν_{YX}. How well do your estimates compare with the experimental values in Table 5.3(b)? Can you suggest reasons for any discrepancies?

5.38 Proceed as in the previous problem, except change the fiber material to Kevlar 49.

5.39 Proceed as in Prob. 5.37, except change the fiber material to T-300 graphite.

5.40 Proceed as in Prob. 5.37, except change the fiber material to GY-70 graphite.

5.41 For unidirectional E-glass fibers used to reinforce epoxy, employ the reinforcement and matrix properties given in Table 5.3(a), and in the note below the table, to estimate E_X and E_Y for several volume fractions of reinforcement ranging from zero to 100%. Plot curves of E_X versus V_r, and E_Y versus V_r, on the same graph, and comment on the trends.

---

[3]Materials properties for these problems may be found in Tables 5.2 and 5.3, including the footnote to the latter.

5.42 A sheet of epoxy reinforced with 60% unidirectional Kevlar 49 fibers has properties as given in Table 5.3(b), where X is the fiber direction. The sheet is subjected to stresses $\sigma_X = 160$, $\sigma_Y = 10$, and $\tau_{XY} = 20$ MPa. Determine the in-plane strains ε_X, ε_Y, and γ_{XY} that result.

5.43 A sheet of epoxy reinforced with 60% unidirectional E-glass fibers has properties as given in Table 5.3(b), where X is the fiber direction. Strains $\varepsilon_X = 0.0030$, $\varepsilon_Y = -0.0020$, and $\gamma_{XY} = 0.0025$ are measured. Estimate the applied stresses σ_X, σ_Y, and τ_{XY}.

5.44 In a composite material, an epoxy matrix is reinforced with GY-70 type graphite fibers. The volume percentage of fibers is 70%, and all are oriented in the same direction. For a sheet of this material in the X-Y plane, with fibers in the X-direction, strains $\varepsilon_X = 0.0050$ and $\varepsilon_Y = 0.0010$ are measured. Estimate the applied stresses σ_X and σ_Y. Reinforcement and matrix properties are given in Table 5.3(a) and in the note below the table.

5.45 Graphite-epoxy material with 65% unidirectional fibers by volume was subjected to two experiments: (1) A stress of 150 MPa was applied parallel to the fibers, as in Fig. 5.15(a). The resulting strains parallel and transverse to this stress direction were measured from strain gages as $\varepsilon_X = 1138 \times 10^{-6}$ and $\varepsilon_Y = -372 \times 10^{-6}$. (2) A stress of 11.2 MPa was applied transverse to the fibers, as in Fig. 5.15(c). The resulting strains parallel and transverse to this stress direction were measured from strain gages as $\varepsilon_Y = 1165 \times 10^{-6}$ and $\varepsilon_X = -22 \times 10^{-6}$. However, the accuracy of the latter ε_X measurement is compromised by the very small value of strain involved.

   (a) Estimate the constants E_X, E_Y, ν_{XY}, and ν_{YX} for this composite material.

   (b) If the elastic modulus of the epoxy matrix is approximately 3.5 GPa, estimate the elastic modulus of the graphite fibers.

5.46 A composite material is to be made from type E-glass fibers embedded in a matrix of ABS plastic, with all fibers to be aligned in the same direction. For the composite, the elastic modulus parallel to the reinforcement must be at least 48 GPa, and the elastic modulus perpendicular to the reinforcement must be at least 5.0 GPa.

   (a) What minimum volume fraction of fibers will satisfy both requirements?

   (b) For the composite material with volume fraction of fibers chosen in (a), estimate the elastic moduli in the parallel and perpendicular directions, the shear modulus, and the major and minor Poisson's ratios.

5.47 A composite material is to be made from silicon carbide (SiC) fibers embedded in a matrix of an aluminum alloy, with all fibers to be aligned in the same direction. For the composite, the elastic modulus parallel to the reinforcement must be at least 220 GPa, and the elastic modulus perpendicular to the reinforcement must be at least 100 GPa. Proceed as in (a) and (b) of Prob. 5.46.

5.48 A composite material is to be made of tungsten wire aligned in a single direction in an aluminum alloy matrix. The elastic modulus parallel to the fibers must be at least 225 GPa, and the elastic modulus perpendicular to the fibers must be at least 100 GPa. Proceed as in (a) and (b) of Prob. 5.46.

5.49 A composite material is to be made by embedding unidirectional SiC fibers in a titanium alloy metal matrix. For the composite, the elastic modulus in the fiber direction must be at least 250 GPa, and the shear modulus must be at least 60 GPa. Proceed as in (a) and (b) of Prob. 5.46.

5.50 A composite material is needed that has unidirectional fiber or wire reinforcement embedded in a metal matrix. The elastic modulus parallel to the reinforcement must be at least 170 GPa, and the elastic modulus perpendicular to the reinforcement must be at least 85 GPa.

    (a) If the matrix material is a magnesium alloy and the volume fraction of reinforcement is 60%, what is the minimum elastic modulus required for the reinforcement material?

    (b) Name two materials listed in Table 5.2 that might be reasonable candidates for the reinforcement material.

6

Review of Complex and Principal States of Stress and Strain

OBJECTIVES

- For plane stress, develop the equations for transformation of axes, and apply these to determine principal normal and shear stresses. Include graphical representation by Mohr's circle, as well as extension to generalized plane stress.
- Explore three-dimensional states of stress, with emphasis on principal normal stresses, principal axes, principal shear stresses, and maximum shear stress.
- Review complex states of strain, applying the fact that the mathematics and analysis procedures are analogous to those for stress.

6.1 INTRODUCTION

Components of machines, vehicles, and structures are subjected to applied loadings that may include tension, compression, bending, torsion, pressure, or combinations of these. As a result, complex states of normal and shear stress occur that vary in magnitude and direction with location in the component. The designer must ensure that the material of the component does not fail as a result of these stresses. To accomplish this, locations where the stresses are the most severe must be identified, and then further analysis of the stresses at these locations is needed.

At any point in a component where the stresses are of interest, it is first necessary to note that the magnitudes of the stresses vary with direction. By considering all possible directions, the most severe stresses at a given location can be found. The stresses involved are called *principal stresses*, and the particular directions in which they act are the *principal axes*. Both principal normal stresses and principal shear stresses are of interest. The main purpose of this chapter is to present the procedures for determining these principal stresses and their directions.

Treatment of the topic begins with the relatively simple case of *plane stress*, where the stresses acting on one orthogonal plane are zero. We next extend the topic to the general case of three-dimensional states of stress, and then conclude the chapter by considering states of strain. The degree of detail is limited to what is needed as background for later chapters. Full detail can be found in any of a number of relatively advanced books on mechanics of materials and similar subjects, such as Boresi (2003), Timoshenko (1970), and Ugural (2012).

The material presented in this chapter is especially needed for Chapter 7, which employs principal stresses to analyze the effect of complex states of stress on yielding of ductile materials and fracture of brittle materials. It is also needed as background for a number of other chapters later in the book, as we consider such topics as brittle fracture of cracked members, failure due to cyclic loading, plastic deformation of materials and components, and time-dependent behavior.

6.2 PLANE STRESS

Plane stress is of practical interest, as it occurs at any free (unloaded) surface, and surface locations often have the most severe stresses, as in bending of beams and torsion of circular shafts.

Consider any given point in a solid body, and assume that an x-y-z coordinate system has been chosen for this point. The material at this point is, in general, subjected to six components of stress, σ_x, σ_y, σ_z, τ_{xy}, τ_{yz}, and τ_{zx}, as illustrated on a small element of material in Fig. 6.1. If the three components of stress acting on one of the three pairs of parallel faces of the element are all zero, then a state of plane stress exists. Taking the unstressed plane to be parallel to the x-y plane gives

$$\sigma_z = \tau_{yz} = \tau_{zx} = 0 \tag{6.1}$$

Equilibrium of forces on the element of Fig. 6.1 requires that the moments must sum to zero about both the x- and y-axes, requiring in turn that the components of τ_{yz} and τ_{zx} acting on the other two planes must also be zero.

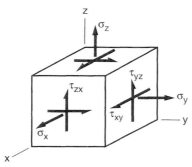

Figure 6.1   The six components needed to completely describe the state of stress at a point.

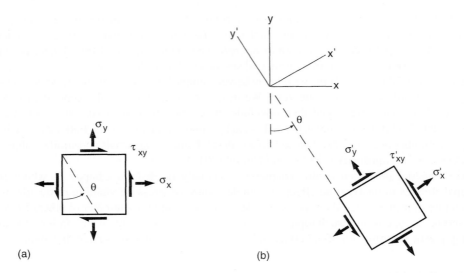

(a)   (b)

Figure 6.2   The three components needed to describe a state of plane stress (a), and an equivalent representation of the same state of stress for a rotated coordinate system (b).

Hence, the components remaining are σ_x, σ_y, and τ_{xy}, as illustrated on a square element of material in Fig. 6.2(a). Note that the square element is simply the cubic element viewed parallel to the z-axis. Positive directions are as shown, with the sign convention as follows: (1) Tensile normal stresses are positive. (2) Shear stresses are positive if the arrows on the positive facing sides of the element are in the directions of the positive x-y coordinate axes.

6.2.1 Rotation of Coordinate Axes

The same state of plane stress may be described on any other coordinate system, such as x'-y' in Fig. 6.2(b). This system is related to the original one by an angle of rotation θ, and the values of the stress components change to σ_x', σ_y', and τ_{xy}' in the new coordinate system. However, it is important to recognize that the new quantities do not represent a new state of stress, but rather an equivalent representation of the original one.

We may obtain the values of the stress components in the new coordinate system by considering the freebody diagram of a portion of the element, as indicated by the dashed line in Fig. 6.2(a). The resulting freebody is shown in Fig. 6.3. Equilibrium of forces in both the x- and y-directions provides two equations, which are sufficient to evaluate the unknown normal and shear stress components σ and τ on the inclined plane. The stresses must first be multiplied by the unequal areas of the sides of the triangular element to obtain forces. For convenience, the hypotenuse is taken to be of unit length, as is the thickness of the element normal to the diagram.

Summing forces in the x-direction, and then in the y-direction, gives two equations:

$$\sigma \cos \theta - \tau \sin \theta - \sigma_x \cos \theta - \tau_{xy} \sin \theta = 0 \tag{6.2}$$

$$\sigma \sin \theta + \tau \cos \theta - \sigma_y \sin \theta - \tau_{xy} \cos \theta = 0 \tag{6.3}$$

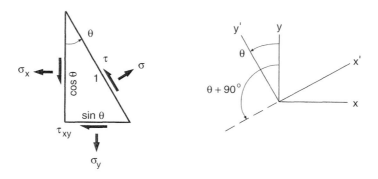

Figure 6.3 Stresses on an oblique plane.

Solving for the unknowns σ and τ, and also invoking some basic trigonometric indentities, yields

$$\sigma = \frac{\sigma_x + \sigma_y}{2} + \frac{\sigma_x - \sigma_y}{2} \cos 2\theta + \tau_{xy} \sin 2\theta \tag{6.4}$$

$$\tau = -\frac{\sigma_x - \sigma_y}{2} \sin 2\theta + \tau_{xy} \cos 2\theta \tag{6.5}$$

The desired complete state of stress in the new coordinate system may now be obtained. Equations 6.4 and 6.5 give σ_x' and τ_{xy}' directly, and substitution of $\theta + 90°$ gives σ_y'. Note that θ is positive in the counterclockwise (CCW) direction, as this was the direction taken as positive in developing these equations. This process of determining the equivalent representation of a state of stress on a new coordinate system is called *transformation of axes*, so the preceding equations are called the *transformation equations*.

6.2.2 Principal Stresses

The equations just developed give the variation of σ and τ with direction in the material, the direction being specified by the angle θ relative to the originally chosen x-y coordinate system. Maximum and minimum values of σ and τ are of special interest and can be obtained by analyzing the variation with θ.

Taking the derivative $d\sigma/d\theta$ of Eq. 6.4 and equating the result to zero gives the coordinate axes rotations for the maximum and minimum values of σ:

$$\tan 2\theta_n = \frac{2\tau_{xy}}{\sigma_x - \sigma_y} \tag{6.6}$$

Two angles θ_n separated by $90°$ satisfy this relationship. The corresponding maximum and minimum normal stresses from Eq. 6.4, called the *principal normal stresses*, are

$$\sigma_1, \sigma_2 = \frac{\sigma_x + \sigma_y}{2} \pm \sqrt{\left(\frac{\sigma_x - \sigma_y}{2}\right)^2 + \tau_{xy}^2} \tag{6.7}$$

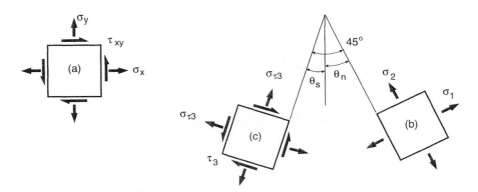

Figure 6.4 A state of plane stress (a), and the special coordinate systems that contain the principal normal stresses (b) and the principal shear stress (c).

Also, the shear stress at the θ_n orientation is found to be zero. The resulting equivalent representation of the original state of stress is illustrated by Fig. 6.4(b).

As noted, the shear stress is zero on the planes where the principal normal stresses occur. The converse is also true: If the shear stress is zero, then the normal stresses are the principal normal stresses.

Similarly, Eq. 6.5 and $d\tau/d\theta = 0$ give the coordinate axes rotation for the maximum shear stress:

$$\tan 2\theta_s = -\frac{\sigma_x - \sigma_y}{2\tau_{xy}} \tag{6.8}$$

The corresponding shear stress from Eq. 6.5 is

$$\tau_3 = \sqrt{\left(\frac{\sigma_x - \sigma_y}{2}\right)^2 + \tau_{xy}^2} \tag{6.9}$$

This is the maximum shear stress in the x-y plane and is called the *principal shear stress*. Also, the two orthogonal planes where this shear stress occurs are found to have the same normal stress of

$$\sigma_{\tau 3} = \frac{\sigma_x + \sigma_y}{2} \tag{6.10}$$

where the special subscript indicates that this is the normal stress that accompanies τ_3. This second equivalent representation of the original state of stress is illustrated by Fig. 6.4(c).

Equations 6.6 and 6.8 indicate that $2\theta_n$ and $2\theta_s$ differ by $90°$. Hence, if both $2\theta_n$ and $2\theta_s$ are considered to be limited to the range $\pm 90°$, then one of these must be negative—that is, clockwise (CW)—and we can write

$$|\theta_n - \theta_s| = 45° \tag{6.11}$$

In addition, τ_3 and the accompanying normal stress can be expressed in terms of the principal normal stresses σ_1 and σ_2 by substituting Eqs. 6.9 and 6.10 into the two relations represented by Eq. 6.7.

Solving these then gives

$$\tau_3 = \frac{|\sigma_1 - \sigma_2|}{2}, \qquad \sigma_{\tau 3} = \frac{\sigma_1 + \sigma_2}{2} \tag{6.12}$$

The absolute value is necessary for τ_3, due to the two roots of Eq. 6.9.

Example 6.1

At a point of interest on the free surface of an engineering component, the stresses with respect to a convenient coordinate system in the plane of the surface are $\sigma_x = 95$, $\sigma_y = 25$, and $\tau_{xy} = 20$ MPa. Determine the principal normal and shear stresses and their coordinate system rotations. Also determine the maximum normal stress and the maximum shear stress.

Solution   Substitution of the given values into Eq. 6.6 gives the angle to the coordinate axes for the principal normal stresses:

$$\tan 2\theta_n = \frac{2\tau_{xy}}{\sigma_x - \sigma_y} = \frac{4}{7}, \qquad \theta_n = 14.9° \quad \text{(CCW)} \qquad \textbf{Ans.}$$

Substitution into Eq. 6.7 gives the principal normal stresses:

$$\sigma_1, \sigma_2 = \frac{\sigma_x + \sigma_y}{2} \pm \sqrt{\left(\frac{\sigma_x - \sigma_y}{2}\right)^2 + \tau_{xy}^2}$$

$$\sigma_1, \sigma_2 = 60 \pm 40.3 = 100.3, 19.7 \text{ MPa} \qquad \textbf{Ans.}$$

The corresponding planes and state of stress are shown in Fig. E6.1(b). Note that the direction for the larger of the two principal normal stresses is chosen so that it is more nearly aligned with the larger of the original σ_x and σ_y than with the smaller.

Alternatively, a more rigorous procedure is to use $\theta = \theta_n = 14.9°$ in Eq. 6.4, which gives $\sigma = \sigma_x' = \sigma_1 = 100.3$ MPa. Use of $\theta = \theta_n + 90° = 104.9°$ in Eq. 6.4 then gives the normal stress in the other orthogonal direction, $\sigma = \sigma_y' = \sigma_2 = 19.7$ MPa. The zero value of τ at $\theta = \theta_n$ can also be verified by using Eq. 6.5.

For the equivalent representation where the maximum shear stress in the x-y plane occurs, Eq. 6.8 gives

$$\tan 2\theta_s = -\frac{\sigma_x - \sigma_y}{2\tau_{xy}} = -\frac{7}{4}, \qquad \theta_s = -30.1° = 30.1° \quad \text{(CW)} \qquad \textbf{Ans.}$$

The stresses for this rotation of the coordinate system may be obtained from σ_1 and σ_2 as previously calculated and from Eq. 6.12:

$$\tau_3 = \frac{|\sigma_1 - \sigma_2|}{2} = \pm 40.3 \text{ MPa}, \qquad \sigma_{\tau 3} = \frac{\sigma_1 + \sigma_2}{2} = 60 \text{ MPa} \qquad \textbf{Ans.}$$

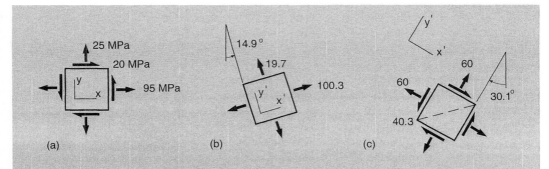

Figure E6.1 Example of a state of stress (a) and its equivalent representations that contain the principal normal stresses (b) and the principal shear stress (c).

This representation of the state of stress is shown as Fig. E6.1(c). The uncertainty as to the sign of the shear stress can be resolved by noting that the positive shear diagonal (dashed line) must be aligned with the larger of σ_1 and σ_2. Alternatively, a more rigorous procedure is to use $\theta = \theta_s = -30.1°$ in Eq. 6.5, which gives $\tau_3 = 40.3$ MPa. The positive sign indicates that the shear stress is positive in the new x'-y' coordinate system.

As for any case of plane stress, the largest of σ_1 and σ_2 is the maximum normal stress that occurs on any plane at this point in the material, so that $\sigma_{max} = 100.3$ MPa (**Ans.**). However, we cannot determine τ_{max} from what has been presented so far. Note that the principal shear stress τ_3 is merely the largest shear stress for any rotation in the x-y plane, and the true maximum shear stress may lie on planes that we have not yet considered. (See Section 6.3.2 and Ex. 6.4.)

6.2.3 Mohr's Circle

A convenient graphical representation of the transformation equations for plane stress was developed by Otto Mohr in the 1880s. On σ versus τ coordinates, these equations can be shown to represent a circle, called *Mohr's circle*, which is developed as follows.

Although it may not be immediately apparent, Eqs. 6.4 and 6.5 do represent a circle on a σ-τ plot in parametric from, where 2θ is the parameter. This can be shown by combining these two equations to eliminate 2θ. First, isolate all terms containing 2θ on one side of Eq. 6.4. Then square both sides of Eqs. 6.4 and 6.5, sum the result, and invoke simple trigonometric identities to eliminate 2θ, obtaining

$$\left(\sigma - \frac{\sigma_x + \sigma_y}{2}\right)^2 + \tau^2 = \left(\frac{\sigma_x - \sigma_y}{2}\right)^2 + \tau_{xy}^2 \tag{6.13}$$

This equation is of the form

$$(\sigma - a)^2 + (\tau - b)^2 = r^2 \tag{6.14}$$

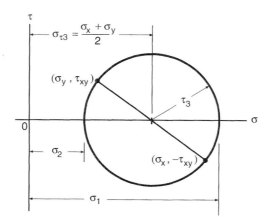

Figure 6.5 Mohr's circle and principal stresses corresponding to a given state of plane stress $(\sigma_x, \sigma_y, \tau_{xy})$.

which is the equation of a circle on a plot of σ versus τ with center at coordinates (a, b) and radius r, where

$$a = \frac{\sigma_x + \sigma_y}{2}, \qquad b = 0, \qquad r = \sqrt{\left(\frac{\sigma_x - \sigma_y}{2}\right)^2 + \tau_{xy}^2} \qquad (6.15)$$

Comparison with Eqs. 6.9 and 6.10 reveals that

$$a = \sigma_{\tau 3}, \qquad r = \tau_3 \qquad (6.16)$$

Mohr's circle is illustrated in Fig. 6.5. The center is seen to be located a distance $\sigma_{\tau 3}$ from the origin along the horizontal σ-axis, with $\sigma_{\tau 3}$ being simply the average of the two normal stresses, σ_x and σ_y. It is evident that the radius τ_3 is indeed the maximum shear stress in the x-y plane. Also, the maximum and minimum normal stresses occur along the σ-axis and are given by

$$\sigma_1, \sigma_2 = a \pm r = \frac{\sigma_x + \sigma_y}{2} \pm \tau_3 \qquad (6.17)$$

Noting Eq. 6.9, this is seen to be equivalent to Eq. 6.7.

In using Mohr's circle, difficulties with the signs of shear stresses can be avoided by adopting the convention shown in Fig. 6.6. The complete state of shear stress is considered to be split into two portions as shown. The portion that causes clockwise rotation is considered positive, and the portion that causes counterclockwise rotation is considered negative. For normal stresses, tension is positive, and compression negative.[1]

---

[1] By the sign convention employed for Fig. 6.3 and the associated equations, a shear stress on the σ_x planes causing counterclockwise rotation is positive. Hence, the suggested sign convention for Mohr's circle reverses the sign for τ_{xy} on the σ_x planes, while leaving the sign unchanged for τ_{xy} on the σ_y planes. Other valid options for handling these signs exist as described in various textbooks on elementary mechanics of materials.

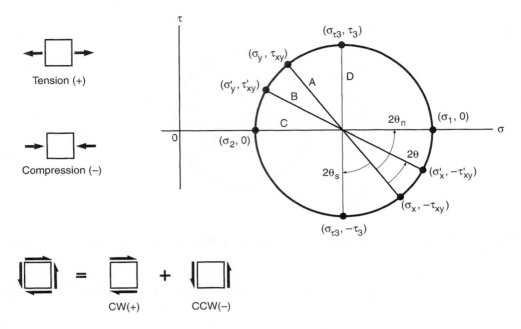

Figure 6.6 Sign convention and diameters of special interest for Mohr's circle.

If this is done, the two ends of a diameter of the circle can be used to represent the stresses on orthogonal planes in the material. This is illustrated by diameter A in Fig. 6.6. Note that the normal and shear stresses that occur together on one orthogonal plane provide the coordinate point for one end of the diameter, and those for the other plane give the opposite end.

A rotation of this diameter by an angle 2θ on the circle gives the state of stress for a coordinate axis rotation of θ in the same direction in the material. This is illustrated by diameter B in Fig. 6.6, which corresponds to the situation of Fig. 6.2(b). If the diameter is rotated by an angle $2\theta_n$ until it becomes horizontal, the principal normal stresses are obtained. Also, if the diameter is rotated by an angle $2\theta_s$ until it becomes vertical, the state of stress obtained contains the principal shear stress. These special choices of coordinate axes are illustrated by diameters C and D in Fig. 6.6, and they correspond to Fig. 6.4(b) and (c), respectively.

Example 6.2

Repeat Example 6.1, using Mohr's circle. Recall that the original state of stress is $\sigma_x = 95$, $\sigma_y = 25$, and $\tau_{xy} = 20$ MPa.

Solution   The circle is obtained by plotting two points that lie at opposite ends of a diameter, as shown in Fig. E6.2.

$$(\sigma, \tau) = (\sigma_x, -\tau_{xy}) = (95, -20) \text{ MPa}$$

$$(\sigma, \tau) = (\sigma_y, \tau_{xy}) = (25, 20) \text{ MPa}$$

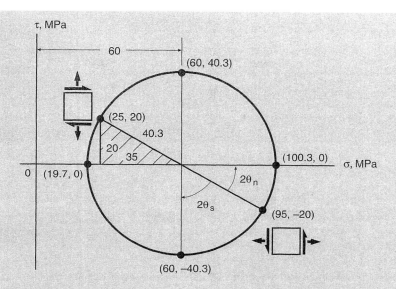

Figure E6.2 Mohr's circle corresponding to the state of stress of Fig. E6.1.

A negative sign is applied to τ_{xy} for the point associated with σ_x, because the shear arrows on the same planes as σ_x tend to cause a counterclockwise rotation. Similarly, a positive sign is used for τ_{xy} when associated with σ_y, due to the clockwise rotation. The center of the circle must lie on the σ-axis at a point halfway between σ_x and σ_y:

$$(\sigma, \tau)_{\text{ctr.}} = \left(\frac{\sigma_x + \sigma_y}{2}, 0 \right) = (60, 0)\ \text{MPa}$$

From the preceding coordinate points, the shaded right triangle shown has a base of 35 and an altitude of 20 MPa. The hypotenuse is the radius of the circle and is also the principal shear stress:

$$\tau_3 = \sqrt{35^2 + 20^2} = 40.3\ \text{MPa} \qquad\qquad \textbf{Ans.}$$

The angle with the σ-axis is

$$\tan 2\theta_n = \frac{20}{35}, \qquad 2\theta_n = 29.74°\ \ \text{(CCW)} \qquad\qquad \textbf{Ans.}$$

A counterclockwise rotation of the diameter of the circle by this $2\theta_n$ gives the horizontal diameter that corresponds to the principal normal stresses. Their values are obtained from the center location and radius of the circle:

$$\sigma_1 = \frac{\sigma_x + \sigma_y}{2} + \tau_3 = 60 + 40.3 = 100.3 \, \text{MPa} \qquad\qquad \textbf{Ans.}$$

$$\sigma_2 = \frac{\sigma_x + \sigma_y}{2} - \tau_3 = 60 - 40.3 = 19.7 \, \text{MPa} \qquad\qquad \textbf{Ans.}$$

The resulting state of stress is the same as previously illustrated in Fig. E6.1(b). Note that the counterclockwise rotation $2\theta_n$ on the circle corresponds to a rotation of $\theta_n = 14.9°$ in the same direction in the material.

The diameter corresponding to the original state of stress must be rotated clockwise to obtain the equivalent representation that contains the principal shear stress. Since this is $90°$ from the σ-axis, the angle of rotation is

$$2\theta_s = 90° - 2\theta_n = 60.26° \quad \text{(CW)} \qquad\qquad \textbf{Ans.}$$

so that $\theta_s = 30.1°$ clockwise. The coordinates of the ends of this vertical diameter give the same state of stress with τ_3 as previously shown in Fig. E6.1(c).

As already noted for Ex. 6.1, we have $\sigma_{\text{max}} = 100.3 \, \text{MPa}$ (**Ans.**), but we cannot determine τ_{max} at this point.

6.2.4 Generalized Plane Stress

Consider a state of stress where two components of shear stress are zero, such as $\tau_{yz} = \tau_{zx} = 0$. Such a situation is illustrated in a three-dimensional view in Fig. 6.7(a). It can also be illustrated by a diagram in the x-y plane, where the z-direction is normal to the paper, as shown in (b). The freebody of a portion of this unit cube is shown in (c). This freebody is similar to that employed previously for plane stress—specifically, Fig. 6.3. The only difference is the presence of the stress σ_z. The equations of equilibrium in the x-y plane are the same as before.

Hence, all of the equations previously developed for the x-y plane apply to this case as well. This includes the equations for the principal normal stresses in the x-y plane, σ_1 and σ_2, and also those for the principal shear stress and the accompanying normal stress, τ_3 and $\sigma_{\tau 3}$. It is simply necessary to note that σ_z remains unchanged for all rotations of the coordinate axes in the x-y plane. Moreover, since Mohr's circle was also derived from the same equilibrium equations, it can also be employed for the x-y plane.

Since this category of stress state is closely related to plane stress, we will call it *generalized plane stress*. For example, such a state of stress occurs in a thick-walled tube with closed ends loaded by internal pressure and torsion, as illustrated in Fig. A.6(a) in Appendix A. Note that, for the r-t-x coordinate system shown, two shear components are zero, with the only nonzero shear being τ_{tx}. The three normal stresses, σ_r, σ_t, and σ_x, generally have nonzero values. (The only exception is that $\sigma_r = 0$ at $R = r_2$.)

As will be apparent from the discussion of three-dimensional states of stress given later in this chapter, there are always three principal normal stresses, σ_1, σ_2, and σ_3. For generalized plane stress

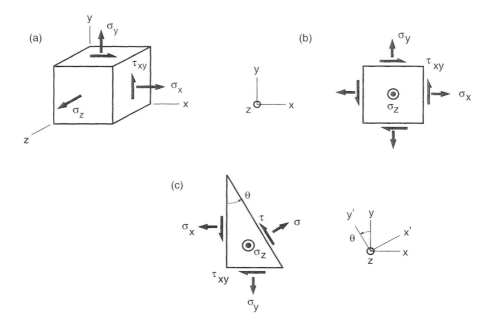

Figure 6.7   State of generalized plane stress where two components of shear stress are zero.

with $\tau_{yz} = \tau_{zx} = 0$, we obtain σ_1 and σ_2 from Eq. 6.7 or from Mohr's circle, and the third principal normal stress turns out to be $\sigma_3 = \sigma_z$. Also, since ordinary plane stress is simply a special case of generalized plane stress where $\sigma_z = 0$, the third principal normal stress in this case is simply $\sigma_3 = \sigma_z = 0$.

6.3 PRINCIPAL STRESSES AND THE MAXIMUM SHEAR STRESS

Consider any state of stress on an x-y-z coordinate system, as in Fig. 6.1. There is, in all cases, an equivalent representation on a new coordinate system of *principal axes*, 1-2-3, where no shear stresses are present, as illustrated by Fig. 6.8(a). The three normal stresses for the 1-2-3 coordinate system are *principal normal stresses*, σ_1, σ_2, and σ_3. Of these, one is the maximum normal stress acting on any plane, another is the minimum normal stress acting on any plane, and the remaining one has an intermediate value.

For x-y plane stress or generalized plane stress, the values of σ_1 and σ_2 and their directions may be found, as described in the previous section of this chapter, by using Eqs. 6.6 and 6.7. In Fig. 6.4, the directions of σ_1 and σ_2 are the 1-2 axes, with these directions being determined by the θ_n rotation from the original x-y axes. Further, the 3-axis is the z-axis, with $\sigma_3 = \sigma_z$.

However, for the general three-dimensional case, the 1-2-3 axes are unique directions that may all differ from the original x-y-z directions. The general procedure for finding σ_1, σ_2, and σ_3 and the corresponding 1-2-3 axes will be considered in the next section of this chapter. However, before proceeding with this somewhat advanced topic, it is useful to consider principal shear stresses and the maximum shear stress, and also to revisit plane stress.

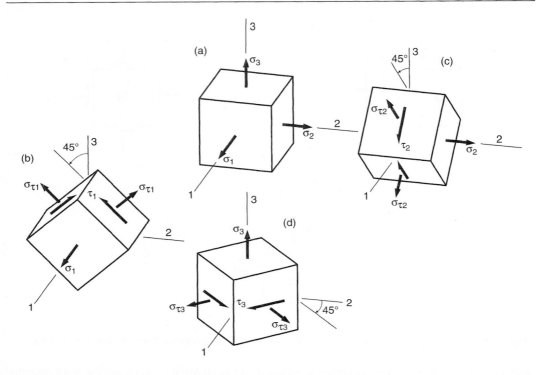

Figure 6.8 Principal normal stresses and principal axes (a), and principal shear stresses (b), (c), (d). In (b), rotation of the unit cube 45° about the axis of σ_1 gives the planes where τ_1 acts. Similar rotation about σ_2 gives the τ_2 planes (c), and about σ_3 the τ_3 planes (d).

6.3.1 Principal Shear Stresses and Maximum Shear Stress

In Fig. 6.8(a), if the equivalent state of stress is found for a 45° rotation about any of the 1, 2, or 3 axes, a shear stress is encountered that is the largest for any rotation about that axis. The three shear stresses that result are called the *principal shear stresses*, τ_1, τ_2, and τ_3. These are each accompanied by normal stresses that are the same on the two shear planes, $\sigma_{\tau 1}$, $\sigma_{\tau 2}$, and $\sigma_{\tau 3}$, respectively. For the planes containing each pair of principal axes, 1-2, 2-3, and 3-1, we have a state of generalized plane stress, so that relationships similar to Eq. 6.12 apply for each 45° rotation. Hence, the three principal shear stresses and the accompanying normal stresses are given by

$$\tau_1 = \frac{|\sigma_2 - \sigma_3|}{2}, \qquad \tau_2 = \frac{|\sigma_1 - \sigma_3|}{2}, \qquad \tau_3 = \frac{|\sigma_1 - \sigma_2|}{2} \qquad (6.18)$$

$$\sigma_{\tau 1} = \frac{\sigma_2 + \sigma_3}{2}, \qquad \sigma_{\tau 2} = \frac{\sigma_1 + \sigma_3}{2}, \qquad \sigma_{\tau 3} = \frac{\sigma_1 + \sigma_2}{2} \qquad (6.19)$$

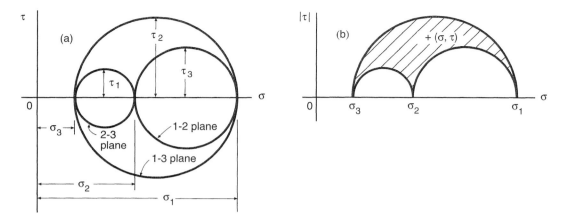

Figure 6.9 Mohr's circles for a three-dimensional state of stress.

The maximum shear stress for any plane in the material is the largest of the three principal shear stresses:

$$\tau_{\max} = \text{MAX}(\tau_1, \tau_2, \tau_3) \tag{6.20}$$

Mohr's circles may be applied for the rotations of Fig. 6.8 about each of the principal axes. The three circles that result are shown in Fig. 6.9. Two of the circles lie inside the largest one, and each is tangent along the σ-axis to the other two. The radii of these circles are the principal shear stresses, τ_1, τ_2, and τ_3, and the centers are located along the σ-axis at the points given by the three $\sigma_{\tau i}$ values. Also, each plane where one of these principal shear stresses occurs is seen to be a 45° rotation away from the corresponding planes of principal normal stress, which is consistent with the previous discussion and with Fig. 6.8.

Example 6.3

For the following state of stress, determine the principal normal stresses, the principal axes, and the principal shear stresses:

$$\sigma_x = 100, \qquad \sigma_y = -60, \qquad \sigma_z = 40\,\text{MPa}$$

$$\tau_{xy} = 80, \qquad \tau_{yz} = \tau_{zx} = 0\,\text{MPa}$$

Also determine the maximum normal stress and the maximum shear stress.

Solution   Since there is only one nonzero component of shear stress, we have a state of generalized plane stress, and the stress normal to the plane of the nonzero shear stress is one of the principal normal stresses:

$$\sigma_3 = \sigma_z = 40\,\text{MPa}$$ **Ans.**

Mohr's circle may then be employed for the x-y plane just as for a two-dimensional problem. The two ends of a diameter are

$$\left(\sigma_x, -\tau_{xy}\right) = (100, -80), \qquad \left(\sigma_y, \tau_{xy}\right) = (-60, 80)\,\text{MPa}$$

The resulting circle is shown in Fig. E6.3(a).

Simple geometry, as in Ex. 6.2, is next needed to locate the ends of the horizontal diameter. In particular, the center of the circle is located at a σ value of

$$a = \frac{\sigma_x + \sigma_y}{2} = \frac{100 - 60}{2} = 20\,\text{MPa}$$

From the cross-hatched triangle, the radius of the circle is

$$r = \sqrt{80^2 + 80^2} = 113.1\,\text{MPa}$$

This gives the two remaining principal normal stresses:

$$\sigma_1, \sigma_2 = a \pm r = 133.1, -93.1\,\text{MPa}$$ **Ans.**

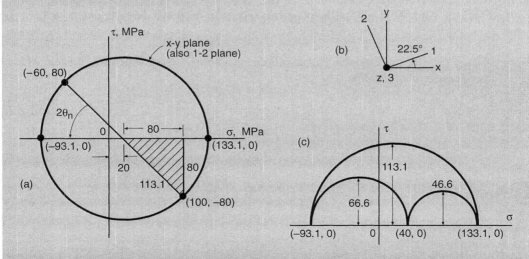

Figure E6.3 Mohr's circle, principal axes, and principal stresses for the three-dimensional state of stress example.

From Fig. E6.3(a), the directions for these stresses are given by a rotation θ_n relative to the original x-y axes:

$$\tan 2\theta_n = 80/80 = 1.00, \qquad 2\theta_n = 45°, \qquad \theta_n = 22.5°\,(\text{CCW})$$

This rotation gives the 1-2 principal axes. Since the third principal stress σ_3 is coincident with σ_z, the, the 1-2-3 principal axes are as shown in Fig. E6.3(b).

The maximum normal stress is the largest of σ_1, σ_2, σ_3, so that $\sigma_{max} = 133.1\,\text{MPa}$ (**Ans.**).

The points $(\sigma_1, 0)$, $(\sigma_2, 0)$, and $(\sigma_3, 0)$ now fix the circles for the three principal planes, as shown in Fig. E6.5(c). The radii of these circles are the principal shear stresses:

$$\tau_1 = \frac{|\sigma_2 - \sigma_3|}{2} = \frac{|-93.1 - 40|}{2} = 66.6\,\text{MPa} \qquad \textbf{Ans.}$$

$$\tau_2 = \frac{|\sigma_1 - \sigma_3|}{2} = \frac{|133.1 - 40|}{2} = 46.6\,\text{MPa} \qquad \textbf{Ans.}$$

$$\tau_3 = \frac{|\sigma_1 - \sigma_2|}{2} = \frac{|133.1 - (-93.1)|}{2} = 113.1\,\text{MPa} \qquad \textbf{Ans.}$$

The largest of these is $\tau_{max} = 113.1\,\text{MPa}$. 　　　　　　　　　　　　　　　　　　　　　　　　　　　**Ans.**

Comments   The principal normal stresses and directions could have been determined from Eqs. 6.6 and 6.7 rather than from Mohr's circle. If desired, the three circles could then still be plotted from the values of σ_1, σ_2, and σ_3, with half circles as in (c) being sufficient to allow τ_1, τ_2, and τ_3 to be visualized.

6.3.2 Plane Stress Revisited

Consider plane stress in the x-y plane, so that $\sigma_z = \tau_{yz} = \tau_{zx} = 0$. If the principal normal stresses in the x-y plane are σ_1 and σ_2, then the third principal normal stress σ_3 is zero. Even for this situation, shear stresses are in general present on all of the principal shear planes of Fig. 6.8. From Eq. 6.18, for the case of $\sigma_z = \sigma_3 = 0$, the principal shear stresses are

$$\tau_1 = \frac{|\sigma_2 - \sigma_3|}{2} = \frac{|\sigma_2|}{2}, \qquad \tau_2 = \frac{|\sigma_1 - \sigma_3|}{2} = \frac{|\sigma_1|}{2}, \qquad \tau_3 = \frac{|\sigma_1 - \sigma_2|}{2} \qquad (6.21)$$

Thus, in a sense, there is no such thing as a state of plane stress, as stresses occur on planes associated with choices of coordinate axes that are not in the x-y plane. Furthermore, it is hazardous

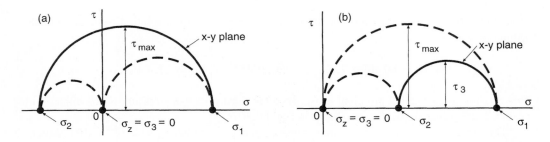

Figure 6.10   Plane stress in the *x-y* plane reconsidered as a three-dimensional state of stress. In case (a), the maximum shear stress lies in the *x-y* plane, but in case (b) it does not.

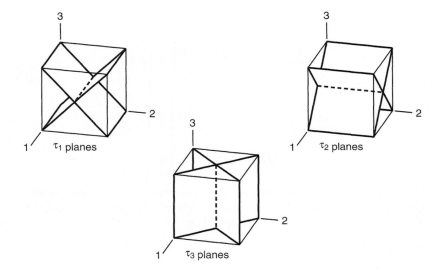

Figure 6.11   Orientations of the planes of principal shear relative to the principal normal stress cube.

to confine one's attention to the *x-y* plane, as one of the principal shear stresses τ_1, τ_2, or τ_3 may be larger than the one of these that is the τ_3 of Eq. 6.9 obtained from analysis of the stresses in the *x-y* plane. From Eq. 6.21, this in fact occurs whenever the two principal normal stresses in the *x-y* plane are of the same sign.

Mohr's circles further illustrate the situation, as shown in Fig. 6.10. The circles are defined by the points σ_1, σ_2, and σ_3 on the σ-axis, where one of these is $\sigma_z = 0$, so that two of the circles must pass through the origin. If the principal normal stresses in the *x-y* plane are of opposite sign, then the circle for the *x-y* plane is the largest, and τ_3 for the *x-y* plane is the maximum shear stress for all possible choices of coordinate axes. This case is illustrated by (a). However, if the principal normal stresses for the *x-y* plane are of the same sign, as in (b), then one of the

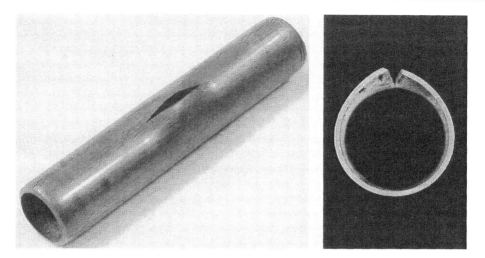

Figure 6.12   Failure of a 15 mm diameter copper water pipe due to excess pressure from freezing. In the cross section on the right, note that failure occurred on a plane inclined 45° to the tube surface, which is the plane of the maximum shear stress. (Photos by R. A. Simonds.)

other circles is the largest. The radius of the largest circle now corresponds to a shear stress that cannot be found by rotations in the x-y plane, and which acts on planes that are inclined to the x-y plane.

Consider Fig. 6.11, where the planes of principal shear from Fig. 6.8 are shown within the principal normal stress cube. For plane stress, we have defined σ_1 and σ_2 as the principal normal stresses found by a coordinate system rotation in the x-y plane. Hence, the 1-2 plane is also the x-y plane. Where either τ_1 or τ_2 is the maximum shear stress, the planes on which this shear stress acts are seen from Fig. 6.11 to be inclined relative to the x-y plane by 45° angles. Failure of a pressurized tube along such an inclined plane of maximum shear stress is shown in Fig. 6.12.

Example 6.4
What is the maximum shear stress for the situation analyzed in Examples 6.1 and 6.2?

Solution   Recall that the original state of stress is $\sigma_x = 95$, $\sigma_y = 25$, and $\tau_{xy} = 20$ MPa. Also, the principal normal and shear stresses already found by analysis confined to the x-y plane are

$$\sigma_1 = 100.3, \qquad \sigma_2 = 19.7, \qquad \tau_3 = 40.3 \text{ MPa}$$

The third principal normal stress is $\sigma_3 = \sigma_z = 0$. Equation 6.18 then gives the remaining principal shear stresses:

$$\tau_1 = \frac{|\sigma_2 - \sigma_3|}{2} = \frac{|19.7 - 0|}{2} = 9.8 \, \text{MPa}$$

$$\tau_2 = \frac{|\sigma_1 - \sigma_3|}{2} = \frac{|100.3 - 0|}{2} = 50.1 \, \text{MPa}$$

The maximum shear stress is thus τ_2, which does not lie in the x-y plane, but acts on planes inclined 45° to the x-y plane, so that $\tau_{\max} = 50.1 \, \text{MPa}$ (**Ans.**). This situation was expected, since the principal stresses σ_1 and σ_2 in the x-y plane are of the same sign.

Example 6.5

A pipe with closed ends has a wall thickness of 10 mm and an inner diameter of 0.60 m. It is filled with a gas at 20 MPa pressure and is subjected to a torque about its long axis of 1200 kN·m. Determine the three principal normal stresses and the maximum shear stress. Neglect any effects of the discontinuity associated with the end closure.

Solution   The thin-walled tube approximations of Figs. A.7 and A.8 apply, and the combination of pressure and torsion give stresses as shown in Fig. E6.5. From thickness $t = 10$ mm, the inner, outer, and average radii are, respectively,

$$r_1 = 300, \qquad r_2 = r_1 + t = 310, \qquad r_{\text{avg}} = r_1 + t/2 = 305 \, \text{mm}$$

The hoop and longitudinal stresses due to the pressure are then

$$\sigma_t = \frac{pr_1}{t} = \frac{(20 \, \text{MPa})(300 \, \text{mm})}{10 \, \text{mm}} = 600 \, \text{MPa}, \qquad \sigma_x = \frac{pr_1}{2t} = 300 \, \text{MPa}$$

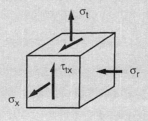

Figure E6.5

There is also a radial stress

$$\sigma_r = 0 \, \text{(outside)}, \qquad \sigma_r = -p = -20 \, \text{MPa (inside)}$$

The shear stress due to the torsion is

$$\tau_{tx} = \frac{T}{2\pi r_{\text{avg}}^2 t} = \frac{1200 \times 10^6 \, \text{N} \cdot \text{mm}}{2\pi (305 \, \text{mm})^2 (10 \, \text{mm})} = 205.3 \, \text{MPa}$$

Since we have a state of generalized plane stress, the principal normal stresses are

$$\sigma_1, \sigma_2 = \frac{\sigma_t + \sigma_x}{2} \pm \sqrt{\left(\frac{\sigma_t - \sigma_x}{2}\right)^2 + \tau_{tx}^2} = 450 \pm 254.3 = 704.3, \, 195.7 \, \text{MPa}$$

$$\sigma_3 = \sigma_r, \qquad \sigma_3 = 0 \, \text{(outside)}, \qquad \sigma_3 = -20 \, \text{(inside)} \qquad\qquad \textbf{Ans.}$$

From Eqs. 6.18 and 6.20, the maximum shear stress is

$$\tau_{\text{max}} = \text{MAX}\left(\frac{|\sigma_2 - \sigma_3|}{2}, \frac{|\sigma_1 - \sigma_3|}{2}, \frac{|\sigma_1 - \sigma_2|}{2}\right)$$

$$\tau_{\text{max}} = 352.1 \, \text{MPa (outside)}, \qquad \tau_{\text{max}} = 362.1 \, \text{MPa (inside)}$$

Note that σ_1 and σ_3 give the controlling choice in each case. The larger value for the two locations is, of course, the final answer—specifically, $\tau_{\text{max}} = 362.1 \, \text{MPa}$ (**Ans.**).

6.4 THREE-DIMENSIONAL STATES OF STRESS

In the general three-dimensional case, all six components of stress may be present: σ_x, σ_y, σ_z, τ_{xy}, τ_{yz}, and τ_{zx}. This general case can be analyzed to obtain transformation equations that permit values of the stress components to be evaluated for any choice of coordinate axes in three dimensions. This is accomplished by considering the freebody of a portion of the stress cube of Fig. 6.1 as cut off by an oblique plane in Fig. 6.13. Equilibrium of forces is then applied to this cube portion, as shown in Fig. 6.14.

The stresses on the cube portion are shown in Fig. 6.14(a) and some needed geometry in (b) and (c). The stresses on the original x-y, y-z, and z-x planes are the same as in Fig. 6.1. On the new oblique plane, there is a normal stress σ and a shear stress τ. In (b), the normal to the oblique plane, which is the direction of σ, is described by angles θ_x, θ_y, θ_z to the x, y, z axes, respectively. The cosines of these angles are useful, $l = \cos\theta_x$, $m = \cos\theta_y$, $n = \cos\theta_z$, and are called the *direction cosines*. By applying equilibrium of forces to this cube portion, σ and τ can be evaluated in terms of the stresses on the original x-y-z coordinate system for any direction (l, m, n) of the normal. Further analysis can be performed to find the maximum and minimum values of σ, and also an intermediate value, which are found to be accompanied by zero τ and to have orthogonal

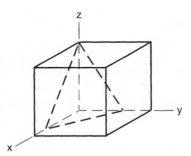

Figure 6.13   An oblique plane in a three-dimensional coordinate system.

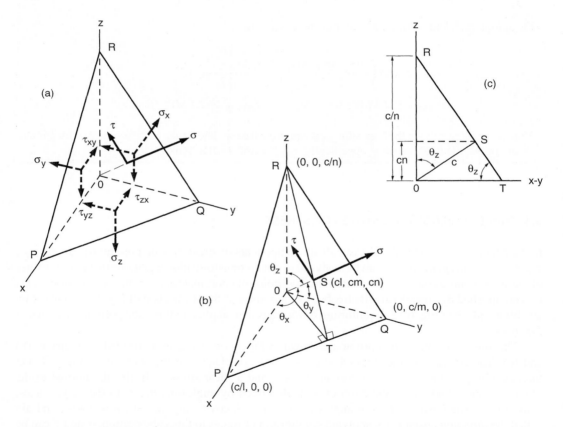

Figure 6.14   Stresses on the cube portion formed by an oblique plane (a), and associated geometry (b), (c). If the oblique plane is normal to a principal axis, then $\sigma = \sigma_i$ and $\tau = 0$, where σ_i is any one of σ_1, σ_2, or σ_3.

directions. These are of course the *principal normal stresses*, σ_1, σ_2, and σ_3. Their directions, 1-2-3, are the *principal axes*, as in Fig. 6.8(a). Interestingly, if the point (σ, τ) for any desired plane is plotted on Mohr's circle as in Fig. 6.9(b), it will always lie within the shaded area. A geometric construction to locate this point was derived by Otto Mohr, as described in the book by Ugural (2012).

Rather than analyzing the rather complex general case, we can proceed directly to the principal normal stresses by invoking equilibrium of forces on the cube portion for the special case $\sigma = \sigma_i$, $\tau = 0$, where σ_i is any one of σ_1, σ_2, σ_3. To aid us in this process, we first need to address some of the details of the geometry of the oblique plane, including the relative areas of the four faces of the cube portion.

6.4.1 Geometry and Areas

Consider right triangle O-T-R in Fig. 6.14(b), which is shown in a two-dimensional view as (c). Point T is located by extending line R-S to the x-y plane, where R is the z-axis intercept and S is the point where the normal intersects the oblique plane. If the distance $\overline{OS}$ along the normal from the origin to the oblique plane is denoted c, the coordinates of point S are (cl, cm, cn). For the z-direction, this can be seen in Fig. 6.14(c), where $c_z = c\,(\cos\theta_z) = cn$, and similarly for the other two directions. Also, from right triangle O-S-R, the z-axis intercept is distance $\overline{OR} = c/\cos\theta_z = c/n$, and similarly for the other two axes intercepts. Hence, we now have the coordinates of points P, Q, R, and S, as shown in (b).

Using these coordinates to write $\overline{RS}$ and $\overline{PQ}$ as vectors, we find that the dot product of these is zero, indicating that the two lines are perpendicular, $\overline{RS} \perp \overline{PQ}$. Since $\overline{RO}$ is perpendicular to any line in the x-y plane, we have $\overline{RO} \perp \overline{PQ}$ as well, and the plane of triangle O-T-R is perpendicular to line $\overline{PQ}$, so that any line in this plane is also perpendicular, giving $\overline{RT} \perp \overline{PQ}$ and $\overline{OT} \perp \overline{PQ}$. Further, from (c), angle O-T-R is seen to equal θ_z, due to mutually perpendicular sides, so that $\overline{RT}\,(\cos\theta_z) = \overline{OT}$.

We can now find the needed areas A of the triangular faces of the cube portion. Due to the perpendicularities noted previously, and since $\overline{RT}(\cos\theta_z) = \overline{OT}$, we have

$$A_{PQR} = \frac{\overline{PQ} \times \overline{RT}}{2}, \qquad A_{PQO} = A_{xy} = \frac{\overline{PQ} \times \overline{OT}}{2} = A_{PQR}(\cos\theta_z) = nA_{PQR} \qquad (6.22)$$

Hence, the area $A_{PQO} = A_{xy}$ of the x-y face is obtained simply by multiplying the area A_{PQR} of the oblique face by the direction cosine to the z-axis, $n = \cos\theta_z$. An analogous result applies for the y-z and z-x faces, so that the areas of the three orthogonal faces are simply related to the area of the oblique face by multiplying by appropriate direction cosines:

$$A_{yz} = lA_{PQR}, \qquad A_{zx} = mA_{PQR}, \qquad A_{xy} = nA_{PQR} \qquad (6.23)$$

6.4.2 Principal Normal Stresses from Equilibrium of Forces

We are now ready to apply equilibrium of forces to the cube portion for the special case $\sigma = \sigma_i$, $\tau = 0$, where σ_i is any one of the principal normal stresses $\sigma_1, \sigma_2, \sigma_3$. First, note that the components of σ_i in the x, y, z directions are $l_i\sigma_i$, $m_i\sigma_i$, $n_i\sigma_i$, respectively, where subscripts i have been added to indicate direction cosines for the particular principal normal stress σ_i. Multiplying stresses by areas to obtain forces and summing in the x-direction of Fig. 6.14(a), we obtain

$$l_i\sigma_i A_{PQR} - \sigma_x A_{yz} - \tau_{xy} A_{zx} - \tau_{zx} A_{xy} = 0 \qquad \text{(a)}$$

$$-l_i\sigma_i A_{PQR} + \sigma_x l_i A_{PQR} + \tau_{xy} m_i A_{PQR} + \tau_{zx} n_i A_{PQR} = 0 \qquad \text{(b)}$$

(6.24)

where (b) is obtained from (a) by invoking Eq. 6.23 and multiplying through by -1. Dividing (b) by A_{PQR}, we obtain the first of the following three equations:

$$(\sigma_x - \sigma_i)l_i + \tau_{xy}m_i + \tau_{zx}n_i = 0$$

$$\tau_{xy}l_i + (\sigma_y - \sigma_i)m_i + \tau_{yz}n_i = 0 \qquad (6.25)$$

$$\tau_{zx}l_i + \tau_{yz}m_i + (\sigma_z - \sigma_i)n_i = 0$$

The second two are similarly obtained by summing forces in the other two directions.

Equation 6.25 represents a homogeneous, linear system in variables l_i, m_i, n_i, which has a nontrivial solution only if the following determinant relationship is satisfied:

$$\begin{vmatrix} (\sigma_x - \sigma) & \tau_{xy} & \tau_{zx} \\ \tau_{xy} & (\sigma_y - \sigma) & \tau_{yz} \\ \tau_{zx} & \tau_{yz} & (\sigma_z - \sigma) \end{vmatrix} = 0 \qquad (6.26)$$

Expanding this determinant gives a cubic equation:

$$\sigma^3 - \sigma^2(\sigma_x + \sigma_y + \sigma_z) + \sigma(\sigma_x\sigma_y + \sigma_y\sigma_z + \sigma_z\sigma_x - \tau_{xy}^2 - \tau_{yz}^2 - \tau_{zx}^2)$$

$$-(\sigma_x\sigma_y\sigma_z + 2\tau_{xy}\tau_{yz}\tau_{zx} - \sigma_x\tau_{yz}^2 - \sigma_y\tau_{zx}^2 - \sigma_z\tau_{xy}^2) = 0 \qquad (6.27)$$

This cubic always has three real roots, which are the principal normal stresses, $\sigma_1, \sigma_2, \sigma_3$.

An alternative means of expressing this relationship is

$$\sigma^3 - \sigma^2 I_1 + \sigma I_2 - I_3 = 0 \qquad (6.28)$$

where

$$I_1 = \sigma_x + \sigma_y + \sigma_z$$

$$I_2 = \sigma_x\sigma_y + \sigma_y\sigma_z + \sigma_z\sigma_x - \tau_{xy}^2 - \tau_{yz}^2 - \tau_{zx}^2 \qquad (6.29)$$

$$I_3 = \sigma_x\sigma_y\sigma_z + 2\tau_{xy}\tau_{yz}\tau_{zx} - \sigma_x\tau_{yz}^2 - \sigma_y\tau_{zx}^2 - \sigma_z\tau_{xy}^2$$

These quantities are called *stress invariants*, as they have the same values for all choices of coordinate system. For example, $\sigma_x + \sigma_y + \sigma_z = \sigma_x' + \sigma_y' + \sigma_z' = $ constant. Hence, the sum of the normal stresses I_1 for the stress state as represented on the original x-y-z coordinate system is the same as the sum for the equivalent representation on any other coordinate system, x'-y'-z', including the coordinate system given by the principal directions, 1-2-3.

Determining values for the principal normal stresses thus consists of finding the three roots of the cubic equation in one of the forms just given. In doing so, it is common practice to assign the subscripts 1, 2, and 3, in order, to the maximum, intermediate, and minimum values. However, this convention is not a necessity, and it is useful in working numerical problems to relax this requirement and allow the numbers to be assigned as convenient. We will write all equations involving principal stresses in general form, so that it is not necessary to assume that the subscripts are assigned in any particular order.

6.4.3 Directions for the Principal Normal Stresses

Now consider finding the directions for the principal normal stresses—that is, the principal axes 1-2-3 of Fig. 6.8(a). To proceed, the values of the principal normal stresses, $\sigma_1, \sigma_2, \sigma_3$, first need to be determined, as described previously. Then one of these is substituted as σ_i into Eqs. 6.25, which are then solved simultaneously with

$$l_i^2 + m_i^2 + n_i^2 = 1 \qquad (6.30)$$

to give the values of l_i, m_i, and n_i. Note that Eq. 6.30 is required by geometry, and that only two of the three elements of Eq. 6.25 will be found to be independent, so that the third will not aid in the solution. To find all three principal axes, the process is repeated for each of $\sigma_1, \sigma_2,$ and σ_3.

In presenting the direction cosines, it is conventional to minimize negative signs. This can be accomplished by replacing one or more sets of direction cosines by its negative, which is merely a vector pointing in the opposite direction along the same line. For example, $(l_1, m_1, n_1) = (0.300, -0.945, -0.130)$ can be replaced by $(-0.300, 0.945, 0.130)$. Also, the three sets of direction cosines should represent a right-hand coordinate system. This can be accomplished by checking the vector cross product.

$$(l_1, m_1, n_1) \times (l_2, m_2, n_2) = (l_3, m_3, n_3) \qquad (6.31)$$

If this is not obeyed, then replace one direction cosine vector with its negative so as to both satisfy Eq. 6.31 and minimize negative signs. Alternatively, the first two direction cosine vectors can be obtained by solving Eqs. 6.25 and 6.30, and the third from Eq. 6.31, so that the right-hand system convention is automatically satisfied.

Example 6.6

For the same state of stress as in Ex. 6.3, determine the principal normal stresses by treating this as a three-dimensional problem. Recall that the given state of stress is $\sigma_x = 100$, $\sigma_y = -60$, $\sigma_z = 40$, $\tau_{xy} = 80$, and $\tau_{yz} = \tau_{zx} = 0$ MPa.

Solution   Substitute these given stresses into Eq. 6.29 to obtain values for the stress invariants:

$$I_1 = 80, \qquad I_2 = -10,800, \qquad I_3 = -496,000$$

These values correspond to units of MPa for stresses, as employed throughout this solution. The cubic relationship of Eq. 6.28 is thus

$$\sigma^3 - \sigma^2 I_1 + \sigma I_2 - I_3 = 0, \qquad \sigma^3 - 80\sigma^2 - 10,800\sigma + 496,000 = 0$$

For a number of values of σ, calculate the corresponding values of $f(\sigma)$:

$$\sigma^3 - 80\sigma^2 - 10,800\sigma + 496,000 = f(\sigma)$$

Then use these values to plot the cubic equation as in Fig. E6.6.

It is evident that there are three roots where the curve crosses the σ-axis, where $f(\sigma) = 0$. From the graph, these roots can be seen to be roughly 130, 40, and -90 MPa. Starting with each of these rough values in turn, apply trial and error, Newton's method, or another numerical procedure, as implemented in various widely available computer software. Accurate values are

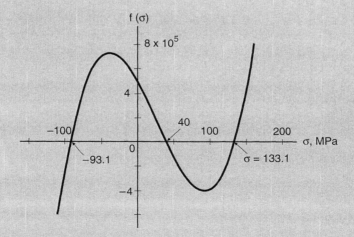

Figure E6.6   Graph of the example cubic equation, showing the three roots that are principal normal stresses.

obtained as follows:

$$\sigma_1 = 133.1, \qquad \sigma_2 = -93.1, \qquad \sigma_3 = 40.0 \, \text{MPa} \qquad\qquad \textbf{Ans.}$$

These are numbered consistently with the Ex. 6.3 solution. The maximum normal stress is the largest of σ_1, σ_2, σ_3, so that $\sigma_{max} = 133.1 \, \text{MPa}$. Principal shear stresses τ_1, τ_2, τ_3 and the maximum shear stress, τ_{max}, can then be calculated as already done in Ex. 6.3.

Comments   Note that we did not take advantage of the fact that this is a state of generalized plane stress. Hence, the foregoing procedure can be applied for any state of stress, as for cases where there are no zero stress components for the original x-y-z system. Where there are zero components, the determinate form of the cubic, Eq. 6.26, may be useful. In this particular case, Eq. 6.26 gives

$$\begin{vmatrix} (100 - \sigma) & 80 & 0 \\ 80 & (-60 - \sigma) & 0 \\ 0 & 0 & (40 - \sigma) \end{vmatrix} = 0$$

Using the last column to expand yields

$$(40 - \sigma)[(100 - \sigma)(-60 - \sigma) - 6400] = 0, \qquad (\sigma - 40)(\sigma^2 - 40\sigma - 12{,}400) = 0$$

Hence, from the $(\sigma - 40)$ factor, it is evident that one root is $\sigma_3 = 40.0 \, \text{MPa}$. The remaining two can be found by applying the quadratic formula to the equation that is the other factor.

Example 6.7

Find the direction cosines for each principal normal stress axis for the stress state of Ex. 6.6.

Solution   The principal stresses as already determined in Ex. 6.6 are needed:

$$\sigma_1 = 133.1, \qquad \sigma_2 = -93.1, \qquad \sigma_3 = 40 \, \text{MPa}$$

Equation 6.25 must now be applied for each of these stresses. Substituting for σ_1, and also for $\sigma_x, \sigma_y, \sigma_z, \tau_{xy}, \tau_{yz},$ and τ_{zx} on the original coordinate axes, we have

$$(100 - 133.1)l_1 + 80m_1 = 0$$

$$80l_1 + (-60 - 133.1)m_1 = 0$$

$$(40 - 133.1)n_1 = 0$$

The last of these is satisfied only by $n_1 = 0$, and the first two both give the same result:

$$l_1 = 2.414m_1$$

Combining these results with Eq. 6.30 gives

$$(2.414m_1)^2 + m_1^2 + 0^2 = 1, \qquad m_1 = 0.383$$

The value of l_1 is then easily obtained, so that the three values are

$$l_1 = 0.924, \qquad m_1 = 0.383, \qquad n_1 = 0 \qquad\qquad \textbf{Ans.}$$

Similar solutions for $\sigma_2 = -93.1$ and for $\sigma_3 = 40\,\text{MPa}$ give the direction cosines for the other two principal axes:

$$l_2 = -0.383, \qquad m_2 = 0.924, \qquad n_2 = 0$$
$$l_3 = 0, \qquad m_3 = 0, \qquad n_3 = 1$$

$$\textbf{Ans.}$$

The right-handedness of the 1-2-3 system of the direction cosines needs to be checked by using Eq. 6.31. We have

$$\begin{vmatrix} \mathbf{i} & \mathbf{j} & \mathbf{k} \\ l_1 & m_1 & n_1 \\ l_2 & m_2 & n_2 \end{vmatrix} = l_3\mathbf{i} + m_3\mathbf{j} + n_3\mathbf{k}, \qquad \begin{vmatrix} \mathbf{i} & \mathbf{j} & \mathbf{k} \\ 0.924 & 0.383 & 0 \\ -0.383 & 0.924 & 0 \end{vmatrix} = 1.000\mathbf{k}$$

where $\mathbf{i}, \mathbf{j}, \mathbf{k}$ are unit vectors for the x, y, z directions, respectively, and the cross product is done in determinate form. The l_3, m_3, n_3 direction cosines from the preceding analysis are confirmed, and no sign changes are needed.

Comments   From Fig. E6.3(b), the angles between the principal axes and the x, y, z axes are as follows:

1-axis: $\theta_x = 22.5°,\quad \theta_y = 67.5°,\quad \theta_z = 90°$
2-axis: $\theta_x = 112.5°,\quad \theta_y = 22.5°,\quad \theta_z = 90°$
3-axis: $\theta_x = 90°,\qquad \theta_y = 90°,\qquad \theta_z = 0°$

The cosines of these angles are seen to agree with the values of the direction cosines that have just been found. For a state of stress with no zero components in the original x-y-z system, there would be no 90° or 0° angles, so none of the direction cosines would be zero or unity.

6.5 STRESSES ON THE OCTAHEDRAL PLANES

Consider an oblique plane oriented relative to the 1-2-3 principal axes, as shown in Fig. 6.15(a). A normal stress σ and a shear stress τ act on this plane. The direction of the normal to the oblique plane is specified by the angles α, β, and γ to the principal axes.

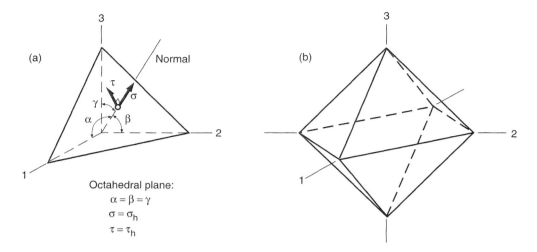

Figure 6.15 Octahedral plane shown relative to the principal normal stress axes (a), and the octahedron formed by the similar such planes in all octants (b).

For the special case where $\alpha = \beta = \gamma$, the oblique plane intersects the principal axes at equal distances from the origin and is called the *octahedral plane*. Based on equilibrium of forces, the normal stress on this plane can be shown to be the average of the principal normal stresses:

$$\sigma_h = \frac{\sigma_1 + \sigma_2 + \sigma_3}{3} \tag{6.32}$$

The quantity σ_h is called the *octahedral normal stress* or the *hydrostatic stress* and was considered in Chapter 5. Equilibrium also permits the shear stress on the same plane, called the *octahedral shear stress*, to be evaluated:

$$\tau_h = \frac{1}{3}\sqrt{(\sigma_1 - \sigma_2)^2 + (\sigma_2 - \sigma_3)^2 + (\sigma_3 - \sigma_1)^2} \tag{6.33}$$

In each octant of the principal axes coordinate system, there is a similar plane where the normal makes equal angles with the axes. The stresses on all eight such planes are the same and are σ_h and τ_h. These planes can be thought of as forming an octahedron, as shown in Fig. 6.15(b). Noting that opposite faces of the octahedron correspond to a single plane, the octahedral stresses act on four planes.

By evaluating the stress invariants, Eq. 6.29, for the special case of the principal normal stresses, and after some manipulation, σ_h and τ_h can be written in terms of the invariants:

$$\sigma_h = \frac{I_1}{3}, \qquad \tau_h = \frac{1}{3}\sqrt{2\left(I_1^2 - 3I_2\right)} \tag{6.34}$$

Substitution of the general form of the invariants and manipulation then gives

$$\sigma_h = \frac{\sigma_x + \sigma_y + \sigma_z}{3} \tag{6.35}$$

$$\tau_h = \frac{1}{3}\sqrt{(\sigma_x - \sigma_y)^2 + (\sigma_y - \sigma_z)^2 + (\sigma_z - \sigma_x)^2 + 6(\tau_{xy}^2 + \tau_{yz}^2 + \tau_{zx}^2)} \tag{6.36}$$

These more general expressions may be used to compute σ_h and τ_h for stresses described with respect to any coordinate system, so that it is not necessary to first determine the principal stresses. Since the octahedral stresses σ_h and τ_h are functions of the stress invariants, these quantities are themselves invariant. Hence, any equivalent representation of a given state of stress will give the same values of σ_h and τ_h.

The octahedral shear stress is an important quantity, as it is used as a basis for predicting yielding and other types of material behavior under complex states of stress. This is considered starting in the next chapter, as is the similar use of the maximum shear stress. Since $\tau_{\max}$ occurs on only two planes, τ_h occurs twice as frequently as does $\tau_{\max}$. (Compare Figs. 6.8 and 6.15.) Also, for all possible states of stress, it can be shown that τ_h is always similar in magnitude to $\tau_{\max}$, with the ratio $\tau_h/\tau_{\max}$ being confined to the range 0.866 to unity, or more precisely, $\sqrt{3}/2$ to unity.

6.6 COMPLEX STATES OF STRAIN

In the discussion of complex states of stress, it was noted that equilibrium of forces leads to transformation equations for obtaining an equivalent representation of a given state of stress on a new set of coordinate axes. Of particular interest are two sets of axes, one containing the principal normal stresses, and the other the principal shear stresses. The mathematics involved is common to all physical quantities classed as *symmetric second-order tensors*, as distinguished from vectors, which are first-order tensors, or scalars, which are zero-order tensors.

Strain is also a symmetric second-order tensor and so is governed by similar equations. In this case, the basis of the equations is simply the geometry of deformation. Detailed analysis (see the References) gives equations that are identical to those for stress, except that shear strains are divided by two. Hence, the various equations developed for stress can be used for strain by changing the variables as follows:

$$\sigma_x, \sigma_y, \sigma_z \rightarrow \varepsilon_x, \varepsilon_y, \varepsilon_z, \qquad \tau_{xy}, \tau_{yz}, \tau_{zx} \rightarrow \frac{\gamma_{xy}}{2}, \frac{\gamma_{yz}}{2}, \frac{\gamma_{zx}}{2} \tag{6.37}$$

These apply in general and also to the special case where the x-y-z axes are axes of principal strain, 1-2-3.

Advanced textbooks on continuum mechanics, theory of elasticity, and similar subjects often redefine shear strains as being half as large as the usual *engineering shear strains* used here, calling these *tensor shear strains*, so that the equations become identical to those for stress. However, we will continue to use engineering shear strains.

6.6.1 Principal Strains

Principal normal strains and *principal shear strains* occur in a similar manner as for stresses. For *plane strain*, where $\varepsilon_z = \gamma_{yz} = \gamma_{zx} = 0$, modifying Eqs. 6.6 and 6.7 according to Eq. 6.37 gives the axis rotations and values for the principal normal strains:

$$\tan 2\theta_n = \frac{\gamma_{xy}}{\varepsilon_x - \varepsilon_y}$$

$$\varepsilon_1, \varepsilon_2 = \frac{\varepsilon_x + \varepsilon_y}{2} \pm \sqrt{\left(\frac{\varepsilon_x - \varepsilon_y}{2}\right)^2 + \left(\frac{\gamma_{xy}}{2}\right)^2} \qquad (6.38)$$

Equations 6.8 through 6.10 are similarly modified to obtain the axis rotation and value for the principal shear strain in the x-y plane, and also the accompanying normal strain:

$$\tan 2\theta_s = -\frac{\varepsilon_x - \varepsilon_y}{\gamma_{xy}}$$

$$\gamma_3 = \sqrt{(\varepsilon_x - \varepsilon_y)^2 + (\gamma_{xy})^2}, \qquad \varepsilon_{\gamma 3} = \frac{\varepsilon_x + \varepsilon_y}{2} \qquad (6.39)$$

As for the stress equations, θ is positive counterclockwise. Positive normal strains correspond to extension, negative ones to contraction. Positive shear strain causes a distortion corresponding to a positive shear stress, in that the long diagonal of the resulting parallelogram has a positive slope. (Look ahead to Fig. E6.8(a) for an example of a positive shear strain.) Direct use of these equations can be replaced by Mohr's circle in a manner similar to its use for stress. In accordance with Eq. 6.37, the σ-axis becomes an ε-axis, and the τ-axis becomes a $\gamma/2$-axis.

For three-dimensional states of strain, the principal strains can be obtained by modifying Eqs. 6.26 and 6.18 with the use of Eq. 6.37:

$$\begin{vmatrix} (\varepsilon_x - \varepsilon) & \dfrac{\gamma_{xy}}{2} & \dfrac{\gamma_{zx}}{2} \\[2ex] \dfrac{\gamma_{xy}}{2} & (\varepsilon_y - \varepsilon) & \dfrac{\gamma_{yz}}{2} \\[2ex] \dfrac{\gamma_{zx}}{2} & \dfrac{\gamma_{yz}}{2} & (\varepsilon_z - \varepsilon) \end{vmatrix} = 0 \qquad (6.40)$$

$$\gamma_1 = |\varepsilon_2 - \varepsilon_3|, \qquad \gamma_2 = |\varepsilon_1 - \varepsilon_3|, \qquad \gamma_3 = |\varepsilon_1 - \varepsilon_2| \qquad (6.41)$$

6.6.2 Special Considerations for Plane Stress

For cases of plane stress, $\sigma_z = \tau_{yz} = \tau_{zx} = 0$, the Poisson effect results in normal strains ε_z occurring in the out-of-plane direction, so that the state of strain is three-dimensional. If the material is isotropic, or if the material is orthotropic and a material symmetry plane is parallel to the x-y

plane, no shear strains γ_{yz} or γ_{zx} occur. This creates a situation analogous to that for generalized plane stress, where σ_z is present, but $\tau_{yz} = \tau_{zx} = 0$. Hence, one of the principal normal strains is $\varepsilon_z = \varepsilon_3$, and the other two can be obtained from Eq. 6.38. In addition, Mohr's circle can be used for the x-y plane.

For isotropic, linear-elastic materials, ε_z can be obtained from Hooke's law in the form of Eq. 5.26. Taking $\sigma_z = 0$ and adding Eqs. 5.26(a) and (b) leads to

$$\sigma_x + \sigma_y = \frac{E}{1 - \nu}(\varepsilon_x + \varepsilon_y) \tag{6.42}$$

Substituting this into Eq. 5.26(c) with $\sigma_z = 0$ gives ε_z in terms of the normal strains in the x-y plane:

$$\varepsilon_z = \frac{-\nu}{1 - \nu}(\varepsilon_x + \varepsilon_y) \tag{6.43}$$

Since $\tau_{yz} = \tau_{zx} = 0$, Eq. 5.27 gives $\gamma_{yz} = \gamma_{zx} = 0$, and it is confirmed that ε_z is one of the principal normal strains.

Consider an orthotropic material under x-y plane stress where the x-y plane is a plane of symmetry of the material. (This is the situation for most sheets and plates of composite materials.) The strain ε_z is still one of the principal normal strains, as $\gamma_{yz} = \gamma_{zx} = 0$ holds in this case also. Hence, the strains in the x-y plane can still be analyzed with Eqs. 6.38 and 6.39, and Mohr's circle for the x-y plane can still be used. However, ε_z cannot be obtained from Eq. 6.43, as the more general form of Hooke's law for orthotropic materials (Eq. 5.44) is needed.

The principal axes for stress and strain coincide for isotropic materials. Hence, Hooke's law can be applied to the principal strains, and the resulting stresses are the principal stresses, and vice versa. However, this is not the case for orthotropic materials unless the principal normal stress axes are perpendicular to the planes of material symmetry.

Example 6.8

At a point on a free (unloaded) surface of an engineering component made of an aluminum alloy, the following strains exist: $\varepsilon_x = -0.0005$, $\varepsilon_y = 0.0035$, and $\gamma_{xy} = 0.003$. Determine the principal normal and shear strains. Assume that no yielding of the material has occurred.

Solution   Since the material is expected to be isotropic, ε_z can be obtained from Eq. 6.43, and this is one of the principal normal strains. We obtain

$$\varepsilon_3 = \varepsilon_z = \frac{-0.345}{1 - 0.345}(-0.0005 + 0.0035) = -0.00158 \qquad \textbf{Ans.}$$

where Poisson's ratio from Table 5.2 is used, and application of this equation based on elastic behavior is valid due to the absence of yielding. Substituting the given strains into Eqs. 6.38 and 6.39 gives the axis rotations and values for the other two principal normal strains and for one of the principal shear strains:

$$\tan 2\theta_n = -\frac{3}{4}, \qquad \theta_n = -18.4° = 18.4° \quad (CW)$$

$$\varepsilon_1, \varepsilon_2 = 0.004, -0.001 \qquad\qquad\qquad \textbf{Ans.}$$

$$\tan 2\theta_s = \frac{4}{3}, \qquad \theta_s = 26.6° \quad (CCW)$$

$$\gamma_3 = 0.005, \qquad \varepsilon_{\gamma 3} = 0.0015 \qquad\qquad \textbf{Ans.}$$

The resulting states of strain are shown in Fig. E6.8 as (b) and (c). Signs and directions are determined in a manner similar to that used previously for stresses. In particular, the larger of the two principal normal strains takes a direction such that it is more nearly aligned with the larger of the original ε_x and ε_y than with the smaller. Also, the principal shear strain causes a distortion

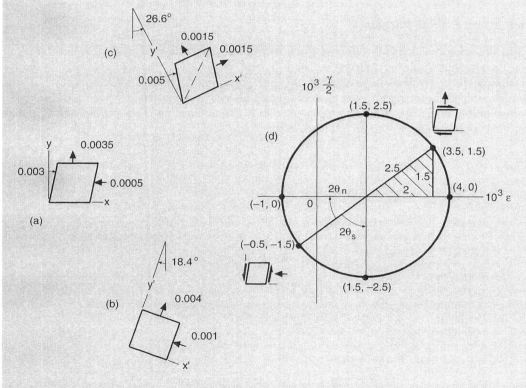

Figure E6.8 A state of strain (a) and the equivalent representations corresponding to principal normal strains (b) and the principal shear strain in the x-y plane (c). Mohr's circle for this case is shown in (d).

such that the long diagonal (dashed line) of the resulting parallelogram is aligned with the larger of ε_1 and ε_2.

The remaining two principal shear strains can be obtained from Eq. 6.41:

$$\gamma_1 = |\varepsilon_2 - \varepsilon_3| = 0.00058, \qquad \gamma_2 = |\varepsilon_1 - \varepsilon_3| = 0.00558 \qquad \textbf{Ans.}$$

The same result for the in-plane strains can be obtained by using Mohr's circle on a plot of ε versus $\gamma/2$ as shown. Two ends of a diameter are given by

$$\left(\varepsilon_x, -\frac{\gamma_{xy}}{2}\right) = (-0.0005, -0.0015), \qquad \left(\varepsilon_y, \frac{\gamma_{xy}}{2}\right) = (0.0035, 0.0015)$$

Analysis on the circle proceeds in a manner similar to that for stress. (See Fig. E6.8(d).) The special dual sign convention needed for shear strain corresponds to that for the shear stress which would produce the distortion, clockwise rotation being positive, as in Fig. 6.6.

6.6.3 Strain Gage Rosettes

Strain gages are small metal-foil sensors that may be bonded to the surface of a material to measure the longitudinal strain in a direction parallel to the alignment of the thin elements of the foil. Deformation of the material is duplicated in the gage, which changes its resistance by a small amount to provide a measurement of strain. A coordinated group of strain gages called a *rosette* is often used to obtain strain measurements in more than one direction. Two common configurations of three-gage rosettes are shown in Fig. 6.16.

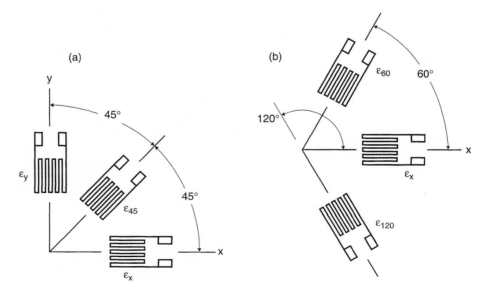

Figure 6.16 Two strain gage rosette configurations for measurements in three directions.

To completely characterize the in-plane strains at a point, ε_x, ε_y, and γ_{xy} are needed. There is no direct way of measuring shear strain, but γ_{xy} can be calculated if longitudinal strains are measured in three different directions. Transformation equations analogous to those of Section 6.2.1 for stress are needed to calculate the shear strain, and sometimes also ε_x and/or ε_y, if the measured strains are not aligned with the desired x-y directions.

Example 6.9

Consider a strain gage rosette mounted on the unloaded free surface of an engineering component, as shown in Fig. 6.16(a). Note that longitudinal strains ε_x, ε_y, and ε_{45} are measured in x- and y-directions and in a third direction 45° from the other two. Develop an equation for calculating the shear strain γ_{xy} from the three measurements that are available, so that the in-plane state of strain, ε_x, ε_y, and γ_{xy}, is completely known.

Solution   Convert the stress transformation relationship of Eq. 6.4 to the corresponding equation for normal strain by substitutions from Eq. 6.37:

$$\varepsilon_\theta = \frac{\varepsilon_x + \varepsilon_y}{2} + \frac{\varepsilon_x - \varepsilon_y}{2}\cos 2\theta + \frac{\gamma_{xy}}{2}\sin 2\theta$$

Substituting $\theta = 45°$ gives

$$\varepsilon_{45} = \frac{\varepsilon_x + \varepsilon_y}{2} + \frac{\gamma_{xy}}{2}$$

Solving for γ_{xy} then provides the desired result:

$$\gamma_{xy} = 2\varepsilon_{45} - \varepsilon_x - \varepsilon_y \qquad\qquad \textbf{Ans.}$$

6.7 SUMMARY

For a general state of stress, given by components $\sigma_x, \sigma_y, \sigma_z, \tau_{xy}, \tau_{yz}$, and τ_{zx}, there is one choice of a new coordinate system where shear stresses are absent and where the maximum and minimum normal stresses occur along with an intermediate normal stress. These special stresses are the principal normal stresses, σ_1, σ_2, and σ_3, and they may be obtained by solving the cubic equation given by the determinant

$$\begin{vmatrix} (\sigma_x - \sigma) & \tau_{xy} & \tau_{zx} \\ \tau_{xy} & (\sigma_y - \sigma) & \tau_{yz} \\ \tau_{zx} & \tau_{yz} & (\sigma_z - \sigma) \end{vmatrix} = 0 \qquad (6.44)$$

If there is only one nonzero component of shear stress, such as τ_{xy}, the principal normal stresses are

$$\sigma_1, \sigma_2 = \frac{\sigma_x + \sigma_y}{2} \pm \sqrt{\left(\frac{\sigma_x - \sigma_y}{2}\right)^2 + \tau_{xy}^2}, \qquad \sigma_3 = \sigma_z \qquad \text{(a, b)} \qquad (6.45)$$

One method of evaluating Eq. 6.45(a) and obtaining the corresponding axis rotation is to use Mohr's circle.

The principal shear stresses occur on planes inclined 45° with respect to the principal normal stress axes. These are given by

$$\tau_1 = \frac{|\sigma_2 - \sigma_3|}{2}, \qquad \tau_2 = \frac{|\sigma_1 - \sigma_3|}{2}, \qquad \tau_3 = \frac{|\sigma_1 - \sigma_2|}{2} \qquad (6.46)$$

One of the values τ_1, τ_2, τ_3 is the maximum shear stress that occurs for all possible choices of coordinate axes. For x-y plane stress, special care is needed that all three of Eq. 6.46 are considered, because the principal shear stress in the x-y plane may not be the largest. It is useful to envision three different Mohr's circles, one for each plane perpendicular to a principal normal stress axis. The radii of these are the principal shear stresses.

The octahedral normal and shear stresses occur on planes that intercept the principal normal stress axes at equal distances from the origin. Their values are given by

$$\sigma_h = \frac{\sigma_1 + \sigma_2 + \sigma_3}{3} \qquad (6.47)$$

$$\tau_h = \frac{1}{3}\sqrt{(\sigma_1 - \sigma_2)^2 + (\sigma_2 - \sigma_3)^2 + (\sigma_3 - \sigma_1)^2} \qquad (6.48)$$

where σ_h is also called the hydrostatic stress.

Principal normal strains and principal shear strains occur in a manner analogous to principal stresses. The same equations apply by replacing stresses with strains as follows:

$$\sigma_x, \sigma_y, \sigma_z \rightarrow \varepsilon_x, \varepsilon_y, \varepsilon_z, \qquad \tau_{xy}, \tau_{yz}, \tau_{zx} \rightarrow \frac{\gamma_{xy}}{2}, \frac{\gamma_{yz}}{2}, \frac{\gamma_{zx}}{2} \qquad (6.49)$$

Even plane stress causes a three-dimensional state of strain. However, for isotropic materials, and also for orthotropic materials stressed in a plane of material symmetry, the out-of-plane shear strains γ_{yz} and γ_{zx} are zero, permitting two-dimensional analysis to be performed in the x-y plane, despite the presence of a nonzero ε_z.

NEW TERMS AND SYMBOLS

axes rotation angles: θ_n and θ_s

direction cosines: l, m, n

generalized plane stress

Mohr's circle

octahedral normal (hydrostatic) stress, σ_h

octahedral planes

octahedral shear stress, τ_h

plane strain

plane stress

principal axes (1, 2, 3)

principal normal strains: ε_1, ε_2, ε_3

principal normal stresses: σ_1, σ_2, σ_3

principal shear strains: γ_1, γ_2, γ_3

principal shear stresses: τ_1, τ_2, τ_3

strain gage rosette

stress invariants: I_1, I_2, I_3

transformation equations

transformation of axes

REFERENCES

BORESI, A. P., and R. J. SCHMIDT. 2003. *Advanced Mechanics of Materials,* 6th ed., John Wiley, Hoboken, NJ. (See also the 2nd ed. of this book, same title, 1952, by F. B. Seely and J. O. Smith.)

DIETER, G. E., Jr. 1986. *Mechanical Metallurgy*, 3d ed., McGraw-Hill, New York.

MENDELSON, A. 1968. *Plasticity: Theory and Applications*, Macmillan, New York. (Reprinted by R. E. Krieger, Malabar, FL, 1983).

TIMOSHENKO, S. P., and J. N. GOODIER. 1970. *Theory of Elasticity*, 3d ed., McGraw-Hill, New York.

UGURAL, A. C., and S. K. FENSTER. 2012. *Advanced Strength and Applied Elasticity*, 5th ed., Prentice Hall, Upper Saddle River, NJ.

PROBLEMS AND QUESTIONS

Sections 6.2 and 6.3

6.1 A state of stress that occurs at a point on the free surface of a solid body is $\sigma_x = 6$ MPa, $\sigma_y = 6$ MPa and $\tau_{xy} = 2$ MPa.

   (a) Evaluate the two principal normal stresses and the one principal shear stress that can be found by coordinate system rotations in the x-y plane, and give the coordinate system rotations.

   (b) Determine the maximum normal stress and the maximum shear stress at this point.

6.2 to 6.9

   Proceed as in Prob. 6.1, but use the indicated stress from the table given below:

Table P6.2

Problem No.	σ_x, MPa	σ_y, MPa	τ_{xy}, MPa
6.2	−5	5	−5
6.3	32	−10	−20
6.4	21	131	0
6.5	35	21	7
6.6	345	138	69
6.7	125	−80	30
6.8	−50	40	−50
6.9	60	80	20

6.10 An element of material is subjected to the following state of stress: $\sigma_x = 4, \sigma_y = -5,$ $\sigma_z = -3, \tau_{xy} = -2, \tau_{yz} = \tau_{zx} = 0$. Determine the following:

   (a) Principal normal stresses and principal shear stresses.

   (b) Maximum normal stress and maximum shear stress.

   (c) Directions of the principal normal stress axes.

6.11 to 6.14

   Proceed as in Prob. 6.10, but use the indicated stresses from the table given below:

Table P6.11

Problem No.	Stress Components, MPa					
	σ_x	σ_y	σ_z	τ_{xy}	τ_{yz}	τ_{zx}
6.11	14	−56	70	0	0	0
6.12	200	0	250	100	0	0
6.13	345	138	−69	69	0	0
6.14	60	90	200	33	0	0

6.15 Consider the following state of plane stress: $\sigma_x = 200$ MPa, $\sigma_y = 100$ MPa and $\tau_{xy} = 0$ MPa.

    (a) Determine the principal normal stresses and the maximum shear stress.

    (b) Show that, for such a special case of x-y plane stress, where $\tau_{xy} = 0$ MPa, the in-plane principal normal stress σ_1 and σ_2 are always the same as σ_x and σ_y as to both the values and directions.

6.16 For the strain measurements on the surface of the mild steel part of Prob. 5.17, estimate the maximum normal stress and the maximum shear stress. Assume that no yielding has occurred.

6.17 For the strain measurements on the surface of the titanium alloy part of Prob. 5.18, estimate the maximum normal stress and the maximum shear stress. Assume that no yielding has occurred.

6.18 A spherical pressure vessel has a wall thickness of 2.5 mm and an inner diameter of 150 mm, and it contains a liquid at 1.2 MPa pressure. Determine the maximum normal stress and the maximum shear stress, and also describe the planes on which these act.

6.19 A pipe with closed ends has an outer diameter of 80 mm and wall thickness of 2.0 mm. It is subjected to an internal pressure of 10 MPa and a bending moment of 2.0 kN·m. Determine the maximum normal stress and the maximum shear stress. Neglect the localized effects of the end closure.

6.20 Proceed as in Prob. 6.19, except let a torque of 3.0 kN·m be applied instead of the bending moment given, while the 10 MPa pressure is still present.

6.21 A tube has an outer diameter of 60 mm and wall thickness of 3.0 mm. It is subjected to a bending moment of 1.8 kN·m and a torque of 2.5 kN·m. Determine the maximum normal stress and the maximum shear stress.

6.22 A solid shaft of diameter 50 mm is subjected to a bending moment $M = 3.0$ kN·m and a torque $T = 2.5$ kN·m. Determine the maximum normal stress and the maximum shear stress.

6.23 A solid shaft of diameter d is subjected to a bending moment M and a torque T.

    (a) Derive an expression for the maximum shear stress as a function of d, M, and T.

    (b) If $M = 2.0$ kN-m, what is the smallest diameter such that the maximum shear stress does not exceed 100 MPa?

6.24 A thin-walled tube with closed ends has an inside radius of 80 mm and a wall thickness of 6 mm. It is subjected to an internal pressure of 20 MPa, a torque of 60 kN·m, and an axial compressive force of 200 kN. Determine the maximum normal stress and the maximum shear stress.

6.25 A solid shaft of diameter 50 mm is subjected to an axial load $P = 200$ kN and a torque $T = 1.5$ kN·m. Determine the maximum normal stress and the maximum shear stress.

6.26 A solid shaft of diameter d is subjected to an axial load P and a torque T.

(a) Derive an expression for the maximum shear stress as a function of d, P, and T.

(b) If $P = 200$ kN and $T = 1.5$ kN·m, what is the smallest diameter such that the maximum shear stress does not exceed 100 MPa?

6.27 A simply supported beam 0.50 m long has a rectangular cross section of depth $2c = 60$ mm and thickness $t = 40$ mm. A vertical force $P = 40$ kN is applied at midspan, as in Fig. A.4(a), and also an axial force $F = 100$ kN is applied along its length. Determine the maximum normal stress and the maximum shear stress.

6.28 Consider an internally pressurized thick-walled spherical vessel, as in Fig. A.6(b).

(a) Develop an equation for the maximum shear stress at any radial position in the vessel, expressing this as a function of the radii r_1, r_2, and R, and the pressure p. Also show that the overall maximum shear stress in the vessel occurs at the inner wall.

(b) Assume that the vessel has an inner diameter of 100 mm and an outer diameter of 150 mm and contains an internal pressure of 300 MPa. Then determine the principal normal and shear stresses at the inner wall.

(c) For the same case as in (b), plot the variations of σ_r, σ_t, and τ_{max} versus R.

6.29 Consider an internally pressurized thick-walled tube, as in Fig. A.6(a). Assume that the tube has closed ends, but neglect the localized effects of the end closure.

(a) Develop an equation for the maximum shear stress at any radial position in the vessel, expressing this as a function of the radii r_1, r_2, and R, and the pressure p. Also show that the overall maximum shear stress in the vessel occurs at the inner wall.

(b) Assume that the vessel has an inner diameter of 80 mm, an outer diameter of 100 mm, and contains an internal pressure of 100 MPa. Then determine the principal normal and shear stresses at the inner wall.

(c) For the same case as in (b), plot the variations of σ_r, σ_t, σ_x, and τ_{max} versus R.

6.30 A thick-walled tube has closed ends and is loaded with an internal pressure of 75 MPa and a torque of 30 kN·m. The inner and outer diameters are 80 and 120 mm, respectively.

(a) Determine the maximum shear stress in the tube. Neglect the localized effects of the end closure. (Suggestion: Using Fig. A.6(a), calculate τ_{max} at the inner and outer walls and at several intermediate radial positions.)

(b) Plot the variations of σ_r, σ_t, and σ_x due to the pressure, τ_{tx} due to the torsion, and τ_{max}, all versus R.

6.31 Proceed as in Prob. 6.30(a) and (b), except change the numerical values as follows: internal pressure 90 MPa, torque 15 kN·m, and inner and outer diameters 48 and 78 mm, respectively.

6.32 A rotating annular disc as in Fig. A.9 has inner radius $r_1 = 90$, outer radius $r_2 = 300$, and thickness $t = 50$ mm. It is made of an alloy steel and rotates at a frequency of $f = 120$ revolutions/second.

(a) Calculate values of the radial and tangential stresses, σ_r and σ_t, for a number of values of the variable radius R, and then plot these stresses as a function of R.

(b) Determine the values and locations of the maximum normal stress and the maximum shear stress in the disc.

(Problem continues)

(c) Show that the maximum normal stress and the maximum shear stress are located at the inner radius for any rotating annular disc with constant thickness.

Section 6.4

6.33 Rework Prob. 6.2 by solving the cubic equation and finding the direction cosines for the principal axes. Also, show that your direction cosines are consistent with the axes rotations from Eq. 6.6.

6.34 Rework Prob. 6.11 by solving the cubic equation and finding the direction cosines for the principal axes. Also, show that your direction cosines are consistent with the axes rotations from Eq. 6.6.

6.35 Consider the special case where normal stresses σ_x, σ_y, and σ_z are present, but where the only nonzero shear stress is τ_{xy}, so that $\tau_{yz} = \tau_{zx} = 0$. For determining principal normal stresses, show that the solution of the cubic equation (Eq. 6.26 or 6.27) corresponds to the two equations represented by Eq. 6.7 and the third equation $\sigma_z = \sigma_3$. Also show that for this special case the direction cosine for σ_3 is perpendicular to the x-y plane, that is $(l_3, m_3, n_3) = (0, 0, 1)$.

6.36 An element of material is subjected to the following state of stress: $\sigma_x = -40$, $\sigma_y = 100$, $\sigma_z = 30$, $\tau_{xy} = -50$, $\tau_{yz} = 12$, and $\tau_{zx} = 0$ MPa. Determine the following:

    (a) Principal normal stresses and principal shear stresses.

    (b) Maximum normal stress and maximum shear stress.

    (c) Direction cosines for each principal normal stress axis.

6.37 to 6.43

Proceed as in Prob. 6.36, but use the indicated stresses from Table P6.37.

Table P6.37

Problem	Stress Components, MPa					
No.	σ_x	σ_y	σ_z	τ_{xy}	τ_{yz}	τ_{zx}
6.37	0	0	0	0	100	100
6.38	0	0	50	0	300	300
6.39	100	0	0	50	50	50
6.40	100	−100	0	0	50	50
6.41	65	−120	−45	30	0	50
6.42	25	50	40	20	−30	0
6.43	10	20	−10	−20	10	−30

6.44 Consider the state of stress $\sigma_x = 90$, $\sigma_y = 130$, $\sigma_z = -60$, and $\tau_{xy} = \tau_{yz} = \tau_{zx} = 0$ MPa. Employ the cubic equation (Eq. 6.26 or 6.27) and answer the following:

    (a) Determine the principal normal stresses and the maximum shear stress.

    (b) Show that, for such a special case, where $\tau_{xy} = \tau_{yz} = \tau_{zx} = 0$, the principal normal stresses are always simply $\sigma_1, \sigma_2, \sigma_3 = \sigma_x, \sigma_y, \sigma_z$. Also, show that the x-y-z axes are coincident with the 1-2-3 principal axes.

Section 6.5

6.45 Determine the octahedral normal and shear stresses for the state of stress: $\sigma_x = 32\,\text{MPa}$, $\sigma_y = -10\,\text{MPa}$, and $\tau_{xy} = -20\,\text{MPa}$.

6.46 Determine the octahedral normal and shear stresses for the state of stress: $\sigma_x = 345\,\text{MPa}$, $\sigma_y = 138\,\text{MPa}$, $\sigma_z = -69\,\text{MPa}$ and $\tau_{xy} = 69\,\text{MPa}$.

6.47 Consider a case of plane stress where the only nonzero components for the x-y-z coordinate system chosen are σ_x and τ_{xy}. (For example, this situation occurs at the surface of a shaft under combined bending and torsion.) Develop equations in terms of σ_x and τ_{xy} for the following: maximum normal stress, maximum shear stress, and octahedral shear stress.

6.48 Consider the case of plane stress where the only nonzero components for the x-y-z system chosen are σ_x and σ_y. (For example, this occurs in a thin-walled tube with internal pressure and bending and/or axial loads.) Develop an equation for the octahedral shear stress in terms of σ_x and σ_y.

6.49 Develop an equation for the octahedral shear stress in terms of the principal shear stresses.

6.50 Consider an internally pressurized thick-walled tube, as in Fig. A.6(a). Assume that the tube has closed ends, but neglect the localized effects of the end closure. Develop an equation for the octahedral shear stress τ_h, expressing this as a function of the radii r_1, r_2, and R, and the pressure p. Also, show that the maximum value of τ_h occurs at the inner wall.

6.51 For the thick-walled tube of Prob. 6.30:

    (a) Determine the maximum value of octahedral shear stress in the tube. Neglect the localized effects of the end closure.

    (b) Plot the variation of τ_h versus radius and comment on the trend observed.

6.52 Derive the equations for the octahedral normal and shear stresses, Eqs. 6.32 and 6.33, on the basis of equilibrium of the solid body shown in Fig. 6.15(a). (Suggestions: Note that the three faces in the principal planes are acted upon by principal stresses, σ_1, σ_2, and σ_3. Then sum *forces* normal to the octahedral plane to get σ_h, and parallel to this plane to get τ_h.)

Section 6.6

6.53 For the strains measured on the free surface of a mild steel part in Prob. 5.17, determine the principal normal strains and the principal shear strains. Assume that no yielding has occurred.

6.54 For pure planar shear, where only τ_{xy} is nonzero, verify the principal stresses, strains, and planes shown in Fig. 4.41.

6.55 A strain guage rosette of the type shown in Fig. 6.16(a) is employed to measure strains on the free surface of an aluminum alloy part, with the result being $\varepsilon_x = 1900 \times 10^{-6}$, $\varepsilon_y = 1250 \times 10^{-6}$, and $\varepsilon_{45} = 2375 \times 10^{-6}$. Determine the principal normal strains and the principal shear strains. Assume that no yielding has occurred.

6.56 As mentioned in the previous problem, strains are measured using a strain gauge on the surface of a polycarbonate plastic part as follows: $\varepsilon_x = 0.011$, $\varepsilon_y = 0.0079$, and $\gamma_{xy} = 0.0048$. Determine the principal normal strains and the principal shear strains. Assume that no yielding has occurred. Poisson's ratio can be taken from Table 5.2.

6.57 Consider a strain gage rosette mounted on the unloaded free surface of an engineering component. The rosette is the type shown in Fig. 6.16(b), so that it measures strain in the x-direction and in two additional directions that correspond to counterclockwise rotations from the x-direction of $\theta = 60°$ and $120°$. Develop equations that allow ε_y and γ_{xy} to be calculated from the available measurements, ε_x, ε_{60}, and ε_{120}, so that the in-plane state of strain, ε_x, ε_y, and γ_{xy}, is completely known.

6.58 By modifying the equations for stress, develop equations for the normal and shear strains on the octahedral plane, ε_h and γ_h. Express these in terms of the components of a general three-dimensional state of strain: ε_x, ε_y, ε_z, γ_{xy}, γ_{yz}, γ_{zx}. What is the significance of ε_h? Under what conditions is the octahedral plane for strain the same as the one for stress?

7

Yielding and Fracture under Combined Stresses

7.1   INTRODUCTION
7.2   GENERAL FORM OF FAILURE CRITERIA
7.3   MAXIMUM NORMAL STRESS FRACTURE CRITERION
7.4   MAXIMUM SHEAR STRESS YIELD CRITERION
7.5   OCTAHEDRAL SHEAR STRESS YIELD CRITERION
7.6   DISCUSSION OF THE BASIC FAILURE CRITERIA
7.7   COULOMB–MOHR FRACTURE CRITERION
7.8   MODIFIED MOHR FRACTURE CRITERION
7.9   ADDITIONAL COMMENTS ON FAILURE CRITERIA
7.10 SUMMARY

OBJECTIVES

- Develop and employ three basic criteria for predicting failure under multiaxial stresses: maximum normal stress fracture criterion, maximum shear stress yield criterion, and octahedral shear stress yield criterion.
- Compare and discuss these basic criteria as to applicability and extensions.
- Explore fracture of brittle materials under multiaxial stresses in tension or compression, where either of two modes of fracture may occur, tension or shear, with the degree of compression affecting the shear mode.

7.1 INTRODUCTION

Engineering components may be subjected to complex loadings in tension, compression, bending, torsion, pressure, or combinations of these, so that at a given point in the material, stresses often occur in more than one direction. If sufficiently severe, such combined stresses can act together to cause the material to yield or fracture. Predicting the safe limits for use of a material under combined stresses requires the application of a *failure criterion*.

A number of different failure criteria are available, some of which predict failure by yielding, others failure by fracture. The former are specifically called *yield criteria*, the latter *fracture criteria*.

275

In the present chapter, failure criteria will be considered on the basis of values of stress. Their application involves calculating an effective value of stress that characterizes the combined stresses, and then this value is compared with the yield or fracture strength of the material. A given material may fail by either yielding or fracture, depending on its properties and the state of stress, so that, in general, the possibility of either event occurring first must be considered.

7.1.1 Need for Failure Criteria

The need for careful consideration of failure criteria is illustrated by the examples of Fig. 7.1. For these examples, the material is assumed to be a ductile engineering metal, the behavior of which approximates the ideal elastic, perfectly plastic case. A uniaxial tension test provides the elastic modulus E, and the yield strength σ_o, as shown in (a). Now assume that a transverse compression of equal magnitude to the tension is also applied, as shown in (b). In this case, the tension σ_y

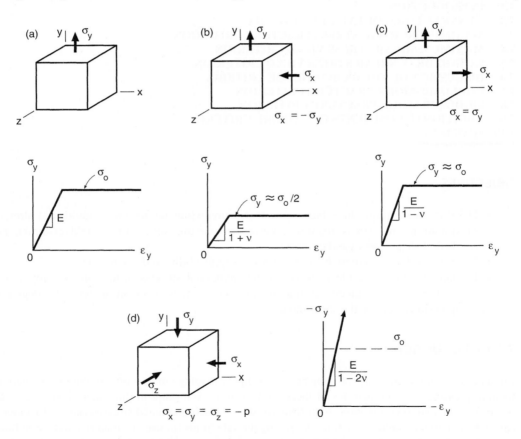

Figure 7.1   Yield strengths for a ductile metal under various states of stress: (a) uniaxial tension, (b) tension with transverse compression, (c) biaxial tension, and (d) hydrostatic compression.

necessary to cause yielding is experimentally observed to be only about half of the value from the uniaxial test. This result is easily verified by conducting a simple torsion test on a thin-walled tube, where the desired state of stress exists at an orientation of 45° to the tube axis. (Recall Fig. 4.41.)

Now consider another example, namely, a transverse tension σ_x of equal magnitude to σ_y, as illustrated in (c). Since transverse compression lowered the yield strength, intuition suggests that transverse tension might increase it. But an experiment will show that the effect of the transverse tension on yielding is small or absent. The experiment could be done by pressurizing a thin-walled spherical vessel until it yielded, or by a combination of pressure and tension on a thin-walled tube. If the material is changed to a brittle one—say, gray cast iron—neither tensile nor compressive transverse stresses have much effect on its fracture.

An additional experimental fact of interest is that it is difficult, and perhaps impossible, to yield a ductile material if it is tested under simple hydrostatic stress, where $\sigma_x = \sigma_y = \sigma_z$, in either tension or compression. This is illustrated in Fig. 7.1(d). Hydrostatic tension is difficult to achieve experimentally, but hydrostatic compression consists of simply placing a sample of material in a pressurized chamber.

Hence, failure criteria are needed that are capable of predicting such effects of combined states of stress on yielding and fracture. Although both yield and fracture criteria should in general be employed, materials that typically behave in a ductile manner generally have their usefulness limited by yielding, and those that typically behave in a brittle manner are usually limited by fracture.

7.1.2 Additional Comments

An alternative to failure criteria based on stress is to specifically analyze cracks in the material by the use of the special methods of *fracture mechanics*. Such an approach is not considered in this chapter, but is instead the sole topic of the next chapter.

In most of the treatment that follows, materials are assumed to be isotropic and homogeneous. Failure criteria for anisotropic materials is a rather complex topic that is considered only to a limited extent.

Note that the effect of a complex state of stress on deformation prior to yielding has already been discussed in Chapter 5. For example, the initial elastic slopes in Fig. 7.1 are readily obtained from Hooke's law in the form of Eq. 5.26. The yield criteria considered in this chapter predict the beginning of plastic deformation, beyond which point Hooke's law ceases to completely describe the stress–strain behavior. Detailed treatment of stress–strain behavior beyond yielding is an advanced topic called *plasticity*, which is considered to an extent in Chapter 12.

The discussion in this chapter relies rather heavily on the review of complex states of stress in the previous chapter, specifically, transformation of axes, Mohr's circle, principal stresses, and octahedral stresses.

7.2 GENERAL FORM OF FAILURE CRITERIA

In applying a yield criterion, the resistance of a material is given by its yield strength. Yield strengths are most commonly available as tensile yield strengths σ_o, determined from uniaxial tests and based on a plastic strain offset, as described in Chapter 4. To apply a fracture criterion, the ultimate strengths in tension and compression, σ_{ut} and σ_{uc}, are needed. In tension tests on materials that behave in a brittle manner, yielding is in most cases not a well-defined event, and the ultimate strength and fracture events occur at the same point. Hence, using σ_{ut} for brittle materials is the same as using the engineering fracture strength, σ_f.

Failure criteria for isotropic materials can be expressed in the mathematical form

$$f(\sigma_1, \sigma_2, \sigma_3) = \sigma_c \quad \text{(at failure)} \tag{7.1}$$

where failure (yielding or fracture) is predicted to occur when a specific mathematical function f of the principal normal stresses is equal to the failure strength of the material, σ_c, as from a uniaxial test. The failure strength is either the yield strength σ_o, or the ultimate strength, σ_{ut} or σ_{uc}, depending on whether yielding or fracture is of interest.

A requirement for a valid failure criterion is that it must give the same result regardless of the original choice of the coordinate system in a problem. This requirement is met if the criterion can be expressed in terms of the principal stresses. It is also met by any criterion where f is a mathematical function of one or more of the stress invariants given in the previous chapter as Eq. 6.29.

If any particular case of Eq. 7.1 is plotted in *principal normal stress space* (three-dimensional coordinates of σ_1, σ_2, and σ_3), the function f forms a surface that is called the *failure surface*. A failure surface can be either a *yield surface* or a *fracture surface*. In discussing failure criteria, we will proceed by considering various specific mathematical functions f, hence various types of failure surface.

Consider a point in an engineering component where the applied loads result in particular values of the principal normal stresses, σ_1, σ_2, and σ_3, and where the materials property σ_c is known, and also where a specific function f has been chosen. It is then useful to define an *effective stress*, $\bar{\sigma}$, which is a single numerical value that characterizes the state of applied stress. In particular,

$$\bar{\sigma} = f(\sigma_1, \sigma_2, \sigma_3) \tag{7.2}$$

where f is the same function as in Eq. 7.1. Thus, Eq. 7.1 states that failure occurs when

$$\bar{\sigma} = \sigma_c \quad \text{(at failure)} \tag{7.3}$$

Failure is not expected if $\bar{\sigma}$ is less than σ_c:

$$\bar{\sigma} < \sigma_c \quad \text{(no failure)} \tag{7.4}$$

Also, the safety factor against failure is

$$X = \frac{\sigma_c}{\bar{\sigma}} \tag{7.5}$$

In other words, the applied stresses can be increased by a factor X before failure occurs. For example, if $X = 2$, the applied stresses can be doubled before failure is expected.[1]

---

[1] Safety factors may also be expressed in terms of applied loads, according to Eq. 1.3. If loads and stresses are proportional, as is frequently the case, then safety factors on stress are identical to those on load. But caution is needed if such proportionality does not exist, as for problems of buckling and surface contact loading.

We will now proceed to discuss various specific failure criteria, some of which are appropriate for yielding, and others for fracture. In doing so, unless otherwise noted, the subscripts for principal stresses σ_1, σ_2, and σ_3 will not be assumed to be assigned in any particular order relative to their magnitudes.

7.3 MAXIMUM NORMAL STRESS FRACTURE CRITERION

Perhaps the simplest failure criterion is that failure is expected when the largest principal normal stress reaches the uniaxial strength of the material. This approach is reasonably successful in predicting fracture of brittle materials under tension-dominated loading.

To simplify the discussion, let us assume for the present that we have a material which fractures if an ultimate strength σ_u is exceeded in either tension or compression. That is, we are temporarily assuming that $\sigma_{ut} = |\sigma_{uc}| = \sigma_u$, where σ_{ut} is the ultimate strength in tension and $|\sigma_{uc}|$ is the ultimate strength in compression, expressed as a positive value.

For such a material, a maximum normal stress fracture criterion would be specified by a function f as follows:

$$\sigma_u = \text{MAX}(|\sigma_1|, |\sigma_2|, |\sigma_3|) \qquad \text{(at fracture)} \qquad (7.6)$$

where the notation MAX indicates that the largest of the values separated by commas is chosen. Absolute values are used so that compressive principal stresses can be considered. A particular set of applied stresses can then be characterized by the effective stress

$$\bar{\sigma}_N = \text{MAX}(|\sigma_1|, |\sigma_2|, |\sigma_3|) \qquad (7.7)$$

where the subscript specifies the maximum normal stress criterion. Hence, fracture is expected when $\bar{\sigma}_N$ is equal to σ_u, but not when it is less, and the safety factor against fracture is

$$X = \frac{\sigma_u}{\bar{\sigma}_N} \qquad (7.8)$$

7.3.1 Graphical Representation of the Normal Stress Criterion

For plane stress, such as $\sigma_3 = 0$, this fracture criterion can be graphically represented by a square on a plot of σ_1 versus σ_2, as shown in Fig. 7.2(a). Any combination of σ_1 and σ_2 that plots within the square box is safe, and any on its perimeter corresponds to fracture. Note that the box is the region that satisfies

$$\text{MAX}(|\sigma_1|, |\sigma_2|) \leq \sigma_u \qquad (7.9)$$

Equations for the four straight lines that form the borders of this safe region are obtained as shown in Fig. 7.2(b):

$$\sigma_1 = \sigma_u, \qquad \sigma_1 = -\sigma_u, \qquad \sigma_2 = \sigma_u, \qquad \sigma_2 = -\sigma_u \qquad (7.10)$$

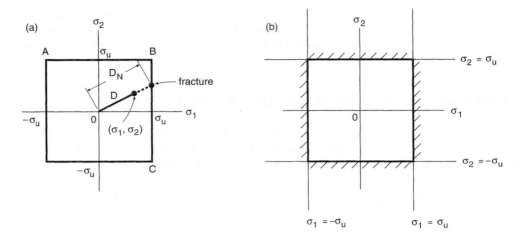

Figure 7.2   Failure locus for the maximum normal stress fracture criterion for plane stress.

For the general case, where all three principal normal stresses may have nonzero values, Eq. 7.6 indicates that the safe region is bounded by

$$\sigma_1 = \pm\sigma_u, \qquad \sigma_2 = \pm\sigma_u, \qquad \sigma_3 = \pm\sigma_u \qquad (7.11)$$

Each of the preceding equalities represents a pair of parallel planes normal to one of the principal axes and intersecting each at $+\sigma_u$ and $-\sigma_u$. The failure surface is therefore simply a cube, as illustrated in Fig. 7.3. If any one of σ_1, σ_2, or σ_3 is zero, then only the two-dimensional region formed by the intersection of the cube with the plane of the remaining two principal stresses needs to be considered. Such an intersection is shown for the case of $\sigma_3 = 0$, and the result is, of course, the square of Fig. 7.2.

7.3.2 Discussion

Consider a point on the surface of an engineering component, where plane stress prevails, so that $\sigma_3 = 0$. Further, assume that increasing the applied load causes σ_1 and σ_2 to both increase with their ratio σ_2/σ_1 remaining constant, a situation called *proportional loading*. For example, for pressure loading of a thin-walled tube with closed ends, the stresses maintain the ratio $\sigma_2/\sigma_1 = 0.5$, where σ_1 is the hoop stress and σ_2 the longitudinal stress.

In such a case, a graphical interpretation of the safety factor may be made, as illustrated in Fig. 7.2(a). Let D be the straight-line distance from the origin to the (σ_1, σ_2) point corresponding to the applied stress. Then extend this straight line until it strikes the fracture line, and denote the overall distance from the origin as D_N. The safety factor against fracture is the ratio of these lengths:

$$X = \frac{D_N}{D} \qquad (7.12)$$

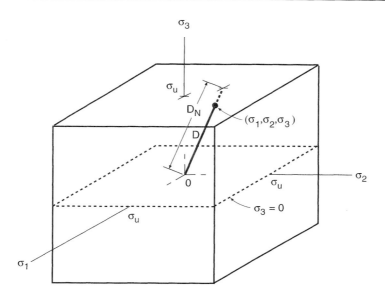

Figure 7.3   Three-dimensional failure surface for the maximum normal stress fracture criterion.

Such a graphical interpretation of the safety factor, and specifically Eq. 7.12, also applies in the general three-dimensional case, as illustrated in Fig. 7.3. The distances D and D_N are still measured along a straight line, but in this case the line may be inclined relative to all three principal axes. Evaluation of the safety factor in terms of lengths of lines for proportional stressing is valid for any physically reasonable failure surface, such as the others to be discussed subsequently.

For real materials that normally behave in a brittle manner, the ultimate strength in compression is usually considerably larger than that in tension, and the behavior in multiaxial compression is more complex than suggested by any form of a maximum normal stress criterion. Hence, for engineering use, the idealized fracture criterion just described needs to be restricted to tension-dominated loading, which can be accomplished with the formulas

$$\bar{\sigma}_{NT} = \mathrm{MAX}(\sigma_1, \sigma_2, \sigma_3), \qquad X = \frac{\sigma_{ut}}{\bar{\sigma}_{NT}} \qquad \text{(a)}$$

$$\text{where } \bar{\sigma}_{NT} > 0, \text{ and } |\sigma_{\max}| > |\sigma_{\min}| \qquad \text{(b)}$$

(7.13)

This modified criterion is subject to the limitations that the maximum principal normal stress be both positive and larger in magnitude than any principal normal stress that is negative (compressive). These restrict its use to cases where the D_N line in Fig. 7.2 strikes the failure criterion within A-B-C, or in Fig. 7.3 strikes one of the three positive-facing sides of the cube. Note that the safety factor is obtained by comparing this redefined effective stress $\bar{\sigma}_{NT}$ to the ultimate strength in tension, σ_{ut}. More discussion on compressive behavior and failure criteria for brittle materials will be given later, and in fact, this is the emphasis of Sections 7.7 and 7.8 near the end of this chapter.

Example 7.1

A sample of gray cast iron is subjected to the state of generalized plane stress of Ex. 6.3. Gray cast iron normally behaves in a brittle manner, and this particular material has ultimate strengths in tension and compression of $\sigma_{ut} = 214$ and $|\sigma_{uc}| = 770$ MPa, respectively. What is the safety factor against fracture?

Solution   In Ex. 6.3, the given state of stress is $\sigma_x = 100$, $\sigma_y = -60$, $\sigma_z = 40$, $\tau_{xy} = 80$, and $\tau_{yz} = \tau_{zx} = 0$ MPa. From these, principal normal stresses $\sigma_1 = 133.1$, $\sigma_2 = -93.1$, and $\sigma_3 = 40$ MPa are calculated. Equation 7.13 thus gives

$$\bar{\sigma}_{NT} = \text{MAX}(\sigma_1, \sigma_2, \sigma_3) = \text{MAX}(133.1, -93.1, 40.0) = 133.1 \text{ MPa}$$

$$X = \sigma_{ut}/\bar{\sigma}_{NT} = (214 \text{ MPa})/(133.1 \text{ MPa}) = 1.61 \qquad \textbf{Ans.}$$

The limitations accompanying Eq. 7.13 need to be checked. Clearly, $\bar{\sigma}_{NT} > 0$. Also, $|\sigma_{\text{max}}| = 133.1$, and $|\sigma_{\text{min}}| = 93.1$ MPa, so that $|\sigma_{\text{max}}| > |\sigma_{\text{min}}|$, and the answer above is valid as to this being a tension-dominated case.

7.4 MAXIMUM SHEAR STRESS YIELD CRITERION

Yielding of ductile materials is often predicted to occur when the maximum shear stress on any plane reaches a critical value τ_o, which is a material property:

$$\tau_o = \tau_{\text{max}} \qquad \text{(at yielding)} \qquad (7.14)$$

This is the basis of the *maximum shear stress yield criterion*, also often called the Tresca criterion. For metals, such an approach is logical because the mechanism of yielding on a microscopic size scale is the slip of crystal planes, which is a shear deformation that is expected to be controlled by a shear stress. (See Chapter 2.)

7.4.1 Development of the Maximum Shear Stress Criterion

From the previous chapter, recall that the maximum shear stress is the largest of the three principal shear stresses, which act on planes oriented at $45°$ relative to the principal normal stress axes, as illustrated in Fig. 6.8. These principal shear stresses may be obtained from the principal normal stresses by Eq. 6.18, which is repeated here for convenience:

$$\tau_1 = \frac{|\sigma_2 - \sigma_3|}{2}, \qquad \tau_2 = \frac{|\sigma_1 - \sigma_3|}{2}, \qquad \tau_3 = \frac{|\sigma_1 - \sigma_2|}{2} \qquad (7.15)$$

Hence, this yield criterion can be stated as follows:

$$\tau_o = \text{MAX}\left(\frac{|\sigma_1 - \sigma_2|}{2}, \frac{|\sigma_2 - \sigma_3|}{2}, \frac{|\sigma_3 - \sigma_1|}{2}\right) \qquad \text{(at yielding)} \qquad (7.16)$$

The yield stress in shear, τ_o, for a given material could be obtained directly from a test in simple shear, such as a thin-walled tube in torsion. However, only uniaxial yield strengths σ_o from tension tests are commonly available, so that it is more convenient to calculate τ_o from σ_o. In a uniaxial tension test, at the stress defined as the yield strength, we have

$$\sigma_1 = \sigma_o, \qquad \sigma_2 = \sigma_3 = 0 \tag{7.17}$$

Substitution of these values into the yield criterion of Eq. 7.16 gives

$$\tau_o = \frac{\sigma_o}{2} \tag{7.18}$$

In the uniaxial test, note that the maximum shear stress occurs on planes oriented at 45° with respect to the applied stress axis. This fact and Eq. 7.18 are easily verified with Mohr's circle, as shown in Fig. 7.4.

Equation 7.16 can thus be written in terms of σ_o as

$$\frac{\sigma_o}{2} = \text{MAX}\left(\frac{|\sigma_1 - \sigma_2|}{2}, \frac{|\sigma_2 - \sigma_3|}{2}, \frac{|\sigma_3 - \sigma_1|}{2}\right) \qquad \text{(at yielding)} \tag{7.19}$$

or

$$\sigma_o = \text{MAX}(|\sigma_1 - \sigma_2|, |\sigma_2 - \sigma_3|, |\sigma_3 - \sigma_1|) \qquad \text{(at yielding)} \tag{7.20}$$

The effective stress is most conveniently defined as in Eq. 7.3, so that it equals the uniaxial strength σ_o at the point of yielding. That is,

$$\bar{\sigma}_S = \text{MAX}(|\sigma_1 - \sigma_2|, |\sigma_2 - \sigma_3|, |\sigma_3 - \sigma_1|) \tag{7.21}$$

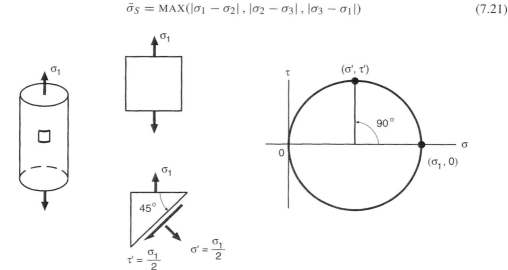

Figure 7.4   The plane of maximum shear in a uniaxial tension test.

where the subscript S specifies the maximum shear stress criterion. The safety factor against yielding is then

$$X = \frac{\sigma_o}{\bar{\sigma}_S} \tag{7.22}$$

7.4.2 Graphical Representation of the Maximum Shear Stress Criterion

For plane stress, such as $\sigma_3 = 0$, the maximum shear stress criterion can be represented on a plot of σ_1 versus σ_2, as shown in Fig. 7.5(a). Points on the distorted hexagon correspond to yielding, and points inside are safe. This failure locus is obtained by substituting $\sigma_3 = 0$ into the yield criterion of Eq. 7.20:

$$\sigma_o = \text{MAX}(|\sigma_1 - \sigma_2|, |\sigma_2|, |\sigma_1|) \tag{7.23}$$

The region of no yielding, where $\bar{\sigma}_S < \sigma_o$, is thus the region bounded by the lines

$$\sigma_1 - \sigma_2 = \pm\sigma_o, \qquad \sigma_2 = \pm\sigma_o, \qquad \sigma_1 = \pm\sigma_o \tag{7.24}$$

These lines are shown in Fig. 7.5(b). Note that the first equation gives a pair of parallel lines with a slope of unity, and the other two give pairs of lines parallel to the coordinate axes.

For the general case, where all three principal normal stresses may have nonzero values, the boundaries of the region of no yielding are obtained from Eq. 7.20:

$$\sigma_1 - \sigma_2 = \pm\sigma_o, \qquad \sigma_2 - \sigma_3 = \pm\sigma_o, \qquad \sigma_1 - \sigma_3 = \pm\sigma_o \tag{7.25}$$

Each of these equations gives a pair of inclined planes which are parallel to the principal stress direction that does not appear in the equation. For example, the first equation represents a pair of planes parallel to the σ_3 direction.

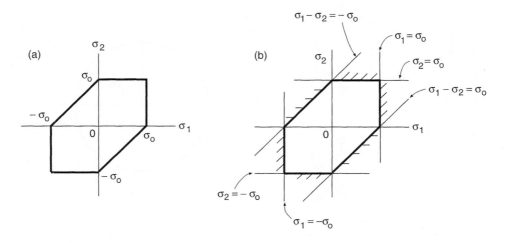

Figure 7.5   Failure locus for the maximum shear stress yield criterion for plane stress.

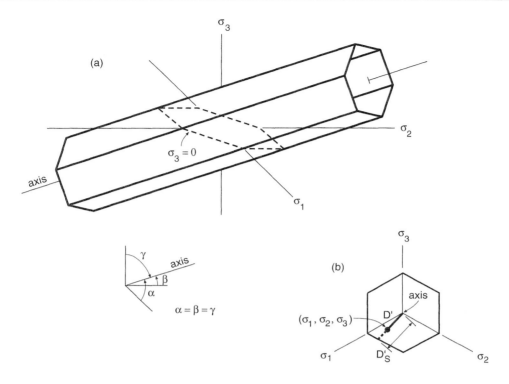

Figure 7.6 Three-dimensional failure surface for the maximum shear stress yield criterion.

These three pairs of planes form a tube with a hexagonal cross section, as shown in Fig. 7.6. The axis of the tube is the line $\sigma_1 = \sigma_2 = \sigma_3$. This direction corresponds to the normal to the octahedral plane in the octant where the principal normal stresses are all positive—specifically, the $\alpha = \beta = \gamma$ line of Fig. 6.15. If the tube is viewed along this line, a regular hexagon is seen, as shown in (b).

If any one of σ_1, σ_2, or σ_3 is zero, then the intersection of the tube with the plane of the remaining two stresses gives a distorted hexagon failure locus, as already shown in Fig. 7.5(a).

7.4.3 Hydrostatic Stresses and the Maximum Shear Stress Criterion

Consider the special case of a stress state where the principal normal stresses are all equal, so that there is a state of pure hydrostatic stress σ_h:

$$\sigma_1 = \sigma_2 = \sigma_3 = \sigma_h \tag{7.26}$$

For example, the material could be subjected to a simple pressure loading p, so that $\sigma_h = -p$. This case corresponds to a point along the axis of the hexagonal cylinder of Fig. 7.6. For any such point, the effective stress $\bar{\sigma}_S$ from Eq. 7.21 is always zero, and the safety factor against yielding is thus infinite.

Hence, the maximum shear stress criterion predicts that hydrostatic stress alone does not cause yielding. This seems surprising, but is in fact in agreement with experimental results for metals under hydrostatic compression. Testing in hydrostatic tension is essentially impossible, but it is likely that brittle fracture without yielding would occur at a high stress level even in normally ductile materials.

Interpretation of the safety factor in terms of lengths of lines from the origin in principal stress space, as discussed earlier, is also valid for the maximum shear stress criterion. Since stresses are expected to affect yielding only to the extent that they deviate from the axis of the hexagonal tube, the projections of lengths normal to this axis can also be used:

$$X = \frac{D'_S}{D'} \tag{7.27}$$

Here, D'_S is the projected distance corresponding to yielding, and D' to the applied stress, as shown in Fig. 7.6(b).

Example 7.2

Consider the pipe with closed ends of Ex. 6.5, with wall thickness 10 mm and inner diameter 0.60 m, subjected to 20 MPa internal pressure and a torque of 1200 kN·m. What is the safety factor against yielding at the inner wall if the pipe is made of the 18 Ni maraging steel of Table 4.2?

Solution   The hoop, longitudinal, and radial stresses due to pressure, and the shear stress due to torsion, are calculated in Ex. 6.5 as $\sigma_t = 600$, $\sigma_x = 300$, $\sigma_r = -20$ (inside), and $\tau_{tx} = 205.3$ MPa. These give principal normal stresses at the inner wall of

$$\sigma_1 = 704.3, \qquad \sigma_2 = 195.7, \qquad \sigma_3 = -20 \text{ MPa}$$

The effective stress for the maximum shear stress criterion from Eq. 7.21 is

$$\bar{\sigma}_S = \text{MAX}\left(|\sigma_1 - \sigma_2|, |\sigma_2 - \sigma_3|, |\sigma_3 - \sigma_1|\right)$$
$$\bar{\sigma}_S = \text{MAX}\left(|704.3 - 195.7|, |195.7 - (-20)|, |(-20) - 704.3|\right) = 724.3 \text{ MPa}$$

The yield strength for this material from Table 4.2 is 1791 MPa, so the safety factor against yielding for the inner wall is

$$X = \sigma_o/\bar{\sigma}_S = (1791 \text{ MPa})/(724.3 \text{ MPa}) = 2.47 \qquad \textbf{Ans.}$$

Comment   For the outer wall, revising the preceding calculation with $\sigma_r = \sigma_3 = 0$ gives $\bar{\sigma}_S = 704.3$ MPa and $X = 2.54$. The slightly lower value of $X = 2.47$ is thus the controlling one.

Example 7.3

A solid shaft of diameter d is made of AISI 1020 steel (as rolled) and is subjected to a tensile axial force of 200 kN and a torque of 1.50 kN·m.

- **(a)** What is the safety factor against yielding if the diameter is 50 mm?
- **(b)** For the situation of (a), what adjusted value of diameter is required to obtain a safety factor against yielding of 2.0?

Solution   **(a)** The applied axial force P and torque T produce stresses as shown in Fig. E7.3, which may be evaluated on the basis of Figs. A.1 and A.2:

$$\sigma_x = \frac{P}{A} = \frac{4P}{\pi d^2}, \qquad \tau_{xy} = \frac{Tc}{J} = \frac{T(d/2)}{\pi d^4/32} = \frac{16T}{\pi d^3}$$

Note that σ_x is uniformly distributed, and τ_{xy} is evaluated at the surface of the shaft where it is highest. Hence, we have a state of plane stress with $\sigma_y = 0$. The principal normal stresses are $\sigma_3 = \sigma_z = 0$ and

$$\sigma_1, \sigma_2 = \frac{\sigma_x + \sigma_y}{2} \pm \sqrt{\left(\frac{\sigma_x - \sigma_y}{2}\right)^2 + \tau_{xy}^2} = \frac{2P}{\pi d^2} \pm \sqrt{\left(\frac{2P}{\pi d^2}\right)^2 + \left(\frac{16T}{\pi d^3}\right)^2}$$

Viewing the foregoing as $\sigma_1, \sigma_2 = a \pm r$, and noting that $r > a$, the three Mohr's circles must be configured as in Fig. 6.10(a), rather than (b). Hence, σ_1 and σ_2 determine the maximum shear stress and so also $\bar{\sigma}_S$:

$$\bar{\sigma}_S = \text{MAX}\left(|\sigma_1 - \sigma_2|, |\sigma_2 - \sigma_3|, |\sigma_3 - \sigma_1|\right) = |\sigma_1 - \sigma_2|$$

$$\bar{\sigma}_S = 2\sqrt{\left(\frac{2P}{\pi d^2}\right)^2 + \left(\frac{16T}{\pi d^3}\right)^2} = \frac{4}{\pi d^2}\sqrt{P^2 + \left(\frac{8T}{d}\right)^2} = 159.1 \, \text{MPa}$$

Substituting $P = 200{,}000$ N, $T = 1.50 \times 10^6$ N·mm, and $d = 50$ mm, gives $\bar{\sigma}_S$ in units of N/mm^2 = MPa. Employing this value with the yield strength $\sigma_o = 260$ MPa of the given material from Table 4.2, we have

$$X = \sigma_o/\bar{\sigma}_S = (260 \, \text{MPa})/(159.1 \, \text{MPa}) = 1.63 \qquad \textbf{Ans.}$$

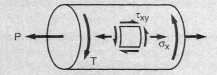

Figure E7.3

(b) To achieve a safety factor of $X = 2.0$ with a modified value of diameter d, we need

$$\bar{\sigma}_S = \sigma_o/X = (260\,\text{MPa})/2.0 = 130\,\text{MPa}$$

Substituting this and the given P and T into the equation for $\bar{\sigma}_S$ developed earlier gives

$$130\,\text{MPa} = \frac{4}{\pi d^2}\sqrt{(200{,}000\ \text{N})^2 + \left(\frac{8(1.50 \times 10^6\ \text{N·mm})}{d}\right)^2}$$

This cannot be solved for d in a closed-form manner, so trial and error or other iterative procedure is required to obtain

$$d = 54.1\,\text{mm} \qquad\qquad \textbf{Ans.}$$

As might be expected, increasing the safety factor to 2.0 from that found in (a) requires a larger diameter.

7.5 OCTAHEDRAL SHEAR STRESS YIELD CRITERION

Another yield criterion often used for ductile metals is the prediction that yielding occurs when the shear stress on the octahedral planes reaches the critical value

$$\tau_h = \tau_{ho} \qquad \text{(at yielding)} \tag{7.28}$$

where τ_{ho} is the value of octahedral shear stress τ_h necessary to cause yielding. The resulting *octahedral shear stress yield criterion*, also often called either the von Mises or the distortion energy criterion, represents an alternative to the maximum shear criterion.

A physical justification for such an approach is as follows: Since hydrostatic stress σ_h is observed not to affect yielding, it is logical to find the plane where this occurs as the normal stress, and then to use the remaining stress τ_h as the failure criterion. Another justification is to note that, although yielding is caused by shear stresses, τ_{max} occurs on only two planes in the material, whereas τ_h is never very much smaller and occurs on four planes. (Compare Figs. 6.8 and 6.15.) Hence, on a statistical basis, τ_h has a greater chance of finding crystal planes that are favorably oriented for slip, and this may overcome its disadvantage of being slightly smaller than τ_{max}.

7.5.1 Development of the Octahedral Shear Stress Criterion

From the previous chapter, Eq. 6.33, the shear stress on the octahedral planes is

$$\tau_h = \frac{1}{3}\sqrt{(\sigma_1 - \sigma_2)^2 + (\sigma_2 - \sigma_3)^2 + (\sigma_3 - \sigma_1)^2} \tag{7.29}$$

so that the failure criterion is

$$\tau_{ho} = \frac{1}{3}\sqrt{(\sigma_1 - \sigma_2)^2 + (\sigma_2 - \sigma_3)^2 + (\sigma_3 - \sigma_1)^2} \qquad \text{(at yielding)} \qquad (7.30)$$

As was done for the maximum shear stress criterion, it is useful to express the critical value in terms of the yield strength from a tension test. Substitution of the uniaxial stress state with $\sigma_1 = \sigma_o$ and $\sigma_2 = \sigma_3 = 0$ into the octahedral shear criterion gives

$$\tau_{ho} = \frac{\sqrt{2}}{3}\sigma_o \qquad (7.31)$$

From the three-dimensional geometry of the octahedral planes, as described in the previous chapter, it can be shown that the plane on which the uniaxial stress acts is related to the octahedral plane by a rotation through the angle α of Fig. 6.15, where

$$\alpha = \cos^{-1}\left(\frac{1}{\sqrt{3}}\right) = 54.7^\circ \qquad (7.32)$$

The same result can also be obtained from Mohr's circle by noting that, in uniaxial tension, the normal stress on the octahedral plane is

$$\sigma_h = \frac{\sigma_1 + \sigma_2 + \sigma_3}{3} = \frac{\sigma_1}{3} \qquad (7.33)$$

Locating the point that satisfies this on Mohr's circle leads to the aforementioned values of α and τ_{ho}, as shown in Fig. 7.7.

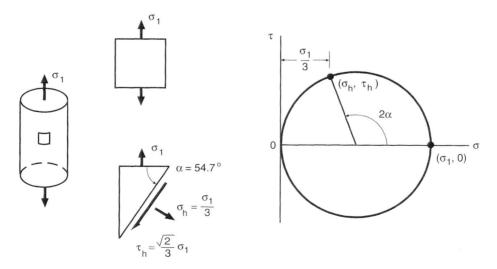

Figure 7.7   The plane of octahedral shear in a uniaxial tension test.

Combining Eqs. 7.30 and 7.31 gives the yield criterion in the desired form, expressed in terms of the uniaxial yield strength:

$$\sigma_o = \frac{1}{\sqrt{2}}\sqrt{(\sigma_1 - \sigma_2)^2 + (\sigma_2 - \sigma_3)^2 + (\sigma_3 - \sigma_1)^2} \qquad \text{(at yielding)} \qquad (7.34)$$

As before, the effective stress for this theory is most conveniently defined so that it equals the uniaxial strength σ_o at the point of yielding:

$$\bar{\sigma}_H = \frac{1}{\sqrt{2}}\sqrt{(\sigma_1 - \sigma_2)^2 + (\sigma_2 - \sigma_3)^2 + (\sigma_3 - \sigma_1)^2} \qquad (7.35)$$

Here, the subscript H specifies that this effective stress is determined by the octahedral shear stress criterion. Also, the corresponding safety factor is $X = \sigma_o/\bar{\sigma}_H$. This effective stress may also be determined directly for any state of stress, without the necessity of first determining principal stresses, by modifying Eq. 7.35 with the use of Eqs. 6.33 and 6.36. The result is

$$\bar{\sigma}_H = \frac{1}{\sqrt{2}}\sqrt{(\sigma_x - \sigma_y)^2 + (\sigma_y - \sigma_z)^2 + (\sigma_z - \sigma_x)^2 + 6(\tau_{xy}^2 + \tau_{yz}^2 + \tau_{zx}^2)} \qquad (7.36)$$

7.5.2 Graphical Representation of the Octahedral Shear Stress Criterion

For plane stress, such as $\sigma_3 = 0$, the octahedral shear stress criterion can be represented on a plot of σ_1 versus σ_2, as shown in Fig. 7.8. This elliptical shape can be obtained by substituting $\sigma_3 = 0$ into

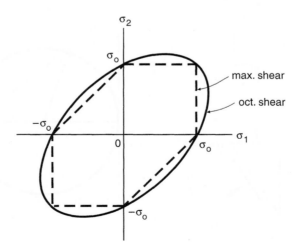

Figure 7.8   Failure locus for the octahedral shear stress yield criterion for plane stress, and comparison with the maximum shear criterion.

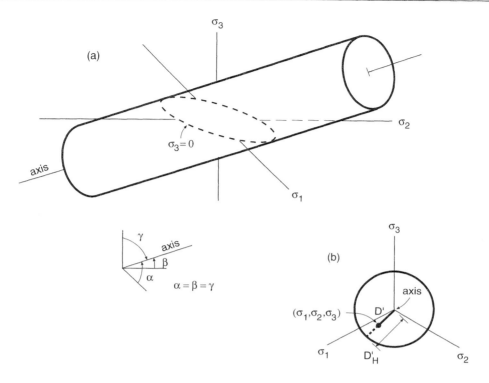

Figure 7.9 Three-dimensional failure surface for the octahedral shear stress yield criterion.

the failure criterion in the form of Eq. 7.34:

$$\sigma_o = \frac{1}{\sqrt{2}}\sqrt{(\sigma_1 - \sigma_2)^2 + \sigma_2^2 + \sigma_1^2} \tag{7.37}$$

Manipulation gives

$$\sigma_o^2 = \sigma_1^2 - \sigma_1\sigma_2 + \sigma_2^2 \tag{7.38}$$

which is the equation of an ellipse with its major axis along the line $\sigma_1 = \sigma_2$ and which crosses the axes at the points $\pm\sigma_o$. Note that the ellipse has the distorted hexagon of the maximum shear criterion inscribed within it as shown.

For the general case, where all three principal normal stresses may have nonzero values, the boundary of the region of no yielding, as specified by Eq. 7.34, represents a circular cylindrical surface with its axis along the line $\sigma_1 = \sigma_2 = \sigma_3$. This is illustrated in Fig. 7.9. The view along the cylinder axis, giving simply a circle, is also shown. If any one of σ_1, σ_2, or σ_3 is zero, then the intersection of the cylindrical surface with the plane of the remaining two principal stresses gives an ellipse, as in Fig. 7.8.

Thus, we have a situation similar to that for the maximum shear stress criterion, where hydrostatic stress is predicted to have no effect on yielding. In particular, substitution of

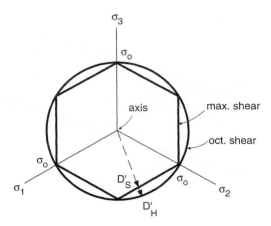

Figure 7.10   Comparison of yield surfaces for the maximum shear and octahedral shear stress criteria.

$\sigma_1 = \sigma_2 = \sigma_3 = \sigma_h$ into Eq. 7.35 gives $\bar{\sigma}_H = 0$, and a safety factor against yielding of infinity. Safety factors against yielding may be similarly interpreted in terms of distances from the cylinder axis, as illustrated in Fig. 7.9(b). The hexagonal-tube yield surface of the maximum shear criterion is in fact inscribed within the cylindrical surface of the octahedral shear criterion. A view along the common axis of both gives the comparison of Fig. 7.10.

7.5.3 Energy of Distortion

In applying stresses to an element of material, work must be done, and for an elastic material, all of this work is stored as potential energy. This internal strain energy can be partitioned into one portion associated with volume change and another portion associated with distorting the shape of the element of material. Hydrostatic stress is associated with the energy of volume change, and since hydrostatic stress alone does not cause yielding, the remaining (distortional) portion of the total internal strain energy is a logical candidate for the basis of a failure criterion. When this approach is taken, the resulting failure criterion is found to be the same as the octahedral shear stress criterion. (See Nadai (1950) or Boresi (2003) for details.)

Example 7.4
Repeat Ex. 7.2, except use the octahedral shear stress yield criterion.

First Solution   For the closed-end pipe, the hoop, longitudinal, and radial stresses due to internal pressure, and the shear stress due to torsion, are calculated in Ex. 6.5 as $\sigma_t = 600$, $\sigma_x = 300$, $\sigma_r = -20$ (inside), and $\tau_{tx} = 205.3$ MPa. These give principal normal stresses of $\sigma_1 = 704.3$, $\sigma_2 = 195.7$, and $\sigma_3 = -20$ MPa. The effective stress for the octahedral shear stress criterion from Eq. 7.35 is

$$\bar{\sigma}_H = \frac{1}{\sqrt{2}}\sqrt{(\sigma_1 - \sigma_2)^2 + (\sigma_2 - \sigma_3)^2 + (\sigma_3 - \sigma_1)^2}$$

$$\bar{\sigma}_H = \frac{1}{\sqrt{2}}\sqrt{(704.3 - 195.7)^2 + (195.7 - (-20))^2 + ((-20) - 704.3)^2} = 644.1 \, \text{MPa}$$

The yield strength for the 18 Ni maraging steel material from Table 4.2 is 1791 MPa, so that the safety factor against yielding for the inner wall is

$$X = \sigma_o/\bar{\sigma}_H = (1791 \, \text{MPa})/(644.1 \, \text{MPa}) = 2.78 \qquad \textbf{Ans.}$$

Comments For the outer wall, revising the preceding calculation with $\sigma_r = \sigma_3 = 0$ gives $\bar{\sigma}_H = 629.6 \, \text{MPa}$ and $X = 2.84$. The slightly lower value of $X = 2.78$ is thus the controlling one. Note that both safety factors are somewhat higher than those for the maximum shear criterion from Ex. 7.2.

Second Solution For the octahedral shear criterion, the step of determining principal normal stresses is not necessary, as the solution can proceed directly from the stresses on the original r-t-x coordinate system with the use of Eq. 7.36.

$$\bar{\sigma}_H = \frac{1}{\sqrt{2}}\sqrt{(\sigma_r - \sigma_t)^2 + (\sigma_t - \sigma_x)^2 + (\sigma_x - \sigma_r)^2 + 6(\tau_{rt}^2 + \tau_{tx}^2 + \tau_{xr}^2)}$$

$$\bar{\sigma}_H = \frac{1}{\sqrt{2}}\sqrt{(-20 - 600)^2 + (600 - 300)^2 + (300 - (-20))^2 + 6(0 + 205.3^2 + 0)} = 644.1 \, \text{MPa}$$

As expected, $\bar{\sigma}_H$ is the same as for the first solution, and $X = 2.78$ (**Ans.**) is similarly obtained for the inner wall.

Example 7.5

A block of material is subjected to equal compressive stresses in the x- and y-directions, and it is confined by a rigid die so that it cannot deform in the z-direction, as shown in Fig. E7.5. Assume that there is no friction against the die and also that the material behaves in an elastic, perfectly plastic manner, with uniaxial yield strength σ_o.

   (a) Determine the stress $\sigma_x = \sigma_y$ necessary to cause yielding, expressing this as a function of σ_o and elastic constants of the material.
   (b) What is the value of σ_y at yielding if the material is an aluminum alloy with uniaxial yield strength $\sigma_o = 300 \, \text{MPa}$ and elastic constants as in Table 5.2?

Solution   **(a)** Apply Hooke's law for the z-direction, Eq. 5.26(c), letting $\sigma_x = \sigma_y$, and noting that preventing deformation in the z-direction requires that the strain in that direction be zero ($\varepsilon_z = 0$):

$$\varepsilon_z = \frac{1}{E}\left[\sigma_z - \nu(\sigma_x + \sigma_y)\right], \qquad 0 = \frac{1}{E}\left[\sigma_z - \nu(\sigma_y + \sigma_y)\right], \qquad \sigma_z = 2\nu\sigma_y$$

Here, solving the second expression for σ_z gives the third. Since there are no shear stresses, the x-y-z axes are also the principal axes, 1-2-3, and the principal normal stresses are

$$\sigma_1 = \sigma_x = \sigma_y, \qquad \sigma_2 = \sigma_y, \qquad \sigma_3 = \sigma_z = 2\nu\sigma_y$$

The effective stress for the octahedral shear criterion is

$$\bar{\sigma}_H = \frac{1}{\sqrt{2}}\sqrt{(\sigma_1 - \sigma_2)^2 + (\sigma_2 - \sigma_3)^2 + (\sigma_3 - \sigma_1)^2}$$

$$\bar{\sigma}_H = \frac{1}{\sqrt{2}}\sqrt{(\sigma_y - \sigma_y)^2 + (\sigma_y - 2\nu\sigma_y)^2 + (2\nu\sigma_y - \sigma_y)^2} = \sigma_y(1 - 2\nu)$$

Since $\bar{\sigma}_H = \sigma_o$ at the point of yielding, the desired result is

$$\sigma_y = \frac{\sigma_o}{1 - 2\nu} \qquad\qquad \textbf{Ans.}$$

(b) For the aluminum alloy with uniaxial yield strength $\sigma_o = 300\,\text{MPa}$, assume that $\sigma_o = -300\,\text{MPa}$ applies for uniaxial compression. Substituting this and $\nu = 0.345$ from Table 5.2,

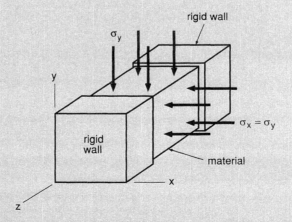

Figure E7.5 Block of material stressed equally in two directions, with rigid walls preventing deformation in the third direction.

the stress to cause yielding is

$$\sigma_y = \frac{-300\,\text{MPa}}{1 - 2(0.345)} = -967.7\,\text{MPa} \qquad\qquad \textbf{Ans.}$$

Discussion   If the same block of material is not confined in the z-direction, the stress in that direction is zero, and an analysis similar to the previous one gives simply $\sigma_y = \sigma_o$. However, preventing deformation in the z-direction is seen to cause a stress $\sigma_z = 2\nu\sigma_y$ to develop, which in turn causes the value of $\sigma_x = \sigma_y$ at yielding to substantially exceed the uniaxial yield strength. Hence, constraining the deformation makes it more difficult to yield the material. This occurs because the stresses σ_x, σ_y, and σ_z all have the same sign and so combine to create significant hydrostatic stress, which in effect subtracts from the ability of the applied stresses to cause yielding. For this particular situation, the maximum shear stress criterion gives an identical result.

7.6 DISCUSSION OF THE BASIC FAILURE CRITERIA

The three failure criteria discussed so far, namely, the maximum normal stress, maximum shear stress, and octahedral shear stress criteria, may be considered to be the basic ones among a larger number that are available. It is useful at this point to discuss these basic approaches. We will also consider some design issues and some additional failure criteria that are modifications or combinations of the basic ones.

7.6.1 Comparison of Failure Criteria

Both the maximum shear stress and the octahedral shear stress criteria are widely used to predict yielding of ductile materials, especially metals. Recall that both of these indicate that hydrostatic stress does not affect yielding, and also that the hexagonal-tube yield surface of the maximum shear criterion is inscribed within the circular-cylinder surface of the octahedral shear criterion. Hence, these two criteria never give dramatically different predictions of the yield behavior under combined stress, there being no state of stress where the difference exceeds approximately 15%. This can be seen in Fig. 7.10, where the distance from the cylinder axis to the two yield surfaces differs by a maximum amount at the various points where the circle is farthest from the hexagon. From geometry, the distances at these points have the ratio $2/\sqrt{3} = 1.155$. Hence, safety factors and effective stresses for a given state of stress cannot differ by more than this. For plane stress, $\sigma_3 = 0$, such a maximum deviation occurs for pure shear, where $\sigma_1 = -\sigma_2 = |\tau|$, and also for $\sigma_1 = 2\sigma_2$, as in pressure loading of a thin-walled tube with closed ends.

However, note that, in some situations, the maximum shear and octahedral shear yield criteria do give dramatically different predictions than a maximum normal stress criterion. Compare the tubular yield surfaces of either with the cube of Fig. 7.3, and consider states of stress near the tube axis ($\sigma_1 = \sigma_2 = \sigma_3$), but well beyond the boundaries of the cube. For plane stress, the three failure criteria compare as shown in Fig. 7.11. Where both principal stresses have the same sign, the maximum shear stress criterion is equivalent to a maximum normal stress criterion. However, if the principal stresses are opposite in sign, the normal stress criterion differs considerably from the other two.

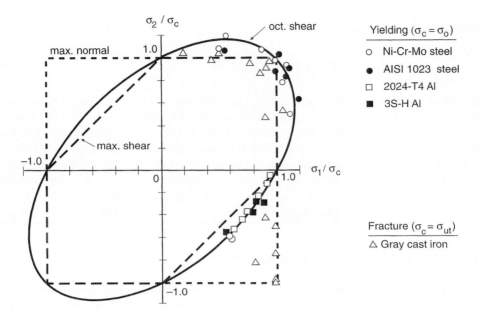

Figure 7.11 Plane stress failure loci for three criteria. These are compared with biaxial yield data for ductile steels and aluminum alloys, and also with biaxial fracture data for gray cast iron. (The steel data are from [Lessells 40] and [Davis 45], the aluminum data from [Naghdi 58] and [Marin 40], and the cast iron data from [Coffin 50] and [Grassi 49].)

The most convenient method of comparing failure criteria experimentally is to test thin-walled tubes under various combinations of axial, torsion, and pressure loading, thus producing various states of plane stress. Some data obtained in this manner for yielding of ductile metals and fracture of a brittle cast iron are shown in Fig. 7.11. The cast iron data follow the normal stress criterion, whereas the yield data tend to fall between the two yield criteria, perhaps agreeing better, in general, with the octahedral shear criterion. The maximum shear criterion is more conservative, and on the basis of experimental data for ductile metals similar to that in Fig. 7.11, this criterion seems to represent a lower limit that is infrequently violated.

The maximum difference of 15% between the two yield criteria is relatively small compared with safety factors commonly used and with various uncertainties usually involved in mechanical design, so a choice between the two is not a matter of major importance. If conservatism is desired, the maximum shear criterion could be chosen.

7.6.2 Load Factor Design

The manner of determining safety factors just described follows *allowable stress design*, where the stresses analyzed correspond to the loads expected in actual service, and a single safety factor X is calculated that applies to all sources of loading.

   An alternative is *load factor design*, where each load expected in actual service is multiplied by a load factor Y, which is similar to a safety factor. The loads so increased are used to determine stresses, so that the failure condition is analyzed. For yield and fracture criteria, effective stresses $\bar{\sigma}$ calculated with the increased loads are then equated to the material's failure stress, such as the yield strength, σ_o, or the ultimate tensile strength, σ_{ut}, as appropriate. Load factors Y may differ for different sources of loading to reflect circumstances such as different uncertainties in the actual values of the various load inputs. Ideally, the Y values would be based on statistical analysis of loads measured in service.

   We will use the following nomenclature: The value of a load P expected in actual service is denoted $\hat{P}$, and the load factor for this load is Y_P. Then the increased (factored) load used in analysis of the failure condition is $P_f = Y_P \hat{P}$.

Example 7.6

Consider the situation of Ex. 7.3(b), where a solid shaft of diameter d is made of AISI 1020 steel (as rolled) and is subjected in service to an axial force $P = 200\,\text{kN}$ and a torque $T = 1.50\,\text{kN·m}$. What diameter is required if load factors of $Y_P = 1.60$ and $Y_T = 2.50$ are required for the axial force and torque, respectively?

Solution   The factored loads for analysis of the failure condition are

$$P_f = Y_P \hat{P} = 1.60(200{,}000\,\text{N}) = 320{,}000\,\text{N}$$

$$T_f = Y_T \hat{T} = 2.50(1.50 \times 10^6\,\text{N·mm}) = 3.75 \times 10^6\,\text{N·mm}$$

Then we modify the Ex. 7.3 solution, proceeding similarly, except for employing P_f and T_f. The maximum shear stress yield criterion thus gives

$$\bar{\sigma}_S = \text{MAX}\left(|\sigma_1 - \sigma_2|, |\sigma_2 - \sigma_3|, |\sigma_3 - \sigma_1|\right) = |\sigma_1 - \sigma_2|$$

$$\bar{\sigma}_S = 2\sqrt{\left(\frac{2P_f}{\pi d^2}\right)^2 + \left(\frac{16T_f}{\pi d^3}\right)^2} = \frac{4}{\pi d^2}\sqrt{P_f^2 + \left(\frac{8T_f}{d}\right)^2} = \sigma_o = 260\,\text{MPa}$$

where the effective stress is now equated directly to the yield strength of the AISI 1020 steel, as the stresses have already been increased by load factors. Substituting P_f and T_f and solving iteratively gives $d = 55.5\,\text{mm}$ (**Ans.**).

Comment   If the preceding solution is repeated with $Y_P = Y_T = 2.00$, the same answer ($d = 54.1\,\text{mm}$) as in Ex. 7.3 is obtained. As employed here, load factors that all have the same value are mathematically equivalent to safety factors.

7.6.3 Stress Raiser Effects

Engineering components necessarily have complex geometry that causes stresses to be locally elevated—for example, holes, fillets, grooves, keyways, and splines. Such *stress raisers* are often collectively termed *notches*. (See Appendix A, Section A.6.) Consider components made of ductile materials, such as most steels, aluminum alloys, titanium alloys, and other structural metals, and also many polymeric materials. In this case, the material can yield in a small local region without significantly compromising the strength of the component. This is due to the ability of the material to deform at the notch and shift some of the stress to adjacent regions, which behavior is called *stress redistribution*. Final failure does not occur until yielding spreads over the entire cross section, as discussed in Section A.7 in the context of fully plastic yielding. (See Figs. A.10 and A.14.)

As a result of a ductile material's ability to tolerate local yielding, stress raiser effects are not usually included in applying yield criteria for static design. In other words, net section nominal stresses, such as S in Figs. A.11 and A.12, are used with the yield criterion, rather than local stresses $\sigma = k_t S$ that include the notch effect. (However, where cyclic loading may cause fatigue cracking, stress raiser effects do need to be considered, as treated in detail in Chapters 10, 13, and 14.)

In modern industry, critical components are likely to be analyzed on a digital computer by the method of *finite elements*. Linear-elastic behavior is usually assumed, and color-coded plots are often made of the magnitude of the *von Mises stress*, which is simply our octahedral effective stress, $\bar{\sigma}_H$. (See the back cover of this book for examples of such plots.) This affords an opportunity to visualize the size of any regions that exceed the yield strength. Where yielding occurs over regions of worrisome size, design changes need to be made, and the analysis repeated, to be sure that the change was successful. It is often not feasible to make a design so conservative as to eliminate all yielding for severe loading conditions that may occur only rarely.

The preceding argument does not apply to brittle (nonductile) materials, such as glass, stone, ceramics, PMMA and some other polymeric materials, and gray cast iron and some other cast metals. Brittle materials are not capable of deforming sufficiently to shift locally high stresses elsewhere, which is illustrated in Fig. A.10(e). Therefore, the locally elevated stress, $\sigma = k_t S$, should be compared with the failure criterion. In tension-dominated situations, brittle materials fail if the local stress reaches the ultimate tensile strength, according to the maximum normal stress fracture criterion of Eq. 7.13. As a rough guide, a brittle material can be defined as one with less than 5% elongation in a tension test. However, there is an interesting exception to the foregoing recommendation: Where the inherent flaws in a brittle material are relatively large, these may overwhelm the effect of a small stress raiser so that it has little effect. For example, gray cast iron is not sensitive to small stress raisers, as its behavior is dominated by relatively large graphite flakes. (See Fig. 3.7.) In contrast, glass is weakened by a scratch.

7.6.4 Yield Criteria for Anisotropic and Pressure-Sensitive Materials

Several empirical modifications have been suggested so that the octahedral shear stress criterion can be used for *anisotropic* or pressure-sensitive materials. Anisotropic materials have different properties in different directions. Consider anisotropic materials that are orthotropic, possessing symmetry about three planes oriented 90° to each other. For example, such anisotropy can occur in rolled plates of metals where the yield strength may differ somewhat between the rolling, transverse, and thickness directions. The anisotropic yield criterion described in Hill (1998) for this case is

$$H \left(\sigma_X - \sigma_Y \right)^2 + F \left(\sigma_Y - \sigma_Z \right)^2 + G \left(\sigma_Z - \sigma_X \right)^2 + 2N\tau_{XY}^2 + 2L\tau_{YZ}^2 + 2M\tau_{ZX}^2 = 1 \qquad (7.39)$$

where the X-Y-Z axes are aligned with the planes of material symmetry, and H, F, G, N, L, and M are empirical constants for the material. Let σ_{oX}, σ_{oY}, and σ_{oZ} be the uniaxial yield strengths in the three directions, and let τ_{oXY}, τ_{oYZ}, and τ_{oZX} be shear yield strengths on the respective orthogonal planes. The empirical constants can be evaluated from the various yield strengths as follows:

$$H + G = \frac{1}{\sigma_{oX}^2}, \qquad H + F = \frac{1}{\sigma_{oY}^2}, \qquad F + G = \frac{1}{\sigma_{oZ}^2}$$

$$2N = \frac{1}{\tau_{oXY}^2}, \qquad 2L = \frac{1}{\tau_{oYZ}^2}, \qquad 2M = \frac{1}{\tau_{oZX}^2}$$

$$(7.40)$$

The Hill criterion as just described can also be used with reasonable success as a *fracture* criterion for orthotropic composite materials. The equations are the same, except that the various yield strengths are replaced by the corresponding ultimate strengths. However, different values of the constants are generally needed for tension versus compression, and other complexities exist for composite materials that may not be fully predicted by this criterion.

If a material has different yield strengths in tension and compression, this suggests that a dependence on hydrostatic stress needs to be added. One proposed yield criterion for this situation is

$$(\sigma_1 - \sigma_2)^2 + (\sigma_2 - \sigma_3)^2 + (\sigma_3 - \sigma_1)^2 + 2\left(|\sigma_{oc}| - \sigma_{ot}\right)(\sigma_1 + \sigma_2 + \sigma_3) = 2\,|\sigma_{oc}|\,\sigma_{ot} \qquad (7.41)$$

where σ_{ot} and σ_{oc} are the yield strengths in tension and compression, respectively, with the negative sign on σ_{oc} being removed by use of the absolute value.

Polymers often have somewhat higher yield strengths in compression than in tension, with the ratio $|\sigma_{oc}|/\sigma_{ot}$ often being in the range from 1.2 to 1.35. This is illustrated by biaxial test results for three such materials in Fig. 7.12. The behavior expected from Eq. 7.41 with a typical value of $|\sigma_{oc}|/\sigma_{ot} = 1.3$ is plotted. The resulting off-center ellipse is in reasonable agreement with the data.

In some exceptional cases, the yield strength of ductile metals has been observed to be decreased by hydrostatic compression. See the review of Lewandowski (1998) for details and a discussion of the physical mechanism involved, which is associated with upper/lower yield point behavior.

7.6.5 Fracture in Brittle Materials

The maximum normal stress criterion gives reasonably accurate predictions of fracture in brittle materials, as long as the normal stress having the largest absolute value is tensile. However, deviations from this criterion occur if the normal stress having the largest absolute value is compressive. Data illustrating this trend for gray cast iron are shown in Fig. 7.13. A prominent feature of the deviation is that the ultimate strength in compression is higher than that in tension by more than a factor of three.

Recall from Chapters 2 and 3 that brittle materials, such as ceramics and glasses and some cast metals, commonly contain large numbers of randomly oriented microscopic cracks or other planar interfaces that cannot support significant tensile stress. For example, the numerous flaws in

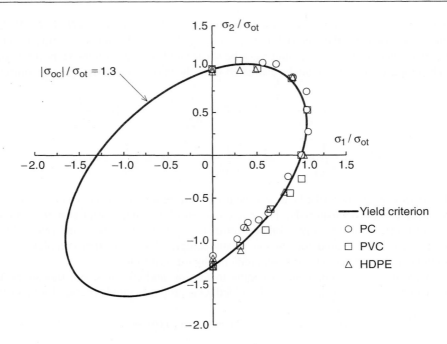

Figure 7.12 Biaxial yield data for various polymers compared with a modified octahedral shear stress theory. (Data from [Raghava 72].)

natural stone have this effect, as do the graphite flakes in gray cast iron. Tensile normal stresses are expected to open these flaws and therefore to cause them to grow. Thus, failure is expected to occur on the plane where the maximum tensile normal stress occurs and to be controlled by this stress. For example, gray cast iron fails normal to the maximum tensile stress in both tension and torsion, as seen in the photographs of Figs. 4.13 and 4.42.

However, if the dominant stresses are compressive, the planar flaws (cracks, etc.) tend to have their opposite sides pressed together so that they have less effect on the behavior. This explains the higher strengths in compression for brittle materials. Also, failure occurs on planes inclined to the planes of principal normal stress and more nearly aligned with planes of maximum shear. (See the compressive fractures of gray iron and concrete in Figs. 4.23 and 4.24.)

One possibility for handling the differing behavior of brittle materials in tension and compression is simply to modify the maximum normal stress criterion so that the compressive and tensile ultimate strengths differ. This would give the off-center square shown in Fig. 7.13, which still does not agree with the data. In addition, any successful fracture criterion should predict that even brittle materials do not fail under hydrostatic compression, which is in agreement with both observation and intuition.

Therefore, additional failure criteria need to be considered that are capable of predicting the behavior of brittle materials. A number of such criteria exist, and we will consider two of the simpler ones in the portions of this chapter that follow.

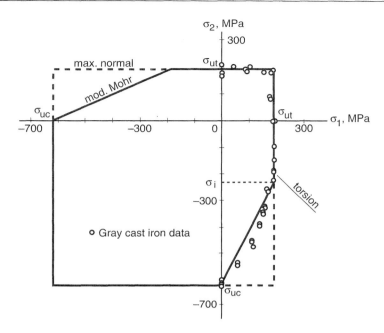

Figure 7.13 Biaxial fracture data of gray cast iron compared with two fracture criteria. (Data from [Grassi 49].)

7.7 COULOMB–MOHR FRACTURE CRITERION

In the Coulomb–Mohr (C–M) criterion, fracture is hypothesized to occur on a given plane in the material when a critical combination of shear and normal stress acts on this plane. In the simplest application of this approach, the mathematical function giving the critical combination of stresses is assumed to be the linear relationship

$$|\tau| + \mu\sigma = \tau_i \qquad \text{(at fracture)} \tag{7.42}$$

where τ and σ are the stresses acting on the fracture plane and μ and τ_i are constants for a given material. This equation forms a line on a plot of σ versus $|\tau|$, as shown in Fig. 7.14. The intercept with the τ axis is τ_i, and the slope is $-\mu$, where both τ_i and μ are defined as positive values.

Now consider a set of applied stresses, which can be specified in terms of the principal stresses, σ_1, σ_2, and σ_3, and plot the Mohr's circles for the principal planes on the same axes as Eq. 7.42. The failure condition is satisfied if the largest of the three circles is tangent to (just touches) the Eq. 7.42 line. If the largest circle does not touch the line, a safety factor greater than unity exists. Intersection of the largest circle and the line is not permissible, as this indicates that failure has already occurred. The line is therefore said to represent a *failure envelope* for Mohr's circle.

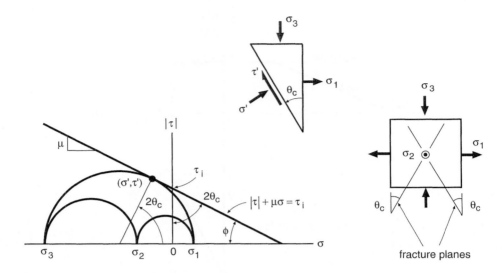

Figure 7.14   Coulomb–Mohr fracture criterion as related to Mohr's circle, and predicted fracture planes.

The point of tangency of the largest circle to the line occurs at a point (σ', τ') that represents the stresses on the plane of fracture. The orientation of this predicted plane of fracture can be determined from the largest circle. In particular, fracture is expected to occur on a plane that is rotated by an angle θ_c relative to the plane normal to the maximum principal stress (σ_1), where rotations in the material are half of the $2\theta_c$ rotation on Mohr's circle. There are two possible planes, as illustrated in Fig. 7.14. Also, from the geometry shown, the slope constant μ can also be specified by an angle ϕ, where

$$\tan\phi = \mu, \qquad \phi = 90° - 2\theta_c \qquad \text{(a, b)} \tag{7.43}$$

The shear stress τ' that causes failure is thus affected by the normal stress σ' acting on the same plane. Such behavior is logical for materials where a brittle shear fracture is influenced by numerous small and randomly oriented planar flaws. More compressive σ' is expected to cause more friction between the opposite faces of the flaws, thus increasing the τ' necessary to cause fracture.

7.7.1 Development of the Coulomb–Mohr Criterion

It is convenient to express the C–M criterion in terms of principal normal stresses with the aid of Fig. 7.14. For the present, we will assume (with signs considered) that σ_1 is the largest principal normal stress, σ_3 the smallest, and σ_2 intermediate; that is, $\sigma_1 \geq \sigma_2 \geq \sigma_3$. Using the radius from the center of the largest Mohr's circle to the (σ', τ') point, we can express σ' and τ' in terms of σ_1 and σ_3:

$$\sigma' = \frac{\sigma_1 + \sigma_3}{2} + \left|\frac{\sigma_1 - \sigma_3}{2}\right| \cos 2\theta_c, \qquad |\tau'| = \left|\frac{\sigma_1 - \sigma_3}{2}\right| \sin 2\theta_c \tag{7.44}$$

These relationships can now be substituted into Eq. 7.42. After doing so, it is useful to make additional substitutions that arise from trigonometry.

$$\cos 2\theta_c = \sin \phi, \quad \sin 2\theta_c = \cos \phi, \quad \mu = \tan \phi = \frac{\sin \phi}{\cos \phi}, \quad \sin^2 \phi + \cos^2 \phi = 1 \qquad (7.45)$$

After some algebraic manipulation, we obtain three alternative forms of the desired expression:

$$|\sigma_1 - \sigma_3| + (\sigma_1 + \sigma_3) \sin \phi = 2\tau_i \cos \phi \qquad \text{(a)}$$

$$|\sigma_1 - \sigma_3| + m(\sigma_1 + \sigma_3) = 2\tau_i \sqrt{1 - m^2} \qquad \text{(b)} \qquad (7.46)$$

$$|\sigma_1 - \sigma_3| + m(\sigma_1 + \sigma_3) = |\sigma_{uc}'| (1 - m) \qquad \text{(c)}$$

Equation (b) arises from (a) through the definition of a new constant, $m = \sin \phi$, and form (c) will be derived shortly. It is also useful to note that additional manipulation using the trigonometric expressions of Eq. 7.45 gives

$$m = \sin \phi = \frac{\mu}{\sqrt{1 + \mu^2}}, \qquad \mu = \frac{m}{\sqrt{1 - m^2}} \qquad \text{(a, b)} \qquad (7.47)$$

Assume that the failure envelope, as given by Eq. 7.42 or 7.46, is known for a given material. We can then calculate the strength that is expected in simple compression, σ_{uc}', where the prime is included to indicate that the value is calculated from the envelope, as distinguished from the value σ_{uc} from an actual test. The principal stresses for this situation are $\sigma_3 = \sigma_{uc}', \sigma_1 = \sigma_2 = 0$. Substituting these into Eq. 7.46(b) and noting that σ_{uc}' has a negative value gives

$$-\sigma_{uc}'(1 - m) = 2\tau_i \sqrt{1 - m^2}, \qquad \sigma_{uc}' = -2\tau_i \sqrt{\frac{1 + m}{1 - m}} \qquad \text{(a, b)} \qquad (7.48)$$

Algebraic manipulation of (a) yields the desired result (b) in explicit form. The corresponding Mohr's circle and fracture planes are illustrated in Fig. 7.15(a). Also, substituting Eq. 7.48(a) into Eq. 7.46(b) gives the envelope equation in the form of Eq. 7.46(c). In the latter, the quantity $|\sigma_{uc}'| = -\sigma_{uc}'$ is employed, so that the correct result is obtained regardless of how the sign of σ_{uc}' is entered.

Similarly, the strength expected in simple tension, σ_{ut}', can be calculated from the failure envelope by substituting the appropriate principal stresses, $\sigma_1 = \sigma_{ut}', \sigma_2 = \sigma_3 = 0$, into Eq. 7.46(b). The result is

$$\sigma_{ut}' = 2\tau_i \sqrt{\frac{1 - m}{1 + m}} \qquad (7.49)$$

The corresponding Mohr's circle and fracture planes for this case are illustrated in Fig. 7.15(b). Additionally, consider a test in simple torsion, as illustrated in Fig. 7.16, where τ_u' is the fracture

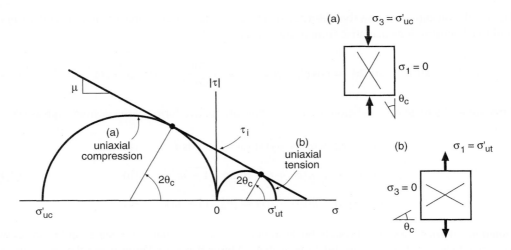

Figure 7.15 Fracture planes predicted by the Coulomb–Mohr criterion for uniaxial tests in tension and compression.

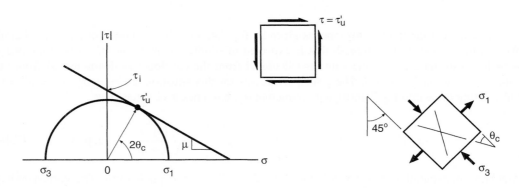

Figure 7.16 Pure torsion and the fracture planes predicted by the Coulomb–Mohr criterion.

strength in shear expected from the failure envelope. Substituting the appropriate principal stresses, $\sigma_1 = -\sigma_3 = \tau'_u$, $\sigma_2 = 0$, into Eq. 7.46(b) gives

$$\tau'_u = \tau_i \sqrt{1 - m^2} \tag{7.50}$$

If experimental data from several triaxial compression tests at various stress levels are available, then a linear least squares fit can be employed to obtain constants for the failure envelope line. Two constants are needed: (1) the slope, as specified by any one of μ, ϕ, θ_c, or m, and (2) the

Table 7.1   Strengths and Coulomb–Mohr Fitting Constants for Some Brittle Materials

	Tension	Compression			Coulomb–Mohr Fit		
Material[1]	σ_{ut}, MPa	$|\sigma_{uc}|$, MPa	m	b, MPa	μ	τ_i, MPa	θ_c, deg
Siliceous sandstone[2]	3[7]	100	0.700	33.37	0.979	23.35	22.8
Granite rock[3]	13.4	143	0.824	22.00	1.455	19.42	17.3
Sand–cement mortar[4]	2.8[7]	31.8	0.497	17.11	0.573	9.86	30.1
Concrete[5]	1.7	45.3	0.631	17.90	0.814	11.54	25.4
Gray cast iron[6]	214	770	0.276	557.8	0.287	290.1	37.0

Notes: [1]The values listed will vary significantly depending on the origin of the material. Based on data from [2][Jaeger 69], [3][Karfakis 03], [4][Campbell 62], and [5][Hobbs 71]. [6]Values not fitted, but estimated from measured σ_{uc} and θ_c. [7]Value estimated from similar material.

intercept τ_i. First, write Eq. 7.46(b) as

$$|\sigma_1 - \sigma_3| = -m(\sigma_1 + \sigma_3) + 2\tau_i\sqrt{1 - m^2} \tag{7.51}$$

Then fit a linear relationship

$$y = ax + b \tag{7.52}$$

where

$$y = |\sigma_1 - \sigma_3|, \qquad x = \sigma_1 + \sigma_3 \qquad \text{(a)}$$
$$a = -m, \qquad b = 2\tau_i\sqrt{1 - m^2} \qquad \text{(b)} \tag{7.53}$$

Values of m and b from fits of this type for a few materials are given in Table 7.1, along with the corresponding values of μ, τ_i, and θ_c, calculated from m and b with the use of Eqs. 7.47, 7.53(b), and 7.43, respectively. Also, the last line of the table gives estimated constants for gray cast iron.

Example 7.7

Test data are given in Table E7.7(a) for static fracture of siliceous sandstone, including simple tension, simple compression, and two tests in compression with lateral pressure p surrounding all sides of the test specimen. The applied stresses at fracture are denoted σ_3, and the lateral stresses as $\sigma_1 = \sigma_2 = -p$.

(a) Fit the data to Eq. 7.51 to obtain values of m and τ_i that describe the Coulomb–Mohr failure envelope line. Also, calculate μ, ϕ, and θ_c.

(b) Plot the resulting failure envelope line, along with the largest Mohr's circles, for each test. Does the line reasonably represent the test data?

(c) Also, calculate the ultimate strengths in compression and tension, σ'_{uc} and σ'_{ut}, that correspond to the fitted C–M failure envelope, and compare these with the actual values from the tests.

Table E7.7

(a) Given Stresses		(b) Calculated Values		
σ_3 MPa	$\sigma_1 = \sigma_2$ MPa	y $\lvert\sigma_1 - \sigma_3\rvert$	x $\sigma_1 + \sigma_3$	Center $(\sigma_1 + \sigma_3)/2$
3	0	—	—	1.5
−100	0	100	−100	−50
−700	−100	600	−800	−400
−1230	−200	1030	−1430	−715

Source: Data in [Jaeger 69] pp. 75 and 156.

Solution   (a) Values of y and x are calculated from Eq. 7.53(a), as given in Table E7.7(b). A linear least squares fit of these values, with the simple tension test not being included, yields

$$a = -0.6995, \qquad b = 33.37\,\text{MPa}$$

Equation 7.53(b) then gives

$$m = -a = 0.6995, \qquad \tau_i = \frac{b}{2\sqrt{1-m^2}} = \frac{33.37\,\text{MPa}}{2\sqrt{1-0.6995^2}} = 23.35\,\text{MPa} \qquad \textbf{Ans.}$$

The additional values desired can then be calculated from Eqs. 7.47 and 7.43:

$$\phi = \sin^{-1} m = 44.39°, \qquad \mu = \tan\phi = 0.9789, \qquad \theta_c = \frac{90° - \phi}{2} = 22.81° \qquad \textbf{Ans.}$$

(b) The failure envelope line is then given by substituting the constants obtained into Eq. 7.42:

$$\lvert\tau\rvert + 0.9789\sigma = 23.35\,\text{MPa} \qquad \textbf{Ans.}$$

This line is plotted in Figs. E7.7(a) and (b), where the latter shows the region near the origin in more detail. Also plotted are the largest Mohr's circles from each test, where the centers of each are calculated in Table E7.7(b) as a convenience. The line is in reasonable agreement with the circles for the three tests in compression, but it is far above the circle for the simple tension test.

(c) The values of the strengths in simple compression and tension expected from the fitted envelope, σ'_{uc} and σ'_{ut}, are obtained by substituting m and τ_i from the previous fit into Eqs. 7.48 and 7.49:

$$\sigma'_{uc} = -111.1, \qquad \sigma'_{ut} = 19.63\,\text{MPa} \qquad \textbf{Ans.}$$

The value of σ'_{uc} is about 10% larger than $\sigma_{uc} = -100\,\text{MPa}$, which is perhaps within statistical scatter. But σ'_{ut} is drastically larger than $\sigma_{ut} = 3\,\text{MPa}$, and the fitted envelope obviously does not agree with the tension test data.

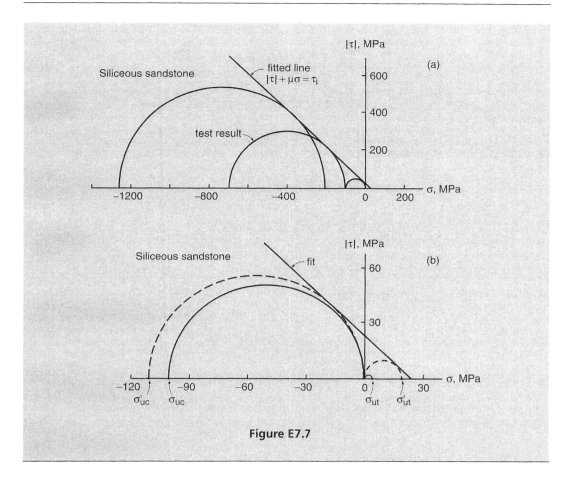

Figure E7.7

7.7.2 Graphical Representation of the Coulomb–Mohr Criterion

If the assumption $\sigma_1 \geq \sigma_2 \geq \sigma_3$ is dropped, so that there are no restrictions on the relative magnitudes of the principal normal stresses, Eq. 7.46 needs to be expanded into three relationships. For the form of Eq. 7.46(c), these are

$$|\sigma_1 - \sigma_2| + m(\sigma_1 + \sigma_2) = |\sigma'_{uc}|(1 - m) \qquad \text{(a)}$$

$$|\sigma_2 - \sigma_3| + m(\sigma_2 + \sigma_3) = |\sigma'_{uc}|(1 - m) \qquad \text{(b)} \qquad (7.54)$$

$$|\sigma_3 - \sigma_1| + m(\sigma_3 + \sigma_1) = |\sigma'_{uc}|(1 - m) \qquad \text{(c)}$$

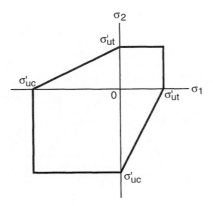

Figure 7.17   Failure locus for the Coulomb–Mohr fracture criterion for plane stress.

Note that these actually represent six equations due to the absolute values, fracture being predicted if any one of them is satisfied. For plane stress with $\sigma_3 = 0$, these reduce to

$$|\sigma_1 - \sigma_2| + m(\sigma_1 + \sigma_2) = \left|\sigma'_{uc}\right|(1 - m) \qquad \text{(a)}$$

$$|\sigma_2| + m(\sigma_2) = \left|\sigma'_{uc}\right|(1 - m) \qquad \text{(b)} \qquad\qquad (7.55)$$

$$|\sigma_1| + m(\sigma_1) = \left|\sigma'_{uc}\right|(1 - m) \qquad \text{(c)}$$

The six lines represented by the latter equations form the boundaries of the region of no failure, as shown in Fig. 7.17. The unequal fracture strengths in tension and compression that correspond to the envelope line can be related by combining Eqs. 7.48 and 7.49 and substituting $-\left|\sigma'_{uc}\right| = \sigma'_{uc}$:

$$\sigma'_{ut} = \left|\sigma'_{uc}\right| \frac{1 - m}{1 + m} \tag{7.56}$$

For the general case of a three-dimensional state of stress, Eq. 7.54 represents six planes that give a failure surface as shown in Fig. 7.18. The surface forms a vertex along the line $\sigma_1 = \sigma_2 = \sigma_3$ at the point

$$\sigma_1 = \sigma_2 = \sigma_3 = \left|\sigma'_{uc}\right| \frac{1 - m}{2m} \tag{7.57}$$

Hence, the value of m, or of the closely related constant μ, determines where the vertex is formed. Higher values of m or μ indicate that the six planes are tilted more abruptly relative to one another and form a vertex closer to the origin. If any one of σ_1, σ_2, or σ_3 is zero, the intersection of this surface with the plane of the remaining two principal stresses forms the shape of Fig. 7.17.

From comparison of Eqs. 7.25 and 7.54, it is evident that the C–M criterion with $m = 0$ is equivalent to a maximum shear stress criterion. Figure 7.17 then takes the same, more symmetrical

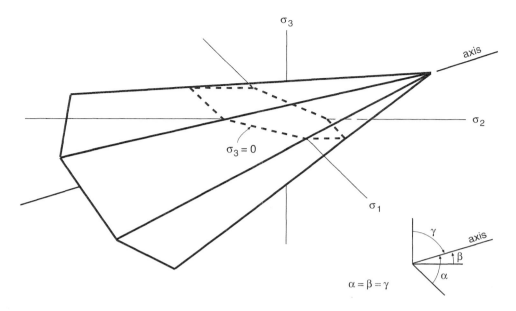

Figure 7.18   Three-dimensional failure surface for the Coulomb–Mohr fracture criterion.

shape as Fig. 7.5. The vertex of the failure surface is moved to infinity, and its cross sections become perfect hexagons, all of the same size. Thus, the C–M criterion contains the maximum shear criterion as a special case.

7.7.3 Effective Stress for the Coulomb–Mohr Criterion

We can define an *effective stress* for the C–M criterion, as was done for other failure criteria earlier in this chapter. To proceed, first note that Eq. 7.54 describes the failure surface. If the stresses actually applied are such that the left-hand sides of all of (a), (b), and (c) are less than $|\sigma'_{uc}|(1 - m)$, then a safety factor against fracture exists that is greater than unity. Consider the following three quantities arising from Eq. 7.54:

$$C_{12} = \frac{1}{1 - m}\Big[|\sigma_1 - \sigma_2| + m(\sigma_1 + \sigma_2)\Big] \qquad \text{(a)}$$

$$C_{23} = \frac{1}{1 - m}\Big[|\sigma_2 - \sigma_3| + m(\sigma_2 + \sigma_3)\Big] \qquad \text{(b)} \qquad\qquad (7.58)$$

$$C_{31} = \frac{1}{1 - m}\Big[|\sigma_3 - \sigma_1| + m(\sigma_3 + \sigma_1)\Big] \qquad \text{(c)}$$

If the applied stresses cause any one of these quantities to reach $|\sigma'_{uc}|$, then fracture is expected. Hence, the effective stress, $\bar{\sigma}_{CM}$, and the corresponding safety factor against fracture, X_{CM}, may be defined as

$$\bar{\sigma}_{CM} = \text{MAX}(C_{12}, C_{23}, C_{31}), \qquad X_{CM} = \frac{|\sigma'_{uc}|}{\bar{\sigma}_{CM}} \qquad \text{(a)}$$
(7.59)
$$\bar{\sigma}_{CM} = 0, \quad X_{CM} = \infty, \quad \text{if MAX} \leq 0 \qquad \text{(b)}$$

Situation (b) arises when the combination of stresses is such that a line from the origin through the point $(\sigma_1, \sigma_2, \sigma_3)$ never intersects the failure surface of the type shown in Fig. 7.18. For example, this occurs for $\sigma_1 = \sigma_2 = \sigma_3 = -p$, where p is pressure.

Ideally, values of σ'_{uc} and m for use in these equations would be available from fitting a failure envelope. However, only σ_{uc} from test data in simple compression may be available. In this case, σ'_{uc} should be estimated as being the same as σ_{uc}, and an estimate of m is needed. This might be obtained by measuring the fracture angle θ_c from the simple compression tests, and then applying Eqs. 7.43(b) and 7.47(a) to estimate $m = \sin\phi = \sin(90° - 2\theta_c)$. Or m might be known approximately from experience with similar material. For example, the paper by Paul (1961) suggests a generic value for any gray cast iron of $\phi = 20°$, corresponding to $\theta_c = 35°$ and $m = 0.342$.

7.7.4 Discussion

For the C–M criterion with a positive nonzero value of μ, which gives a downward-sloping failure envelope line as in Fig. 7.14, the predicted behavior is consistent with a number of observations that are typical of brittle materials. First, the fracture strength in compression is greater than that in tension, with the difference increasing with the value of μ. Test data showing different strengths in tension and compression have already been presented in Fig. 7.13 for gray cast iron. Data for a ceramic material are shown in Fig. 7.19. (See also Table 3.10 for data on additional materials.)

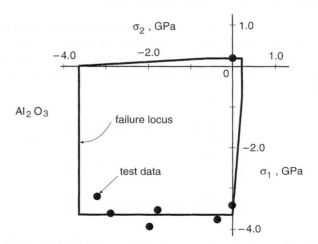

Figure 7.19   Test data and failure locus for biaxial compression of the ceramic alumina, Al_2O_3. Each point plotted is the average from three or four tests as reported by [Sines 75].

The plane of fracture in compression is often observed to be an acute angle relative to the loading axis on the order of $\theta_c = 20°$ to $40°$. (See the fractured compression specimens of cast iron and concrete in Figs. 4.23 and 4.24, and compare with Fig. 7.15.) From Eq. 7.43, this corresponds approximately to μ values in the range 1.2 to 0.2.

However, the fracture planes predicted for a tension test are incorrect. Brittle materials generally fail in tension on planes near the plane normal to the maximum tension stress—that is, normal to the specimen axis—not on planes as shown in Fig. 7.15. Failures of brittle materials in torsion generally also occur on planes normal to the maximum tension stress, not on the planes predicted by the C–M theory, as in Fig. 7.16. (See the broken tension and torsion specimens of cast iron in Figs. 4.13 and 4.42.) Moreover, the fracture strengths in tension, compression, and shear are not typically related to one another as predicted by a single value of m used with the previous equations.

The situation of the maximum tension stress controlling the behavior in tension and torsion, in disagreement with the C–M criterion, can be handled by using the C–M criterion in combination with the maximum normal stress fracture criterion. This combination, called the *modified Mohr fracture criterion*, will be discussed in Section 7.8.

An alternative form of Eq. 7.46 is sometimes employed. Returning to the $\sigma_1 \geq \sigma_2 \geq \sigma_3$ assumption, so that only Eq. 7.46(c) is needed, some algebraic manipulation yields

$$\sigma_3 = h\sigma_1 - |\sigma'_{uc}|, \qquad \text{where} \quad h = \frac{1+m}{1-m} \tag{7.60}$$

In some cases, a linear relationship does not fit the data very well, so Eq. 7.60 is generalized to a power equation:

$$\sigma_3 = -k(-\sigma_1)^a - |\sigma_{uc}| \qquad (\sigma_3 \leq \sigma_2 \leq \sigma_1) \tag{7.61}$$

The quantities k and a are fitting constants, and σ_{uc} is the strength in simple compression from test data. Where this nonlinear relationship is needed, the value of a is typically less than unity and in the range 0.7 to 0.9. A nonlinear relationship between σ_3 and σ_1 implies a curved failure envelope line, rather than a straight line as in Eq. 7.42 and Fig. 7.14. A curved failure envelope is indeed sometimes observed, especially for tests under rather large confining pressures, where failure of the normally brittle material is controlled by ductile yielding rather than by fracture.

In most tests for obtaining C–M envelope fits, the σ_3 at failure is a larger compressive value than $\sigma_1 = \sigma_2$ from lateral pressure; these are called Type I tests, as in Ex. 7.7. Another option is to increase $\sigma_3 = \sigma_2$ to fracture while σ_1 is held at a smaller compressive value; this is called a Type II test. The C–M envelopes for Type II tests in general appear to be above those for Type I tests. So the intermediate principal stress σ_2 does have an effect, contrary to the assumption implicit in the C–M criterion that it does not. Although a more general approach would be desirable, it appears to be reasonable to use the envelope from Type I tests as a conservative approximation.

7.8 MODIFIED MOHR FRACTURE CRITERION

As already noted, the Coulomb–Mohr fracture criterion does not agree with behavior of brittle materials in tension and torsion. This difficulty can be handled by using the C–M criterion in combination with the maximum normal stress fracture criterion, as illustrated in Fig. 7.20. In particular, the C–M failure locus from compression-dominated behavior is truncated and replaced by the maximum normal stress criterion wherever its predictions exceed the latter. This combination is called the modified Mohr (M-M) fracture criterion.

7.8.1 Details of the Modified Mohr Criterion

For the σ_1 versus σ_2 failure locus for biaxial stresses of Fig. 7.20(a), note that, for simple tension, and also for biaxial stresses that are both positive, fracture is controlled by σ_{ut}, as measured in a simple tension test, not by the larger value σ_{ut}' expected from the C–M criterion and Eq. 7.49 or 7.56. Looking at the σ versus $|\tau|$ failure envelope, as in Fig. 7.20(b), we see that a vertical line at σ_{ut} truncates the sloping line of the C–M criterion, so that, again, σ_{ut}' does not correspond to the real behavior.

For simple compression, $\sigma_{uc} \approx \sigma_{uc}'$ is indicated in Fig. 7.20(a) and (b), with these two quantities differing only due to statistical scatter in real data, and perhaps due to minor deviations of the compression-dominated behavior from a linear C–M envelope. (If there are major deviations from linearity, as when Eq. 7.61 applies, a more general approach is needed.)

Tension-dominated behavior generally extends at least to, and often somewhat beyond, the $\sigma_1 = -\sigma_2$ line in Fig. 7.20(a) corresponding to simple torsion. (See the data of Figs. 7.11 and 7.13.) Hence, in torsion, fracture is expected to occur at $\tau_u = \sigma_{ut}$, not at the larger value τ_u' from the C–M criterion and Eq. 7.50.

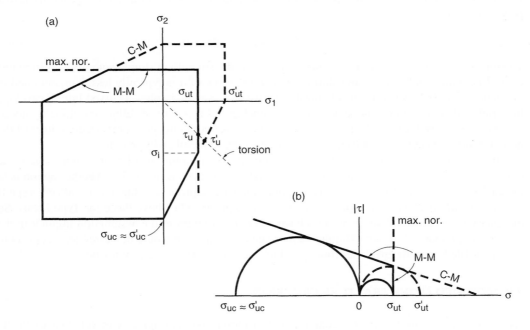

Figure 7.20   The modified Mohr (M-M) fracture criterion, formed by the maximum normal stress criterion truncating the Coulomb–Mohr (C–M) criterion.

The intersection of the C–M and the maximum normal stress parts of the M-M failure locus for biaxial stress occurs at a stress σ_i, as shown in Fig. 7.20(a). In particular, there is usually a biaxial state of stress, $\sigma_1 = \sigma_{ut}, \sigma_2 = \sigma_i, \sigma_3 = 0$, with σ_i negative, where both the C–M and maximum normal stress criteria are obeyed. Substituting this combination of stresses into Eq. 7.54(a) and solving for σ_i gives

$$\sigma_i = -|\sigma_{uc}'| + \sigma_{ut} \frac{1+m}{1-m} \qquad (\sigma_{ut} \leq \sigma_{ut}') \qquad (7.62)$$

In three dimensions, the M-M failure locus is similar to Fig. 7.21. The three positive faces of the maximum normal stress cube truncate the C–M failure surface. (Compare Fig. 7.21 with Figs. 7.3 and 7.18.) Note that the three positive faces of the normal stress cube correspond to

$$\sigma_1 = \sigma_{ut}, \qquad \sigma_2 = \sigma_{ut}, \qquad \sigma_3 = \sigma_{ut} \qquad (7.63)$$

Hence, the failure surface is given by these three planes in addition to the six planes corresponding to Eq. 7.54. Fracture is expected when any one of the nine planes is reached. The two failure surfaces intersect, and the two theories agree, along six edges of these faces. (Four of these edges can be seen, and two are hidden, in Fig. 7.21.) For plane stress, a failure locus as in Fig. 7.20(a), solid line, is obtained as the intersection of the failure surface with a plane such as $\sigma_3 = 0$.

The M-M criterion requires three materials constants: (1) the slope of the C–M failure envelope, as specified by any one of μ, ϕ, θ_c, and m; (2) the intercept τ_i of the C–M failure envelope, which

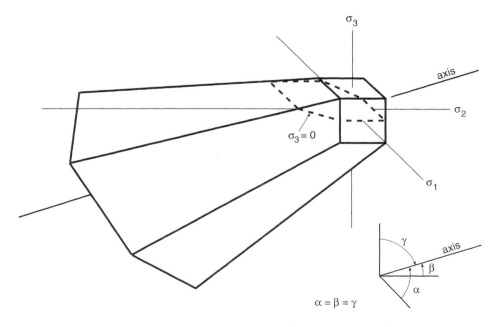

Figure 7.21 Three-dimensional failure surface for the modified Mohr fracture criterion. The Coulomb–Mohr surface is truncated by three faces of the maximum normal stress cube.

can be specified by σ'_{uc} used with Eq. 7.48; and (3) the ultimate tensile strength σ_{ut} from test data in simple tension. As already noted, the estimate $\sigma'_{uc} \approx \sigma_{uc}$ may be employed if there are insufficient compression-dominated data for making a C–M envelope fit. But then m or one of its allied constants must be known, such as an observed fracture angle θ_c from simple compression tests. Equation 7.62 presents an additional opportunity to estimate m. In particular, if biaxial data as in Fig. 7.13 are available and give a reasonably distinct value of σ_i, then m may be obtained by solving Eq. 7.62:

$$m = \frac{|\sigma'_{uc}| - \sigma_{ut} + \sigma_i}{|\sigma'_{uc}| + \sigma_{ut} + \sigma_i} \qquad (7.64)$$

Some caution is obviously needed in employing values of m estimated without the benefit of data suitable for fitting the C–M failure envelope.

More general, but more complex, methods are available that do not require a linear C–M failure envelope line. (See books by Nadai (1950), Jaeger (2007), Chen (1988), and Munz (1999) for discussion and details.) However, the linear assumption is often employed, as in the ASTM test method for triaxial compression of rock.

7.8.2 Effective Stresses and Safety Factor for the Modified Mohr Criterion

For the M-M criterion, effective stresses for its C–M and maximum normal stress components can be determined. Each of these gives a safety factor against fracture, the lowest of which is the controlling one. The effective stress and safety factor for the C–M criterion have already been described by Eqs. 7.58 and 7.59, which may be employed in the same form here. For the maximum normal stress component, the effective stress of Eq. 7.13(a) applies to include the three positive faces of the normal stress cube:

$$\bar{\sigma}_{NP} = \text{MAX}(\sigma_1, \sigma_2, \sigma_3), \qquad X_{NP} = \frac{\sigma_{ut}}{\bar{\sigma}_{NP}} \qquad \text{(a)}$$

$$\bar{\sigma}_{NP} = 0, \quad X_{NP} = \infty, \quad \text{if MAX} \leq 0 \qquad \text{(b)} \qquad (7.65)$$

Here, the subscripts are changed to NP, as this differs by removal of the restrictions of Eq. 7.13(b). We will now use the normal stress criterion up to the intersection with the C–M criterion, as at the stress σ_i of Fig. 7.20, which generally exceeds the previous limitation by a small amount. The situation of Eq. 7.65(b) arises when the combination of stresses is such that a line from the origin through the point $(\sigma_1, \sigma_2, \sigma_3)$ never intersects one of the positive faces of the maximum normal stress cube.

The overall and controlling safety factor for the M-M criterion is then the smallest of the values from Eqs. 7.59 and 7.65:

$$X_{MM} = \text{MIN}(X_{CM}, X_{NP}) \qquad \text{(a)}$$

$$\frac{1}{X_{MM}} = \text{MAX}\left(\frac{\bar{\sigma}_{CM}}{|\sigma'_{uc}|}, \frac{\bar{\sigma}_{NP}}{\sigma_{ut}}\right) \qquad \text{(b)} \qquad (7.66)$$

Form (b) gives the same result and is convenient for numerical calculations, as it avoids generating infinite values when either or both of $\bar{\sigma}_{CM}$ or $\bar{\sigma}_{NP}$ are zero.

Example 7.8

A gray cast iron has a tensile strength of 214 MPa and a compressive strength of 770 MPa, where these values are averages from three tests of each type on a single batch of material. Also, in the compression tests, the fracture was observed to occur on a plane inclined to the direction of loading by an angle averaging $\theta_c = 37°$.

(a) Assuming that the modified Mohr criterion applies, calculate m and σ_i values for this material.

(b) If a shaft of diameter 30 mm of this material is subjected to a torque of 500 N·m, estimate the safety factor against fracture.

(c) What is the safety factor against fracture if a 100 kN compressive force is applied to the shaft in addition to the torque?

Solution   (a) The value of m can be obtained from $\theta_c = 37°$ and Eqs. 7.43 and 7.47.

$$\phi = 90° - 2\theta_c = 16°, \qquad m = \sin\phi = 0.2756 \qquad\qquad \textbf{Ans.}$$

To calculate σ_i, use $\sigma'_{uc} = \sigma_{uc} = -770$ MPa, as well as $\sigma_{ut} = 214$ MPa, with m in Eq. 7.62.

$$\sigma_i = -|\sigma'_{uc}| + \sigma_{ut}\frac{1+m}{1-m} = -393.1 \text{ MPa} \qquad\qquad \textbf{Ans.}$$

(b) The shear stress at the shaft surface due to a torque T is obtained from the shaft radius of $r = 15$ mm and expressions from Appendix A:

$$\tau_{xy} = \frac{Tr}{J}, \qquad J = \frac{\pi r^4}{2}$$

$$\tau_{xy} = \frac{2T}{\pi r^3} = \frac{2(500,000 \text{ N·mm})}{\pi(15 \text{ mm})^3} = 94.31 \text{ MPa}$$

Noting that there is a state of plane stress with this τ_{xy} and $\sigma_x = \sigma_y = 0$, the in-plane principal normal stresses from Eq. 6.7 are

$$\sigma_1, \sigma_2 = \frac{\sigma_x + \sigma_y}{2} \pm \sqrt{\left(\frac{\sigma_x - \sigma_y}{2}\right)^2 + \tau_{xy}^2} = 94.31, -94.31 \text{ MPa}$$

The third principal normal stress is $\sigma_3 = 0$.

We now have all of the quantities needed to obtain C_{12}, C_{23}, and C_{31} from Eq. 7.58:

$$C_{12} = 260.4, \qquad C_{23} = 94.31, \qquad C_{31} = 166.09 \text{ MPa}$$

These, along with the principal normal stresses, σ_1, σ_2, and σ_3 give the effective stresses and safety factors for the C–M and maximum normal stress components of the M-M failure criterion.

From Eqs. 7.59 and 7.65, we obtain

$$\bar{\sigma}_{CM} = \text{MAX}(C_{12}, C_{23}, C_{31}) = 260.4\,\text{MPa}, \qquad X_{CM} = \frac{|\sigma'_{uc}|}{\bar{\sigma}_{CM}} = \frac{770\,\text{MPa}}{260.4\,\text{MPa}} = 2.96$$

$$\bar{\sigma}_{NP} = \text{MAX}(\sigma_1, \sigma_2, \sigma_3) = 94.31\,\text{MPa}, \qquad X_{NP} = \frac{\sigma_{ut}}{\bar{\sigma}_{NP}} = \frac{214\,\text{MPa}}{94.31\,\text{MPa}} = 2.27$$

Finally, from Eq. 7.66, the controlling safety factor is the smaller of the two:

$$X_{MM} = \text{MIN}(X_{CM}, X_{NP}) = 2.27 \qquad\qquad \textbf{Ans.}$$

(c) The additional compressive force causes a stress of

$$\sigma_x = \frac{P}{A} = \frac{-100,000\,\text{N}}{\pi(15\,\text{mm})^2} = -141.47\,\text{MPa}$$

so the overall state of plane stress and the resulting principal normal stresses are now

$$\sigma_x = -141.47, \qquad \sigma_y = 0, \qquad \tau_{xy} = 94.31\,\text{MPa}$$
$$\sigma_1 = 47.16, \qquad \sigma_2 = -188.63, \qquad \sigma_3 = 0\,\text{MPa}$$

The latter, with the same m, σ'_{uc}, and σ_{ut} values as before, give the following from Eqs. 7.58, 7.59, 7.65, and 7.66:

$$C_{12} = 271.7, \qquad C_{23} = 188.63, \qquad C_{31} = 83.05\,\text{MPa}$$

$$\bar{\sigma}_{CM} = \text{MAX}(C_{12}, C_{23}, C_{31}) = 271.7\,\text{MPa}, \qquad X_{CM} = \frac{|\sigma'_{uc}|}{\bar{\sigma}_{CM}} = \frac{770\,\text{MPa}}{271.7\,\text{MPa}} = 2.83$$

$$\bar{\sigma}_{NP} = \text{MAX}(\sigma_1, \sigma_2, \sigma_3) = 47.16\,\text{MPa}, \qquad X_{NP} = \frac{\sigma_{ut}}{\bar{\sigma}_{NP}} = \frac{214\,\text{MPa}}{47.16\,\text{MPa}} = 4.54$$

$$X_{MM} = \text{MIN}(X_{CM}, X_{NP}) = 2.83 \qquad\qquad \textbf{Ans.}$$

Discussion   In (b), X_{NP} is the smaller of the two safety factors, so that the maximum normal stress component of the M-M failure criterion is controlling. But in (c), X_{CM} is smaller, so the C–M component is controlling.

Example 7.9

A block of the granite rock of Table 7.1 is subjected to a confining pressure on all sides of $p = 150\,\text{MPa}$, due to the weight of rock above, as well as a shear stress τ_{xy}, as shown in Fig. E7.9(a).

(a) What value of shear stress τ_{xy} will cause the block to fracture?
(b) What is the largest value of τ_{xy} that can be allowed if a safety factor of 2.0 against fracture is desired?

Solution   (a) Since a fit was done to obtain the constants in Table 7.1 for this material, it is preferable to employ σ'_{uc} from Eq. 7.48, rather than the tabulated value of σ_{uc} from a simple compression test. Using $m = 0.824$ and $\tau_i = 19.42\,\text{MPa}$ from Table 7.1, we find that the value is

$$\sigma'_{uc} = -2\tau_i\sqrt{\frac{1+m}{1-m}} = -2(19.42\,\text{MPa})\sqrt{\frac{1+0.824}{1-0.824}} = -125.0\,\text{MPa}$$

The given state of stress is $\sigma_x = \sigma_y = \sigma_z = -p = -150\,\text{MPa}$, and unknown τ_{xy}, with $\tau_{yz} = \tau_{zx} = 0\,\text{MPa}$. This is a state of generalized plane stress, so that one principal normal stress is $\sigma_3 = \sigma_z = -150\,\text{MPa}$, and the other two are

$$\sigma_1,\ \sigma_2 = \frac{\sigma_x + \sigma_y}{2} \pm \sqrt{\left(\frac{\sigma_x - \sigma_y}{2}\right)^2 + \tau_{xy}^2} = -150 \pm \tau_{xy}\ \text{MPa}$$

Since σ_1 and σ_2 are determined by adding and subtracting the same value from $\sigma_3 = -150\,\text{MPa}$, the three Mohr's circles must be configured as in Fig. E7.9(b), with the circle formed by σ_1 and σ_2 being the largest. Hence, C_{12} is the largest and controlling value for Eqs. 7.58 and 7.59, so C_{23} and C_{31} can be disregarded. Assuming for the present that the C–M component controls, we have

$$C_{12} = \frac{1}{1-m}\left[|\sigma_1 - \sigma_2| + m(\sigma_1 + \sigma_2)\right] = \bar{\sigma}_{CM} = \frac{|\sigma'_{uc}|}{X_{CM}}$$

$$\left|(-150 + \tau_{xy}) - (-150 - \tau_{xy})\right| + 0.824(-300) = (1 - 0.824)(125.0)/1.00\,\text{MPa}$$

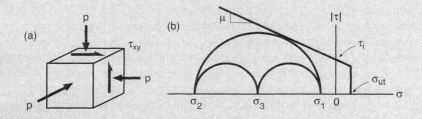

(a)

(b)

Figure E7.9

where $X_{CM} = 1.00$ is substituted so that the point of fracture is analyzed. Solving for τ_{xy} yields

$$\tau_{xy} = 134.6 \, \text{MPa} \qquad \qquad \textbf{Ans.}$$

This value gives σ_1, $\sigma_2 = -150 \pm \tau_{xy} = -15.4, -284.6 \, \text{MPa}$. Hence, Eq. 7.65 gives $\bar{\sigma}_{NP} = 0$ and infinite X_{NP}, so the maximum normal stress component does not control, and the preceding solution is valid.

   (b) Proceeding as before, except for substituting $X_{CM} = 2.00$, gives $\tau_{xy} = 129.1 \, \text{MPa}$ (**Ans.**). This value corresponds to σ_1, $\sigma_2 = -20.9, -279.1 \, \text{MPa}$, so Eq. 7.65 again gives $\bar{\sigma}_{NP} = 0$, and this solution is also valid.

Comment   In the solution for (b), the safety factor of $X_{CM} = 2.00$ is, in effect, applied both to the pressure and to τ_{xy}. Due to increased pressure making fracture more difficult, it turns out that only a small decrease in τ_{xy} is needed to achieve the safety factor. From an engineering viewpoint, if the pressure is considered not to vary, it would be wise to apply the desired safety factor of $X = 2.00$ to only the shear stress that is allowed to vary, so that the solution for (b) becomes $\tau_{xy} = 134.6/2.00 = 67.3 \, \text{MPa}$. This would be the same as a *load factor design* approach, with $Y_p = 1.00$ applied to the pressure and $Y_\tau = 2.00$ applied to τ_{xy}. (See Section 7.6.2.)

7.9 ADDITIONAL COMMENTS ON FAILURE CRITERIA

To gain additional perspective on the subject of this chapter, we will engage in some limited further discussion on brittle versus ductile behavior and on time-dependent effects.

7.9.1 Brittle Versus Ductile Behavior

Engineering materials that are commonly classed as ductile are those for which the static strength in engineering applications is generally limited by yielding. Many metals and polymers fit into this category. In contrast, the usefulness of materials commonly classed as brittle is generally limited by fracture. In a tension test, brittle materials exhibit no well-defined yielding behavior, and they fail after only a small elongation, on the order of 5% or less. Examples are gray cast iron and certain other cast metals, and also stone, concrete, other ceramics, and glasses.

   However, normally brittle materials may exhibit considerable ductility when tested under loading such that the hydrostatic component σ_h of the applied stress is highly compressive. Such an experiment can be conducted by testing the material in a chamber that is already pressurized, as in Fig. 4.27. The surprising result of large plastic deformations in a normally brittle material is illustrated by some stress–strain curves for limestone in Fig. 7.22.

   Also, materials normally considered ductile fail with increased ductility if the hydrostatic stress is compressive, or reduced ductility if it is tensile. For example, although the initial yielding of metals is insensitive to hydrostatic stress, the point of fracture is affected. Data showing this for a steel are given in Fig. 7.23, where the true fracture stress and strain are seen to increase with

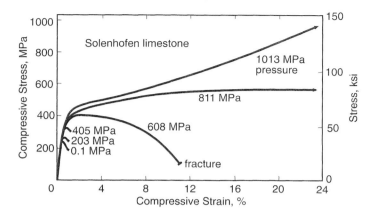

Figure 7.22 Stress–strain data for limestone cylinders tested under axial compression with various hydrostatic pressures ranging from one to 10,000 atmospheres. The applied compressive stress plotted is the stress in the *pressurized laboratory*, that is, the compression in excess of pressure. (Adapted from [Griggs 36]; used with permission; © 1936 The University of Chicago Press.)

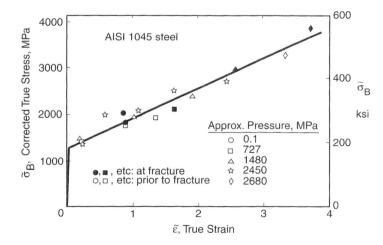

Figure 7.23 Effect of pressures ranging from one to 26,500 atmospheres on the tensile behavior of a steel, specifically AISI 1045 with *HRC* = 40. Stress in the *pressurized laboratory* is plotted. (Data from [Bridgman 52] pp. 47–61.)

pressure—that is, with hydrostatic compression. The fracture event appears to shift to a later point along a common stress–strain curve.

To explain such behavior, it is useful to adopt the viewpoint that fracture and yielding are separate events and that either one may occur first, depending on the combination of material and stress state involved. In three-dimensional principal normal stress space, the limiting surface for

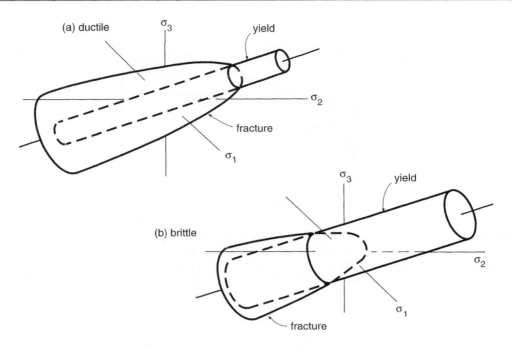

Figure 7.24   Relationships of the limiting surfaces for yielding and fracture for materials that usually behave in a ductile manner, and also for materials that usually behave in a brittle manner.

yielding (at least for metals) is taken to be a cylinder or other prismatic shape that is symmetrical about the line $\sigma_1 = \sigma_2 = \sigma_3$, such as the surfaces of Figs. 7.6 and 7.9. Limiting surfaces for fracture are, in general, similar to those for the modified Mohr theory (as discussed previously and illustrated in Fig. 7.21), although the boundaries may actually be smooth curves.

The situation is illustrated in Fig. 7.24. For certain states of stress, the yield surface is encountered first, whereas for others the fracture surface is encountered first. The relative dimensions of the two surfaces change for different materials. For normally ductile materials, fracture prior to yielding is not expected, except for stress states involving a large hydrostatic tension. The stress may be increased by varying amounts beyond yielding before fracture occurs, depending on the amount of hydrostatic compression. However, for normally brittle materials, there is a contrasting behavior, as fracture occurs prior to yielding, except for stress states involving a large hydrostatic compression. Thus, if a wide range of stress states are of interest for any material, it is important to consider the possibility that either yielding or fracture may occur first.

7.9.2 Time-Dependent Effects of Cracks

As already noted, normally brittle materials usually contain, or easily develop, small flaws or other geometric features that are equivalent to small cracks. Brittle failure generally occurs as a result of such cracks growing and joining. This process is often time dependent, principally because it is affected by the presence of moisture (water) or other substances that react chemically with the material. Time-dependent cracking causes the fracture behavior to be dependent on the loading rate. Also, if the stress is held constant, failure can occur after some time has elapsed at a stress that would not cause fracture if maintained for only a short time. Thus, the approaches of this chapter should be used with some caution to assure that the material properties employed are realistic with respect to time-related effects.

7.10 SUMMARY

Design to avoid yielding or fracture in nominally uncracked material requires the use of a failure criterion, which is a procedure for summarizing a complex state of stress as an effective stress $\bar{\sigma}$ that can be compared to the material's strength. For yielding of ductile materials, the relevant materials strength property is the yield strength σ_o, so that a safety factor can be calculated as

$$X = \frac{\sigma_o}{\bar{\sigma}} \qquad (7.67)$$

Two yield criteria are available that are reasonably accurate for isotropic materials, namely, the maximum shear stress criterion and the octahedral shear stress criterion. The effective stresses for these are, respectively,

$$\bar{\sigma}_S = \text{MAX}(|\sigma_1 - \sigma_2|, |\sigma_2 - \sigma_3|, |\sigma_3 - \sigma_1|) \qquad (7.68)$$

$$\bar{\sigma}_H = \frac{1}{\sqrt{2}}\sqrt{(\sigma_1 - \sigma_2)^2 + (\sigma_2 - \sigma_3)^2 + (\sigma_3 - \sigma_1)^2} \qquad (7.69)$$

Effective stresses, and hence safety factors, from these two criteria never differ by more than 15%. In their basic forms, according to these two equations, both predict that hydrostatic stresses have no effect. Modifications can be used to predict yielding in anisotropic or pressure-sensitive materials.

The application of safety factors, as just described, is called allowable stress design. An alternative is load factor design, where the applied loads are increased by factors Y that can vary for different load inputs, and the failure condition is analyzed. In particular, $\bar{\sigma} = \sigma_o$ is employed, where $\bar{\sigma}$ is calculated from stresses that include load factors.

In applying yield criteria to ductile materials, the stresses employed are usually the nominal ones—that is, the stresses do not include the localized stress raiser effect at notches. This is justified, as ductile materials can deform beyond yielding in a small region without causing failure of the component. But this is not the case for brittle materials, for which stress raiser effects should be considered in fracture criteria.

For brittle materials, no single basic failure criterion suffices to describe the fracture behavior. The modified Mohr criterion is a reasonable choice. It is a combination of the maximum normal stress criterion, which is used where the stresses are dominated by tension, and the Coulomb–Mohr criterion. The latter assumes that fracture occurs when the combination of normal and shear stress on any plane in the material reaches a critical value given by

$$|\tau| + \mu\sigma = \tau_i \qquad (7.70)$$

where μ and τ_i are material constants. The Coulomb–Mohr criterion can be considered to be a shear stress criterion in which the limiting shear stress increases for greater amounts of hydrostatic compression.

In applying the modified Mohr criterion, values are needed for three material constants. These can be the ultimate strengths in tension and compression, σ_{ut} and σ_{uc}, and one additional constant, either μ or the closely related constant m. A value for μ or m can be estimated from the inclination of the fracture plane in compression tests.

Under high hydrostatic compression, normally brittle materials behave in a ductile manner, and ductile materials fracture at higher true stresses and strains than otherwise. Such behavior can be explained by considering yielding and fracture to be independent events with different failure surfaces. The possibility of either occurring first should generally be considered.

Fracture may be time dependent due to crack growth effects, so caution is needed in applying failure criteria that use materials constants from short-term tests.

NEW TERMS AND SYMBOLS

(a) Terms

allowable stress design

anisotropic yield criterion

effective stresses: $\bar{\sigma}_{NT}, \bar{\sigma}_S, \bar{\sigma}_H, \bar{\sigma}_{CM}$

failure criterion (stress based)

failure surface

fracture criteria:

   Coulomb–Mohr

   maximum normal stress

   modified Mohr

load factor design

principal normal stress space

proportional loading

safety factor

ultimate strengths:

   compression, σ_{uc}

   shear, τ_u

   tension, σ_{ut}

yield criteria:

   maximum shear stress

   octahedral shear stress

(b) Constants for the Coulomb–Mohr (C–M) and Modified Mohr (M-M) Criteria

μ, τ_i	Slope and intercept, respectively, of the C–M failure envelope line
$m, \|\sigma'_{uc}\|$	Constants for the C–M criterion, expressed in terms of principal normal stresses
ϕ	C–M failure envelope slope angle, $\tan \phi = \mu$, $\sin \phi = m$
θ_c	Fracture angle, $\theta_c = (90° - \phi)/2$
σ_i	For the modified Mohr criterion, stress where the maximum normal and C–M portions of the failure surface agree

REFERENCES

ASTM. 2010. *Annual Book of ASTM Standards*, ASTM International, West Conshohocken, PA. See No. D7012, "Compressive Strength and Elastic Moduli of Intact Rock Core Specimens under Varying States of Stress and Temperatures," Vol. 04.09.

BORESI, A. P., and R. J. SCHMIDT. 2003. *Advanced Mechanics of Materials*, 6th ed., John Wiley, Hoboken, NJ. (See also the 2d ed. of this book, same title, 1952, by F. B. Seely and J. O. Smith.)

CHEN, W. F., and D. J. HAN. 1988. *Plasticity for Structural Engineers*, Springer-Verlag, New York.

HILL, R. 1998. *The Mathematical Theory of Plasticity*, Oxford University Press, Oxford, UK.

JAEGER, J. C., N. G. W. COOK, and R. W. Zimmerman. 2007. *Fundamentals of Rock Mechanics*, 4th ed., John Wiley, Hoboken, NJ.

LEWANDOWSKI, J. J., and P. LOWHAPHANDU. 1998. "Effects of Hydrostatic Pressure on Mechanical Behavior and Deformation Processing of Materials," *International Materials Reviews*, vol. 43, no. 4, pp. 145–187.

MUNZ, D., and T. FETT. 1999. *Ceramics: Mechanical Properties, Failure Behavior, Materials Selection*, Springer-Verlag, Berlin.

NADAI, A. 1950. *Theory of Flow and Fracture of Solids*, 2nd ed., McGraw-Hill, New York.

PAUL, B. 1961. "A Modification of the Coulomb-Mohr Theory of Fracture," *Jnl. of Applied Mechanics, Trans. ASME*, Ser. E., vol. 28, no. 2, pp. 259–268.

PROBLEMS AND QUESTIONS

Section 7.3

7.1 An engineering component is made of the Boron carbide (B_4C) ceramic of Table 3.10. The most severely stressed point is subjected to the following state of stress: $\sigma_x = 35$, $\sigma_y = 21$, $\tau_{xy} = 7$, and $\sigma_z = \tau_{yz} = \tau_{zx} = 0$ MPa. Determine the safety factor against fracture.

7.2 In an engineering component made of zirconia (ZrO_2), the most severely stressed point is subjected to the following state of stress: $\sigma_x = 125$, $\sigma_y = -80$, $\tau_{xy} = 30$ and $\sigma_z = \tau_{yz} = \tau_{zx} = 0$ MPa. Determine the safety factor against fracture. The material has a tensile strength of 147 MPa and a compressive strength of 2100 MPa.

7.3 An engineering component is made of the silicon nitride (Si_3N_4) ceramic of Table 3.10. The most severely stressed point is subjected to the following state of stress: $\sigma_x = 60$, $\sigma_y = 90$, $\sigma_z = 200$, $\tau_{xy} = 33$, and $\tau_{yz} = \tau_{zx} = 0$ MPa. Determine the safety factor against fracture.

7.4 In an engineering component made of AISI 1020 steel as rolled, the most severely stressed point is subjected to the following state of stress: $\sigma_x = 200$, $\sigma_y = 0$, $\sigma_z = 250$, $\tau_{xy} = 100$ and $\tau_{yz} = \tau_{zx} = 0$ MPa. Determine the safety factor against fracture. The material has a yield strength of 260 MPa and an ultimate tensile strength of 441 MPa.

Sections 7.4 and 7.5[2]

7.5 In an engineering component made of SAE 308 cast aluminum, the most severely stressed point is subjected to the following state of stress: $\sigma_x = 32$, $\sigma_y = -10$, $\tau_{xy} = -20$, and $\sigma_z = \tau_{yz} = \tau_{zx} = 0$ MPa. Determine the safety factor against yielding by (a) the maximum shear stress criterion, and (b) the octahedral shear stress criterion.

7.6 In an engineering component made of AISI 4142 steel (as quenched), the most severely stressed point is subjected to the following state of stress: $\sigma_x = 345$, $\sigma_y = 138$, $\sigma_z = -69$, $\tau_{xy} = 69$, and $\tau_{yz} = \tau_{zx} = 0$ MPa. Determine the safety factor against yielding by (a) the maximum shear stress criterion, and (b) the octahedral shear stress criterion.

---

[2]Use materials properties from Tables 4.2 and 5.2. Unless otherwise indicated, these yield criteria problems may be worked by either the maximum shear stress criterion or the octahedral shear stress criterion.

7.7 In an engineering component made of ductile cast iron A 536 (65-45-12) material, the most severely stressed point is subjected to the following state of stress: $\sigma_x = -50$, $\sigma_y = 120$, $\sigma_z = 40$, $\tau_{xy} = -60$, $\tau_{yz} = 14$, and $\tau_{zx} = 0$ MPa. Determine the safety factor against yielding by (a) the maximum shear stress criterion, and (b) the octahedral shear stress criterion.

7.8 In an engineering component, the most severely stressed point is subjected to the following state of stress: $\sigma_x = 345$, $\sigma_y = 138$, $\tau_{xy} = 69$, and $\sigma_z = \tau_{yz} = \tau_{zx} = 0$ MPa. What minimum yield strength is required for the material if a safety factor of 2.5 against yielding is required? Employ (a) the maximum shear stress criterion, and (b) the octahedral shear stress criterion.

7.9 In an engineering component, the most severely stressed point is subjected to the following state of stress: $\sigma_x = 14$, $\sigma_y = -56$, $\sigma_z = 70$, and $\tau_{xy} = \tau_{yz} = \tau_{zx} = 0$ MPa. What minimum yield strength is required for the material if a safety factor of 2.0 against yielding is required? Employ (a) the maximum shear stress criterion, and (b) the octahedral shear stress criterion.

7.10 In Fig. 7.1, for each case (a), (b), (c), and (d) that is shown, sketch the three Mohr's circles corresponding to the principal shear stresses. Then, for each case, employ the maximum shear stress criterion to determine σ_y at yielding as a function of the uniaxial yield strength. Do you confirm the predictions indicated?

7.11 Strains are measured on the surface of part made from 7075-T6 aluminum and are as follows: $\varepsilon_x = 3600 \times 10^{-6}$, $\varepsilon_y = 150 \times 10^{-6}$, and $\gamma_{xy} = 700 \times 10^{-6}$. Assume that no yielding has occurred and also that no loading is applied directly to the surface, so that $\sigma_z = \tau_{yz} = \tau_{zx} = 0$ MPa. What is the safety factor against yielding?

7.12 A strain gauge rosette, as in Ex. 6.9, is applied to the surface of a component made of Ti-6A1-4V (solution treated and aged). Assume that no yielding has occurred and also that no loading is applied directly to the surface, so that $\sigma_z = \tau_{yz} = \tau_{zx} = 0$ MPa. Strains are measured as follows: $\varepsilon_x = 1200 \times 10^{-6}$, $\varepsilon_y = -650 \times 10^{-6}$, and $\varepsilon_{45} = 1900 \times 10^{-6}$. What is the safety factor against yielding?

7.13 A strain gauge rosette, as in Ex. 6.9, is applied to the surface of a component made of AISI 1020 steel (as rolled). Assume that no yielding has occurred, and also that no loading is applied directly to the surface, so that $\sigma_z = \tau_{yz} = \tau_{zx} = 0$ MPa. Strains are measured as follows: $\varepsilon_x = 290 \times 10^{-6}$, $\varepsilon_y = -860 \times 10^{-6}$, and $\varepsilon_{45} = -190 \times 10^{-6}$. What is the safety factor against yielding?

7.14 A solid circular shaft subjected to pure torsion must be designed to avoid yielding, with a safety factor X. Find the required diameter as a function of the torque T and the yield strength σ_o, using (a) the maximum shear stress criterion, and (b) the octahedral shear stress criterion. How much do these two sizes differ?

7.15 A solid circular shaft has a diameter of 50 mm and is made of AISI 1020 steel (as rolled). It is subjected to a tensile axial force of 100 kN, a bending moment of 800 N·m, and a torque of 1500 N·m. Determine the safety factor against yielding.

7.16 A pipe with closed ends has an outer diameter of 80 mm and a wall thickness of 3.0 mm. It is subjected to an internal pressure of 20 MPa and a bending moment of 2.0 kN·m. Determine the safety factor against yielding if the material is 7075-T6 aluminum.

7.17 A thin-walled tube with closed ends has an inside radius $r_1 = 80$ mm and a wall thickness $t = 6$ mm. It is made of AISI 4142 steel tempered at 450°C and is subjected to an internal pressure of 20 MPa, a torque of 60 kN·m, and a compressive axial force of 200 kN. Determine the safety factor against yielding.

7.18 A solid shaft of diameter d is made of ASTM A514, T1 structural steel and is subjected to a tensile axial force of 200 kN and a torque of 1.5 kN.m. What is the safety factor against yielding if the diameter is 50 mm? Use the octahedral shear stress yield criterion.

7.19 A solid shaft is subjected to a tensile axial force of 300 kN, a bending moment of 5.0 kN·m, and a torque of 9.0 kN·m. A safety factor against yielding of 2.75 is required. What is the smallest permissible value of diameter d if the material is 18 Ni (250) maraging steel?

7.20 A vertical force of 50 kN is applied at mid-span of a simply supported beam, as in Fig. A.4(a). The beam is made of AISI 1020 steel (as rolled), it is 1.0 m long, and it has an I-shaped cross section. The dimensions, as defined in Fig. A.2(d), are $h_2 = 150$, $h_1 = 135$, $b_2 = 100$, and $b_1 = 96$ mm, with loading in the y-direction of Fig. A.2(d).

    (a) For an arbitrary location along the beam length, qualitatively sketch the variations of bending stress and of transverse shear stress through the depth of the beam.

    (b) Determine the safety factor against yielding, checking any points of possible maximum stress. (Suggestion: The transverse shear stress at the center of the beam, $y = 0$, may be approximated as $\tau_{xy} = V/A_{\text{web}}$.)

7.21 A circular tube must support a bending moment of 4.5 kN·m and a torque of 7.0 kN·m. It is made of ASTM A514 (T1) structural steel and has a wall thickness of 3.0 mm.

    (a) What is the safety factor against yielding if the outside diameter is 80 mm?

    (b) For the situation of (a), what adjusted value of outside diameter with the same thickness is required to obtain a safety factor against yielding of 1.5?

7.22 A circular tube must support an axial load of 60 kN tension and a torque of 1.0 kN·m. It is made of 7075-T6 aluminum and has an inside diameter of 46.0 mm.

    (a) What is the safety factor against yielding if the wall thickness is 2.5 mm?

    (b) For the situation of (a), what adjusted value of thickness with the same inside diameter is required to obtain a safety factor against yielding of 2.0?

7.23 Consider a solid circular shaft subjected to bending and torsion, so that the state of stress of interest involves only a normal stress σ_x and a shear stress τ_{xy}, with all other stress components being zero, as in Fig. P7.23. Develop a design equation for the shaft, giving diameter d as a function of yield strength, safety factor, bending moment M, and torque T. Employ (a) the maximum shear stress criterion, and (b) the octahedral shear stress criterion.

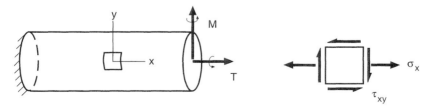

Figure P7.23

7.24 A thin-walled tube with closed ends has an inner diameter of 40 mm and a wall thickness of 2.5 mm. It contains a pressure of 10 MPa and is subjected to a torque of 3000 N·m.

(a) What is the safety factor against yielding if the material is ASTM A514 (T1) structural steel.

(b) Is the design adequate? If not, suggest a new choice of material.

7.25 A piece of a ductile metal is confined on two sides by a rigid die, as shown in Fig. P7.25. A uniform compressive stress σ_z is applied to the surface of the metal. Assume that there is no friction against the die, and also that the material behaves in an elastic, perfectly to plastic manner with uniaxial yield strength σ_o. Derive an equation for the value of σ_z necessary to cause yielding in terms of σ_o and the elastic constants of the material. Is the value of σ_z that causes yielding affected significantly by Poisson's ratio? Employ (a) the maximum shear stress criterion, and (b) the octahedral shear stress criterion. (c) For each yield criterion, what stress σ_z is expected to cause yielding if the material is ductile cast iron A536 (65-45-12)?

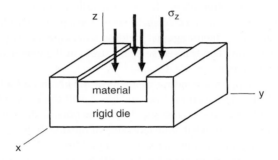

Figure P7.25

7.26 Repeat Prob. 7.25(c) for the case where the die material is AISI 4142 steel.

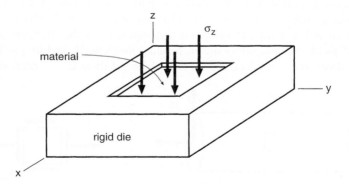

Figure P7.26

7.27 Consider the situation of Fig. E7.5, where a piece of material is stressed in two directions and restrained from deforming in the third direction by rigid, but smooth, walls. Generalize the loading such that $\sigma_x = \lambda\sigma_y$, where λ may vary between $+1$ and -1, and derive the corresponding expression for σ_y at yielding that is analogous to the result of Ex. 7.5(a). Comment on how the stress at yielding is affected by λ.

7.28 A block of 7075-T6 aluminum is subjected to a confining pressure on all sides of $p = 120\,\text{MPa}$, along with a shear stress τ_{xy} as shown in Fig. P7.28.

    (a) Employ octahedral shear stress criterion and find the largest value of τ_{xy} that can be applied if the safety factor against yielding must be 2.5.

    (b) Is there a large effect of the pressure p on the τ_{xy} required to cause yielding? Briefly discuss the effect of p as to whether the effect is large, small or absent and explain why.

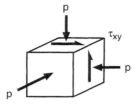

Figure P7.28

7.29 A block of AISI 4142 steel (as quenched) is subjected to a stress $\sigma_z = -100\,\text{MPa}$, along with a shear stress τ_{xy}, as shown in Fig. P7.29.

    (a) Based on octahedral shear stress criterion, find the largest valued of τ_{xy} that can be applied if the safety factor against yielding must be 2.0.

    (b) Is there a large effect of σ_z on the τ_{xy} required to cause yielding? Briefly discuss the effect of σ_z as to whether the effect is large, small or absent, and explain why.

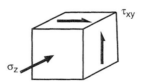

Figure P7.29

7.30 A thick-walled tube with closed ends has inner and outer radii of 30 and 50 mm, respectively. It contains an internal pressure of 160 MPa and is also subjected to a torque of 30 kN·m. The material is AISI 4142 steel tempered at 450°C. What is the safety factor against yielding? (Note: Check inside, outside, and several intermediate values of radius, as the most severely stressed location is not known.)

7.31 A thick-walled tube with closed ends has inner and outer radii of 25 and 50 mm, respectively. It contains an internal pressure of 100 MPa and is also subjected to a torque of 75 kN·m. The material is 18 Ni maraging steel (250). What is the safety factor against yielding? (Note: Check inside, outside, and several intermediate values of radius, as the most severely stressed location is not known.)

7.32 A thick-walled tube with closed ends has inner and outer radii of 25 and 35 mm, respectively. It contains an internal pressure of 25 MPa and is also subjected to a torque of 8.0 kN·m. The material is 7075-T6 aluminum and a safety factor of 2.0 against yielding is required.

    (a) What is the safety factor against yielding? Does it meet the required value?

    (b) Assume that the inner radius is fixed at its given value. What adjusted value of the outer radius is required to meet the safety factor?

7.33 Consider a thick-walled tube with closed ends having inner radius r_1, outer radius r_2, and loaded only with an internal pressure p. Assume that, in a design situation, values of r_1 and p are fixed, as well as a safety factor X against yielding. Further, a candidate material with yield strength σ_o has been selected.

    (a) Develop an equation for the outer radius r_2 that is required as a function of the other variables involved, that is, find $r_2 = f(r_1, p, X, \sigma_o)$.

    (b) What r_2 is required for $r_1 = 40$ mm, $p = 100$ MPa, $X = 4.0$, and $\sigma_o = 1791$ MPa, where the latter corresponds to the 18 Ni maraging steel of Table 4.2.

7.34 A rotating annular disc, as in Fig. A.9, has inner radius $r_1 = 50$, outer radius $r_2 = 200$, and thickness $t = 30$ mm. It is made of 2024-T4 aluminum and rotates at a frequency of $f = 230$ revolutions/second.

    (a) What is the safety factor against yielding?

    (b) If a safety factor of 2.0 against yielding is required, what is the highest permissible rotational frequency?

7.35 A solid circular shaft 1.0 m long must support a bending moment $M = 1.0$ kN·m and a torque $T = 1.5$ kN·m. A safety factor of $X = 2.0$ against yielding is required.

    (a) What shaft diameter d is required if the material is AISI 1020 steel? What is the resulting mass of the shaft?

    (b) Also, consider the possibility of making the shaft out of 2024-T4 aluminum, 7075-T6 aluminum, or one of the tempers of AISI 4140 steel from Prob. 4.33. Calculate the required diameter and mass for each.

    (c) Select a material for the shaft from among those considered in (a) and (b). Assume that the shaft must be both light in weight and inexpensive, and also not prone to sudden fracture. See Table 3.13 for useful data.

Section 7.6

7.36 For the situation of Prob. 7.21, what outside diameter is needed if load factors $Y_M = 1.50$ and $Y_T = 1.80$ are required for moment and torque, respectively?

7.37 For a shaft loaded in bending and torsion, as in Prob. 7.23, develop a design equation for the diameter d as a function of yield strength, bending moment M, torque T, and load factors Y_M and Y_T for moment and torque, respectively. Employ (a) the maximum shear stress criterion, and (b) the octahedral shear stress criterion.

7.38 A shaft made of gray cast iron is loaded in torsion and contains a groove as in Fig. A.12(d). Dimensions are $d_2 = 52.5$, $d_1 = 50$, and $\rho = 3.75$ mm. The material has a tensile strength of

214 MPa and a compressive strength of 770 MPa. For a safety factor of 3.0 against fracture, what is the highest torque that can be applied to the shaft? Note that S in Fig. A.12(d) is the nominal shear stress, and $k_t S$ is the shear stress in the bottom of the groove.

7.39 A block of the polycarbonate (PC) plastic of Table 4.3 is loaded in compression and confined by a rigid die on two sides, as in Fig. P7.25. The compressive yield strength is 20% higher than the tensile yield strength.

    (a) Estimate the value of σ_z necessary to cause yielding.

    (b) Qualitatively sketch the yield locus for plane stress, in this case $\sigma_x = \sigma_3 = 0$, and show the location of the point corresponding to your answer to (a).

7.40 Specialize the anisotropic yield criterion of Hill, Eq. 7.39, to the case of plane stress. If the yield strengths σ_{oX}, σ_{oY}, and τ_{oXY} are known, can the needed constants be obtained so that the criterion can be used? If not, suggest an additional test on the material and explain how you would use the result to evaluate the needed constants.

7.41 An unusual new material is hypothesized to fail when the absolute value of the hydrostatic stress exceeds a critical value. That is,

$$\left| \frac{\sigma_x + \sigma_y + \sigma_z}{3} \right| = \sigma_{hc}$$

However, there is also a possibility that this material obeys either the maximum normal stress failure criterion or the maximum shear stress failure criterion.

    (a) Does the equation given constitute a possible failure theory? Why or why not?

    (b) Consider a uniaxial test, and on this basis define a convenient effective stress.

    (c) In three-dimensional principal normal stress space, describe the failure surface corresponding to the equation given. Also describe the failure locus for the special case of plane stress.

    (d) Describe a critical experiment, consisting of one or a few mechanical tests, and a minimum of experimentation, that provides a definitive choice among the aforementioned three criteria. Note that some of the mechanical tests that are feasible are uniaxial tension and compression, torsion of tubes and rods, internal and external pressure of closed-end tubes, biaxial tension in pressurized diaphragms, and hydrostatic compression.

Section 7.7

7.42 The results of two tests on diabase rock are given in Table P7.42: (1) a uniaxial compression test, and (2) a confined compression test with lateral pressure $\sigma_1 = \sigma_2$.

    (a) Assume that the Coulomb–Mohr fracture criterion applies, and use the results of these tests to determine the slope and intercept constants μ and τ_i for Eq. 7.42.

    (b) Accurately plot the resulting $|\tau|$ versus σ failure envelope line. Also accurately plot the corresponding σ_1 versus σ_2 (biaxial stress) failure locus similar to Fig. 7.17.

Table P7.42

Test No.	σ_3, MPa	$\sigma_1 = \sigma_2$, MPa
1	-225.7	0
2	-548.0	-30.3

Source: Data in [Karfakis 03].

7.43 Test data are given in Table P7.43 for siltstone from Virginia under simple tension, simple compression, and compression with lateral pressure. The values of σ_3 correspond to fracture. Proceed as in Ex. 7.7 for these data.

Table P7.43

σ_3 MPa	$\sigma_1 = \sigma_2$ MPa
21.9	0
-185.4	0
-278	-7.10
-291	-10.49
-343	-14.34
-345	-19.65
-392	-23.1

Source: Data from [Karfakis 03].

7.44 Test data are given in Table P7.44 for mortar, made from Portland cement and Sydney sand, under simple compression and compression with lateral pressure. The values of σ_3 correspond to failure, which occurred as distinct fractures, except for the highest value of lateral compression, where the peak compressive stress occurred after considerable nonlinear deformation. The data are taken from three different batches of nominally identical mortar, and the tests were done after approximately 200 days of aging. Proceed as in Ex. 7.7 for these data.

Table P7.44

σ_3 MPa	$\sigma_1 = \sigma_2$ MPa
-32.1	0
-33.8	0
-29.5	0
-61.0	-8.27
-61.0	-8.27
-102.7	-22.1
-104.8	-22.1
-148.9	-41.4
-159.3	-41.4

Source: Data in [Campbell 62].

7.45 Test data are given in Table P7.45 for Portland cement concrete, made with Thames Valley flint gravel as the aggregate, under simple tension, simple compression, and compression with lateral pressure. The values of σ_3 correspond to failure, which occurred as distinct fractures for lateral pressures of zero and 2.5 MPa. For the higher lateral pressures, the peak compressive stress occurred after considerable nonlinear deformation, with an array of internal splitting cracks being observed. The tests were done after 56 days of aging, and any water appearing in compression was allowed to drain from the ends of the specimen. Proceed as in Ex. 7.7 for these data.

Table P7.45

σ_3 MPa	$\sigma_1 = \sigma_2$ MPa
1.70	0
−45.3	0
−58.8	−2.5
−72.0	−5.0
−96.2	−10.0
−117.6	−15.0
−137.5	−20.0
−155.2	−25.0

Source: Data in [Hobbs 71].

7.46 Consider the test data of Table P7.45, but ignore the simple tension test on the first line.
   (a) Fit these data to the alternative form of the C–M criterion of Eq. 7.60, where h and $|\sigma'_{uc}|$ are the fitting constants.
   (b) Also fit these data to Eq. 7.61, where k and a are the fitting constants, and $|\sigma_{uc}|$ is the value from the simple compression test.
   (c) Comment on the relative success of the two equations in representing the data.

Section 7.8
7.47 For the situation of Ex. 7.8, accurately plot the σ_1-σ_2 failure locus for plane stress, as in Fig. 7.20(a). Then use this plot to graphically verify the two safety factors.
7.48 A brittle material has an ultimate tensile strength of 300 MPa, and for compression-dominated behavior, it has a Coulomb–Mohr failure envelope line given by $\tau_i = 387$ MPa and $\mu = 0.259$.
   (a) Accurately plot the limiting modified-Mohr failure envelope on σ versus $|\tau|$ coordinates.
   (b) Calculate σ'_{uc} and σ_i, and then accurately plot the biaxial failure locus on σ_1 versus σ_2 coordinates.
   (c) Graphically determine the safety factor for the following cases of biaxial principal stresses:

    (1) $\sigma_1 = 200$, $\sigma_2 = -100\,\text{MPa}$

    (2) $\sigma_1 = 100$, $\sigma_2 = -600\,\text{MPa}$

    (3) $\sigma_1 = -300$, $\sigma_2 = -600\,\text{MPa}$

  (d) Confirm the values from (c) by applying Eq. 7.66.

7.49 In a compression test, a cylinder of unreinforced concrete has an ultimate strength of 27.2 MPa, and the fracture is observed to occur on a plane inclined to the direction of loading by an angle of approximately $\theta_c = 25°$. If this same concrete is subjected to lateral (compressive) stresses of $\sigma_1 = \sigma_2 = -10\,\text{MPa}$, estimate the stress σ_3 necessary to cause failure in compression. (Suggestion: If the tensile strength is needed, this may be estimated as 10% of the compressive strength.)

7.50 A cylinder of the mortar of Table 7.1 is subjected to an axial compressive stress σ_z of 50 MPa, along with equal lateral compressive stresses, $\sigma_x = \sigma_y$.

  (a) What is the safety factor against fracture if the lateral compressive stresses are 12 MPa?

  (b) Let σ_z remain unchanged. But let the lateral compression be reduced, that is, $|\sigma_x| = |\sigma_y| < 12\,\text{MPa}$. Can $\sigma_x = \sigma_y$ approach zero without fracture occurring? At what value of $\sigma_x = \sigma_y$ is fracture expected to occur?

7.51 A building column 400 mm in diameter is made of the sandstone of Table 7.1.

  (a) What is the safety factor against fracture if the column is subjected to a compressive force of 1250 kN?

  (b) What is the safety factor against fracture if the column is subjected to a torque of 20 kN·m?

  (c) What is the safety factor against fracture if the column is subjected at the same time to both the 1250 kN compressive force and the 20 kN·m torque?

  (d) Compare the safety factors calculated in (a), (b), and (c), and explain the trends in their values.

7.52 A block of the concrete of Table 7.1 is loaded with a pressure p applied to all sides, and also with a shear stress, $\tau_{xy} = 30\,\text{MPa}$, as shown in Fig. P7.28.

  (a) Will the block fracture if $p = 40\,\text{MPa}$?

  (b) What smallest value of p such that the block will not fracture?

7.53 A block of the mortar of Table 7.1 is loaded with a shear stress $\tau_{xy} = 1.0\,\text{MPa}$, and also with a normal stress σ_z, as shown in Fig. P7.29.

  (a) What is the safety factor against fracture if $\sigma_z = 0$?

  (b) What is the safety factor against fracture if σ_z is 15 MPa compression?

  (c) For the safety factor to be not less than 2.5, what is the most severe compressive σ_z that can be applied?

7.54 Consider a 50 mm diameter shaft of the gray cast iron of Table 7.1. If a safety factor of 3.0 against fracture is required, what is the largest torque that can be applied along with a compressive axial force of 250 kN?

7.55 A building column 400 mm in diameter is made of the sandstone of Table 7.1. It resists a compressive force P and a torque $T = 34{,}000$ N·m, and a safety factor of 4.0 against fracture is required.

  (a) What is the largest compressive force P that can be permitted?

(b) If only the torsion is applied, that is $P = 0$, is the safety factor requirement met? If not, what minimum value of compressive force P must be applied to satisfy the safety factor?

7.56 A thick-walled tube has inner and outer radii of 30 and 50 mm, respectively, and it is made of the gray cast iron of Table 7.1.

    (a) What is the safety factor against fracture for an internal pressure of 20 MPa?

    (b) What is the safety factor against fracture if a compressive axial force of 700 kN is applied, in addition to the internal pressure in part (a)?

8

Fracture of Cracked Members

OBJECTIVES

- Understand the effects of cracks on materials and why the *fracture toughness*, K_{Ic}, is a measure of a material's ability to resist failure due to a crack. Explore trends in K_{Ic} with material and with variables such as temperature, loading rate, and processing.
- Evaluate the effects of cracks in engineering components, using linear-elastic fracture mechanics and applying the *stress intensity factor*, K, to combine stress, geometry, and crack size to characterize the severity of a crack situation.
- Analyze the effects of plasticity in cracked members, including plastic zone sizes, constraint effects due to plate thickness, and fully plastic limit loads, and briefly introduce advanced fracture mechanics methods.

8.1 INTRODUCTION

The presence of a crack in a component of a machine, vehicle, or structure may weaken it so that it fails by fracturing into two or more pieces. This can occur at stresses below the material's yield strength, where failure would not normally be expected. As an example, photographs from a propane tank truck failure caused in part by pre-existing cracks are shown in Fig. 8.1. Where cracks are difficult to avoid, a special methodology called *fracture mechanics* can be used to aid in selecting materials and designing components to minimize the possibility of fracture.

334

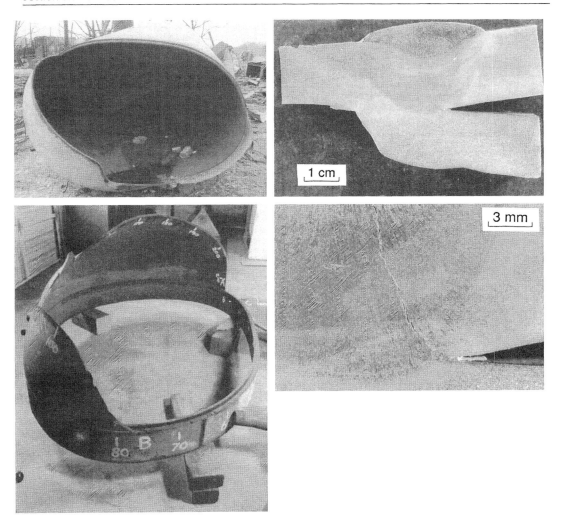

Figure 8.1   Photographs from a propane tank truck that exploded due to fracture from initial environmental cracks in welds. Typical initial cracks are shown from a region that did not participate in the final failure. (Photos courtesy of H. S. Pearson, Pearson Testing Labs, Marietta, GA, lower left, upper and lower right, published in [Pearson 86]; copyright © ASTM; reprinted with permission.)

In addition to cracks themselves, other types of flaws that are cracklike in form may easily develop into cracks, and these need to be treated as if they were cracks. Examples include deep surface scratches or gouges, voids in welds, inclusions of foreign substances in cast and forged materials, and delaminations in layered materials. For example, a photograph of a crack starting from a large inclusion in the wall of a forged steel artillery tube is shown in Fig. 8.2.

Figure 8.2 Crack (light area) growing from a large nonmetallic inclusion (dark area within) in an AISI 4335 steel artillery tube. The inclusion was found by inspection, and the tube was not used in service, but rather was tested under cyclic loading to study its behavior. (Photo courtesy of J. H. Underwood, U.S. Army Armament RD&E Center, Watervliet, NY.)

The study and use of fracture mechanics is of major engineering importance simply because cracks or cracklike flaws occur more frequently than we might at first think. For example, the periodic inspections of large commercial aircraft frequently reveal cracks, sometimes numerous cracks, that must be repaired. Cracks or cracklike flaws also commonly occur in ship structures, bridge structures, pressure vessels and piping, heavy machinery, and ground vehicles. They are also a source of concern for various parts of nuclear reactors.

Prior to the development of fracture mechanics in the 1950s and 1960s, specific analysis of cracks in engineering components was not possible. Engineering design was based primarily on tension, compression, and bending tests, along with failure criteria for nominally uncracked material—that is, the methods discussed in Chapters 4 and 7. Such methods automatically include the effects of the microscopic flaws that are inherently present in any sample of material. But they provide no means of accounting for larger cracks, so their use involves the implicit assumption that no unusual cracks are present. Notch-impact tests, as described in Section 4.8, do represent an attempt to deal with cracks. These tests provide a rough guide for choosing materials that resist failure due to cracks, and they aid in identifying temperatures where particular materials are brittle. But there is no direct means of relating the fracture energies measured in notch-impact tests to the behavior of an engineering component.

In contrast, fracture mechanics provides materials properties that can be related to component behavior, allowing specific analysis of strength and life as limited by various sizes and shapes of cracks. Hence, it provides a basis for choosing materials and design details so as to minimize the possibility of failure due to cracks.

Effective use of fracture mechanics requires inspection of components, so that there is some knowledge of what sizes and geometries of cracks are present or might be present. For example, periodic inspections are commonly performed on large aircraft and bridges so that a crack cannot grow to a dangerous size before it is found and repaired. Methods of inspection for cracks include not only simple visual examination, but also sophisticated means such as X-ray photography and ultrasonics. (In the latter method, reflections of high-frequency sound waves are used to reveal the presence of a crack.) Repairs necessitated by cracks may involve replacing a part or modifying it, as by machining away a small crack to leave a smooth surface, or by reinforcing the cracked region in some manner.

In this chapter, we will introduce fracture mechanics and study its application to failure under static loading. Later, in Chapter 11, we will consider growth of cracks due to cyclic loading.

8.2 PRELIMINARY DISCUSSION

Before introducing the details of fracture mechanics, it is useful to make some observations concerning the general nature of cracks and their effects.

8.2.1 Cracks as Stress Raisers

Consider an elliptical hole in a plate of material, as illustrated in Fig. 8.3(a). For purposes of discussion, the hole is assumed to be small compared with the width of the plate and to be aligned with its major axis perpendicular to the direction of a uniform stress, S, applied remotely. The uniform stress field is altered in the neighborhood of the hole, as illustrated for one particular case in Fig. 8.3(b).

The most notable effect of the hole is its influence on the stress σ_y parallel to S. Far from the hole, this stress is equal to S. If examined along the x-axis of (b), the value of σ_y rises sharply near the hole and has a maximum value at the edge of the hole. This maximum value depends on the proportions of the ellipse and its tip radius ρ:

$$\sigma_y = S\left(1 + 2\frac{c}{d}\right) = S\left(1 + 2\sqrt{\frac{c}{\rho}}\right) \tag{8.1}$$

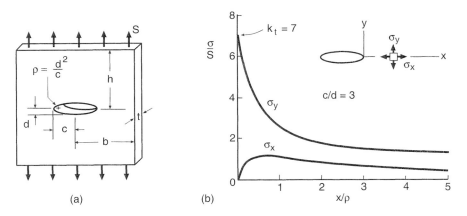

Figure 8.3   Elliptical hole in a wide plate under remote uniform tension, and the stress distribution along the x-axis near the hole for one particular case.

A stress concentration factor for the ellipse can be defined as the ratio of the maximum stress to the remote stress: $k_t = \sigma_y / S$.

Consider a narrow ellipse where the half-height d approaches zero, so that the tip radius ρ also approaches zero, which corresponds to an ideal slitlike crack. In this case, σ_y becomes infinite, as does k_t. Hence, a sharp crack causes a severe concentration of stress and is special in that the stress is theoretically infinite if the crack is ideally sharp.

8.2.2 Behavior at Crack Tips in Real Materials

An infinite stress cannot, of course, exist in a real material. If the applied load is not too high, the material can accommodate the presence of an initially sharp crack in such a way that the theoretically infinite stress is reduced to a finite value. This is illustrated in Fig. 8.4. In ductile materials, such as many metals, large plastic deformations occur in the vicinity of the crack tip. The region within which the material yields is called the *plastic zone*. Intense deformation at the crack tip results in the sharp tip being blunted to a small, but nevertheless nonzero, radius. Hence, the stress is no longer infinite, and the crack is open near its tip by a finite amount, δ, called the *crack-tip opening displacement* (CTOD).

In other types of material, different behaviors occur that have a similar effect of relieving the theoretically infinite stress by modifying the sharp crack tip. In some polymers, a region containing elongated voids develops, with a fibrous structure bridging the crack faces, which is called a *craze zone*. In brittle materials such as ceramics, a region containing a high density of tiny cracks may develop at the crack tip.

In all three cases, the crack tip experiences intense deformation and develops a finite separation near its tip. The very high stress that would ideally exist near the crack tip is spread over a larger region and is said to be *redistributed*. A finite value of stress that can be resisted by the material thus

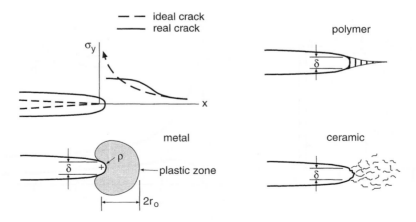

Figure 8.4 Finite stresses and nonzero radii at tips of cracks in real materials. A region of intense deformation forms due to plasticity, crazing, or microcracking.

exists near the crack tip, and the stresses somewhat farther away are higher than they would be for an ideal crack.

8.2.3 Effects of Cracks on Strength

If the load applied to a member containing a crack is too high, the crack may suddenly grow and cause the member to fail by fracturing in a brittle manner—that is, with little plastic deformation. From the theory of fracture mechanics, a useful quantity called the *stress intensity factor*, K, can be defined. Specifically, K is a measure of the severity of a crack situation as affected by crack size, stress, and geometry. In defining K, the material is assumed to behave in a linear-elastic manner, according to Hooke's law, Eq. 5.26, so that the approach being used is called *linear-elastic fracture mechanics* (LEFM).

A given material can resist a crack without brittle fracture occurring as long as this K is below a critical value K_c, called the *fracture toughness*. Values of K_c vary widely for different materials and are affected by temperature and loading rate, and secondarily by the thickness of the member. Thicker members have lower K_c values until a worst-case value is reached, which is denoted K_{Ic} and called the *plane strain fracture toughness*. Hence, K_{Ic} is a measure of a given material's ability to resist fracture in the presence of a crack. Some values of this property are given for various materials in Tables 8.1 and 8.2.

For example, consider a crack in the center of a wide plate of stressed material, as illustrated in Fig. 8.5. In this case, K depends on the remotely applied stress S and the crack length a, measured from the centerline as shown:

$$K = S\sqrt{\pi a} \qquad (a \ll b) \tag{8.2}$$

This equation is accurate only if a is small compared with the half-width b of the member. For a given material and thickness with fracture toughness K_c, the critical value of remote stress necessary to cause fracture is thus

$$S_c = \frac{K_c}{\sqrt{\pi a}} \tag{8.3}$$

Hence, longer cracks have a more severe effect on strength than do shorter ones, as might be expected.

Some test data illustrating the effect of different crack lengths on strength are shown in Fig. 8.5. These particular data correspond to 2014-T6 aluminum plates of thickness $t = 1.5\,\text{mm}$, tested at $-195°\text{C}$. Note that the failure data fall far below the material's yield strength σ_o. This behavior cannot be explained merely by yielding and the loss of cross-sectional area due to the crack, which is indicated by the dotted line. (See Fig. A.16(a), which gives the dotted line as $S = P/(2bt) = \sigma_o(1 - a/b)$.) Substituting the K_c value for this case into Eq. 8.3 gives the solid curve, which agrees quite well with most of the data, indicating a degree of success for LEFM. However, as the stress S approaches the material's yield strength σ_o, the data fall below Eq. 8.3, as shown by the dashed line. This deviation occurs because Eq. 8.2 assumes that linear-elastic behavior is exhibited and so is accurate only if the plastic zone is small, which is not the case for the failures at high stresses for short cracks.

Table 8.1   Fracture Toughness and Corresponding Tensile Properties for Representative Metals at Room Temperature

Material	Toughness K_{Ic}	Yield σ_o	Ultimate σ_u	Elong. $100\varepsilon_f$	Red. Area %RA
	$MPa\sqrt{m}$ (ksi$\sqrt{in}$)	MPa (ksi)	MPa (ksi)	%	%
(a) Steels					
AISI 1144	66 (60)	540 (78)	840 (122)	5	7
ASTM A470-8 (Cr-Mo-V)	60 (55)	620 (90)	780 (113)	17	45
ASTM A517-F	187 (170)	760 (110)	830 (121)	20	66
AISI 4130	110 (100)	1090 (158)	1150 (167)	14	49
18-Ni maraging air melted	123 (112)	1310 (190)	1350 (196)	12	54
18-Ni maraging vacuum melted	176 (160)	1290 (187)	1345 (195)	15	66
300-M 650°C temper	152 (138)	1070 (156)	1190 (172)	18	56
300-M 300°C temper	65 (59)	1740 (252)	2010 (291)	12	48
(b) Aluminum and Titanium Alloys (L-T Orientation)					
2014-T651	24 (22)	415 (60)	485 (70)	13	—
2024-T351	34 (31)	325 (47)	470 (68)	20	—
2219-T851	36 (33)	350 (51)	455 (66)	10	—
7075-T651	29 (26)	505 (73)	570 (83)	11	—
7475-T7351	52 (47)	435 (63)	505 (73)	14	—
Ti-6Al-4V annealed	66 (60)	925 (134)	1000 (145)	16	34

Sources: Data in [Barsom 87] p. 172, [Boyer 85] pp. 6.34, 6.35, and 9.8, [MILHDBK 94] pp. 3.10–3.12 and 5.3, and [Ritchie 77].

Table 8.2   Fracture Toughness of Some Polymers and Ceramics at Room Temperature

Material Polymers[1]	K_{Ic}		Material Ceramics[2]	K_{Ic}	
	MPa$\sqrt{\text{m}}$	(ksi$\sqrt{\text{in}}$)		MPa$\sqrt{\text{m}}$	(ksi$\sqrt{\text{in}}$)
ABS	3.0	(2.7)	Soda-lime glass	0.76	(0.69)
Acrylic	1.8	(1.6)	Magnesia, MgO	2.9	(2.6)
Epoxy	0.6	(0.55)	Alumina, Al_2O_3	4.0	(3.6)
PC	2.2	(2.0)	Al_2O_3, 15% ZrO_2	10	(9.1)
PET	5.0	(4.6)	Silicon carbide	3.7	(3.4)
Polyester	0.6	(0.55)	SiC		
PS	1.15	(1.05)	Silicon nitride	5.6	(5.1)
PVC	2.4	(2.2)	Si_3N_4		
PVC	3.35	(3.05)	Dolomitic limestone	1.30	(1.18)
rubber mod.			Westerly granite	0.89	(0.81)
			Concrete	1.19	(1.08)

Notes: [1,2]See Tables 4.3 and 3.10, respectively, for additional properties of similar materials.
Sources: Data in [ASM 88] p. 739, [Karfakis 90], [Kelly 86] p. 376, [Shah 95] p. 176, and [Williams 87] p. 243.

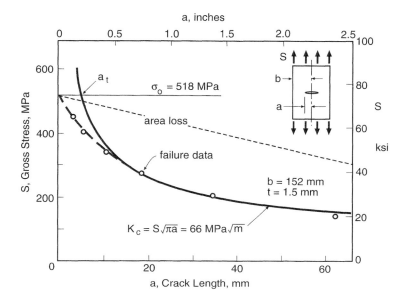

Figure 8.5   Failure data for cracked plates of 2014-T6 Al tested at −195°C. (Data from [Orange 67].)

8.2.4 Effects of Cracks on Brittle Versus Ductile Behavior

Consider the crack length where the failure stress predicted by LEFM equals the yield strength, identified as a_t in Fig. 8.5. Substituting $S_c = \sigma_o$ into Eq. 8.3 gives its value:

$$a_t = \frac{1}{\pi} \left(\frac{K_c}{\sigma_o} \right)^2 \tag{8.4}$$

On an approximate basis, cracks longer than this *transition crack length* will cause the strength to be limited by brittle fracture, rather than by yielding. Thus, if cracks of length around or greater than the a_t of a given material are likely to be present, fracture mechanics should be employed in design. Conversely, for crack lengths below a_t, yielding dominated behavior is expected, so that there will be little or no strength reduction due to the crack.

Note that Eq. 8.4 is based on the assumed case of a wide, center-cracked plate, and that a_t will differ for other geometric cases. It is nevertheless useful to employ a_t values from Eq. 8.4 as representative quantities in comparing different materials.

Consider two materials, one with low σ_o and high K_c, and the other with an opposite combination, namely, high σ_o and low K_c. These combinations of properties cause a relatively large a_t for the low-strength material, but a small a_t for the high-strength one. Compare Figs. 8.6(a) and (b). Thus, cracks of moderate size may not affect the low-strength material, but they may severely limit the usefulness of the high-strength one. Such an inverse trend between yield strength and fracture toughness is fairly common within any given class of materials. Low strength in a tension test is usually accompanied by high ductility and also by high fracture toughness. Conversely, high strength is usually associated with low ductility and low fracture toughness. Trends of this nature for AISI 1045 steel are illustrated in Fig. 8.7.

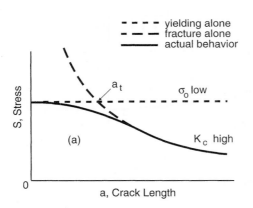
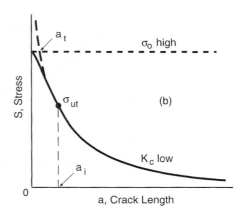

Figure 8.6 Transition crack length a_t for a low-strength, high-toughness material (a), and for a high-strength, low-toughness material (b). If (b) contains internal flaws a_i, its strength in tension σ_{ut} is controlled by brittle fracture.

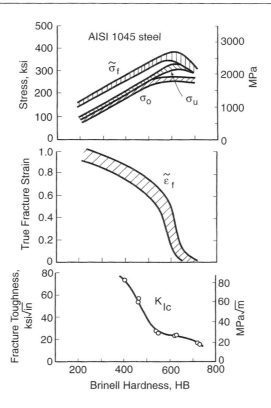

Figure 8.7 Comparison of properties from tension tests and fracture toughness tests for AISI 1045 steel, all plotted as functions of hardness, which is varied by heat treatment. (Illustration courtesy of R. W. Landgraf, Howell, MI.)

The relative sensitivity to flaws associated with different a_t values for different materials helps to explain a number of sudden engineering failures that occurred in the 1950s and 1960s. New high-strength materials, such as steels and aluminum alloys developed for the aerospace industry, had sufficiently low fracture toughness that they were sensitive to rather small cracks. One example was the British-made Comet passenger airliner, two of which failed at high altitude in the 1950s, with considerable loss of life in the resulting crashes. Other examples are the late 1950s failures of rocket motor cases for the Polaris missile, and the F-111 aircraft crash in 1969. Such failures accelerated the development of fracture mechanics and led to its adoption by the U.S. Air Force as the basis of their *damage tolerant design* requirements.

Also, some apparently mysterious brittle failures in normally ductile steels occurred in the 1940s and earlier. These were finally understood years later to be due to cracks that were sufficiently large to exceed even the relatively large a_t value of the ductile steel. One example of this is the failure in Boston in 1919 of a large tank, about 90 feet in diameter and 50 feet high, that contained 2 million gallons of molasses. Other examples include welded Liberty Ships and tankers that broke completely in two during and shortly after World War II, and other ship and bridge failures.

8.2.5 Internally Flawed Materials

As already discussed in earlier chapters, many brittle materials naturally contain small cracks or cracklike flaws. This is generally true for glass, natural stone, ceramics, and some cast metals. The interpretation can be made that these materials have a high yield strength, but this strength can never be reached under tensile loading because of earlier failure due to small flaws and a low fracture toughness. Such a viewpoint is supported by the fact that brittle materials have considerably higher strengths under compression than under tension, because the flaws simply close under compression and thus have a much reduced effect.

Denoting the inherent flaw size in such a material as a_i, Eq. 8.3 gives the ultimate strength in tension:

$$\sigma_{ut} = \frac{K_c}{\sqrt{\pi a_i}} \tag{8.5}$$

This situation is illustrated in Fig. 8.6(b). New cracks of size around or below a_i have little effect, as they are no worse than the flaws already present. The material is thus said to be *internally flawed*. Also, since the flaws actually present may vary considerably from sample to sample, there is generally a large statistical scatter in σ_{ut}.

8.3 MATHEMATICAL CONCEPTS

A cracked body can be loaded in any one or a combination of the three displacement modes shown in Fig. 8.8. Mode I is called the *opening mode* and consists of the crack faces simply moving apart. For Mode II, the *sliding mode*, the crack faces slide relative to one another in a direction normal to the leading edge of the crack. Mode III, the *tearing mode*, also involves relative sliding of the crack faces, but now the direction is parallel to the leading edge. Mode I is caused by tension loading, whereas the other two are caused by shear loading in different directions, as shown. Most cracking problems of engineering interest involve primarily Mode I and are due to tension stresses, so we will limit most of our discussion to this case.

Energy methods were employed in the earliest work on fracture mechanics, reported by A. A. Griffith in 1920. This approach is expressed by a concept called the *strain energy release rate*, G. Later work led to the concept of a stress intensity factor, K, and to the proof that G and K are directly related.

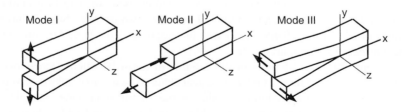

Figure 8.8 The basic modes of crack surface displacement. (Adapted from [Tada 85]; used with permission.)

8.3.1 Strain Energy Release Rate, G

Consider a cracked member under a Mode I force P, where the crack has length a, as shown in Fig. 8.9. Assume that the behavior of the material is linear-elastic, which requires that the force versus displacement behavior also be linear. In a manner similar to a linear spring, potential energy U is stored in the member, as a result of the elastic strains throughout its volume, as shown in Fig. 8.9(a). Note that v is the displacement at the point of loading and $U = Pv/2$ is the triangular area under the P-v curve.

If the crack moves ahead by a small amount da while the displacement is held constant, the stiffness of the member decreases, as shown by (b). This results in the potential energy decreasing by an amount dU; that is, U decreases due to a release of this amount of energy. The rate of change of potential energy with increase in crack area is defined as the strain energy release rate

$$G = -\frac{1}{t}\frac{dU}{da} \tag{8.6}$$

Here, the change in crack area is $t(da)$, and the negative sign causes G to have a positive value. Thus, G characterizes the energy per unit crack area required to extend the crack, and as such is expected to be the fundamental physical quantity controlling the behavior of the crack.

In the original concept by Griffith, all of the potential energy released was thought to be used in the creation of the new free surface on the crack faces. This is approximately true for materials that crack with essentially no plastic deformation, as for the glass tested by Griffith. However, in more ductile materials, a majority of the energy may be used in deforming the material in the plastic zone at the crack tip. In applying G to metals in the 1950s, G. R. Irwin showed that the concept was applicable even under these circumstances if the plastic zone was small.

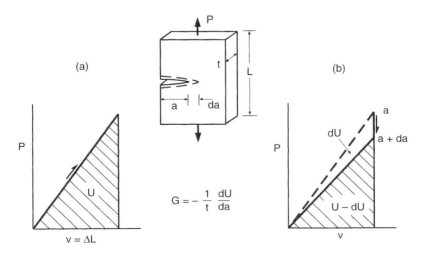

Figure 8.9 Potential energies for two neighboring crack lengths and the energy change dU used to define the strain energy release rate G.

As listed in the References, Barsom (1987) is a collection of papers reporting some of the early work on fracture mechanics by Griffith, Irwin, and others.

8.3.2 Stress Intensity Factor, *K*

The stress intensity factor concept, which has already been introduced, needs to be defined in a more complete manner. In general terms, K characterizes the magnitude (intensity) of the stresses in the vicinity of an ideally sharp crack tip in a linear-elastic and isotropic material.

A coordinate system for describing the stresses in the vicinity of a crack is shown in Fig. 8.10. The polar coordinates r and θ lie in the x-y plane, which is normal to the plane of the crack, and the z-direction is parallel to the leading edge of the crack. For any case of Mode I loading, the stresses near the crack tip depend on r and θ as follows:

$$\sigma_x = \frac{K_I}{\sqrt{2\pi r}} \cos\frac{\theta}{2} \left[1 - \sin\frac{\theta}{2} \sin\frac{3\theta}{2} \right] + \cdots \qquad \text{(a)}$$

$$\sigma_y = \frac{K_I}{\sqrt{2\pi r}} \cos\frac{\theta}{2} \left[1 + \sin\frac{\theta}{2} \sin\frac{3\theta}{2} \right] + \cdots \qquad \text{(b)}$$

$$\tau_{xy} = \frac{K_I}{\sqrt{2\pi r}} \cos\frac{\theta}{2} \sin\frac{\theta}{2} \cos\frac{3\theta}{2} + \cdots \qquad \text{(c)} \qquad\qquad \text{(8.7)}$$

$$\sigma_z = 0 \qquad\qquad \text{(plane stress)} \qquad\qquad \text{(d)}$$

$$\sigma_z = \nu\left(\sigma_x + \sigma_y\right) \quad \text{(plane strain; } \varepsilon_z = 0\text{)} \qquad\qquad \text{(e)}$$

$$\tau_{yz} = \tau_{zx} = 0 \qquad\qquad \text{(f)}$$

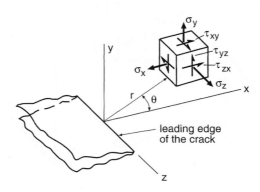

Figure 8.10   Three-dimensional coordinate system for the region of a crack tip. (Adapted from [Tada 85]; used with permission.)

These equations are derived on the basis of the *theory of linear elasticity*, as described in any standard text on that subject, and they are said to describe the *stress field* near the crack tip. Higher order terms that are not of significant magnitude near the crack tip are omitted. These equations predict that the stresses rapidly increase near the crack tip. Confirmation of this characteristic of the stress field is provided by a photograph of stress contours in a clear plastic specimen in Fig. 8.11.

If the cracked member is relatively thin in the z-direction, plane stress with $\sigma_z = 0$ applies. However, if it is relatively thick, a more reasonable assumption may be plane strain, $\varepsilon_z = 0$, in which case Hooke's law, specifically Eq. 5.26(c), requires that σ_z depend on the other stresses and Poisson's ratio, ν, according to Eq. 8.7(e).

The nonzero stress components in Eq. 8.7 are seen to all approach infinity as r approaches zero—that is, upon approaching the crack tip. Note that this is specifically caused by these stresses being proportional to the inverse of $\sqrt{r}$. Thus, a mathematical singularity is said to exist at the crack tip, and no value of stress at the crack tip can be given. Also, all of the nonzero stresses of Eq. 8.7 are proportional to the quantity K_I, and the remaining factors merely give the variation with r and θ. Hence, the magnitude of the stress field near the crack tip can be characterized by giving the

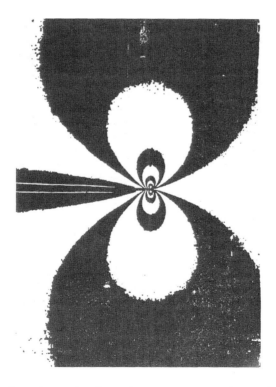

Figure 8.11 Contours of maximum in-plane shear stress around a crack tip. These were formed by the photoelastic effect in a clear plastic material. The two thin white lines entering from the left are the edges of the crack, and its tip is the point of convergence of the contours. (Photo courtesy of C. W. Smith, Virginia Tech, Blacksburg, VA.)

value of the factor K_I. On this basis, K_I is a measure of the severity of the crack. Its definition in a formal mathematical sense is

$$K_I = \lim_{r,\theta \to 0} \left(\sigma_y \sqrt{2\pi r} \right) \tag{8.8}$$

It is generally convenient to express K_I as

$$K_I = FS\sqrt{\pi a} \tag{8.9}$$

where the factor F is needed to account for different geometries. For example, if a central crack in a plate is relatively long, Eq. 8.2 needs to be modified, as the proximity of the specimen edge causes F to increase above unity. The quantity F is a function of the ratio a/b, as shown in Fig. 8.12, curve (a). Curves (b) and (c) show the variation of F with a/b for two additional cases of cracked members under tension, specifically, for double-edge-cracked plates and for single-edge-cracked plates.

8.3.3 Additional Comments on *K* and *G*

For loading in Mode II or III, analogous, but distinct, stress field equations exist, and stress intensities K_{II} and K_{III} can be defined in a manner analogous to K_I. However, most practical applications involve Mode I. As a convenience, the subscript on K_I will be dropped, and K without such a subscript is understood to denote K_I, that is, $K = K_I$.

The quantities G and K can be shown to be related as follows:

$$G = \frac{K^2}{E'} \tag{8.10}$$

where E' is obtained from the material's elastic modulus E and Poisson's ratio ν:

$$
\begin{aligned}
E' &= E && \text{(plane stress; } \sigma_z = 0\text{)} \\
E' &= \frac{E}{1 - \nu^2} && \text{(plane strain; } \varepsilon_z = 0\text{)}
\end{aligned}
\tag{8.11}
$$

Equation 8.10 and the dependence of G on load versus displacement behavior, Eq. 8.6, can be exploited to evaluate K. Slopes on P-v curves, as in Fig. 8.9, are employed in a procedure called the *compliance method*. See any book on fracture mechanics or Tada (2000) for details.

Since G and K are directly related according to Eq. 8.10, only one of these concepts is generally needed. We will primarily employ K, which is consistent with most engineering-oriented publications on fracture mechanics.

8.4 APPLICATION OF *K* TO DESIGN AND ANALYSIS

For fracture mechanics to be put to practical use, values of stress intensity K must be determined for crack geometries that may exist in structural components. Extensive analysis work has been published, and also collected into handbooks, giving equations or plotted curves that enable K values to be calculated for a wide variety of cases. A special section of the References at the

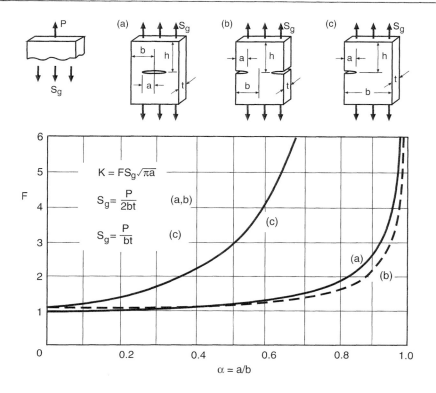

Values for small a/b and limits for 10% accuracy:

    (a) $K = S_g\sqrt{\pi a}$ (b) $K = 1.12 S_g\sqrt{\pi a}$ (c) $K = 1.12 S_g\sqrt{\pi a}$

        $(a/b \le 0.4)$ $(a/b \le 0.6)$ $(a/b \le 0.13)$

Expressions for any $\alpha = a/b$:

$$\text{(a)}\quad F = \frac{1 - 0.5\alpha + 0.326\alpha^2}{\sqrt{1 - \alpha}} \qquad\qquad (h/b \ge 1.5)$$

$$\text{(b)}\quad F = \left(1 + 0.122\cos^4\frac{\pi\alpha}{2}\right)\sqrt{\frac{2}{\pi\alpha}\tan\frac{\pi\alpha}{2}} \qquad (h/b \ge 2)$$

$$\text{(c)}\quad F = 0.265\,(1 - \alpha)^4 + \frac{0.857 + 0.265\alpha}{(1 - \alpha)^{3/2}} \qquad (h/b \ge 1)$$

Figure 8.12   Stress intensity factors for three cases of cracked plates under tension. Geometries, curves, and equations labeled (a) all correspond to the same case, and similarly for (b) and (c). (Equations as collected by [Tada 85] pp. 2.2, 2.7, and 2.11.)

end of this chapter lists several such handbooks. What will be done in this portion of the chapter is to give certain fundamental equations for calculating K and also examples of the type of information available from handbooks.

8.4.1 Mathematical Forms Used to Express K

It has already been noted that K can be related to applied stress and crack length by an equation of the form

$$K = F S_g \sqrt{\pi a}, \qquad F = F(\text{geometry}, a/b) \tag{8.12}$$

The quantity F is a dimensionless function that depends on the geometry and loading configuration, and usually also on the ratio of the crack length to another geometric dimension, such as the member width or half-width, b, as defined for three cases in Fig. 8.12. Additional examples for F are given in Figs. 8.13 and 8.14, specifically, for bending of single-edge-cracked plates and for various loadings on a circumferentially cracked round bar. In these examples, crack length a is measured from either the surface or the centerline of loading, and the width dimension b is consistently defined as the maximum possible crack length, so that for $a/b = 1$, the member is completely cracked. For each case in Figs. 8.12 to 8.14, polynomials or other mathematical expressions are given that may be employed to calculate F within a few percent for any $\alpha = a/b$. Where trigonometric functions appear, the arguments for these are in units of radians.

Applied forces or bending moments are often characterized by determining a nominal or average stress. In fracture mechanics, it is conventional to use the gross section nominal stress, S_g, calculated under the assumption that no crack is present. Note that this convention is followed for each case in Figs. 8.12 to 8.14. The subscript g is added merely to avoid any possibility of confusion, as net section stresses, S_n, based on the remaining uncracked area, could be used. The use of S_g rather than S_n is convenient, as the effect of crack length is then confined to the F and $\sqrt{a}$ factors. In general, the manner of defining nominal stress S is arbitrary, but consistency with F is necessary. The function F must be redefined and its values changed if the definition of S is changed, and also if the definition of a or b is changed.

It is sometimes convenient to work directly with applied loads (forces), with the following equation being useful for planar geometries:

$$K = F_P \frac{P}{t\sqrt{b}}, \qquad F_P = F_P(\text{geometry}, a/b) \tag{8.13}$$

Here, P is force, t is thickness, and b is the same as before. The function F_P is a new dimensionless geometry factor. Examples are given in Figs. 8.15 and 8.16. Equating K from Eqs. 8.12 and 8.13 allows F_P to be related to the previously defined F:

$$F_P = F \frac{S_g t \sqrt{\pi a b}}{P} \tag{8.14}$$

This relationship can be used to obtain the function F_P for any of the cases where F is given in Figs. 8.12 to 8.14. Expressing K in terms of F_P has the advantage that the dependence on crack length is confined to the dimensionless function F_P.

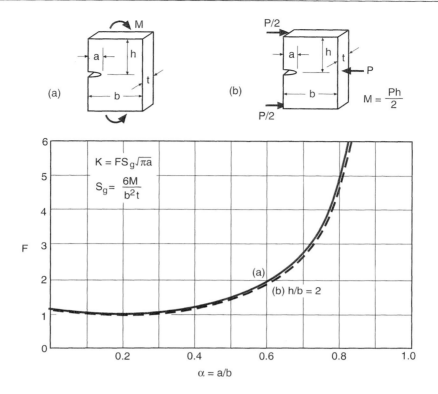

Values for small *a/b* and limits for 10% accuracy:

$$(a, b) \quad K = 1.12 S_g \sqrt{\pi a} \qquad (a/b \le 0.4)$$

Expressions for any $\alpha = a/b$:

$$(a) \quad F = \sqrt{\frac{2}{\pi \alpha} \tan \frac{\pi \alpha}{2}} \left[\frac{0.923 + 0.199 \left(1 - \sin \dfrac{\pi \alpha}{2} \right)^4}{\cos \dfrac{\pi \alpha}{2}} \right] \qquad \text{(large } h/b)$$

(b) *F* is within 3% of (a) for $h/b = 4$, and within 6% for $h/b = 2$, at any a/b:

$$F = \frac{1.99 - \alpha \left(1 - \alpha \right) \left(2.15 - 3.93 \alpha + 2.7 \alpha^2 \right)}{\sqrt{\pi} \left(1 + 2\alpha \right) \left(1 - \alpha \right)^{3/2}} \qquad (h/b = 2)$$

Figure 8.13 Stress intensity factors for two cases of bending. Geometries, curves, and equations labeled (a) all correspond to the same case, and similarly for (b). Case (b) with $h/b = 2$ is the ASTM standard bend specimen. (Equations from [Tada 85] p. 2.14, and [ASTM 97] Std. E399.)

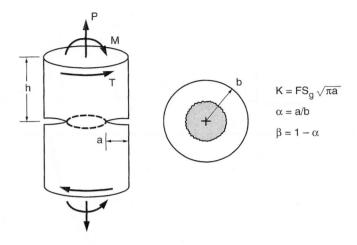

$$K = FS_g \sqrt{\pi a}$$
$$\alpha = a/b$$
$$\beta = 1 - \alpha$$

(a) Axial load P: $\quad S_g = \dfrac{P}{\pi b^2},$ $\qquad F = 1.12$ $\qquad (10\%, \ a/b \leq 0.21)$

$$F = \frac{1}{2\beta^{1.5}}\left[1 + \frac{1}{2}\beta + \frac{3}{8}\beta^2 - 0.363\beta^3 + 0.731\beta^4\right]$$

(b) Bending moment M: $\quad S_g = \dfrac{4M}{\pi b^3},$ $\qquad F = 1.12$ $\qquad (10\%, a/b \leq 0.12)$

$$F = \frac{3}{8\beta^{2.5}}\left[1 + \frac{1}{2}\beta + \frac{3}{8}\beta^2 + \frac{5}{16}\beta^3 + \frac{35}{128}\beta^4 + 0.537\beta^5\right]$$

(c) Torsion T, $K = K_{\text{III}}$: $\quad S_g = \dfrac{2T}{\pi b^3},$ $\qquad F = 1.00$ $\qquad (10\%, a/b \leq 0.09)$

$$F = \frac{3}{8\beta^{2.5}}\left[1 + \frac{1}{2}\beta + \frac{3}{8}\beta^2 + \frac{5}{16}\beta^3 + \frac{35}{128}\beta^4 + 0.208\beta^5\right]$$

Figure 8.14   Stress intensities for a round shaft with a circumferential crack, including limits on the constant F for 10% accuracy and expressions for any $\alpha = a/b$. For torsion (c), the stress intensity is for the shear Mode III. (Equations from [Tada 85] pp. 27.1, 27.2, and 27.3.)

8.4.2 Discussion

Mathematically closed-form solutions for K exist primarily for $a/b = 0$, that is, for members that are large (ideally infinite) compared with the crack. However, these solutions are often reasonably accurate to surprisingly large values of a/b. Corresponding equations for K are given in Figs. 8.12 to 8.15, along with limits on $\alpha = a/b$ for 10% accuracy. For example, for a center-cracked plate, Fig. 8.12(a) indicates that $F = 1$ is within 10% for $a/b \leq 0.4$. As a second

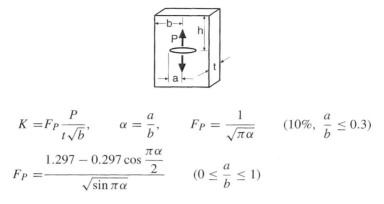

$$K = F_P \frac{P}{t\sqrt{b}}, \qquad \alpha = \frac{a}{b}, \qquad F_P = \frac{1}{\sqrt{\pi\alpha}} \qquad (10\%, \ \frac{a}{b} \leq 0.3)$$

$$F_P = \frac{1.297 - 0.297 \cos\dfrac{\pi\alpha}{2}}{\sqrt{\sin\pi\alpha}} \qquad (0 \leq \frac{a}{b} \leq 1)$$

Figure 8.15   Stress intensity factor for forces applied to the faces of a central crack in a plate with $h/b \geq 2$. A simple expression is given for F_P that is within 10% for a limited range of $\alpha = a/b$, as is an expression valid for any α. (Equations from [Tada 85] pp. 2.22 and 2.23.)

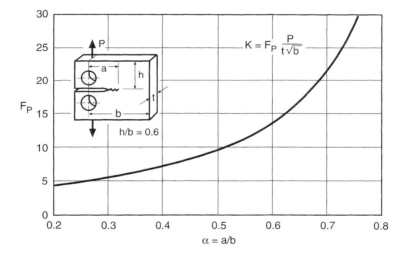

$$F_P = \frac{2+\alpha}{(1-\alpha)^{3/2}} (0.886 + 4.64\alpha - 13.32\alpha^2 + 14.72\alpha^3 - 5.6\alpha^4) \qquad (a/b \geq 0.2)$$

Figure 8.16   Stress intensity factor for the ASTM standard compact specimen, as determined from $F_P = F_P(\alpha)$, where $\alpha = a/b$. (Equation from [Srawley 76].)

example, for a single-edge-cracked plate, Fig. 8.12(c) indicates that $F = 1.12$ is within 10% for $a/b \leq 0.13$.

An edge-cracked tension member, Fig. 8.12(c), can be thought of as being similar to a center-cracked plate (a) that has been split in half. Since the crack dimension a is consistently defined for the two cases, the additional relatively modest factor of 1.12 is associated with the effect of the new free surface. In fact, for Mode I cracks with loading applied far from the crack, this same factor $F = 1.12$ applies, for small a/b, to any through-thickness surface crack in a plate and to any circumferential surface crack in a round bar. Thus, it applies to all of the surface crack cases of Figs. 8.12 to 8.14, with the exception of the Mode III case of Fig. 8.14(c).

For relatively long cracks where the simple infinite body solutions become inaccurate, the polynomial-type equations for calculating F or F_P are needed. These were obtained by various researchers and handbook authors by performing numerical analysis for a number of relative crack lengths a/b. Mathematical expressions $F = F(a/b)$ or $F_P = F_P(a/b)$ were then fitted that give close agreement with the calculated values. Such fitted expressions are, of course, valid only for the range of a/b covered in analysis, but these are now often available for all possible a/b from zero to unity, as for each case in Figs. 8.12 to 8.15. (In Fig. 8.16, note that the expression is valid for $0.2 \le a/b \le 1$.) Some of the numerical methods that apply to such analysis are the *finite element*, *boundary integral equation*, and *weight function* methods. See the book by Anderson (2005) for an introductory discussion of numerical analysis of cracked bodies.

In Figs. 8.12 to 8.14, with the exception of Fig. 8.13(b), the equations apply for uniform, bending, or torsional stresses applied an infinite distance h from the crack. However, the errors for finite h are generally negligible at $h/b = 3$ and begin to be significant ($>5\%$) only at h/b around 1 or 2, which is indicated where the details are known.

Example 8.1

A center-cracked plate, as in Fig. 8.12(a), has dimensions $b = 50\,\text{mm}$, $t = 5\,\text{mm}$, and large h; a force of $P = 50\,\text{kN}$ is applied.

    (a) What is the stress intensity factor K for a crack length of $a = 10\,\text{mm}$?
    (b) For $a = 30\,\text{mm}$?
    (c) What is the critical crack length a_c for fracture if the material is 2014-T651 aluminum?

Solution   **(a)** To calculate K for $a = 10\,\text{mm}$, using Fig. 8.12(a), we need

$$S_g = \frac{P}{2bt} = \frac{50{,}000\,\text{N}}{2(50\,\text{mm})(5\,\text{mm})} = 100\,\text{MPa}, \qquad \alpha = \frac{a}{b} = \frac{10\,\text{mm}}{50\,\text{mm}} = 0.200$$

Since $\alpha \le 0.4$, it is within 10% to use $F = 1$. Thus,

$$K = S_g\sqrt{\pi a} = (100\,\text{MPa})\sqrt{\pi(0.010\,\text{m})} = 17.7\,\text{MPa}\sqrt{\text{m}} \qquad \textbf{Ans.}$$

where crack length a is entered in units of meters to obtain the desired units for K of $\text{MPa}\sqrt{\text{m}}$.

    (b) For $a = 30\,\text{mm}$, we have $\alpha = a/b = (30\,\text{mm})/(50\,\text{mm}) = 0.600$. This does not satisfy $\alpha \le 0.4$, so the more general expression for F from Fig. 8.12(a) is needed:

$$F = \frac{1 - 0.5\alpha + 0.326\alpha^2}{\sqrt{1-\alpha}} = 1.292$$

$$K = FS_g\sqrt{\pi a} = 1.292\,(100\,\text{MPa})\sqrt{\pi(0.030\,\text{m})} = 39.7\,\text{MPa}\sqrt{\text{m}} \qquad \textbf{Ans.}$$

(c) Table 8.1 gives $K_{Ic} = 24\,\text{MPa}\sqrt{\text{m}}$ for 2014-T651 Al. Since a_c is not known, F cannot be determined directly. First, assume that $\alpha \le 0.4$ is satisfied, in which case $F \approx 1$. Then

$$K_{Ic} \approx S_g \sqrt{\pi a_c}$$

Solving for a_c gives

$$a_c \approx \frac{1}{\pi} \left(\frac{K_{Ic}}{S_g} \right)^2 = \frac{1}{\pi} \left(\frac{24\,\text{MPa}\sqrt{\text{m}}}{100\,\text{MPa}} \right)^2 = 0.0183\,\text{m} = 18.3\,\text{mm} \qquad \textbf{Ans.}$$

This corresponds to $\alpha = a_c/b = (18.3\,\text{mm})/(50\,\text{mm}) = 0.37$, which satisfies $\alpha \le 0.4$, so that the estimated $F \approx 1$ is acceptable and the result obtained is reasonably accurate.

If it is not desired to use the 10% approximation on F, an iterative solution is needed. Toward that end, substitute the expression for F into the equation for K:

$$K = \frac{1 - 0.5(a/b) + 0.326(a/b)^2}{\sqrt{1 - (a/b)}} S_g \sqrt{\pi a}$$

Then, using the values $K = K_{Ic} = 24\,\text{MPa}\sqrt{\text{m}}$, $b = 0.050\,\text{m}$, and $S_g = 100\,\text{MPa}$, solve for a by trial and error, Newton's method, or another numerical procedure, as implemented in various widely available computer software. The result is

$$a_c = 0.01627\,\text{m} = 16.3\,\text{mm} \qquad \textbf{Ans.}$$

which value is seen to differ somewhat from the previous one. (The actual value of F that corresponds to this a_c is $F_c = 1.061$.)

A graphical procedure could also be used to obtain this result: Select a number of values of a, and for each of these calculate $\alpha = a/b$. Then calculate F by using the polynomial-type expression as in (b), and calculate K, obtaining values such as those in Table E8.1. Next, plot the resulting values of K versus a as in Fig. E8.1. Finally, enter this graph with the desired value of $K = K_{Ic} = 24\,\text{MPa}\sqrt{\text{m}}$, and read the corresponding crack length as accurately as the graph permits, giving $a_c = 16.3\,\text{mm}$ (**Ans.**).

Table E8.1

Calc. No.	a mm	$\alpha = a/b$	F	$K = FS_g\sqrt{\pi a}$ MPa$\sqrt{\text{m}}$
1	10	0.20	1.021	18.1
2	15	0.30	1.051	22.8
3	20	0.40	1.100	27.6

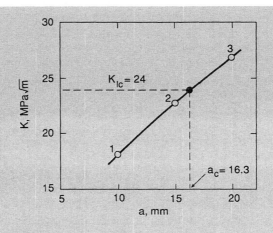

Figure E8.1

Comment   For (c), an iterative or graphical solution is optional in this case, but is necessary in other cases where a limit on α for 10% accuracy in K is exceeded.

8.4.3 Safety Factors

Where cracks may be present, safety factors against yielding, as examined in Chapter 7, need to be supplemented by safety factors against brittle fracture. Depending on the particular situation, either yielding or fracture might control the design.

Since stress S_g and K are proportional according to $K = F S_g \sqrt{\pi a}$, a safety factor X against fracture for stress can be accomplished by applying the same factor to K. Hence, if S_g and a are the stress and crack length that are expected to occur in actual service, the safety factor on K, and thus on S_g, is

$$X_K = \frac{K_{Ic}}{K} = \frac{K_{Ic}}{F S_g \sqrt{\pi a}} \tag{8.15}$$

It may also be useful to compare the service crack length a with the crack length a_c that is expected to cause failure at the service stress S_g. The value of a_c is available from

$$K_{Ic} = F_c S_g \sqrt{\pi a_c} \tag{8.16}$$

where F_c is evaluated at a_c. Combining the previous two equations leads to the following safety factor on crack length:

$$X_a = \frac{a_c}{a} = \left(\frac{F}{F_c} X_K \right)^2 \tag{8.17}$$

Because X_K is squared, safety factors on crack length must be rather large to achieve reasonable safety factors on K and stress.

For example, if F does not change very much between a and a_c, so that $F \approx F_c$, then Eq. 8.17 reduces to $X_a = X_K^2$, so that $X_K = \sqrt{X_a}$. Hence, a safety factor of $X_a = 4$ is needed to achieve $X_K = 2$, and $X_a = 9$ is needed to achieve $X_K = 3$. This is very important in design, as it means that crack lengths must be guaranteed to be quite small compared with the critical value a_c for fracture.

If the crack length expected to occur in actual service is relatively small, safety factors against yielding may be calculated simply by comparing the service stress S_g with the material's yield strength σ_o:

$$X_o = \sigma_o / S_g \tag{8.18}$$

However, for applied stresses that are multiaxial, S_g must be replaced by an effective stress $\bar{\sigma}$ for one of the yield criteria of Chapter 7. Since S_g is the stress on the gross area, the preceding calculation gives the safety factor against yielding as if no crack were present.

A more advanced method for calculating the safety factor against yielding is to compare the applied load with the *fully plastic limit load*. The latter is an estimate of the load necessary to cause yielding over the entire cross section that remains after subtracting the crack area, so that the effect of the crack in reducing the cross-sectional area is included. See Section A.7.2 for more explanation, and note that Fig. A.16 gives fully plastic forces and moments, P_o and M_o, for some simple cases of cracked members. Hence, this type of safety factor against yielding is given by one of

$$X_o' = P_o / P, \qquad X_o' = M_o / M \tag{8.19}$$

as may apply for a given case, where P and M are values of force and moment for actual service.

Values chosen for safety factors must reflect the consequences of failure and whether or not the values of the variables that affect the calculation are well known, as well as sound engineering judgment. If possible, statistical information should be employed for variables such as stress, crack size and shape, and materials properties. (See Section B.4 for a discussion of statistical variation in materials properties.) Also, minimum safety factors may be set by design code, company policy, or governmental regulation. Where the applied loads are well known and there are no unusual circumstances, reasonable values for safety factors in stress are three against fracture and two against yielding. The larger value for fracture is suggested because of the greater statistical scatter in K_{Ic} compared with yield strength, and also because brittle fracture is a more sudden, catastrophic mode of failure than yielding.

Example 8.2

Consider the situation of Ex. 8.1, where a center-cracked plate of 2014-T651 aluminum, with dimensions $b = 50$ and $t = 5$ mm, is subjected in service to a force of $P = 50$ kN.

  (a) What is the largest crack length a that can be permitted for a safety factor against fracture of 3.0 in stress?
  (b) What safety factor on crack length results from the safety factor in stress of (a)?
  (c) What is the safety factor against yielding?

Solution　　(a) Equation 8.15 gives the highest value of K that can be allowed:

$$K = \frac{K_{Ic}}{X_K} = \frac{24\,\text{MPa}\sqrt{\text{m}}}{3.0} = 8.0\,\text{MPa}\sqrt{\text{m}}$$

Hence, this K is employed to obtain the largest crack length that can be permitted:

$$K = FS_g\sqrt{\pi a}, \qquad 8.0\,\text{MPa}\sqrt{\text{m}} = F(100\,\text{MPa})\sqrt{\pi a}$$

Assuming that $F = 1$ is sufficiently accurate, solving for a gives

$$a = 2.04\,\text{mm} \qquad\qquad\qquad \textbf{Ans.}$$

Since $\alpha = a/b = (2.04\,\text{mm})/(50\,\text{mm}) = 0.0408$, we are well within the limit for 10% accuracy on K, and this result is reasonably accurate. If F is allowed to vary, as in Ex. 8.1(c), essentially the same result is obtained: $a = 2.03\,\text{mm}$ (**Ans.**).

　　(b) In Ex. 8.1(c), the crack length causing failure at the service stress is calculated to be $a_c = 16.3\,\text{mm}$. Comparing this with the value of a from part (a) of this example gives the safety factor on crack length:

$$X_a = a_c/a = (16.3\,\text{mm})/(2.03\,\text{mm}) = 8.03 \qquad\qquad \textbf{Ans.}$$

　　(c) The safety factor against yielding, calculated as if no crack is present, is given by Eq. 8.18 and is

$$X_o = \sigma_o/S_g = (415\,\text{MPa})/(100\,\text{MPa}) = 4.15 \qquad\qquad \textbf{Ans.}$$

where the yield strength value is from Table 8.1. A more detailed calculation that uses the fully plastic limit force as in Eq. 8.19 is

$$X_o' = \frac{P_o}{P} = \frac{2bt\sigma_o(1 - a/b)}{P} = \frac{2(50\,\text{mm})(5\,\text{mm})(415\,\text{MPa})}{50{,}000\,\text{N}}\left(1 - \frac{2.03\,\text{mm}}{50\,\text{mm}}\right) = 3.98 \quad \textbf{Ans.}$$

where the expression for P_o is obtained from Fig. A.16(a), and P is the actual service force.

Comments　　The safety factor on crack length is rather large, as expected. Either of the safety factors against yielding is higher than $X_K = 3.0$, indicating that this member is closer to brittle fracture that to yielding; that is, $X_K = 3.0$ is the controlling safety factor.

Example 8.3

An engineering member made of titanium 6Al-4V (annealed) is a plate loaded in tension that may have a crack in one edge, as shown in Fig. 8.12(c). The applied force is $P = 55\,\text{kN}$, the width is $b = 40\,\text{mm}$, and the crack may be as long as $a = 6\,\text{mm}$. If a safety factor of 3.0 in stress is required, what minimum plate thickness t is required?

Solution   The stress intensity $K = F S_g \sqrt{\pi a}$ must be below K_{Ic} by a safety factor $X_K = 3.0$. Noting this and substituting the expression for S_g from Fig. 8.12(c) gives

$$K = \frac{K_{Ic}}{X_K} = F \frac{P}{bt} \sqrt{\pi a}, \qquad \frac{66 \, \text{MPa}\sqrt{\text{m}}}{3.0} = F \frac{55{,}000 \, \text{N}}{(40 \, \text{mm})(t, \text{mm})} \sqrt{\pi (0.006 \, \text{m})}$$

where K_{Ic} is from Table 8.1. Note that $F = 1.12$ with 10% accuracy up to $\alpha = 0.13$. But $\alpha = a/b = (6 \, \text{mm})/(40 \, \text{mm}) = 0.15$ is beyond this limit, so F must be calculated by substituting this α into the appropriate polynomial-type expression. The result is

$$F = 0.265(1 - \alpha)^4 + \frac{0.857 + 0.265\alpha}{(1 - \alpha)^{3/2}} = 1.283$$

Substituting this F and solving gives $t = 11.01 \, \text{mm}$ (**Ans.**).

However, we need to check that the safety factor is also met for yielding. The fully plastic limit force, from Fig. A.16(d), is

$$P_o = bt\sigma_o \left[-\alpha + \sqrt{2\alpha^2 - 2\alpha + 1} \right]$$

$$P_o = (40 \, \text{mm})(11.01 \, \text{mm})(925 \, \text{MPa}) \left[-0.15 + \sqrt{2(0.15)^2 - 2(0.15) + 1} \right] = 290{,}400 \, \text{N}$$

where the yield strength is from Table 8.1. Hence, the safety factor against yielding is

$$X'_o = \frac{P_o}{P} = \frac{290.4 \, \text{kN}}{55 \, \text{kN}} = 5.28$$

which exceeds the required value, so the preceding result of $t = 11.01 \, \text{mm}$ is the final answer.

8.5 ADDITIONAL TOPICS ON APPLICATION OF *K*

Following the basic treatment of the previous section, it is useful to consider some additional topics related to the application of K to design and analysis. These topics include some special cracked member configurations, superposition for handling combined loading, cracks inclined to the stress direction, and also leak-before-break for pressure vessels.

8.5.1 Cases of Special Interest for Practical Applications

The handbooks listed in the References contain a wide variety of additional useful cases. These include not only additional situations of cracked plates and shafts, but also cracked tubes, discs, stiffened panels, etc., including three-dimensional cases.

In practical applications, cracks having shapes that approximate a circle, half-circle, or quarter-circle may occur, as illustrated in Fig. 8.17. Half-circular surface cracks as in (b) and (d) are especially common. Evaluation of stress intensities for these complex three-dimensional cases is aided by the existence of an exact solution for a circular crack of radius a in an infinite body under uniform stress S:

$$K = \frac{2}{\pi} S \sqrt{\pi a} \qquad (8.20)$$

For embedded (internal) circular cracks, Fig. 8.17(a), this solution is still within 10% for members of finite size, subject to the limits $a/t < 0.5$ and $a/b < 0.5$.

For half-circular surface cracks or quarter-circular corner cracks, and for a values that are small compared with the other dimensions, the stress intensities are elevated compared with Eq. 8.20 by a factor around 1.13 or 1.14, giving F values as shown in Fig. 8.17 for cases (b), (c), and (d). These F values specifically apply for points where the crack front intersects the surface, where K has its maximum value. They may be applied for either tension or bending, with 10% accuracy, within the limits indicated. (Note that the factors of 1.13 or 1.14 on K, compared with the circular crack case, are analogous to the previously discussed free surface factor of 1.12 for cracks in flat plates.)

More detail is shown for the half-circular surface crack case in Fig. 8.18. The equations given are based on the paper by Newman (1986), as fitted there to finite element analyses. Note that K is affected by the proximity of the boundary in two directions and also varies around the periphery of the crack; that is, K varies with both a/b and a/t and also with θ. Stresses for tension and bending, S_t and S_b, respectively, are defined as in Fig. 8.17(b), and three functions f_a, f_b, and f_w, are needed. Figure 8.18 gives an equation for f_w that is accurate for $a/b < 0.5$, where $f_w = 1$ if either or both of a/b and a/t are small. Also given are f_a and f_b for the surface points, $\theta = 0$ and $180°$, and for the deepest point, $\theta = 90°$. The θ variation is rather small, as shown in Fig. 8.18(b) for two different a/t values. For small a/b and a/t, note that $f_w = f_b = 1$, giving $f_a = 1.144$ at the surface and $f_a = 1.04$ at the deepest point. The former value corresponds to $F = 1.144(2/\pi) = 0.728$ in Fig. 8.17(b).

An exact solution also exists for an elliptical crack in an infinite body under uniform stress. With reference to Fig. 8.19(a), this solution is

$$K = S \sqrt{\frac{\pi a}{Q}} f_\phi, \qquad f_\phi = \left[\left(\frac{a}{c} \right)^2 \cos^2 \phi + \sin^2 \phi \right]^{1/4} \qquad (a/c \leq 1) \qquad (8.21)$$

where the angle ϕ specifies a particular location P around the elliptical crack front. The quantity Q is called the *flaw shape factor*. It is given exactly by

$$\sqrt{Q} = E(k) = \int_0^{\pi/2} \sqrt{1 - k^2 \sin^2 \beta}\, d\beta, \qquad k^2 = 1 - \left(\frac{a}{c} \right)^2 \qquad (8.22)$$

$E(k)$ is the standard *elliptic integral of the second kind*, values of which are given in most books of mathematical tables and in analogous computer software packages. However, Q may be closely

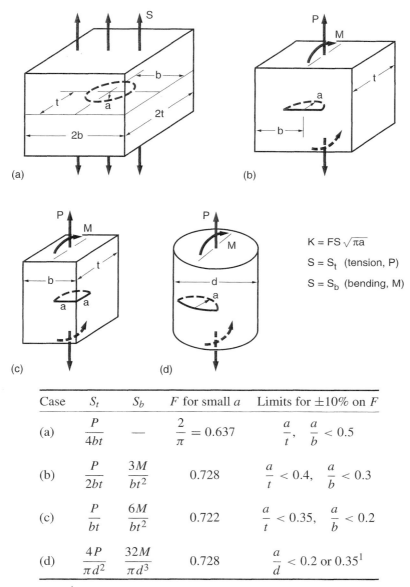

Case	S_t	S_b	F for small a	Limits for $\pm 10\%$ on F
(a)	$\dfrac{P}{4bt}$	—	$\dfrac{2}{\pi} = 0.637$	$\dfrac{a}{t},\ \dfrac{a}{b} < 0.5$
(b)	$\dfrac{P}{2bt}$	$\dfrac{3M}{bt^2}$	0.728	$\dfrac{a}{t} < 0.4,\ \dfrac{a}{b} < 0.3$
(c)	$\dfrac{P}{bt}$	$\dfrac{6M}{bt^2}$	0.722	$\dfrac{a}{t} < 0.35,\ \dfrac{a}{b} < 0.2$
(d)	$\dfrac{4P}{\pi d^2}$	$\dfrac{32M}{\pi d^3}$	0.728	$\dfrac{a}{d} < 0.2$ or 0.35 [1]

Note: [1]Different limits for tension or bending, respectively.

Figure 8.17   Stress intensity factors for (a) an embedded circular crack under uniform tension normal to the crack plane, and related cases: (b) half-circular surface crack, (c) quarter-circular corner crack, and (d) half-circular surface crack in a shaft, where the latter is more precisely a portion of a circular arc with center on the surface. (Based on [Newman 86] and [Raju 86].)

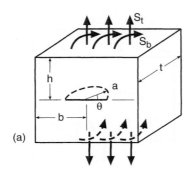

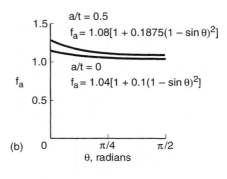

(a)　　　(b)

Functional forms for $a/b < 0.5,\ h/b > 1$:

$$K = f_a f_w \frac{2}{\pi}(S_t + f_b S_b)\sqrt{\pi a}, \qquad f_w = \sqrt{\sec\left(\frac{\pi a}{2b}\sqrt{\frac{a}{t}}\right)}$$

$$\text{where } f_a = f_a(a/t,\ \theta), \qquad f_b = f_b(a/t)$$

Expressions for $\theta = 0$ and 180° (surface) for any $\alpha = a/t$:

$$f_a = (1.04 + 0.2017\alpha^2 - 0.1061\alpha^4)(1.1 + 0.35\alpha^2), \qquad f_b = 1 - 0.45\alpha$$

Expressions for $\theta = 90°$ (deepest point) for any $\alpha = a/t$:

$$f_a = 1.04 + 0.2017\alpha^2 - 0.1061\alpha^4, \qquad f_b = 1 - 1.34\alpha - 0.03\alpha^2$$

Figure 8.18 Stress intensity factors for rectangular cross sections as in (a) for half-circular surface cracks under tension and/or bending. The general form for K is given, as well as particular equations for the surface and deepest point for any a/t. Also, (b) shows the variation with θ for $a/t = 0$ and 0.5 as given by f_a. (Equations from [Newman 86].)

approximated by the expression given in Fig. 8.19. Note that Eq. 8.21 reduces to Eq. 8.20 for a circular crack, $a/c = 1$.

With respect to variation with the angle ϕ, the maximum K from Eq. 8.21 occurs at $\phi = 90°$, where $f_\phi = 1$, corresponding to points D on the minor axis of the ellipse. The minimum K occurs at $\phi = 0$, where $f_\phi = \sqrt{a/c}$, corresponding to points E on the major axis of the ellipse. Denoting the maximum K as K_D, this value may be employed for finite-size members, within 10%, for $a/t < 0.4$ and $c/b < 0.2$.

In a manner similar to the circular crack, the closed-form solution for an embedded elliptical crack may be applied in modified form to related cases. For example, for a half-elliptical surface crack under uniform stress, multiplying by a free surface factor of 1.12 allows K_D to be approximated. Limitations for 10% accuracy are given in Fig. 8.19, as case (b). For surface cracks

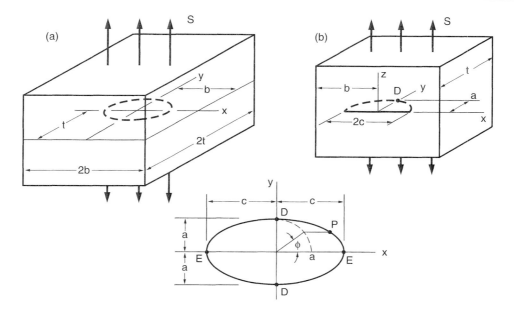

$$K_D = F_D S \sqrt{\frac{\pi a}{Q}}, \qquad Q \approx 1 + 1.464 \left(\frac{a}{c}\right)^{1.65} \qquad (a/c \leq 1)$$

Case	Values for small $a/t, c/b$	Limits for 10% accuracy
(a)	$F_D = 1$	$a/t < 0.4,\ c/b < 0.2$
(b)	$F_D \approx 1.12$	$a/t < 0.3,$[1] $c/b < 0.2$

Note: [1]Except limit to $a/t < 0.16$ if $a/c < 0.25$.

Figure 8.19   Stress intensity factors for (a) an embedded elliptical crack and (b) a similar half-elliptical surface crack. The equations give K_D at point D for a uniform tension normal to the crack plane. (Based on [Newman 86].)

with $a/c \leq 1$, equations giving F_D for any a/t are

$$F_D = \left[g_1 + g_2(a/t)^2 + g_3(a/t)^4\right] f_w, \qquad g_1 = 1.13 - 0.09(a/c)$$

$$g_2 = -0.54 + \frac{0.89}{0.2 + a/c}, \qquad g_3 = 0.5 - \frac{1}{0.65 + a/c} + 14(1 - a/c)^{24}$$

$$f_w = \sqrt{\sec\left(\frac{\pi c}{2b}\sqrt{\frac{a}{t}}\right)} \qquad (c/b < 0.5)$$

(8.23)

except that these are limited to $a/t < 0.75$ for $a/c < 0.2$. The foregoing equations are from Newman (1986). This and other sources, notably Raju (1982, 1986) and Murakami (1987), together give K solutions for a wide variety of cases of elliptical, half-elliptical, and quarter-elliptical cracks in plates, shafts, and tubes, under both tension and bending loads.

Example 8.4

A pressure vessel made of ASTM A517-F steel operates near room temperature and has a wall thickness of $t = 50\,\text{mm}$. A surface crack was found in the vessel wall during an inspection. It has an approximately semi-elliptical shape, as in Fig. 8.19(b), with surface length $2c = 40\,\text{mm}$ and depth $a = 10\,\text{mm}$. The stresses in the region of the crack, as calculated without considering the presence of the crack, are approximately uniform through the thickness and are $S_z = 300\,\text{MPa}$ normal to the crack plane and $S_x = 150\,\text{MPa}$ parallel to the crack plane, where the coordinate system of Fig. 8.19 is used. What is the safety factor against brittle fracture? Would you remove the pressure vessel from service?

Solution   From Table 8.1(a), we see that this material has a fracture toughness of $K_{Ic} = 187\,\text{MPa}\sqrt{\text{m}}$ and a yield strength of $\sigma_o = 760\,\text{MPa}$ at room temperature. The K for the given stresses and crack can be estimated from Fig. 8.19(b). Since $c = 20\,\text{mm}$, we have $a/c = 0.5$. Also, we have $a/t = 0.2$ and large b, for which $F_D = 1.12$ is a reasonable approximation. The quantity Q is needed:

$$Q = 1 + 1.464 \left(\frac{a}{c}\right)^{1.65} = 1.466$$

Hence, the maximum K, which occurs at the point of maximum depth of the elliptical crack, is approximately

$$K = K_D = F_D S_z \sqrt{\frac{\pi a}{Q}} \approx 1.12(300\,\text{MPa})\sqrt{\frac{\pi(0.010\,\text{m})}{1.466}} = 49.2\,\text{MPa}\sqrt{\text{m}}$$

The stress-based safety factor against brittle fracture is

$$X_K = \frac{K_{Ic}}{K} = \frac{187}{49.2} = 3.80 \qquad\qquad \textbf{Ans.}$$

This is a reasonably high value, so it would be safe to continue using the pressure vessel until repairs are convenient. However, the crack should be checked frequently to be sure that it is not growing. In addition, the ASME or other design code for pressure vessels is likely to apply, and it should be consulted in this situation.

Comment   Stresses parallel to the plane of a crack do not affect K, so the given S_x does not enter the calculation. (See Section 8.5.4 for further discussion of this point.)

8.5.2 Cracks Growing from Notches

Another situation that is often of practical interest is a crack growing from a stress raiser, such as a hole, notch, or fillet. The example of a pair of cracks growing from a circular hole in a wide plate

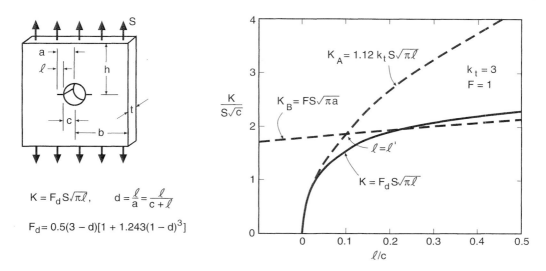

Figure 8.20   Stress intensities for a pair of cracks growing from a circular hole in a remotely loaded wide plate, $a \ll b, h$. (Equation from [Tada 85] p. 19.1.)

is used to illustrate this situation in Fig. 8.20. The solid line shown is from numerical analysis and is closely approximated by the equation given. If the crack is short compared with the hole radius, the solution is the same as for a surface crack in an infinite body, except that the stress is $k_t S$, being amplified by the stress concentration factor, in this case $k_t = 3$ from Fig. A.11(a):

$$K_A = 1.12 \, k_t S \sqrt{\pi l} \tag{8.24}$$

In this equation, l is the crack length measured from the hole surface. Once the crack has grown far from the hole, the solution is the same as for a single long crack of tip-to-tip length $2a$, for which

$$K_B = F S \sqrt{\pi a} \tag{8.25}$$

where $F = 1$ for this particular case of a wide plate. Hence, for long cracks, the width of the hole acts as part of the crack, and the fact that the material removed to make the hole is missing from the crack faces is of little consequence. The exact K first follows K_A, then falls below it and approaches K_B, agreeing exactly for large l beyond the range of the plot of Fig. 8.20.

Most cases of a crack at an internal or surface notch can be roughly approximated by using K_A for crack lengths up to that where $K_A = K_B$, and then using K_B for all longer crack lengths. Equations 8.24 and 8.25 apply, with the k_t and $F = F(a/b)$ for the particular case being used, and with the nomenclature being generalized as in Fig. 8.21. Note that k_t and S in Eq. 8.24 must be consistently defined and also that F in Eq. 8.25 is usually consistent with S_g calculated from gross area. Hence, the values k_{tn} used with net section stress S_n that are usually available need to be converted to values k_{tg} that are consistent with S_g, which can be accomplished by using the relationship $k_{tn} S_n = k_{tg} S_g$. The crack length where $K_A = K_B$, labeled as $l = l'$ in Fig. 8.20, can

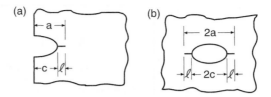

Figure 8.21 Nomenclature for cracks growing from notches.

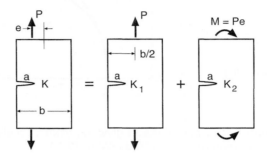

Figure 8.22 Eccentric loading of a plate with an edge crack, and the superposition used to obtain K.

then be obtained from the preceding equations:

$$l' = \frac{c}{\left(1.12\dfrac{k_{tg}}{F}\right)^2 - 1}$$ (8.26)

The resulting values of l' are typically in the range 0.1ρ to 0.2ρ, where ρ is the notch-tip radius.

More refined estimates of K for cracks at notches may be made, as described by Kujawski (1991) and in earlier work that he references. Also, the various handbooks give solutions for specific cases.

8.5.3 Superposition for Combined Loading

Stress intensity solutions for combined loading can be obtained by superposition—that is, by adding the contributions to K from the individual load components. For example, consider an eccentric load applied a distance e from the centerline of a member with a single edge crack, as shown in Fig. 8.22. This eccentric load is statically equivalent to the combination of a centrally applied tension load and a bending moment. The contribution to K from the centrally applied tension may be determined from Fig. 8.12(c):

$$K_1 = F_1 S_1 \sqrt{\pi a}, \qquad S_1 = \frac{P}{bt}$$ (8.27)

The contribution from bending may be determined from Fig. 8.13(a):

$$K_2 = F_2 S_2 \sqrt{\pi a}, \qquad S_2 = \frac{6M}{b^2 t} = \frac{6Pe}{b^2 t} \tag{8.28}$$

Hence, the total stress intensity due to the eccentric load is obtained by summing the two solutions and using substitutions from the previous equations; it is

$$K = K_1 + K_2 = \frac{P}{bt} \left(F_1 + \frac{6F_2 e}{b} \right) \sqrt{\pi a} \tag{8.29}$$

where the particular a/b that applies is used to separately determine F_1 and F_2 for tension and bending, respectively.

Ingenious use of superposition sometimes allows handbook solutions to be employed for cases not obviously included. For example, consider the case of a central crack in a plate with a pair of prying forces. Values of K for this case, here denoted K_1, are available from Fig. 8.15. This K_1 can be considered to be the superposition of three loadings, as shown in Fig. 8.23(a). The two cases denoted K_2 have the same solution, and K_3 is simply the center-cracked plate from Fig. 8.12(a). Hence, superposition requires that $K_1 = K_2 + K_2 - K_3$, where the K_3 loading is subtracted from $2K_2$ to obtain K_1. This allows K_2 to be determined from the known solutions for K_1 and K_3, with details being given as the equations for case (a) in Fig. 8.23.

Similar superposition is shown in Fig. 8.23(b) for the related case of an infinite array of collinear cracks with prying forces. Here, K_1 and K_3 have known closed-form solutions, as given in the case (b) equations, so that a closed-form expression for K_2 is readily obtained. Figure 8.23 also gives some approximations for these solutions that are within 10% for the indicated ranges of $\alpha = a/b$. Note that K_2 from Fig. 8.23(a) or (b) is of special interest for applications where tension in a sheet of material is reacted by a concentrated force due to a bolt or a rivet, or a row of bolts or rivets. In particular, these K_2 solutions provide K_B (see Section 8.5.2) for cracks growing from one hole, or a row of holes, as shown in Fig. 8.24.

8.5.4 Cracks Inclined or Parallel to an Applied Stress

Consider a crack that is inclined to the applied stress, as in Fig. 8.25. Such a situation is difficult to handle because there is not only an opening (tensile) mode stress intensity K_I, but also a sliding (shear) mode K_{II}, with these varying with θ as shown. A reasonable, but approximate, approach to such cases is to treat them as opening mode (K_I) situations, with the crack length being the projection normal to the stress direction—that is, along the x-axis of Fig. 8.25—giving

$$K = S\sqrt{\pi a \cos \theta} \tag{8.30}$$

where $F = 1$ for this particular example of a wide plate.

Stresses parallel to a crack can generally be ignored in calculating the opening mode K. Note that this is the case in Fig. 8.25, where K_I is zero for $\theta = 90°$. As an additional example, consider a crack in a pressure vessel wall, as in Fig. 8.26. Only the stress σ_t that is normal to the plane of the crack affects K, and the stress parallel to the crack, such as σ_x, may be ignored in calculating K.

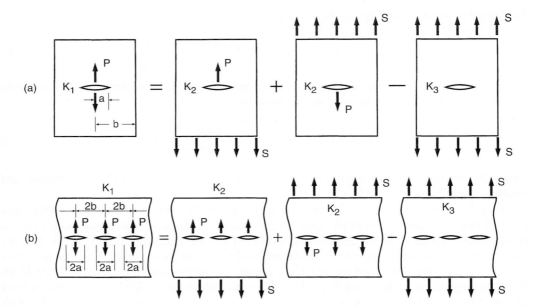

Superposition for either (a) or (b): ($t =$ thickness)

$$K_1 = K_2 + K_2 - K_3, \qquad \text{so that } K_2 = \frac{1}{2}(K_1 + K_3), \qquad \text{where } S = \frac{P}{2bt}$$

(a) Single crack in finite-width plate for any $\alpha = a/b$:

$$K_1 = F_{P1}\frac{P}{t\sqrt{b}}, \qquad K_3 = F_3 S\sqrt{\pi a}, \qquad K_2 = \frac{P}{2t\sqrt{b}}\left(F_{P1} + \frac{F_3\sqrt{\pi\alpha}}{2}\right)$$

F_{P1} is F_P from Fig. 8.15, and F_3 is F from Fig. 8.12(a).

(b) Infinite array of collinear cracks, exact solutions for any $\alpha = a/b$:

$$K_1 = \frac{P}{t\sqrt{b}}\frac{1}{\sqrt{\sin\pi\alpha}}, \qquad K_3 = S\sqrt{2b\tan\frac{\pi\alpha}{2}}, \qquad K_2 = \frac{P}{2t\sqrt{b}}\left(\frac{1}{\sqrt{\sin\pi\alpha}} + \sqrt{\frac{1}{2}\tan\frac{\pi\alpha}{2}}\right)$$

Approximations within 10%: (Note limits for (a) or (b), respectively, below each equation.)

$$K_2 = \frac{P}{2t\sqrt{b}}\left(\frac{1}{\sqrt{\pi\alpha}} + \frac{\sqrt{\pi\alpha}}{2}\right), \qquad K_2 = \frac{0.89P}{t\sqrt{b}}$$

$$(\alpha \leq 0.32 \text{ or } 0.38) \qquad\qquad (0.12 \leq \alpha \leq 0.57 \text{ or } 0.65)$$

Figure 8.23   Superposition to obtain solutions for cases of a single crack (a), or a row of cracks (b), loaded on one side. (Arguments of trigonometric functions are in radians.)

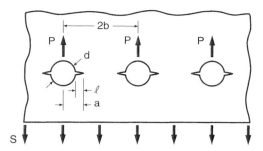

Figure 8.24 Row of holes loaded on one side, with cracks on both sides of each hole.

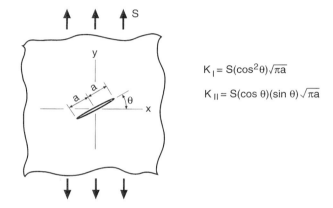

$$K_I = S(\cos^2\theta)\sqrt{\pi a}$$

$$K_{II} = S(\cos\theta)(\sin\theta)\sqrt{\pi a}$$

Figure 8.25 Angled crack in an infinite plate under remote tension and the resulting stress intensity factors.

8.5.5 Leak-Before-Break Design of Pressure Vessels

In a thin-walled pressure vessel with a crack growing in the wall, two possibilities exist: (1) The crack may gradually extend and penetrate the wall, causing a leak before sudden brittle fracture can occur. (2) Sudden brittle fracture may occur prior to the vessel leaking. Since a brittle fracture in a pressure vessel may involve explosive release of the vessel contents, a leak is by far preferable. Also, a leak is easily detected from a pressure drop or from the escape of vessel contents. Hence, pressure vessels should be designed to leak before they fracture.

A crack in a pressure vessel may grow in size due to the influence of the cyclic loading associated with pressure changes, or due to hostile chemical attack on the material. (See Chapter 11.) A crack usually starts from a surface flaw and extends in a plane normal to the maximum stress in the vessel wall, as shown in Fig. 8.26(a). Early in its progress, the crack will often grow with the surface length $2c$ continuing to be approximately twice the depth a, so that $c \approx a$. If no brittle fracture occurs, the growth will proceed in a pattern similar to that shown, resulting in a through-wall crack with surface length $2c$ that is approximately twice the thickness, $2t$, as in (b). However, sudden brittle fracture will occur before the crack penetrates the wall unless the material has sufficient

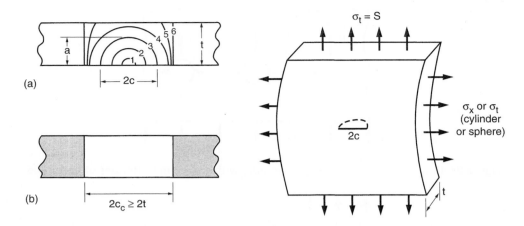

Figure 8.26   A crack in the wall of a pressure vessel, showing (a) its growth from a small surface flaw and (b) the minimum critical size of a through-wall crack to provide leak-before-break.

fracture toughness to support a through-wall crack of at least this size:

$$c_c \geq t \qquad (8.31)$$

Such a through-wall crack may be analyzed as a central crack in a plate, as in Fig. 8.12(a). Since the plate is wide compared with the crack length, $F = 1$, with c_c being the crack length a, and the maximum stress σ_t is S. Making these substitutions into $K = FS\sqrt{\pi a}$, and also substituting K_{Ic} for K, and then solving for c_c, we have

$$c_c = \frac{1}{\pi} \left(\frac{K_{Ic}}{\sigma_t} \right)^2 \qquad (8.32)$$

Hence, c_c may be calculated and compared with the thickness to determine whether the *leak-before-break condition* is met.

The equations just developed apply where the crack starts from a small surface flaw. If the initial flaw is located inside the wall, penetration of the wall may occur with a surface length $2c$ that is less than twice the thickness, so that the c_c value from Eq. 8.32 will be more than sufficient. However, if the initial flaw has considerable length along the surface, the crack may have $2c$ larger than twice the thickness, or $c > t$, when it penetrates the wall. In this case, c_c from Eq. 8.32 will not provide leak-before-break. This latter circumstance is best avoided by adequate inspection and repair to assure that no initial surface defects of size approaching $c > t$ are present.

Example 8.5

A spherical pressure vessel is made of ASTM A517-F steel and operates at room temperature. The inner diameter is 1.5 m, the wall thickness is 10 mm, and the maximum pressure is 6 MPa. Is the leak-before-break condition met? What is the safety factor on K relative to K_{Ic}, and what is the safety factor against yielding?

Solution   From Fig. A.7(b), the maximum stress in the vessel wall is

$$\sigma_t = \frac{pr_1}{2t} = \frac{(6\,\text{MPa})(750\,\text{mm})}{2(10\,\text{mm})} = 225\,\text{MPa}$$

Combining this value with $K_{Ic} = 187\,\text{MPa}\sqrt{\text{m}}$ from Table 8.1, the critical crack length is

$$c_c = \frac{1}{\pi}\left(\frac{K_{Ic}}{\sigma_t}\right) = \frac{1}{\pi}\left(\frac{187\,\text{MPa}\sqrt{\text{m}}}{225\,\text{MPa}}\right)^2 = 0.220\,\text{m} = 220\,\text{mm}$$

This far exceeds the wall thickness of $t = 10$ mm, so the leak-before-break condition is met.
When the vessel leaks, the crack length along the surface is $2c = 2t$, so that $c = t = 10$ mm.
At this point, the stress intensity factor is

$$K = FS\sqrt{\pi a} = 1(225\,\text{MPa})\sqrt{\pi(0.01\,\text{m})} = 39.9\,\text{MPa}\sqrt{\text{m}}$$

Here, the situation is treated as a center crack in a wide plate, as in Fig. 8.12(a), with substitutions $F = 1$, $S = \sigma_t$, and $a = c$. Hence, the safety factor on K is

$$X_K = \frac{K_{Ic}}{K} = \frac{187\,\text{MPa}\sqrt{\text{m}}}{39.9\,\text{MPa}\sqrt{\text{m}}} = 4.69 \qquad\qquad \textbf{Ans.}$$

This is a reasonable value, so the vessel is safe from brittle fracture.
Noting that the principal stresses are $\sigma_1 = \sigma_2 = 225$ MPa and $\sigma_3 \approx 0$, we conclude that the effective stress from Eq. 7.21 is $\bar{\sigma}_S = 225$ MPa, and the safety factor against yielding is

$$X_o = \frac{\sigma_o}{\bar{\sigma}_S} = \frac{760\,\text{MPa}}{225\,\text{MPa}} = 3.38 \qquad\qquad \textbf{Ans.}$$

where the yield strength is also from Table 8.1. Hence, yielding is unlikely.

8.6 FRACTURE TOUGHNESS VALUES AND TRENDS

In fracture toughness testing, an increasing displacement is applied to an already cracked specimen of the material of interest until it fractures. The arrangement used for a *bend specimen* is shown in Fig. 8.27. Growth of the crack is detected by observing the force versus displacement (P-v) behavior, as in Fig. 8.28. A deviation from linearity on the P-v plot, or a sudden drop in force due to rapid cracking, identifies a point P_Q corresponding to an early stage of cracking. The value of K, denoted K_Q, is then calculated for this point. If there is some tearing of the crack prior to final fracture, K_Q may be somewhat lower than the value K_c corresponding to the final fracture of the specimen.

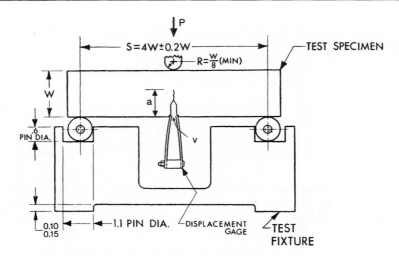

Figure 8.27   Fixtures for a fracture toughness test on a bend specimen. The dimension *W* corresponds to our *b*. (Adapted from [ASTM 97] Std. E399; copyright © ASTM; reprinted with permission.)

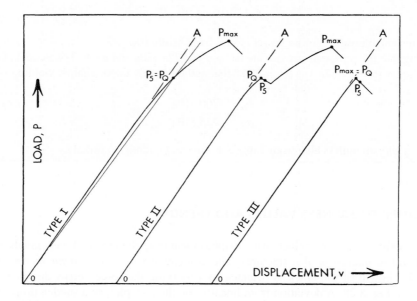

Figure 8.28   Types of force vs. displacement behavior that can occur in a fracture toughness test. (From [ASTM 97] Std. E399; copyright © ASTM; reprinted with permission.)

Figure 8.29   Compact specimens of two different sizes, $b = 5.1$ and $61\,\text{cm}$. (Photo courtesy of E. T. Wessel, Haines City, FL; used with permission of Westinghouse Electric Corp.)

In addition to bend specimens, various other specimen geometries are used, such as the *compact specimen* geometry of Fig. 8.16. For these, the thickness is usually $t = 0.5b$. Figures 8.29 and 8.30 are photographs of untested and tested compact specimens.

Fracture toughness testing of metals based on LEFM principles is governed by several ASTM standards, notably Standard Nos. E399 and E1820. Similar tests are also done for other types of material, as in Standard No. D5045 on plastics (polymers) and No. C1421 on ceramics. A situation addressed in these standards is that K_Q decreases with increasing specimen thickness t, as illustrated by test data in Fig. 8.31. This occurs because the behavior is affected by the plastic zone at the crack tip in a manner that depends on thickness. Once the thickness obeys the following relationship involving the yield strength, no further decrease is expected:

$$t \geq 2.5 \left(\frac{K_Q}{\sigma_o} \right)^2 \tag{8.33}$$

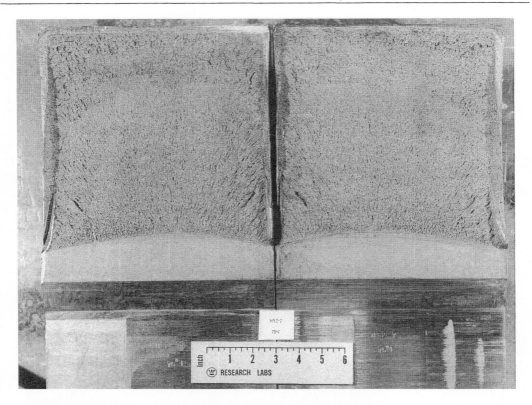

Figure 8.30 Fracture surfaces from a K_{Ic} test on A533B steel that used a compact specimen of dimensions $t = 25$, $b = 51$ cm. (Photo courtesy of E. T. Wessel, Haines City, FL; used with permission of Westinghouse Electric Corp.)

Values of K_Q meeting this requirement are denoted as K_{Ic} to distinguish them as worst-case values. In engineering design that employs material of thickness such that K_Q is somewhat greater than K_{Ic}, values of K_{Ic} can be used, while recognizing that this provides some extra conservatism. Such an approach is often necessary, since only K_{Ic} values are widely available, as in Tables 8.1 and 8.2.

A later section of this chapter will consider in more detail plastic zone size effects and other aspects of fracture toughness testing. We will now proceed to discuss the trends in K_{Ic} with material, temperature, loading rate, and other influences.

8.6.1 Trends in K_{Ic} with Material

Values of K_{Ic} for engineering metals are generally in the range 20 to 200 MPa$\sqrt{m}$. For increasing strength within a given class of engineering metal, it has already been noted that fracture toughness decreases along with tensile ductility. See Figs. 1.6 and 8.7. As a further example, the effect on K_{Ic} of heat treating the alloy steel AISI 4340 to various strength levels is shown in Fig. 8.32.

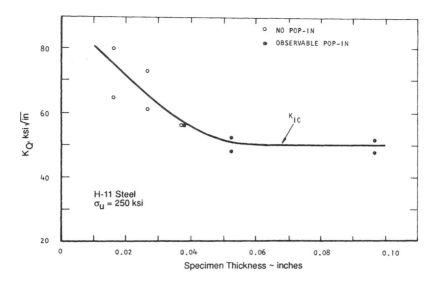

Figure 8.31 Effect of thickness on fracture toughness of an alloy steel heat treated to the high strength of $\sigma_u = 1720$ MPa. (Adapted from [Steigerwald 70]; copyright © ASTM; reprinted with permission.)

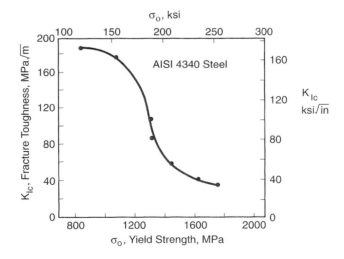

Figure 8.32 Fracture toughness vs. yield strength for AISI 4340 steel quenched and tempered to various strength levels. (Adapted from an illustration courtesy of W. G. Clark, Jr., Westinghouse Science and Technology Ctr., Pittsburgh, PA.)

Polymers that are useful as engineering materials typically have K_{Ic} values in the range 1 to 5 MPa$\sqrt{\text{m}}$. Although these are low values, most polymers are used at low stresses due to their low ultimate strengths, so that under typical usage the likelihood of fracture is roughly similar to that for metals. Modifying a low-ductility polymer with ductile particles such as rubber increases its fracture toughness. The addition of short chopped fibers or other stiff reinforcement may decrease toughness if crack growth paths are available that do not intersect the reinforcement. Conversely, long fibers, and especially continuous ones, in a polymer matrix composite may obstruct crack growth to the point that the toughness is in the range of that for metals.

Ceramics have low values of fracture toughness, also in the range 1 to 5 MPa$\sqrt{\text{m}}$, as might be expected from their low ductility. This range of K_{Ic} values is similar to that for polymers, but it is quite low in view of the fact that ceramics are high-strength materials. Indeed, their strengths in tension are usually limited by the inherent flaws in the material, as discussed near the beginning of this chapter. Recent efforts in materials development have led to modifications to ceramics that increase toughness somewhat. For example, alumina (Al_2O_3) toughened with a second phase of 15% zirconia (ZrO_2) has $K_{Ic} \approx 10$ MPa$\sqrt{\text{m}}$. This occurs because high stress causes a phase transformation (crystal structure change) in the zirconia, which increases its volume by several percent. Thus, when the crack tip encounters a zirconia grain, the increase in volume is sufficient to cause a local compressive stress that retards further extension of the crack.

Fracture toughness exhibits more statistical variation than other materials properties, such as yield strength. Coefficients of variation are often 10% and may reach 20%. Taking 15% as a typical value, about one out of ten values from a large sample are expected to be 19% below the mean, one out of a hundred 35% below, and one out of a thousand 46% below. Safety factors used in design need to reflect this rather large uncertainty. (See Appendix B near the end of this book for additional discussion of statistical variation and also for some sample statistical data on fracture toughness.)

8.6.2 Effects of Temperature and Loading Rate

Fracture toughness generally increases with temperature; illustrative test data for a low-alloy steel and a ceramic are shown in Figs. 8.33 and 8.34. An especially abrupt change in toughness over a relatively small temperature range occurs in metals with a BCC crystal structure, notably in steels with ferritic–pearlitic and martensitic structures. The temperature region where the rapid transition occurs varies considerably for different steels, as illustrated in Fig. 8.35. There is usually a *lower shelf* of approximately constant K_{Ic} below the transition region, and an *upper shelf* above it, corresponding to a higher approximately constant K_{Ic}. (Only one set of data in Fig. 8.35 covers a sufficient range to exhibit an upper shelf.) Such *temperature-transition* behavior is similar to that observed in Charpy or other notch-impact tests, as discussed in Chapter 4.

The distinct temperature-transition behavior in BCC metals is difficult to explain merely on the basis of the increase in ductility associated with the temperature range involved. It is, in fact, due to a shift in the physical mechanism of fracture. Below the temperature transition, the fracture mechanism is identified as *cleavage*, and above it, as *dimpled rupture*. Microphotographs of fracture surfaces exhibiting these mechanisms are shown in Fig. 8.36. Cleavage is fracture with little plastic

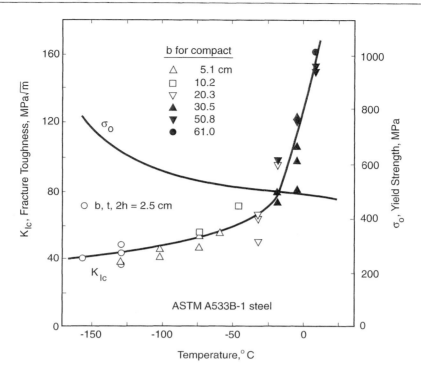

Figure 8.33 Fracture toughness and yield strength versus temperature for a nuclear pressure vessel steel. Compact specimens and one nonstandard geometry were used in sizes indicated. (Adapted from [Clark 70]; copyright © ASTM; reprinted with permission.)

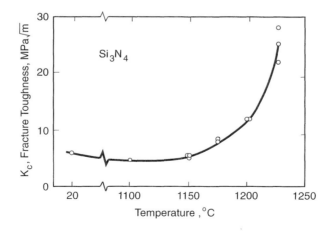

Figure 8.34 Fracture toughness vs. temperature for a silicon nitride ceramic. (Adapted from [Munz 81]; copyright © ASTM; reprinted with permission.)

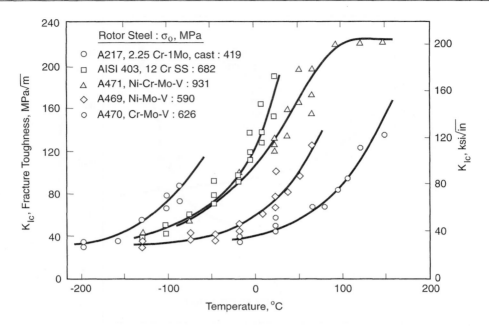

Figure 8.35   Fracture toughness vs. temperature for several steels used for turbine-generator rotors. (Data from [Logsdon 76].)

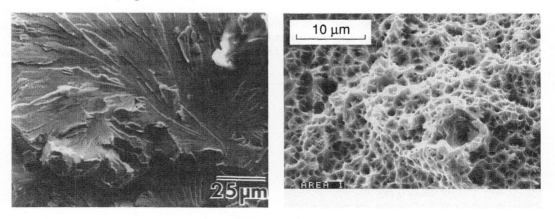

Figure 8.36   Cleavage fracture surface (left) in a 49Co-49Fe-2V alloy, and dimpled rupture (right) in a low-alloy steel. (Photos courtesy of A. Madeyski, Westinghouse Science and Technology Ctr., Pittsburgh, PA.)

deformation along specific crystal planes that have low resistance. Dimpled rupture, also called *microvoid coalescence*, involves the plasticity-induced formation, growth, and joining of tiny voids in the material. This process leaves the rough and highly dimpled fracture appearance seen in the photograph.

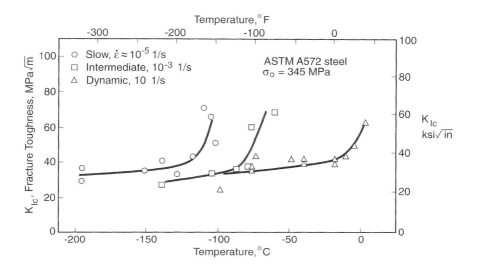

Figure 8.37 Effect of loading rate on the fracture toughness of a structural steel. Approximate strain rates at the edge of the plastic zone are given; the slowest corresponds to an ordinary test. (Adapted from [Barsom 75]; reprinted with permission from *Engineering Fracture Mechanics*; © 1975 Elsevier, Oxford, UK.)

Data on the K_{Ic} versus temperature behavior of steels and other materials is useful in selecting specific materials for service, as it is important to avoid high-stress use of a material at a temperature where its fracture toughness is low. Combinations of material and service temperature that are on the upper shelf should be employed wherever possible.

The statistical variation in fracture toughness is especially large within the temperature transition region. For example, note the degree of scatter about the trend lines in Figs. 8.33 and 8.35. Also, the position of the transition may shift by as much as 50°C for different batches of the same steel. Hence, special care is needed in engineering design within the temperature transition region. A conservative approach would be to use the lower shelf toughness value, which is often around 40 MPa$\sqrt{m}$ for steel.

A higher rate of loading usually lowers the fracture toughness, having an effect similar to decreasing the temperature. The effect can be thought of as causing a temperature shift in the K_{Ic} behavior, as illustrated by test data in Fig. 8.37. Since notch-impact tests involve a high rate of loading, these typically give a higher transition temperature than K_{Ic} tests run at ordinary rates. Some illustrative test data are shown in Fig. 8.38.

8.6.3 Microstructural Influences on K_{Ic}

Seemingly small variations in chemical composition or processing of a given material can significantly affect fracture toughness. For example, sulfide inclusions in steels apparently have effects on a microscopic level that facilitate fracture. The resulting influence of sulfur content on toughness of an alloy steel is shown in Fig. 8.39.

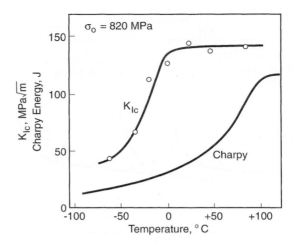

Figure 8.38   Comparison of temperature-transition behaviors for K_{Ic} and Charpy tests on a 2.25Cr-1Mo steel. (Adapted from [Marandet 77]; copyright © ASTM; reprinted with permission.)

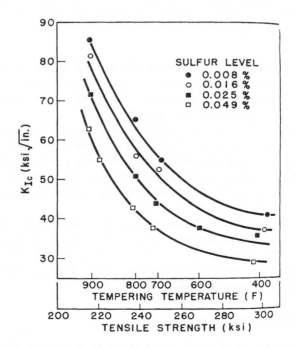

Figure 8.39   Effect of sulfur content on the fracture toughness of AISI 4345 steel. (From [Wei 65]; copyright © ASTM; reprinted with permission.)

Fracture toughness is generally more sensitive than other mechanical properties to anisotropy and planes of weakness introduced by processing. For example, in forged, rolled, or extruded metal, the crystal grains are elongated and/or flattened in certain directions, and fracture is easier where the crack grows parallel to the planes of the flattened grains. Nonmetallic inclusions and voids may also become elongated and/or flattened so that they also cause the fracture properties to vary with direction. Thus, fracture toughness tests are often conducted for various specimen orientations relative to the original piece of material. The six possible combinations of crack plane and direction in a rectangular section of material are shown in Fig. 8.40. Fracture toughness data for three of these possibilities are also given for some typical aluminum alloys.

Neutron radiation affects the pressure vessel steels used in nuclear reactors by introducing large numbers of point defects (vacancies and interstitials) into the crystal structure of the material. This causes increased yield strength, but decreased ductility, and the fracture toughness transition temperature may increase substantially, as shown by test data in Fig. 8.41. As a result, there is a large decrease in fracture toughness over a range of temperatures. Such *radiation embrittlement* is obviously a major concern in nuclear power plants and is an important factor in determining their service life.

8.6.4 Mixed-Mode Fracture

If a crack is not normal to the applied stress, or if there is a complex state of stress, a combination of fracture Modes I, II, and III may exist. For example, a situation involving combined Modes I and II is shown in Fig. 8.25. Such a situation is complex because the crack may change direction so that it does not grow in its original plane, and also because the two fracture modes do not act independently, but rather interact. Tests analogous to the K_{Ic} test to determine K_{IIc} or K_{IIIc} are difficult to conduct and are not standardized, so that toughness values for the other modes are generally not known.

The situation is analogous to the need for a yield criterion for combined stresses. Several combined-mode fracture criteria exist, but there is currently no general agreement on which is best. Any successful theory must predict mixed-mode fracture data of the type shown in Fig. 8.42. These particular data suggest that an elliptical curve could be used as an empirical fit, which is useful where both K_{Ic} and K_{IIc} are known.

$$\left(\frac{K_I}{K_{Ic}} \right)^2 + \left(\frac{K_{II}}{K_{IIc}} \right)^2 = 1 \tag{8.34}$$

8.7 PLASTIC ZONE SIZE, AND PLASTICITY LIMITATIONS ON LEFM

Near the beginning of this chapter, it was noted that real materials cannot support the theoretically infinite stresses at the tip of a sharp crack, so that upon loading, the crack tip becomes blunted and a region of yielding, crazing, or microcracking forms. We will now pursue yielding at crack tips in more detail. It is significant that the region of yielding, called the *plastic zone*, must not be excessively large if the LEFM theory is to be applied.

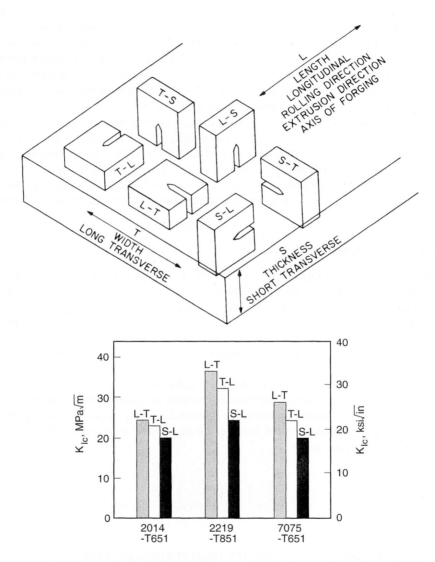

Figure 8.40   Designations for crack plane and growth direction in rectangular sections, and some corresponding effects on fracture toughness in plates of three aluminum alloys. (Top from [ASTM 97] Std. E399; copyright © ASTM; reprinted with permission. Bottom from data in [MILHDBK 94] pp. 3.10 and 3.11.)

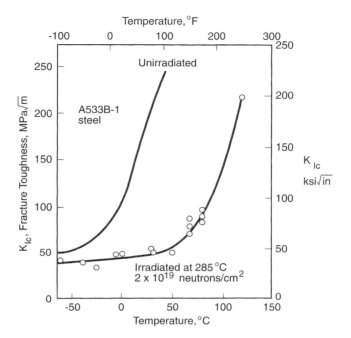

Figure 8.41   Effect of neutron irradiation on fracture toughness of a nuclear pressure vessel steel. (Adapted from [Bush 74]; copyright © ASTM; reprinted with permission.)

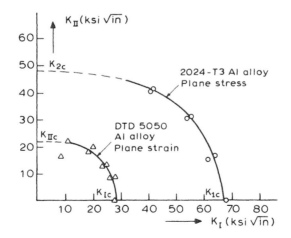

Figure 8.42   Combined mode fracture in two aluminum alloys. (From [Broek 86] p. 378; reprinted by permission of Kluwer Academic Publishers.)

8.7.1 Plastic Zone Size for Plane Stress

An equation for estimating plastic zone sizes for plane stress situations can be developed from the elastic stress field equations, Eq. 8.7, with $\sigma_z = 0$. In the plane of the crack, where $\theta = 0$, these simplify to

$$\sigma_x = \sigma_y = \frac{K}{\sqrt{2\pi r}}, \qquad \sigma_z = \tau_{xy} = \tau_{yz} = \tau_{zx} = 0 \qquad \text{(a, b)} \qquad (8.35)$$

Since all shear stress components along $\theta = 0$ are zero, σ_x, σ_y, and σ_z are principal normal stresses. Applying either the maximum shear stress or the octahedral shear stress yield criterion of the previous chapter, we estimate that yielding occurs at $\sigma_x = \sigma_y = \sigma_o$, where σ_o is the yield strength. Substituting this and solving for r gives

$$r_{o\sigma} = \frac{1}{2\pi} \left(\frac{K}{\sigma_o} \right)^2 \qquad (8.36)$$

This is simply the distance ahead of the crack tip where the elastic stress distribution exceeds the yield criterion for plane stress, as illustrated in Fig. 8.43. Note that elastic, perfectly plastic behavior is assumed.

Due to yielding within the plastic zone, the stresses are lower than the values from the elastic stress field equations. The yielded material thus offers less resistance than expected, and large deformations occur, which in turn cause yielding to extend even farther than $r_{o\sigma}$, as also illustrated. The commonly used estimate is that yielding actually extends to about $2r_{o\sigma}$. Hence, the final estimate of plastic zone size for plane stress is

$$2r_{o\sigma} = \frac{1}{\pi} \left(\frac{K}{\sigma_o} \right)^2 \qquad (8.37)$$

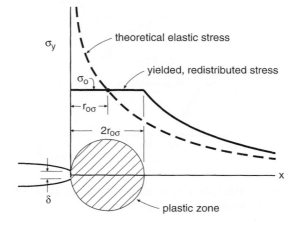

Figure 8.43 Plastic zone size estimate for plane stress, showing the approximate effect of redistribution of stress.

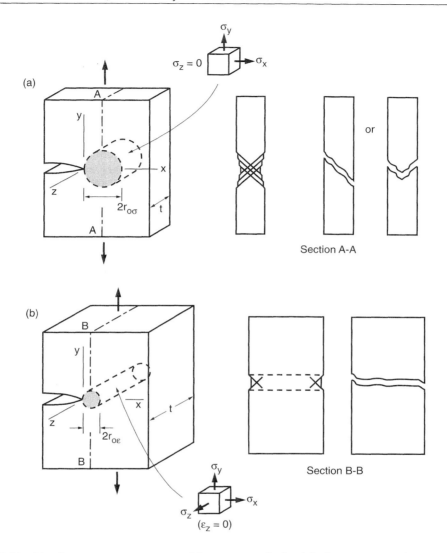

Figure 8.44 Plastic zone, stress state, and fracture mode for (a) plane stress and (b) plane strain.

As might be expected, the plastic zone size increases if the stress (hence K) is increased, and it is smaller for the same K for materials with higher σ_o. The plane stress plastic zone and the stress state within it near the crack tip are illustrated in Fig. 8.44(a).

8.7.2 Plastic Zone Size for Plane Strain

Consider a cracked member where the thickness is large compared with the plastic zone size, as in Fig. 8.44(b). The material outside the plastic zone is subjected to relatively low stresses σ_x and

σ_y, and thus relatively small Poisson contraction in the z-direction. This makes it difficult for the material inside the plastic zone to deform in the z-direction, as its length in the z-direction is held nearly constant by the surrounding material. Hence, the behavior is said to approximate *plane strain*, defined by $\varepsilon_z = 0$. As a result, a tensile stress develops in the z-direction, which elevates the value of $\sigma_x = \sigma_y$ necessary to cause yielding, in turn decreasing the plastic zone size relative to that for plane stress.

To explore this in more detail, note that $\varepsilon_z = 0$, when substituted with $\sigma_x = \sigma_y$ into Hooke's law, Eq. 5.26, gives a stress in the z-direction of $\sigma_z = 2\nu\sigma_y$. Substituting these stresses into either the octahedral shear stress yield criterion or the maximum shear stress yield criterion gives a stress at yielding of $\sigma_x = \sigma_y = \sigma_0/(1 - 2\nu)$; that is, $\sigma_x = \sigma_y = 2.5\sigma_0$ for a typical value of Poisson's ratio of $\nu = 0.3$. This situation has already been analyzed as Ex. 7.5, except that the stresses there were compressive, but the same result as just stated is obtained for tensile stresses. Hence, the constrained deformation creates a tensile hydrostatic stress that, in effect, subtracts from the ability of the applied stresses $\sigma_x = \sigma_y$ to cause yielding, resulting in an apparent elevation of the yield strength.

The more refined estimate by G. R. Irwin suggests that the effect is somewhat smaller, with yielding around $\sigma_y = \sqrt{3}\sigma_0$. Proceeding as for the plane stress estimate, except for using the latter value of σ_y, we obtain

$$2r_{o\varepsilon} = \frac{1}{3\pi}\left(\frac{K}{\sigma_o}\right)^2 \tag{8.38}$$

This is noted to be one-third as large as the plane-stress value.

The plastic zone size equations given are based on simple assumptions and should be considered to be rough estimates only. The particular estimates given follow the early work of G. R. Irwin.

8.7.3 Plasticity Limitations on LEFM

If the plastic zone is sufficiently small, there will be a region outside of it where the elastic stress field equations (Eq. 8.7) still apply, called the *region of K-dominance*, or the *K-field*. This is illustrated in Fig. 8.45. The existence of such a region is necessary for LEFM theory to be applicable. The K-field surrounds and controls the behavior of the plastic zone and crack tip area, which can be thought of as an incompletely understood "black box." Thus, K continues to characterize the severity of the crack situation, despite the occurrence of some limited plasticity. However, if the plastic zone is so large that it eliminates the K-field, then K no longer applies.

As a practical matter, it is necessary that the plastic zone be small compared with the distance from the crack tip to any boundary of the member, such as distances a, $(b - a)$, and h for a cracked plate, as in Fig. 8.46(a). A distance of $8r_o$ is generally considered to be sufficient. Note from Eqs. 8.37 and 8.38 that $8r_o$ is four times the plastic zone size, which can be either $2r_{o\sigma}$ or $2r_{o\varepsilon}$, depending on which applies. Since $2r_{o\sigma}$ is larger than $2r_{o\varepsilon}$, an overall limit on the use of LEFM is

$$a, (b - a), h \geq \frac{4}{\pi}\left(\frac{K}{\sigma_o}\right)^2 \qquad \text{(LEFM applicable)} \tag{8.39}$$

This must be satisfied for all three of a, $(b - a)$, and h. Otherwise, the situation too closely approaches gross yielding with a plastic zone extending to one of the boundaries, as shown in

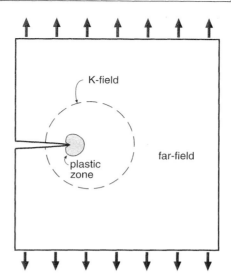

Figure 8.45   A crack and its plastic zone, and the larger K-field that must exist for LEFM to be applicable.

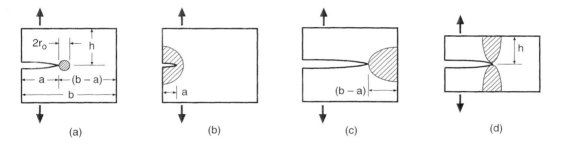

Figure 8.46   Small plastic zone compared with planar dimensions (a), and situations where LEFM is invalid due to the plastic zones being too large compared with (b) crack length, (c) uncracked ligament, and (d) member height.

Fig. 8.46(b), (c), or (d). As discussed in Section 8.9, a value of K calculated beyond the applicability of LEFM underestimates the severity of the crack.

8.7.4 Plane Stress Versus Plane Strain

If the thickness is not large compared with the plastic zone, Poisson contraction in the thickness direction occurs freely around the crack tip, resulting in yielding on shear planes inclined through the thickness, as shown in Fig. 8.44(a). Fracture under plane stress also occurs along such inclined planes.

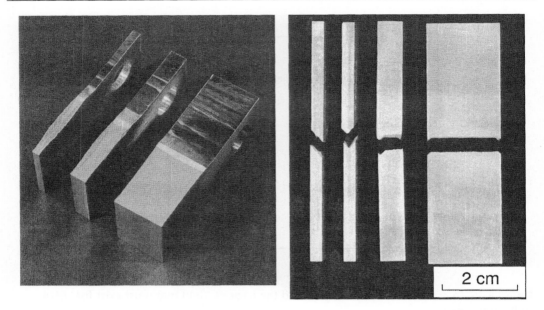

Figure 8.47 Fracture surfaces (left) and cross sections showing profiles of fractures (right) for toughness tests on compact specimens ($b = 51$ mm) of 7075-T651 aluminum. The thinnest specimens shown have typical plane stress fractures on inclined planes; the intermediate thickness has mixed behavior; and the thickest specimens have flat plane-strain fractures. (Photos by R. A. Simonds.)

However, for thick members, the geometric constraint limits the strain ε_z in the thickness direction, giving rise to a transverse stress σ_z. As already discussed, this σ_z has the effect of elevating the stress σ_y at yielding and reducing the plastic zone size. Yielding on through-thickness shear planes is no longer possible, and a flat fracture occurs over most of the thickness, as illustrated in Fig. 8.44(b). Photographs of broken specimens showing plane stress, plane strain, and mixed fractures are shown in Fig. 8.47.

On the basis of empirical observation of the trends in fracture behavior, especially the thickness effect on toughness, as in Fig. 8.31, it has become generally accepted that a fully developed situation of plane strain does not occur unless the thickness satisfies the relationship given earlier as Eq. 8.33. In addition, the distances from the crack tip to the in-plane boundaries must be similarly large compared with the plastic zone. Otherwise, deformation in the x- or y-direction can occur, as in Fig. 8.46, reducing the degree of constraint. Thus, the overall requirement for plane strain is

$$t, a, (b - a), h \geq 2.5 \left(\frac{K}{\sigma_o} \right)^2 \qquad \text{(plane strain)} \qquad (8.40)$$

Comparison with Eq. 8.38 indicates that this corresponds to the various dimensions all being larger than $47r_{o\varepsilon}$, or about 24 times the plane strain plastic zone size $2r_{o\varepsilon}$. Note that the requirements on the in-plane dimensions of Eq. 8.39 are less stringent than Eq. 8.40, so that the limits on the use of LEFM are automatically satisfied if plane strain is satisfied.

Example 8.6

For the situation of Ex. 8.1:

    (a) For $a = 10$ mm, determine whether or not plane strain applies and whether or not LEFM is valid. Also estimate the plastic zone size.

    (b) Do the same for the estimated $a_c = 16.3$ mm.

Solution   **(a)** Plane strain applies if Eq. 8.40 is satisfied. Use $t = 5$ mm, $b = 50$ mm, and K as calculated in Ex. 8.1(a), and also $\sigma_o = 415$ MPa for 2014-T651 Al, to obtain

$$t, a, (b-a), h \geq 2.5 \left(\frac{K}{\sigma_o} \right)^2 = 2.5 \left(\frac{17.7\,\text{MPa}\sqrt{\text{m}}}{415\,\text{MPa}} \right)^2 ?$$

$$5, 10, 40, \text{large } h \geq 0.0045\,\text{m} = 4.5\,\text{mm}?$$

Yes, the test is successful, so *plane strain applies and LEFM is applicable* **(Ans.)**. The plastic zone size is then estimated as the value for plane strain from Eq. 8.38:

$$2r_{o\varepsilon} = \frac{1}{3\pi} \left(\frac{K}{\sigma_o} \right)^2 = \frac{1}{3\pi} \left(\frac{17.7\,\text{MPa}\sqrt{\text{m}}}{415\,\text{MPa}} \right)^2 = 0.19\,\text{mm} \qquad \textbf{Ans.}$$

    (b) For $a_c = 16.3$ mm and $K = K_{Ic} = 24$ MPa$\sqrt{\text{m}}$, the plane strain test is similarly applied.

$$5, 16.3, 33.7, \text{large } h \geq 2.5 \left(\frac{24\,\text{MPa}\sqrt{\text{m}}}{415\,\text{MPa}} \right)^2 = 8.4\,\text{mm}?$$

No, the test fails, and *plane strain does not apply* **(Ans.)**. But LEFM may still be applicable if Eq. 8.39 is satisfied. Thus, we ask,

$$a, (b-a), h \geq \frac{4}{\pi} \left(\frac{K}{\sigma_o} \right)^2 = \frac{4}{\pi} \left(\frac{24\,\text{MPa}\sqrt{\text{m}}}{415\,\text{MPa}} \right)^2 ?$$

$$16.3, 33.7, \text{large } h \geq 4.3\,\text{mm}?$$

Yes, the test is successful, and *LEFM is applicable* **(Ans.)**. The plastic zone size is then estimated as the value for plane stress from Eq. 8.37:

$$2r_{o\sigma} = \frac{1}{\pi} \left(\frac{K}{\sigma_o} \right)^2 = \frac{1}{\pi} \left(\frac{24\,\text{MPa}\sqrt{\text{m}}}{415\,\text{MPa}} \right)^2 = 1.06\,\text{mm} \qquad \textbf{Ans.}$$

Comment   Due to the state of plane stress in (b), the use of K_{Ic} is conservative. The actual K_c may be somewhat higher than K_{Ic}, and the a_c value therefore larger than estimated.

8.8 DISCUSSION OF FRACTURE TOUGHNESS TESTING

The preceding discussion on plastic zone size and the condition of plane strain permits us to now engage in a more detailed discussion of certain aspects of fracture toughness testing.

8.8.1 Standard Test Methods

Test methods for evaluating fracture toughness on the basis of LEFM include requirements similar to Eq. 8.40 to qualify a test result as a valid measurement of K_{Ic}. For example, ASTM Standard No. E399, which applies to metallic materials, explicitly requires that Eq. 8.40 be met for $(b - a)$, and then the remaining items in Eq. 8.40 are included by recommending that a/b and t/b be near 0.5, and by using specimen geometries where h/b is around 0.5 or greater.

The force versus displacement (P-v) behavior in a fracture toughness test may be similar to Fig. 8.28, Types I, II, or III. Since the plastic zone is required by Eq. 8.40 to be quite small, any nonlinearity in the P-v curve must be due to growth of the crack. A smooth curve as in Type I is caused by a steady tearing type of fracture called *slow-stable crack growth*. In other cases, the crack may suddenly grow a short distance, which is called a *pop-in* (II), or it may suddenly grow to complete failure (III).

The K_{Ic} test standard for metals handles the problem of defining the beginning of cracking by drawing a line with a slope that is 95% as large as the initial elastic slope (O-A) in the test. A force P_Q is identified as the point where this line crosses the P-v curve, or as any larger peak value prior to the crossing point. The stress intensity factor is then evaluated with the use of P_Q and the initial crack length:

$$K_Q = f(a_i, P_Q) \tag{8.41}$$

If this K_Q satisfies Eq. 8.40, it is then considered to be a *valid* K_{Ic} value. However, there is one additional requirement designed to assure that the test involves sudden fracture with little slow-stable crack growth, specifically that the maximum load reached cannot exceed P_Q by 10%.

If the plane strain condition is not satisfied in the test, then it is necessary to use a larger test specimen so that the comparisons of Eq. 8.40 are more favorable. As a result, quite large specimens may be required for materials with relatively low yield strength but high fracture toughness. For example, the large compact specimen of Fig. 8.29 (with $b = 61$ cm) was required to obtain the K_{Ic} value plotted for 10°C for A533B steel in Fig. 8.33.

A successful fracture toughness test requires an initially sharp flaw, called a *precrack*, that is equivalent to a natural crack; otherwise the measured K_{Ic} will be artificially elevated. For metals, this is achieved by using cyclic loading at a low level to start a natural fatigue crack at the end of a machined slot. For plastics (polymers), the usual procedure is to press a razor blade into the material at the end of the machined slot.

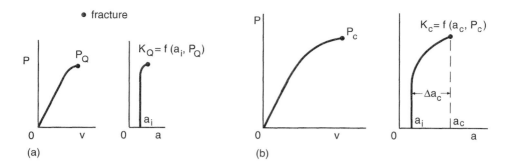

Figure 8.48 Load vs. displacement and load vs. crack extension behavior during fracture toughness tests under plane strain (a) and plane stress (b).

8.8.2 Effect of Thickness on Fracture Behavior

Fracture under the highly constrained conditions of plane strain generally occurs rather suddenly, with little crack growth prior to final fracture. Also, the fracture surface is quite flat. In contrast, plane stress fractures tend to have sloping or V-shaped surfaces inclined at about 45° on planes of maximum shear stress, as already illustrated by Figs. 8.44 and 8.47. The final fracture in plane stress is usually preceded by considerable slow-stable crack growth, as shown in Fig. 8.48. These behaviors correlate with the thickness effect on toughness, as in Fig. 8.31. Flat plane-strain fractures occur where the thickness is sufficient to reach the lower plateau of the curve—that is, the minimum toughness K_{Ic}. Inclined or V-shaped plane-stress fractures occur for relatively thin members, for which the toughness may be well above K_{Ic}. Fracture toughness values K_{Ic} meeting the requirements for plane strain are expected to be minimum values that can be safely used in design for any thickness.

Where a thickness less than that required for plane strain fracture in a given material is used in an engineering application, K_{Ic} may involve an undesirably large degree of conservatism. It may then be useful to use K_Q data for the particular thickness of interest. Also, a toughness K_c can be defined that corresponds to the point of final fracture, as illustrated in Fig. 8.48(b). Since the amount of slow-stable crack growth may be considerable, the crack extension Δa_c from the initial length a_i to the final length a_c needs to be measured. The corresponding K can then be calculated from the load P_c at the point of final fracture.

8.9 EXTENSIONS OF FRACTURE MECHANICS BEYOND LINEAR ELASTICITY

If Eq. 8.39 is not satisfied, so that LEFM does not apply due to excessive yielding, several methods still exist for analyzing cracked members. Excessive yielding causes K to no longer correctly characterize the magnitude of the stress field around the crack tip—specifically, K underestimates the severity of the crack. An introduction to various approaches for extending fracture mechanics beyond linear elasticity follows.

However, before proceeding, it is useful to take note of the concept of a *fully plastic yielding load*. For a given cracked member, the fully plastic force P_o, or moment M_o, is the load or moment necessary to cause yielding to spread across the entire remaining uncracked portion of the cross-sectional area. Large and unstably increasing strains and deflections occur once P_o or M_o is exceeded. If the stress–strain curve of the material is idealized as being elastic, perfectly plastic, then lower bound estimates of fully plastic loads may be made, as described in Appendix A, Section A.7. Some particular results are given in Fig. A.16.

Three approaches to extending fracture mechanics beyond linear elasticity will now be introduced: (1) the plastic zone adjustment, (2) the J-integral, and (3) the crack-tip opening displacement (CTOD).

8.9.1 Plastic Zone Adjustment

Consider the redistributed stress near the plastic zone, as in Fig. 8.43. The stresses outside of the plastic zone are similar to those for the elastic stress field equations for a hypothetical crack of length $a_e = a + r_{o\sigma}$, that is, a hypothetical crack with its tip near the center of the plastic zone. This in turn leads to modifying K, increasing it, to account for this yielding by using a_e in place of the actual crack length a.

Where the form $K = FS\sqrt{\pi a}$ is used, the modified value is

$$K_e = F_e S \sqrt{\pi a_e} = F_e S \sqrt{\pi(a + r_{o\sigma})}, \qquad \text{where } r_{o\sigma} = \frac{1}{2\pi}\left(\frac{K_e}{\sigma_o}\right)^2 \qquad (8.42)$$

The F used is the value corresponding to a_e/b, and $r_{o\sigma}$ is calculated by using K_e in Eq. 8.36. An iterative calculation is generally involved in using this equation, as $F_e = F(a_e/b)$ cannot be determined in advance, since $r_{o\sigma}$ and hence a_e depend on K_e. If F is not significantly changed for the new crack length a_e, then no iteration is required, and the modified value K_e is related to the unmodified value $K = FS\sqrt{\pi a}$ by

$$K_e = \frac{K}{\sqrt{1 - \frac{1}{2}\left(\frac{FS}{\sigma_o}\right)^2}} \qquad (8.43)$$

In some situations with a high degree of constraint, such as embedded elliptical cracks or half-elliptical surface cracks, it may be appropriate to use the plane strain plastic zone size to make the adjustment. Replacing $r_{o\sigma}$ with $r_{o\varepsilon}$ in the previous equations gives a relationship similar to Eq. 8.43, differing in that the $\frac{1}{2}$ in the denominator is replaced by $\frac{1}{6}$.

Such modified K values allow LEFM to be extended to somewhat higher stress levels than permitted by the limitation of Eq. 8.39. However, large amounts of yielding still cannot be analyzed. The use of even adjusted crack lengths becomes increasingly questionable if the stress approaches a value that would cause yielding fully across the uncracked section of the member. It is suggested that the use of plastic zone adjustments be limited to loads below 80% of the fully plastic force or moment—that is, below $0.8P_o$ or $0.8M_o$.

Example 8.7

Problem 8.48 concerns a test on a double-edge-cracked plate of 7075-T651 aluminum, for which $a = 5.7$, $b = 15.9$, and $t = 6.35$ mm. A value of $K_Q = 37.3$ MPa$\sqrt{m}$ is calculated for the force $P_Q = 50.3$ kN, but the test for applicability of LEFM (Eq. 8.39) is not met. Calculate the fully plastic force. If it is reasonable to do so, also apply the plastic zone adjustment to obtain a revised value of K_Q.

Solution   Figure A.16(a) also applies to the geometry of Fig. 8.12(b), so that the fully plastic load is

$$P_o = 2bt\sigma_o \left(1 - \frac{a}{b}\right)$$

$$P_o = 2(0.0159 \text{ m})(0.00635 \text{ m})(505 \text{ MPa}) \left(1 - \frac{5.7 \text{ mm}}{15.9 \text{ mm}}\right)$$

$$P_o = 0.0654 \text{ MN} = 65.4 \text{ kN} \qquad\qquad \textbf{Ans.}$$

where the yield strength of 7075-T651 Al from Table 8.1 is used. Comparing P_o with P_Q gives

$$\frac{P_Q}{P_o} = \frac{50.3 \text{ kN}}{65.4 \text{ kN}} = 0.77$$

Since this ratio is less than 0.80, it is reasonable to apply the plastic zone adjustment.

From Fig. 8.12(b), the value $\alpha = a/b = 0.358$ that applies is well within the range $\alpha \leq 0.6$, where $F \approx 1.12$. Hence, F can be taken as unchanged for a_e and Eq. 8.43 applies. Thus, we have

$$K_{Qe} = \frac{K_Q}{\sqrt{1 - \frac{1}{2}\left(\frac{FS}{\sigma_o}\right)^2}} = \frac{37.3 \text{ MPa}\sqrt{m}}{\sqrt{1 - \frac{1}{2}\left(\frac{1.12 \times 249 \text{ MPa}}{505 \text{ MPa}}\right)^2}} = 40.5 \text{ MPa}\sqrt{m} \qquad \textbf{Ans.}$$

where $S = S_g = P_Q/2bt$ is used.

Comment   This adjusted K is 40% above the value from Table 8.1 of $K_{Ic} = 29$ MPa$\sqrt{m}$. The probable explanation for the difference is that K_{Qe} includes an effect of increased toughness for plane stress.

8.9.2 The *J*-Integral

An advanced approach to fracture based on the *J*-integral concept is capable of handling even large amounts of yielding. In a formal mathematical sense, the *J*-integral is defined as the quantity obtained from evaluating a particular line integral around a path enclosing the crack tip. The material is assumed to be elastic—that is, to recover all strain on unloading—but the stress–strain curve may be nonlinear. For our present purposes, it is sufficient to define *J* as the generalization of the

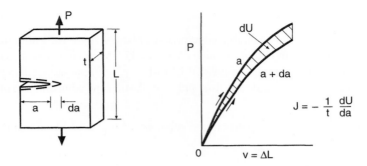

Figure 8.49   Definition of the J-integral in terms of the potential energy difference for cracks of slightly different length.

strain energy release rate, G, to cases of nonlinear-elastic stress–strain curves. This is illustrated in Fig. 8.49. However, for most cases of engineering interest, the nonlinear stress–strain (and hence, P-v) behavior is due to elasto-plastic behavior, as in metals. For elasto-plastic materials, J loses the physical interpretation related to potential energy. But it retains significance as a measure of the intensity of the elasto-plastic stress and strain fields around the crack tip. Values can still be determined experimentally or analytically by the use of P-v curves, as in Fig. 8.49, but the two different P-v curves for crack lengths a and $(a + da)$ need to be obtained from independent tests on two different members, rather than by extending the crack da after a single member is loaded.

The J-integral can be used as the basis of fracture toughness tests, according to ASTM Standard No. E1820. Since the plasticity limitations of LEFM can now be exceeded, the need for large test specimens is removed. For example, in A533B steel at room temperature, a fracture toughness J_{Ic} can be obtained from the small specimen in Fig. 8.29, without the need for testing the large one. Thus, J_{Ic} can be used to estimate an equivalent value of K_{Ic} by using Eq. 8.10 with J replacing G:

$$K_{IcJ} = \sqrt{J_{Ic}E'} \tag{8.44}$$

Here, E' is from Eq. 8.11. Fracture toughness testing to determine J_{Ic} is summarized in the section that follows.

In engineering applications where crack extension and fracture under plastic loading need to be considered, the J-integral is a candidate for use, as is the CTOD approach, which is discussed later. (See Section 8.9.4.) One important area of such application is pressure vessels, especially nuclear pressure vessels. Note that an attempt to use K beyond its region of validity will generally cause the results of engineering calculations to be nonconservative, that is, to be in error on the unsafe side. For example, consider the case of a center-cracked plate, as in Fig. 8.12(a), where the crack length a is small compared with the half-width b. For plane stress, the modified (equivalent) value K_J, which includes the plasticity effect, is approximately

$$K_J = \sqrt{JE}, \qquad K_J \approx K\sqrt{1 + \frac{\varepsilon_p}{\varepsilon_e\sqrt{n}}} \tag{8.45}$$

Here, $K = S\sqrt{\pi a}$ is from LEFM, and ε_e and ε_p are the elastic and plastic strains corresponding to the applied stress. The quantity n is the strain-hardening exponent for a stress versus plastic strain relationship of the form $\sigma = H\varepsilon_p^n$, where $n \approx 0.1$ to 0.2 is typical for metals. (See Chapter 12 for a detailed discussion of such stress–strain curves.) If the plastic strain ε_p is small, the second term under the radical disappears, and $K_J = K$. However, beyond yielding, ε_p increases rapidly, and K_J can become much larger than K. Hence, use of K can be substantially nonconservative.

The use of the J-integral in engineering applications requires that one be able to determine J for various geometries and crack lengths for the particular material's nonlinear stress–strain curve. Handbooks by Kumar (1981) and Zahoor (1989) give extensive tables for calculating J, and the books by Anderson (2005) and Saxena (1998) also provide useful information.

8.9.3 Fracture Toughness Tests for J_{Ic}

One complexity encountered in J_{Ic} testing is that nonlinearity in the P-v behavior is now due to a combination of crack growth and plastic deformation. Hence, the beginning of cracking beyond the initial precrack cannot be determined in a straightforward manner from the P-v curve, and special means are needed to directly measure crack growth. A common method of doing so is the *unloading compliance method*, which involves periodically unloading the sample by a small amount, while measuring the P-v behavior, as illustrated in Fig. 8.50. The slopes of the P-v lines during unloading and reloading, such as m_5 in the illustration, are a measure of the elastic stiffness of the sample, which decreases as the crack increases its length, permitting the crack length to be

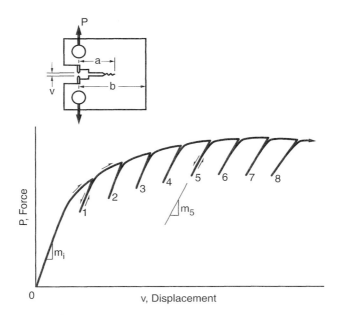

Figure 8.50   Force versus displacement (P-v) behavior during an elasto-plastic fracture toughness test with periodic elastic unloadings.

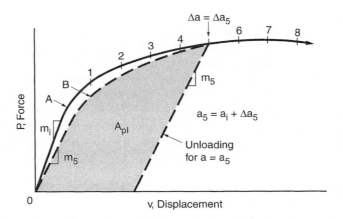

Figure 8.51 Area A_{pl} for calculating the J-integral. Curve A is the actual $P\text{-}v$ record for the growing crack, whereas curve B is the hypothetical $P\text{-}v$ curve for a stationary (nongrowing) crack of length a_5.

calculated at various points during the test. (Note that the small elastic unloadings have no significant effect on the cracking behavior.)

Another approach, called the *potential drop method*, is based on the fact that the electrical resistance of the specimen increases as its cross-sectional area decreases due to crack growth. A current is passed through the specimen, and the voltage (potential) across the crack is measured and used to calculate the crack length. The unloading compliance and potential drop methods have the advantage of allowing crack extension data to be obtained from a single sample. However, the most accurate method is to test several nominally identical test specimens and remove the load after varying amounts of crack extension in different specimens. Then the samples are heated to tint (slightly oxidize) the fresh fracture surface so that it is easily observed, next they are broken into two pieces, and finally the amounts of crack growth are measured through a microscope.

Values of the J-integral are needed for the points along the $P\text{-}v$ record, such as point 5 in Fig. 8.50, where crack lengths have been determined. For the standard bend specimen, Fig. 8.13(b) with $h/b = 2$, and the standard compact specimen, Fig. 8.16, an approximate procedure has been developed for determining J directly from the $P\text{-}v$ record of the test. To do so, the current crack length, $a = a_i + \Delta a$, is needed, where a_i is the initial precrack length and Δa is the crack extension. Also needed is the area A_{pl} shown in Fig. 8.51. This is the area under the force versus displacement curve for loading and then unloading a hypothetical test member originally containing a stationary (nongrowing) crack of length $a = a_i + \Delta a$. Hence, the hypothetical loading slope, such as m_5, is somewhat lower than the actual initial load slope m_i. Also, this $P\text{-}v$ curve differs from, and deviates below, the actual one, as the actual curve corresponds to an initial crack of length a_i, with crack growth by gradual tearing to the current Δa value.

Given the current crack length a and area A_{pl}, the J value can be determined as follows:

$$J = J_{el} + J_{pl}, \qquad J_{el} = \frac{K^2(1 - \nu^2)}{E} \tag{8.46}$$

The elastic term J_{el} is obtained from the stress intensity K and the elastic constants of the material

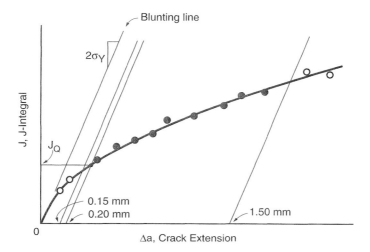

Figure 8.52   The *J*-integral versus Δa curve, or *R*-curve, from an elasto-plastic fracture toughness test. The intersection with the 0.2 mm offset line gives J_Q, the provisional J_{Ic} value.

as indicated. Further, K is calculated from the applied force P and the crack length a just as if there were no yielding, as from Fig. 8.13(b) or Fig. 8.16. The plastic term J_{pl} is given by

$$J_{pl} = \frac{\eta A_{pl}}{t\,(b - a)} \tag{8.47}$$

where t, a, and b are defined as in Fig. 8.13(b) or 8.16. For the bend specimen, if the displacement v is the deflection at the point of load application, then $\eta = 1.9$, or if v is the crack mouth displacement, as in Fig. 8.27, then η is a somewhat larger value that varies with a/b. For the compact specimen, $\eta = 2 + 0.522(1 - a/b)$.

In ASTM Standard No. E1820, two alternate procedures are described. For the *basic test method*, the crack extension Δa is assumed to be small, so that $a = a_i + \Delta a$ can be approximated as being equal to the initial crack length a_i, with Eqs. 8.46 and 8.47 being applied on this basis. For the area A_{pl} of Fig. 8.51, a small crack extension gives solid and dashed loading curves *A* and *B* that approximately coincide, so that the actual loading curve *A* can be employed. Also, a small correction is applied to the J values so obtained to account for the effect of the actual crack extension Δa. The more detailed *resistance curve test method* in Standard E1820 is applicable for single specimen tests, such as the unloading compliance test of Fig. 8.50. In this method, values of J are calculated in an incremental manner by updating the value at each point of crack length measurement, and in the process making an adjustment so that the value is based on the new stationary-crack P-v curve, such as curve *B* in Fig. 8.51. The calculated values of J determined by either method are then plotted versus the change in crack length, Δa, to form a curve, called the *R-curve*, as shown in Fig. 8.52.

Before the crack begins to tear through the material, the intense local plastic deformation at the crack tip causes an increase in the crack-tip opening displacement, CTOD, or δ, of Fig. 8.4. This plastic blunting effect causes the tip of the crack to move forward by a distance of about $\delta/2$, giving the J versus Δa curve an initial, or *blunting line*, slope of approximately

$$\frac{J}{\Delta a} = 2\sigma_Y, \qquad \text{where } \sigma_Y = \frac{\sigma_o + \sigma_u}{2} \tag{8.48}$$

The quantities σ_o and σ_u are the tensile yield and ultimate strengths of the material.

Lines are then drawn on the J-Δa curve that are parallel to this blunting line and which intersect the Δa axis at 0.15 mm and 1.5 mm. A curve is fitted through the data between these lines, and J_Q is defined as the intersection of this curve and a third parallel line that intersects the Δa axis at 0.2 mm. Hence, J_Q corresponds to a crack extension by tearing of 0.2 mm (0.008 in), which value does not include the apparent extension due to plastic blunting. Finally, J_Q is qualified as a fracture toughness, J_{Ic}, if the test meets the size requirement

$$t, (b - a) > 10 \left(\frac{J_Q}{\sigma_Y} \right) \tag{8.49}$$

An equivalent K_{Ic} can then be calculated from J_{Ic} by Eq. 8.44.

Note that the crack extension at J_Q is quite small, so that the material may have considerable reserve toughness beyond J_{Ic} due to an ability to withstand tearing crack growth. It is thus sometimes useful to employ the full R-curve and consider this behavior in engineering applications.

8.9.4 Crack-Tip Opening Displacement (CTOD)

The elastic stress field analysis employed for K can also be used to estimate the displacements separating the crack faces. Then, pursuing logic that partially parallels that for plastic zone sizes, it is possible to make an estimate of the separation of the crack faces near the tip—that is, of the CTOD, which is denoted δ. For ductile materials, this estimate is

$$\delta \approx \frac{K^2}{E\sigma_o} \approx \frac{J}{\sigma_o} \tag{8.50}$$

where δ is illustrated in Fig. 8.4. In this equation, the yield strength σ_o is sometimes replaced by the higher stress σ_Y of Eq. 8.48. Experimentally determined values of δ are also used as the basis of fracture toughness tests, so that the toughness is expressed as a critical value δ_c, as in ASTM Standard Nos. E1290 and E1820.

Values of δ may be determined for situations of engineering interest, such as a flaw in a pressure vessel wall, and then compared with δ_c. Hence, the CTOD concept also provides an engineering approach to fracture beyond linear elasticity.

8.10 SUMMARY

Using linear-elastic fracture mechanics (LEFM), the severity of a crack in a component can be characterized by the value of a special variable called the stress intensity factor, $K = FS\sqrt{\pi a}$, where S is stress and a is crack length, both consistently defined relative to the dimensionless quantity F. Use of K depends on the behavior being dominated by linear-elastic deformation, so that the zone of yielding (plasticity) at the crack tip must be relatively small. Simple equations and handbooks provide values of F for a wide range of cases of cracked bodies, some examples of which are given in Figs. 8.12 to 8.14 and also Figs. 8.17 to 8.20. The value of F depends on the crack and member geometry; the loading configuration, such as tension or bending; and the ratio of the crack length to the width of the member, such as the ratio a/b. Some notable values of F for relatively short cracks under tension stress are as follows:

$$
\begin{aligned}
F &= 1.00 && \text{(center-cracked plate)} \\
F &= 1.12 && \text{(through-thickness or circumferential surface crack)} \\
F &= 0.73 && \text{(half-circular surface crack)} \\
F &= 0.72 && \text{(quarter-circular corner crack)}
\end{aligned}
\tag{8.51}
$$

It is sometimes convenient to express K in terms of an applied force P by using the differently defined dimensionless quantity F_P according to Eq. 8.13.

The value of K for which a given material begins to crack significantly is called K_Q, and the value for failure is called K_c. Slow-stable crack growth may follow K_Q until K_c is reached, and both of these may decrease with increased member thickness. If the plastic zone surrounding the crack tip is quite small compared with the thickness and is very well isolated relative to the boundaries of the member, then a state of plane strain is established. Under plane strain, only limited slow-stable crack growth occurs, so that K_Q and K_c have similar values to each other, and K_Q becomes the standard plane-strain fracture toughness, K_{Ic}. A value of K_{Ic} represents a worst-case fracture toughness that can be safely used for any thickness. The flowchart of Fig. 8.53 gives the requirement for plane strain and the plastic zone sizes, and the situation concerning K_{Ic} is also summarized.

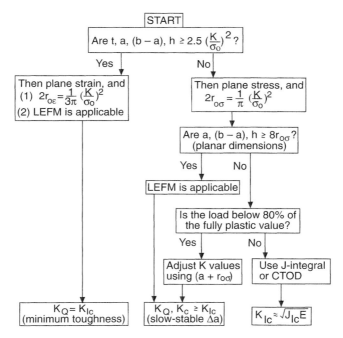

Figure 8.53 Flowchart for distinguishing between plane stress and plane strain, for deciding what fracture mechanics approach is needed, and for identifying what is expected from toughness testing.

Values of K_{Ic} for a given material generally decrease along with ductility if the material is processed to achieve higher strength. For a given material and processing, K_{Ic} generally increases with temperature, sometimes exhibiting a rather abrupt change over a narrow range of temperatures, and also having relatively constant lower shelf and upper shelf values on opposite sides of the temperature transition. Increased loading rate causes K_{Ic} to decrease, having the effect of shifting the transition to a higher temperature. The microstructure of the material may affect K_{Ic}, as in the detrimental effect of sulfur in some steels, the effect of crystal grain orientation from rolling of aluminum alloys, and radiation embrittlement of pressure vessel steels.

If the plastic zone is too large, LEFM is no longer valid. Modest amounts of yielding can be handled by using adjusted values K_e calculated by adding half of the plastic zone size to the crack length. However, above about 80% of the fully plastic force or moment, P_o or M_o, more general methods such as the J-integral or the crack-tip opening displacement (CTOD, δ) are needed. The flowchart of Fig. 8.53 also provides a guide for determining which of the various approaches is required in a given situation.

NEW TERMS AND SYMBOLS

(a) Terms

bend specimen
blunting line
cleavage
compact specimen
crack-tip opening displacement (CTOD): δ, δ_c
dimpled rupture
fracture modes I, II, and III
fracture toughness: K_c, K_{Ic}
fully plastic force, moment: P_o, M_o
internally flawed material
J-integral: J, J_{Ic}
K-field
linear-elastic fracture mechanics (LEFM)
mixed-mode fracture

plane strain constraint
plastic zone
pop-in
precrack
R-curve
slow-stable crack growth
strain energy release rate, G
stress intensity factor, K
stress redistribution
superposition
temperature transition
transition crack length, a_t
unloading compliance

(b) Nomenclature

a	Crack length
a_c	Critical (at fracture) crack length
a_e	Plastic-zone-adjusted crack length
b	Maximum possible crack length; member width or half-width
c	Major axis of elliptical crack; notch dimension analogous to a
F	Dimensionless function $F(a/b)$ for $K = FS\sqrt{\pi a}$
F_P	Dimensionless function $F_P(a/b)$ for $K = F_P P/(t\sqrt{b})$
h	Member half-height
J	Value of the J-integral
J_{Ic}	Plane strain fracture toughness in terms of J

K	Stress intensity factor for a Mode I crack
K_I, K_{II}, K_{III}	Stress intensity factors for the three fracture modes
K_{Ic}	Plane strain fracture toughness
K_c	Fracture toughness
K_e	Plastic-zone-adjusted K
K_J, K_{IcJ}	Plasticity-modified K based on J
K_Q	Provisional fracture toughness
P_c	Critical (at fracture) force
P_Q	Force for calculating K_Q
$r_{o\varepsilon}$	Half the estimated plastic zone size for plane strain
$r_{o\sigma}$	Half the estimated plastic zone size for plane stress
S_g	Gross section S (based on area before cracking)
t	Thickness
U	Potential strain energy
v	Displacement
α	Ratio a/b

REFERENCES

(a) General References

ANDERSON, T. L. 2005. *Fracture Mechanics: Fundamentals and Applications*, 3d ed., CRC Press, Boca Raton, FL.

ASTM. 2010. *Annual Book of ASTM Standards*, ASTM International, West Conshohocken, PA. See: No. E399, "Standard Test Method for Plane-Strain Fracture Toughness of Metallic Materials," Vol. 03.01; also Nos. E561, E1290, and E1820 in Vol. 03.01; No. D5045 in Vol. 08.02; No. D6068 in Vol. 08.03; No. C1421 in Vol. 15.01.

BARSOM, J. M., ed. 1987. *Fracture Mechanics Retrospective: Early Classic Papers (1913–1965)*, RPS-1, ASTM International, West Conshohocken, PA.

BARSOM, J. M., and S. T. ROLFE. 1999. *Fracture and Fatigue Control in Structures*, 3d ed., ASTM International, West Conshohocken, PA.

BROEK, D. 1988. *The Practical Use of Fracture Mechanics*, Kluwer Academic Pubs., Dordrecht, The Netherlands.

HERTZBERG, R. W. 1996. *Deformation and Fracture Mechanics of Engineering Materials*, 4th ed., John Wiley, New York.

JOYCE, J. A. 1996. *Manual on Elastic-Plastic Fracture: Laboratory Test Procedures*, ASTM Manual Series, MNL 27, Am. Soc. for Testing and Materials, West Conshohocken, PA.

LAWN, B. 1993. *Fracture of Brittle Solids*, 2d ed., Cambridge University Press, Cambridge, UK.

MIEDLAR, P. C., A. P. BERENS, A. GUNDERSON, and J. P. GALLAGHER. 2002. *USAF Damage Tolerant Design Handbook: Guidelines for the Analysis and Design of Damage Tolerant Aircraft Structures*, 3 vols., University of Dayton Research Institute, Dayton, OH.

MILNE, I., B. KARIHALOO, and R. O. RITCHIE, eds. 2003. *Comprehensive Structural Integrity*, 10 vols., Elsevier Ltd., Oxford, England.

SAXENA, A. 1998. *Nonlinear Fracture Mechanics for Engineers*, CRC Press, Boca Raton, FL.

WILLIAMS, J. G. 2001. *Fracture Mechanics of Polymers*, Ellis Horwood Ltd., Hemel Hempstead, England.

(b) Handbooks and Other Sources of Stress Intensity and J-Integral Solutions

DOWLING, N. E. 1987. "J-Integral Estimates for Cracks in Infinite Bodies," *Engineering Fracture Mechanics*, vol. 26, no. 3, pp. 333–348.

KUJAWSKI, D. 1991. "Estimations of Stress Intensity Factors for Small Cracks at Notches," *Fatigue of Engineering Materials and Structures*, vol. 14, no. 10, pp. 953–965.

KUMAR, V., M. D. GERMAN, and C. F. SHIH. 1981. *An Engineering Approach for Elastic-Plastic Fracture Analysis*, EPRI NP-1931, Electric Power Research Institute, Palo Alto, CA.

MURAKAMI, Y., ed. 1987. *Stress Intensity Factors Handbook*, vols. 1 and 2, 1987; vol. 3, 1992, Pergamon Press, Oxford, UK. Also vols. 4 and 5, 2001, Elsevier, Amsterdam.

NEWMAN, J. C., JR., and I. S. RAJU. 1986. "Stress-Intensity Factor Equations for Cracks in Three-Dimensional Finite Bodies Subjected to Tension and Bending Loads," *Computational Methods in the Mechanics of Fracture*, S. N. Atluri, ed., Elsevier Science Publishers, New York.

RAJU, I. S., and J. C. NEWMAN, JR. 1982. "Stress-Intensity Factors for Internal and External Surface Cracks in Cylindrical Vessels," *Jnl. of Pressure Vessel Technology*, ASME, vol. 104, Nov. 1982, pp. 293–298.

RAJU, I. S., and J. C. NEWMAN, JR. 1986. "Stress-Intensity Factors for Circumferential Surface Cracks in Pipes and Rods Under Tension and Bending Loads," *Fracture Mechanics, Seventeenth Volume*, J. H. Underwood et al., eds., ASTM STP 905, American Society for Testing and Materials, West Conshohocken, PA.

ROOKE, D. P., and D. J. CARTWRIGHT. 1976. *Compendium of Stress Intensity Factors*, Her Majesty's Stationery Office, London.

TADA, H., P. C. PARIS, and G. R. IRWIN. 2000. *The Stress Analysis of Cracks Handbook*, 3d ed., ASME Press, American Society of Mechanical Engineers, New York.

ZAHOOR, A. 1989. *Ductile Fracture Handbook*, 3 vols., EPRI NP-6301-D, Electric Power Research Institute, Palo Alto, CA.

(c) Sources for Material Properties and Databases

CES. 2009. *CES Selector 2009*, database of materials and processes, Granta Design Ltd, Cambridge, UK. (See *http://www.grantadesign.com*.)

CINDAS. 2010. *Aerospace Structural Metals Database (ASMD)*, CINDAS LLC, West Lafayette, IN. (See *https://cindasdata.com*.)

MMPDS. 2010. *Metallic Materials Properties Development and Standardization Handbook*, MMPDS-05, U.S. Federal Aviation Administration; distributed by Battelle Memorial Institute, Columbus, OH. (See *http://projects.battelle.org/mmpds*; replaces MIL-HDBK-5.)

SKINN, D. A., J. P. GALLAGHER, A. F. BERENS, P. D. HUBER, and J. SMITH, compilers. 1994. *Damage Tolerant Design Handbook*, 5 vols., CINDAS/USAF CRDA Handbooks Operation, Purdue University, West Lafayette, IN. (See *https://cindasdata.com*.)

PROBLEMS AND QUESTIONS

Section 8.2

8.1 Look at Fig. 8.32, and perform the following tasks:

    (a) Obtain approximate values of fracture toughness K_{Ic} for AISI 4340 steel heat treated to yield strengths of 1000 and 1800 MPa.

    (b) For each of these yield strengths, calculate the transition crack length a_t, and comment on the significance of the values obtained.

8.2 Look at Fig. 8.33, and perform the following tasks:

    (a) Obtain approximate values of fracture toughness K_{Ic} and yield strength σ_o for A533B steel at temperatures of $-100°C$ and $+0°C$.

    (b) For each temperature, make a plot of stress versus crack length, showing the *yielding alone* line, and the *fracture alone* curve, as in Fig. 8.6.

    (c) Then compare these plots, and comment on the engineering use of this steel at these two temperatures.

8.3 For each metal in Table 8.1, do the following:

    (a) Calculate the transition crack length a_t.

    (b) Plot these as data points on a logarithmic scale, versus yield strength σ_o on a linear scale, using different symbols for steels, aluminum alloys, and titanium alloys.

    (c) Comment on the values obtained and on any trends with yield strength.

8.4 Using Tables 8.1 and 8.2, perform these tasks:

    (a) Calculate transition crack lengths *at* for the following materials: steels AISI 1144, ASTM A517, and 300-M (both tempers); aluminum alloys 2219-T851 and 7075-T651; polymers ABS and epoxy; soda-lime glass; and the ceramic SiC. Refer to Table 3.10 or 4.3 for tensile properties for the ceramics and polymers. For brittle materials where the yield strength σ_o is not available, replace it with the ultimate tensile strength σ_u.

    (b) Comment on the values obtained and any trends observed for the different classes of material. Which particular materials do you think are likely to be internally flawed?

Sections 8.3 and 8.4

8.5 Define the following concepts in your own words: (a) Modes I, II, and III, (b) crack-tip singularity, (c) stress intensity factor K, (d) strain energy release rate G, and (e) fracture toughness K_{Ic}.

8.6 For center-cracked plates in tension, as in Fig. 8.12(a), accurate values of F from numerical results are given in the Tada (2000) handbook, as listed in Table P8.6

    (a) Compare these values with the expression for F from Fig. 8.12(a) that is recommended for any α. What is its accuracy for $\alpha \leq 0.8$?

    (b, c) Two approximations for F that are sometimes employed for center-cracked plates are

$$F = \sqrt{\sec \frac{\pi \alpha}{2}}, \qquad F = \sqrt{\frac{2}{\pi \alpha} \tan \frac{\pi \alpha}{2}} \qquad \text{(b, c)}$$

    where the arguments of the trigonometric functions are in radians. Compare each of these with the numerical values, and characterize the accuracy of each for $\alpha \leq 0.8$.

Table P8.6

$\alpha = a/b$	0	0.1	0.2	0.3	0.4	0.5	0.6	0.7	0.8	0.9
$F = F(\alpha)$	1.000	1.006	1.025	1.058	1.109	1.187	1.303	1.488	1.816	2.578

8.7 An engineering member is to be made of 18-Ni maraging steel (vacuum melted). The member is a plate loaded in tension, and it may have a crack in one edge as shown in Fig. 8.12(c). The dimensions are width $b = 35$ and $t = 5$ mm, and the crack may be as long as $a = 10$ mm. The member must resist a tension force of $P = 50$ kN. Determine: (a) the safety factor against brittle fracture, (b) the safety factor against fully plastic yielding, and (c) the overall (controlling) safety factor.

8.8 A center-cracked plate of AISI 1144 steel has dimensions, as defined in Fig. 8.12(a), of $b = 50$ and $t = 5$ mm, and it is subject to a tension force of $P = 100$ kN.

   (a) What are the safety factors against brittle fracture and against fully plastic yielding if the crack length is $a = 10$ mm?

   (b) Proceed as in (a) but use $a = 30$ mm.

   (c) Assume that this plate is an engineering component and comment on its safety for the two different crack lengths.

8.9 A beam with a rectangular cross section has dimensions, as defined in Fig. 8.13, of $b = 40$ and $t = 10$ mm. The beam is made of 7475-T7351 aluminum and is subjected to a bending moment of $M = 900$ N·m.

   (a) If a through-thickness edge crack of length $a = 5$ mm is present, what is the safety factor against brittle fracture?

   (b) Repeat (a) for a crack length of 10 mm.

   (c) What is the critical crack length for fracture?

   (d) What crack length can be allowed if a safety factor of 3.0 against brittle fracture is required?

8.10 A tension member made of 2014-T651 aluminum has dimensions, as defined in Fig. 8.12(c), of $b = 50$ and $t = 5$ mm. A safety factor of 3.0 against failure by either brittle fracture or fully plastic yielding is required.

   (a) If there is a through-thickness crack in one edge of length $a = 10$ mm, what is the highest tension force P that can be permitted in service.

   (b) If the force in service is $P = 5.0$ kN, what is the largest crack length that can safely exist in the member?

8.11 A rectangular beam made of ABS plastic is $b = 20$ mm deep and $t = 10$ mm thick. As shown in Fig. 8.13(a), a bending moment M is applied, and a through-thickness edge crack may be present. For a safety factor against brittle fracture of 2.5 in stress, what is the largest crack length a that can be allowed if (a) $M = 20$ N·m, and (b) $M = 5.0$ N·m?

8.12 An engineering member is made of 300-M (650°C temper) steel. It is in the shape of a plate loaded in tension and may have a crack in one edge, as shown in Fig. 8.12(c). The dimensions are width $b = 80$ mm and thickness $t = 20$ mm, and the member must resist a tension force of $P = 150$ kN. Determine the length a of the largest edge crack that can be permitted such that the safety factor against brittle fracture is not less than 3.5, and also the safety factor against fully plastic yielding is not less than 2.5.

8.13 An engineering member is to be made of an aluminum alloy. It is in the shape of a plate loaded in tension that may have a crack in one edge, as shown in Fig. 8.12(c). The dimensions are width $b = 40$ mm and thickness $t = 4.0$ mm, and the crack may be as long as $a = 8.0$ mm. The member must resist a tension force of $P = 7.5$ kN.

(a) For a safety factor of 2.8 against brittle fracture, what minimum fracture toughness K_{Ic} is required?

(b) For a safety factor of 2.0 against fully plastic yielding, what minimum yield strength σ_o is required?

(c) Given your results from (a) and (b), select an aluminum alloy from Table 8.1 that meets both requirements.

8.14 A tension member has width $b = 50$ mm and thickness $t = 5$ mm. An axial force P is applied, and the member may contain an edge crack as deep as $a = 10$ mm, as in Fig. 8.12(c).

(a) Estimate the force P at failure if the material is the ASTM A517-F steel of Table 8.1.

(b) Also estimate the force P at failure if the material is the AISI 4130 steel from Table 8.1.

(c) Which material would be the best choice if the member is to be used in an engineering application? Why?

8.15 Bending members, as in Fig. 8.13(a), of depth $b = 40$ mm and thickness $t = 10$ mm are made of 18-Ni maraging steel (vacuum melted). In service, the bending moment may be as high as $M = 5$ kN·m, and members with edge cracks larger than $a = 1$ mm are normally found in inspection and scrapped.

(a) Estimate the moment M necessary to cause failure in this situation. What is the safety factor?

(b) Assume that some of these members were accidentally not inspected and found their way into actual service with cracks as large as $a = 10$ mm. Replacement is expensive. Assume that you are the engineer who must make the decision on replacement. What would you decide? Support your decision with additional calculations as needed.

8.16 A beam with a rectangular cross section has dimensions, as defined in Fig. 8.13(a), of $b = 50$ and $t = 10$ mm. The beam is made of 7475-T7351 aluminum and is subjected to a bending moment of $M = 1.0$ kN·m. A through-thickness edge crack of length as large as $a = 4$ mm may be present. Safety factors of 2.0 against yielding and 3.5 against brittle fracture are needed.

(a) Are the safety factor requirements met?

(b) If not, what new beam depth b is needed, assuming that t and the other values given remain unchanged?

8.17 For a round shaft with a circumferential crack, as in Fig. 8.14, derive equations for (a) the fully plastic force P_o, and (b) the fully plastic moment M_o. Express these as functions of crack length a, shaft radius b, and yield strength σ_o.

8.18 A circular shaft of 50 mm diameter is subjected to bending and contains a circumferential surface crack of depth $a = 10$ mm, as in Fig. 8.14. The shaft is made of the ASTM A517-F steel of Table 8.1. Estimate the bending moment M that will cause the shaft to fail.

8.19 A thin-walled tube, as in Fig. P8.19, is loaded with an internal pressure p and has a longitudinal through-wall crack of length $2a$. Stress intensity factors f or this case from Tada (2000) are

$$K = F(pr_{\text{avg}}/t)\sqrt{\pi a}, \qquad \text{where } F = F(\lambda), \qquad \lambda = a/\sqrt{r_{\text{avg}}t}$$

$$F = \sqrt{1 + 1.25\lambda^2} \quad \text{for } \lambda \leq 1, \qquad \text{and } F = 0.6 + 0.9\lambda \quad \text{for } 1 \leq \lambda \leq 5$$

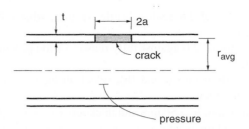

Figure P8.19

The material is titanium 6Al-4V alloy (annealed), the pressure is $p = 40\,\text{MPa}$, and the tube dimensions are $r_{\text{avg}} = 50$ and $t = 4\,\text{mm}$. A crack of tip-to-tip length $2a = 20\,\text{mm}$ may be present. What is the safety factor against fracture? What is the safety factor against yielding with no crack present? Is the tube safe to use if failure could present a safety hazard?

8.20 A structural member has dimensions and area moment of inertia as shown in Fig. P8.20, and it contains a crack of length $a = 15\,\text{mm}$, as also shown. This member is made of A572 structural steel (Fig. 8.37) and may be subjected in service to dynamic loading at temperatures as low as $-30°\text{C}$.

    (a) What bending moment about the x-axis will cause brittle fracture of the beam, where the sense of the moment is such that the crack is subjected to a tensile stress? (Suggestions: Evaluate K approximately by noting that the cracked flange of the beam is essentially an edge-cracked tension member. Also, verify that $K_{Ic} \approx 40\,\text{MPa}\sqrt{\text{m}}$ from Fig. 8.37.)

    (b) The structural design code used for this beam permits a moment of $176\,\text{kN·m}$ to be applied in service, which is based on a safety factor of 1.67 against yielding. Compare this value with your result from (a) and comment on the difference.

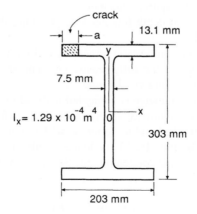

Figure P8.20

8.21 A stiffener in aircraft structure is a T-section, as shown in Fig. P8.21, and is made of 7075-T651 aluminum. A crack of length a may be present in the bottom of the web as shown. A bending moment of $180\,\text{N}\cdot\text{m}$ is applied about the x-axis, such that the crack is subjected to tensile stresses.

    (a) To enable stress calculations, locate the y-centroid of the T-section and its area moment of inertia about the centriodal x-axis. (Answers: $c = 25.36\,\text{mm}$, $\bar{I}_x = 31{,}538\,\text{mm}^4$.)

    (b) If the crack has length $a = 1.5\,\text{mm}$, what is the safety factor against brittle fracture?

    (c) What is the largest crack length a that can be permitted if a safety factor against brittle fracture of 3.0 is considered adequate?

    (d) Consider the possibility of changing the material to the more expensive 7475-T7351 aluminum alloy. What are some possible advantages and disadvantages of making this change? Support your comments with calculations where possible.

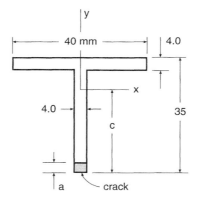

Figure P8.21

8.22 A tube having inner radius $r_1 = 45\,\text{mm}$ and outer radius $r_2 = 50\,\text{mm}$ is subjected to a bending moment of $8.0\,\text{kN}\cdot\text{m}$. It is made of annealed titanium 6Al-4V. As shown in Fig. P8.22, the tube has a through-wall crack of width $2a = 10\,\text{mm}$, located at an angle $\theta = 50°$ relative to the bending axis. Estimate the safety factor, considering both brittle fracture and fully plastic yielding. Use reasonable approximations as needed to reach a solution.

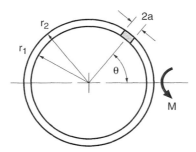

Figure P8.22

Section 8.5

8.23 A large part in a turbine-generator unit operates near room temperature and is made of ASTM A470-8 steel. A surface crack has been found that is roughly a semi-ellipse, with surface length $2c = 60$ mm and depth $a = 20$ mm. The stress normal to the plane of the crack is 200 MPa, and the member width and thickness are large compared with the crack size. What is the safety factor against brittle fracture? Should the power plant continue to operate if failure of this part is likely to cause costly damage to the remainder of the unit?

8.24 A solid circular shaft 40 mm in diameter is made of the steel 300-M (300°C temper). It is subjected to a bending moment of 2 kN·m and may contain a half-circular surface crack, as in Fig. 8.17(d).

   (a) What crack size a_c will cause brittle fracture?

   (b) What crack size a must be found by inspection to achieve a safety factor in stress of 3.5 against brittle fracture?

   (c) Calculate the ratio of the crack size from (a) to that from (b), and comment on the significance of this value.

8.25 A beam with a rectangular cross section, as in Fig. 8.17(c), is made of 2219-T851 aluminum and must withstand a bending moment of M = 150 N·m. The thickness is $b = 20$ mm, and a quarter-circular corner crack as large as $a = 1$ mm may be present.

   (a) What beam depth t is required for a safety factor 3.0 against brittle fracture?

   (b) For the beam depth t as calculated in (a), is the design adequate with respect to possible fully plastic failure? (Suggestion: Make a conservative estimate of M_o by assuming that the crack extends across the full thickness b.)

8.26 A round rod of silicon nitride ceramic is loaded as a simply supported beam under a uniformly distributed force, as in Fig. A.4(b). The rod diameter is 10 mm, the length between supports is 120 mm, and the distributed force is $w = 3.0$ N/mm.

   (a) If a half-circular surface crack as deep as 0.5 mm may be present, what is the safety factor against brittle fracture?

   (b) If a safety factor of 4.0 is required, what is the largest permissible depth for a half-circular surface crack?

8.27 Solid circular shafts made of titanium 6Al-4V (annealed) are subjected in service to bending, with a moment $M = 6.0$ kN·m. Half-circular surface cracks, as in Fig. 8.17(d), may exist in the part. From nondestructive inspection, it is expected that no cracks larger than $a = 5.0$ mm are present.

   (a) What shaft diameter is required to resist yielding with a safety factor of 2.0 if no crack is present?

   (b) For an inspection-size crack, what shaft diameter is required to resist brittle fracture with a safety factor of 3.0?

   (c) What shaft diameter should actually be used?

8.28 A shaft of diameter 60 mm has a circumferential surface crack, as in Fig. 8.14, of depth $a = 10$ mm. The shaft is made of the 18-Ni maraging steel (air melted) of Table 8.1.

   (a) If the shaft is loaded with a bending moment of 2 kN·m, what is the safety factor against brittle fracture?

(b) If an axial tensile force of 120 kN is combined with the bending moment, what is the safety factor?

8.29 A solid circular shaft has a diameter of 50 mm and is made of 7075-T651 aluminum. The shaft contains a half-circular surface crack, as in Fig. 8.17(d), of depth $a = 10$ mm, and it is subjected to a bending moment of $M = 600$ N·m. What is the largest axial force P that can be applied along with M such that the safety factor against brittle fracture is not less than 4.0?

8.30 A tension member made of the AISI 4130 steel of Table 8.1 has dimensions, as defined in Fig. 8.12(c), of $b = 50$ and $t = 10$ mm. A safety factor of 3.5 against brittle fracture is required.

    (a) If there is a through-thickness crack in one edge of length $a = 5$ mm, what is the highest tension force P that can be permitted in service?

    (b) The force P may be off the center of the width dimension b of the member (eccentric) by as much as 5 mm. In this case, and for the same $a = 5$ mm, what is the highest force P that can be permitted in service?

8.31 A tube made of soda-lime glass has an inner radius $r_1 = 38$ mm and a wall thickness $t = 4$ mm. A half-circular surface crack of depth $a = 2$ mm is present as shown in Fig. P8.31. What internal pressure will cause fracture of the tube?

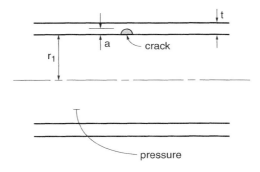

Figure P8.31

8.32 Consider the case of an infinite array of collinear cracks of Fig. 8.23(b), specifically, the K_2 case where the crack faces are loaded on one side.

    (a) For $\alpha = a/b$ in the range 0.01 to 0.99, calculate a number of values of the dimensionless function $F_{P2} = K_2 t \sqrt{b}/P$. Plot these as a function of α, and comment on the somewhat unusual trend observed.

    (b) Verify that the two approximations given near the bottom of Fig. 8.23 are indeed within 10% over the ranges indicated.

8.33 In joining plates of 2024-T351 aluminum, a row of bolt holes is loaded on one side by concentrated forces, as in Fig. 8.24. The remotely applied stress is $S = 60$ MPa, the hole spacing is $2b = 24$ mm, and the hole diameters are 4 mm. Cracks of length $l = 3$ mm are present on each side of each hole. What is the safety factor against failure? Consider both brittle fracture and fully plastic yielding.

8.34 A cylindrical pressure vessel has an inner diameter of 150 mm and a wall thickness of 5 mm, and it contains a pressure of 20 MPa. The safety factor against yielding must be at least $X_o = 2$. Also, a leak-before-break criterion must be met, with a safety factor of at least $X_a = 9$ on crack length, requiring $c_c \geq X_a t$.

    (a) Is the vessel safe if it is made from 300-M steel (300°C temper)?

    (b) From ASTM A517-F steel?

    (c) What minimum fracture toughness is required for the material in this application?

    (d) What is the safety factor on K relative to K_{Ic} due to the $X_a = 9$ requirement?

8.35 A thick-walled tube having inner radius $r_1 = 30$ mm and outer radius $r_2 = 50$ mm contains a pressure of 200 MPa. It is made of the AISI 4130 steel of Table 8.1. As shown in Fig. P8.35, a longitudinal crack is present, with width $2c = 10$ mm and depth $a = 3$ mm. Estimate the safety factors against brittle fracture and against yielding.

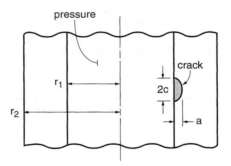

Figure P8.35

8.36 A disc having inner radius $r_1 = 100$ mm and outer radius $r_2 = 400$ mm rotates at 60 revolutions/sec. It is made of ASTM A470-8 steel. As shown in Fig. P8.36, the disc has a quarter-circular corner crack of depth $a = 10$ mm at the inner radius. Estimate the safety factors against brittle fracture and against yielding.

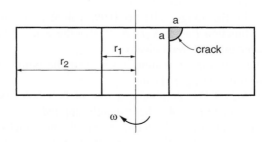

Figure P8.36

Section 8.6

8.37 Assume that each of the rotor steels of Fig. 8.35 except A217 is being considered for use at room temperature (22°C). The design will be such that the highest stress does not exceed half of the respective yield strength in each case. Assuming a flaw geometry that is a half-circular surface crack in a semi-infinite body, determine the largest permissible crack size a for each material if a safety factor of 2.0 against brittle fracture is required. Also comment on how this information might affect the choice among these steels.

8.38 A bending member has dimensions, as defined in Fig. 8.13(a), of width $b = 50$ mm and thickness $t = 20$ mm. A through-thickness crack in the edge subjected to tension stress may be as long as $a = 10$ mm. What moment is expected to cause failure if the material is AISI 4340 steel (Fig. 8.32) with a yield strength of (a) 800 MPa and (b) 1600 MPa? In each case, consider both brittle fracture and fully plastic yielding as possible failure modes. Then (c) comment on whether or not it is beneficial to use the higher strength steel in this case. (Look at Prob. 8.42 for tabulated values from Fig. 8.32.)

8.39 Two plates of A533B-1 steel (Fig. 8.33) are butted together and then welded from one side, with the weld only penetrating halfway, as shown in Fig. P8.39. A uniform tension stress is applied during service in a pressure vessel. Considering both brittle fracture and fully plastic yielding as possible failure modes, estimate the strength of this joint, as affected by the cracklike flaw that exists, for temperatures of (a) −75°C and (b) 200°C. Express your answers as values of gross stress, $S_g = P/(bt)$, calculated as if the joint were solid. Properties for −75°C can be read from Fig. 8.33 as $K_{Ic} \approx 52$ MPa$\sqrt{m}$ and $\sigma_o \approx 550$ MPa. For 200°C, the yield strength is $\sigma_o = 400$ MPa and the (upper shelf) fracture toughness is

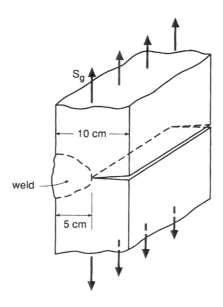

Figure P8.39

$K_{Ic} = 200\,\text{MPa}\sqrt{\text{m}}$. The weld metal has similar properties to the plates. Then (c) comment on the suitability of this steel for use at these two temperatures.

8.40 Consider 300-M steel with properties for 650°C and 300°C tempers as listed in Table 8.1. Solid circular shafts for an engineering application are currently being made from the 650°C temper material and have a diameter of 54 mm. The shafts are loaded with a bending moment of 8.0 kN·m, and nondestructive inspection assures that there are no cracks deeper than $a = 1.0\,\text{mm}$. Also, the design requires a safety factor of at least 2.0 against yielding.

    (a) Is the current design adequate? Assume that any cracks present are half-circular surface cracks as in 8.17(d).

    (b) It has been suggested that a weight and cost savings can be realized by changing to the 300°C temper material with a higher yield strength, and then using a smaller shaft diameter. What minimum shaft diameter would you recommend for the 300°C temper material? Would you recommend a change to the 300°C temper material?

8.41 Consider rapid cooling (thermal shock) of the glass and ceramics listed in Table P8.41, with additional data in Table 8.2. Sudden cooling of a thin surface layer of material causes a stress, as given by Eq. 5.41.

Table P8.41

Material	α $10^{-6}/°C$	E GPa	ν
Soda-lime glass	9.1	69	0.20
MgO	13.5	300	0.18
Al_2O_3	8.0	400	0.22
SiC	4.5	396	0.22
Si_3N_4	2.9	310	0.27

Sources: Tables 3.10, 5.2, P5.30, and [Creyke 82] p. 50.

    (a) Assume that a piece of each material contains a small half-circular surface crack of depth $a = 1.0\,\text{mm}$, and calculate the surface temperature change ΔT necessary to cause fracture for each. Which material is the most resistant to thermal shock? Which is the least?

    (b) Apply the method of Section 3.8.1 to determine the combination of materials properties giving the function f_2 that controls the resistance to thermal shock. Rank the materials according to f_2. Comment on the effects of each of the properties K_{Ic}, α, E, and ν, and rationalize how each affects the resistance to thermal shock.

8.42 A solid round shaft is to be made from the AISI 4340 steel of Fig. 8.32. It must resist a bending moment of $M = 3.8\,\text{kN·m}$, with a safety factor of two against yielding. Also, a half-circular surface crack of depth $a = 1.0\,\text{mm}$ may be present, and a safety factor of three against brittle fracture is needed. Some combinations of yield strength and fracture toughness from Fig. 8.32 are given in Table P8.42.

    (a) For material heat treated to a yield strength of 800 MPa, what shaft diameter is required to resist yielding if the possible crack is ignored? Also, what shaft diameter is required to resist fracture due to the 1 mm crack, where the possibility of yielding is ignored?

    (b) Which value from (a) should be chosen to avoid failure by either cause?

    (c) Repeat (a) for the additional combinations of yield strength and fracture toughness given. What combination of yield strength and shaft diameter gives the most efficient design, such that the diameter, and thus the weight, is minimized?

    (d) Repeat the previous analysis for $a = 0.50$ mm and for $a = 2.0$ mm. Is the choice of a yield strength sensitive to the crack size that might be present?

Table P8.42

σ_o, MPa	800	1000	1200	1300	1400	1600	1800
K_{Ic}, MPa$\sqrt{\text{m}}$	187	182	152	102	65	41	35

8.43 In Fig. 8.40, the fracture toughness of rolled plates of aluminum alloys is seen to vary with orientation. Explain the physical reasons for this behavior and why the toughness for the *L-T* orientation is the highest and that for *S-L* is the lowest.

8.44 Write a paragraph explaining the significance of the data for unirradiated and irradiated A533B-1 steel of Fig. 8.41.

8.45 Consider the choice of a steel for an oil pipeline in a cold climate, such as Alaska or Siberia. What are the desirable characteristics of a material for this application? What types of test data should be available on candidate materials to serve as a basis for the decision?

8.46 A shaft of diameter 20 mm has a circumferential surface crack, as in Fig. 8.14, of depth $a = 1.5$ mm. The shaft is made of the AISI 4130 steel of Table 8.1, and it is loaded with a bending moment of 150 N·m, combined with a torque of 300 N·m. What is the safety factor against brittle fracture? Noting that K_{IIIc} is unknown, a reasonable and probably conservative assumption is to employ a relationship of the same form as Eq. 8.34 and assume that $K_{IIIc} = K_{Ic}/2$.

Sections 8.7, 8.8, and 8.9

8.47 For the situation of Ex. 8.4 under the applied stress given, do the following:

    (a) Determine whether or not plane strain applies and whether or not LEFM is applicable.

    (b) Estimate the plastic zone size, $2r_{o\sigma}$ or $2r_{o\varepsilon}$, whichever applies.

8.48 A double-edge-cracked plate of 7075-T651 aluminum has dimensions, as defined in Fig. 8.12(b), of $b = 15.9$ mm, $t = 6.35$ mm, large h, and sharp precracks with $a = 5.7$ mm. Under tension load, failure by sudden fracture occurred at a force of $P_{max} = 55.6$ kN. Prior to this, there was a small amount of slow-stable crack growth, with the *P-v* curve being similar to Fig. 8.28, Type I, and crossing the 5% slope deviation at $P_Q = 50.3$ kN.

   (a) Calculate K_Q corresponding to P_Q.
   (b) At the K_Q point, determine whether or not plane strain applies and whether or not LEFM is applicable.
   (c) What is the significance of the K_Q calculated?

8.49 A fracture toughness test was conducted on AISI 4340 steel having a yield strength of 1380 MPa. The standard compact specimen used had dimensions, as defined in Fig. 8.16, of $b = 50.8$ mm, $t = 12.95$ mm, and a sharp precrack to $a = 25.4$ mm. Failure occurred suddenly at $P_Q = P_{max} = 15.03$ kN, with the P-v curve resembling Type III of Fig. 8.28.
   (a) Calculate K_Q at fracture.
   (b) Does this value qualify as a valid (plane strain) K_{Ic} value?
   (c) Estimate the plastic zone size at fracture.

8.50 Data are given in Table P8.50 for compact specimens of 7075-T651 aluminum in the same sizes as those photographed in Fig. 8.47. All had dimensions, as defined in Fig. 8.16, of $b = 50.8$ and $h = 30.5$ mm, and initial sharp precracks and thickness as tabulated. For each test, perform the following tasks:
   (a) Calculate K_Q, and determine whether or not K_Q qualifies as a valid (plane strain) K_{Ic}.
   (b) Estimate the plastic zone size at K_Q, using $2r_{o\sigma}$ or $2r_{o\varepsilon}$ as applicable.
   (c) Determine whether analysis by LEFM is applicable.
   (d) Plot K_Q versus thickness t, and comment on the trend observed and its relationship to the fracture surfaces in Fig. 8.47.
   (e) For each test, employ the crack length a_i and Fig. A.16(c) in Appendix A to estimate the fully plastic force. Then compare these values to the highest forces P_{max} reached prior to fracture. What is the significance of the trend observed?

Table P8.50

Test No.	a_i mm	t mm	P_Q kN	Basis of P_Q (See Fig. 8.28.)	P_{max} kN
1	24.1	3.18	2.56	P_5 for Type I	3.96
2	24.7	6.86	4.96	Pop-in, Type II	6.16
3	23.3	19.35	12.00	P_{max} for Type III	12.00

8.51 Consider the form $K = F S_g \sqrt{\pi a}$ and the limitation on LEFM of Eq. 8.39.
   (a) Develop an equation that gives the largest permissible ratio S_g/σ_o as a function of F.
   (b) What is the maximum stress level S_g/σ_o for use of LEFM for $F = 1.00$, $F = 1.12$, and $F = 2/\pi$, corresponding, respectively, to center, edge, and embedded circular cracks in infinite bodies?
   (c) Can you rationalize the trends in Fig. 8.5 on the basis of your results?

8.52 The combinations of crack length and stress corresponding to failure in Fig. 8.5 are given in Table P8.52.

Table P8.52

Test No.	Crack Length a_c, mm	Gross Stress at Fracture S_g, MPa
1	3.00	453
2	5.35	405
3	10.70	342
4	18.43	276
5	34.60	202
6	62.19	142

Source: Data in [Orange 67].

(a) Plot these data, the line for $\sigma_o = 518\,\text{MPa}$, and the curve for $K_c = S\sqrt{\pi a} = 66\,\text{MPa}\sqrt{\text{m}}$, just as they appear in Fig. 8.5.

(b) Also plot a revised curve for $K_c = 66\,\text{MPa}\sqrt{\text{m}}$, where the plastic zone adjustment is used.

(c) Comment on the success of curve (b) in predicting the behavior.

9

Fatigue of Materials: Introduction and Stress-Based Approach

OBJECTIVES

- Explore the cyclic fatigue behavior of materials as a process of progressive damage leading to cracking and failure, including trends for variables such as stress level, geometry, surface condition, environment, and microstructure.
- Review laboratory testing in fatigue, and analyze typical test data to obtain stress–life curves and evaluate mean stress effects.
- Apply engineering methods to estimate fatigue life, including the effects of mean stress, multiaxial stress, and variable-level cyclic loading; also evaluate safety factors in stress and in life.

9.1 INTRODUCTION

Components of machines, vehicles, and structures are frequently subjected to repeated loads, and the resulting cyclic stresses can lead to microscopic physical damage to the materials involved.

416

Even at stresses well below a given material's ultimate strength, this microscopic damage can accumulate with continued cycling until it develops into a crack or other macroscopic damage that leads to failure of the component. This process of damage and failure due to cyclic loading is called *fatigue*. Use of this term arose because it appeared to early investigators that cyclic stresses caused a gradual, but not readily observable, change in the ability of the material to resist stress.

Mechanical failures due to fatigue have been the subject of engineering efforts for more than 150 years. One early study was that of W. A. J. Albert, who tested mine hoist chains under cyclic loading in Germany around 1828. The term *fatigue* was used quite early, as in an 1839 book on mechanics by J. V. Poncelet of France. Fatigue was further discussed and studied in the mid-1800s by a number of individuals in several countries in response to failures of components such as stagecoach and railway axles, shafts, gears, beams, and bridge girders.

The work in Germany of August Wöhler, starting in the 1850s and motivated by railway axle failures, is especially noteworthy. He began the development of design strategies for avoiding fatigue failure, and he tested irons, steels, and other metals under bending, torsion, and axial loads. Wöhler also demonstrated that fatigue was affected not only by cyclic stresses, but also by the accompanying steady (mean) stresses. More detailed studies following Wöhler's lead included those of Gerber and Goodman on predicting mean stress effects. The early work on fatigue and subsequent efforts up to the 1950s are reviewed in a paper by Mann (1958).

Fatigue failures continue to be a major concern in engineering design. Recall from Chapter 1 that the economic costs of fracture and its prevention are quite large, and note that an estimated 80% of these costs involve situations where cyclic loading and fatigue are at least a contributing factor. As a result, the annual cost of fatigue of materials to the U.S. economy is about 3% of the gross national product (GNP), and a similar percentage is expected for other industrial nations. These costs arise from the occurrence or prevention of fatigue failure for ground vehicles, rail vehicles, aircraft of all types, bridges, cranes, power plant equipment, offshore oil well structures, and a wide variety of miscellaneous machinery and equipment, including everyday household items, toys, and sports equipment. For example, wind turbines used in power generation, Fig. 9.1, are subjected to cyclic loads due to rotation and wind turbulence, making fatigue a critical aspect of the design of the blade and other moving parts.

At present, there are three major approaches to analyzing and designing against fatigue failures. The traditional *stress-based approach* was developed to essentially its present form by 1955. Here, analysis is based on the nominal (average) stresses in the affected region of the engineering component. The nominal stress that can be resisted under cyclic loading is determined by considering mean stresses and by adjusting for the effects of stress raisers, such as grooves, holes, fillets, and keyways. Another approach is the *strain-based approach*, which involves more detailed analysis of the localized yielding that may occur at stress raisers during cyclic loading. Finally, there is the *fracture mechanics approach*, which specifically treats growing cracks by the methods of fracture mechanics.

The stress-based approach is introduced in this chapter and further considered in Chapter 10, and the fracture mechanics approach is treated in Chapter 11. Discussion of the strain-based approach is postponed until Chapter 14, as it is necessary to first consider plastic deformation in materials and components in Chapters 12 and 13.

Figure 9.1   Large horizontal-axis wind turbine in operation on the Hawaiian island of Oahu. The blade has a tip-to-tip span of 98 m. (Photo courtesy of the NASA Lewis Research Center, Cleveland, OH.)

9.2 DEFINITIONS AND CONCEPTS

A discussion of the stress-based approach begins with some necessary definitions and basic concepts.

9.2.1 Description of Cyclic Loading

Some practical applications, and also many fatigue tests on materials, involve cycling between maximum and minimum stress levels that are constant. This is called *constant amplitude stressing* and is illustrated in Fig. 9.2.

The *stress range*, $\Delta\sigma = \sigma_{\max} - \sigma_{\min}$, is the difference between the maximum and the minimum values. Averaging the maximum and minimum values gives the *mean stress*, σ_m. The mean stress may be zero, as in Fig. 9.2(a), but often it is not, as in (b). Half the range is called the *stress*

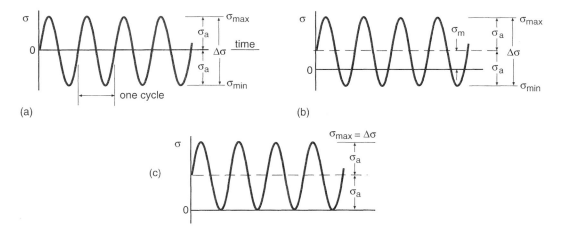

Figure 9.2   Constant amplitude cycling and the associated nomenclature. Case (a) is completely reversed stressing, $\sigma_m = 0$; (b) has a nonzero mean stress σ_m; and (c) is zero-to-tension stressing, $\sigma_{min} = 0$.

amplitude, σ_a, which is the variation about the mean. Mathematical expressions for these basic definitions are

$$\sigma_a = \frac{\Delta\sigma}{2} = \frac{\sigma_{max} - \sigma_{min}}{2}, \qquad \sigma_m = \frac{\sigma_{max} + \sigma_{min}}{2} \qquad \text{(a, b)} \tag{9.1}$$

The term *alternating stress* is used by some authors and has the same meaning as stress amplitude. It is also useful to note that

$$\sigma_{max} = \sigma_m + \sigma_a, \qquad \sigma_{min} = \sigma_m - \sigma_a \tag{9.2}$$

The signs of σ_a and $\Delta\sigma$ are always positive, since $\sigma_{max} > \sigma_{min}$, where tension is considered positive. The quantities σ_{max}, σ_{min}, and σ_m can be either positive or negative.

The following ratios of two of these variables are sometimes used:

$$R = \frac{\sigma_{min}}{\sigma_{max}}, \qquad A = \frac{\sigma_a}{\sigma_m} \tag{9.3}$$

where R is called the *stress ratio* and A the *amplitude ratio*. Some additional relationships derived from the preceding equations are also useful:

$$\sigma_a = \frac{\Delta\sigma}{2} = \frac{\sigma_{max}}{2}(1 - R), \qquad \sigma_m = \frac{\sigma_{max}}{2}(1 + R) \qquad \text{(a, b)}$$

$$R = \frac{1 - A}{1 + A}, \qquad A = \frac{1 - R}{1 + R} \qquad \text{(c, d)} \tag{9.4}$$

Cyclic stressing with zero mean can be specified by giving the amplitude σ_a, or by giving the numerically equal maximum stress, σ_{max}. If the mean stress is not zero, two independent values are needed to specify the loading. Some combinations that may be used are σ_a and σ_m, σ_{max} and R, $\Delta\sigma$ and R, σ_{max} and σ_{min}, and σ_a and A. The term *completely reversed cycling* is used to describe a situation of $\sigma_m = 0$, or $R = -1$, as in Fig. 9.2(a). Also, *zero-to-tension cycling* refers to cases of $\sigma_{min} = 0$, or $R = 0$, as in Fig. 9.2(c).

The same system of subscripts and the prefix Δ are used in an analogous manner for other variables, such as strain ε, force P, bending moment M, and nominal stress S. For example, P_{max} and P_{min} are maximum and minimum force, ΔP is force range, P_m is mean force, and P_a is force amplitude. If there is any possibility of confusion as to what variable is used with the ratios R or A, a subscript should be employed, such as R_ε for strain ratio.

9.2.2 Point Stresses Versus Nominal Stresses

It is important to distinguish between the stress at a point, σ, and the nominal or average stress, S, and for this reason we use two different symbols. *Nominal stress* is calculated from force or moment or their combination as a matter of convenience and is only equal to σ in certain situations. Consider the three cases of Fig. 9.3. For simple axial loading (a), the stress σ is the same everywhere and so is equal to the average value $S = P/A$, where A is the cross-sectional area.

For bending, it is conventional to calculate S from the elastic bending equation, $S = Mc/I$, where c is the distance from neutral axis to edge and I is the area moment of inertia about the bending axis. Hence, $\sigma = S$ at the edge of the bending member, with σ, of course, being less elsewhere, as illustrated in Fig. 9.3(b). However, if yielding occurs, the actual stress distribution becomes nonlinear, and σ at the edge of the member is no longer equal to S. This is also illustrated in Fig. 9.3(b). Despite the limitation to elastic behavior, such values of S are often calculated beyond yielding, and this can lead to confusion. Stresses σ for bending beyond yielding can be obtained by replacing the elastic bending formula with more general analysis, as described in Chapter 13.

For notched members, nominal stress S is conventionally calculated from the net area remaining after removal of the notch. (The term *notch* is used in a generic sense to indicate any stress raiser, including holes, grooves, fillets, etc.) If the loading is axial, $S = P/A$ is used, and for bending, $S = Mc/I$ is calculated on the basis of bending across the net area. Due to the stress raiser effect, such an S needs to be multiplied by an *elastic stress concentration factor*, k_t, to obtain the peak stress at the notch, $\sigma = k_t S$, as illustrated in Fig. 9.3(c). (Values of k_t and corresponding definitions of S are given for some representative cases in Appendix A, Figs. A.11 and A.12.) Note that k_t is based on linear-elastic materials behavior, and the value does not apply if there is yielding. Where yielding occurs even locally at the notch, the actual stress σ is lower than $k_t S$, as also illustrated in Fig. 9.3(c).

Stresses in notched members and other complex geometries may be determined from *finite element analysis* or other numerical methods. Such analysis most commonly considers only linear-elastic materials behavior, so calculated stresses are, again, not correct if yielding occurs—that is, if the calculated stress exceeds the yield strength σ_o.

To avoid confusion, we will strictly observe the distinction between the stress σ at a point of interest and nominal stress S. For axial loading of unnotched members, where $\sigma = S$, we will use σ. However, for bending and notched members, S or $k_t S$ are employed, except where it is truly appropriate to use σ.

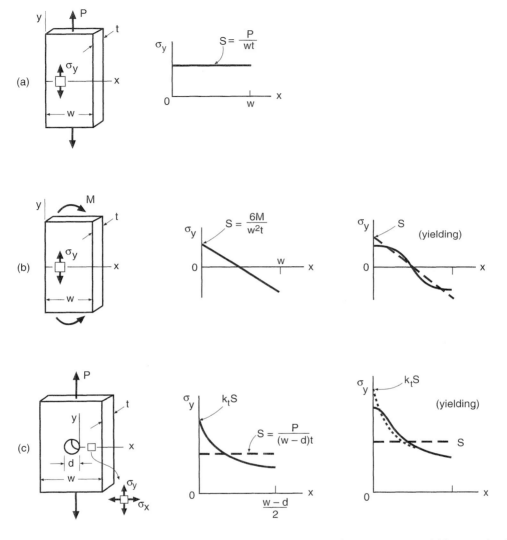

Figure 9.3   Actual and nominal stresses for (a) simple tension, (b) bending, and (c) a notched member. Actual stress distributions σ_y vs. x are shown as solid lines, and hypothetical distributions associated with nominal stresses S as dashed lines. In (c), the stress distribution that would occur if there were no yielding is shown as a dotted line.

9.2.3 Stress Versus Life (*S-N*) Curves

If a test specimen of a material or an engineering component is subjected to a sufficiently severe cyclic stress, a fatigue crack or other damage will develop, leading to complete failure of the member. If the test is repeated at a higher stress level, the number of cycles to failure will be smaller.

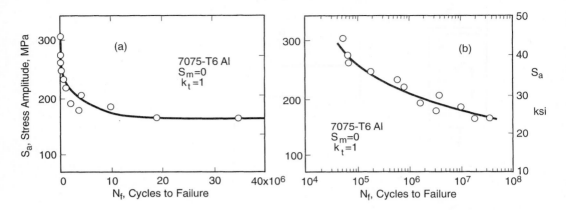

Figure 9.4 Stress versus life (*S-N*) curves from rotating bending tests of unnotched specimens of an aluminum alloy. Identical linear stress scales are used, but the cycle numbers are plotted on a linear scale in (a), and on a logarithmic one in (b). (Data from [MacGregor 52].)

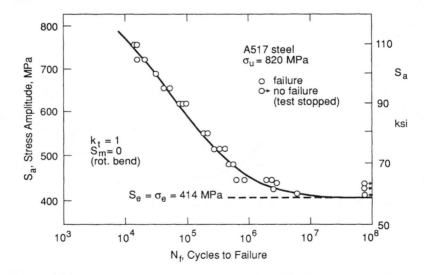

Figure 9.5 Rotating bending *S-N* curve for unnotched specimens of a steel with a distinct fatigue limit. (Adapted from [Brockenbrough 81]; used with permission.)

The results of such tests from a number of different stress levels may be plotted to obtain a *stress–life curve*, also called an *S-N curve*. The amplitude of stress or nominal stress, σ_a or S_a, is commonly plotted versus the number of cycles to failure N_f, as shown in Figs. 9.4 and 9.5.

A group of such fatigue tests giving an *S-N* curve may be run all at zero mean stress, or all at some specific nonzero mean stress, σ_m. Also common are *S-N* curves for a constant value of the stress ratio, R. Although stresses are usually plotted as amplitudes, $\Delta\sigma$ or σ_{max} are sometimes plotted instead. Equations 9.2 and 9.4 can be used to convert S-N curves plotted in one form to another.

The number of cycles to failure changes rapidly with stress level and may range over several orders of magnitude. For this reason, the cycle numbers are usually plotted on a logarithmic scale. The difficulty with a linear plot is illustrated in Fig. 9.4, where the same S-N data are plotted on both linear and logarithmic scales of N_f. On the linear plot, the cycle numbers for the shorter lives cannot be read accurately. A logarithmic scale is also often used for the stress axis.

If S-N data are found to approximate a straight line on a log–linear plot, the following equation can be fitted to obtain a mathematical representation of the curve:

$$\sigma_a = C + D \log N_f \tag{9.5}$$

In this equation, C and D are fitting constants. For data approximating a straight line on a log–log plot, the corresponding equation is

$$\sigma_a = A N_f^B \tag{9.6}$$

This second equation is often used in the slightly different form

$$\sigma_a = \sigma_f'(2N_f)^b \tag{9.7}$$

The fitting constants for the two forms are related by

$$A = 2^b \sigma_f', \qquad B = b \tag{9.8}$$

Constants for Eqs. 9.6 and 9.7 are given in Table 9.1 for several engineering metals. These are based on fitting test data for unnotched axial specimens tested under completely reversed ($\sigma_m = 0$) loading. It is noteworthy that Eq. 9.7 has been widely adopted, with values of σ_f' and b for $\sigma_m = 0$ being tabulated as materials properties.

At short fatigue lives, the high stresses involved may be accompanied by plastic strains, as described in Chapters 12 and 14. Equation 9.7 nevertheless continues to apply for uniaxial test data from unnotched specimens, except that amplitudes of true stress $\tilde{\sigma}_a$ are needed if the strains are quite large. Also, the constant σ_f' is often approximately equal to the true fracture strength $\tilde{\sigma}_f$ from a tension test, which for ductile materials is noted to be a value larger than the engineering ultimate strength σ_u.

In some materials, notably plain-carbon and low-alloy steels, there appears to be a distinct stress level below which fatigue failure does not occur under ordinary conditions. This is illustrated in Fig. 9.5, where the S-N curve appears to become flat and to asymptotically approach the stress amplitude labeled S_e. Such lower limiting stress amplitudes are called *fatigue limits* or *endurance limits*. For test specimens without notches and with a smooth surface finish, these are denoted σ_e and are often considered to be material properties.

The term *fatigue strength* is used to specify a stress amplitude value from an S-N curve at a particular life of interest. Hence, the *fatigue strength* at 10^5 cycles is simply the stress amplitude corresponding to $N_f = 10^5$. Other terms used with S-N curves include *high-cycle fatigue* and

Table 9.1 Constants for Stress–Life Curves for Various Ductile Engineering Metals, From Tests at Zero Mean Stress on Unnotched Axial Specimens

Material	Yield Strength σ_o	Ultimate Strength σ_u	True Fracture Strength $\tilde{\sigma}_{fB}$	$\sigma_a = \sigma'_f(2N_f)^b = AN_f^B$		
				σ'_f	A	$b = B$
(a) Steels						
SAE 1015	228	415	726	1020	927	−0.138
(normalized)	(33)	(60.2)	(105)	(148)	(134)	
Man-Ten	322	557	990	1089	1006	−0.115
(hot rolled)	(46.7)	(80.8)	(144)	(158)	(146)	
RQC-100	683	758	1186	938	897	−0.0648
(roller Q & T)	(99.0)	(110)	(172)	(136)	(131)	
SAE 4142	1584	1757	1998	1937	1837	−0.0762
(Q & T, 450 HB)	(230)	(255)	(290)	(281)	(266)	
AISI 4340	1103	1172	1634	1758	1643	−0.0977
(aircraft quality)	(160)	(170)	(237)	(255)	(238)	
(b) Other Metals						
2024-T4 Al	303	476	631	900	839	−0.102
	(44.0)	(69.0)	(91.5)	(131)	(122)	
Ti-6Al-4V	1185	1233	1717	2030	1889	−0.104
(solution treated and aged)	(172)	(179)	(249)	(295)	(274)	

Notes: The tabulated values have units of MPa (ksi), except for dimensionless $b = B$.
See Table 14.1 for sources and additional properties.

low-cycle fatigue. The former identifies situations of long fatigue life where the stress is sufficiently low that yielding effects do not dominate the behavior. The life where high-cycle fatigue starts varies with material, but is typically in the range 10^2 to 10^4 cycles. In the low-cycle range, the more general strain-based approach of Chapter 14 is particularly useful, as this deals specifically with the effects of plastic deformation.

Example 9.1

Some values of stress amplitude and corresponding cycles to failure are given in Table E9.1 from tests on the AISI 4340 steel of Table 9.1. The tests were done on unnotched, axially loaded specimens under zero mean stress.

(a) Plot these data on log–log coordinates. If this trend seems to represent a straight line, obtain rough values for the constants for A and B of Eq. 9.6 from two widely separated points on a line drawn through the data.

(b) Obtain refined values for A and B, using a linear least-squares fit of $\log N_f$ versus $\log \sigma_a$.

Table E9.1

σ_a, MPa	N_f, cycles
948	222
834	992
703	6 004
631	14 130
579	43 860
524	132 150

Source: Data in [Dowling 73].

Solution   **(a)** The plotted data are shown in Fig. E9.1. They do seem to fall along a straight line, and the first and last points represent the line well. Denote these points as (σ_1, N_1) and (σ_2, N_2), and apply the equation $\sigma_a = AN_f^B$ to both:

$$\sigma_1 = AN_1^B, \qquad \sigma_2 = AN_2^B$$

Then divide the second equation into the first, and take logarithms of both sides:

$$\frac{\sigma_1}{\sigma_2} = \left(\frac{N_1}{N_2}\right)^B, \qquad \log\frac{\sigma_1}{\sigma_2} = B\log\frac{N_1}{N_2}$$

Solving for B gives

$$B = \frac{\log\sigma_1 - \log\sigma_2}{\log N_1 - \log N_2} = \frac{\log(948\,\text{MPa}) - \log(524\,\text{MPa})}{\log 222 - \log 132,150} = -0.0928 \qquad \textbf{Ans.}$$

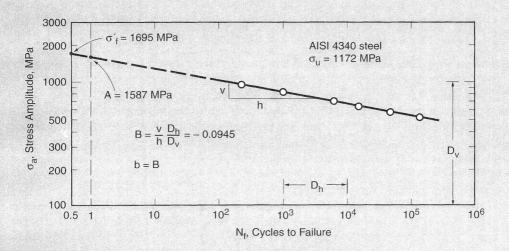

Figure E9.1

Once B is known, A can be calculated from either point:

$$A = \frac{\sigma_1}{N_1^B} = \frac{948\,\text{MPa}}{222^{-0.0928}} = 1565\,\text{MPa}$$ **Ans.**

   (b) Since the stress is chosen in each test, σ_a is the independent variable, and N_f is the dependent one. Hence, to proceed with a least-squares fit, solve Eq. 9.6 for N_f, and then take the logarithm of both sides:

$$N_f = \left(\frac{\sigma_a}{A}\right)^{1/B}, \qquad \log N_f = \frac{1}{B}\log\sigma_a - \frac{1}{B}\log A$$

This is a straight line on a log–log plot, so

$$y = mx + c$$

where y is the dependent variable and x is the independent one. Then

$$y = \log N_f, \qquad x = \log\sigma_a, \qquad m = 1/B, \qquad c = -\frac{1}{B}\log A$$

Performing a linear least-squares fit on this basis gives

$$m = -10.582, \qquad c = 33.87$$

so that

$$B = 1/m = -0.0945, \qquad A = 10^{-cB} = 1587$$ **Ans.**

The resulting line is plotted on Fig. E9.1.

Discussion   The values of A and B from Solutions (a) and (b) are seen to agree approximately with each other and with the values in Table 9.1, which are based on a larger set of data.

   From Eq. 9.6, the coefficient A is seen to be the σ_a intercept at $N_f = 1$. This is shown in Fig. E9.1. The exponent B is the slope as directly measured on a log–log plot with the same scales on both axes. In Fig. E9.1, since the logarithmic decades on the σ_a axis are twice as large as those on the N_f axis, $D_v/D_h = 2$, the slope v/h measured directly from the graph must be divided by 2 to graphically determine a value of B.

   Also, σ_f' and b for Eq. 9.7 may be obtained directly from A and B. Using Eq. 9.8 with the values from the least-squares fit, we get

$$b = B = -0.0945, \qquad \sigma_f' = \frac{A}{2^b} = \frac{1587\,\text{MPa}}{2^{-0.0945}} = 1695\,\text{MPa}$$

From Eq. 9.7, the constant σ_f' is noted to be the σ_a intercept at one-half cycle, $N_f = 0.5$, which is also shown in Fig. E9.1.

9.2.4 Safety Factors for *S-N* Curves

Consider a stress level $\hat{\sigma}_a$ and a number of cycles $\hat{N}$ that are expected to occur in actual service. As illustrated in Fig. 9.6, this combination must fall below the stress–life curve $\sigma_a = f(N_f)$ that corresponds to failure, so that there is an adequate safety factor. At Point (1), the stress amplitude σ_{a1} corresponds to failure at the desired service life $\hat{N}$. Comparing σ_{a1} with the service stress $\hat{\sigma}_a$ provides the safety factor in stress:

$$X_S = \frac{\sigma_{a1}}{\hat{\sigma}_a} \qquad (N_f = \hat{N}) \tag{9.9}$$

An alternative is to employ Point (2), where the failure life N_{f2} corresponds to the service stress $\hat{\sigma}_a$. Comparing N_{f2} with the service life $\hat{N}$ gives the safety factor in life:

$$X_N = \frac{N_{f2}}{\hat{N}} \qquad (\sigma_a = \hat{\sigma}_a) \tag{9.10}$$

Safety factors in stress for fatigue should be similar in magnitude to other stress-based safety factors, as discussed in previous chapters, typically in the range $X_S = 1.5$ to 3.0, depending on the consequences of failure and whether or not the values of $\hat{\sigma}_a$ and $\hat{N}$ are well known. However, fatigue lives are quite sensitive to the value of stress, so relatively large safety factors in life are needed to achieve reasonable safety factors in stress. Hence, safety factors in life need to be in the range $X_N = 5$ to 20 or more.

For example, consider stress–life curves of the form of Eq. 9.6, and apply this relationship to points analogous to (1) and (2) in Fig. 9.6:

$$\sigma_{a1} = A\hat{N}^B, \qquad \hat{\sigma}_a = A N_{f2}^B \qquad \text{(a, b)} \tag{9.11}$$

Substituting these into Eq. 9.9 and noting Eq. 9.10 allows X_S and X_N to be related:

$$X_S = \frac{A\hat{N}^B}{A N_{f2}^B} = \left(\frac{1}{X_N}\right)^B = X_N^{-B}, \qquad X_N = X_S^{-1/B} \qquad \text{(a, b)} \tag{9.12}$$

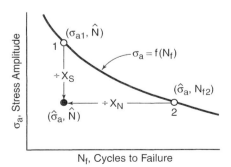

Figure 9.6 Stress–life curve and the stress amplitude and number of cycles expected in actual service, $\hat{\sigma}_a$ and $\hat{N}$, giving safety factors X_S in stress and X_N in life.

Hence, for the Eq. 9.6 form of stress–life curve, a given safety factor in stress corresponds to a particular safety factor in life, and vice versa. The same relationship applies for the alternative form of Eq. 9.7 by substituting $b = B$. For other forms of stress–life curve that do not form a straight line on a log–log plot, the X_N that corresponds to a given X_S will vary with life.

Values around $B = -0.1$ are typical of stress–life curves for unnotched axial specimens of engineering metals, as in Table 9.1. Stress–life curves from tests on notched engineering components typically have exponents around $B = -0.2$ and welded structural steel members around $B = -1/3$. Applying Eq. 9.12 for these values of B, we get the following safety factors in life X_N corresponding to $X_S = 2$, and also safety factors in stress for $X_N = 10$:

B	$-1/B$	X_N for $X_S = 2$	X_S for $X_N = 10$
-0.1	10	1024	1.26
-0.2	5	32	1.58
-0.333	3	8	2.15

We see that a quite large safety factor in life is needed to achieve even a modest safety factor in stress, especially for shallow S-N curves where $-1/B$ is large.

From Appendix B, Table B.4, a typical coefficient of variation for fatigue strength is $\delta_x = 10\%$. With reference to Table B.3, this implies a 0.1% failure rate, or 1 out of 1000, at a stress $3.09 \times 10\% = 30.9\%$ below the mean. This in turn corresponds to a stress of 69.1% of the mean and to a safety factor in stress of $X_S = 1/0.691 = 1.45$. Similarly, a 0.01% failure rate, 1 out of 10,000, corresponds to $3.72 \times 10\% = 37.2\%$ below the mean, implying a safety factor of $X_S = 1/0.628 = 1.59$. Particular cases will of course have more or less variation than the typical δ_x. Also, the foregoing logic assumes that there is no error in the S-N curve itself. Hence, these failure rates and corresponding safety factors X_S should be considered to be only a rough guide. Nevertheless, they do suggest that safety factors in stress for fatigue should generally be larger than 1.5.

Example 9.2

For the AISI 4340 steel of Table 9.1, a stress amplitude of $\hat{\sigma}_a = 500$ MPa will be applied in service for $\hat{N} = 2000$ cycles. What are the safety factors in stress and in life?

Solution   The safety factor in life can be determined by applying Eq. 9.6 to calculate the life corresponding to Point (2) in Fig. 9.6. We obtain

$$\sigma_a = \hat{\sigma}_a = A N_{f2}^B, \qquad N_{f2} = \left(\frac{\hat{\sigma}_a}{A}\right)^{1/B} = \left(\frac{500\,\text{MPa}}{1643\,\text{MPa}}\right)^{1/(-0.0977)} = 1.942 \times 10^5 \text{ cycles}$$

$$X_N = \frac{N_{f2}}{\hat{N}} = \frac{1.942 \times 10^5}{2000} = 97.1$$

Ans.

where the material constants A and B are from Table 9.1.

The safety factor in stress can be calculated from the stress amplitude σ_{a1} corresponding to Point (1), which is obtained by substituting $\hat{N} = 2000$ cycles into Eq. 9.6:

$$\sigma_{a1} = AN_f^B = A\hat{N}^B = 1643(2000)^{-0.0977} = 782\,\text{MPa}$$

Hence, the safety factor in stress is

$$X_S = \frac{\sigma_{a1}}{\hat{\sigma}_a} = \frac{782\,\text{MPa}}{500\,\text{MPa}} = 1.564 \qquad\qquad \textbf{Ans.}$$

However, due to the Eq. 9.6 form of the stress–life curve, this latter calculation can be accomplished more efficiently from X_N and Eq. 9.12:

$$X_S = X_N^{-B} = 97.1^{-(-0.0977)} = 1.564$$

Discussion   Note that the modest value of safety factor in stress of $X_S = 1.56$ corresponds to the quite large safety factor in life of $X_N = 97.1$, as expected from the rather large value of $-1/B = 10.2$ for the stress–life curve.

9.3 SOURCES OF CYCLIC LOADING

Some practical applications involve cyclic loading at a constant amplitude, but irregular load versus time histories are more commonly encountered. Examples are given in Figs. 9.7 to 9.10. Loads on components of machines, vehicles, and structures can be divided into four categories, depending on their source. *Static loads* do not vary and are continuously present. *Working loads* change with time and are incurred as a result of the function performed by the component. *Vibratory loads* are relatively high-frequency cyclic loads that arise from the environment or as a secondary effect of the function of the component. These are often caused by fluid turbulence or by the roughness of solid surfaces in contact with one another. *Accidental loads* are rare events that do not occur under normal circumstances.

For example, consider highway bridges. Static loads are caused by the always-present weight of the structure and roadway. Cyclic working loads are caused by the weights of vehicles, especially heavy trucks, moving across the bridge. Vibratory loads are added to the working loads and are caused by tires interacting with the roughness of the roadway, including the bouncing of vehicles after hitting potholes. Long-span bridges are also subject to vibratory loading due to wind turbulence. Accidental loading could be caused by a truck hitting an overpass bridge because the truck was too high for the clearance available, or by an earthquake.

Working loads and vibratory loads, and often their combined effects, are the cyclic loads that can cause fatigue failure. However, the damage due to cyclic loads is greater if the static loads are more severe, so these also need to be considered. Accidental loads may play an additional role, themselves causing fatigue failure, or damaging a component so that it is more susceptible to fatigue caused by subsequent, more ordinary loads.

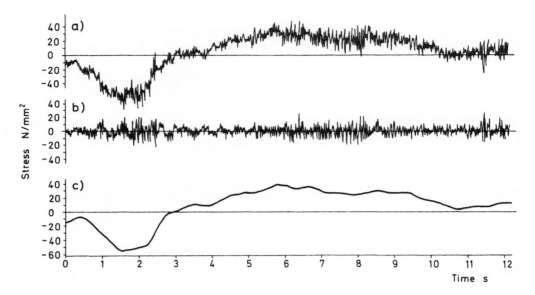

Figure 9.7 Sample record of stresses at the steering knuckle arm of a motor vehicle, including the original stress–time history (a), and the separation of this into the vibratory load due to roadway roughness (b) and the working load due to maneuvering the vehicle (c). (From [Buxbaum 73]; used with permission; first published by AGARD/NATO.)

    S-N curves from constant amplitude testing can be used to estimate fatigue lives for irregular load-time histories. The methodology will be introduced near the end of this chapter.

9.4 FATIGUE TESTING

Materials testing to obtain *S-N* curves is a widespread practice. Several ASTM Standards address stress-based fatigue testing for metals, especially Standard No. E466. The resulting data and curves are widely available in the published literature, including various handbooks, as listed in a special section of the References. An understanding of the basis of these tests is useful in effectively employing their results for engineering purposes.

9.4.1 Test Apparatus

One of the machines employed by Wöhler tested a pair of rotating test specimens subjected to cantilever bending, as shown in Fig. 9.11. Springs supplied a constant force through a bearing, permitting rotation of the specimen, so that the bending moment varied linearly with distance from the spring. In such a *rotating bending test*, any point on the specimen is subjected to a sinusoidally varying stress as it rotates from the tension (top) side of the beam to the compression (bottom) side, completing one cycle each time the specimen rotates 360°.

    Equipment for rotating bending tests operating on similar principles is still in use today. A variation involving four-point bending has probably been more widely used than any other type of

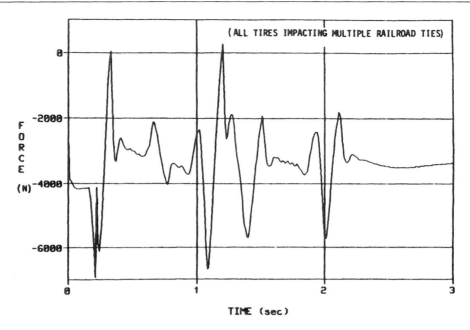

Figure 9.8   Calculated force on the front left lower ball joint in an automobile suspension, recorded while the tires were impacting railroad ties. (From [Thomas 87]; used with permission; © Society of Automotive Engineers.)

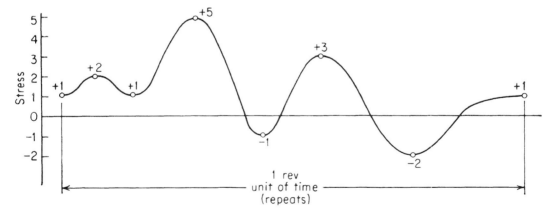

Figure 9.9   Loads during each revolution of a helicopter rotor. Feathering of the blade and interaction with the air cause these dynamic loads. (From [Boswell 59]; used with permission.)

fatigue testing machine; this is illustrated in Fig. 9.12. The two bearings near each end of the test specimen permit the load to be applied while the specimen rotates, and two bearings outside of these provide support. A hanging weight usually provides the constant force. Four-point bending has the advantage of providing a constant bending moment and zero shear over the length of the

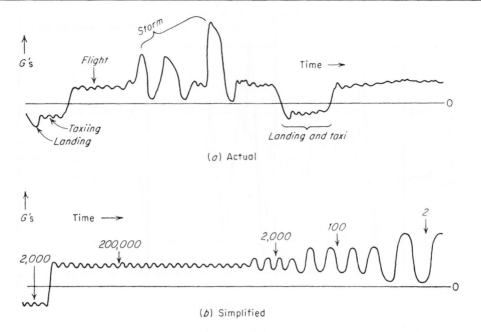

Figure 9.10 Loads for one flight of a fixed-wing aircraft (a), and a simplified version of this loading (b). Working loads occur due to takeoffs, maneuvers, and landings, and there are vibratory loads due to runway roughness and air turbulence, as well as wind gust loads in storms. (From [Waisman 59]; used with permission.)

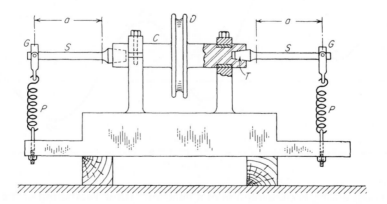

Figure 9.11 Rotating cantilever beam fatigue testing machine used by Wöhler. *D*, drive pulley; *C*, arbor; *T*, tapered specimen butt; *S*, specimen; *a*, moment arm; *G*, loading bearing; *P*, loading spring. (From [Hartmann 59]; used with permission.)

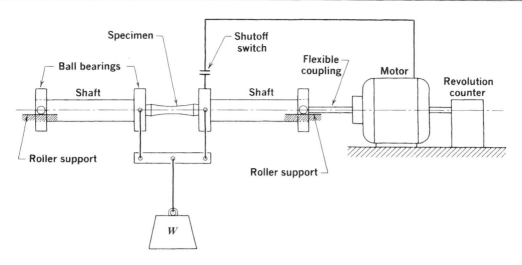

Figure 9.12   The R. R. Moore rotating beam fatigue testing machine. (From [Richards 61] p. 382; reprinted by permission of PWS-Kent Publishing Co., Boston.)

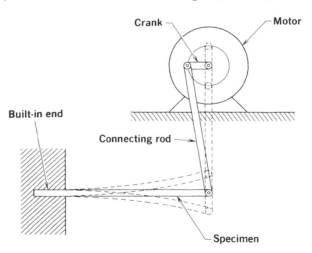

Figure 9.13   A reciprocating cantilever bending fatigue testing machine based on controlled deflections from a rotating eccentric. (From [Richards 61] p. 383; reprinted by permission of PWS-Kent Publishing Co., Boston.)

specimen. For all forms of rotating bending test, the cyclic stress has a mean value of zero. This is because the distance from the neutral axis of bending to a given point on the specimen surface varies symmetrically about zero as the circular cross section rotates.

A rotating crank can be used in a *reciprocating bending test* to achieve a nonzero mean stress, as shown in Fig. 9.13. Geometric changes in the apparatus that effectively alter the length of the

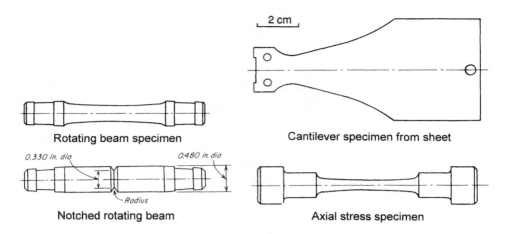

Figure 9.14   Various fatigue test specimens, all shown to the same scale. (Adapted from [Hartmann 59]; used with permission.)

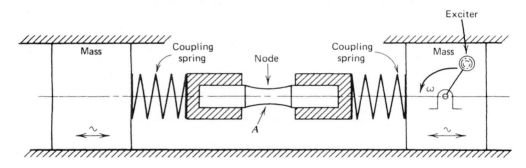

Figure 9.15   Axial fatigue testing machine based on a resonant vibration caused by a rotating eccentric mass. (From [Collins 93] p. 179; reprinted by permission of John Wiley & Sons, Inc. copyright © 1993 by John Wiley & Sons, Inc.)

connecting rod from the eccentric drive give different mean deflections and, hence, different mean stresses. The test specimens are often flat, with the width tapered the proper amount to give a constant bending stress, despite the linearly varying moment. One of the test specimens shown in Fig. 9.14 is of this type. If yielding occurs in such a test, the stresses cannot be readily determined from the deflections, and the force or specimen strain must be specifically measured. Axial stressing with various mean levels can be achieved by a modification of this device.

A cyclic stress with zero mean level can be achieved by exciting a *resonant vibration* in an elastic system, such as the axial testing machine based on a rotating eccentric mass shown in Fig. 9.15. More complex resonant devices capable of providing mean stresses are also used, and similar principles can be applied to bending or torsion. In addition, the vibration can be induced by other means, such as electromagnetic, piezoelectric, or acoustic effects. Frequencies of cycling up to 100 kHz are possible with some of these special techniques. At such very high frequencies, active cooling of the specimen is required to avoid overheating.

Modifications and elaborations of simple mechanical devices, as just described, allow fatigue tests to be run in torsion, combined bending and torsion, biaxial bending, etc. Test specimens made of thin-walled tubes may be subjected to cyclic fluid pressure to obtain biaxial stresses. All of the test equipment described so far is best suited to constant amplitude loading at a constant frequency of cycling. However, additional complexity can be added to some of these machines to achieve a slowly changing amplitude or mean level.

Closed-loop servohydraulic testing machines (Fig. 4.4) are also widely used for fatigue testing. This equipment is expensive and complex, but it has important advantages over all other types of fatigue testing equipment. The test specimens can be subjected to constant amplitude cycling with controlled loads, strains, or deflections, and the amplitude, mean, and cyclic frequency can be set to a desired value by the electronic controls of the machine. Also, any irregular loading history available as an electrical signal can be enforced upon a test specimen. Highly irregular histories similar to Figs. 9.7 to 9.10 can thus be used in tests that closely simulate actual service conditions. Closed-loop machines are often controlled by computers, and the test results monitored by computers.

In most of the test apparatus described, the frequency is fixed by the speed of an electric motor or by the natural frequency of a resonant vibratory device. This fixed frequency is usually in the range from 10 to 100 Hz. At the latter value, a test to 10^7 cycles takes 28 hours, a test to 10^8 cycles takes 12 days, and a test to 10^9 cycles takes almost four months. These long test times place a practical limit on the range of lives that can be studied. If very long lives are of interest, one possibility is to use a special high-frequency resonant vibration testing device. However, the frequency may affect the test results, so it is not clear that an *S-N* curve obtained at, say, 20 kHz can be applied to service loading at a much lower frequency.

9.4.2 Test Specimens

Specimens for evaluating the fatigue resistance of materials are designed to fit the test apparatus used. Some examples are shown in Fig. 9.14, and two fractures from fatigue tests are shown in Fig. 9.16. The simplest test specimens, called *unnotched* or *smooth specimens*, have no stress raiser in the region where failure occurs. A variety of specimens containing stress raisers, called *notched specimens*, are also used. These permit the evaluation of materials under conditions more closely approaching those in an actual component. Notched test specimens are characterized by the value of the elastic stress concentration factor k_t.

Actual structural components, or portions of components, such as bolted or welded joints, are often subjected to fatigue testing. Structural assemblies, or even entire structures or vehicles, are also sometimes tested. Examples are tests of aircraft wings or tail sections, or of automobile suspension systems. A test of an entire automobile has already been illustrated by Fig. 1.13.

9.5 THE PHYSICAL NATURE OF FATIGUE DAMAGE

When viewed at a sufficiently small size scale, all materials are anisotropic and inhomogeneous. For example, engineering metals are composed of an aggregate of small crystal grains. Within each

Figure 9.16 Photographs of broken 7075-T6 aluminum fatigue test specimens: unnotched axial specimen, 7.6 mm diameter (left); and plate 19 mm wide with a round hole (right). In the unnotched specimen, the crack started in the flat region with slightly lighter color, and cracks in the notched specimen started on each side of the hole. (Photos by R. A. Simonds.)

grain, the behavior is anisotropic due to the crystal planes, and if a grain boundary is crossed, the orientation of these planes changes. Inhomogeneities exist not only due to the grain structure, but also because of tiny voids or particles of a different chemical composition than the bulk of the material, such as hard silicate or alumina inclusions in steel. Multiple phases, involving grains or other regions of more than one chemical composition, are also common, as discussed in Chapter 3. As a result of such nonuniform microstructure, stresses are distributed in a nonuniform manner when viewed at the size scale of this microstructure. Regions where the stresses are severe are usually the points where fatigue damage starts. The details of the behavior at a microstructural level vary widely for different materials due to their different bulk mechanical properties and their different microstructures.

For ductile engineering metals, crystal grains that have an unfavorable orientation relative to the applied stress first develop slip bands. As discussed in Chapter 2, slip bands are regions where there is intense deformation due to shear motion between crystal planes. A sequence of photographs showing this process is presented as Fig. 9.17. Also, the slip band damage previously illustrated in Fig. 2.22 was caused by cyclic loading. Additional slip bands form as more cycles are applied, and their number may become so large that the rate of formation slows, with the number of slip bands approaching a saturation level. Individual slip bands become more severe, and some develop into cracks within grains, which then spread into other grains, joining with other similar cracks, and producing a large crack that propagates to failure.

For materials of somewhat limited ductility, such as high-strength metals, the microstructural damage is less widespread and tends to be concentrated at defects in the material. A small crack develops at a void, inclusion, slip band, grain boundary, or surface scratch, or there may be a sharp flaw initially present that is essentially a crack. This crack then grows in a plane generally normal to the

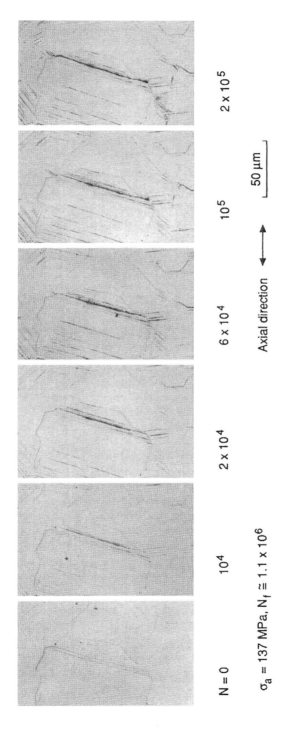

N = 0 10^4 2×10^4 6×10^4 10^5 2×10^5

$\sigma_a = 137$ MPa, $N_f \cong 1.1 \times 10^6$

Axial direction ⟷

⊢ 50 μm ⊣

Figure 9.17 The process of slip band damage during cyclic loading developing into a crack in an annealed 70Cu-30Zn brass. (Photos courtesy of Prof. H. Nisitani, Kyushu Sangyo University, Fukuoka, Japan. Published in [Nisitani 81]; reprinted with permission from *Engineering Fracture Mechanics*, Pergamon Press, Oxford, UK.)

437

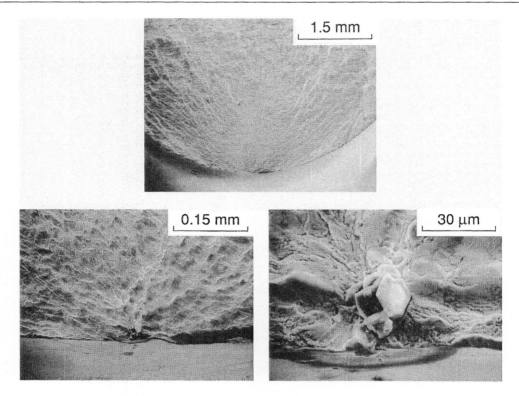

Figure 9.18   Fatigue crack origin in an unnotched axial test specimen of AISI 4340 steel having $\sigma_u = 780$ MPa, tested at $\sigma_a = 440$ MPa with $\sigma_m = 0$. The inclusion that started the crack can be seen at the two higher magnifications. (SEM photos by A. Madeyski, Westinghouse Science and Technology Ctr., Pittsburgh, PA; see [Dowling 83] for related data.)

tensile stress until it causes failure, sometimes joining with other cracks in the process. Photographs of progressive damage of this type have already been presented as Fig. 1.8. An example of a fatigue fracture initiating from an inclusion is shown in Fig. 9.18. Thus, the process in limited-ductility materials is characterized by *propagation* of a few defects, in contrast to the more widespread *damage intensification* that occurs in highly ductile materials. In fibrous composite materials, fatigue damage is generally characterized by increasing numbers of fiber breaks and delamination spreading over a relatively large area. The final failure involves an irregular geometry of pulled-out fibers and separated layers, rather than a distinct crack.

S-N curves can be plotted not only for failure, but also for numbers of cycles required to reach various stages of the damage process, as illustrated in Fig. 9.19. The curves in one case are for slip-band-dominated damage in an annealed, nearly pure, aluminum alloy. For the other case, a precipitation hardened aluminum alloy, *S-N* curves are given for the first detected crack and for failure.

Where failure is dominated by growth of a crack, the resulting fracture, when viewed macroscopically, generally exhibits a relatively smooth area near its origin. This can be seen in Figs. 9.16, 9.18, and 9.20. The portion of the fracture associated with growth of the fatigue crack is

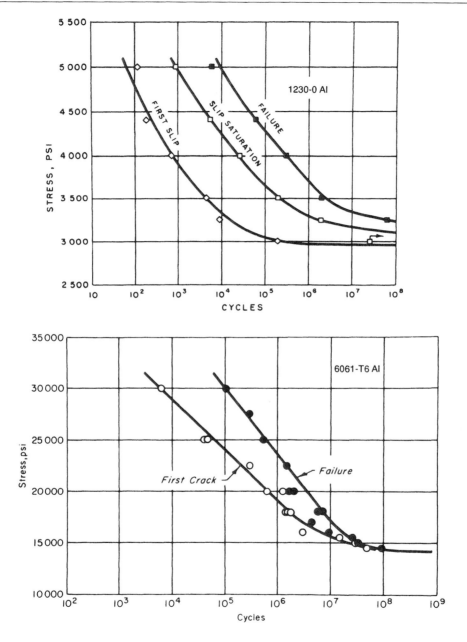

Figure 9.19   Stress–life curves for completely reversed bending of smooth specimens, showing various stages of fatigue damage in an annealed 99% aluminum (1230-0), and in a hardened 6061-T6 aluminum alloy. (Adapted from [Hunter 54] and [Hunter 56]; copyright © ASTM; reprinted with permission.)

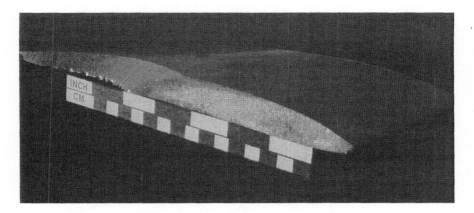

Figure 9.20   Fatigue failure of an aluminum alloy airplane propeller. The failure began at a small gouge on the bottom edge, approximately 2 cm from the right end of the scale. (Photo by R. A. Simonds; sample loaned for photo by Prof. J. L. Lytton of Virginia Tech, Blacksburg, VA.)

Figure 9.21   Fracture surfaces for fatigue and final brittle fracture in an 18 Mn steel member. (Photo courtesy of A. Madeyski, Westinghouse Science and Technology Ctr., Pittsburgh, PA.)

usually fairly flat and is oriented normal to the applied tensile stress. Rougher surfaces generally indicate more rapid growth, where the rate of growth usually increases as the crack proceeds. Curved lines concentric about the crack origin, called *beach marks*, are often present and mark the progress of the crack at various stages, as seen in Fig. 9.20 and more clearly in Fig. 9.21. Beach marks indicate changes in the texture of the fracture surface as a result of the crack being delayed or

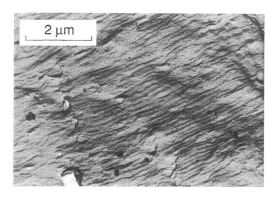

Figure 9.22 Fatigue striations spaced approximately $0.12 \, \mu$m apart, from a fracture surface of a Ni-Cr-Mo-V steel. (Photo courtesy of A. Madeyski, Westinghouse Science and Technology Ctr., Pittsburgh, PA. Published in [Madeyski 78]; copyright © ASTM; reprinted with permission.)

accelerated, which may occur due to an altered stress level, temperature, or chemical environment. Beach marks may also be caused by discoloration due to greater amounts of corrosion on older portions of the fracture surface.

After the crack has reached a sufficient size, a final failure occurs that may be ductile, involving considerable deformation, or brittle and involving little deformation. The final fracture area is usually rough in texture, and in ductile materials forms a *shear lip*, inclined at approximately 45° to the applied stress. These features can be seen in Figs. 9.16, 9.20, and 9.21. Microscopic examination of fatigue fracture surfaces in ductile materials often reveals the presence of marks left by the progress of the crack on each cycle. These are called *striations* and can be seen in Fig. 9.22.

9.6 TRENDS IN *S-N* CURVES

S-N curves vary widely for different classes of materials, and they are affected by a variety of factors. Any processing that changes the static mechanical properties or microstructure is also likely to affect the *S-N* curve. Additional factors of importance include mean stress, member geometry, chemical environment, temperature, cyclic frequency, and residual stress. Some typical *S-N* curves for metals have already been presented, and curves for several polymers are shown in Fig. 9.23.

9.6.1 Trends with Ultimate Strength, Mean Stress, and Geometry

Smooth specimen fatigue limits of steels are often about half of the ultimate tensile strength, which is illustrated in Fig. 9.24. Values drop below $\sigma_e \approx 0.5\sigma_u$ at high-strength levels where most steels have limited ductility. This indicates that a reasonable degree of ductility is helpful in providing resistance to cyclic loading. Lack of appreciation for this fact can lead to fatigue failures in situations where fatigue was not previously a problem, as in substituting high-strength materials to save weight in vehicles. Similar correlations exist for other metals, but the fatigue limits are generally lower than half the ultimate. This is illustrated for wrought aluminum alloys by Fig. 9.25.

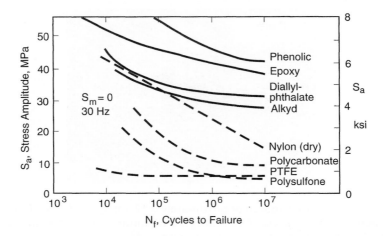

Figure 9.23 Stress–life curves from cantilever bending of mineral and glass-filled thermosets (solid lines) and unfilled thermoplastics (dashed lines). (Adapted from [Riddell 74]; used with permission.)

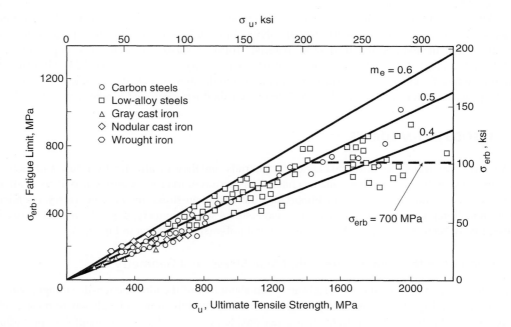

Figure 9.24 Rotating bending fatigue limits, or failure stresses for 10^7 to 10^8 cycles, from polished specimens of various ferrous metals. The slopes $m_e = \sigma_{erb}/\sigma_u$ indicate the average and approximate extremes of the data for $\sigma_u < 1400$ MPa. (From data compiled by [Forrest 62].)

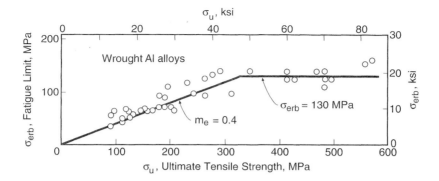

Figure 9.25   Fatigue strengths in rotating bending at 5×10^8 cycles for various tempers of common wrought aluminum alloys, including 1100, 2014, 2024, 3003, 5052, 6061, 6063, and 7075 alloys. The slope $m_e = \sigma_{erb}/\sigma_u$ indicates the average behavior for $\sigma_u < 325$ MPa. (Adapted from R. C. Juvinall, *Stress, Strain, and Strength*, 1967; [Juvinall 67] p. 215; reproduced with permission; ©1967 The McGraw-Hill Companies, Inc.)

Figures 9.24 and 9.25 apply for a uniaxial state of stress and for zero mean stress, so the values need to be adjusted for other situations. For example, for a state of pure shear stress due to torsion, the fatigue limit for zero mean stress can be estimated from the bending value by

$$\tau_{er} = \sigma_{erb}/\sqrt{3} = 0.577\sigma_{erb} \tag{9.13}$$

Glass-fiber-reinforced thermoplastics are typically tested under zero-to-maximum tension or bending. Such composites may have various reinforcement details, such as continuous unidirectional fibers, random chopped fiber mats, or short chopped fibers for injection molding. Their *S-N* curves for $R \approx 0$ are sometimes approximated by a relationship of the form of Eq. 9.5, namely,

$$\sigma_{\max} = \sigma_u(1 - 0.1 \log N_f) \tag{9.14}$$

where σ_u is the ultimate tensile strength. The constant 0.1 determines the slope of the resulting straight line on a log–linear plot. See the paper by Adkins (1988) in the References for more detail.

An important influence on *S-N* curves that will be considered in some detail later in this chapter is the effect of mean stress. For a given stress amplitude, tensile mean stresses give shorter fatigue lives than for zero mean stress, and compressive mean stresses give longer lives. Some test data illustrating this are shown in Fig. 9.26. Note that such an effect of mean stress lowers or raises the *S-N* curve, so that for a given life, the stress amplitude which can be allowed is lower if the mean stress is tensile, or higher if it is compressive.

Stress raisers (notches) shorten the life—that is, lower the *S-N* curve—more so if the elastic stress concentration factor k_t is higher. An example of this effect is shown in Fig. 9.27. Another important trend is that notches have a relatively more severe effect on high-strength, limited-ductility materials. Notch effects are treated in detail in the next chapter, and also later in Chapter 14.

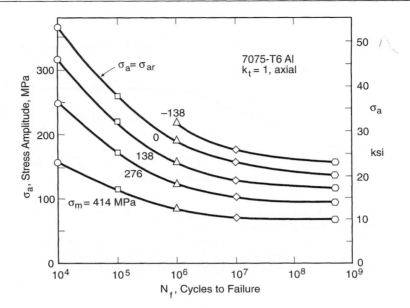

Figure 9.26   Axial loading *S-N* curves at various mean stresses for unnotched specimens of an aluminum alloy. The curves connect average fatigue strengths for a number of lots of material. (Data from [Howell 55].)

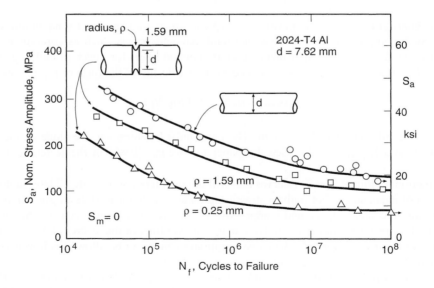

Figure 9.27   Effects of notches having $k_t = 1.6$ and 3.1 on rotating bending *S-N* curves of an aluminum alloy. (Adapted from [MacGregor 52].)

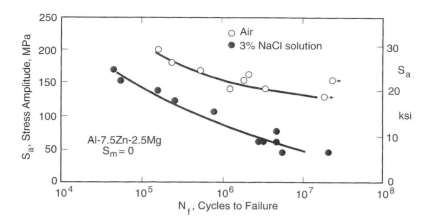

Figure 9.28   Effect of a salt solution similar to seawater on the bending fatigue behavior of an aluminum alloy. (Data from [Stubbington 61].)

9.6.2 Effects of Environment and Frequency of Cycling

Hostile chemical environments can accelerate the initiation and growth of fatigue cracks. One mechanism is the development of corrosion pits, which then act as stress raisers. In other cases, the environment causes cracks to grow faster by chemical reactions and dissolution of material at the crack tip. For example, testing in a salt solution similar to seawater lowers the *S-N* curve of one aluminum alloy as shown in Fig. 9.28.

Even the moisture and gases in air can act as a hostile environment, especially at high temperature. Time-dependent deformation (creep) is also more likely at high temperature, and when combined with cyclic loading, creep may have a synergistic effect that unexpectedly shortens the life. In general, chemical or thermal effects are greater if more time is available for them to occur. This leads to the fatigue life varying with frequency of cycling in such situations, the life in cycles being shorter for slower frequencies. Such effects are evident in Fig. 9.29.

Polymers may increase in temperature during cyclic loading, as these materials often produce considerable internal energy due to their viscoelastic deformation, which must be dissipated as heat. The effect is compounded because such materials have a poor ability to conduct heat away to their surroundings. A consequence of this is that the *S-N* curve is affected not only by frequency, but also by specimen thickness, since thinner test specimens are more efficient at conducting their heat away.

9.6.3 Effects of Microstructure

Any change in the microstructure or surface condition has the potential of altering the *S-N* curve, especially at long fatigue lives. In metals, resistance to fatigue is generally enhanced by reducing the size of inclusions and voids, by small grain size, and by a dense network of dislocations. However, special processing aimed at improvements due to microstructure may not be successful unless it can be accomplished without substantially decreasing the ductility. Some *S-N* curves for brass illustrating effects due to microstructure are shown in Fig. 9.30. In this material, a higher degree

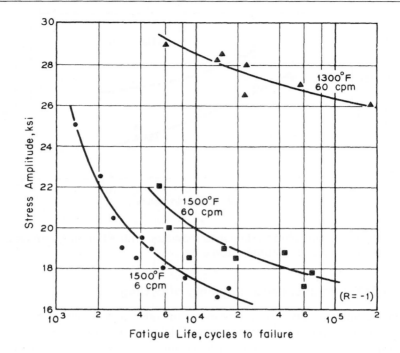

Figure 9.29 Temperature and frequency effects on axial *S-N* curves for the nickel-base alloy Inconel. (Illustration from [Gohn 64] of data in [Carlson 59]; used with permission.)

of cold work by drawing increases the dislocation density and hence the fatigue strength. Larger grain sizes are obtained by more thorough annealing, thus lowering the fatigue strength.

Microstructures of materials often vary with direction, such as the elongation of grains and inclusions in the rolling direction of metal plates. Fatigue resistance may be lower in directions where the stress is normal to the long direction of such an elongated or layered grain structure. Similar effects are especially pronounced in fibrous composite materials, where the properties and structure are highly dependent on direction. Fatigue resistance is higher where larger numbers of fibers are parallel to the applied stress, and especially low for stresses normal to the plane of a laminated structure.

9.6.4 Residual Stress and Other Surface Effects

Internal stresses in the material, called *residual stresses*, have an effect similar to an applied mean stress. Hence, compressive residual stresses are beneficial. These can be introduced by permanently stretching a thin surface layer, yielding it in tension. The underlying material then attempts to recover its original size by elastic deformation, forcing the surface layer into compression.

One means of doing this is by bombarding the surface with small steel or glass shot, which is called *shot peening*. Another is by sufficient bending to yield a thin surface layer, which is called *presetting*. However, the latter has an opposite (hence harmful) effect on the other side of a bending

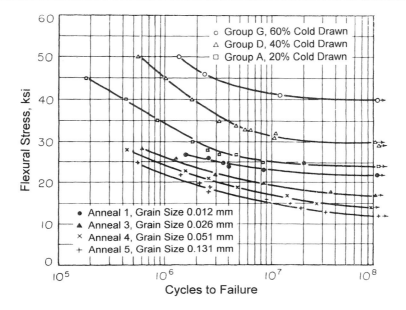

Figure 9.30   Influence of grain size and cold work on rotating bending *S-N* curves for 70Cu-30Zn brass. (From [Sinclair 52]; used with permission.)

member, so the procedure is useful only if the bending in service is expected to be primarily in one direction, as for leaf springs in ground vehicle suspensions. Various combinations of presetting and shot peening affect the *S-N* curves of steel leaf springs under zero-to-maximum bending, as shown in Fig. 9.31. The effects correlate as expected with measured residual stresses.

Smoother surfaces that result from more careful machining in general improve resistance to fatigue, although some machining procedures are harmful, as they introduce tensile residual stresses. Various surface treatments, such as carburizing or nitriding of steels, may alter the microstructure, chemical composition, or residual stress of the surface and therefore affect the fatigue resistance. Plating, such as nickel or chromium plating of steel, generally introduces tensile residual stresses and is therefore often harmful. Also, the deposited material itself may have poorer resistance to fatigue than the base material, so cracks easily start there and then grow into the base material. Shot peening after plating can help by changing the residual stress to compression.

Welding results in geometries that involve stress raisers, and residual stresses often occur as a result of uneven cooling from the molten state. Unusual microstructure may exist, as well as porosity or other small flaws. Hence, the presence of welds generally reduces fatigue strength and requires special attention.

9.6.5 Fatigue Limit Behavior

Many steels and some other materials appear to exhibit a distinct *fatigue limit* —that is, a safe stress below which fatigue failure appears to never occur, as in Fig. 9.5. For other materials, such

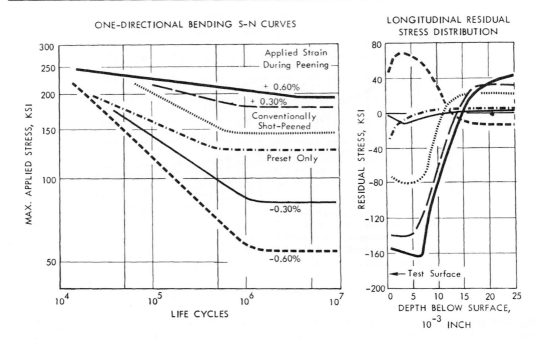

Figure 9.31 *S-N* curves for zero-to-maximum bending, and residual stresses, for variously shot peened steel leaf springs. (From [Mattson 59]; courtesy of General Motors Research Laboratories.)

as many nonferrous metals, the stress–life curve is observed to continuously decrease as far as test data are available. This can be seen for aluminum alloys in Figs. 9.4 and 9.27 and for brass in Fig. 9.30.

The fatigue limit concept is widely employed in engineering design. Even materials that do not have a distinct fatigue limit are sometimes assumed to have such behavior for design purposes. In this case, the fatigue strength at an arbitrary long life is defined as the fatigue limit, where beyond this life the stress–life curve decreases only very gradually. Such an assumption for a life of 5×10^8 cycles is the basis for the data of Fig. 9.25.

Due to the long test times that are required to reach lives beyond 10^7 cycles, most fatigue data that are available are limited to this range. However, recent test data extending to 10^9 cycles and beyond have exhibited the surprising behavior of a drop in the stress–life curve beyond the flat region in the 10^6 to 10^7 cycles range. Such behavior has been observed in a number of steels and other engineering metals, with one set of data being shown in Fig. 9.32. Detailed study reveals that there are two competing mechanisms of fatigue failure: failure that begins from surface defects and failure that begins from internal nonmetallic inclusions. The former dominates the behavior up to around 10^7 cycles and exhibits the apparent fatigue limit, but the latter causes failures at lower stresses and very long lives. Hence, where very large numbers of cycles are applied in service, the concept of a safe stress may not be valid. See the book by Bathias (2005) for more detail.

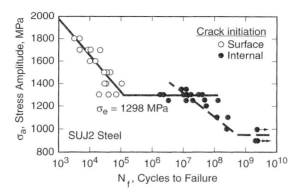

Figure 9.32 Stress–life curve extending into the very long life range for a bearing steel with hardness $HV = 778$, corresponding to $\sigma_u \approx 2350$ MPa, containing 1% carbon and 1.45% chromium. The specimens were tested by T. Sakai and M. Takeda at Ritsumeikan University in lab air at 52.5 Hz using a cantilever-type rotating bending apparatus. (Adapted from [Sakai 00]; used with permission of the Society of Materials Science, Japan.)

There are additional problems with the fatigue limit concept. These arise from the fact that the fatigue limit occurs because the progressive damage process is difficult to initiate below this level. But if the fatigue process can somehow start, then it can proceed below the fatigue limit. Hence, corrosion may cause small pits or other surface damage that allows fatigue cracks to initiate, with the result that the stress–life curve for corroded material may continue downward below the usual fatigue limit.

A similar effect can occur where large numbers of cycles at low stress are combined in the loading history with occasional severe cycles. High stress levels tend to initiate fatigue damage at a number of cycles N that is only a small fraction of the failure life N_f at that level. Hence, the occurrence of a small number of severe cycles can cause damage that can then be propagated to failure by stresses below the usual fatigue limit.

Test data illustrating this for a low-strength steel are given in Fig. 9.33. For the data points corresponding to *periodic overstrain*, the material was subjected to a severe cycle at intervals of 10^5 cycles. Although the cumulative life fraction, $\Sigma N / N_f$, for the overstrain cycles never exceeded a few percent, there was a large effect on the life, with failure now occurring below the fatigue limit σ_e, close to the extrapolation of the line of Eq. 9.7. Test results from studies by several investigators suggest that such behavior occurs for all steels with a distinct fatigue limit, and similar behavior is likely for any other metal with a distinct fatigue limit.

Behavior as just described is one type of a *sequence effect*, which is any situation where prior loading at one stress level affects the behavior at a second stress level. See Section 14.6 for more discussion and illustrative data.

9.6.6 Statistical Scatter

If multiple fatigue tests are run at one stress level, there is always considerable statistical scatter in the fatigue life. Some *S-N* data illustrating this are shown in Fig. 9.34. The scatter arises

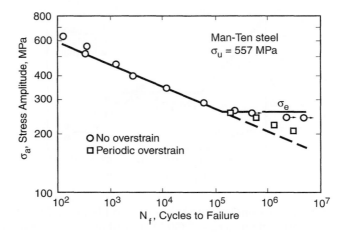

Figure 9.33 Stress–life data for a low-strength steel tested under constant amplitude cycling with zero mean stress. Periodic overstrain tests included severe cycles applied every 10^5 cycles, but with their $\Sigma N/N_f$ not exceeding a few percent. (Data from [Brose 74].)

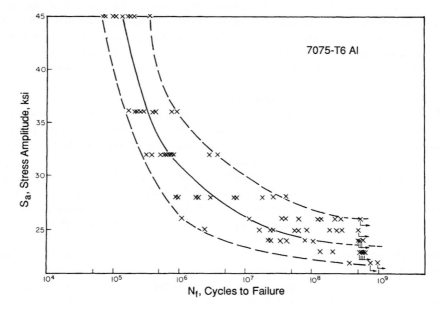

Figure 9.34 Scatter in rotating bending *S-N* data for an unnotched aluminum alloy. (Adapted from [Grover 66] p. 44.)

due to sample-to-sample variation in materials properties, internal defect sizes, and surface roughness, as well as imperfect control of test variables, such as humidity and specimen alignment. If the statistical scatter in cycles to failure N_f is considered, a skewed distribution usually occurs,

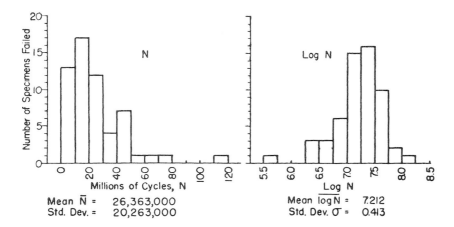

Figure 9.35 Distribution of fatigue lives for 57 small specimens of 7075-T6 aluminum tested at $S_a = 207$ MPa (30 ksi) in rotating bending. (From [Sinclair 53]; used with permission of ASME.)

as in Fig. 9.35 (left). However, if the logarithm of N_f is treated as the variable, then a reasonably symmetrical distribution is generally obtained, as shown on the right. Use of a standard Gaussian (also called normal) statistical distribution of $\log N_f$ is then possible, which is equivalent to a *lognormal* distribution of N_f. Other statistical models are also used, such as the Weibull distribution. The scatter in $\log N_f$ is almost always observed to increase with life, which can be seen in Fig. 9.34.

Statistical analysis of fatigue data permits the average *S-N* curve to be established, along with additional *S-N* curves for various probabilities of failure. An example is shown in Fig. 9.36. Such a family of *S-N-P* curves gives detail on the statistical scatter. Since *S-N* curves are affected by a variety of factors, such as surface finish, frequency of cycling, temperature, hostile chemical environments, and residual stresses, probabilities of failure from *S-N-P* curves determined on the basis of laboratory data should be considered only as estimates. Additional safety margins are usually needed in design to account for complexities and uncertainties that are not included in such data.

9.7 MEAN STRESSES

S-N curves that include data for various mean stresses are widely available for commonly used engineering metals, and sometimes for other materials. In this section, we will consider the effect of mean stress in some detail, including equations that have been developed to estimate the effect where specific data are not available.

9.7.1 Presentation of Mean Stress Data

One procedure used for developing data on mean stress effects is to select several values of mean stress, running tests at various stress amplitudes for each of these. The results can be plotted as a family of *S-N* curves, each for a different mean stress, as already illustrated in Fig. 9.26.

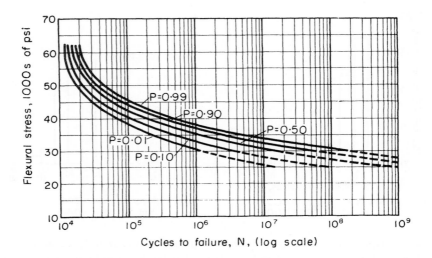

Figure 9.36   Family of rotating bending *S-N* curves for various probabilities of failure, *P*, from data for small unnotched specimens of 7075-T6 aluminum. (From [Sinclair 53]; used with permission of ASME.)

An alternative means of presenting the same information is a *constant-life diagram*, as shown in Fig. 9.37. This is done by taking points from the *S-N* curves at various values of life in cycles, and then plotting combinations of stress amplitude and mean stress that produce each of these lives. Interpolation between the lines on either type of plot can be used to obtain fatigue lives for various applied stresses. The constant-life diagram presentation shows clearly that, to maintain the same life, increasing the mean stress in the tensile direction must be accompanied by a decrease in stress amplitude.

Another procedure often used for developing data on mean stress effect is to choose several values of the stress ratio, $R = \sigma_{min}/\sigma_{max}$, running tests at various stress levels for each of these. A different family of *S-N* curves is obtained, with each corresponding to a different R value. An example is shown in Fig. 9.38. In this example, the σ_{max} values are plotted. *S-N* curves for constant values of R provide the same information, but in different form, than *S-N* curves for constant values of mean stress.

9.7.2 Normalized Amplitude-Mean Diagrams

Let the stress amplitude for the particular case of zero mean stress be designated σ_{ar}. On a constant-life diagram, σ_{ar} is thus the intercept at $\sigma_m = 0$ of the curve for any particular life. The graph can then be normalized in a useful way by plotting values of the ratio σ_a/σ_{ar} versus the mean stress σ_m. The result of so normalizing the data of Fig. 9.37 is shown in Fig. 9.39. Such a *normalized amplitude-mean diagram* forces agreement at $\sigma_m = 0$, where $\sigma_a/\sigma_{ar} = 1$, and tends to consolidate the data at various mean stresses and lives into a single curve. This provides

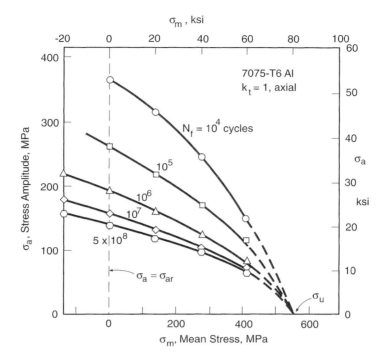

Figure 9.37   Constant-life diagram for 7075-T6 aluminum, taken from the *S-N* curves of Fig. 9.26.

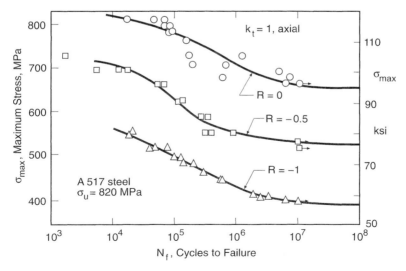

Figure 9.38   Stress–life curves for axial loading of unnotched A517 steel for constant values of the stress ratio *R*. (Adapted from [Brockenbrough 81]; used with permission.)

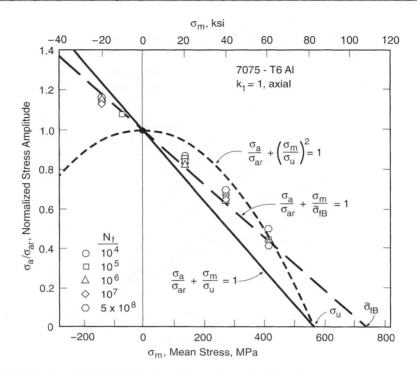

Figure 9.39　Normalized amplitude-mean diagram for 7075-T6 aluminum based on Fig. 9.37.

an opportunity to fit a single curve that gives an equation representing the data. For values of stress amplitude approaching zero, the mean stress should approach the ultimate strength of the material, so that a line or curve representing such data should also pass through the point $(\sigma_m, \sigma_a/\sigma_{ar}) = (\sigma_u, 0)$.

A straight line is often used, as illustrated by the solid line in Fig. 9.39. This is justified by the observation that, for tensile mean stresses, most data for ductile materials tend to lie near or beyond such a line, as is the case in Fig. 9.39. Hence, the straight line is generally conservative—that is, the error is such that it causes extra safety in life estimates. The equation of this line is

$$\frac{\sigma_a}{\sigma_{ar}} + \frac{\sigma_m}{\sigma_u} = 1 \tag{9.15}$$

This relationship is also used for fatigue limits, for which σ_a and σ_{ar} become σ_e and σ_{er}, respectively. Equation 9.15 and the corresponding straight line on the normalized plot were developed by Smith (1942) from an early proposal by Goodman, and they are called the *modified Goodman equation* and *line*, respectively.

9.7.3 Additional Mean Stress Equations

A variety of other equations have been proposed in attempts to more closely fit the central tendency of data of this type. One of the earliest to be employed was the *Gerber parabola*; this is also shown in Fig. 9.39 and gives the equation

$$\frac{\sigma_a}{\sigma_{ar}} + \left(\frac{\sigma_m}{\sigma_u}\right)^2 = 1 \qquad (\sigma_m \geq 0) \tag{9.16}$$

This particular equation is limited to tensile mean stresses, as it incorrectly predicts a harmful effect of compressive mean stresses.

Improved agreement for ductile metals is often possible by replacing σ_u in Eq. 9.15 with either: (a) the corrected true fracture strength $\tilde{\sigma}_{fB}$ from a tension test, as defined in Section 4.5, or (b) the constant σ_f' from the unnotched axial *S-N* curve for $\sigma_m = 0$, in the form of Eq. 9.7. The corresponding new equations are

$$\frac{\sigma_a}{\sigma_{ar}} + \frac{\sigma_m}{\tilde{\sigma}_{fB}} = 1, \qquad \frac{\sigma_a}{\sigma_{ar}} + \frac{\sigma_m}{\sigma_f'} = 1 \qquad \text{(a, b)} \tag{9.17}$$

Such modification of the Goodman line was proposed by J. Morrow in the first edition of the Society of Automotive Engineers' *Fatigue Design Handbook* (Graham, 1968). The constant σ_f' is often approximately equal to $\tilde{\sigma}_{fB}$, and both of these values are somewhat higher than σ_u for ductile metals. Hence, the higher intercept value on the σ_m axis, as shown by the dashed line in Fig. 9.39, tends to give better agreement with test data for both tensile and compressive mean stress than does the use of σ_u.

Equation 9.17(b) with σ_f' generally gives reasonable results for steels. However, for some aluminum alloys, $\tilde{\sigma}_{fB}$ and σ_f' may differ significantly, and this is associated with the stress–life data not fitting the form of Eq. 9.7 very well at short lives. In these cases, better agreement with test data is obtained by employing Eq. 9.17(a) with $\tilde{\sigma}_{fB}$.

An additional relationship that is frequently employed is the Smith, Watson, and Topper (SWT) equation. Two equivalent forms are

$$\sigma_{ar} = \sqrt{\sigma_{max}\sigma_a} \qquad (\sigma_{max} > 0) \qquad \text{(a)}$$

$$\tag{9.18}$$

$$\sigma_{ar} = \sigma_{max}\sqrt{\frac{1-R}{2}} \qquad (\sigma_{max} > 0) \qquad \text{(b)}$$

either of which may be chosen as a matter of convenience. Noting that $\sigma_{max} = \sigma_m + \sigma_a$, we see that form (a) includes the same variables as the other mean stress equations. Form (b) may be obtained from (a) by employing Eq. 9.4(a) to eliminate σ_a. The SWT relationship has the advantage of not relying on any material constant.

The final expression that we will consider is the Walker equation, which employs a materials constant γ. Two equivalent forms are

$$\sigma_{ar} = \sigma_{max}^{1-\gamma}\sigma_a^{\gamma} \qquad (\sigma_{max} > 0) \qquad \text{(a)}$$

$$\tag{9.19}$$

$$\sigma_{ar} = \sigma_{max}\left(\frac{1-R}{2}\right)^{\gamma} \qquad (\sigma_{max} > 0) \qquad \text{(b)}$$

Fitting of data for more than one mean stress or R-ratio is needed to obtain γ, which will be described in Chapter 10. Note that the SWT relationship may be thought of as a special case of the Walker one where $\gamma = 0.5$. Neither the SWT nor the Walker equations can be shown as a single curve on a plot of σ_a/σ_{ar} versus σ_m, as in Fig. 9.39. But they both do form a single curve on a plot of σ_a/σ_{ar} versus σ_m/σ_{ar}, so that comparisons to test data can be done on this basis.

Considering all of the mean stress equations given, neither the Goodman nor the Gerber equations are very accurate, with the former often being overly conservative, and the latter often nonconservative. The Morrow relationship in the form of Eq. 9.17(a) is usually reasonably accurate, but suffers from the value of the true fracture strength $\tilde{\sigma}_{fB}$ not always being known. Equation 9.17(b) with σ_f' fits data very well for steels, but should be avoided for aluminum alloys and perhaps for other nonferrous metals. The SWT expression of Eq. 9.18 is a good choice for general use and fits data particularly well for aluminum alloys. The Walker relationship, Eq. 9.19, is the best choice where data exist for fitting the value of γ.

A recent paper (Dowling, 2009) provides a comparison of these mean stress equations for a number of sets of fatigue test data. In that study, it is noted that the Walker constant γ decreases for higher strength metals, indicating an increasing sensitivity to mean stress. For steels, the data analyzed give the following equation for estimating γ from the ultimate tensile strength:

$$\gamma = -0.000200\,\sigma_u + 0.8818 \qquad (\sigma_u \text{ in MPa}) \tag{9.20}$$

9.7.4 Life Estimates with Mean Stress

Let the equation representing the amplitude-mean behavior, such as Eq. 9.17(b), be solved for the completely reversed stress σ_{ar}:

$$\sigma_{ar} = \frac{\sigma_a}{1 - \dfrac{\sigma_m}{\sigma_f'}} \tag{9.21}$$

Substituting values of stress amplitude σ_a and mean stress σ_m gives a stress amplitude σ_{ar} that is expected to produce the same life at zero mean stress as the (σ_a, σ_m) combination. Hence, σ_{ar} can be thought of as an *equivalent completely reversed stress amplitude*. Substituting σ_{ar} into a stress–life curve for zero mean stress thus provides a life estimate for the (σ_a, σ_m) combination.

For example, assume that the *S-N* curve for completely reversed loading is known and has the form of Eq. 9.7. Since tests at $\sigma_m = 0$ are employed to obtain the constants σ_f' and b, the stress amplitude σ_a corresponds to the special case denoted σ_{ar}, so that, for our present purposes, the equation needs to be written as

$$\sigma_{ar} = \sigma_f'(2N_f)^b \tag{9.22}$$

Combining this with Eq. 9.21 yields a more general stress–life equation that applies for nonzero mean stress:

$$\sigma_a = (\sigma_f' - \sigma_m)(2N_f)^b \tag{9.23}$$

Note that this reduces to Eq. 9.7 for the special case of $\sigma_m = 0$. On a log–log plot, Eq. 9.23 produces a family of σ_a-N_f curves for different values of mean stress, which are all parallel straight lines.

Any of the preceding mean stress equations can be similarly employed to generalize the stress–life equation. As a further example, combining Eq. 9.22 with the SWT relationship of Eq. 9.18 gives

$$\sqrt{\sigma_{max}\sigma_a} = \sigma'_f(2N_f)^b \qquad (\sigma_{max} > 0) \qquad \text{(a)}$$

$$\sigma_{max}\sqrt{\frac{1-R}{2}} = \sigma'_f(2N_f)^b \qquad (\sigma_{max} > 0) \qquad \text{(b)} \qquad\qquad (9.24)$$

$$N_f = \infty \qquad\qquad\qquad (\sigma_{max} \le 0) \qquad \text{(c)}$$

where either of the two forms (a) and (b) may be used, as convenient. Note that (c) is necessary, as σ_{ar} from Eq. 9.18 is zero if σ_{max} is zero and is undefined if σ_{max} is negative. Hence, the SWT equation predicts that fatigue failure is not possible unless the cyclic stress ranges into tension.

The equivalent completely reversed stress σ_{ar} is also useful as a means of assessing the success of any given mean stress equation in a way that makes the accuracy of life estimates apparent. Assume that fatigue life data N_f are available for various combinations of stress amplitude and mean, σ_a and σ_m, or for various combinations of σ_{max} and R. Values of σ_{ar} can then be calculated for each test, and then these all plotted versus the corresponding N_f values. If the mean stress equation is successful, then all of the σ_{ar} data will agree closely with the stress–life curve for zero mean stress, such as Eq. 9.22. This will be demonstrated by one of the examples that follow.

Example 9.3

The AISI 4340 steel of Table 9.1 is subjected to cyclic loading with a tensile mean stress of $\sigma_m = 200\,\text{MPa}$.

    (a) What life is expected if the stress amplitude is $\sigma_a = 450\,\text{MPa}$?
    (b) Also estimate the σ_a versus N_f curve for this σ_m value.

First Solution   **(a)** The *S-N* curve from Table 9.1 for zero mean stress is given by constants $\sigma'_f = 1758\,\text{MPa}$ and $b = -0.0977$ for Eq. 9.7. Life estimates may be made for nonzero σ_m by entering Eq. 9.7 with values of equivalent completely reversed stress σ_{ar}:

$$\sigma_{ar} = \sigma'_f\left(2N_f\right)^b = 1758\left(2N_f\right)^{-0.0977}\text{MPa}$$

Calculating σ_{ar} from Eq. 9.21 gives

$$\sigma_{ar} = \frac{\sigma_a}{1 - \dfrac{\sigma_m}{\sigma'_f}} = \frac{450}{1 - \dfrac{200}{1758}} = 507.8\,\text{MPa}$$

Solving the life equation for N_f and substituting σ_{ar} produces the desired result:

$$N_f = \frac{1}{2}\left(\frac{\sigma_{ar}}{\sigma_f'}\right)^{1/b} = \frac{1}{2}\left(\frac{507.8}{1758}\right)^{1/(-0.0977)} = 166{,}000 \text{ cycles} \qquad \textbf{Ans.}$$

Noting that Eqs. 9.7 and 9.21 were combined to obtain Eq. 9.23, we get the same result in fewer steps by solving the latter for N_f:

$$N_f = \frac{1}{2}\left(\frac{\sigma_a}{\sigma_f' - \sigma_m}\right)^{1/b} = \frac{1}{2}\left(\frac{450}{1758 - 200}\right)^{1/(-0.0977)} = 166{,}000 \text{ cycles} \qquad \textbf{Ans.}$$

(b) The σ_a versus N_f curve for $\sigma_m = 200$ MPa may be obtained from Eq. 9.23, with σ_a left as a variable.

$$\sigma_a = (\sigma_f' - \sigma_m)(2N_f)^b = (1758 - 200)(2N_f)^{-0.0977} = 1558(2N_f)^{-0.0977} \text{ MPa} \qquad \textbf{Ans.}$$

Second Solution   **(a)** An alternative is to employ Eq. 9.24 with $\sigma_{max} = \sigma_m + \sigma_a = 650$ MPa. First, solve Eq. 9.24 for N_f, and then substitute as appropriate:

$$N_f = \frac{1}{2}\left(\frac{\sqrt{\sigma_{max}\sigma_a}}{\sigma_f'}\right)^{1/b} = \frac{1}{2}\left(\frac{\sqrt{650 \times 450}}{1758}\right)^{1/(-0.0977)} = 86{,}900 \text{ cycles} \qquad \textbf{Ans.}$$

(b) The σ_a versus N_f curve for $\sigma_m = 200$ MPa may be obtained from the foregoing by retaining σ_a in variable form:

$$N_f = \frac{1}{2}\left(\frac{\sqrt{(200 + \sigma_a)\sigma_a}}{1758}\right)^{1/(-0.0977)} \qquad (\sigma_a \text{ in MPa}) \qquad \textbf{Ans.}$$

Discussion   For (a), the N_f value is seen to differ between the two solutions, which were based on the Morrow and SWT mean stress equations, respectively. In general, these approaches can be expected to agree only roughly. The equations for σ_a versus N_f for part (b) also differ, with the one for the second solution being a gradual curve, rather than a straight line, on log–log coordinates.

Example 9.4

The aluminum alloy 2024-T4 is subjected to cyclic loading between $\sigma_{min} = 172$ and $\sigma_{max} = 430$ MPa. What life is expected?

Solution   Since the SWT relationship generally works well for aluminum alloys, we will use this. The form of Eq. 9.24(b) is the most convenient, for which we need

$$R = \frac{\sigma_{min}}{\sigma_{max}} = \frac{172}{430} = 0.40$$

Constants $\sigma_f' = 900\,\text{MPa}$ and $b = -0.102$ are available for this material from Table 9.1. Solving Eq. 9.24(b) for N_f and substituting gives

$$N_f = \frac{1}{2}\left(\frac{\sigma_{max}}{\sigma_f'}\sqrt{\frac{1-R}{2}}\right)^{1/b} = \frac{1}{2}\left(\frac{430}{900}\sqrt{\frac{1-0.40}{2}}\right)^{1/(-0.102)} = 255{,}000\text{ cycles}\qquad\textbf{Ans.}$$

Example 9.5

Fatigue data for unnotched, axially loaded specimens tested at various mean stresses are given in Table E9.5 for the same AISI 4340 steel as in Table 9.1. Additional data for zero mean stress are given in Ex. 9.1. Plot σ_{ar} versus N_f for all data for the mean stress equations of (a) Goodman, Eq. 9.15, and (b) Morrow with σ_f', Eq. 9.17(b). On each plot, also show the stress–life line from the constants in Table 9.1. Then comment on the success of each equation in correlating the data.

Solution   (a) Materials properties $\sigma_u = 1172\,\text{MPa}$, $\sigma_f' = 1758\,\text{MPa}$, and $b = -0.0977$ are needed from Table 9.1. Solving the Goodman relationship of Eq. 9.15 for σ_{ar} gives

$$\sigma_{ar} = \frac{\sigma_a}{1 - \dfrac{\sigma_m}{\sigma_u}}$$

Then calculate σ_{ar} for each (σ_a, σ_m) combination in Table E9.5. For example, for the first test listed, with $N_f = 73{,}780$ cycles, the value is

$$\sigma_{ar} = \frac{379\,\text{MPa}}{1 - \dfrac{621\,\text{MPa}}{1172\,\text{MPa}}} = 806.1\,\text{MPa}$$

Table E9.5

σ_a, MPa	σ_m, MPa	N_f, cycles	σ_a, MPa	σ_m, MPa	N_f, cycles
379	621	73 780	310	414	445 020
345	621	83 810	552	207	45 490
276	621	567 590	483	207	109 680
517	414	31 280	414	207	510 250
483	414	50 490	586	−207	208 030
414	414	84 420	552	−207	193 220
345	414	437 170	483	−207	901 430
345	414	730 570			

Source: Data in [Dowling 73]. Note: All prestrained 10 cycles at $\varepsilon_a = 0.01$.

Similarly calculating all of the σ_{ar} values and plotting these versus N_f gives Fig. E9.5(a). The data points from Table E9.1 are also plotted, for which no calculation is needed, as $\sigma_{ar} = \sigma_a$ due to $\sigma_m = 0$. Also shown is the log–log straight line corresponding to Eq. 9.22, $\sigma_{ar} = \sigma_f'(2N_f)^b$.

In Fig. E9.5(a), the data for tensile mean stress are seen to lie well above the Eq. 9.22 line for zero mean stress, increasingly so for larger σ_m. The data being above the line indicates that the Goodman equation is conservative with respect to these data for tensile mean stress. But the overall correlation is quite poor. (**Ans.**)

(**b**) For the equation of Morrow with σ_f', the same procedure is followed, except for the use of Eq. 9.17(b), which is already solved for σ_{ar} as Eq. 9.21. The calculation for the first test listed in Table E9.5, with $N_f = 73{,}780$ cycles, is

$$\sigma_{ar} = \frac{\sigma_a}{1 - \dfrac{\sigma_m}{\sigma_f'}} = \frac{379\,\text{MPa}}{1 - \dfrac{621\,\text{MPa}}{1758\,\text{MPa}}} = 586.0\,\text{MPa}$$

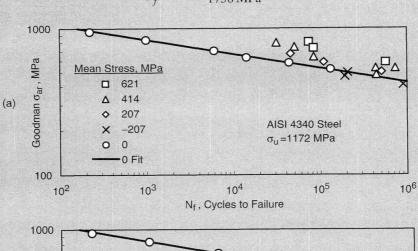

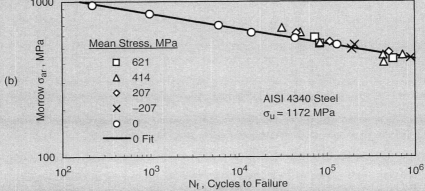

Figure E9.5

Similarly, calculating all of the values and plotting versus N_f, while also including the Table E9.1 data and the Eq. 9.22 line, gives Fig. E9.5(b).

The correlation of the data with the line for zero mean stress is now much improved, and no clear trends are seen except for some scatter. Hence, the equation of Morrow with σ_f' provides a reasonably accurate representation of these data. (**Ans.**)

9.7.5 Safety Factors with Mean Stress

The discussion in Section 9.2.4 on safety factors can be generalized to include cases with nonzero mean stress. One option is to apply the logic of Fig. 9.6 with the stress amplitude σ_a simply replaced by an equivalent completely reversed stress amplitude, σ_{ar}. The stress–life curve is then $\sigma_{ar} = f(N_f)$, and safety factors in stress and life are calculated by generalizing Eqs. 9.9 and 9.10:

$$X_S = \left.\frac{\sigma_{ar1}}{\hat{\sigma}_{ar}}\right|_{N_f=\hat{N}}, \qquad X_N = \left.\frac{N_{f2}}{\hat{N}}\right|_{\sigma_{ar}=\hat{\sigma}_{ar}} \qquad \text{(a, b)} \qquad (9.25)$$

The value of $\hat{\sigma}_{ar}$ is calculated from the stress amplitude $\hat{\sigma}_a$ and mean stress $\hat{\sigma}_m$ expected to occur in actual service, with the use of Eq. 9.18 or 9.21 or other similar mean stress relationship. Also, for stress–life curves of the form of Eq. 9.7, the two safety factors are related by $X_S = X_N^{-b}$ from Eq. 9.12.

A second option is to multiply $\hat{\sigma}_a$ and $\hat{\sigma}_m$ by load factors Y_a and Y_m, respectively, to calculate a value of equivalent completely reversed stress σ_{ar1}' that cannot exceed the stress–life curve at the desired service life $\hat{N}$, so that $\sigma_{ar1}' \leq f(\hat{N})$ is required. For example, the Morrow σ_{ar} expression of Eq. 9.21 is used with the stress–life curve of Eq. 9.22 as follows:

$$\sigma_{ar1}' = \frac{Y_a\hat{\sigma}_a}{1 - \dfrac{Y_m\hat{\sigma}_m}{\sigma_f'}}, \qquad \sigma_{ar1}' \leq \sigma_f'(2\hat{N})^b \qquad \text{(a, b)} \qquad (9.26)$$

The SWT expression of Eq. 9.18, with $\sigma_{\max} = \sigma_m + \sigma_a$ substituted, is employed as

$$\sigma_{ar1}' = \sqrt{(Y_m\hat{\sigma}_m + Y_a\hat{\sigma}_a)Y_a\hat{\sigma}_a}\,, \qquad \sigma_{ar1}' \leq \sigma_f'(2\hat{N})^b \qquad \text{(a, b)} \qquad (9.27)$$

The load factor approach has the advantage that different values can be assigned to Y_a and Y_m, which may be desirable if the value of one of $\hat{\sigma}_a$ or $\hat{\sigma}_m$ is more uncertain than the other.

Assume that the same load factor is applied for both the stress amplitude and mean, $Y = Y_a = Y_m$. This common load factor can be factored out of Eq. 9.27, so that $\sigma_{ar1}' = Y\sqrt{\hat{\sigma}_{\max}\hat{\sigma}_a} = Y\hat{\sigma}_{ar}$. Comparison with Eq. 9.25(a) gives $Y = X_S$, so that the load factor and the safety factor in stress are equivalent if SWT is employed. Such $Y = X_S$ equivalence also applies for the Walker mean stress relationship, Eq. 9.19, but not for the Morrow or Goodman equations, as the latter mathematical forms do not allow similar factoring.

Example 9.6

Man-Ten steel is subjected in service to a stress amplitude of 180 MPa and a mean stress of 100 MPa for 20,000 cycles.

    (a) What are the safety factors in stress and in life?
    (b) What load factor $Y = Y_a = Y_m$ corresponds to the 20,000 cycle service life?

Solution   **(a)** Constants for this material are available from Table 9.1, which will be used as needed. If we choose the Morrow mean stress equation, $\hat{\sigma}_{ar}$ is calculated from Eq. 9.21, and then the corresponding life is available from Eq. 9.22:

$$\hat{\sigma}_{ar} = \frac{\hat{\sigma}_a}{1 - \dfrac{\hat{\sigma}_m}{\sigma'_f}} = \frac{180\,\text{MPa}}{1 - \dfrac{100\,\text{MPa}}{1089\,\text{MPa}}} = 198.2\,\text{MPa}$$

$$N_{f2} = \frac{1}{2}\left(\frac{\hat{\sigma}_{ar}}{\sigma'_f}\right)^{1/b} = \frac{1}{2}\left(\frac{198.2\,\text{MPa}}{1089\,\text{MPa}}\right)^{1/(-0.115)} = 1.359 \times 10^6\,\text{cycles}$$

Hence, the safety factor in life from Eq. 9.25(b) is

$$X_N = \frac{N_{f2}}{\hat{N}} = \frac{1.359 \times 10^6}{20,000} = 67.93 \qquad\qquad \textbf{Ans.}$$

The safety factor in stress can be obtained from this value and Eq. 9.12(a), for which $B = b$.

$$X_S = X_N^{-b} = (67.93)^{-(-0.115)} = 1.624 \qquad\qquad \textbf{Ans.}$$

    (b) To obtain the load factor, we employ Eq. 9.26(b) to obtain σ'_{ar1}, with an equality applying, as we wish to compute the failure point:

$$\sigma'_{ar1} = \sigma'_f(2\hat{N})^b = (1089\,\text{MPa})(2 \times 20,000)^{-0.115} = 322.0\,\text{MPa}$$

Then, substituting the known quantities into Eq. 9.26(a) gives

$$\sigma'_{ar1} = \frac{Y_a\hat{\sigma}_a}{1 - \dfrac{Y_m\hat{\sigma}_m}{\sigma'_f}}, \qquad 322.0\,\text{MPa} = \frac{Y_a(180\,\text{MPa})}{1 - \dfrac{Y_m(100\,\text{MPa})}{1089\,\text{MPa}}}$$

Invoking $Y = Y_a = Y_m$ as specified and solving gives $Y = 1.536$ (**Ans.**).

Discussion   As expected, the load factor Y does not have the same value as X_S. If we rework this problem, choosing the SWT mean stress equation, we obtain identical values $X_S = Y = 1.434$.

9.8 MULTIAXIAL STRESSES

In engineering components, cyclic loadings that cause complex states of stress are common. Some examples are biaxial stresses due to cyclic pressure in tubes or pipes, combined bending and torsion of shafts, and bending of sheets or plates about more than one axis. Steady applied loads that cause mean stresses may also be combined with such cyclic loads. An additional complexity is that different sources of cyclic loading may differ in phase or frequency or both. For example, if a steady bending stress is applied to a thin-walled tube under cyclic pressure, there are different stress amplitudes and mean stresses in two directions, as shown in Fig. 9.40. The axial and hoop directions are the directions of principal stress and remain so as the pressure fluctuates.

If a steady torsion is instead applied, a more complex situation exists, as illustrated in Fig. 9.41. At times when the pressure is momentarily at zero, the principal stress directions are controlled by the shear stress and are oriented 45° to the tube axis. However, for nonzero values of pressure, these directions rotate to become more closely aligned with the axial and hoop directions, but never reaching them, except for the limiting case where the stresses σ_x and σ_y due to pressure are large

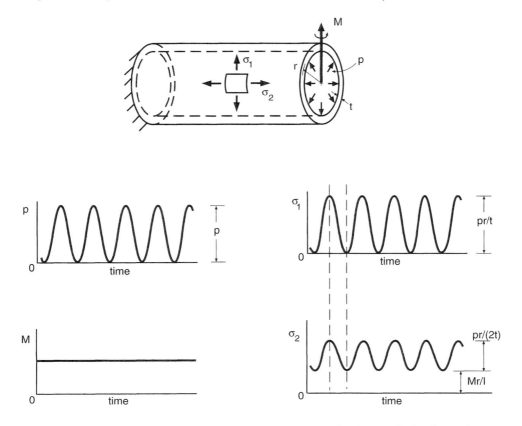

Figure 9.40 Combined cyclic pressure and steady bending of a thin-walled tube with closed ends. The principal directions are constant.

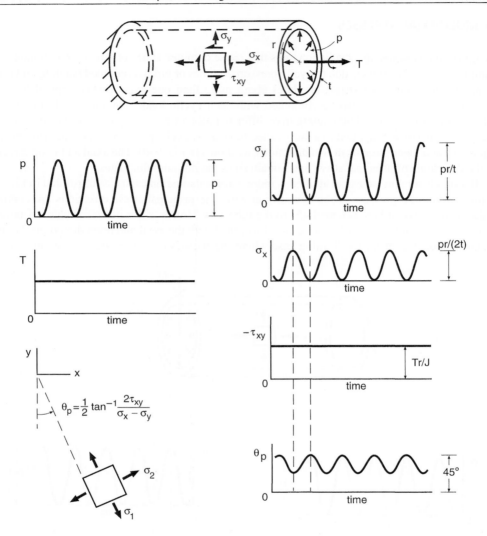

Figure 9.41   Combined cyclic pressure and steady torsion of a thin-walled tube with closed ends. The principal directions oscillate during each cycle.

compared with the τ_{xy} caused by torsion. Additional complexities could exist. For example, the bending moment in Fig. 9.40 or the torque in Fig. 9.41 could also be cyclic loads, and the frequency of cycling of the bending or torsion could differ from that of the pressure.

9.8.1 One Approach to Multiaxial Fatigue

Consider the simple situation where all cyclic loads are completely reversed and have the same frequency, and further where they are either in-phase or $180°$ out-of-phase with one another. Also, assume for the present that there are no steady (noncyclic) loads present. For ductile engineering metals, it is reasonable in this case to assume that the fatigue life is controlled by the cyclic amplitude of the octahedral shear stress. The amplitudes of the principal stresses, σ_{1a}, σ_{2a}, and σ_{3a} can then be employed to compute an *effective stress amplitude* using a relationship similar to that employed for the octahedral shear yield criterion:

$$\bar{\sigma}_a = \frac{1}{\sqrt{2}}\sqrt{(\sigma_{1a} - \sigma_{2a})^2 + (\sigma_{2a} - \sigma_{3a})^2 + (\sigma_{3a} - \sigma_{1a})^2} \tag{9.28}$$

This is identical to Eq. 7.35, except that all stress quantities are amplitudes. In applying this equation, amplitudes considered to be in-phase are positive, and those 180° out-of-phase are negative.

The life may then be estimated by using $\bar{\sigma}_a$ to enter an *S-N* curve for completely reversed uniaxial stress. Note that the *S-N* curves most commonly available are from bending or axial tests, which do involve a uniaxial state of stress and can therefore be used directly with $\bar{\sigma}_a$ values. (However, difficulties arise for *S-N* curves for bending where yielding occurred in the tests.) For plane stress with $\sigma_3 = 0$, Eq. 9.28 predicts an elliptical failure locus on a plot of σ_{1a} versus σ_{2a}, analogous to the locus for the octahedral shear yield criterion. Some experimental data are compared with such a locus in Fig. 9.42.

If steady (noncyclic) loads are present, these alter the effective stress amplitude $\bar{\sigma}_a$ in a manner analogous to the mean stress effect under uniaxial loading. One approach is to assume that the controlling mean stress variable is proportional to the steady value of the hydrostatic stress. On this basis, an *effective mean stress* can be calculated from the mean stresses in the three

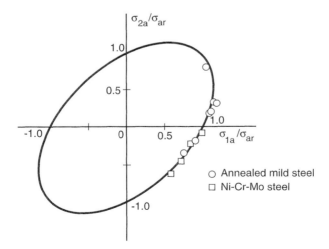

Figure 9.42 Octahedral shear stress criterion compared with 10^7 cycle fatigue strengths for completely reversed biaxial loading. (From the data of Sawert and Gough as compiled by [Sines 59].)

principal directions:

$$\bar{\sigma}_m = \sigma_{1m} + \sigma_{2m} + \sigma_{3m} \tag{9.29}$$

Using stress invariants as discussed in Chapter 6, we can compute these effective stress amplitudes and means from the amplitudes and means of the stress components for any convenient coordinate axes:

$$\bar{\sigma}_a = \frac{1}{\sqrt{2}}\sqrt{(\sigma_{xa} - \sigma_{ya})^2 + (\sigma_{ya} - \sigma_{za})^2 + (\sigma_{za} - \sigma_{xa})^2 + 6(\tau_{xya}^2 + \tau_{yza}^2 + \tau_{zxa}^2)}$$

$$\bar{\sigma}_m = \sigma_{xm} + \sigma_{ym} + \sigma_{zm} \tag{9.30}$$

The quantities $\bar{\sigma}_a$ and $\bar{\sigma}_m$ can be combined into an *equivalent completely reversed uniaxial stress* by generalizing Eq. 9.21 or other mean stress relationship:

$$\sigma_{ar} = \frac{\bar{\sigma}_a}{1 - \dfrac{\bar{\sigma}_m}{\sigma_f'}} \tag{9.31}$$

Values of σ_{ar} may be used to enter a completely reversed S-N curve for uniaxial stress, such as Eq. 9.22, and the life thus determined.

For uniaxial loading with a mean stress, only σ_{1a} and σ_{1m} are nonzero, and Eq. 9.31 reduces to Eq. 9.21, as it should. For pure shear, as in torsion, only the amplitude and mean of the shear stress, τ_{xya} and τ_{xym}, are nonzero. Hence, Eq. 9.30 gives simply

$$\bar{\sigma}_a = \sqrt{3}\tau_{xya}, \qquad \bar{\sigma}_m = 0 \tag{9.32}$$

Note that $\bar{\sigma}_m$ is zero even if a mean shear stress is present. This somewhat surprising prediction that mean shear stress has no effect is in fact in agreement with experimental observation. For additional detail on this point and on multiaxial stress effects in general, see Sines (1959) and Socie (2000) in the References.

9.8.2 Discussion

For situations where the principal axes rotate during cyclic loading, the applicability of the equations just given is questionable. This also applies if cyclic loads occur at more than one frequency, or if there is a difference in phase (other than 180°) between them. A number of other approaches exist. For example, the *critical plane approach* involves finding the maximum shear strain amplitude and the plane on which it acts, and then using the maximum normal stress acting on this plane to obtain a mean stress effect. Some discussion of this method is given in Chapter 14.

Example 9.7

An unnotched solid circular shaft of diameter 50 mm is made of the alloy Ti-6Al-4V of Table 9.1. A zero-to-maximum ($R = 0$) cyclic torque of $T = 10$ kN·m is applied, together with a zero-to-maximum cyclic bending moment of $M = 7.5$ kN·m, with the two cyclic loads being applied in phase at the same frequency. How many load cycles can be applied before fatigue failure is expected?

Solution   Employing Figs. A.1 and A.2 in Appendix A, the stresses at the shaft surface at points in time where both the torque and the moment reach their maximum values are

$$\tau_{xy\ max} = \frac{Tc}{J} = \frac{Tr}{\pi r^4/2} = \frac{2(0.010\ \text{MN·m})}{\pi(0.025\ \text{m})^3} = 407.4\ \text{MPa}$$

$$\sigma_{x\ max} = \frac{Mc}{I} = \frac{Mr}{\pi r^4/4} = \frac{4(0.0075\ \text{MN·m})}{\pi(0.025\ \text{m})^3} = 611.2\ \text{MPa}$$

where all other stress components, σ_y, σ_z, τ_{yz}, and τ_{zx}, are zero. Since both of these stresses are applied at $R = 0$, the amplitudes and means are

$$\tau_{xya} = \tau_{xym} = \frac{407.4}{2} = 203.7, \qquad \sigma_{xa} = \sigma_{xm} = \frac{611.2}{2} = 305.6\ \text{MPa}$$

The effective stress amplitude and mean may then be calculated from Eq. 9.30:

$$\bar{\sigma}_a = \frac{1}{\sqrt{2}}\sqrt{(305.6 - 0)^2 + 0 + (0 - 305.6)^2 + 6(203.7^2 + 0 + 0)} = 466.8\ \text{MPa}$$

$$\bar{\sigma}_m = 305.6 + 0 + 0 = 305.6\ \text{MPa}$$

The equivalent completely reversed stress amplitude σ_{ar} can now be obtained from Eq. 9.31 and the life then estimated by substituting σ_{ar} into Eq. 9.22:

$$\sigma_{ar} = \frac{\bar{\sigma}_a}{1 - \dfrac{\bar{\sigma}_m}{\sigma_f'}} = \frac{466.8}{1 - \dfrac{305.6}{2030}} = 549.5\ \text{MPa}$$

$$N_f = \frac{1}{2}\left(\frac{\sigma_{ar}}{\sigma_f'}\right)^{1/b} = \frac{1}{2}\left(\frac{549.5\ \text{MPa}}{2030\ \text{MPa}}\right)^{1/(-0.104)} = 1.43 \times 10^5\ \text{cycles} \qquad \textbf{Ans.}$$

The material constants σ_f' and b are from Table 9.1.

Discussion   Yielding at the peak load is a possibility. The most severe stresses occur when the bending and torque reach their peak values, $\tau_{xy} = 407.4$ and $\sigma_x = 611.2$ MPa. Substituting these into Eq. 7.36 gives an effective stress of $\bar{\sigma}_H = 933.5$ MPa. Comparison with the yield strength from Table 9.1 gives a safety factor against yielding of $X_o = 1.27$. Hence, there is no yielding, but the safety factor is not very large.

9.9 VARIABLE AMPLITUDE LOADING

As discussed earlier in this chapter, fatigue loadings in practical applications usually involve stress amplitudes that change in an irregular manner. We will now consider methods of making life estimates for such loadings.

9.9.1 The Palmgren–Miner Rule

Consider a situation of variable amplitude loading, as illustrated in Fig. 9.43. A certain stress amplitude σ_{a1} is applied for a number of cycles N_1, where the number of cycles to failure from the S-N curve for σ_{a1} is N_{f1}. The fraction of the life used is then N_1/N_{f1}. Now let another stress amplitude σ_{a2}, corresponding to N_{f2} on the S-N curve, be applied for N_2 cycles. An additional fraction of the life N_2/N_{f2} is then used. The *Palmgren–Miner rule* simply states that fatigue failure is expected when such life fractions sum to unity—that is, when 100% of the life is exhausted:

$$\frac{N_1}{N_{f1}} + \frac{N_2}{N_{f2}} + \frac{N_3}{N_{f3}} + \cdots = \sum \frac{N_j}{N_{fj}} = 1 \tag{9.33}$$

This simple rule was employed by A. Palmgren in Sweden in the 1920s for predicting the life of ball bearings, and then it was applied in a more general context by B. F. Langer in 1937. However, the rule was not widely known or used until its appearance in 1945 in a paper by M. A. Miner.

A particular sequence of loading may be repeatedly applied to an engineering component, or, for a continually varying load history, a typical sample may be available. Under these circumstances, it is convenient to sum cycle ratios over one repetition of a given load sequence and then multiply the result by the number of repetitions required for the summation to reach unity:

$$B_f \left[\sum \frac{N_j}{N_{fj}} \right]_{\text{one rep.}} = 1 \tag{9.34}$$

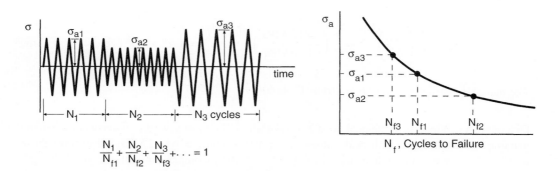

Figure 9.43   Use of the Palmgren–Miner rule for life prediction for variable amplitude loading which is completely reversed.

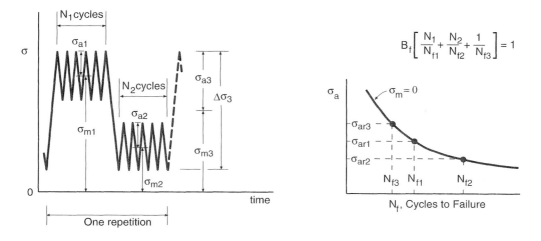

Figure 9.44   Life prediction for a repeating stress history with mean level shifts.

Here, B_f is the number of repetitions to failure. The application of this equation is illustrated in Fig. 9.44.

Some cycles of the variable amplitude loading may involve mean stresses. Equivalent completely reversed stresses then need to be calculated before applying a completely reversed S-N curve, or else a life equation applied that already incorporates mean stress effects, such as Eq. 9.23 or 9.24. In addition, the stress ranges caused by changing the mean level also need to be considered in summing cycle ratios. For example, in Fig. 9.44, the cycles at amplitude-mean combinations $(\sigma_{a1}, \sigma_{m1})$ and $(\sigma_{a2}, \sigma_{m2})$ are obvious. However, one additional cycle $(\sigma_{a3}, \sigma_{m3})$ also needs to be considered. In fact, this cycle will cause most of the fatigue damage if σ_{a1} and σ_{a2} are small, so that omitting it could result in a seriously nonconservative life estimate. The task of identifying cycles can be handled in a comprehensive manner by *cycle counting*, as described in the next subsection.

Consider service loading that includes stress cycles at contrasting high and low levels. A relatively small number of severe cycles can have a significant effect on the life estimated by the Palmgren–Miner rule, depending on their contribution to the summation of cycle ratios. However, as discussed in Section 9.6.5, there is an additional sequence effect of the severe cycles. In particular, a small number of severe cycles may initiate damage that can then be propagated by low stresses, even stresses below the fatigue limit from constant amplitude tests. Therefore, where cycles both above and below the fatigue limit occur, it is recommended that the stress–life relationship of the form of Eqs. 9.6 or 9.7 be extrapolated below the fatigue limit, as a straight line on a log–log plot, for the purpose of making life estimates. Hence, stresses below the fatigue limit are not assumed to give infinite life. One procedure that has some support in experimental results is to assume that there is a revised fatigue limit at half of the one from constant amplitude testing. (In Ritchie (2003), see Chapter 4.03 for additional comments and literature references.)

Example 9.8

The stress history shown in Fig. E9.8 is repeatedly applied as a uniaxial stress to an unnotched member made of the AISI 4340 steel of Table 9.1. Estimate the number of repetitions required to cause fatigue failure.

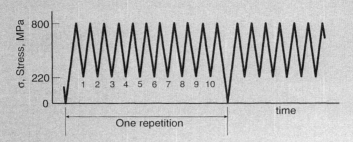

Figure E9.8

Solution   In one repetition of the history, the stress rises from zero to 800 MPa and later returns to zero, forming one cycle with $\sigma_{min} = 0$ and $\sigma_{max} = 800$ MPa. There are also 10 cycles with $\sigma_{min} = 220$ and $\sigma_{max} = 800$ MPa. A table is useful, with all stress values being in MPa:

j	N_j	σ_{min}	σ_{max}	σ_a	σ_m	N_{fj}	N_j/N_{fj}
1	1	0	800	400	400	1.36×10^5	7.37×10^{-6}
2	10	220	800	290	510	1.54×10^6	6.51×10^{-6}

$$\Sigma = 1.388 \times 10^{-5}$$

Each of the two levels of cycling forms a line in the table. The values of stress amplitude σ_a, and mean stress σ_m, and the corresponding life N_f, are calculated from Eqs. 9.1 and 9.23.

$$\sigma_a = \frac{\sigma_{max} - \sigma_{min}}{2}, \qquad \sigma_m = \frac{\sigma_{max} + \sigma_{min}}{2}, \qquad N_f = \frac{1}{2}\left(\frac{\sigma_a}{\sigma'_f - \sigma_m}\right)^{1/b}$$

Constants $\sigma'_f = 1758$ MPa and $b = -0.0977$ from Table 9.1 are used. The life in repetitions to failure B_f may then be estimated from the N and N_f values in the table by using the Palmgren–Miner rule in the form of Eq. 9.34.

$$B_f = 1 \bigg/ \left[\sum \frac{N_j}{N_{fj}}\right]_{\text{one rep.}} = 1/1.388 \times 10^{-5} = 72,000 \text{ repetitions} \qquad \textbf{Ans.}$$

9.9.2 Cycle Counting for Irregular Histories

For highly irregular variations of load with time, such as those in Figs. 9.7 to 9.10, it is not obvious how individual events should be isolated and defined as cycles so that the Palmgren–Miner rule can be employed. In past years, there was considerable uncertainty and debate concerning the proper procedure, and a number of different methods were proposed and used. However, a consensus has emerged that the best approach is a procedure called *rainflow cycle counting*, developed by Prof. T. Endo and his colleagues in Japan around 1968, or certain other procedures that are essentially equivalent.

An irregular stress history consists of a series of *peaks* and *valleys*, which are points where the direction of loading changes, as illustrated in Fig. 9.45. Also of interest are *ranges*—that is, stress differences—measured between peaks and valleys or between valleys and peaks. A *simple range* is measured between a peak and the next valley, or between a valley and the next peak. An *overall range* is measured between a peak and a valley that is not the next one, but is one that occurs later, or between a valley and a later peak. In Fig. 9.45, $\Delta\sigma_{AB}$ and $\Delta\sigma_{BC}$ are simple ranges, and $\Delta\sigma_{AD}$ and $\Delta\sigma_{DG}$ are overall ranges.

In performing rainflow cycle counting, a cycle is identified or *counted* if it meets the criterion illustrated in Fig. 9.46. A peak-valley-peak or valley-peak-valley combination X-Y-Z in the loading history is considered to contain a cycle if the second range, $\Delta\sigma_{YZ}$, is greater than or equal to the first range, $\Delta\sigma_{XY}$. If the second range is indeed larger or equal, then a cycle equal to the first range ($\Delta\sigma_{XY}$) is counted. The mean value for this cycle, specifically the average of σ_X and σ_Y, is also of interest.

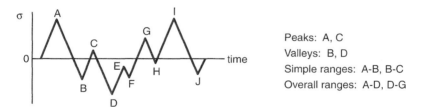

Figure 9.45   Definitions for irregular loading.

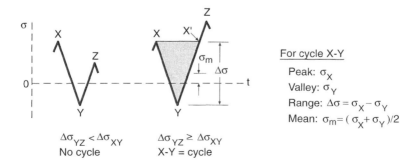

Figure 9.46   Condition for counting a cycle with the rainflow method.

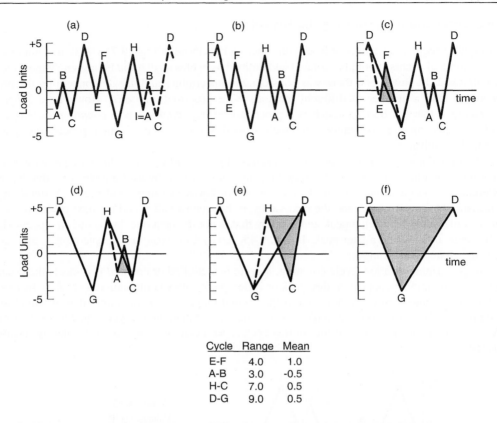

Cycle	Range	Mean
E-F	4.0	1.0
A-B	3.0	-0.5
H-C	7.0	0.5
D-G	9.0	0.5

Figure 9.47 Example of rainflow cycle counting. (Adapted from [ASTM 97] Std. E1049; copyright © ASTM; reprinted with permission.)

The complete procedure is described as follows, with the use of the example of Fig. 9.47: Assume that the stress history given is to be repeatedly applied, so that it can be taken to begin at any peak or valley. On this basis, it is convenient to move a portion of the history to the end, so that a sequence is obtained that begins and ends with the highest peak or lowest valley. Figures 9.47(a) and (b) illustrate this. We can then proceed with cycle counting, starting at the beginning of the rearranged history and using the criterion of Fig. 9.46. If a cycle is counted, this information is recorded, and its peak and valley are assumed not to exist for purposes of further cycle counting, as illustrated for cycle *E-F* in (c). If no cycle can be counted at the current location, we then move ahead until a count can be made. For example, in (d), after *E-F* is counted, the counting condition is next met for *A-B*.

Counting is complete when all of the history is exhausted. For this example, the cycles counted are *E-F*, *A-B*, *H-C*, and *D-G*, and they have ranges and means as tabulated at the bottom of Fig. 9.47. Note that some of the cycles counted correspond to simple ranges in the original history, specifically *E-F* and *A-B*, and others to overall ranges, specifically *H-C* and *D-G*. The largest

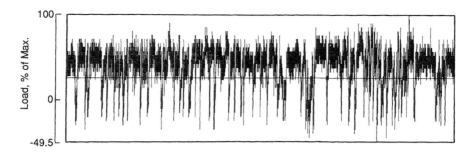

Range	−15	−10	−5	0	5	10	15	20	25	30	35	40	45	50	55	60	65	70	75	All
								Mean												
20	4	1	5	2	2	5	—	—	3	6	15	27	29	32	22	12	6	2	—	173
25	2	4	3	9	8	10	4	6	2	7	17	37	36	43	33	13	7	1	2	244
30	1	1	5	3	1	1	4	3	—	4	13	20	20	23	20	8	6	1	—	134
35	1	1	4	2	3	2	—	1	3	2	8	17	16	11	11	7	2	—	—	91
40	—	1	1	1	2	1	1	—	—	4	7	15	16	9	8	2	—	—	—	68
45	—	1	—	4	3	—	—	—	—	2	1	9	7	2	3	1	—	—	—	33
50	—	—	2	2	2	1	—	—	—	2	2	3	3	1	1	1	1	—	—	21
55	—	—	1	1	—	—	—	—	—	2	2	4	4	2	—	1	—	1	—	18
60	—	1	1	—	—	—	—	—	—	1	1	3	2	1	—	—	—	—	—	10
65	—	—	—	—	—	—	—	—	—	—	2	1	—	—	—	—	—	—	—	3
70	—	—	—	—	—	—	—	—	—	—	2	—	1	—	—	—	—	—	—	3
75	—	—	—	—	—	1	—	—	—	—	1	2	—	—	—	—	—	—	—	4
80	—	—	—	—	—	—	—	—	—	—	—	—	—	—	—	—	—	—	—	—
85	—	—	—	—	1	—	1	3	3	—	—	—	—	—	—	—	—	—	—	8
90	—	—	—	—	—	—	—	4	—	—	—	—	—	—	—	—	—	—	—	4
95	—	—	—	—	—	1	—	1	4	1	—	—	—	—	—	—	—	—	—	7
100	—	—	—	—	—	—	—	5	3	1	—	—	—	—	—	—	—	—	—	9
105	—	—	—	—	—	—	—	3	3	3	—	—	—	—	—	—	—	—	—	9
110	—	—	—	—	—	—	—	2	3	—	—	—	—	—	—	—	—	—	—	5
115	—	—	—	—	—	—	—	3	—	—	—	—	—	—	—	—	—	—	—	3
120	—	—	—	—	—	1	—	1	1	—	—	—	—	—	—	—	—	—	—	3
125	—	—	—	—	—	—	—	2	—	—	—	—	—	—	—	—	—	—	—	2
130	—	—	—	—	—	—	—	—	—	—	—	—	—	—	—	—	—	—	—	—
135	—	—	—	—	—	—	1	—	—	—	—	—	—	—	—	—	—	—	—	1
140	—	—	—	—	—	—	—	—	—	—	—	—	—	—	—	—	—	—	—	—
145	—	—	—	—	—	—	—	—	—	—	—	—	—	—	—	—	—	—	—	—
150	—	—	—	—	—	—	—	1	—	—	—	—	—	—	—	—	—	—	—	1

Figure 9.48   An irregular load vs. time history from a ground vehicle transmission, and a matrix giving numbers of rainflow cycles at various combinations of range and mean. The range and mean values are percentages of the peak load; in constructing the matrix, these were rounded to the discrete values shown. (Load history from [Wetzel 77] pp. 15–18.)

range counted is always the one between the highest peak and the lowest valley, D-G for this example.

For lengthy histories, it is convenient to present the results of rainflow cycle counting as a matrix giving the numbers of cycles occurring at various combinations of range and mean. An example of this is shown in Fig. 9.48. Note that values of range and mean are rounded off to discrete values to give a matrix of manageable size. Cycle counting is often applied directly to load histories, with this being the case for Fig. 9.48.

Additional information on cycle counting can be found in ASTM Standard No. E1049 and in the *SAE Fatigue Design Handbook* (Rice, 1997). The latter reference also contains relevant computer programs.

Example 9.9

At a location of interest in a member made of the alloy Ti-6Al-4V of Table 9.1, the material is repeatedly subjected to the uniaxial stress history of Fig. E9.9(a). Estimate the number of repetitions necessary to cause fatigue failure.

Solution   Cycle counting is needed, as shown in Fig. E9.9(b). Point A has the highest absolute value of stress, so no reordering is needed. Thus, cycle counting can start at the first point at level A and finish when the history returns to this point at A'. By considering event A_1-B_1-A_2, a cycle A_1-B_1 is counted, followed by two additional similar cycles, A_2-B_2 and A_3-B_3. Next, event A_4-C_1-D_1 is considered, but no cycle is counted. Then event C_1-D_1-C_2 yields cycle C_1-D_1, followed by additional similar cycles, with a total of 100 cycles C-D being counted. At this point, all peaks and valleys have participated in cycles, except A_4, E, and A'. These form the final major cycle between the highest peak and the lowest valley.

The results of the cycle counting are summarized in Table E9.9, including the maximum and minimum stresses for each of the three levels of cycling. Stress amplitudes σ_a are calculated for each line in the table from Eq. 9.1(a), with all stress values tabulated being in units of MPa. Values of N_f are then determined from σ_{max} and σ_a on the basis of the SWT equation and

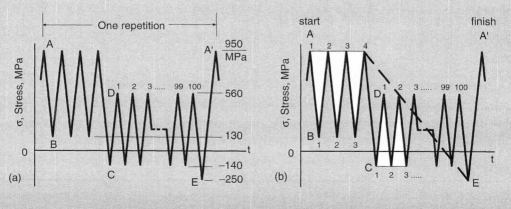

Figure E9.9

Table E9.9

Cycle	j	N_j	σ_{min}	σ_{max}	σ_a	N_{fj}	N_j/N_{fj}
A-B	1	3	130	950	410	4.21×10^4	7.12×10^{-5}
C-D	2	100	-140	560	350	1.14×10^6	8.74×10^{-5}
A-E	3	1	-250	950	600	6.75×10^3	1.481×10^{-4}

$$\Sigma = 3.068 \times 10^{-4}$$

constants σ_f' and b for Ti-6Al-4V from Table 9.1. Hence, Eq. 9.24(a) is solved for N_f to make the calculations:

$$N_f = \frac{1}{2}\left(\frac{\sqrt{\sigma_{max}\sigma_a}}{\sigma_f'}\right)^{1/b}$$

Next, the ratios N_j/N_{fj} are calculated for each level of cycling, and the sum of these is employed in Eq. 9.34 to finally yield the estimated number of repetitions to failure:

$$B_f = 1 \Big/ \left[\sum \frac{N_j}{N_{fj}}\right]_{\text{one rep.}} = 1/3.068 \times 10^{-4} = 3259 \text{ repetitions} \qquad \textbf{Ans.}$$

9.9.3 Equivalent Stress Level and Safety Factors

For making life estimates for variable amplitude loading, an alternative procedure is to calculate an *equivalent constant amplitude stress* level that causes the same life as the variable history if applied for the same number of cycles. Since the Palmgren–Miner rule is the basis of the equation that we will develop for calculating the equivalent stress, this method is simply a different route to making the same calculation.

Consider a repeating or sample load history containing N_B rainflow cycles, so that the number of cycles to failure is $N_f = B_f N_B$, where B_f is the number of repetitions to failure. For each cycle, an equivalent completely reversed stress amplitude σ_{ar} can be computed from the stress amplitude and mean. To proceed, apply the Palmgren–Miner rule in the form of Eq. 9.34:

$$B_f\left[\sum_{j=1}^{N_B} \frac{N_j}{N_{fj}}\right] = 1, \qquad N_{fj} = \frac{1}{2}\left(\frac{\sigma_{arj}}{\sigma_f'}\right)^{1/b} \qquad (\text{a, b}) \qquad (9.35)$$

Here, the life N_{fj} for each σ_{arj} is calculated from Eq. 9.22. Then treat each cycle individually, so that each $N_j = 1$, and substitute the N_{fj} values from (b) into (a) to obtain

$$\frac{N_f}{N_B}\left[\sum_{j=1}^{N_B} 2\left(\frac{\sigma_{arj}}{\sigma_f'}\right)^{-1/b}\right] = 1, \qquad \sigma_f'(2N_f)^b\left[\sum_{j=1}^{N_B}(\sigma_{arj})^{-1/b}\Big/ N_B\right]^b = 1 \qquad (\text{a, b}) \quad (9.36)$$

where N_f/N_B has been substituted for B_f and (a) is rearranged and raised to the power b to obtain (b).

From Eq. 9.7, we note that the desired equivalent constant amplitude stress, which we will denote σ_{aq}, must be related to the number of cycles to failure by $\sigma_{aq} = \sigma'_f(2N_f)^b$. Hence, if we isolate the quantity $\sigma'_f(2N_f)^b$ in Eq. 9.36(b) onto one side of the equality, then what is on the other side gives the desired σ_{aq}:

$$\sigma_{aq} = \left[\sum_{j=1}^{N_B} (\sigma_{arj})^{-1/b} \Big/ N_B \right]^{-b} , \qquad \sigma_{aq} = \left[\sum_{j=1}^{k} N_j (\sigma_{arj})^{-1/b} \Big/ N_B \right]^{-b} \qquad \text{(a, b)} \quad (9.37)$$

Equivalent form (b) is convenient where there are repeated cycles numbering N_j at each of k different levels. It is derived from (a) by combining the cycles at each level, so that the products $N_j(\sigma_{arj})^{-1/b}$ are summed over the k different levels. Equation 9.37 applies for any power-law form of stress–life curve, such as Eq. 9.6, for which $\sigma_{aq} = AN_f^B$ and B replaces b.

To determine safety factors, the logic of Fig. 9.6 applies, with the stress amplitude σ_a now generalized to σ_{aq}, and the stress–life curve becoming $\sigma_{aq} = \sigma'_f(2N_f)^b$. The safety factors in stress and life are calculated by generalizing Eqs. 9.9 and 9.10:

$$X_S = \frac{\sigma_{aq1}}{\hat{\sigma}_{aq}}\bigg|_{N_f=\hat{N}} , \qquad X_N = \frac{N_{f2}}{\hat{N}}\bigg|_{\sigma_{aq}=\hat{\sigma}_{aq}} \qquad \text{(a, b)} \qquad (9.38)$$

The value of $\hat{\sigma}_{aq}$ is calculated from the stress history expected in service by using Eq. 9.37. Also, Eq. 9.12 relates the two safety factors, so that $X_S = X_N^{-b}$.

A load factor approach can also be applied. The entire stress history could be scaled by a single load factor Y, or different components of the loading could be assigned different load factors. The life from the factored stress history must not be less than the desired service life $\hat{N}$. For the Eq. 9.7 form of stress–life curve, this is the same as requiring that the equivalent constant amplitude stress from Eq. 9.37 for the factored stress history must obey $\sigma'_{aq1} \leq \sigma'_f(2\hat{N})^b$. For the Eq. 9.7 form with either the SWT or Walker mean stress equations, a single load factor Y applied to all stresses in the history will always have the same value as the safety factor in stress, $Y = X_S$. But different values will be obtained for the Morrow or Goodman mean stress equations, $Y \neq X_S$, which arise from an extension of the logic in the last paragraph of Section 9.7.5.

Example 9.10

Consider the stress history and material of Ex. 9.8.

    (a) Estimate the life using the equivalent constant amplitude stress method.
    (b) If the given stress history is expected to be applied in service for 1000 repetitions, what are the safety factors in stress and in life?

Solution   **(a)** Since there are repeated cycles at different levels of cycling, Eq. 9.37(b) is convenient, where $k = 2$ in this case. Cycle counting and calculation of stress amplitudes and means are the same as for Ex. 9.8, and the same materials constants σ'_f and b for AISI 4340 steel are

Table E9.10

j	N_j	σ_{min}	σ_{max}	σ_a	σ_m	σ_{arj}	$N_j(\sigma_{arj})^{-1/b}$
1	1	0	800	400	400	517.8	6.036×10^{27}
2	10	220	800	290	510	408.5	5.330×10^{27}

$N_B = 11$							$\Sigma = 1.137 \times 10^{28}$

employed. Then σ_{ar} is calculated for each of level of cycling from the Morrow mean stress relationship, Eq. 9.21. Values are given in Table E9.10, where all stresses are in MPa units. Next, the corresponding products $N_j(\sigma_{arj})^{-1/b}$ are computed, and the sum of these obtained as required for Eq. 9.37(b). Also, summing the N_j values gives N_B.

We then employ Eq. 9.37(b) to calculate σ_{aq}, substituting the sum Σ from the table, along with N_B and the material constant b:

$$\sigma_{aq} = \left[\sum_{j=1}^{k} N_j(\sigma_{arj})^{-1/b} \bigg/ N_B \right]^{-b} = [1.137 \times 10^{28}/11]^{-(-0.0977)} = 435.8 \text{ MPa}$$

Finally, substitute this value as σ_a in Eq. 9.7 and solve for N_f to obtain

$$N_f = \frac{1}{2} \left(\frac{\sigma_{aq}}{\sigma_f'} \right)^{1/b} = \frac{1}{2} \left(\frac{435.8 \text{ MPa}}{1758 \text{ MPa}} \right)^{1/(-0.0977)} = 792,300 \text{ cycles}$$

$$B_f = \frac{N_f}{N_B} = \frac{792,300}{11} = 72,000 \text{ repetitions} \qquad\qquad\qquad \textbf{Ans.}$$

where the number of repetitions to failure is also calculated. As expected, the same result is obtained as for Ex. 9.8.

(b) The safety factor in life can be calculated from Eq. 9.38(b) and then the safety factor in stress from Eq. 9.12(a):

$$X_N = \frac{N_{f2}}{\hat{N}} = \frac{B_{f2}}{\hat{B}} = \frac{72,000}{1000} = 72.0, \qquad X_S = X_N^{-b} = (72.0)^{-(-0.0977)} = 1.52 \quad \textbf{Ans.}$$

Discussion   Note that by using Eq. 9.12, both safety factors can be obtained from the original solution of Ex. 9.8 without invoking the σ_{aq} value. Alternatively, the safety factor in stress can also be calculated from Eq. 9.38(a) by entering Eq. 9.7 with $\hat{N} = \hat{B}N_B = 11,000$ cycles to obtain $\sigma_{aq1} = 661.9$ MPa. Comparison with $\hat{\sigma}_{aq} = 435.8$ MPa from (a) then gives the same value, $X_S = 1.52$.

9.10 SUMMARY

Fatigue of materials is the process of accumulated damage and then failure due to cyclic loading. Engineering efforts over more than 150 years, aimed at preventing fatigue failure, led first to the development of a stress-based approach. This approach emphasizes stress versus life curves and nominal (average) stresses. More sophisticated approaches, namely the strain-based approach and the fracture mechanics approach, have arisen in recent years.

Cyclic stressing between constant maximum and minimum values can be described by giving values of the stress amplitude and mean, σ_a and σ_m. Alternatively, we can specify $\sigma_{\max}$ and the ratio R, or $\Delta\sigma$ and R, where $R = \sigma_{\min}/\sigma_{\max}$. Useful relationships among these quantities are given by Eqs. 9.1 to 9.4. It is important to distinguish between the actual stress σ at a point and any nominal (average) stress S that might be calculated.

Stress versus life (S-N) curves are commonly plotted in terms of stress amplitude versus cycles to failure. Such curves can be obtained from a variety of test apparatus, ranging from relatively simple rotating bending machines to sophisticated closed-loop servohydraulic equipment. The most basic S-N curve is considered to be the one for zero mean stress, which is the only case that can be tested by means of rotating bending.

S-N curves vary with the material and its prior processing. They are also affected by mean stress and geometry, especially the presence of notches, and also by surface finish, chemical and thermal environment, frequency of cycling, and residual stress. Some equations for representing S-N curves are

$$\sigma_a = \sigma_f'(2N_f)^b, \qquad \sigma_a = C + D \log N_f \tag{9.39}$$

The first of these gives a straight line on log–log coordinates, the second a straight line on log–linear coordinates.

Estimates of mean stress effects for unnotched members may be made by using equations such as that of Morrow, or of Smith, Watson, and Topper:

$$\sigma_{ar} = \frac{\sigma_a}{1 - \dfrac{\sigma_m}{\sigma_f'}}, \qquad \sigma_{ar} = \sqrt{\sigma_{\max}\sigma_a} \tag{9.40}$$

In such an equation, the applied combination of stress amplitude σ_a and mean stress σ_m is expected to result in the same life as the stress amplitude σ_{ar} applied at zero mean stress. Values of σ_{ar}, called the *equivalent completely reversed stress amplitude*, may be used to enter a curve of σ_a versus N_f from completely reversed loading. The preceding equations may also be generalized for making life estimates for simple cases of multiaxial loading. The quantities σ_a and σ_m are replaced by an effective stress amplitude $\bar\sigma_a$, which is proportional to the amplitude of the octahedral shear stress, and an effective mean stress $\bar\sigma_m$, which is proportional to the hydrostatic stress due to mean stresses in three directions.

If more than one amplitude or mean level occurs, life estimates may be made by summing cycle ratios in the Palmgren–Miner rule:

$$\sum \frac{N_j}{N_{fj}} = 1 \tag{9.41}$$

The alternative form given by Eq. 9.34 is useful for sequences of loading that occur repeatedly. Cycles introduced by changing mean levels need to be considered in making such life estimates, and rainflow cycle counting is needed for highly irregular load versus time histories. Stress cycles below the fatigue limit should not be assigned infinite life if they occur in the same loading history as occasional cycles that are substantially above the fatigue limit. The Palmgren–Miner rule may be applied by summing cycle ratios, as in Eq. 9.41, or by calculating an *equivalent constant amplitude stress* σ_{aq} that causes the same life as the variable history if applied for the same number of cycles. (See Eq. 9.37.)

NEW TERMS AND SYMBOLS

beach marks

completely reversed cycling

constant amplitude

constant-life diagram

elastic stress concentration factor, k_t

equivalent completely reversed stress
    amplitude, σ_{ar}

equivalent constant amplitude stress, σ_{aq}

fatigue (of materials)

fatigue limit, σ_e

fatigue strength

fracture mechanics approach

Gerber parabola

high-cycle fatigue

low-cycle fatigue

maximum stress, σ_{max}

mean stress, σ_m

minimum stress, σ_{min}

modified Goodman line

Morrow equation

nominal stress, S

normalized amplitude-mean diagram

notch (stress raiser)

Palmgren–Miner rule

peak, valley

point stress, σ

rainflow cycle counting

residual stress

rotating bending test

safety factor in life, X_N

safety factor in stress, X_S

sequence effect

S-N curve

static load

strain-based approach

stress amplitude, σ_a

stress-based approach

stress range, $\Delta\sigma$

stress ratio, R

striations

SWT equation

vibratory load

Walker equation

working load

zero-to-tension cycling

REFERENCES

(a) General References

ASTM. 2010. *Annual Book of ASTM Standards*, ASTM International, West Conshohocken, PA. See: No. E466, "Standard Practice for Conducting Force Controlled Constant Amplitude Axial Fatigue Tests of Metallic Materials," Vol. 03.01; No. E739, "Standard Practice for Statistical Analysis of Linear or Linearized Stress-life (*S-N*) and Strain-Life (*ε-N*) Fatigue Data," Vol. 03.01; No. E1049, "Standard Practices for Cycle

Counting in Fatigue Analysis," Vol. 03.01; No. F1801, "Standard Practice for Corrosion Fatigue Testing of Metallic Implant Materials," and others in Vol. 13.01; and No. D3479, "Standard Test Method for Tension-Tension Fatigue of Polymer Matrix Composite Materials," Vol. 15.03.

BATHIAS, C., and P. C. PARIS. 2005. *Gigacycle Fatigue in Mechanical Practice*, Marcel Dekker, New York.

DRAPER, JOHN. 2008. *Modern Metal Fatigue Analysis*, Engineering Materials Advisory Services, Cradley Heath, West Midlands, England.

DOWLING, N. E., C. A. CALHOUN, and A. ARCARI. 2009. "Mean Stress Effects in Stress-Life Fatigue and the Walker Equation," *Fatigue and Fracture of Engineering Materials and Structures,* vol. 32, no. 3, pp. 163–179. Also, *Erratum,* vol. 32, no. 10, p. 866.

GRAHAM, J. A., J. F. MILLAN, and F. J. APPL, eds. 1968. *Fatigue Design Handbook*, SAE Pub. No. AE-4, Society of Automotive Engineers, Warrendale, PA.

LAMPMAN, S. R., ed., 1996. *ASM Handbook, Vol. 19: Fatigue and Fracture*, ASM International, Materials Park, OH.

MANN, J. Y. 1958. "The Historical Development of Research on the Fatigue of Materials and Structures," *The Jnl. of the Australian Inst. of Metals*, Nov. 1958, pp. 222–241.

RICE R. C., ed. 1997. *Fatigue Design Handbook*, 3d ed., SAE Pub. No. AE-22, Society of Automotive Engineers, Warrendale, PA.

RITCHIE, R. O., and Y. MURAKAMI, eds. 2003. *Cyclic Loading and Fatigue*, Vol. 4 of *Comprehensive Structural Integrity: Fracture of Materials from Nano to Macro*, I. Milne, R. O. Ritchie, and B. Karihaloo, eds., Elsevier Ltd., Oxford, UK.

SINES, G. and J. L. WAISMAN. 1959. *Metal Fatigue*, McGraw-Hill, New York.

SMITH, J. O. 1942. "The Effect of Range of Stress on the Fatigue Strength of Metals," Bulletin No. 334, University of Illinois, Engineering Experiment Station, Urbana, IL. See also Bulletin No. 316, Sept. 1939.

SMITH, K. N., P. WATSON, and T. H. TOPPER. 1970. "A Stress-Strain Function for the Fatigue of Metals," *Journal of Materials*, ASTM, vol. 5, no. 4, Dec. 1970, pp. 767–778.

SOCIE, D. F. and G. B. MARQUIS. 2000. *Multiaxial Fatigue*, Society of Automotive Engineers, Warrendale, PA.

(b) Sources of Material Properties and Databases

ADKINS, D. W. and R. G. KANDER. 1988. "Fatigue Performance of Glass Reinforced Thermoplastics," Paper No. 8808-010, *Proc. of the 4th Annual Conf. on Advanced Composites*, Sept. 1988, Dearborn, MI. Sponsored by ASM International, Materials Park, OH.

BOLLER, C. and T. SEEGER. 1987. *Materials Data for Cyclic Loading*, 5 vols., Elsevier Science Pubs., Amsterdam. See also *Supplement 1*, 1990, by A. Baumel and T. Seeger.

CINDAS. 2010. *Aerospace Structural Metals Database (ASMD)*, CINDAS LLC, West Lafayette, IN. (See *https://cindasdata.com.*)

HOLT, J. M., H. MINDLIN, and C. Y. HO, eds. 1996. *Structural Alloys Handbook*, CINDAS LLC, West Lafayette, IN. (See *https://cindasdata.com.*)

KAUFMAN, J. G., ed. 1999. *Properties of Aluminum Alloys: Tensile, Creep, and Fatigue Data at High and Low Temperatures*, ASM International, Materials Park, OH.

MCKEEN, L. W. 2010. *Fatigue and Tribiological Properties of Plastics and Elastomers*, 2nd ed., Plastics Design Library, William Andrew (Elsevier), Norwich, NY.

MMPDS. 2010. *Metallic Materials Properties Development and Standardization Handbook*, MMPDS-05, U.S. Federal Aviation Administration; distributed by Battelle Memorial Institute, Columbus, OH. (See *http://projects.battelle.org/mmpds*; replaces MIL-HDBK-5.)

NIMS. 2010. *Fatigue Data Sheets*, periodically updated database, National Institute of Materials Science, Tsukuba, Ibaraki, Japan. (See *http://mits.nims.go.jp/index_en.html.*)

SAE. 2002. *Technical Report on Low Cycle Fatigue Properties: Ferrous and Non-Ferrous Materials*, Document No. J1099, Society of Automotive Engineers, Warrendale, PA.

SHIOZAWA, K. and T. SAKAI, eds. 1996. *Data Book on Fatigue Strength of Metallic Materials*, 3 Vols., Elsevier Science, Amsterdam.

PROBLEMS AND QUESTIONS

Section 9.2

9.1 Verify each item of Eq. 9.4, starting from any of Eqs. 9.1 to 9.3 or preceding items of Eq. 9.4.

9.2 Write definitions in your own words for point stress σ, nominal stress S, and the product $k_t S$. Give an example of a situation where $\sigma = S$, and also give an example where $\sigma \neq S$.

9.3 For an *S-N* curve of the form of Eq. 9.5, two points (N_1, σ_1) and (N_2, σ_2) are known.

    (a) Develop equations for the constants C and D as a function of these values.

    (b) Apply your result from (a) to the data in Fig. 9.5 for $N_f < 10^6$ cycles, evaluating C and D to obtain an equation that gives a reasonable representation of these data.

9.4 The steel 50CrMo4 can be assumed to have an *S-N* curve of the form of Eq. 9.6. Some fatigue test data for unnotched specimens under axial stress, with zero mean stress, are given in Table P9.4.

    (a) Plot these data on log–log coordinates, and determine approximate values for the constants A and B.

    (b) Obtain refined values for A and B, using a linear least-squares fit to $\log N_f$ versus $\log \sigma_a$. Then calculate σ_f' and b for Eq. 9.7.

Table P9.4

σ_a MPa	N_f cycles
675	14 000
578	55 000
600	58 000
559	61 000
563	165 000
540	270 000

Source: Data in [Baumel 90].

9.5 Proceed as in Prob. 9.4, but use the data in Table P9.5 for unnotched, axially loaded specimens of 2024-T3 aluminum tested under zero mean stress.

Table P9.5

σ_a MPa	N_f cycles
331	43 000
276	112 000
241	172 000
207	231 000
190	546 000
179	1 165 000

Source: Data in [Baumel 90].

9.6 Proceed as in Prob. 9.4, but use the data in Table P9.6 for unnotched, axially loaded specimens of 50CrMo4 tested under zero mean stress.

Table P9.6

σ_a MPa	N_f cycles
537	38 000
475	45 000
463	47 000
447	140 000
450	185 000
438	190 000

Source: Data in [Baumel 90].

9.7 Proceed as in Prob. 9.4, but use the data in Table P9.7 for unnotched, axially loaded specimens of 50CrMo4 tested under zero mean stress.

Table P9.7

σ_a MPa	N_f cycles
448	30 000
448	85 000
414	144 000
469	252 000
372	351 000
459	520 000
345	701 000

Source: Data in [Berns 91].

9.8 Proceed as in Prob. 9.4, but use the data in Table P9.8 for unnotched, axially loaded specimens of 6Al-4V Titanium tested under zero mean stress.

Table P9.8

σ_a MPa	N_f cycles
293	45 000
241	90 000
207	160 000
174	700 000
152	1 200 000

Source: Data in [Grover 51a] and [Illg 56].

9.9 For the SAE 1015 steel in Table 9.1, a life of 1.94×10^5 cycles to failure is calculated for the stress amplitude of $\sigma_a = 500$ MPa that is expected to occur in service. To assure that no failures occur, the suggestion is made that parts of this type should be replaced when the number of cycles applied reaches $\frac{1}{3}$ of this life.

    (a) What are the safety factors in life and in stress corresponding to this suggestion?

    (b) Is the suggestion a good one? Briefly explain the logic of your answer.

9.10 A part made of Ti-6Al-4V (solution treated and aged) will be subjected in service to a stress amplitude of $\sigma_a = 500$ MPa, and the desired service life is 60,000 cycles.

    (a) What are the safety factors in stress and in life? Do these seem reasonable for an actual engineering application? Explain why or why not.

    (b) If a safety factor of 1.3 in stress is considered adequate, how many cycles can be applied in service before the part is replaced?

9.11 A part made of the Man-Ten (hot rolled) steel of Table 9.1 is subjected in service to a stress amplitude of $\sigma_a = 150$ MPa. If a safety factor of 1.5 on stress is considered adequate, how many cycles can be allowed to occur in service before the part is replaced? What is the corresponding safety factor on life?

Sections 9.3 to 9.6

9.12 Describe the likely sources of cyclic loading for a sailboat mast. Consider static loads, working loads, vibratory loads, and accidental loads.

9.13 For a bicycle pedal crank arm, answer the same question as in Prob. 9.12.

9.14 For the suspension springs in an automobile, answer the same question as in Prob. 9.12.

9.15 For the *fork* of a fork-lift truck, answer the same question as in Prob. 9.12.

9.16 Describe how a rotating bending fatigue testing machine works, and identify its major advantages and disadvantages.

9.17 Describe how a closed-loop servohydraulic fatigue testing machine works, and identify its major advantages and disadvantages.

9.18 For the *S-N* curves of Fig. 9.19, explain how the damage develops differently for the two aluminum alloys and how this correlates with the prior processing of the alloys. Comment on the fractions of the failure life required to develop observable damage. (Sections 3.2 and 3.4 may be useful.)

9.19 Define *beach marks* and *striations*, and explain the differences between these.

9.20 Explain the significance of statistical scatter in fatigue life, especially how this may affect the use of *S-N* curves for engineering purposes.

Section 9.7

9.21 The SAE 1015 steel of Table 9.1 is subjected to a stress amplitude of $\sigma_a = 200$ MPa. Using the Morrow equation, estimate the life for mean stresses σ_m of (a) zero, (b) 80 MPa tension, and (c) 80 MPa compression.

9.22 Proceed as in Prob. 9.21 except use the SWT equation.

9.23 Proceed as in Prob. 9.21 except use the Walker equation with $\gamma = 0.735$.

9.24 The AISI 4340 steel of Table 9.1 is subjected to cyclic loading at a stress amplitude of $\sigma_a = 600$ MPa. Using the Morrow equation, estimate the life for mean stresses σ_m of (a) zero, (b) 200 MPa tension, and (c) 200 MPa compression.

9.25 Proceed as in Prob. 9.24, except use the SWT equation.

9.26 Proceed as in Prob. 9.24, except use the Walker equation with $\gamma = 0.65$.

9.27 The aluminum alloy 2024-T4 is subjected to a stress amplitude of $\sigma_a = 250$ MPa. Using the Morrow equation in the true fracture strength form, estimate the life for mean stresses σ_m of (a) zero, (b) 120 MPa tension, and (c) 120 MPa compression.

9.28 Proceed as in Prob. 9.27 except use the SWT equation.

9.29 For RQC-100 steel, using the Morrow equation, obtain equations relating stress amplitude σ_a and life N_f for mean stresses σ_m of (a) 200 MPa tension, (b) zero, and (c) 200 MPa compression. Then plot these on log–log coordinates, and comment on the trends observed.

9.30 Proceed as in Prob. 9.29, except change the material to 2024-T4 aluminum and use the SWT equation.

9.31 Consider the data for AISI 4340 steel at various mean stresses from Tables E9.1 and E9.5.
   (a) Prepare a plot of these data similar to Fig. 9.39. (Suggestion: Start by calculating σ_{ar} from each N_f value, using constants from Table 9.1.)
   (b) On plot (a), add lines for Eqs. 9.15, 9.16, 9.17(a), and 9.17(b), and briefly discuss the success of these equations in representing the data.

9.32 Consider the data for AISI 4340 steel at various mean stresses from Tables E9.1 and E9.5.
   (a) Calculate σ_{ar} values for the SWT mean stress relationship, Eq. 9.18, for the combined data from both tables, and plot these versus life. Add the σ_{ar} versus N_f line from the constants in Table 9.1, and comment on the success of the correlation.
   (b) Repeat (a), except use σ_{ar} values for the Walker relationship, Eq. 9.19, with $\gamma = 0.65$.

9.33 For axially loaded, unnotched specimens of titanium 6Al-4V, Table P9.5 gives fatigue test data for zero mean stress, and Table P9.33 gives additional data at various nonzero mean stresses. Combine the data from Tables P9.5 and P9.33 into a single data set and proceed as follows:
   (a) For the Goodman relationship, Eq. 9.15, calculate σ_{ar} for each test, and plot these versus N_f. Add the line from the fit to the zero mean stress data of Prob. 9.5, and comment on the success of the correlation.

(b, c, d) Proceed as in (a) for the mean stress relationships of (b) Morrow with $\tilde{\sigma}_{fB}$, (c) Morrow with σ'_f, and (d) SWT.

Table P9.33

σ_a, MPa	σ_m, MPa	N_f, cycles	σ_a, MPa	σ_m, MPa	N_f, cycles
293	592	45 000	778	−130	4 500
241	646	90 000	594	−312	132 000
207	668	160 000	529	−354	540 000
174	685	700 000			

Source: Data in [Baumel 90].

9.34 For axially loaded, unnotched specimens of 50CrMo4 steel, Table P9.6 gives fatigue test data for mean stresses of approximately zero, and Table P9.34 gives additional data at various nonzero mean stresses. Combine the data from Tables P9.6 and P9.34 into a single data set and proceed as follows:

(a) For the Goodman relationship, Eq. 9.15, calculate σ_{ar} for each test, and plot these versus N_f. Add the line from the fit to the zero mean stress data of Prob. 9.6, and comment on the success of the correlation.

(b, c, d) Proceed as in (a) for the mean stress relationships of (b) Morrow with $\tilde{\sigma}_{fB}$, (c) Morrow with σ'_f, and (d) SWT.

Table P9.34

σ_a, MPa	σ_m, MPa	N_f, cycles	σ_a, MPa	σ_m, MPa	N_f, cycles
537	125	38 000	675	−225	14 000
447	267	140 000	578	−193	55 000
475	475	45 000	600	−200	58 000
463	463	47 000	559	−135	61 000
450	450	185 000	563	−188	165 000
438	438	190 000	540	−180	270 000

Source: Data in [Baumel 90].

9.35 For axially loaded, unnotched specimens of 2024-T3 aluminum, Table P9.8 gives fatigue test data for zero mean stress. Table P9.35 gives additional data for nonzero mean stresses, specifically, for various combinations of σ_{max} and $R = \sigma_{min}/\sigma_{max}$, with N_f being given in thousands of cycles. Combine the data from Tables P9.8 and P9.35 into a single data set and proceed as follows:

(a) For the Goodman relationship, Eq. 9.15, calculate σ_{ar} for each test, and plot these versus N_f. Add the line from the fit to the zero mean stress data of Prob. 9.8, and comment on the success of the correlation.

(b, c, d) Proceed as in (a) for the mean stress relationships of (b) Morrow with $\tilde{\sigma}_{fB}$, (c) Morrow with σ'_f, and (d) SWT.

Table P9.35

$\sigma_{\max}$, MPa	R	N_f, 10^3 cycles	$\sigma_{\max}$, MPa	R	N_f, 10^3 cycles
469	0.6	252	345	−0.3	67
459	0.6	520	310	−0.3	132
448	0.4	85	241	−0.3	353
414	0.4	144	448	−0.6	6.2
372	0.4	351	372	−0.6	18.2
345	0.4	701	331	−0.6	43
448	0.02	30	276	−0.6	112
386	0.02	60	241	−0.6	172
362	0.02	85	207	−0.6	231
310	0.02	156	190	−0.6	546
260	0.02	355	179	−0.6	1165
414	−0.3	24			

Source: Data in [Grover 51a].

9.36 The steel SAE 4142 (450 HB) will be subjected in service to a stress amplitude $\sigma_a = 500$ MPa and a mean stress $\sigma_m = 450$ MPa. A service life of 8,000 cycles is desired. What are the safety factors in stress and in life?

9.37 Aluminum alloy 2024-T4 will be subjected in service to a stress amplitude $\sigma_a = 200$ MPa and a mean stress $\sigma_m = 250$ MPa. A service life of 5000 cycles is desired. What are the safety factors in stress and in life?

9.38 The AISI 4340 steel of Table 9.1 will be subjected in service to a stress amplitude $\sigma_a = 400$ MPa and a mean stress $\sigma_m = 100$ MPa. A service life of 3000 cycles is desired. What are the safety factors in stress and in life?

9.39 The alloy Ti-6Al-4V of Table 9.1 is employed in a service situation where the stress amplitude is fixed at $\sigma_a = 350$ MPa, but where the mean stress can vary. A mean stress $\sigma_m = 200$ MPa is expected in service and a service life of 12,000 cycles is desired.

    (a) What is the safety factor in life?

    (b) What load factor $Y = Y_a = Y_m$ corresponds to the 12,000 cycle service life?

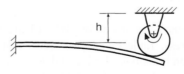

Figure P9.39

9.40 Man-Ten steel will be subjected in service to a stress amplitude $\sigma_a = 100$ MPa and a mean stress $\sigma_m = 200$ MPa. A service life of 4000 cycles is desired. The value of the amplitude is less certain than that of the mean, so the load factor for the amplitude is desired to be twice that for the mean, $Y_a = 2Y_m$.

    (a) What is the safety factor in life?

    (b) What load factor $Y_a = 2Y_m$ corresponds to the desired service life?

Section 9.8

9.41 The alloy Ti-6Al-4V of Table 9.1 is used to make a cylindrical pressure vessel having closed ends with an inner diameter of 250 mm and wall thickness of 2.5 mm.

    (a) What repeatedly applied pressure will cause fatigue failure in 10^5 cycles? (Neglect the stress raiser effect of the end closure or other geometric discontinuities.)

    (b) For the pressure from (a), what is the safety factor against yielding?

9.42 An unnotched solid circular shaft is made of SAE 4142 steel (450 HB). It has a diameter of 50 mm and is loaded in cyclic torsion between zero and a torque of 20 kN·m.

    (a) How many torsion cycles are expected to result in fatigue failure?

    (b) What is the safety factor against yielding?

    (c) What shaft diameter is needed if 100,000 cycles are expected in service and the safety factor on life must be at least 20?

    (d) What shaft diameter is needed if the safety factor against yielding must be at least 1.5?

    (e) What diameter is needed if requirements of (c) and (d) are both satisfied?

Section 9.9

9.43 An un-notched member of the AISI4340 steel of Table 9.1 is subjected to uniaxial cyclic stressing at zero mean stress. The amplitude is at first $\sigma_a = 517$ MPa for 31,280 cycles, followed by $\sigma_a = 444$ MPa for 84,620 cycles. If the stress is then changed to 550 MPa, how many cycles can be applied at this third level before fatigue failure is expected?

9.44 At a location of interest in an engineering component made of 2024-T4 aluminum, the material is repeatedly subjected to the uniaxial stress history shown in Fig. P9.44. Estimate the number of repetitions necessary to cause fatigue failure.

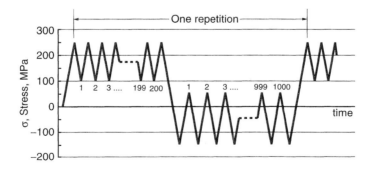

Figure P9.44

9.45 At a location of interest in an engineering component, the material is repeatedly subjected to the uniaxial stress history shown in Fig. P9.45. The component is made of SAE 4142 steel (450 HB). Estimate the number of repetitions necessary to cause fatigue failure.

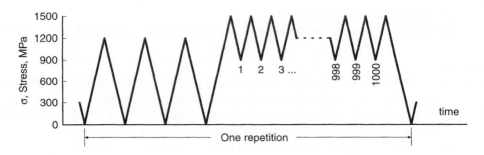

Figure P9.45

9.46 At a location of interest in a member made of the alloy Ti-6Al-4V of Table 9.1, the material is repeatedly subjected to the uniaxial stress history shown in Fig. P9.46. Estimate the number of repetitions necessary to cause fatigue failure.

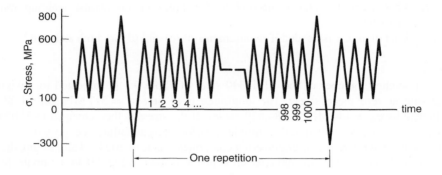

Figure P9.46

9.47 At a location of interest in a member made of the alloy Ti-6Al-4V of Table 9.1, the material is repeatedly subjected to the uniaxial stress history shown in Fig. P9.47. Estimate the number of repetitions necessary to cause fatigue failure.

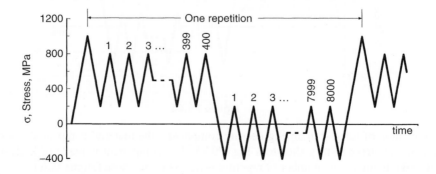

Figure P9.47

9.48 At a location of interest in a member made of the SAE 1015 steel of Table 9.1, the material is repeatedly subjected to the uniaxial stress history shown in Fig. P9.48. Estimate the number of repetitions necessary to cause fatigue failure.

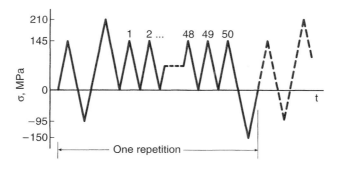

Figure P9.48

9.49 At a location of interest in an engineering component, the material is repeatedly subjected to the uniaxial stress history shown in Fig. P9.49. The component is made of RQC-100 steel. Estimate the number of repetitions necessary to cause fatigue failure.

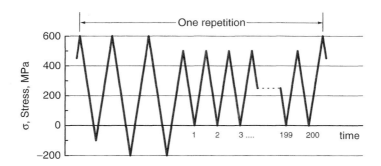

Figure P9.49

9.50 At a location of interest in an engineering component, the material is repeatedly subjected to the uniaxial stress history shown in Fig. P9.50. The component is made of the AISI 4340 steel of Table 9.1. Estimate the number of repetitions necessary to cause fatigue failure.

9.51 The history of Fig. 9.47(a) is repeatedly applied as a uniaxial stress on an unnotched member of 2024-T4 aluminum, with stress values σ being given by 1 unit = 60 MPa.

    (a) Estimate the number of repetitions required to cause fatigue failure.

    (b) If 1000 repetitions of the stress history are expected in service, what are the safety factors in stress and in life?

9.52 Rework Ex. 9.9, using the equivalent stress method of Section 9.9.3.

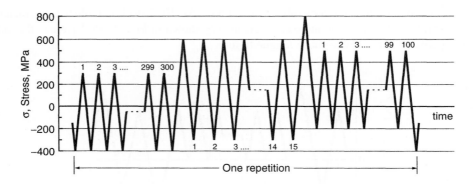

Figure P9.50

9.53 For the situation of Ex. 9.9, assume that 500 repetitions of the given stress history are expected in service. What are the safety factors in stress and in life? Do these values seem adequate for a real engineering situation?

9.54 Assume that the history of Fig. 9.9 is a bending stress on the main rotor shaft of the helicopter. The shaft is made of the alloy Ti-6Al-4V of Table 9.1. With the stress concentration factor of a notch included, one stress unit in Fig. 9.9 is equivalent to 50 MPa.

    (a) How many rotor revolutions can be applied before fatigue failure is expected? What is the estimated life in hours of flight if each rotor revolution requires 0.3 seconds?

    (b) A service life of 2000 flight hours is required, with a load factor of 1.5 uniformly applied to all stresses. Is this requirement met?

10

Stress-Based Approach to Fatigue: Notched Members

OBJECTIVES

- Understand the effects of notches (stress raisers) on fatigue strength, and apply traditional engineering methods for evaluating long-life fatigue strength and for estimating *S-N* curves.
- Evaluate mean stress effects for notched members.
- Analyze fatigue strength and life where *S-N* curves from tests on actual components are available.

10.1 INTRODUCTION

Geometric discontinuities that are unavoidable in design, such as holes, fillets, grooves, and keyways, cause the stress to be locally elevated and so are called *stress raisers*. Stress raisers, here generically termed *notches* for brevity, require special attention, as their presence reduces the resistance of a component to fatigue failure. This is simply a consequence of the locally higher stresses causing fatigue cracks to start at such locations.

Figure 10.1 provides an example of a notch in an engineering component, in particular, the attachment of blades in a steam turbine. Despite careful design to minimize the severity of the notch, a fatigue crack nevertheless developed as shown. Figure 10.2 illustrates the effect of a notch on the

Figure 10.1   Steam turbine rotor with blades attached and the *fir tree* type of connection at the blade root. On the lower right, a fatigue crack can be seen running across the blade root just above the base of the blade. (Photos courtesy of Neville F. Rieger, STI Technologies, Inc., Rochester, NY. Reprinted with permission of the Electric Power Research Institute, EPRI, from *Failure Analysis of Fossil Low Pressure Turbine Blade Group*.)

S-N curve for an aluminum alloy tested in rotating bending. Plotting nominal bending stress versus life for both the smooth and notched members shows that the fatigue strength is lowered substantially by the notch. Such effects clearly need to be included in engineering design and analysis.

Textbooks on mechanical design and similar sources describe traditional methods of applying a stress-based approach to fatigue of notched members. This chapter first reviews and discusses these traditional methods. Following this, we consider the use of fatigue test data for notched engineering components as an alternative to the empirical estimates of the traditional methods. Note that Chapter 14 covers the more advanced strain-based approach to fatigue, which treats notched members in a more detailed and rigorous manner than does any type of a stress-based approach.

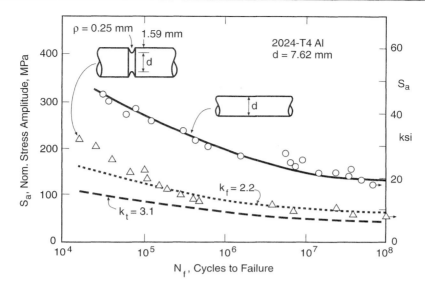

Figure 10.2   Effect of a notch on the rotating bending *S-N* behavior of an aluminum alloy, and comparisons with strength reductions using k_t and k_f. (Data from [MacGregor 52].)

10.2 NOTCH EFFECTS

The elastic stress concentration factor k_t may be employed to characterize the severity of a notch, where $k_t = \sigma/S$ is the ratio of the local notch (point) stress σ to the nominal (average) stress S. (These quantities have already been defined and discussed in Section 9.2.2 with the aid of Fig. 9.3. Also, Figs. A.11 and A.12 in Appendix A give k_t values for typical cases.) Although the k_t concept is useful for analyzing notch effects in fatigue, additional influences need to be considered, which we will now discuss.

10.2.1 The Fatigue Notch Factor k_f and Causes of $k_f < k_t$

If a simplistic view is taken, we would expect unnotched (smooth) and notched members to have the same fatigue life if the stress $\sigma = S$ in the smooth member is the same as the stress $\sigma = k_t S$ at the notch in the notched member. Hence, on a plot of S versus life N_f, the effect of a notch should be to reduce the stress amplitude corresponding to any given life by the factor k_t. An example of such an estimate is the lower line in Fig. 10.2. However, it is seen that the actual test data lie above this estimate, so that the notch has less effect than expected on the basis of k_t. The actual reduction factor at long fatigue lives—specifically, at $N_f = 10^6$ to 10^7 cycles or greater—is called the *fatigue notch factor* and is denoted k_f. It is given by

$$k_f = \frac{\sigma_{ar}}{S_{ar}} \tag{10.1}$$

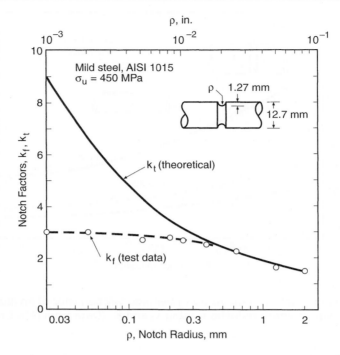

Figure 10.3 Fatigue notch factors for various notch radii based on fatigue limits from rotating bending of mild steel. (Data from [Frost 59].)

where k_f is formally defined only for completely reversed stresses, σ_{ar} for the smooth member, and S_{ar} for the notched member.

If the notch has a large radius ρ at its tip, k_f may be essentially equal to k_t. However, for small ρ, the previously noted discrepancy may be quite large, so that k_f is considerably smaller than k_t. Some values of k_f illustrating this variation with ρ for notched bars of mild steel are shown in Fig. 10.3. As will be discussed in the following sections, more than one physical cause of this behavior may exist.

10.2.2 Process Zone Size and Weakest-Link Effects

The stress in a notched member decreases rapidly with increasing distance from the notch, as illustrated in Fig. 10.4. The slope $d\sigma/dx$ of the stress distribution is called the *stress gradient*, and the magnitude of this quantity is especially large near sharp notches. It is generally agreed that the $k_f < k_t$ effect is associated with this stress gradient, and several detailed explanations have been suggested on this basis.

One argument made on the basis of stress gradients is that the material is not sensitive to the peak stress, but rather to the average stress that acts over a region of small, but finite, size. In other words, some finite volume of material must be involved for the fatigue damage process to proceed.

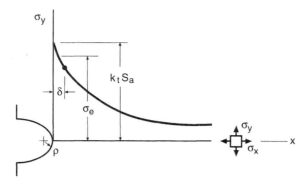

Figure 10.4 Interpretation of the fatigue limit as the average stress over a finite distance δ ahead of the notch.

The size of the active region can be characterized by a dimension δ, called the *process zone size*, as illustrated in Fig. 10.4. Thus, the stress that controls the initiation of fatigue damage is not the highest stress at $x = 0$, but rather the somewhat lower value that is the average out to a distance $x = \delta$. This average stress is then expected to be the same as the smooth specimen fatigue limit σ_e, so that k_f is estimated by

$$k_f = \frac{\left(\text{average } \sigma_y \text{ out to } x = \delta\right)}{S_a} = \frac{\sigma_e}{S_a} \tag{10.2}$$

which is less than k_t. The ratio k_f / k_t falls further below unity—that is, the discrepancy increases—if the notch radius ρ is smaller. This is because the drop in stress with increasing distance x away from the notch is more abrupt if ρ is smaller. Such a trend is consistent with observations, as in Fig. 10.3.

A result of this type might be expected due to discrete microstructure, such as crystal grains, having the effect of equalizing the stress over a small dimension, so that the peak stress is actually lowered. However, no generally applicable correlation of trends in k_f with microstructural features has been established.

Another possible stress gradient effect involves a *weakest-link* argument based on statistics. Recall that the fatigue damage process may initiate in a crystal grain that has an unfavorable orientation of its slip planes relative to the planes of applied shear stress, or in other cases at an inclusion, void, or other microscopic stress raiser. Many potential damage initiation sites occur within the volume of a smooth specimen. However, at a sharp notch, there is a possibility that no such damage initiation site occurs in the small region where the stress is near its peak value. Hence, on the average, the notched member will be more resistant to fatigue than expected if the comparison is made on the basis of the local notch stress, $\sigma_a = k_t S_a$.

10.2.3 Crack Growth Effect

A third possible effect is related to the fact that a crack may start quickly in a sharply notched member during cyclic loading, so that the fatigue behavior is dominated by *crack growth*. Consider cyclic loading of a notched member under a nominal stress S. Then let a smooth member be cycled under a stress σ_s, such that its stress is the same as that at the notch in the notched member, $\sigma_s = k_t S$. Therefore, on the basis of k_t, the same fatigue life is expected in smooth and notched members. However, in the notched member, the crack is growing into a region of rapidly decreasing stress, as in Fig. 10.4, whereas this does not occur in the smooth member. As a result, the crack in the notched member will require more cycles to grow than the one in the smooth member, extending the life in the notched member and resulting in a $k_f < k_t$ effect.

A more specific rationalization is possible by noting that the growth of cracks under cyclic loading is controlled by the stress intensity factor, K, of fracture mechanics. Consider the variation in K for a crack growing from a notch, as in Fig. 8.20. For a short surface crack of length l in an unnotched (smooth) plate of material under axial stress σ_s, we may obtain K from Fig. 8.12(c).

$$K_s = 1.12\sigma_s\sqrt{\pi l} \qquad (10.3)$$

Now, considering a crack in the notched member, the situation described in Section 8.5.2 applies. In particular, the stress intensity may be approximated as K_A up to the crack length l' of Eq. 8.26, and by K_B beyond l'. If the stress in the smooth member is the same as that at the notch, $\sigma_s = k_t S$, then K_s for the smooth member is similar to K_A for the notched member up to $l = l'$. However, beyond l', the value of K in the notched member no longer increases very rapidly and falls well below that for the smooth member.

Hence, the lower values of K in the notched member will cause cracks to grow slower than in the smooth member, causing longer lives and thus a higher S-N curve than expected on the basis of k_t. Since l' is generally in the range 0.1ρ to 0.2ρ, its value is smaller for sharper notches, so the smooth and notched specimen K values for sharper notches diverge at smaller crack lengths. This explains the trend of a greater $k_f < k_t$ effect for sharper notches. Moreover, in sharply notched members, cracks are observed to start due to the high stress and strain at the notch tip, but then to fail to grow as the K value is too low. The stress below which such *nonpropagating cracks* exist determines the fatigue limit of the sharply notched member.

10.2.4 Reversed Yielding Effect

Finally, there is a fourth effect that is caused by *reversed yielding* at the notch during cyclic loading. In this case, the plastic strains that occur cause the actual stress amplitude σ_a at the notch to be less than $k_t S_a$, as illustrated in Fig. 10.5. This gives a life that is longer than expected from $k_t S_a$, in effect raising the S-N curve. Such behavior occurs at high stress levels corresponding to short fatigue lives in most engineering metals, and it occurs even at long lives in a few very ductile metals. However, there is little or no yielding at long lives, say, around 10^6 or 10^7 cycles, for most engineering metals, so this explanation alone is insufficient. (Yielding effects at short lives are considered in detail later in Chapter 14 with the use of the strain-based approach.)

To summarize, fracture mechanics analysis of cracks growing from notches suggests that the presence of cracks is a major cause of the $k_f < k_t$ effect. This argument is further supported by the occurrence of nonpropagating cracks in sharply notched members. Reversed yielding is clearly also a factor at short lives, and the process zone and weakest-link effects may play a further role. In general, however, the situation is quite complex and is not completely understood.

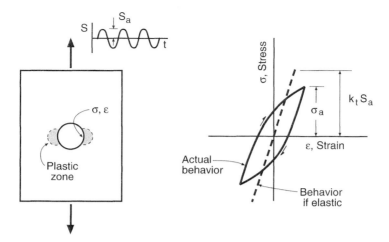

Figure 10.5   Effect of reversed yielding in a small region near the notch on the stress amplitude.

This circumstance has resulted in the development of several empirical approaches, which are considered next.

10.3 NOTCH SENSITIVITY AND EMPIRICAL ESTIMATES OF k_f

A useful concept in dealing with notch effects is the *notch sensitivity*

$$q = \frac{k_f - 1}{k_t - 1} \tag{10.4}$$

If the notch has its maximum possible effect, so that $k_f = k_t$, then $q = 1$. The value of q decreases from unity if $k_f < k_t$, having a minimum value of $q = 0$ where $k_f = 1$, which corresponds to the notch having no effect. The value of q between 0 and 1 is therefore a convenient measure of how severely a given member is affected by a notch. An example of the variation of q with material and notch radius is shown in Fig. 10.6. For a given material, q increases with notch radius, and within a given class of materials, q increases with ultimate tensile strength. Hence, the discrepancy between k_f and k_t is greatest for highly ductile materials and for sharp notches, and least for low-ductility materials and blunt notches.

Values of q and hence k_f may be estimated from empirical material constants that are independent of notch radius. Peterson (1974) employs

$$q = \frac{1}{1 + \dfrac{\alpha}{\rho}} \tag{10.5}$$

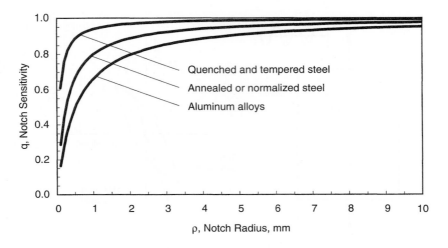

Figure 10.6   Notch sensitivities q for the typical α values of Peterson, from Eq. 10.6.

where α is a material constant having dimensions of length, with some typical values being as follows:

$$\alpha = 0.51 \text{ mm } (0.02 \text{ in})$$ (aluminum alloys)
$$\alpha = 0.25 \text{ mm } (0.01 \text{ in})$$ (annealed or normalized low-carbon steels)   (10.6)
$$\alpha = 0.064 \text{ mm } (0.0025 \text{ in})$$ (quenched and tempered steels)

These typical values correspond to the curves plotted in Fig. 10.6.

Peterson also provides more detail on the variation of α with strength for steels, as shown in Fig. 10.7. Values of α from this curve may be calculated within a few percent accuracy by the fitted expression

$$\log \alpha = 2.654 \times 10^{-7} \sigma_u^2 - 1.309 \times 10^{-3} \sigma_u + 0.01103$$

$$\alpha, \text{ mm} = 10^{\log \alpha} \qquad (345 \leq \sigma_u \leq 2070 \text{ MPa})$$ (10.7)

where σ_u is the ultimate tensile strength in MPa units. Figure 10.7 and Eq. 10.7 apply to axial or bending loading, and approximate values of α for torsion are obtained by multiplying values from Eq. 10.7 by 0.6.

Empirical curves giving either q or α can therefore be used to obtain k_f. It is convenient in making such calculations to solve Eq. 10.4 for k_f:

$$k_f = 1 + q(k_t - 1)$$ (10.8)

Combining this with Eq. 10.5 gives k_f directly from α:

$$k_f = 1 + \frac{k_t - 1}{1 + \dfrac{\alpha}{\rho}}$$ (10.9)

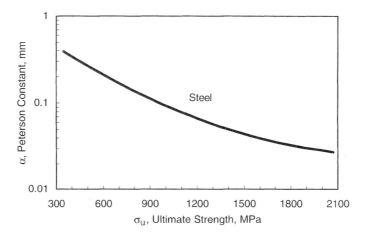

Figure 10.7   Peterson constant α as a function of ultimate tensile strength for carbon and low-alloy steels. Typical values from [Peterson 59] closely fit the curve shown.

Another frequently used empirical formulation for q and the resulting equation for k_f are

$$q = \frac{1}{1 + \sqrt{\dfrac{\beta}{\rho}}}, \qquad k_f = 1 + \frac{k_t - 1}{1 + \sqrt{\dfrac{\beta}{\rho}}} \qquad (10.10)$$

where β is a different material constant. These particular expressions represent a simplification of an equation developed by H. Neuber. Typical values of β for steels and for heat-treated aluminum alloys are plotted in Fig. 10.8. Fitting the curve for steel, with σ_u in MPa units, gives

$$\log \beta = -1.079 \times 10^{-9} \sigma_u^3 + 2.740 \times 10^{-6} \sigma_u^2 - 3.740 \times 10^{-3} \sigma_u + 0.6404$$

$$\beta, \mathrm{mm} = 10^{\log \beta} \qquad (345 \leq \sigma_u \leq 1725 \,\mathrm{MPa}) \tag{10.11}$$

and fitting the one for aluminum gives

$$\log \beta = -9.402 \times 10^{-9} \sigma_u^3 + 1.422 \times 10^{-5} \sigma_u^2 - 8.249 \times 10^{-3} \sigma_u + 1.451, \qquad \beta, \mathrm{mm} = 10^{\log \beta} \tag{10.12}$$

The accuracy of β from these expressions is within a few percent of the original graphs developed by Kuhn, as replotted in Fig. 10.8.

Equations 10.9 and 10.10, and a number of other analogous equations in the literature, are based on the process zone, weakest link, and similar hypotheses as reviewed by Peterson (1959). However, research related to k_f has continued, as in the paper by Harkegard (2010). The equations presented here and other similar ones should be viewed as somewhat crude estimates based on empirical data. Note that the equations for estimating k_f are intended for relatively mild notches,

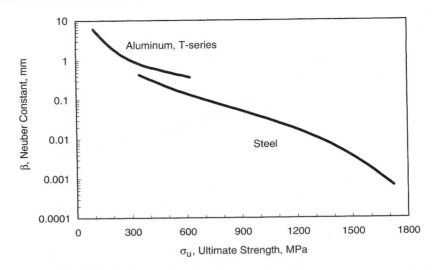

Figure 10.8   Neuber constant β as a function of ultimate tensile strength for carbon and low-alloy steels and for solution treated and aged (T-series) aluminum alloys. Curves from [Kuhn 52] and [Kuhn 62] are replotted.

such as those intentionally used in mechanical design. If the notch is relatively deep and sharp, so that it is cracklike in form, it will generally be more accurate to simply assume that the notch is already a crack. Its behavior can then be predicted from fracture mechanics.

Example 10.1
Consider the rotating bending member of Fig. 10.3, and, specifically, a notch radius of $\rho = 0.4\,\text{mm}$.

    (a) Determine k_t and then estimate k_f.
    (b) Estimate the completely reversed bending moment amplitude that can be applied for 10^6 cycles.

Solution   **(a)** The geometry and loading correspond to Fig. A.12(c). Values of the ratios d_2/d_1 and ρ/d_1 are determined and used to obtain k_t from this graph. We have

$$d_2 = 12.7\,\text{mm}, \qquad \rho = 0.4\,\text{mm}, \qquad d_1 = 12.7 - 2(1.27) = 10.16\,\text{mm}$$

$$\frac{d_2}{d_1} = \frac{12.7}{10.16} = 1.25, \qquad \frac{\rho}{d_1} = \frac{0.4}{10.16} = 0.0394, \qquad k_t = 2.7 \qquad \textbf{Ans.}$$

where a judgmental interpolation between the curves for $d_2/d_1 = 1.11$ and 1.43 is needed.

A value of k_f could be obtained from either the Peterson constant α or the Neuber constant β. Entering Fig. 10.7 with the materials ultimate tensile strength $\sigma_u = 450\,\text{MPa}$ gives $\alpha \approx 0.3\,\text{mm}$, which, with Eq. 10.9, gives

$$k_f = 1 + \frac{k_t - 1}{1 + \dfrac{\alpha}{\rho}} = 1 + \frac{2.7 - 1}{1 + \dfrac{0.3\,\text{mm}}{0.4\,\text{mm}}} = 1.97 \qquad \textbf{Ans.}$$

Essentially the same result is obtained by starting with the fit to the Peterson curve, Eq. 10.7, which gives $\alpha = 0.299\,\text{mm}$. Using Neuber, $\beta = 0.259\,\text{mm}$ is obtained from Eq. 10.11, resulting in $k_f = 1.94$ from Eq. 10.10.

(b) The fatigue limit for completely reversed ($\sigma_m = 0$) loading of unnotched material is estimated from Fig. 9.24 as half the ultimate strength, or $\sigma_{er} = 225\,\text{MPa}$. Dividing by k_f gives the fatigue limit with the notch effect included:

$$S_{er} = \frac{\sigma_{er}}{k_f} = \frac{225\,\text{MPa}}{1.97} = 114.1\,\text{MPa}$$

From the definition of S in Fig. A.12(c), the moment amplitude for infinite life is

$$M_a = \frac{\pi d_1^3 S_{er}}{32} = \frac{\pi (10.16\,\text{mm})^3 (114.1\,\text{N/mm}^2)}{32} = 11{,}740\,\text{N·mm} = 11.74\,\text{N·m} \qquad \textbf{Ans.}$$

In an actual engineering situation, a safety factor is required. For example, for a safety factor of $X_S = 2$ in stress, the highest moment actually allowed in service would be $\hat{M}_a = M_a/2 = 5.87\,\text{N·m}$.

Comment   Such close agreement between the two differently calculated k_f values in (a) is ideally expected, but often does not occur. Note that these values agree only roughly with the experimental value of $k_f \approx 2.5$ from Fig. 10.3.

10.4 ESTIMATING LONG-LIFE FATIGUE STRENGTHS (FATIGUE LIMITS)

In applications involving relatively low stresses applied for large numbers of cycles, design against fatigue may require only that the fatigue strength at long lives on the order of 10^6 to 10^8 cycles be known. Such values are often available in the literature from rotating bending fatigue tests on smoothly polished samples. For situations that differ from standard test conditions as to type of loading, size, surface finish, etc., modified values are often estimated on the basis of trends observed in existing data.

10.4.1 Estimation of Smooth Specimen Fatigue Limits

Distinct fatigue limits, where the *S-N* curve appears to become horizontal at long lives, are observed for many low-strength carbon and alloy steels and for some stainless steels, irons, molybdenum alloys, titanium alloys, and polymers. But for many other materials, such as aluminum, magnesium, copper, and nickel alloys, and for some stainless steels, and also for high-strength carbon and alloy steels, *S-N* curves generally continue to decrease slowly at the longest lives that have been studied. Fatigue strengths at long lives from rotating bending tests on smoothly polished specimens are commonly tabulated as materials properties. These fatigue strengths are often loosely termed *fatigue limits*, even if there is no distinct horizontal region on the *S-N* curve.

It is convenient to consider the ratio of the fatigue limit to the ultimate tensile strength, namely,

$$m_e = \frac{\sigma_{erb}}{\sigma_u} \tag{10.13}$$

where σ_{erb} is the polished specimen fatigue limit for completely reversed loading in bending, often rotating bending. A value around $m_e = 0.5$ is common for low- and intermediate-strength steels, as discussed in Section 9.6.1 and as shown in Fig. 9.24. A similar plot for fatigue strengths of wrought aluminum alloys at $N_f = 5 \times 10^8$ cycles is given in Fig. 9.25. For aluminum alloys, a value of $m_e = 0.4$ applies for the lower strength levels. For both steels and aluminums, m_e decreases beyond a certain ultimate tensile strength level; that is, the fatigue limit fails to keep up with the increased static strength. The fatigue limit appears to level off around 700 MPa for many steels, and around 130 MPa for wrought aluminum alloys. This trend is associated with the fact that a degree of ductility is helpful in providing fatigue resistance, and high-strength alloys generally have limited ductility.

Some other typical m_e values are 0.4 for cast irons at $N_f = 10^7$ cycles, 0.35 for wrought magnesium alloys at $N_f = 10^8$ cycles, and 0.5 for titanium alloys at $N_f = 10^7$ cycles. Data are given in various materials property sources (see the Chapter 9 References). Systematic collections of long-life fatigue strength data are not generally available for the less commonly used metals or for polymers and composites, but data on particular materials of these types can sometimes be found in the literature.

10.4.2 Factors Affecting Long-Life Fatigue Strength

If a notch is present, the fatigue strength at long lives is reduced by the factor k_f, as discussed in detail in Section 10.3. A variety of additional factors may also affect the long-life fatigue strength, often reducing it. For example, axial loading produces a lower fatigue strength than bending, typically by 10% or more. This is thought to be because the process zone, weakest link, or related effects due to a stress gradient act to a limited extent in bending, as described earlier for notches. Such effects are beneficial and can occur in bending (or torsion) due to the stress variation with depth in the material, but not for axial loading, where the stress is uniform. Another factor is that a slight, but unknown, eccentricity of the axial load may cause some bending that is not included in the stress calculation, $S = P/A$.

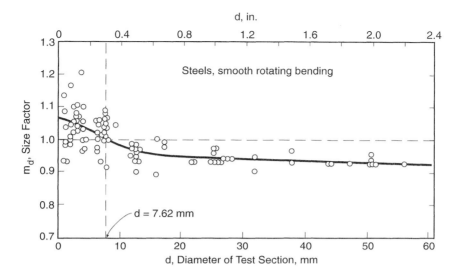

Figure 10.9 Effect of size on the fatigue limit of smoothly polished specimens of steels tested in rotating bending. Values are plotted of m_d, the ratio of the fatigue limit to that for the frequently used 7.62 mm (0.3 in.) specimen diameter. (Data from [Heywood 62] p. 23.)

The state of stress also has an effect on fatigue strength, as described in Chapter 9, where an octahedral shear stress criterion is suggested for ductile materials. For example, for pure torsion, such an approach gives an estimate of the fatigue limit in shear from Eq. 9.13, specifically, $\tau_{er} = 0.577\sigma_{erb}$.

For large-size members in bending or torsion, stress gradient effects would be expected to cause fatigue strengths to decrease with member size, and such a *size effect* is in fact observed. A size effect is expected specifically because the decrease of stress with depth is less abrupt in larger cross sections, so that a larger volume of material is subjected to relatively high stress. Some test data for steel shafts are shown in Fig. 10.9. As a result of this effect, fatigue limits from small (typically, 8 mm diameter) rotating bending test specimens need to be decreased for application to larger sizes.

If the *surface finish* is rougher than the polished surface of a typical smooth test specimen, the long-life fatigue strength is reduced. Careful grinding reduces the fatigue limit around 10%, and more ordinary machining by 20% or more. Relatively rough surfaces that are unmodified after forging or casting may cause the fatigue limit to be less than half of the smooth specimen value. Some typical reduction factors for various surface conditions for steel are given in Fig. 10.10. Note that the reductions are greater for increased ultimate tensile strength. This occurs because surface roughness acts as a stress raiser (notch), and as previously discussed, higher strength materials are relatively more sensitive to notches. Surface finish effects are complicated by other factors that may accompany them, such as residual stresses from machining or heat treating, and also by surface compositional or microstructural changes that may occur during some types of processing, such as hot rolling or forging.

10.4.3 Reduction Factors for the Fatigue Limit

Combinations of effects such as those just described are common in engineering situations. What is usually done is to multiply reduction factors for the various effects to obtain an adjusted fatigue limit σ_{er}, which is lower than σ_{erb}:

$$\sigma_{er} = m_t m_d m_s m_o \sigma_{erb} \qquad \text{(a)}$$

$$\sigma_{er} = m_e m_t m_d m_s m_o \sigma_u = m \sigma_u \qquad \text{(b)}$$

$$(10.14)$$

Here, (a) is chosen if the bending fatigue strength σ_{erb} is known and (b) if only the ultimate strength σ_u is known. In (b), the quantity m is a combined reduction factor that includes m_e from Eq. 10.13. Specifically,

$$m = m_e m_t m_d m_s m_o \qquad (10.15)$$

The various factors account for the effects of type of loading (m_t), size (m_d), surface finish (m_s), and any other effects (m_o) that may be involved, such as elevated temperature, corrosion, etc. Any one of these factors obviously has no effect if the value is unity, and a value of 0.9 corresponds to a 10% reduction, etc. Some examples are $m_t = 0.58$ for torsion from Eq. 9.13, $m_d = 0.95$ for diameters around 25 mm from Fig. 10.9, and $m_s = 0.8$ for a machined surface in low-strength steel from Fig. 10.10.

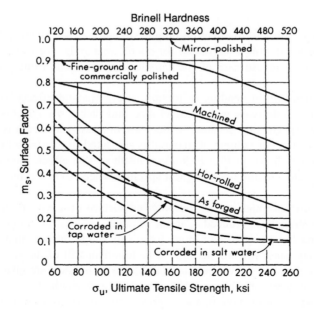

Figure 10.10 Effect of various surface finishes on the fatigue limit of steel. Values are plotted of m_s, the ratio of the fatigue limit to that for polished specimens. (Adapted from R. C. Juvinall, *Stress, Strain, and Strength*, 1967; [Juvinall 67] p. 234; reproduced with permission; © 1967 the McGraw-Hill Companies, Inc.)

Table 10.1   Parameters for Estimating Fatigue Limits

Parameter	Applicability	Juvinall (2006)	Budynas (2011)
Bending fatigue limit factor: m_e	Steels, $\sigma_u \leq 1400\,\text{MPa}$[1]	0.5	0.5
	High-strength steels	≤ 0.5	$\sigma_{erb} = 700\,\text{MPa}$
	Cast irons; Al alloys if $\sigma_u \leq 328\,\text{MPa}$	0.4	—
	Higher strength Al	$\sigma_{erb} = 131\,\text{MPa}$	—
	Magnesium alloys	0.35	—
Load type factor: m_t	Bending	1.0	1.0
	Axial	1.0	0.85
	Torsion	0.58	0.59
Size (stress gradient) factor: m_d	Bending or torsion[2,3,4]	1.0 ($d < 10\,\text{mm}$) 0.9 ($10 \leq d < 50$)	$1.24 d^{-0.107}$ ($3 \leq d \leq 51\,\text{mm}$)
	Axial[2,3]	0.7 to 0.9 ($d < 50$)[5]	1.0
Surface finish factor: m_s	Polished	1.0	1.0
	Ground[6]	See Fig. 10.10	$1.58\sigma_u^{-0.085}$
	Machined[6]	See Fig. 10.10	$4.51\sigma_u^{-0.265}$
Life for fatigue limit point: N_e, cycles	Steels, cast irons	10^6	10^6
	Aluminum alloys	5×10^8	—
	Magnesium alloys	10^8	—

Notes:[1] Juvinall specifically gives a hardness limit, $HB \leq 400$. [2]Diameter d is in mm units. [3]For Juvinall, for $50 \leq d < 100\,\text{mm}$, decrease the values of m_d by 0.1 relative to the values for $d < 50\,\text{mm}$, and for $100 \leq d < 150\,\text{mm}$ decrease by 0.2. [4]For Budynas, use $1.51 d^{-0.157}$ for $51 < d \leq 254\,\text{mm}$, and for nonrotating bending, replace d with $d_e = 0.37d$ for round sections, and with $d_e = 0.808\sqrt{ht}$ for rectangular sections (Fig. A.2). [5]Use 0.9 for accurately concentric loading, and a lower value otherwise. [6]For Budynas, substitute σ_u in MPa.

Recommended factors from the design books of Juvinall (2006) and of Budynas (2011) are given in Table 10.1. Note that the former addresses several metals, but the latter only steels. (Table 10.1 will be considered in detail later in Section 10.7 on estimating S-N curves.)

If the starting point for the estimate is the ultimate tensile strength, then the fatigue limit, as a nominal stress for a notched member, S_{er}, is obtained by applying Eq. 10.14(b) along with k_f:

$$S_{er} = \frac{\sigma_{er}}{k_f} = \frac{m\sigma_u}{k_f} \tag{10.16}$$

This discussion on estimating fatigue limits would be incomplete without reminding the reader of Section 9.6.5, where it is noted that some materials have a surprising drop in the S-N curve at very long lives, so that failures occur below the apparent fatigue limit. Also, corrosion damage and occasional severe cycles may cause the S-N curve to continue downward below the fatigue limit from constant amplitude tests.

Example 10.2

Consider again the notched bending member of Fig. 10.3. Modify the 10^6 cycles fatigue strength (fatigue limit) estimate of Ex. 10.1 to include additional factors as just discussed. Assume that the notch surface is finished by grinding.

Solution The minor diameter of 12.7 mm gives a size effect of around $m_d = 0.96$ from Fig. 10.9, and the ground surface finish gives $m_s = 0.90$ from Fig. 10.10. Combining these with $m_e = 0.5$ from Fig. 9.24, as used before, gives the revised estimate for unnotched material from Eq. 10.14(b):

$$\sigma_{er} = m_e m_d m_s \sigma_u = 0.5 \times 0.96 \times 0.90 \times 450 = 194.4\,\text{MPa}$$

Note that m_t and m_o are omitted, as no reduction is made for these; that is, $m_t = 1$ and $m_o = 1$. Using the same k_f as before, the fatigue limit for the notched member is estimated as

$$S_{er} = \frac{\sigma_{er}}{k_f} = \frac{194.4\ \text{MPa}}{1.97} = 98.7\,\text{MPa} \qquad \textbf{Ans.}$$

Second Solution Since the AISI (SAE) 1015 steel material is included in Table 9.1, the $m_e = 0.50$ estimate can be bypassed in favor of the fatigue strength at 10^6 cycles calculated from Eq. 9.7:

$$\sigma_a = \sigma_f'(2N_f)^b = 1020(2 \times 10^6)^{-0.138} = 137.7\,\text{MPa}$$

Modifying this value for size and surface finish and applying k_f gives a second estimate for the fatigue limit of the notched member:

$$S_{er} = \frac{m_d m_s \sigma_a}{k_f} = \frac{0.96 \times 0.90 \times 137.7\ \text{MPa}}{1.97} = 60.4\,\text{MPa} \qquad \textbf{Ans.}$$

Comment The second value is considerably lower than the first. The difference is in part due to the ultimate strength for the Table 9.1 material being lower than for the Fig. 10.3 material of nominally the same type. Also, the Table 9.1 constants correspond to axial loading, which is known to give fatigue strengths around 10% lower than for bending. The remaining discrepancy is still around 35%, which highlights the rough nature of estimates of this type.

10.5 NOTCH EFFECTS AT INTERMEDIATE AND SHORT LIVES

At intermediate and short fatigue lives in ductile materials, the reversed yielding effect of Fig. 10.5 becomes increasingly important as higher stresses, and therefore shorter lives, are considered. One consequence of this behavior is that the ratio of the smooth specimen to notched specimen fatigue strengths becomes even less than k_f, so that it is useful to define a fatigue notch factor k_f' that varies with life:

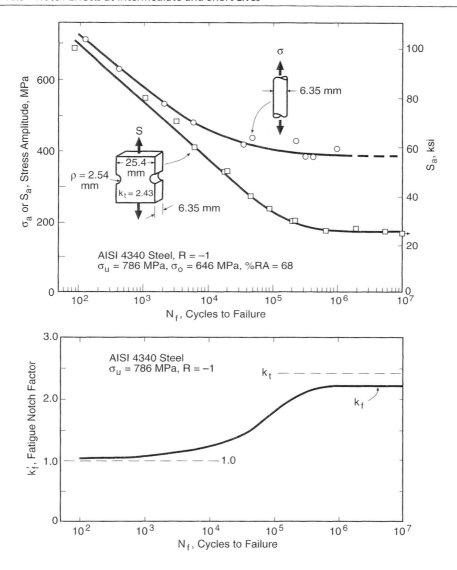

Figure 10.11 Test data for a ductile metal illustrating variation of the fatigue notch factor with life. The S-N data (top) are used to obtain $k'_f = \sigma_a / S_a$ (bottom). The notches are half-circular cutouts. Nominal stress S is defined on the basis of the net area, as in Fig. A.11(b).

$$k'_f = f(N_f) = \frac{\sigma_{ar}}{S_{ar}} \qquad (10.17)$$

Data illustrating this effect are shown in Fig. 10.11. As is typical for ductile metals, k'_f decreases from k_f at long lives to a value near unity at short lives.

Considering completely reversed loading, these trends can be rationalized by idealizing the behavior of the material as elastic, perfectly plastic with yield strength σ_o, as illustrated in Fig. 10.12. There are three possible situations: (a) no yielding, (b) local yielding, and (c) full yielding. If the stress at the notch never exceeds the yield strength, which is satisfied if $k_t S_a \leq \sigma_o$, there is *no yielding*. In this case, ignoring effects other than yielding for the present, k'_f is expected to be equal to k_t:

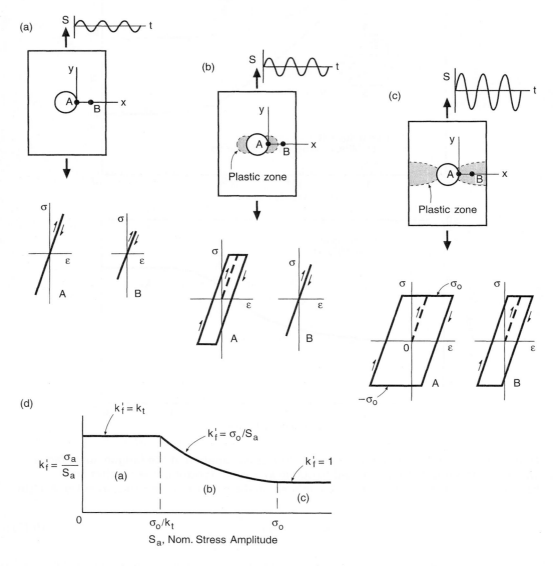

Figure 10.12 Cyclic yielding for a notched member of an ideal elastic, perfectly plastic material. There are three possibilities: (a) no yielding, (b) local yielding, and (c) full yielding. The fatigue notch factor is thus expected to vary with the stress level, as in (d).

$$k'_f = k_t \qquad \text{(no yielding; } k_t S_a \le \sigma_o \text{)} \qquad (10.18)$$

Assume that the loading is sufficiently severe to cause yielding, at least locally at the notch—in other words, assume that $k_t S_a > \sigma_o$. Completely reversed loading will then cause yielding to occur in both tension and compression on each loading cycle, as illustrated in Fig. 10.12(b). If this reversed yielding does not spread over the entire cross section, the situation is described as *local yielding*. Since the stress amplitude at the notch is equal to σ_o, the value of k'_f is expected to be

$$k'_f = \frac{\sigma_o}{S_a} \qquad \text{(local yielding; } k_t S_a > \sigma_o \text{)} \qquad (10.19)$$

In the extreme case of *full yielding*, the reversed yielding spreads across the entire cross section, as in (c). This causes the stress amplitude over the net section to be uniform and equal to σ_o, so that the nominal stress amplitude is also equal to σ_o. Hence, the notch has little effect, and

$$k'_f \approx 1 \qquad \text{(full yielding; } S_a \approx \sigma_o \text{)} \qquad (10.20)$$

Such behavior is similar to the spreading of yielding across the cross section in static loading, as in Fig. A.10 in Appendix A, except that now reversed yielding in both tension and compression on each cycle of loading is involved.

The expected trends in k'_f for the three situations are summarized by the preceding equations, as shown in Fig. 10.12(d). The indicated trends of k'_f with stress will produce a variation with life similar to the lower curve of Fig. 10.11. However, the difference between k_f and k_t at long lives indicates that at least one effect in addition to yielding is acting.

In applying the stress-based approach, *S-N* curves for notched members may need to be estimated. An empirical approach rather than analysis as just described is sometimes used to make adjustments for yielding effects at short and intermediate lives. For example, once k_f for long life has been estimated, k'_f at $N_f = 10^3$ cycles can be estimated from curves based on test data, as in Fig. 10.13. A graphical interpolation is then used to obtain k'_f for lives between $N_f = 10^3$ and 10^6.

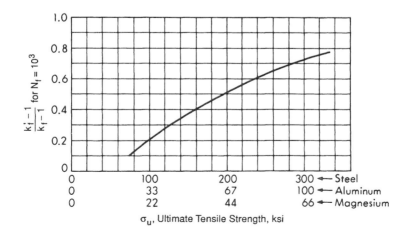

Figure 10.13 Curve based on empirical data for estimating the fatigue notch factor k'_f at $N_f = 1000$ cycles. (Adapted from R. C. Juvinall, *Stress, Strain, and Strength*, 1967; [Juvinall 67] p. 260; reproduced with permission; © 1967 the McGraw-Hill Companies, Inc.)

Study of the particular curves shown indicates that k'_f at $N_f = 10^3$ approaches k_f for high-strength (usually brittle, low-ductility) metals, and k'_f approaches unity for low-strength (usually ductile) metals. This is precisely what is expected on the basis of a reversed yielding effect, as just discussed. Empirical estimates of entire S-N curves for notched members are discussed in a later section of this chapter.

10.6 COMBINED EFFECTS OF NOTCHES AND MEAN STRESS

The empirical expressions and curves for k_f and k'_f are based on trends and data observed under completely reversed loading. Hence, these values cannot be applied directly if mean stresses are present. The most common approach to handling mean stresses for notched members is to apply the Goodman relationship, Eq. 9.15, with nominal stresses. However, mean stress adjustments for notched members are complicated by the effects of local yielding at the notch. The Smith, Watson, and Topper (SWT) method, Eq. 9.18, and the Walker relationship, Eq. 9.19, offer useful alternatives. Detailed discussion follows.

10.6.1 Goodman Equation for Notched Members

Consider the fully plastic yielding behavior of a notched member, as illustrated in Fig. A.10 and discussed in Section A.7. If the material is quite ductile, as for many engineering metals, redistribution of stresses results in an approximately uniform stress at failure. Hence, the ultimate strength of the notched member is not strongly affected by the notch, and in fact may be increased somewhat compared with the value σ_u for unnotched material.

Pursuing this logic leads to applying the Goodman equation in the manner shown by the line labeled *ductile* in Fig. 10.14. The corresponding equation is

$$S_{ar} = \frac{\sigma_{ar}}{k_f} = \frac{S_a}{1 - \dfrac{S_m}{\sigma_u}} \qquad \text{(ductile materials)} \tag{10.21}$$

Compared with unnotched material, the equivalent completely reversed *nominal* stress S_{ar} is reduced by a notch factor k_f. But since there is no corresponding reduction on the mean stress axis, the preceding equation implies that the notch factor for the mean stress is $k_{fm} = 1$.

However, for low-ductility materials, the redistribution of stress does not occur, and the ultimate strength of the notched member is reduced. This suggests the line labeled *brittle* in Fig. 10.14, which corresponds to the equation

$$S_{ar} = \frac{\sigma_{ar}}{k_f} = \frac{S_a}{1 - \dfrac{k_{fm} S_m}{\sigma_u}} \qquad \text{(brittle materials)} \tag{10.22}$$

The notch factor k_{fm} for the mean stress is generally taken to be the same value as for the stress amplitude; that is, $k_{fm} = k_f$.

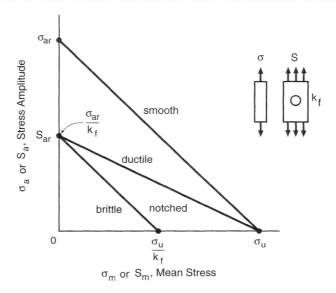

Figure 10.14 Goodman amplitude-mean plots for smooth and notched members of brittle and ductile materials.

The preceding equations are rather widely employed, as is similar use of the Gerber relationship, Eq. 9.16. However, there are some problems in applying them. First, the brittle versus ductile choice is problematical. For example, for metals with reasonable, but somewhat limited, ductility, such as high-strength steels and high-strength aluminum alloys, a notch effect on the mean stress does occur, but mainly at long lives. Hence, we might choose Eq. 10.22, with k_{fm} being treated as a life-dependent variable, but this greatly complicates its application. Second, plotting S_{ar} versus life N_f for test data (as in Ex. 9.5) usually gives a poor correlation, even for unquestionably ductile metals where Eq. 10.21 would be the logical choice.

Third, nominal stress S is an arbitrarily defined quantity, and for complex geometries, there may be more than one possible choice for defining S, or no clear choice at all. Since the arbitrary definition of S affects the value of the ratio S_m/σ_u, numerical results will vary, depending on the definition of S. This situation creates a serious logical problem in applying any mean stress equation to nominal stress where there is a ratio with a materials constant.

The first and second difficulties just noted involve behavior resulting from local yielding at notches. Hence, it is useful to pursue this issue in more detail, which is undertaken next.

10.6.2 Local Yielding Effects

Let the concentration factor for the mean stress in Eq. 10.22 be considered to be a variable,

$$k_{fm} = \frac{\sigma_m}{S_m} \tag{10.23}$$

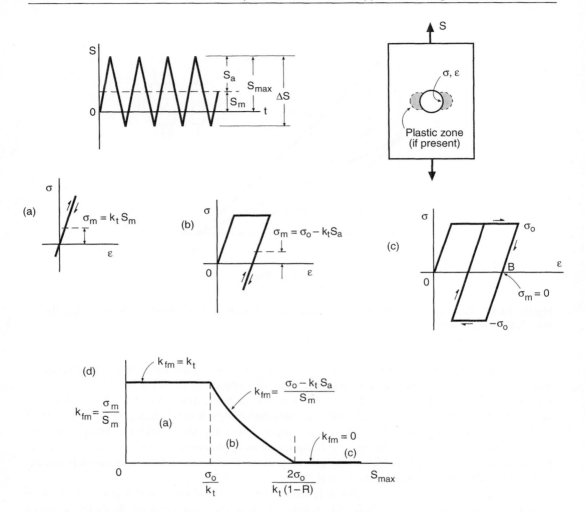

Figure 10.15 A notched member of an elastic, perfectly plastic material under cyclic loading with nonzero mean level. There are three possible stress–strain behaviors at the notch: (a) no yielding, (b) initial yielding, but elastic cycling, and (c) reversed yielding. The concentration factor k_{fm} for mean stress is thus expected to vary with S_{max} as shown in (d).

where S_m is the mean level for the nominal stress and σ_m is the mean level for the local stress at the notch. Also let the behavior of the material be approximated as being elastic, perfectly plastic, and assume that a mean stress is present. There are three possible situations, as illustrated in Fig. 10.15: (a) no yielding, (b) initial yielding, and (c) reversed yielding. There is *no yielding* if neither the peak nor the valley of the load causes the stress $k_t S$ at the notch to exceed the yield strength. In this case, the mean stress at the notch is elevated by the factor k_t, so that $k_{fm} = k_t$ is expected.

Next, assume that either the peak or valley load causes yielding, corresponding to $k_t |S|_{\max} > \sigma_o$. However, also assume that the loading is not sufficiently severe for reversed yielding to occur. We then have the situation shown in Fig. 10.15(b) where there is only *initial yielding*. Since the cyclic stressing is elastic, the notch stress amplitude may be calculated from $\sigma_a = k_t S_a$. On each stress cycle, the maximum stress will return to the same yield strength value σ_o that it had at the first load peak. Hence, for initial yielding in tension, the mean stress is

$$\sigma_m = \sigma_{\max} - \sigma_a = \sigma_o - k_t S_a \tag{10.24}$$

Finally, if the loading is sufficiently severe that $k_t \Delta S > 2\sigma_o$, *reversed yielding* occurs, as shown in (c). The stresses at the notch are

$$\sigma_{\max} = \sigma_o, \qquad \sigma_{\min} = -\sigma_o \tag{10.25}$$

so that

$$\sigma_m = \frac{\sigma_{\max} + \sigma_{\min}}{2} = 0 \tag{10.26}$$

which gives $k_{fm} = 0$.

Hence, the situation can be summarized as

$$k_{fm} = k_t \qquad \text{(no yielding; } k_t |S|_{\max} < \sigma_o\text{)}$$

$$k_{fm} = \frac{\sigma_o - k_t S_a}{|S_m|} \qquad \text{(initial yielding; } k_t |S|_{\max} > \sigma_o\text{)} \tag{10.27}$$

$$k_{fm} = 0 \qquad \text{(reversed yielding; } k_t \Delta S > 2\sigma_o\text{)}$$

where absolute values are used to make the equations applicable for either tensile or compressive S_m. The variation of k_{fm} with $S_{\max}$ is similar to Fig. 10.15(d). Note that local yielding at the notch causes k_{fm} to be less than k_t, even zero in extreme cases.

In view of this analysis, Eq. 10.22 could be used for ductile materials by making k_{fm} a continuous variable according to Eq. 10.27. The value $k_{fm} = 1$ implied by Eq. 10.21 is indeed within the range of zero to k_t given by these equations, but this or any other single value is seen to represent only a crude approximation. This question is discussed in Juvinall (1967), where one of the alternatives suggested is similar to the use of Eq. 10.27, except that k_t is replaced with k_f.

10.6.3 SWT and Walker Equations for Notched Members

Recalling the difficulties noted for the Goodman equation in the simple form of Eq. 10.21, we see that this expression is not an optimum choice for general use. Equation 10.22, with k_{fm} from Eq. 10.27, may represent an improvement. However, the added complexity of this method may not be justified in view of the underlying inaccuracy of the Goodman equation. (See Ex. 9.5.) Also, note that the yield strength on which Eq. 10.27 depends is altered by cyclic loading, as discussed later in

Section 12.5. Moreover, the strain-based method provides a more complete analysis of the effects of local yielding at notches, as covered in Section 14.5, which method should be adopted if it is truly desired to include local yielding effects. Hence, for the present use, it seems appropriate to consider other options.

One possibility is to apply the SWT equation to nominal stress by changing the variable to S in either of the two equivalent forms of Eq. 9.18:

$$S_{ar} = \sqrt{S_{max} S_a} \,, \qquad S_{ar} = S_{max}\sqrt{\frac{1-R}{2}} \qquad \text{(a, b)} \qquad (10.28)$$

For several sets of notched specimen data on steels and aluminum alloys, plotting this S_{ar} versus life N_f gave better results than the Goodman equation. (See Dowling, 2000, and also the Problems at the end of this chapter.)

Another option is to similarly employ the Walker relationship of Eq. 9.19 with nominal stresses:

$$S_{ar} = S_{max}^{1-\gamma} S_a^{\gamma}, \qquad S_{ar} = S_{max}\left(\frac{1-R}{2}\right)^{\gamma} \qquad \text{(a, b)} \qquad (10.29)$$

The constant γ should be specifically fitted to data on the notched member of interest; the procedure for doing so is given in the next section. Where γ is not known from data for at least a case similar to the one of interest, the SWT relationship should be employed, which is, of course, the same as Walker with the default value $\gamma = 0.5$.

Note that there is no ratio of S to a material property in Eq. 10.28 or 10.29, so this logical difficulty with the Goodman equation is removed. Also, the fatigue life curve and the SWT or Walker equation may be expressed in terms of an applied load, such as a force P or a bending moment M, so there is no need to even define a nominal stress. For example, for the SWT equation and a force P, we have

$$P_{ar} = \sqrt{P_{max} P_a} \,, \qquad P_{ar} = P_{max}\sqrt{\frac{1-R}{2}} \qquad \text{(a, b)} \qquad (10.30)$$

Since any reasonable definition of S would be proportional to such an applied load, estimated fatigue lives will be unaffected by the use of a variable such as P in place of S.

Example 10.3

The RQC-100 steel of Table 9.1 is to be used in the form of a plate with a width change under bending, as in Fig. A.11(d). The dimensions are $w_2 = 88$, $w_1 = 80$, $\rho = 4$, and $t = 10\,\text{mm}$. What amplitude of bending moment M_a will result in a life of 10^6 cycles if cycling is applied at mean moment of $M_m = 4\,\text{kN·m}$?

First Solution   One approach is to use Eq. 10.21 for this ductile material. Since the available data are for unnotched material, Eq. 10.21 is used in the form

$$\sigma_{ar} = k_f S_{ar} = \frac{k_f S_a}{1 - \dfrac{S_m}{\sigma_u}}$$

The quantities k_f, S_m, and σ_{ar} need to be evaluated, and then we can solve for S_a, which gives M_a. To estimate k_f, first determine k_t from Fig. A.11(d):

$$\frac{w_2}{w_1} = \frac{88\,\text{mm}}{80\,\text{mm}} = 1.1, \qquad \frac{\rho}{w_1} = \frac{4\,\text{mm}}{80\,\text{mm}} = 0.05, \qquad k_t = 1.85$$

The Peterson constant α is given by Eq. 10.7 used with $\sigma_u = 758\,\text{MPa}$ from Table 9.1. We have

$$\log \alpha = 2.654 \times 10^{-7}(758\,\text{MPa})^2 - 1.309 \times 10^{-3}(758\,\text{MPa}) + 0.01103 = -0.8287$$

$$\alpha = 10^{\log \alpha} = 10^{-0.8287} = 0.148\,\text{mm}$$

Equation 10.9 then gives k_f:

$$k_f = 1 + \frac{k_t - 1}{1 + \dfrac{\alpha}{\rho}} = 1 + \frac{1.85 - 1}{1 + \dfrac{0.148\,\text{mm}}{4\,\text{mm}}} = 1.82$$

We next calculate S_m from the definition of S in Fig. A.11(d):

$$S_m = \frac{6M_m}{w_1^2 t} = \frac{6(0.004\,\text{MN}\cdot\text{m})}{(0.08\,\text{m})^2(0.01\,\text{m})} = 375\,\text{MPa}$$

Constants A and B from Table 9.1 give the completely reversed stress amplitude σ_{ar} at $N_f = 10^6$ for smooth specimens of this material:

$$\sigma_{ar} = A N_f^B = 897(10^6)^{-0.0648} = 366\,\text{MPa}$$

We can now solve the preceding first equation for S_a, substitute the values determined, and finally use the definition of S to get M_a:

$$S_a = \frac{\sigma_{ar}}{k_f}\left(1 - \frac{S_m}{\sigma_u}\right) = \frac{366\,\text{MPa}}{1.82}\left(1 - \frac{375\,\text{MPa}}{758\,\text{MPa}}\right) = 102\,\text{MPa}$$

$$M_a = \frac{w_1^2 t S_a}{6} = \frac{(0.08\,\text{m})^2(0.01\,\text{m})(102\,\text{MPa})}{6} = 0.00109\,\text{MN}\cdot\text{m}$$

$$M_a = 1.09\,\text{kN}\cdot\text{m} \qquad\qquad \textbf{Ans.}$$

Second Solution   The SWT equation can also be employed. From the calculations already done, we obtain

$$S_{ar} = \sigma_{ar}/k_f = 366/1.82 = 201\,\text{MPa}$$

With $S_m = 375\,\text{MPa}$ from the given mean moment, we can apply Eq. 10.28:

$$S_{ar} = \sqrt{S_{max}S_a} = \sqrt{(S_m + S_a)S_a}\,, \qquad 201 = \sqrt{(375 + S_a)S_a}\,\text{MPa}$$

Solving the latter iteratively (or using the quadratic formula) gives $S_a = 87.5\,\text{MPa}$, and calculating the corresponding moment amplitude as before gives $M_a = 0.933\,\text{kN·m}$ (**Ans.**).

10.6.4 Fitting the Walker Equation

As noted, use of the Walker equation requires that a value be known for the special fitting constant γ. This is useful where fatigue life data for more that one mean stress or R-ratio are available for a notched member of interest, or for unnotched materials test specimens. All of the data can then be employed in a single fitting procedure to obtain a stress–life curve with the mean stress effect included. The ability to vary γ to fit the data usually allows accurate representation of the mean stress effect.

Assume that the nominal stress versus life curve for a notched member for zero mean stress is a straight line on a log–log plot, so that it has the same form as Eq. 9.6. Then

$$S_{ar} = AN_f^B \tag{10.31}$$

Combine this with Eq. 10.29(b), and then solve for N_f:

$$S_{ar} = AN_f^B = S_{max}\left(\frac{1-R}{2}\right)^{\gamma}, \qquad N_f = \left[S_{max}\left(\frac{1-R}{2}\right)^{\gamma}\frac{1}{A}\right]^{1/B} \qquad \text{(a, b)} \tag{10.32}$$

Next, take the logarithm to the base 10 of both sides:

$$\log N_f = \frac{1}{B}\log S_{max} + \frac{\gamma}{B}\log\left(\frac{1-R}{2}\right) - \frac{1}{B}\log A \tag{10.33}$$

We can now do a multiple linear regression with independent variables x_1 and x_2 and dependent variable y. We have

$$y = m_1 x_1 + m_2 x_2 + c \tag{10.34}$$

where

$$y = \log N_f, \qquad x_1 = \log S_{max}, \qquad x_2 = \log\left(\frac{1-R}{2}\right) \tag{10.35}$$

$$m_1 = \frac{1}{B}, \qquad m_2 = \frac{\gamma}{B}, \qquad c = -\frac{1}{B}\log A \tag{10.36}$$

Once the fitting constants m_1, m_2, and c are known, the desired values are easily determined:

$$B = \frac{1}{m_1}, \qquad \gamma = Bm_2 = \frac{m_2}{m_1}, \qquad A = 10^{-cB} = 10^{-c/m_1} \tag{10.37}$$

Hence, after the fit is done, so that A, B, and γ are known, the life N_f may be calculated from Eq. 10.32(b) for any cyclic loading given by values of S_{max} and R.

The value of γ is limited to the range zero to 1.0, and γ can be thought of as an inverse measure of the sensitivity to mean stress or to R. Low values of γ correspond to high sensitivity, and values approaching 1.0 to low sensitivity. Note that substituting $\gamma = 1$ into Eq. 10.29 gives $S_{ar} = S_a$, which corresponds to mean stress having no effect.

The original expression of the Walker equation in 1970 employed an equivalent zero-to-maximum ($R = 0$) stress range, $\overline{\Delta S}$. Two forms that may be used interchangeably are

$$\overline{\Delta S} = S_{max}^{1-\gamma} \Delta S^\gamma, \qquad \overline{\Delta S} = S_{max}(1-R)^\gamma \qquad \text{(a, b)} \tag{10.38}$$

Comparison of (b) with Eq. 10.29(b) gives the relationship

$$\overline{\Delta S} = 2^\gamma S_{ar} \tag{10.39}$$

Thus, we may choose either $\overline{\Delta S}$ or S_{ar} as merely different expressions of the same concept, with values being easily converted from one form to the other. Also, data may be fitted to a stress–life curve in terms of $\overline{\Delta S}$ by using a procedure similar to the one for S_{ar}. This gives the same values of γ and B, but the coefficient analogous to A in Eq. 10.31 differs due to Eq. 10.39. We have

$$\overline{\Delta S} = A' N_f^B, \qquad \text{where } A' = 2^\gamma A \tag{10.40}$$

Example 10.4

For double-edge-notched plates of 2024-T3 aluminum under axial load, cycles to failure data are given in Table E10.4(a) for various combinations of maximum stress S_{max} and mean stress S_m. These data are also plotted in Fig. E10.4(a). Fit these data to the Walker equation, using Eq. 10.31, with S_{ar} given by Eq. 10.29, to obtain values of A, B, and γ. The specimen dimensions were $w_1 = 38.10$, $w_2 = 57.15$, notch radius $\rho = 8.06$, and thickness $t = 2.29$ mm, giving $k_t = 2.15$ on the basis of net area. The material's tensile properties were yield 372 MPa and ultimate 503 MPa.

Table E10.4(a)

$S_{\max}$, MPa	S_m, MPa	N_f, cycles	$S_{\max}$, MPa	S_m, MPa	N_f, cycles
241	0	3 500	362	138	3 100
207	0	6 500	338	138	9 300
172	0	17 400	338	138	6 000
138	0	70 000	310	138	21 800
103	0	754 000	276	138	48 300
103	0	210 000	241	138	82 200
303	69	3 000	214	138	128 500
276	69	6 500	214	138	218 700
241	69	14 900	414	207	4 500
207	69	35 000	372	207	9 600
207	69	43 400	345	207	25 700
172	69	124 200	310	207	63 500
152	69	168 700	293	207	152 900
145	69	507 400	276	207	315 500

Source: Data in [Grover 51b].

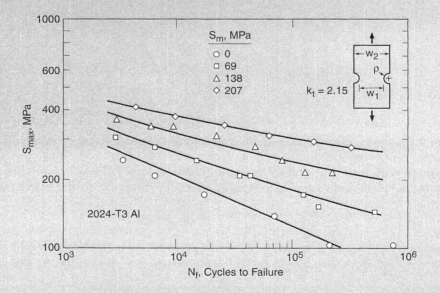

Figure E10.4(a)

Solution   To use the procedure just described, we first employ Eq. 9.4(b) to calculate R for each test. Equation 10.35 then gives values of y, x_1, and x_2 for each test. A few representative values are shown in Table E10.4(b). Next, the multiple linear regression of Eq. 10.34 is performed by widely available computer software.

Table E10.4(b)

	(a) Given Data			(b) Variables for Fitting and Calculated S_{ar}			
S_{max}	S_m	R	N_f	y $\log N_f$	x_1 $\log S_{max}$	x_2 $\log \frac{1-R}{2}$	S_{ar} for $\gamma = 0.7326$
241	0	−1.000	3 500	3.544	2.382	0	241.0
207	0	−1.000	6 500	3.813	2.316	0	207.0
. . . . .	. . . . .	. . . . .	. . . . .	. . . . .	. . . . .	. . . . .	. . . . .
303	69	−0.545	3 000	3.477	2.481	−0.1122	250.7
276	69	−0.500	6 500	3.813	2.441	−0.1249	223.6
. . . . .	. . . . .	. . . . .	. . . . .	. . . . .	. . . . .	. . . . .	. . . . .

The result of the multiple regression is

$$m_1 = -4.598, \qquad m_2 = -3.369, \qquad c = 14.644$$

Equation 10.37 then gives the desired values of A, B, and γ:

$$B = \frac{1}{m_1} = -0.2175, \qquad \gamma = \frac{m_2}{m_1} = 0.7326, \qquad A = 10^{-c/m_1} = 1531 \,\text{MPa}$$

Therefore, Eqs. 10.29 and 10.31 become

$$S_{ar} = S_{max}\left(\frac{1-R}{2}\right)^{0.7326}, \qquad S_{ar} = 1531\, N_f^{-0.2175} \,\text{MPa} \qquad \textbf{Ans.}$$

 Computing S_{ar} from the first equation for each test and plotting versus N_f gives the data points in Fig. E10.4(b). The line from the second equation is also shown. The data are consolidated reasonably well and follow the straight line trend, so this fitting result seems satisfactory. Also, eliminating R from Eq. 10.32(b) by means of Eq. 9.4(b) gives N_f as a function of S_m and S_{max}:

$$N_f = \left[\frac{S_{max}}{A}\left(1 - \frac{S_m}{S_{max}}\right)^{\gamma}\right]^{1/B}$$

Using this with the values for the fitted constants gives the family of curves plotted in Fig. E10.4(a).

Discussion   Where the S_{ar} versus N_f data do not fit a log–log straight line, or where the Walker equation does not consolidate the data into a single trend, another mathematical form may be employed. See MMPDS-05 (Chapter 9 References) for some possibilities.

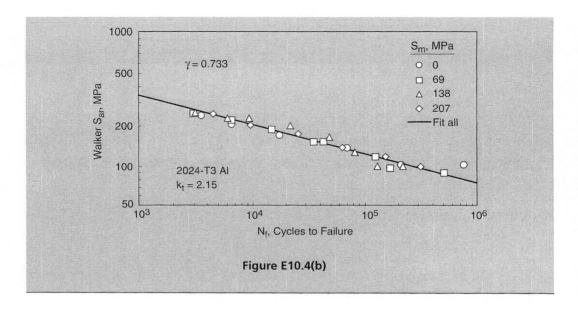

Figure E10.4(b)

10.7 ESTIMATING *S-N* CURVES

Estimates of fatigue limits can be used as part of a procedure for estimating entire *S-N* curves, with most mechanical engineering design books including such a procedure. We will first consider the general methodology that is applied, which is illustrated by Fig. 10.16. Then we will summarize the methods recommended in the design books of Juvinall (2006) and Budynas (2011), where the latter is the current presentation of the Shigley book.

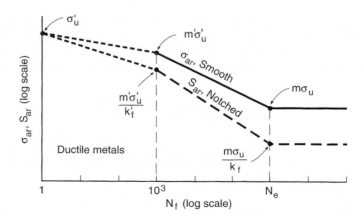

Figure 10.16 Estimating completely reversed *S-N* curves for smooth and notched members according to procedures suggested by Juvinall or Budynas.

10.7.1 Methodology for Estimating *S-N* Curves

A stress–life curve for smooth (unnotched) material at zero mean stress is estimated first. Using the ultimate tensile strength σ_u, the fatigue limit $\sigma_{er} = m\sigma_u$ is obtained as described in Section 10.4. Recall that the factor m is a multiplication of several factors, as in Eq. 10.15. One of these is an estimate of the polished bend specimen fatigue limit as a fraction of σ_u, such as $m_e = 0.5$ for most steels. Additional reduction factors account for effects such as type of loading (m_t), size (m_d), and surface finish (m_s). This provides a point σ_{er} at a long life N_e, such as $N_e = 10^6$ cycles for steels. The curve is assumed to be flat beyond N_e.

Then a point $\sigma'_{ar} = m' \sigma'_u$ is established at $N_f = 10^3$ cycles. The quantity σ'_u is the ultimate tensile strength σ_u for tension or bending, or the ultimate strength in shear τ_u for torsion. Based on the observation that stress levels around this life are not very far below σ_u, the factor m' is typically in the range 0.75 to 0.9. This value may vary with the type of loading, as stress–life curves for axial loading around 10^3 cycles are lower than for bending. Size and surface finish factors are not usually applied at 10^3 cycles, as these effects are observed to act mainly at long lives.

The points at 10^3 and N_e cycles are connected with a straight line on a log–log plot, giving a relationship of the form $\sigma_{ar} = A \, N_f^B$. If very short lives are of interest, another straight line may be employed to connect the 10^3 cycles point with σ'_u at $N_f = 1$ cycle. Hence, the three points forming the stress–life relationship are

$$(\sigma'_u, \ 1), \qquad (\sigma'_{ar}, N_f) = (m'\sigma'_u, \ 10^3), \qquad (\sigma_{er}, N_f) = \ (m\sigma_u, \ N_e) \qquad (10.41)$$

For notched members, the stress–life curve is expressed in terms of nominal (average) stress, S, as defined for various cases in Figs. A.11 and A.12. The stress at the long life point N_e is divided by k_f, becoming a nominal stress $S_{er} = m\sigma_u/k_f$. At 10^3 cycles, the stress value is divided by a short-life notch factor k'_f, becoming $S'_{ar} = m'\sigma'_u/k'_f$. Also, at $N_f = 1$ cycle, the notch is usually assumed to have no effect, so that the value σ'_u is unchanged. The three points on a log–log plot forming the nominal stress versus life relationship are then

$$(\sigma'_u, \ 1), \qquad (S'_{ar}, N_f) = \left(\frac{m'\sigma'_u}{k'_f}, \ 10^3 \right), \qquad (S_{er}, N_f) = \left(\frac{m\sigma_u}{k_f}, \ N_e \right) \qquad (10.42)$$

For agreement with experimental data, k'_f should be somewhat smaller than k_f, more so for lower strength metals, to reflect the effect of yielding as discussed in Section 10.5. Empirical values of k'_f can be obtained from Fig. 10.13 for steels, aluminum alloys, and magnesium alloys. The graph is entered with the ultimate tensile strength σ_u, using a different scale for each material type, giving the value of a quantity that can be used with k_f to obtain k'_f.

Various design textbooks are highly diverse in the handling of k'_f, as are even different editions of the same textbook. Values range over the extremes of $k'_f = 1$ and $k'_f = k_f$, where the former indicates no notch effect at 10^3 cycles, and the latter indicates the same effect as at long lives. The choice $k'_f = k_f$ is sometimes justified as simplifying calculations, but it produces a stress–life relationship that is overly conservative at short lives.

10.7.2 Estimates by the Methods of Juvinall or Budynas

In Juvinall (2006), a procedure is suggested that can be applied to a variety of engineering metals, and a similar approach is used by Budynas (2011) for steels. These approaches are summarized by Tables 10.1 and 10.2, with Table 10.1 giving details for the fatigue limit (N_e) point, and Table 10.2 for the 10^3 cycles point. With reference to Table 10.1, both authors use the factor $m_e = 0.5$ for steels, while noting that m_e falls below this value for high-strength steels, as in Fig. 9.24. Budynas limits the estimated bending fatigue limit for steels, not allowing it to exceed 700 MPa. Juvinall employs m_e factors for other metals as indicated, with the fatigue limit for aluminum alloys not being allowed to exceed 131 MPa. (See Fig. 9.25.)

The load type factors m_t that are employed by the two authors are similar for bending and torsion, but differ for axial loading. However, this m_t difference for axial loading is mostly eliminated by the details of the factors m_d used for size (stress gradient). For bending and torsion, Juvinall reduces m_d in steps for various ranges of diameter, with d being interpreted as the minor diameter or width, such as d_1 or w_1 for various cases in Figs. A.11 and A.12. Budynas uses continuously varying equations for m_d, and also makes special provisions for nonrotating bending and for rectangular sections. (See not only the main table entries, but also the notes below the table.)

For the surface finish factor m_s, Juvinall employs Fig. 10.10 for steels, and suggests $m_s = 1.0$ for gray cast iron, but makes no specific recommendations for other metals. Budynas gives equations for m_s for steels as a function of σ_u, two of which are listed in Table 10.1. Both authors employ $N_e = 10^6$ cycles for steels and cast irons, and Juvinall gives values for some other metals. Both authors also present reduction factors for temperature and for various levels of statistical reliability, but these are not shown in Table 10.1.

For the point at 10^3 cycles, with reference to Table 10.2, Juvinall uses fixed m' values as indicated. Budynas employs $m' = 0.9$ for low-strength steels, and also gives a curve with decreasing m' values for higher strength steels. An equation fitted to this curve is given in Table 10.2. Both authors employ the conservative assumption $k'_f = k_f$, which avoids some mathematical complexities in dealing with cases of combined loading, as when more than one of bending, axial, and torsion loading occur.

In their calculations, both authors work with local notch stresses, $\sigma = k_f S$, and apply these with the stress–life curve for smooth (unnotched) material at zero mean stress, σ_{ar} versus N_f. Although neither author directly employs the S_{ar} versus N_f curve, either method can be used to obtain such a curve by employing the three points of Eq. 10.42.

Table 10.2   Estimates of the S-N Curve Point at 10^3 Cycles

Juvinall (2006)[1]	$m' = 0.9$, $k'_f = k_f$ (bending; torsion with τ_u replacing σ_u)
	$m' = 0.75$, $k'_f = k_f$ (axial)
Budynas (2011)[2]	$m' = 0.90$ ($\sigma_u < 483$ MPa)
(steel only)	$m' = 0.2824x^2 - 1.918x + 4.012$, $x = \log \sigma_u$ ($\sigma_u \geq 483$ MPa)
	$k'_f = k_f$

Notes: [1]Use the estimate $\tau_u \approx 0.8\sigma_u$ for steel, and $\tau_u \approx 0.7\sigma_u$ for other ductile metals. [2] The equation for m' is a fit to the curve given in Budynas (2011).

For nonzero mean stresses, both authors employ local notch stress amplitudes and mean stresses.

$$\sigma_a = k_f S_a , \qquad \sigma_m = k_f S_m \qquad (\sigma_{\max} \leq \sigma_o) \qquad \text{(a)}$$

$$\sigma_a = k_f S_a , \qquad \sigma_m = k_{fm} S_m \qquad (\sigma_{\max} > \sigma_o) \qquad \text{(b)}$$

$$(10.43)$$

Where $\sigma_{\max} = \sigma_a + \sigma_m$ exceeds the yield strength σ_o, local yielding is expected, as in Fig. 10.15(b) or (c), and Eq. 10.43(b) is needed. In this case, Juvinall employs a procedure that is equivalent to the use of Eq. 10.27 with k_f replacing k_t . Budynas gives two options, either Eq. 10.27 with k_f replacing k_t , or $k_{fm} = 1$. (With reference to Fig. 10.15, note that the $k_{fm} = 1$ assumption can be either conservative or nonconservative, depending on the stress levels.)

Given σ_a and σ_m values from Eq. 10.43, Juvinall in effect employs the Goodman mean stress relationship, Eq. 9.15. Budynas gives the option of employing either the Goodman or Gerber relationships, as well as a third option called the ASME elliptic equation.

Example 10.5
A round bar of the aircraft quality AISI 4340 steel of Table 9.1 is subject to nonrotating bending and contains a circumferential groove with a ground surface. The dimensions, as defined in Fig. A.12(c), are $d_1 = 32$, $d_2 = 35$, and $\rho = 1.5$ mm. Assume that the only materials properties known are the yield and ultimate strengths.

   (a) Estimate the completely reversed *S-N* curve for the grooved bar.
   (b) Predict the life for cyclic loading at a nominal stress amplitude of $S_a = 150$ MPa, with a mean of $S_m = 200$ MPa.
   (c) If 5000 cycles are expected in actual service, what are the safety factors in stress and in life?

First Solution   (a) One approach is to use the procedure of Budynas. First, the notch factor k_f is estimated from k_t by using α or β as in previous examples. Figure A.12(c) provides k_t:

$$\frac{d_2}{d_1} = 1.094, \qquad \frac{\rho}{d_1} = 0.047, \qquad k_t = 2.35$$

If we obtain k_f from Eqs. 10.7 and 10.9, it is

$$\alpha = 0.070 \, \text{mm}, \qquad k_f = 2.29$$

The ultimate strength of $\sigma_u = 1172$ MPa from Table 9.1 is needed, and the various m_i factors are evaluated by following the Budynas column of Table 10.1. We obtain

$$m_e = 0.5, \qquad m_t = 1.0$$

For the size factor, Note 4 of Table 10.1 applies, due to the nonrotating bending situation. Using the minimum diameter d_1, we have

$$d_e = 0.37 d_1 = 11.84 \text{ mm}, \qquad m_d = 1.24 d_e^{-0.107} = 0.952$$

The surface finish factor is

$$m_s = 1.58 \, \sigma_u^{-0.085} = 0.867$$

Hence, the overall reduction factor and the estimated fatigue limit are

$$m = m_e m_t m_d m_s = 0.412$$

$$\sigma_{er} = m\sigma_u = 0.412(1172 \text{ MPa}) = 483 \text{ MPa} , \qquad S_{er} = \frac{m\sigma_u}{k_f} = \frac{483 \text{ MPa}}{2.29} = 211 \text{ MPa}$$

Here, σ_{er} and $N_e = 10^6$ cycles provides one point on the estimated stress–life curve for unnotched material, and S_{er} provides the corresponding point on the curve for the notched member.

Table 10.2 is then employed to calculate values needed for the point at 10^3 cycles.

$$m' = 0.2824 x^2 - 1.918 x + 4.012 , \qquad x = \log \sigma_u \quad (\sigma_u \geq 483 \text{ MPa})$$

$$m' = 0.2824 \, (\log 1172)^2 - 1.918 \, (\log 1172) + 4.012 = 0.786$$

$$k_f' = k_f = 2.29$$

Thus, the values for $N_f = 10^3$ cycles, for both unnotched and notched cases, are

$$\sigma_{ar}' = m'\sigma_u' = 0.786(1172 \text{ MPa}) = 921 \text{ MPa} , \qquad S_{ar}' = \frac{m'\sigma_u'}{k_f} = \frac{921 \text{ MPa}}{2.29} = 402 \text{ MPa}$$

Proceeding as in Ex. 9.1(a), the equation of the form $\sigma_{ar} = A N_f^B$ for unnotched material is

$$B = \frac{\log \sigma_{ar}' - \log \sigma_{er}}{\log N_f - \log N_e} = \frac{\log 921 - \log 483}{\log 10^3 - \log 10^6} = -0.0933$$

$$A = \frac{\sigma_{ar}'}{N_f^B} = \frac{921}{1000^{-0.0933}} = 1754 \text{ MPa}$$

$$\sigma_{ar} = 1754 \, N_f^{-0.0933} \text{ MPa} \qquad (10^3 \leq N_f \leq 10^6) \qquad\qquad \textbf{Ans.}$$

This stress–life relationship is shown in Fig. E10.5 (left). Also shown is the similar line obtained by applying the Juvinall procedure, with details from Tables 10.1 and 10.2.

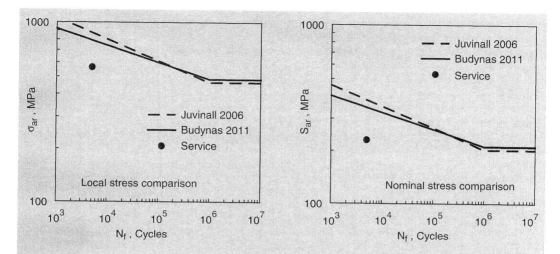

Figure E10.5

For the notched member, since $k'_f = k_f$ applies uniformly over the interval 10^3 to 10^6 cycles, the corresponding stress–life relationship is

$$S_{ar} = \frac{A}{k_f} N_f^B , \quad S_{ar} = 766 \, N_f^{-0.0933} \text{ MPa} \quad (10^3 \le N_f \le 10^6) \qquad \textbf{Ans.}$$

This nominal stress versus life relationship is shown in Fig. E10.5 (right), as is the similar relationship from the Juvinall procedure.

(b) To obtain the life for the given nominal stresses, first multiply the given S_a and S_m by k_f to obtain local stresses at the notch.

$$\sigma_a = k_f S_a = 2.29(150) = 344 , \quad \sigma_m = k_f S_m = 2.29(200) = 458$$

$$\sigma_{\max} = \sigma_a + \sigma_m = 802 \text{ MPa}$$

Since σ_{max} is less than the yield strength of $\sigma_o = 1103$ MPa from Table 9.1, the situation is similar to Fig. 10.15(a), and no special measures are needed to account for yielding effects. One of the mean stress options in the Budynas method is to use the Goodman equation, which gives an equivalent completely reversed stress from Eq. 9.15 of

$$\sigma_{ar} = \frac{\sigma_a}{1 - \sigma_m / \sigma_u} = \frac{344}{1 - 458/1172} = 564 \text{ MPa}$$

The corresponding life from the stress–life relationship developed in (a) is

$$N_f = \left(\frac{\sigma_{ar}}{A} \right)^{1/B} = \left(\frac{564 \text{ MPa}}{1754 \text{ MPa}} \right)^{1/(-0.0933)} = 1.914 \times 10^5 \text{cycles} \qquad \textbf{Ans.}$$

(c) The safety factor in life can then be calculated from the service life of $\hat{N} = 5000$ cycles using Eq. 9.25(b), and the safety factor in stress follows from Eq. 9.12(a).

$$X_N = \frac{N_{f2}}{\hat{N}} = \frac{1.914 \times 10^5}{5000} = 38.3 , \qquad X_S = X_N^{-B} = 38.3^{-(-0.0933)} = 1.405 \qquad \textbf{Ans.}$$

The point $(\hat{\sigma}_{ar}, \hat{N}) = (564 \text{ MPa}, 5000)$ corresponding to the service loading is shown in Fig. E10.5 (left), allowing these safety factors to be visualized.

Second Solution **(a, b)** An alternate procedure is to employ the nominal stress versus life relationship already developed as $S_{ar} = (A/k_f) N_f^B$. Noting the difficulties with the Goodman and similar mean stress relationships, we will apply the SWT equation to the nominal stress.

$$S_{ar} = \sqrt{S_{\max} S_a} = \sqrt{(S_m + S_a) S_a} = \sqrt{(200 + 150)150} = 229 \text{ MPa}$$

The corresponding life is

$$N_f = \left(\frac{S_{ar}}{A/k_f} \right)^{1/B} = \left(\frac{(229 \text{ MPa})2.29}{1754 \text{ MPa}} \right)^{1/(-0.0933)} = 4.14 \times 10^5 \text{ cycles} \qquad \textbf{Ans.}$$

(c) Safety factors then follow as before.

$$X_N = \frac{N_{f2}}{\hat{N}} = \frac{4.14 \times 10^5}{5000} = 82.8 , \qquad X_S = X_N^{-B} = 82.8^{-(-0.0933)} = 1.510 \qquad \textbf{Ans.}$$

The point $(\hat{S}_{ar}, \hat{N}) = (229 \text{ MPa}, 5000)$ corresponding to the service loading is shown in Fig. E10.5 (right), again allowing the safety factors to be visualized.

Discussion The first solution is highly conservative due to the use of $k'_f = k_f$. Entering Fig. 10.13 with $\sigma_u = 1172 \text{ MPa} = 170 \text{ ksi}$ and applying $k_f = 2.29$ gives $k'_f = 1.55$. Modifying the estimated S_{ar} vs. N_f curve with this value would considerably raise the point at $N_f = 10^3$ cycles, thus giving larger safety factors. Also, noting the discussion of the Goodman equation in Sections 9.7 and 10.6, the use of the SWT equation in the second solution should provide greater accuracy.

10.7.3 Discussion

The two methods discussed for estimating S-N curves, and other similar ones, should not be regarded as providing anything more than very rough curves for use in design. Of the two procedures discussed, Juvinall's is the most complete, as it incorporates nonferrous metals. However, the Budynas estimate is more detailed where it does apply for steels. Notably, some of the reduction factors, such as those for size and surface finish, reflect fits to large amounts of test data.

These estimates assume that the *S-N* curve does not decrease beyond the long-life point at N_e, where they assume the existence of a fatigue limit. Recalling the discussion of Section 9.6.5, we note that caution is needed regarding this aspect of the estimates. Where corrosion or occasional severe cycles are involved, it may be wise to regard the (S_{er}, N_e) point on the estimated *S-N* curve not as the beginning of a flat region, but rather as a point on a log–log straight line that continues downward below this point.

Actual fatigue data from tests are always preferable to an estimated *S-N* curve. Thus, such data should be used where possible to aid in estimating the *S-N* curve, or even to replace the estimate entirely. Also, where data are not found in the literature, it will sometimes be appropriate to expend the time and funds necessary to obtain them. It is, in fact, quite common in engineering practice to employ *S-N* curves from tests on engineering components, as described in the next section.

10.8 USE OF COMPONENT *S-N* DATA

It is often advantageous to employ *S-N* data from tests on members that are similar or identical to the engineering component of interest, such as machine or vehicle parts or structural joints. Subassemblies, such as a vehicle suspension system, may also be tested, as may portions of a structure, or even an entire machine, vehicle, or structure.

10.8.1 Bailey Bridge Example

An example is provided by the Bailey bridge panel made from structural steel, as shown in Fig. 10.17. This is one panel of a modular truss for military and temporary civilian bridges used by the British in World War II. Bailey bridges were still being manufactured long after the end of the war, and some were used in situations and for lengths of time (10 years or more) that were not envisioned by the original designers. Hence, a fatigue testing program was undertaken, as reported in a 1970 paper by Webber, to provide information on permissible duration and severity of bridge usage.

Constant amplitude *S-N* data from this work and a fitted curve are shown in Fig. 10.18. The tests were conducted by applying cyclic loads to an assembly of panels, with these loads oriented in a plane corresponding to vertical loads on a bridge, which is the vertical direction in the illustration. Cracks generally started at a weld near the *slot for sway brace* and were visibly growing for at least half of the life, which was defined as complete separation of a truss member. The nominal stresses plotted are bending stresses, calculated by treating the entire panel as a beam, with the bracing averaged as a web and with the location of the critical slot giving the distance from the neutral axis of this beam. All tests employed the same minimum load, corresponding to the dead load of a bridge.

Such a curve is useful in assessing the life expected for Bailey bridges. In particular, values of cycles to failure from the fitted curve may be employed with the Palmgren-Miner rule to make life estimates for various combinations of vehicle weight and numbers of load applications. Note that this curve lacks generality in that it is applicable only to this particular component cycled with the particular minimum stress used. However, it has the major advantage of automatically including the effects of details such as complex geometry, surface finish, residual stresses from fabrication,

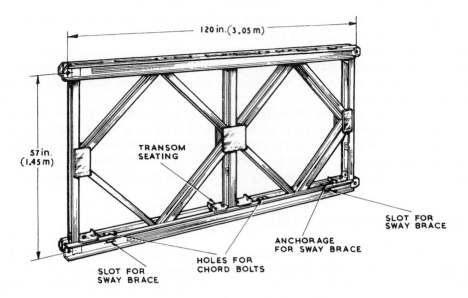

Figure 10.17   Bailey bridge panel. (From [Webber 70]; copyright © ASTM; used with permission.)

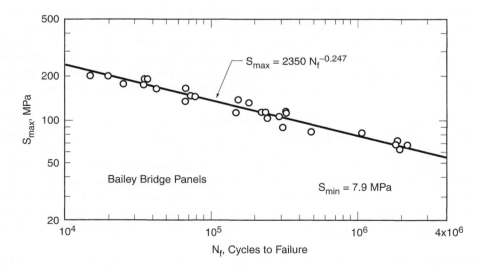

Figure 10.18   Fatigue data at constant S_{min} and fitted line, for Bailey bridge panels in vertical bending, with failure defined as complete separation of a truss member. (Data from [Whitman 60].)

and the unusual metallurgy at welds. Such factors are difficult to evaluate by any means other than a component test.

In a manner similar to the Bailey bridge case, other component *S-N* curves have the disadvantage of lacking generality, but the advantage of automatically including difficult-to-evaluate geometric and fabrication detail.

10.8.2 Mean Stress Effects and Variable Amplitude Life for Components

For the Bailey bridge example, the *S-N* data and the service stresses of interest all correspond to a fixed minimum stress, so there is no need to consider variations in the mean stress. However, many applications of component *S-N* data will require evaluating the effects of mean nominal stress, S_m, which may also be expressed as effects of the *R*-ratio, $R = S_{min}/S_{max}$. For this purpose, the SWT relationship can be employed, with the variable being either nominal stress *S*, as in Eq. 10.28, or an applied force or moment, as in Eq. 10.30. If data are available for more than one value of mean stress or *R*, then the Walker relationship of Eq. 10.29 is recommended. A value of γ needs to be fitted, as described in Section 10.6.4, and the variable can again be either *S* or an applied load. The Goodman, Gerber, and similar equations are not recommended.

For variable amplitude loading, component life estimates can be made by counting cycles and using the Palmgren–Miner rule in the same manner as described in Section 9.9. A nominal stress versus life curve, or a load versus life curve, simply replaces the stress–life curve for unnotched material. An alternative is to use the strain-based approach, as described later in Chapter 14.

Example 10.6
Double-edge-notched plates of 2024-T3 aluminum alloy ($k_t = 2.15$) have a nominal stress versus life relationship of the form of Eq. 10.31, where S_{ar} is given by the Walker relationship, Eq. 10.29, with fitting constants $A = 1530\,\text{MPa}$, $B = -0.217$, and $\gamma = 0.733$. Assume that these plates will be repeatedly subjected in engineering service to the nominal stress history shown in Fig. E10.6.

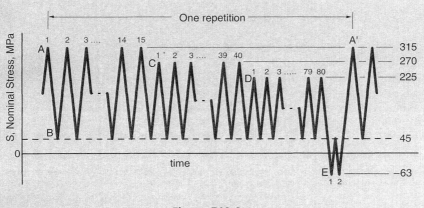

Figure E10.6

(a) Estimate the number of repetitions of the history to cause fatigue failure.
(b) If 60 repetitions of the load history are expected to be applied in service, what are the safety factors in life and in stress?

Table E10.6

j	N_j	S_{min}	S_{max}	R	S_{ar}	N_{fj}	N_j/N_{fj}
1	14	45	315	0.143	169.3	2.55×10^4	5.50×10^{-4}
2	40	45	270	0.167	142.1	5.70×10^4	7.02×10^{-4}
3	80	45	225	0.200	114.9	1.52×10^5	5.28×10^{-4}
4	1	-63	45	-1.400	51.4	6.17×10^6	1.62×10^{-7}
5	1	-63	315	-0.200	216.6	8.17×10^3	1.22×10^{-4}

$$\Sigma = 1.902 \times 10^{-3}$$

Solution   (a) Rainflow cycle counting of the history is first needed, and the results are shown in the first four columns of Table E10.6. Peak A_1 is a suitable starting point, as it is at the highest stress level in the history. The first cycle counted is A_1-B_1, followed by A_2-B_2, etc., up to A_{14}-B_{14}, for 14 cycles at this level. Then 40 cycles B-C and 80 cycles B-D are counted, followed by one cycle E_1-B. Peak/valley points A_{15} and E_2 remain unused, and along with a return to the starting point A', these form major cycle A_{15}-E_2-A'.

Next, apply the Walker mean stress relationship, Eq. 10.29, along with the stress–life curve of Eq. 10.31, with constants A, B, and γ as given. For each stress level, calculate

$$R = S_{min}/S_{max}, \qquad S_{ar} = S_{max}\left(\frac{1-R}{2}\right)^{\gamma}, \qquad N_f = \left(\frac{S_{ar}}{A}\right)^{1/B}$$

where all stresses are in MPa units. The resulting values are given in Table E10.6. Also, calculate and then sum the cycle ratios, N_j/N_{fj}. Finally, the number of repetitions to failure may be evaluated by applying the Palmgren–Miner rule in the form of Eq. 9.34:

$$B_f = 1\bigg/\left[\sum \frac{N_j}{N_{fj}}\right]_{\text{one rep.}} = 1/1.902 \times 10^{-3} = 526 \text{ repetitions} \qquad \textbf{Ans.}$$

(b) With 60 repetitions expected in service, the safety factor in life can be calculated from Eq. 9.10, and the safety factor in stress follows from Eq. 9.12:

$$X_N = \frac{N_f}{\hat{N}} = \frac{B_f}{\hat{B}} = \frac{526}{60} = 8.76, \qquad X_S = X_N^{-B} = 8.76^{-(-0.217)} = 1.60 \qquad \textbf{Ans.}$$

10.8.3 Matching a Component to Notched Specimen Data

Often, *S-N* data exist for notched plate or bar specimens of the component material, as in various handbooks, including MMPDS-05 (Chapter 9 References). It is tempting to match a component to such *S-N* data by looking for a case with a similar elastic stress concentration factor, k_t. However, this does not properly handle notch size (stress gradient) effects, which were discussed earlier in Section 10.2. It is preferable to match the component to test specimens with a similar notch radius ρ, even if the k_t values differ significantly, and then relate the stresses in terms of the value of $k_t S$, the local notch stress for elastic behavior.

Another approach is to match not ρ but the fracture mechanics length parameter l' of Eq. 8.26. For notched members loaded at the same $k_t S$ and having similar l' values, there will be a similar variation of the stress intensity factor K with crack length near the notch. This can be verified for two notched members by plotting $K/(k_{tg} S_g)$ versus crack length for both on the same graph. The approximations of Eqs. 8.24 and 8.25 may be employed—that is, K_A up to l', and K_B beyond. (For consistency with F, gross section stress S_g should be employed. The corresponding stress concentration factor k_{tg} can be obtained from a value k_{tn} based on net area by noting that $k_{tg} S_g = k_{tn} S_n$.) The l' method of matching *S-N* curves is applicable to notches and holes, but requires further development for fillet-type notches. See the paper by Dowling and Wilson (1981) for more detail and discussion.

10.8.4 Component *S-N* Curves for Welded Members

Connections between pieces of metal are often accomplished by welding. This involves applying intense heat to melt filler metal and at the same time melting a small portion of the two pieces to be joined, so that a solid joint is formed upon cooling and solidification. Some typical weld joints are shown in Fig. 10.19, and a few structural details that involve welding are shown in Fig. 10.20.

Welded structural members have complex geometry and metallurgy in the vicinity of the weld, and they may contain porosity or other defects. These defects make it difficult to determine stress concentration factors or to relate the behavior to that of any nonwelded test member. As a result, most design codes that cover welded structural members employ component *S-N* curves based on extensive testing of actual welded members. Several design codes that employ this approach are listed at the end of this chapter in a separate section of the References.

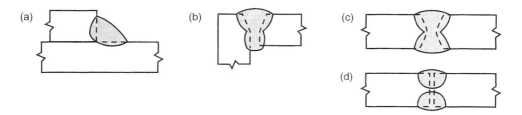

Figure 10.19 Typical welds: (a) fillet weld, (b) corner joint formed by a single-V-groove weld, (c) butt joint formed by a double-V-groove weld, and (d) butt joint formed by a square-groove weld with partial penetration. Dashed lines indicate the base metal shape before welding, and shaded areas indicate the melted and resolidified material.

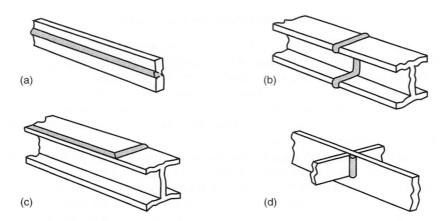

Figure 10.20   A sampling of the numerous structural details involving welding: (a) longitudinal butt weld, (b) transverse butt weld, (c) cover plate attached with fillet welds, and (d) lateral attachment with fillet welds. (Adapted from [AWS 96] p. 16; used with permission.)

Some of the fatigue data on welded structural members used in design code development are shown in Fig. 10.21. The cyclic range of the nominal stress from bending, ΔS, is plotted versus cycles to failure. Members with only longitudinal welds are seen to have considerably higher fatigue strengths than members with transverse welds at the ends of cover plates. Although data for three different structural steels are plotted, the results are insensitive to the particular structural steel involved, but highly sensitive to the geometric detail. Noting the statistical scatter that is evident in these data, *S-N* curves are shown not only for the mean behavior, but also for 95% survival at a confidence level of 95%, where the latter curves are seen to lie near the lower limits of the scatter for the two cases.

Similar data for a variety of cases have been employed to develop *S-N* curves for use in structural design. For example, for structural steel details in nontubular members under tension and/or bending, the American Welding Society (AWS) structural welding design code gives fatigue curves as

$$\Delta S = \left(\frac{C}{N_f} \right)^{0.333}, \qquad \Delta S \geq \Delta S_{TH} \qquad \text{(ksi units)} \qquad \text{(a)}$$

$$\Delta S = \left(\frac{329C}{N_f} \right)^{0.333}, \qquad \Delta S \geq \Delta S_{TH} \qquad \text{(MPa units)} \qquad \text{(b)}$$

(10.44)

where the stresses are given as ranges, and ΔS_{TH} is a *threshold* stress range—that is, a fatigue limit. Structural details are categorized according to the severity of their stress concentration effect, giving a family of *S-N* curves that each obey Eq. 10.44, as shown in Fig. 10.22. The corresponding constants for Eq. 10.44 are given in Table 10.3, as are constants for these same curves expressed in the form

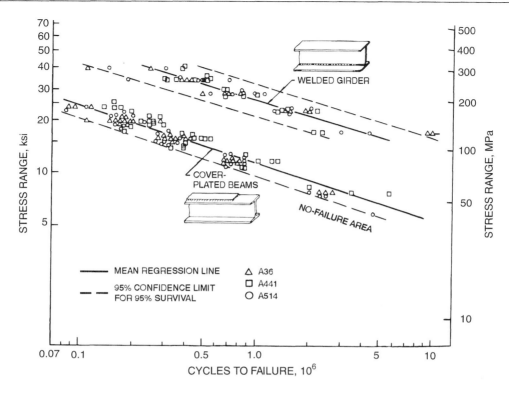

Figure 10.21 Nominal stress range versus millions of cycles to failure for bending tests on welded structural members of three different structural steels. The data for longitudinal welds (top) correspond to AWS category *B*, and that for cover-plated beams (bottom) to category *E*. (From [Jenney 01] p. 276; reprinted with permission.)

$$\Delta S = A' N_f^B, \qquad \Delta S \ge \Delta S_{TH} \tag{10.45}$$

The curves of Fig. 10.22 and Table 10.3 correspond to 95% survival, as in Fig. 10.21.

Plain structural steel with no welding or other stress raiser corresponds to category *A*. Additional categories are then assigned, depending on the geometric detail, as specified in the AWS code. For example, category *B* applies for cases of only mild stress concentration, as for simple longitudinal welds, as in Fig. 10.20(a). The welded girder (upper) data in Fig. 10.21 is also a category *B* case. Category *C* corresponds to somewhat more severe cases, such as transverse welds in a spliced beam, Fig. 10.20(b), except that category *B* may be used if the welds are ground flat to be flush with the adjacent metal. Transverse welds similar to Fig. 10.20(d) are also category *C*. An especially severe stress concentration is caused by a transverse weld at the end of a partial-length cover plate, as in Fig. 10.20(c), and as for the cover-plate (lower) data of Fig. 10.21. If the flange thickness is less than 20 mm, then category *E* applies; otherwise the less favorable category *E'* is used.

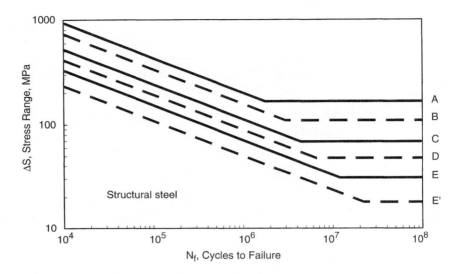

Figure 10.22   Stress–life curves from the AWS design code for various categories of nontubular connections.

Table 10.3   Constants for AWS Fatigue Curves for Nontubular Sections

Category	C, cycles	B	A', MPa	ΔS_{TH}, MPa
A	2.50×10^{10}	−0.3330	19 987	166.0
B	1.20×10^{10}	−0.3330	15 653	110.0
C	4.40×10^{9}	−0.3330	11 207	69.0
D	2.20×10^{9}	−0.3330	8 897	48.0
E	1.10×10^{9}	−0.3330	7 063	31.0
E′	3.90×10^{8}	−0.3330	5 001	18.0

To choose the appropriate category and hence *S-N* curve, we must match the structural detail to a pictorial and explanatory chart in the AWS code. There are also some intermediate categories, such as *B′*, and a special category *F* for shear loading. The same set of curves are employed for all common structural steels, and no mean stress adjustment is made. AWS gives a different set of curves for tubular connections, as for structures made from pipe sections welded together.

The American Association of State Highway and Transportation Officials (AASHTO) employs essentially identical curves, with $B = -\frac{1}{3}$ exactly, while specifying how they are to be applied to the specific case of bridge design. For design involving finite fatigue lives, the *S-N* curves are extended below the threshold (fatigue limit), and a load factor of 0.75 is applied relative to the stresses caused by a *design truck* weighing 90% of the usual legal limit. This factor arises from Palmgren–Miner rule life calculations that consider a spectrum of truck weights, many lighter than the design truck. However, to employ the threshold and thus assume infinite life, the load factor required is 1.50, twice the previous value. On this basis, fatigue damage is expected only for trucks that are 50%

heavier than the design truck, that is, 35% above the usual legal limit. Recalling the discussion in Section 9.6.5, this conservative handling of the fatigue limit is indeed appropriate for the variable amplitude loading experienced by bridges.

Additional, generally similar, weld design codes with *S-N* curves are published by other national and international organizations, some of which are referenced at the end of this chapter.

As noted, the AWS design curves correspond to 95% survival. These curves are shifted relative to the corresponding curves for the mean of the data by approximately a factor of 2.0 in life, which, due to $B = -\frac{1}{3}$, gives a shift in stress by a factor of approximately 1.25. (Note that substituting $X_N = 2.0$ and $B = -\frac{1}{3}$ into Eq. 9.12 gives $X_S = 2.0^{1/3} = 1.26$.) Although AWS does not specify any safety factor beyond that given by the 95% survival curves, an additional margin of safety may be desirable. For example, consider a safety factor of 2.5 in life relative to the 95% survival curve. Combined with the aforementioned factor of 2.0, this gives a safety factor in life relative to the mean of the data of approximately $X_N = 2.5 \times 2.0 = 5.0$. Applying Eq. 9.12 makes this equivalent to a safety factor in stress of $X_N = 5.0^{1/3} = 1.71$.

In applying the Palmgren–Miner rule for variable amplitude loading, we have noted in Chapter 9 that this can be done by calculating an equivalent stress level which is expected to cause the same fatigue life, in cycles, as the variable loading. Adapting Eq. 9.37 to an *S-N* curve of the form of Eq. 10.45, we see that the equivalent stress range ΔS_q and the resulting life are given by

$$\Delta S_q = \left[\sum_{j=1}^{k} N_j (\Delta S_j)^{-1/B} \Big/ N_B \right]^{-B}, \qquad N_f = B_f N_B = \left(\frac{\Delta S_q}{A'} \right)^{1/B} \qquad \text{(a, b)} \qquad (10.46)$$

The preceding applies to a repeating sequence of loading containing N_B cycles with k different stress levels. For each stress level $j = 1, 2, 3, \ldots k$, the quantity N_j is the number of cycles and ΔS_j is the stress range. The overall number of cycles to failure N_f is related to the number of repetitions to failure B_f according to $B_f = N_f / N_B$.

Note that the quantity $f_j = N_j / N_B$ is the fraction of the total number of cycles that occurs at stress range ΔS_j. Making this substitution into Eq. 10.46(a) gives

$$\Delta S_q = \left[\sum_{j=1}^{k} f_j (\Delta S_j)^{-1/B} \right]^{-B}, \qquad \sum_{j=1}^{k} f_j = 1 \qquad (10.47)$$

where the f_j must, of course, sum to unity. For the particular case of $B = -\frac{1}{3}$, Eqs. 10.46(b) and 10.47 give

$$\Delta S_q = \left[\sum_{j=1}^{k} f_j (\Delta S_j)^3 \right]^{1/3}, \qquad N_f = \left(\frac{\Delta S_q}{A'} \right)^{-3} \qquad \text{(a, b)} \qquad (10.48)$$

Equations similar to these may appear in weld design codes and in literature discussing them.

10.9 DESIGNING TO AVOID FATIGUE FAILURE

Where fatigue failure is a concern in design, or where failures have actually occurred, one strategy that can be employed to reduce or eliminate problems is to minimize the severity of stress raisers. This corresponds to minimizing the elastic stress concentration factor k_t, which in turn decreases the fatigue notch factor k_f, thus raising the fatigue limit and the overall *S-N* curve. Other changes in geometric detail, such as reducing eccentricity that causes bending, may also be beneficial. Another strategy is to exploit the mean stress effect by introducing residual (locked-in) stresses that have the same beneficial effect as an applied compressive mean stress. More detailed discussion follows.

10.9.1 Design Details

In design of engineering components, resistance to fatigue failure can be improved by careful attention to detail. For notches such as grooves, fillets, and noncircular holes, stress concentration factors are decreased if the radius of the notch is increased, as study of Figs. A.11 and A.12 in Appendix A will confirm. Other aspects of the geometry also have an effect, such as the relative width of a notched plate or the ratio of the two diameters in a stepped shaft. Hence, within the constraints imposed by functional requirements, geometries can be adjusted to minimize the elastic stress concentration factor k_t. For a given material, k_f will then also be minimized. If more than one material is being considered, the different notch sensitivities q of these also need to be examined.

Consider the example of Fig. 10.23. A relatively small radius occurs in (a) at the diameter step in a shaft. The stress concentration factor k_t can be decreased by increasing the fillet radius while keeping the other dimensions the same. Even better, the radius can be essentially eliminated by using a taper, as in (b). If functional requirements preclude a simple taper, the geometry of (c) has a lower k_t than (a) and could perhaps be used.

Similar principles apply to other design details, such as keyways, as illustrated in Fig. 10.24. A further example is the common *fir tree* design for connecting the roots of turbine blades, shown in Fig. 10.1. Smooth curves with radii as large as permitted by the tight spaces involved are used, and the overall taper tends to distribute the load fairly evenly among the projections (lugs) on the blade root.

Where small motions occur between tightly fitting metal parts, a problem called *fretting* may occur. A metal oxide in the form of a powder is usually present, and there is surface damage that can cause cracks to start and grow. Hence, considerable care is needed in designing certain mechanical connections, such as the press-fitted shaft of Fig. 10.25. Altered geometry to reduce the stresses and to make a more gradual transition into the press fit is helpful, with some possibilities being shown. Since certain combinations of materials are particularly susceptible to this problem, it is often helpful to change one of the materials, or to use a bushing or a surface coating in the joint. Intentional introduction of beneficial compressive residual stresses, as by shot peening, is also often used.

Bolts involve severe stress raisers in the threads and elsewhere, and the tightly fitting surfaces in a bolted connection may also be subject to fretting. Locations where fatigue cracks are likely to start in a bolt, and some changes that can be used to improve the fatigue resistance, are shown in Fig. 10.26. Highly specialized bolt and rivet designs are sometimes used in critical applications. Some bolted connections that might be found in metal aircraft structure are shown

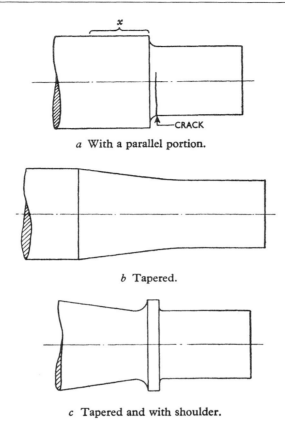

a With a parallel portion.

b Tapered.

c Tapered and with shoulder.

Figure 10.23   The common location (a) of fatigue cracks in a stepped shaft, and (b) reducing the stress raiser effect by using a taper, or (c) by using a taper with a shoulder. (From [Cottell 56]; reprinted by permission of the Council of the Institution of Mechanical Engineers, London, UK.)

in Fig. 10.27. Improved resistance to fatigue is provided by symmetrical geometries that minimize bending stresses in the members being connected, and thus also in the bolts. Tapered or *scarf* joints cause the loads to be more evenly distributed among the bolts, so this feature also is usually beneficial.

In welded joints, special care is needed to minimize the stress-raiser effect. Grinding to smooth the irregular raised shape left when the weld metal solidifies is helpful. Welds may contain a variety of defects, such as shrinkage cracks, porosity, or a groove (undercut) left at the edge of the weld. Inspection to find defects and their subsequent repair is important. Also, partial penetration welds, as in Fig. 10.19(d), essentially constitute built-in cracks, so these should not be allowed in critical areas.

Additional information on design details for various mechanical elements, such as joints, springs, gears, bearings, shafts, etc., may be found in textbooks on mechanical design and in structural design codes, such as those listed in the References.

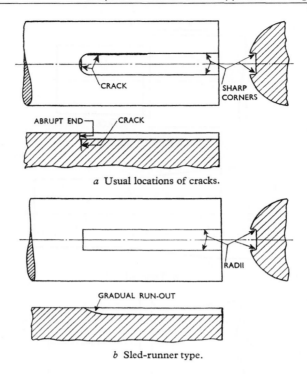

Figure 10.24   Usual location (a) of fatigue cracks in keyways, and an improved design (b) called a *sled-runner* keyway. (From [Cottell 56]; reprinted by permission of the Council of the Institution of Mechanical Engineers, London, UK.)

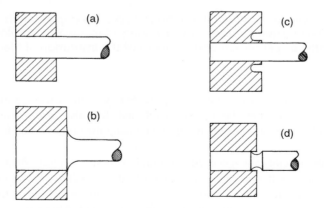

Figure 10.25   Some designs to alleviate stress concentration at a press-fitted shaft. The plain shaft (a) involves a severe stress raiser and is susceptible to fretting. Some possible improvements are (b) enlarging the shaft end, (c) modifying the collar, or (d) grooving the shaft. (Adapted from [Grover 66] p. 211.)

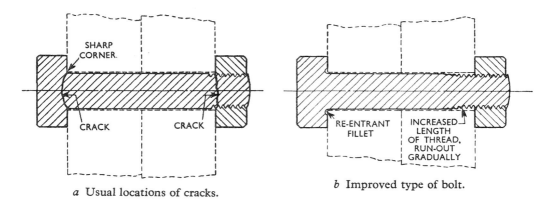

a Usual locations of cracks.

b Improved type of bolt.

Figure 10.26   Usual location (a) of fatigue cracks in a bolt and (b) some measures to improve fatigue resistance. (From [Cottell 56]; reprinted by permission of the Council of the Institution of Mechanical Engineers, London, UK.)

10.9.2 Surface Residual Stresses

Consider a notched member, as in Fig. 10.28, that is subjected to a tensile overload sufficient to cause local yielding. Upon removal of the load, the unyielded material around the plastic zone attempts to recover its original shape, and in so doing forces the yielded material into compression. Other regions away from the notch are in tension, so there is a distribution of stress that sums to zero, as required by equilibrium and the now-zero applied load. These locked-in stresses are called *residual stresses*. If compressive at the notch, they retard fatigue cracking by biasing the mean stress in the compressive direction during subsequent cyclic loading.

If it is assumed that the material is an elastic, perfectly plastic one, the residual stress remaining after removal of a nominal stress S' is thus

$$\sigma_r = \sigma_o - k_t S' \qquad (\sigma_o < k_t S' \leq 2\sigma_o)$$
$$\sigma_r = -\sigma_o \qquad\quad (k_t S' > 2\sigma_o) \tag{10.49}$$

In the first case, corresponding to Fig. 10.28(a), no compressive yielding occurs during unloading, but in the second case, (b), it does, and this results in a residual stress equal to the yield strength in compression. If the overload is compressive, an analogous but opposite effect occurs, giving a tensile and thus harmful residual stress. The preceding equations can still be used if σ_o is replaced by $-\sigma_o$ and S' is used with its negative value.

Compressive surface residual stresses are often intentionally introduced into mechanical components to improve the fatigue strength at long lives. Any method of yielding the surface in tension will result in a compressive residual stress in a manner similar to the notch case. Methods used in addition to tensile overloading of notches include *shot peening*, *cold rolling* of the surface, and overloading in bending, called *presetting*. (See Fig. 9.31.) Shot peening is the most commonly used method and involves bombarding the surface with small, hard, often steel, balls. These cause

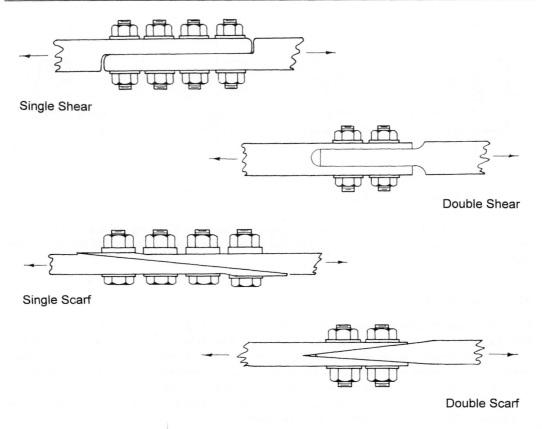

Single Shear

Double Shear

Single Scarf

Double Scarf

Figure 10.27   Some bolted joint details. A single shear joint can be improved by introducing a taper (scarf). Double shear joints minimize bending and can also be tapered. (Adapted from [Grover 66] p. 176.)

biaxial yielding in tension under each point of impact; hence, a biaxial compressive residual stress occurs due to the elastic recovery of the unyielded material beneath. Components commonly shot peened include leaf springs, gears, crankshafts, and turbine blades.

Compressive surface residual stresses can also be produced by surface hardening treatments, as in carburizing or nitriding of steels, or by thermal treatments, notably rapid quenching of steel shafts. Other surface treatments, such as abusive grinding and chrome plating, need to be used with care, as they may introduce harmful tensile residual stresses. Tensile residual stresses often remain after welding, which leads to the common practice of a subsequent *stress relief* heat treatment to remove them.

Surface residual stresses are beneficial only where subsequent yielding does not occur due to loads in service, as this may remove the compressive residual stress or even change it to a harmful tensile one. Additional discussion of residual stress effects on fatigue can be found in Stephens (2001) and in the SAE *Fatigue Design Handbook* (Rice, 1997).

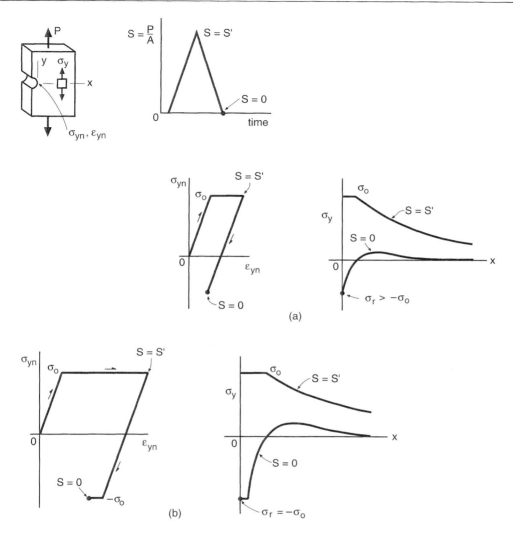

Figure 10.28   Unloading of a notched member after local yielding. Stress–strain behavior at the notch and residual stress distributions are shown for (a) elastic behavior during unloading, and (b) compressive yielding during unloading.

10.10 DISCUSSION

In some cases, engineering components have geometrically smooth contours and relatively large notch radii, such that stresses in fatigue-critical locations can be analyzed in detail, as by the application of stress concentration factors, k_t, or by finite element analysis. However, note that k_t values are based on elastic behavior, and most finite element analysis done in a design environment also assumes elastic behavior. As a result, the stress values are in error if they exceed the yield strength. But if there is indeed little or no yielding, it is reasonable to make fatigue life estimates using the methodology of Chapter 9, applying this to the local stresses as analyzed.

However, the circumstances are often more complex. Specifically, there may be localized yielding. Or there may be relatively sharp notches or complexities—for example, bolted joints or welds—such that detailed analysis of the local stresses is difficult. Estimated *S-N* curves or component *S-N* curves are then needed. However, we recall from the previous discussion that estimated *S-N* curves are recommended only for obtaining rough initial estimates. Wherever possible, these should be replaced by *S-N* data for actual components or for notched members similar to the component.

As discussed in Section 10.8, component *S-N* curves have the advantage of automatically including difficult-to-evaluate geometric and fabrication detail. But there are disadvantages. First, the match between the actual components and the readily available data may be imperfect. Second, the accuracy of life estimates for irregular loading histories can be affected by occasional severe loads during service if these cause local yielding at notches. Such local yielding causes residual stresses, as illustrated in Fig. 10.28. These overload-induced residual stresses may affect the life by shifting the local mean stresses during subsequent cyclic loading. This sequence effect is not accounted for by any mean stress equation that employs nominal stress or load, such as the ones described in this chapter. As a result, when using component *S-N* curves, we may not predict lives for irregular loading histories very well by the Palmgren–Miner rule. This can be overcome to an extent by employing the P–M rule in *relative* form, $\Sigma(N_j/N_{fj}) = D$, where D may differ from unity, having a value based on test data for component geometries and load histories similar to those expected in service. Another option is to apply the Corten–Dolan cumulative damage procedure, which is summarized in Section 5.3 of Graham (1968).

The local yielding effects that cause difficulty for any nominal-stress-based or load-based approach are specifically analyzed by the strain-based approach, as described in Chapter 14. See the discussion of Section 14.6.

In some cases, cracks are present essentially from the beginning of the fatigue life. The use of a crack-growth approach based on fracture mechanics is then indicated; this is treated in Chapter 11. Note that very sharp notches may cause such early initiation of cracks that the life is dominated by crack growth. In particular, this is likely to be the case where k_f requires a large adjustment from k_t.

It can be argued with considerable justification that all but the highest quality welds contain sufficiently severe defects that the life is controlled by crack growth. A crack-growth approach to fatigue of welded members is promising, but this approach has not yet been fully exploited, due to the difficulties caused by the complex geometry involved. The geometric complexity also makes it difficult to apply a strain-based approach to welded members, so that component *S-N* curves are currently the preferred approach for welded members.

10.11 SUMMARY

Stress raisers (notches) reduce fatigue strength and require careful attention to detail in design. The strength reduction is often not as great as would be expected from the elastic stress concentration factor k_t, so special fatigue notch factors are used. These are calculated from k_t and empirical curves, giving the notch sensitivity value q for the material and notch radius of interest. Alternatively, the same empirical information may be expressed in terms of a material constant. For example, Peterson employs a material constant α and the notch radius ρ to estimate k_f:

$$k_f = 1 + \frac{k_t - 1}{1 + \dfrac{\alpha}{\rho}} \tag{10.50}$$

In ductile materials, yielding causes even further reductions in k_f at short lives. A more general variable k_f' that varies with life is then needed. Limiting values of k_f' are k_f at long life and unity at short life.

For engineering situations involving low stresses applied large numbers of times, design may be based on the fatigue strength at a long life of 10^6 cycles or more, called the fatigue limit, and denoted σ_{er} for completely reversed loading. Where specific data are not available, σ_{er} for commonly used metals may be estimated from correlations with the ultimate tensile strength σ_u. In applying σ_{er} values to engineering components, the fatigue notch factor k_f is employed along with additional modifying factors, such as those for type of load, size, and surface finish, to obtain the fatigue limit as a nominal stress, S_{er}, for the notched member. Additional empirical assumptions may be employed to make a rough estimate of an entire S-N curve, as in the procedures of Juvinall or Budynas. However, caution is needed with the concept of a fatigue limit stress, as damage due to occasional severe cycles or corrosion may cause failure at stresses below this level.

In considering mean stress effects for notched members, the Goodman or Gerber equations are often applied to nominal stresses. But application of these is complicated by local yielding at notches, inaccuracy, and sensitivity to the arbitrary definition of nominal stress, S. Thus, it is preferable to employ either the Smith, Watson, and Topper (SWT) equation or the Walker equation, which are, respectively,

$$S_{ar} = \sqrt{S_{\max} S_a}\,, \qquad S_{ar} = S_{\max}^{1-\gamma} S_a^{\gamma} \qquad \text{(a, b)} \tag{10.51}$$

The Walker equation requires data at more than one mean stress or R-ratio to permit fitting a value of γ.

An S-N curve from test data for the actual engineering component of interest is preferable to an estimated one. Lacking this, data from similar components or notched members should be employed if possible. To match a component to notched specimen data, such as might be found in a handbook, look for data for a similar notch radius, ρ, or for a similar length parameter l' of Eq. 8.26, and compare stresses on the basis $k_t S$. For welded structural members, design codes include S-N curves identified with various structural details. These are typically expressed in terms of the range of nominal stress, and the curves are generally the same for all mean stresses and for all structural steels, independent of yield strength.

Design strategies to minimize fatigue failures include avoiding sharp notch radii and intentionally introducing beneficial surface residual stresses.

NEW TERMS AND SYMBOLS

component S-N curve

equivalent stresses, $\overline{\Delta S}$, S_{ar}

estimated S-N curve

fatigue limit:

    polished bend, σ_{erb}

    adjusted, σ_{er}

    notch, S_{er}

fatigue limit life, N_e

fatigue limit ratio, $m_e = \sigma_{erb}/\sigma_u$

fatigue limit reduction factors:

    load type, m_t

    size, m_d

    surface, m_s

fatigue notch factor:

    long life, k_f

    short life, k_f'

    mean stress, k_{fm}

fretting

initial yielding

local yielding

Neuber constant, β

nonpropagating crack

notch sensitivity, q

Peterson constant, α

process zone effect

relative P–M rule

residual stress

reversed yielding

shot peening

size effect

stress gradient, $d\sigma/dx$

stress raiser

surface finish

weakest-link effect

REFERENCES

(a) General References

BUDYNAS, R. G., and J. K. NISBETT. 2011. *Shigley's Mechanical Engineering Design*, 9th ed., McGraw-Hill, New York.

DOWLING, N. E., and S. THANGJITHAM. 2000. "An Overview and Discussion of Basic Methodology for Fatigue," *Fatigue and Fracture Mechanics: 31st Volume*, ASTM STP 1389, G. R. Halford and J. P. Gallagher, eds., ASTM International, West Conshohocken, PA, pp. 3–36.

DOWLING, N. E., and W. K. WILSON. 1981. "Geometry and Size Requirements for Fatigue Life Similitude Among Notched Members," *Advances in Fracture Research*, D. Francois et al., eds., Pergamon Press, Oxford, UK, pp. 581–588.

GRAHAM, J. A., J. F. MILLAN, and F. J. APPL, eds. 1968. *Fatigue Design Handbook*, SAE Pub. No. AE-4, Society of Automotive Engineers, Warrendale, PA.

HARKEGARD, G., and G. HALLERAKER. 2010. "Assessment of Methods for Prediction of Notch Size Effects at the Fatigue Limit Based on Test Data by Bohm and Magin," *International Journal of Fatigue,* vol. 32, no. 10, pp. 1701–1709.

JUVINALL, R. C. 1967. *Stress, Strain, and Strength*, McGraw-Hill, New York.

JUVINALL, R. C., and K. M. MARSHEK. 2006. *Fundamentals of Machine Component Design*, 4th ed., John Wiley, Hoboken, NJ.

LASSEN, T., and N. RECHO. 2006. *Fatigue Life Analyses of Welded Structures: Flaws*, Wiley-ISTE, London.

LEE, Y.-L., M. E. BARKEY, and H.-T. KANG. 2012. *Metal Fatigue Analysis Handbook: Practical Problem-Solving Techniques for Computer-Aided Engineering*, Elsevier Butterworth-Heinemann, Oxford, UK.

LEE, Y.-L., J. PAN, R. B. HATHAWAY, and M. E. BARKEY. 2005. *Fatigue Testing and Analysis: Theory and Practice*, Elsevier Butterworth-Heinemann, Oxford, UK.

MARSH, K. J. 1988. *Full-Scale Fatigue Testing of Components and Structures*, Butterworths, London.

PETERSON, R. E. 1959. "Notch-Sensitivity," *Metal Fatigue*, G. Sines and J. L. Waisman, eds., McGraw-Hill, New York, pp. 293–306.

PETERSON, R. E. 1974. *Stress Concentration Factors*, John Wiley, New York. See also W. D. Pilkey and D. F. Pilkey, *Peterson's Stress Concentration Factors*, 3d ed., John Wiley, New York, 2008.

RICE, R. C., ed. 1997. *Fatigue Design Handbook*, 3d ed., SAE Pub. No. AE-22, Society of Automotive Engineers, Warrendale, PA.

STEPHENS, R. I., A. FATEMI, R. R. STEPHENS, and H. O. FUCHS. 2001. *Metal Fatigue in Engineering*, 2d ed., John Wiley, New York.

WALKER, K. 1970. "The Effect of Stress Ratio During Crack Propagation and Fatigue for 2024-T3 and 7075-T6 Aluminum," *Effects of Environment and Complex Load History on Fatigue Life*, ASTM STP 462, Am. Soc. for Testing and Materials, West Conshohocken, PA, pp. 1–14.

WRIGHT, D. H. 1993. *Testing Automotive Materials and Components*, Society of Automotive Engineers, Warrendale, PA.

(b) Design Codes and Methods for Welded Structure

AASHTO. 2010. *AASHTO LRFD Bridge Design Specifications*, 5th ed., Am. Assoc. of State Highway and Transportation Officials, Washington, DC.

ALUMINUM ASSOCIATION. 2010. *Aluminum Design Manual*, 9th ed., The Aluminum Association, Arlington, VA.

API. 2007. *Recommended Practice for Planning, Designing, and Constructing Fixed Offshore Platforms - Working Stress Design*, API RP-2A-WSD, 21st ed., Am. Petroleum Institute, Washington, DC. See also API RP-2A-LRFD, 1st ed., 2003.

AWS. 2010. *Structural Welding Code: Steel*, 19th ed., AWS D1.1/D1.1M:2010, American Welding Society, Miami, FL.

CEN. 2005. *Eurocode 3: Design of Steel Structures, Part 1-9: Fatigue*, EN 1993-1-9:2005, Comité Européen de Normalisation (European Committee for Standardization), Brussels. See also: BS EN 1993-1-9:2005, British Standards Institution, London; replaces BS 5400-10 and BS 7608.

DONG, P., J. K. HONG, D. OSAGE, and M. PRAGER. 2002. "Master S-N Curve Method for Fatigue Evaluation of Welded Components," *WRC Bulletin 474*, ISSN 043-2326, Welding Research Council, New York.

PROBLEMS AND QUESTIONS

Sections 10.2 and 10.3

10.1 Define the following terms in your own words: (a) notches; (b) *S-N* curve; (c) stress gradient; and (d) reversed yielding.

10.2 Determine k_t, and then estimate k_f for the low carbon steel. Do you agree with the values given? Why might there be a discrepancy in k_f?

10.3 For the notched member of Fig. 9.27 with $\rho = 1.20$ mm, determine k_t and estimate k_f. Then use the unnotched member fatigue strength at 10^8 cycles to estimate S_{er}, for the notched member, and compare to the actual data.

10.4 For the notched member of Fig. 10.11, answer the following:

   (a) Determine your own value of k_t, and then estimate k_f. (Note that the half-circular notch shape gives $w_1 = w_2 - 2\rho$.). Assume $k_t = 3.4$.

    (b) For 10^6 cycles, use your k_f value with the smooth specimen fatigue strength from the S-N curve to estimate the notched specimen strength. How good is the agreement with the test data?

10.5 A double-edge-notched plate is made of AISI 4130 steel and is subjected to an axial force P, as in Fig. A.11(b). Its dimensions are $w_1 = 80$, $w_2 = 88$, $\rho = 4$, and $t = 10$ mm. The steel has an ultimate tensile strength of 1172 MPa, and the fatigue limit for completely reversed ($\sigma_m = 0$) loading of unnotched material can be estimated from Fig. 9.24.

    (a) Determine k_t and then estimate k_f.

    (b) Determine the σ_{ar} value for 10^6 cycles.

10.6 A shaft with a step-down in diameter has dimensions, as defined in Fig. A.12(c), of $d_1 = 11$, $d_2 = 13$, and $\rho = 0.4$ mm. The shaft is subjected to bending and is made of a quenched and tempered low-alloy steel having an ultimate tensile strength of 450 MPa. The fatigue limit for completely reversed ($\sigma_m = 0$) loading of unnotched material can be estimated from Fig. 9.24.

    (a) Determine k_t and then estimate k_f.

    (b) What completely reversed bending moment amplitude M_a can be applied to the notched shaft for 10^6 cycles? A safety factor of 2.0 in stress is required.

10.7 A plate with a round hole is made of the 2024-T4 aluminum of Table 9.1, and it has dimensions of $d = 6$, $w = 30$, and $t = 5$ mm, as defined in Fig. A.11(a). The fatigue limit for completely reversed ($\sigma_m = 0$) loading of unnotched material can be estimated from Fig. 9.25.

    (a) Determine k_t and estimate k_f for loading in tension.

    (b) What completely reversed axial force amplitude P_a can be applied for 5×10^8 cycles without fatigue failure? A safety factor of 2.5 in stress is required.

10.8 A flat plate with a width reduction is made of the AISI 4340 steel of Table 9.1. The bar has dimensions, as defined in Fig. A.11(d), of $w_1 = 20$, $w_2 = 30$, $t = 10$, and $\rho = 2$ mm.

    (a) Determine k_t and estimate k_f for loading in bending.

    (b) What completely reversed bending moment amplitude M_a can be applied for 10^6 cycles without fatigue failure? A safety factor of 1.8 in stress is required.

Section 10.4

10.9 According to Fig. 9.24, most steels with ultimate tensile strengths beyond $\sigma_u = 1400$ MPa have fatigue limits below half the ultimate. However, a few high-strength steels ($\sigma_u = 1700$ to 2000 MPa) have higher fatigue limits than is typical, with the values still being near the $\sigma_{erb} = 0.5\sigma_u$ line. Speculate on how the tensile properties other than σ_u for such steels might compare with those for more ordinary high-strength steels.

10.10 A circular rod made of the RQC-100 steel of Table 9.1 is loaded in bending and has a step change in diameter. The dimensions, as defined in Fig. A.11(d), are $w_1 = 70$, $w_2 = 80$, $t = 8$ mm and $\rho = 4$ mm, and the fillet radius is ground. Estimate the largest completely reversed bending moment amplitude that can be applied for 10^6 cycles.

10.11 A circumferentially grooved round bar made of 7075-T6 aluminum is subjected to 10^8 cycles of completely reversed bending. The bar has dimensions, as defined in Fig. A.12(c), of $d_1 = 15, d_2 = 21.5$, and $\rho = 0.75$ mm. The notch radius ρ has a ground surface finish, which is estimated to reduce the polished specimen fatigue limit of the material (see Fig. 9.25) by a factor $m_s = 0.8$. A safety factor of 1.5 in stress is required.

    (a) What completely reversed moment amplitude M_a can be applied in the actual service of this bar?

    (b) If a completely reversed moment amplitude of $M_a = 13$ N·m will be applied in service, is the design adequate? If not, what new value of notch radius ρ will allow the bar to just meet the required safety factor?

10.12 A circumferentially grooved round shaft of the AISI 4340 steel of Table 9.1 is subjected to torsion. The shaft has dimensions, as defined in Fig. A.12(d), of $d_1 = 20, d_2 = 22$, and $\rho = 1.0$ mm. The notch radius ρ has a ground surface finish. A safety factor of 1.8 in stress is required. What completely reversed torque amplitude T_a can be applied for 10^6 cycles in the actual service of this shaft?

Sections 10.5 and 10.6

10.13 For notched members of ductile materials, explain in your own words why k_f' tends to approach unity at short fatigue lives, and also why k_{fm} tends to approach zero at short fatigue lives.

10.14 Consider the fatigue data for AISI 4340 steel in Fig. 10.11(a), specifically, the S-N curve for the notched member.

    (a) Obtain an equation that approximates the line relating S_a and N_f between 10^2 and 10^5 cycles. (Note that the stress scale is linear and the life scale is logarithmic.)

    (b) One of the same notched members is subjected to constant amplitude cycling at a force amplitude of $P_a = 32$ kN and a mean force of $P_m = 25$ kN. What fatigue life in cycles is expected?

10.15 For the notched member of Fig. 10.11, estimate the repeatedly applied zero-to-maximum nominal stress $S_{\max}$ that corresponds to a life of $N_f = 10^5$ cycles: (a) using Eq. 10.21, and (b) using Eq. 10.28.

10.16 Consider the S-N curve of Fig. 9.27 for the bar of 2024-T4 aluminum with notch radius $\rho = 1.59$ mm. Note that nominal stress S is defined as in Fig. A.12(c). If a similar bar is subjected to a mean bending moment $M_m = 4.0$ N·m, estimate the bending moment amplitude M_a that will cause failure in 10^5 cycles: (a) using Eq. 10.21 and (b) using Eq. 10.28.

10.17 The aluminum alloy 2024-T4 of Table 9.1 is to be used in the form of a plate with a central hole under axial loading, as in Fig. A.11(a). The dimensions are $w = 50, d = 10$, and $t = 20$ mm. For a life of $N_f = 10^7$ cycles, estimate the mean force P_m if the force amplitude is $P_a = 50$ kN: (a) using Eq. 10.21 and (b) using Eq. 10.28.

10.18 Assume that the notched member AISI 4340 Steel of Fig. 10.11 is a component that is required to resist 2000 cycles of a nominal stress amplitude of $S_a = 150$ MPa, applied at a mean level of $S_m = 200$ MPa. Obtain approximate values for the safety factors in both stress and life.

10.19 Consider the 7075-T6 aluminum bending member of Prob. 10.11, with notch radius $\rho = 0.75$ mm. The completely reversed loading fatigue limit of the material, with the surface finish effect included, is $\sigma_{er} = 220$ MPa, and the fatigue notch factor is $k_f = 1.98$. What moment amplitude M_a can be applied for 5×10^6 cycles along with this mean moment such that there is a safety factor of 2 in stress?

10.20 A plate with a width reduction is made of the ASTM A514 structural steel of Table 4.2. It is required to withstand 10^6 cycles of an axial force amplitude of $P_a = 16$ kN, applied along with a mean force of $P_m = 9$ kN. The plate has dimensions, as defined in Fig. A.11(c), of $w_1 = 20$, $w_2 = 24$, $t = 10$, and $\rho = 0.50$ mm. The notch radius ρ has a ground surface finish.

    (a) What is the safety factor in stress?

    (b) If a safety factor of 1.8 in stress is required, what new value of notch radius ρ allows the bar to just meet this requirement?

10.21 Consider the data for notched plates of 2024-T3 aluminum of Ex. 10.4. Fitting the data for zero mean stress to Eq. 10.31 gives $A = 976$ MPa and $B = -0.1750$.

    (a) Using the Goodman relationship of Eq. 10.21, plot S_{ar} versus N_f for all of the data. Also plot the zero-mean-stress fitted line, and comment on the success of the resulting correlation.

    (b) Repeat (a), using the SWT relationship of Eq. 10.28.

    (c) Repeat (a), using the Goodman relationship of Eq. 10.22, with k_{fm} from Eq. 10.27, except replace k_t with k_f.

10.22 For double-edge-notched plates of 7075-T6 aluminum under axial load, cycles to failure data are given in Table P10.22 for various combinations of maximum stress S_{max} and

Table P10.22

S_{max}, MPa	S_m, MPa	N_f, cycles	S_{max}, MPa	S_m, MPa	N_f, cycles
276	0	136	138	69	32 000
224	0	329	121	69	48 500
207	0	917	379	138	169
172	0	2 228	345	138	309
138	0	5 300	310	138	756
112	0	17 800	241	138	2 500
103	0	30 000	224	138	5 500
86.2	0	70 000	207	138	10 500
69.0	0	274 000	190	138	16 800
63.8	0	339 200	172	138	179 000
58.6	0	969 200	155	138	566 500
276	69	374	293	207	4 000
241	69	955	276	207	7 800
207	69	2 000	276	207	10 000
172	69	6 823	259	207	15 000
155	69	13 000	241	207	32 700

Source: Data in [Grover 51b], [Illg 56], and [Naumann 59].

mean stress S_m. The specimen dimensions, as defined in Fig. A.11(b), were $w_1 = 38.10$, $w_2 = 57.15$, notch radius $\rho = 1.45$, and thickness $t = 2.29$ mm, giving $k_t = 4.00$ on the basis of net area. Also, the material's tensile properties were yield 521 MPa and ultimate 572 MPa. Fitting the data for zero mean stress to Eq. 10.31 gives $A = 676$ MPa and $B = -0.1822$.

(a) Using the Goodman relationship of Eq. 10.21, plot S_{ar} versus N_f for all of the data. Also plot the zero-mean-stress fitted line, and comment on the success of the resulting correlation.

(b) Repeat (a), using the SWT relationship of Eq. 10.28.

10.23 Three fatigue test data points from Ex. 10.4 are given in Table P10.23 for notched axial specimens of 2024-T3 aluminum. Assume that the data fit $S_{ar} = A N_f^B$, with S_{ar} given by the Walker relationship, Eq. 10.29. Using these three points, determine approximate values for the fitting constants A, B, and γ. Then employ the resulting γ value to calculate S_{ar} values for the three data points, and plot these versus N_f on a log–log graph. Do the three points lie on the fitted straight line?

Table P10.23

S_{max}, MPa	S_m, MPa	N_f, cycles
241	0	3 500
103	0	210 000
310	207	63 500

10.24 Three fatigue test data points from Probs. 9.5 and 9.33 are given in Table P10.24 for unnotched axial specimens of titanium 6Al-4V. Assume that the data fit $\sigma_{ar} = A N_f^B$, with σ_{ar} given by the Walker relationship, Eq. 9.19. Using these three points, determine approximate values for the fitting constants A, B, and γ. Then employ the resulting γ value to calculate σ_{ar} values for the three data points, and plot these versus N_f on a log–log graph. Do the three points lie on the fitted straight line?

Table P10.24

σ_a, MPa	σ_m, MPa	N_f
892	0	706
385	0	500 000
241	646	90 000

10.25 Consider the notched specimen data of Table P10.22 for 7075-T6 aluminum. Fit these data to the Walker equation, all together as a single set of data. Use $S_{ar} = A N_f^B$, with S_{ar} given by Eq. 10.29, to obtain values of A, B, and γ. Also, on a plot of S_{ar} versus N_f, show data and fitted line, and comment on the success of the fit.

10.26 Consider the unnotched specimen data for AISI 4340 steel of Ex. 9.1 and 9.5. Combine the data from both examples into a single set of data and proceed as follows:

    (a) Fit the data to an equation of the form $\sigma_{ar} = A\,N_f^B$, with σ_{ar} given by the Walker relationship, Eq. 9.19 . Obtain values for the three fitting constants, A, B, and γ.

    (b) On a log–log graph of σ_{ar} vs. N_f , plot both your fitted line and the data, and comment on the success of the fit.

10.27 Consider the unnotched specimen data for titanium 6Al-4V of Tables P9.5 and P9.33. Combine the data from both tables into a single set of data and proceed as in (a) and (b) of Prob. 10.26.

10.28 Consider the unnotched specimen data for 50CrMo4 steel of Tables P9.6 and P9.34. Combine the data from both tables into a single set of data and proceed as in (a) and (b) of Prob. 10.26.

10.29 Consider the unnotched specimen data for 2024-T3 aluminum of Tables P9.8 and P9.35. Combine the data from both tables into a single set of data and proceed as in (a) and (b) of Prob. 10.26.

Section 10.7

10.30 The notched plate in bending of Ex. 10.3, which is made of RQC-100 steel with $\sigma_u = 758$ MPa, is noted to have a value of $k_f = 1.82$. Assume that the notch has a machined surface.

    (a) Estimate the S-N curve for unnotched material according to Budynas.

    (b) What life is expected for a moment amplitude of $M_a = 1.50\,\text{kN·m}$ applied at a mean level of $M_m = 2.00\,\text{kN·m}$?

10.31 The axially loaded plate with a hole of Prob. 10.17, made of 2024-T4 aluminum as in Table 9.1, has a value of $k_f = 2.36$, and the hole is smoothly polished.

    (a) Estimate the S-N curve for unnotched material according to the procedure of Juvinall.

    (b) What life is expected if an axial force amplitude of $P_a = 40\,\text{kN}$ is applied at a mean level of $P_m = 32\,\text{kN}$?

10.32 A circular rod made of the SAE 4142 (450 HB) steel of Table 9.1 is loaded axially and has a step change in diameter. The dimensions, as defined in Fig. A.12(a), are $d_1 = 15$, $d_2 = 18$, and $\rho = 1$ mm, and the fillet radius is ground. Using the S-N curve estimate of Budynas, evaluate the safety factors in both stress and life if the expected service loading is 30,000 cycles at a zero-to-tension force of $P_{\max} = 70$ kN.

10.33 For the AISI 4340 steel notched member of Fig. 10.11, some points on the S-N curve are given in Table P10.33. Note that the notch surface is smoothly polished. Estimate the nominal stress versus life S-N curve according to the procedures of (a) Juvinall and (b) Budynas. Then plot both estimates along with the data and comment on the success of the estimates.

Table P10.33

S_a, MPa	N_f, cycles
696	10^2
617	$10^{2.5}$
538	10^3
459	$10^{3.5}$
379	10^4
300	$10^{4.5}$
231	10^5
193	$10^{5.5}$
176	10^6 to 10^7

10.34 Nominal stress amplitude versus cycles to failure data are given in Table P10.34 for completely reversed ($R = -1$) loading of notched members of normalized SAE 4130 steel with yield strength $\sigma_o = 679$ MPa and ultimate tensile strength $\sigma_u = 807$ MPa. The axially loaded test specimens were double-edge-notched plates, as in Fig. A.11(b), with (net area) nominal stress S defined as shown. The dimensions were $w_1 = 38.10$, $w_2 = 57.15$, notch radius $\rho = 8.06$, and thickness $t = 1.905$ mm, giving an elastic stress concentration factor of $k_t = 2.15$. The notch surface was electropolished. Estimate the nominal stress versus life S-N curve according to the procedures of (a) Juvinall and (b) Budynas. Then plot both estimates along with the data and comment on the success of the estimates.

Table P10.34

S_a, MPa	N_f, cycles
690	190
552	1 075
400	5 779
345	27 000
310	43 000
262	82 000
221	182 000
221	635 000
197	1 712 700
186	2 153 500
172	>10 900 000

Source: Data from [Grover 51b] and [Illg 56].
Note: No failure indicated by ">".

10.35 Nominal stress amplitude versus cycles to failure data are given in Table P10.35 for completely reversed loading of notched members of 2014-T6 aluminum. The axially loaded test specimens were circumferentially notched round bars, with diameter in the bottom of the notch $d_1 = 10.16$, major diameter $d_2 = 12.70$, and notch radius $\rho = 0.813$ mm, giving an elastic stress concentration factor of $k_t = 2.65$. Nominal stress S is defined based on the net area corresponding to d_1, and the notch surface was polished. The material's tensile properties were yield 438 MPa and ultimate 494 MPa. Estimate the nominal stress versus life S-N curve by the method of Juvinall, and graphically compare estimate and data.

Table P10.35

S_a, MPa	N_f,cycles
262	2 100
200	13 300
138	137 000
124	661 000
100	2 420 000
82.7	17 200 000
79.3	27 600 000

Source: Data in [Lazan 52].

10.36 In an engineering failure that actually occurred, the shaft shown in Fig. P10.36 was supported by bearings at its ends and was used in a hoist for lifting ore out of a mine. It was loaded

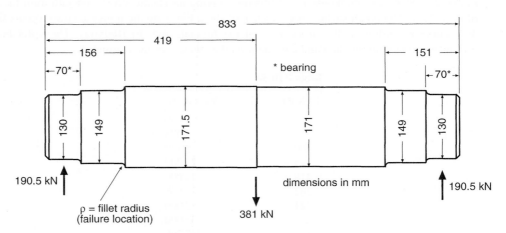

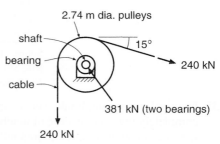

Figure P10.36

in rotating bending by the forces shown and failed after 15 years of service and 2.5×10^7 rotations. An *impact factor* of 1.5 has already been included in the forces given to roughly account for forces exceeding the dead weight of the ore, cable, and bucket. (An impact factor is needed due to such effects as bouncing during loading at the bottom of the mine and acceleration to start moving the ore upward.) The shaft was made of AISI 1040 steel with tensile properties of $\sigma_u = 620$ MPa, $\sigma_o = 310$ MPa, and reduction in area 25%. The design drawings showed a fillet radius of 6.35 mm at the failure location, with a machined surface finish, but measurements on the shaft after failure indicated that it had a radius of only 2 mm. Estimate the safety factor in stress for both the intended and actual fillet radii. Does this error in manufacture explain the failure?

Section 10.8

10.37 In the Bailey bridge work described in the text, variable amplitude tests were also done. In one series of these, numbers of cycles were applied at various stress levels, with a constant $S_{min} = 7.9$ MPa, in a pattern as shown in Fig. P10.37. This loading block contained a total of 24,000 cycles, and it was repeatedly applied, with alternate blocks being done in reverse sequence, until fatigue failure occurred. Table P.10.37(a) gives the total numbers of cycles in each loading block for the various load levels, where the load levels are expressed as percentages of the *peak stress*, which is the highest value of S_{max}. Test data are given in Table P.10.37(b) as average numbers of blocks to failure from multiple tests at each of two peak stress values. Failure in these tests was defined as complete separation of a truss member.

    (a) Calculate the life expected for the two peak stress values of 240 and 209 MPa. Base your calculations on the S_{max} versus N_f equation fitted to constant amplitude data, as shown in Fig. 10.18.

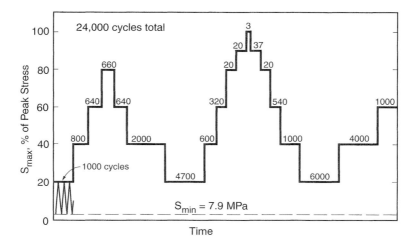

Figure P10.37

(b) Compare your results with the test data. Can you think of reasons for any trends in the calculated versus actual life comparison?

Table P.10.37(a)	
S_{max} Level, % of Peak Stress	Number of Cycles
20	11 700
40	8 400
60	3 140
80	700
90	57
100	3
All	24 000

Table P.10.37(b)	
Peak Stress, MPa	Blocks to Failure
240	33
209	100

Source: Data in [Webber 70].

10.38 Consider double-edge-notched plates of 2024-T3 aluminum alloy with $k_t = 2.15$, as in Ex. 10.4. These have a nominal stress versus life curve of the form $S_{ar} = A\,N_f^B$, where S_{ar} is given by the Walker relationship, Eq. 10.29, with fitting constants $A = 1530$ MPa, $B = -0.217$, $\gamma = 0.733$ and $\sum = 2.9 \times 10^{-3}$. Assume that these plates will be repeatedly subjected in engineering service to the nominal stress history shown in Fig. P10.38.

    (a) Estimate the number of repetitions to failure.

    (b) If 200 repetitions are expected to be applied in service, what are the safety factors in life and in stress?

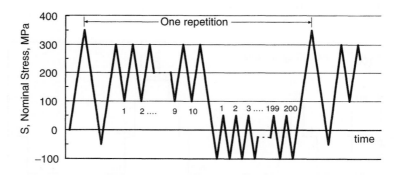

Figure P10.38

10.39 Notched members of the same geometry and material as in Prob. 10.38 are subjected to the nominal stress history shown in Fig. P10.39.

    (a) Estimate the number of repetitions to failure.

    (b) If 600 repetitions are expected to be applied in service, what are the safety factors in life and in stress?

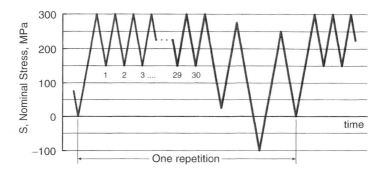

Figure P10.39

10.40 Consider double-edge-notched plates of 7075-T6 aluminum, as in Prob. 10.22, with $k_t = 4.00$. These have a (net section) nominal stress versus life curve of the form $S_{ar} = A\,N_f^B$, where S_{ar} is given by the Walker relationship, Eq. 10.29, with fitting constants[1] of $A = 779\,\text{MPa}$, $B = -0.197$, and $\gamma = 0.486$. Some of these plates were repeatedly subjected to the nominal stress history given by Table P10.40(a). Note that all of the loading cycles had a common minimum level. Each maximum stress level was applied for the number of cycles given, and then the entire sequence was repeated until failure occurred. Six tests were run, with numbers of repetitions of the load history to failure being given in Table P10.40(b).

    (a) Estimate the number of repetitions to failure.

    (b) Compare your calculated life with the test data, and comment on the success of your estimate.

Table P10.40(a)

S_{min}, MPa	S_{max}, MPa	No. of Peaks
48.3	303	47
48.3	231	268
48.3	159	810
48.3	86.2	1810

Table P10.40(b)

Test No.	Repetitions to Failure
1	18.7
2	18.0
3	18.0
4	18.0
5	16.0
6	15.0

Source: Data in [Naumann 62].

10.41 Consider double-edge-notched plates of 7075-T6 aluminum, as in Prob. 10.22, with $k_t = 4.00$. These have a (net section) nominal stress versus life curve of the form $S_{ar} = A\,N_f^B$,

Note: [1]These values were obtained by fitting the full set of 74 data points available from the sources for Table P10.22 for $N_f = 10^2$ to 2×10^6 cycles.

where S_{ar} is given by the Walker relationship, Eq. 10.29, with fitting constants $A = 779$ MPa, $B = -0.197$, and $\gamma = 0.486$. Some of these plates were repeatedly subjected to a variable amplitude axial loading history, as shown in Fig. P10.41. All loading events started from and returned to a base level of $S = 48.3$ MPa, with the nominal stress levels and numbers of cycles being considered representative of aircraft maneuver loads. Stress levels and numbers of events are listed in Table P10.41(a). Six tests were run, and numbers of repetitions of the load history to failure are given in Table P10.41(b).

(a) Estimate the number of repetitions to failure. (Suggestion: Apply rainflow cycle counting, and consider the history to start and finish at either the 336 MPa level or the -67.6 MPa level.)

(b) Compare your calculated life with the test data, and comment on the success of your estimate.

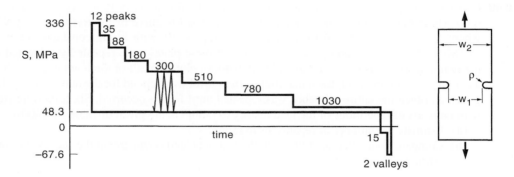

Figure P10.41

Table P10.41(a)

S_{max} or S_{min} MPa	No. of Peaks or Valleys[1]
336	12
292	35
255	88
219	180
181	300
143	510
105	780
67.6	1030
-19.3	15
-67.6	2

Note: [1] All events start at and return to $S = 48.3$ MPa.

Table P10.41(b)

Test No.	Repetitions to Failure
1	13.7
2	12.1
3	12.1
4	11.0
5	11.0
6	10.0

Source: Data in [Naumann 62].

10.42 Several notched members of Man-Ten steel, as shown in Fig. P10.42, were tested under completely reversed constant amplitude loading. Fitting these data yielded the force versus life relationship

$$\Delta P = 379(2N_f)^{-0.223} \text{ kN} \qquad (R = -1)$$

where N_f is the number of cycles to observation of a crack of length 2.5 mm beyond the notch. Similar notched members were also repeatedly subjected to the irregular load history of Fig. 9.48, where this history contains 854 cycles, distributed among various ranges and means as shown. Test results are given in Table P10.42. Note that numbers of repetitions of the history to reach a 2.5 mm crack are given for three different values of the peak force, with three duplicate tests in each case.

  (a) Use the given force–life relationship to calculate the fatigue life expected for each of the three peak force levels in Table P10.42. Note that the range and mean values for the matrix of Fig. 9.48 are expressed as percentages of the peak force.

  (b) Compare your calculations with the test data, preferably on a log–log plot of peak force versus repetitions to cracking. Briefly discuss any trends that are apparent.

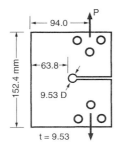

Table P10.42

Peak Force kN	Repetitions to 2.5 mm Crack		
	Test 1	Test 2	Test 3
71.17	8.4	12.8	12.5
35.58	420	154	74
15.57	5800	4270	3755

Source: Data in [Wetzel 77] pp. 7–13.

Figure P10.42

10.43 For structural-steel cover-plated beams, Fig. 10.20(c), the most likely failure location is at the end of the cover plate. For one such beam in a bridge, assume that the AWS design S-N curve for category E' applies, where ΔS is the nominal bending stress range in the beam at the end of the cover plate. The bridge is crossed by numerous vehicles of various weights each day, resulting in approximately 1000 stress cycles of significant magnitude per day. The values of stress at this detail, and the numbers of cycles per day at each stress level, are distributed as in Table P10.43.

  (a) Estimate the number of years of service before fatigue failure at this detail is expected, on the basis of the design S-N curve.

  (b) If the desired service life is 75 years, what are the safety factors in life and in stress?

10.44 A structural detail in a highway bridge that has been in service for 20 years fits AWS category E. When the bridge was designed, a weight limit on trucks of 30 tons was in effect, where 1 ton = 2000 lb = 8.896 kN. Traffic monitoring when the bridge was one year old indicated

Table P10.43

ΔS, MPa	Cycles per day
1.8	121
5.4	335
9.0	255
12.6	136
16.2	76
19.8	48
23.4	16
27.0	9
30.6	3
34.2	1
All	1000

a traffic volume averaging 800 trucks a day, with the numbers and weights of trucks allowing cyclic stress ranges to be determined for the detail, as listed in Table P10.44. (Automobiles and other light vehicles cause insignificant stresses.)

(a) Calculate the equivalent constant level of cyclic stress ΔS_q that is expected to cause the same life as the given stresses if applied for the same number of cycles.

(b) For the given stresses, estimate the life of the detail in years. Given that the usual design life for bridges is 75 years, what are the safety factors in life and in stress?

(c) The traffic volume on the bridge has gradually increased and at the present time is twice the early value—that is, 1600 trucks a day. Moreover, the legislature in the state involved is being lobbied to raise the weight limit on bridges of this type to 40 tons. Estimate the remaining life of the bridge if this change is made. (Suggestion: Assume that the new loading corresponds to increasing all of the stresses in Table P10.44 by the ratio of $40/30 = 1.333$.)   (*Problem continues*)

Table P10.44

ΔS, MPa	% of trucks
2	2.1
6	10.5
10	15.1
14	21.0
18	18.5
22	11.8
26	10.9
30	5.9
34	2.1
38	1.3
42	0.8
Σ	100

(d) You are an engineer who lives in this state. Draft a letter to your state legislator, explaining the expected effect of the weight limit change on the life of the bridge, and giving your opinion as to what the legislature should do.

Section 10.9

10.45 Examine a crank shaft in internal combustion engine.

(a) Draw a sketch of it, and point out any design features that are beneficial in avoiding fatigue failure.

(b) Suggest any design changes that might improve fatigue resistance.

(c) Of what material does this part appear to be made? Try to explain the choice of material from the viewpoints of function, cost, and resistance to fatigue, wear, and other possible failure causes.

10.46 Examine the helical springs in the axle suspension system of a small boat trailer, and then answer (a), (b), and (c), as in Prob. 10.45.

10.47 Examine a cotter joint with sleeve, and then answer (a), (b), and (c) as in Prob. 10.45.

11

Fatigue Crack Growth

OBJECTIVES

- Apply the stress intensity factor K of fracture mechanics to fatigue crack growth and to environmental crack growth, and understand test methods and trends in behavior.
- Explore fatigue crack growth rate curves, da/dN versus ΔK, including fitting common equations and evaluating R-ratio (mean stress) effects.
- Calculate the life to grow a fatigue crack to failure, including cases requiring numerical integration and cases of variable amplitude loading. Employ such calculations to evaluate safety factors and inspection intervals.

11.1 INTRODUCTION

The presence of a crack can significantly reduce the strength of an engineering component due to brittle fracture, as already discussed in Chapter 8. However, it is unusual for a crack of dangerous size to exist initially, although this can occur, as when there is a large defect in the material used to make a component. In a more common situation, a small flaw that was initially present develops into a crack and then grows until it reaches the critical size for brittle fracture.

Crack growth can be caused by cyclic loading, a behavior called *fatigue crack growth*. However, if a hostile chemical environment is present, even a steady load can cause *environmental crack*

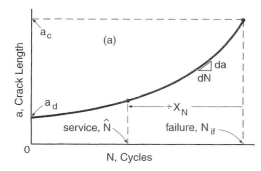
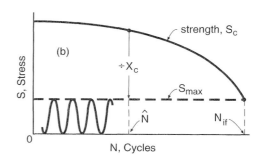

Figure 11.1   Growth of a worst-case crack from the minimum detectable length a_d to failure (a), and the resulting variation in worst-case strength (b).

growth. Both types of crack growth can occur if cyclic loads are applied in the presence of a hostile environment, especially if the cycling is slow or if there are periods of steady load interrupting the cycling. This chapter primarily considers fatigue crack growth, but limited discussion of environmental crack growth is included near the end in Section 11.10.

Engineering analysis of crack growth is often required and can be done with the stress intensity concept, K, of fracture mechanics. Recall from Chapter 8 that K quantifies the severity of a crack situation. Specifically, K depends on the combination of crack length, loading, and geometry given by

$$K = FS\sqrt{\pi a} \tag{11.1}$$

where a is crack length, S is nominal stress, and F is a dimensionless function of geometry and the relative crack length $\alpha = a/b$. The rate of fatigue crack growth is controlled by K. Hence, the dependence of K on a and F causes cracks to accelerate as they grow. The variation of crack length with cycles is thus similar to Fig. 11.1(a).

The analysis and prediction of fatigue crack growth has assumed major importance for large engineered items, especially where safety is paramount, as for large aircraft and for components in nuclear power plants. Note that the stress-based approach to fatigue of Chapters 9 and 10 does not consider cracks in a specific and detailed manner. Hence, this chapter provides an introduction to crack growth, including materials testing, trends in materials behavior, and prediction of the life to grow a crack to failure.

11.2 PRELIMINARY DISCUSSION

Before proceeding in detail, it is useful to describe the general nature of crack growth analysis and the need for it, and further to present some definitions.

11.2.1 Need for Crack Growth Analysis

It has been found from experience that careful inspection of certain types of hardware often reveals cracks. For example, this is the case for large welded components, such as pressure vessels and bridge and ship structure, for metal structure in large aircraft, and for large forgings, as in the rotors of turbines and generators in power plants. Cracks are especially likely to be found in such hardware after some actual service usage has occurred. The possibility of cracks strongly suggests that specific analysis based on fracture mechanics is appropriate.

Let us assume that a certain structural component may contain cracks, but none are larger than a known *minimum detectable length* a_d. This situation could be the result of an inspection that is capable of finding all cracks larger than a_d, so that all such cracks have been repaired, or the parts scrapped. (Inspections for cracks are done by a variety of means, including visual examination, X-ray photography, reflection of ultrasonic waves, and application of electric currents, where in the latter case a crack causes a detectable disturbance in the resulting voltage field.) This worst-case crack of initial length a_d then grows until it reaches a critical length a_c, where brittle fracture occurs after N_{if} cycles of loading. If the number of cycles expected in actual service is $\hat{N}$, then the safety factor on life is

$$X_N = \frac{N_{if}}{\hat{N}} \tag{11.2}$$

This situation is illustrated in Fig. 11.1(a). Such a safety factor is needed because uncertainties exist as to the actual stress that will occur in service, the exact a_d that can be reliably found, and the crack growth rates in the material.

The critical strength for brittle fracture of the member is determined by the current crack length and the fracture toughness K_c for the material and thickness involved:

$$S_c = \frac{K_c}{F\sqrt{\pi a}} \tag{11.3}$$

As the worst-case crack grows, its length increases, causing the worst-case strength S_c to decrease, with failure occurring when S_c reaches $S_{\max}$, the maximum value for the cyclic loading applied in actual service. This is illustrated in Fig. 11.1(b). The safety factor on stress against sudden brittle fracture due to the applied cyclic load is

$$X_c = \frac{S_c}{S_{\max}} \tag{11.4}$$

Such a safety factor is generally needed in addition to X_N because of the possibility of an unexpected high load that exceeds the normal cyclic load. Within the expected actual service life, X_c decreases and has its minimum value at the end of this service life.

It sometimes occurs that the combination of minimum detectable crack length a_d and cyclic stress is such that the safety margin, as expressed by X_N and X_c, is insufficient. Predicted failure prior to reaching the actual service life, $X_N < 1$, may even be the case. *Periodic inspections* for cracks are then necessary, following which any cracks exceeding a_d are repaired, or the part replaced. This ensures that, after each inspection, no cracks larger than a_d exist. Assuming that inspections are done at intervals of N_p cycles, the length of the worst-case crack increases due to growth between inspections, varying as shown in Fig. 11.2. The safety factor on life is then

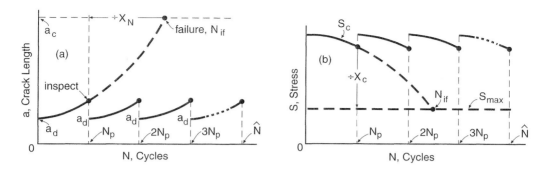

Figure 11.2   Variation of worst-case crack length (a), and strength (b), where periodic inspections are required.

determined by the inspection period:

$$X_N = \frac{N_{if}}{N_p} \tag{11.5}$$

After each inspection, the worst-case strength of the member temporarily increases, as shown in Fig. 11.2(b). The safety factor on stress is lowest just prior to each inspection.

Analysis based on fracture mechanics allows the variations in crack length and strength to be estimated so that safety factors can be evaluated. Where periodic inspections are necessary, fracture mechanics analysis thus permits a safe inspection interval to be set. For example, for large military and civilian aircraft, cracks are so commonly found during periodic inspections that safe operation and economic maintenance are both critically dependent on fracture mechanics analysis. The term *damage-tolerant design* is used to identify this approach of requiring that structures be able to survive even in the presence of growing cracks.

In reality, the detectable crack length a_d is not an absolute limit, as the probability of finding a crack in inspection increases with crack size, but is never 100%. For example, in the aircraft industry, values of a_d for various inspection methods are generally established as the size that can be found with 90% probability at a confidence level of 95%. On this basis, the better inspection methods give a_d values on the order of 1 or 2 mm under normal circumstances. Note that a_d is usually defined as the depth of a surface crack or half the width of an internal crack, on the basis of typical flaw geometries, as in Figs. 8.17 and 8.19. Cracks as small as $a = 0.1$ mm can be found, but a_d values this small can be justified only in special cases.

In addition to design applications, analysis of crack growth life is also useful in situations where an unexpected crack has been found in a component of a machine, vehicle, or structure. The remaining life can be calculated to determine whether the crack may be ignored, whether repair or replacement is needed immediately, or whether this can be postponed until a more convenient time. Situations of this sort have arisen in steel-mill machinery, where an immediate shutdown would disrupt operations and perhaps cause a large employee layoff. Similar situations have also occurred in turbine-generator units in major electrical power plants, where fracture of a large steel component could cause a power outage and expenditures of millions of dollars.

11.2.2 Definitions for Fatigue Crack Growth

Consider a growing crack that increases its length by an amount Δa due to the application of a number of cycles ΔN. The rate of growth with cycles can be characterized by the ratio $\Delta a / \Delta N$ or, for small intervals, by the derivative da/dN. A value of *fatigue crack growth rate, da/dN*, is the slope at a point on an a versus N curve, as in Fig. 11.1(a).

Assume that the applied loading is cyclic, with constant values of the loads P_{max} and P_{min}. The corresponding gross section nominal stresses S_{max} and S_{min} are then also constant. For fatigue crack growth work, it is conventional to use the stress range ΔS and the stress ratio R, which are defined as in Eqs. 9.1 and 9.3:

$$\Delta S = S_{max} - S_{min}, \qquad R = \frac{S_{min}}{S_{max}} \tag{11.6}$$

The primary variable affecting the growth rate of a crack is the range of the stress intensity factor. This is calculated from the stress range ΔS:

$$\Delta K = F \, \Delta S \sqrt{\pi a} \tag{11.7}$$

The value of F depends only on the geometry and the relative crack length, $\alpha = a/b$, just as if the loading were not cyclic. Since, according to Eq. 11.1, K and S are proportional for a given crack length, the maximum, minimum, range, and R-ratio for K during a loading cycle are respectively given by

$$K_{max} = F S_{max} \sqrt{\pi a}, \qquad K_{min} = F S_{min} \sqrt{\pi a}$$

$$\Delta K = K_{max} - K_{min}, \qquad R = \frac{K_{min}}{K_{max}} \tag{11.8}$$

Also, it may be convenient, especially for laboratory test specimens, to use the alternative expression of K in terms of applied force P, as discussed in Chapter 8 relative to Eq. 8.13:

$$\Delta K = F_P \frac{\Delta P}{t\sqrt{b}}, \qquad R = \frac{P_{min}}{P_{max}} \tag{11.9}$$

11.2.3 Describing Fatigue Crack Growth Behavior of Materials

For a given material and set of test conditions, the crack growth behavior can be described by the relationship between cyclic crack growth rate da/dN and stress intensity range ΔK. Test data and a fitted curve for one material are shown on a log–log plot in Fig. 11.3. At intermediate values of ΔK, there is often a straight line on the log–log plot, as in this case. A relationship representing this line is

$$\frac{da}{dN} = C(\Delta K)^m \tag{11.10}$$

where C is a constant and m is the slope on the log–log plot, assuming, of course, that the decades on both log scales are the same length. This equation is identified with Paul Paris, who first used it and who was influential in the first application of fracture mechanics to fatigue in the early 1960s.

At low growth rates, the curve generally becomes steep and appears to approach a vertical asymptote denoted ΔK_{th}, which is called the *fatigue crack growth threshold*. This quantity is interpreted as a lower limiting value of ΔK below which crack growth does not ordinarily occur. At high growth rates, the curve may again become steep, due to rapid unstable crack growth just

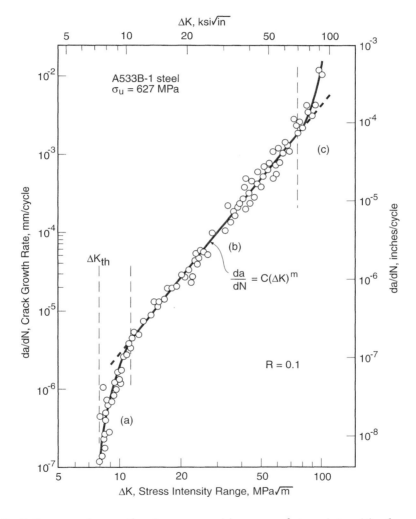

Figure 11.3 Fatigue crack growth rates over a wide range of stress intensities for a ductile pressure vessel steel. Three regions of behavior are indicated: (a) slow growth near the threshold ΔK_{th}, (b) intermediate region following a power equation, and (c) unstable rapid growth. (Plotted from the original data for the study of [Paris 72].)

prior to final failure of the test specimen. Such behavior can occur where the plastic zone is small, in which case the curve approaches an asymptote corresponding to $K_{max} = K_c$, the fracture toughness for the material and thickness of interest. Rapid unstable growth at high ΔK sometimes involves fully plastic yielding. In such cases, the use of ΔK for this portion of the curve is improper, as the theoretical limitations of the K concept are exceeded.

The value of the stress ratio R affects the growth rate in a manner analogous to the effects observed in S-N curves for different values of R or mean stress. For a given ΔK, increasing R increases the growth rate, and vice versa. Some data illustrating this effect for a steel are shown in Fig. 11.4.

Constants C and m for the intermediate region where Eq. 11.10 applies have been suggested by Barsom (1999) for various classes of steel. These apply for $R \approx 0$ and are given in Table 11.1.

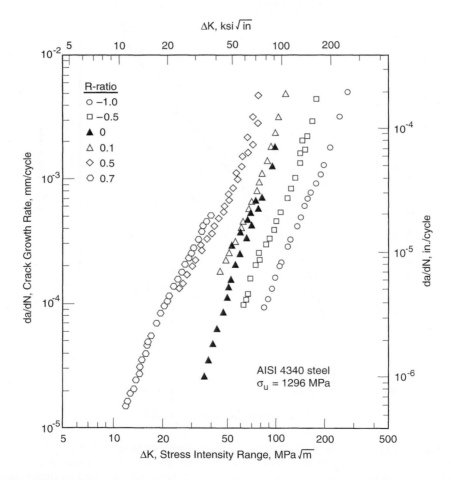

Figure 11.4   Effect of R-ratio on crack growth rates for an alloy steel. For $R < 0$, the compressive portion of the load cycle is here included in calculating ΔK. (Data from [Dennis 86].)

Table 11.1   Constants from Barsom (1999) for Worst-Case da/dN Versus ΔK Curves for Various Classes of Steel for $R \approx 0$

	Constants for $da/dN = C(\Delta K)^m$		
Class of Steel	$C, \frac{\text{mm/cycle}}{(\text{MPa}\sqrt{\text{m}})^m}$	$C, \frac{\text{in/cycle}}{(\text{ksi}\sqrt{\text{in}})^m}$	m
Ferritic-pearlitic	6.89×10^{-9}	3.6×10^{-10}	3.0
Martensitic	1.36×10^{-7}	6.6×10^{-9}	2.25
Austenitic	5.61×10^{-9}	3.0×10^{-10}	3.25

Note: For use with the Walker equation for $R > 0.2$, it is suggested that the given constants be employed as C_0 and m along with an approximate value of $\gamma = 0.5$.

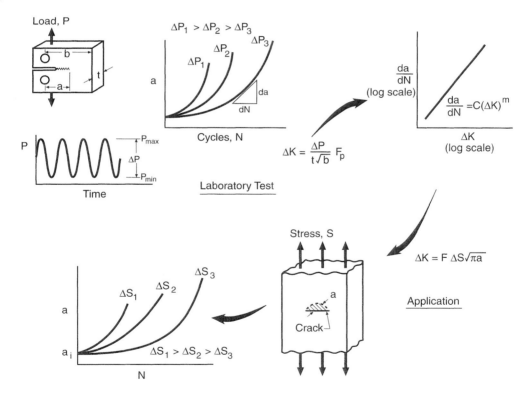

Figure 11.5   Steps in obtaining da/dN versus ΔK data and using it for an engineering application. (Adapted from [Clark 71]; used with permission.)

The value of m is important, as it indicates the degree of sensitivity of the growth rate to stress. For example, if $m = 3$, doubling the stress range ΔS doubles the stress intensity range ΔK, thus increasing the growth rate by a factor of $2^m = 8$.

11.2.4 Discussion

The logical path involved in evaluating the crack growth behavior of a material and using the information is summarized in Fig. 11.5. First, a convenient test specimen geometry is employed in tests at each of several different load levels, so that a wide range of fatigue crack growth rates is obtained. Growth rates are then evaluated and plotted versus ΔK to obtain the da/dN versus ΔK curve. This curve can be used later in an engineering application, with ΔK values being calculated as appropriate for the particular component geometry of interest. Crack length versus cycles curves for a specific initial crack length can then be predicted for the component, leading to life estimates and the determination of safety factors and inspection intervals as discussed earlier.

Example 11.1

Obtain approximate values of constants C and m, and give Eq. 11.10 for the data at $R = 0.1$ in Fig. 11.4.

Solution   These data appear to fall along a straight line on this log–log plot, so it is reasonable to apply Eq. 11.10. Aligning a straight edge with the data gives a line that passes near two points as follows:

$$\left(\Delta K, \frac{da}{dN}\right) = \left(21, 10^{-5}\right) \quad \text{and} \quad \left(155, 10^{-2}\right)$$

Here, units of MPa$\sqrt{\text{m}}$ and mm/cycle are used. Now apply Eq. 11.10 to these two points, denoting them as $(\Delta K_A, da/dN_A)$ and $(\Delta K_B, da/dN_B)$:

$$da/dN_A = C(\Delta K_A)^m, \qquad da/dN_B = C(\Delta K_B)^m$$

Eliminate C between these two equations by dividing one into the other:

$$\frac{da/dN_A}{da/dN_B} = \left(\frac{\Delta K_A}{\Delta K_B}\right)^m$$

Taking logarithms of both sides and solving for m then gives

$$m = \frac{\log\left(da/dN_A\right) - \log\left(da/dN_B\right)}{\log\left(\Delta K_A\right) - \log\left(\Delta K_B\right)} = \frac{\log 10^{-5} - \log 10^{-2}}{\log 21 - \log 155} = 3.456$$

Next, obtain C by substituting this m and either known point into Eq. 11.10:

$$10^{-5}\,\frac{\text{mm}}{\text{cycle}} = C(21\,\text{MPa}\sqrt{\text{m}})^{3.456}, \qquad C = 2.696 \times 10^{-10}\,\frac{\text{mm/cycle}}{(\text{MPa}\sqrt{\text{m}})^m}$$

Note that C has the unusual units indicated that involve the exponent m. Hence, the desired relationship, with constants rounded to three significant figures, is

$$\frac{da}{dN} = 2.70 \times 10^{-10} (\Delta K)^{3.46} \qquad \text{(mm/cycle, MPa}\sqrt{\text{m}}\text{)} \qquad \textbf{Ans.}$$

Discussion   If a more accurate fit is desired, the original source of the data should be consulted for numerical values of the data points and a log–log least squares line of the form $y = mx + b$ obtained. Taking logarithms of both sides of Eq. 11.10 then gives

$$\log \frac{da}{dN} = m \log (\Delta K) + \log C$$

$$y = \log \frac{da}{dN}, \qquad x = \log (\Delta K), \qquad m = m, \qquad b = \log C$$

11.3 FATIGUE CRACK GROWTH RATE TESTING

Standard methods for conducting fatigue crack growth tests have been developed, notably ASTM Standard No. E647. Two commonly used test specimen geometries are the standard compact specimen, Fig 8.16, and center-cracked plates, Fig. 8.12(a).

11.3.1 Test Methods and Data Analysis

In a typical test, constant amplitude cyclic loading is applied to a specimen of a size such that its width dimension b (as defined in Chapter 8) is perhaps 50 mm. Before starting the test, a precrack is necessary. This is accomplished by first machining a sharp notch into the specimen and then starting a crack by cyclic loading at a low level. Cyclic loading is then applied at the higher level to be used for the remainder of the test. The progress of the crack is recorded in terms of the numbers of cycles required for its length to reach each of 10 to 20 or more different values, with these being on the order of 1 mm apart for a specimen of size $b \approx 50$ mm. The resulting crack length data may then be plotted as discrete points versus the corresponding cycle numbers, as in Fig. 11.6.

To measure these crack lengths, one approach is simply to note by visual observation, through a low-power (20 to 50X) microscope, when the crack reaches various lengths that have been previously marked on the specimen. An arrangement for such a test is shown in Fig. 11.7. More sophisticated means may be used to measure crack lengths. For example, as the crack grows, the deflection of the specimen increases, resulting in decreased stiffness. This stiffness change may be measured and used to calculate the crack length. Another approach is to pass an electric current through the specimen and measure changes in the voltage field due to growth of the crack, from which we can obtain its length. Ultrasonic waves can also be reflected from the crack and used to measure its progress.

To obtain growth rates from crack length versus cycles data, a simple and generally suitable approach is to calculate straight-line slopes between the data points, as shown in Fig. 11.6.

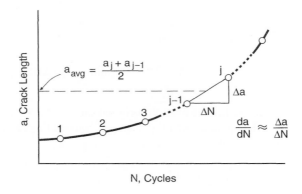

Figure 11.6 Crack growth rates obtained from adjacent pairs of *a* versus *N* data points.

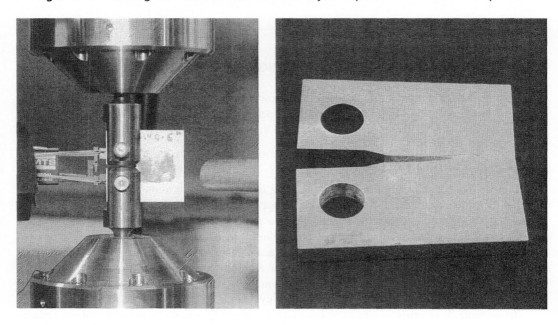

Figure 11.7 Crack growth rate test under way (left) on a compact specimen ($b = 51$ mm), with a microscope and a strobe light used to visually monitor crack growth. Cycle numbers are recorded when the crack reaches each of a number of scribe lines (right). (Photos by R. A. Simonds.)

If the data points are numbered $1, 2, 3 \ldots j$, then the growth rate for the segment ending at point number j is

$$\left(\frac{da}{dN}\right)_j \approx \left(\frac{\Delta a}{\Delta N}\right)_j = \frac{a_j - a_{j-1}}{N_j - N_{j-1}} \qquad (11.11)$$

The corresponding ΔK is calculated from the average crack length during the interval with either of the two equations

$$\Delta K_j = F \, \Delta S \sqrt{\pi a_{\text{avg}}}, \qquad \Delta K_j = F_P \frac{\Delta P}{t\sqrt{b}} \tag{11.12}$$

whichever is more convenient. In the first equation,

$$a_{\text{avg}} = \frac{a_j + a_{j-1}}{2} \tag{11.13}$$

The geometry factor $F = F(\alpha)$ or $F_P = F_P(\alpha)$, where $\alpha = a/b$, is evaluated at the same average crack length, using

$$\alpha_{\text{avg}} = \frac{a_{\text{avg}}}{b} = \frac{a_j + a_{j-1}}{2b} \tag{11.14}$$

The foregoing procedure is valid only if the crack length is measured at fairly short intervals. Otherwise, the growth rate and K may differ so much between adjacent observations that the averaging involved causes difficulties. Detailed requirements are given in the ASTM Standard. Also, curve-fitting methods of evaluating da/dN, which are more sophisticated than simple point-to-point slopes, are sometimes used to smooth the scatter in the a versus N data. Fitting a polynomial over all of the data from a test usually does not work very well, but such a fit applied in an incremental manner to portions of the data works well, as described in the ASTM Standard.

Example 11.2

Crack length versus cycles data are given in Table E11.2(a) from a test on a center-cracked plate of 7075-T6 aluminum. The specimen had dimensions, as defined in Fig. 8.12(a), of $h = 445$, $b = 152.4$, and $t = 2.29$ mm. The force was cycled between zero and a maximum value of $P_{\max} = 48.1$ kN. Obtain da/dN and ΔK values from these data.

Solution   The average growth rate between points 1 and 2 is obtained by applying Eq. 11.11 with $j = 2$:

$$\left(\frac{da}{dN}\right)_2 = \frac{a_2 - a_1}{N_2 - N_1} = \frac{7.62 - 5.08}{18{,}300 - 0} = 1.388 \times 10^{-4} \text{ mm/cycle} \qquad \textbf{Ans.}$$

The corresponding ΔK is evaluated by using the average crack length from Eqs. 11.13 and 11.14 with $j = 2$:

$$a_{\text{avg}} = \frac{a_2 + a_1}{2} = \frac{7.62 + 5.08}{2} = 6.35 \text{ mm}, \qquad \alpha_{\text{avg}} = \frac{a_{\text{avg}}}{b} = \frac{6.35 \text{ mm}}{152.4 \text{ mm}} = 0.0417$$

To evaluate F for this geometry, Fig. 8.12(a) is employed. The value corresponding to α_{avg} is

$$F = \frac{1 - 0.5\alpha + 0.326\alpha^2}{\sqrt{1 - \alpha}} = \frac{1 - 0.5(0.0417) + 0.326(0.0417)^2}{\sqrt{1 - 0.0417}} = 1.001$$

Table E11.2

	(a) Given Data			(b) Calculated Values			
j	a mm	N cycles	da/dN mm/cycle	a_{avg} mm	α_{avg}	F	ΔK MPa$\sqrt{m}$
1	5.08	0	—	—	—	—	—
2	7.62	18 300	1.39×10^{-4}	6.35	0.0417	1.001	9.74
3	10.16	28 300	2.54×10^{-4}	8.89	0.0583	1.002	11.53
4	12.70	35 000	3.79×10^{-4}	11.43	0.0750	1.003	13.09
5	15.24	40 000	5.08×10^{-4}	13.97	0.0917	1.004	14.49
6	17.78	43 000	8.47×10^{-4}	16.51	0.1083	1.006	15.78
7	20.32	47 000	6.35×10^{-4}	19.05	0.1250	1.008	16.99
8	22.86	50 000	8.47×10^{-4}	21.59	0.1417	1.010	18.13
9	25.40	52 000	1.27×10^{-3}	24.13	0.1583	1.013	19.21
10	30.48	57 000	1.02×10^{-3}	27.94	0.1833	1.017	20.77
11	35.56	59 000	2.54×10^{-3}	33.02	0.2167	1.025	22.74
12	40.64	61 000	2.54×10^{-3}	38.10	0.2500	1.034	24.65
13	45.72	62 000	5.08×10^{-3}	43.18	0.2833	1.045	26.52

Source: Data in [Hudson 69].

Hence, using $\Delta S = \Delta P/(2bt)$ in Eq. 11.12, we have

$$(\Delta K)_2 = F \, \Delta S \sqrt{\pi a_{avg}}$$

$$(\Delta K)_2 = 1.001 \frac{48,100 \, \text{N}}{2(152.4 \, \text{mm})(2.29 \, \text{mm})} \sqrt{\pi (0.00635 \, \text{m})} = 9.74 \, \text{MPa}\sqrt{m} \qquad \textbf{Ans.}$$

Similarly applying Eqs. 11.11 to 11.14 with $j = 3$, and then with $j = 4$, etc., gives the additional values seen in Table E11.2(b).

11.3.2 Test Variables

Crack growth tests are most commonly conducted under zero-to-tension loading, $R = 0$, or tension-to-tension loading with a small R value, such as $R = 0.1$. Variations of R in the range 0 to 0.2 have little effect on most materials, and tests in this range are accepted by convention as the standard basis for comparing the effects of various materials, environments, etc. It is usually necessary to test several specimens at different load levels to obtain data over a wide range of growth rates. Such results for a steel are shown in Figs. 11.8 and 11.9. For more complete data, groups of several tests at each of several R values can be conducted. Also, if data are desired in the ΔK_{th} region, a special decreasing load test is needed, as described in ASTM Standard No. E647.

A wide range of variables may affect fatigue crack growth rates in a given material, so that test conditions may be selected to include situations that resemble the anticipated service use of the material. Some of these variables are temperature, frequency of the cyclic load, and hostile chemical environments. Minor variations in the processing or composition of materials may affect fatigue crack growth rates due to the different microstructures that result. Hence, tests on different

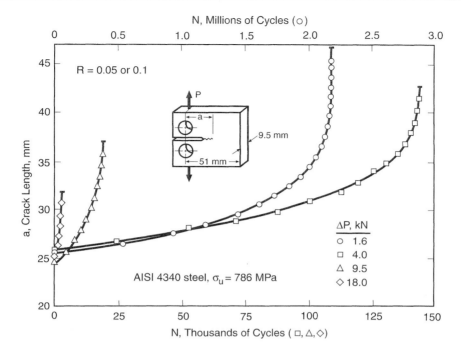

Figure 11.8   Crack length versus cycles data for four different levels of cyclic load applied to compact specimens of an alloy steel.

variations of a material may be conducted to aid in developing materials that can best resist fatigue crack growth.

11.3.3 Geometry Independence of *da/dN* versus ΔK Curves

For a given material and set of test conditions, such as a particular R value, test frequency, and environment, the growth rates should depend only on ΔK. This arises simply from the fact that K characterizes the severity of a combination of loading, geometry, and crack length, and ΔK serves the same function for cyclic loading. Hence, regardless of the load level, crack length, and specimen geometry, all da/dN versus ΔK data for a given set of test conditions should fall together along a single curve, except that some statistical scatter is, of course, expected. This occurs for the different load levels and crack lengths involved in Figs. 11.8 and 11.9. There should be a single trend even if more than one specimen geometry is included in the tests. Some data demonstrating geometry independence are shown in Fig. 11.10.

Such uniqueness of the da/dN versus ΔK curve for different geometries is a crucial test of the applicability of the K concept to both materials testing and engineering applications. (Recall Fig. 11.5.) This uniqueness has been sufficiently verified, so it is not generally necessary to include more than one test specimen geometry in obtaining materials data. However, difficulty with the applicability of ΔK can occur if there is excessive yielding, or for very small cracks, as discussed in Section 11.9 near the end of this chapter.

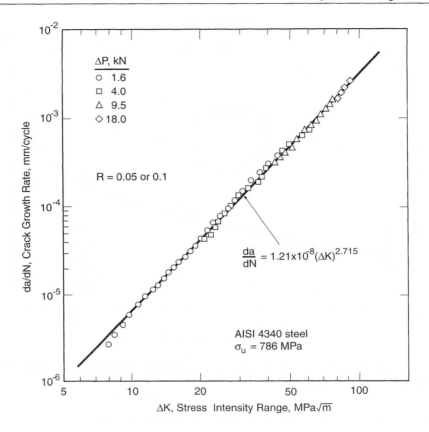

Figure 11.9 Data and least-squares fitted line for da/dN versus ΔK from the a versus N data of Fig. 11.8.

11.4 EFFECTS OF $R = S_{min}/S_{max}$ ON FATIGUE CRACK GROWTH

An increase in the R-ratio of the cyclic loading causes growth rates for a given ΔK to be larger, which has already been illustrated by Fig. 11.4. The effect is usually more pronounced for more brittle materials. For example, the granite rock of Fig. 11.11 shows an extreme effect, being sensitive to increasing R from 0.1 to only 0.2. In contrast, mild steel and other relatively low-strength, highly ductile, structural metals exhibit only a weak R effect in the intermediate growth rate region of the da/dN versus ΔK curve.

11.4.1 The Walker Equation

Various empirical relationships are employed for characterizing the effect of R on da/dN versus ΔK curves. One of the most widely used equations is based on applying the Walker relationship,

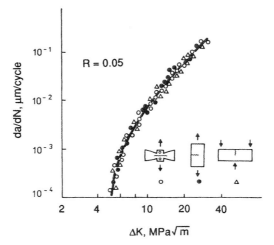

Figure 11.10 Fatigue crack growth rate data for a 0.65% carbon steel, demonstrating geometry independence. (Adapted from [Klesnil 80] p. 111; used with permission.)

Eq. 10.38, to the stress intensity factor K:

$$\overline{\Delta K} = K_{max}(1 - R)^{\gamma} \tag{11.15}$$

Here, γ is a constant for the material and $\overline{\Delta K}$ is an equivalent zero-to-tension ($R = 0$) stress intensity that causes the same growth rate as the actual K_{max}, R combination. By applying Eq. 9.4(a) to K, which gives $\Delta K = K_{max}(1 - R)$, Eq. 11.15 is seen to be equivalent to

$$\overline{\Delta K} = \frac{\Delta K}{(1 - R)^{1-\gamma}} \tag{11.16}$$

Let the constant C in Eq. 11.10 be denoted C_0 for the special case of $R = 0$.

$$\frac{da}{dN} = C_0 (\Delta K)^m \qquad (R = 0) \tag{11.17}$$

Since $\overline{\Delta K}$ is an equivalent ΔK for $R = 0$, we can substitute $\overline{\Delta K}$ for ΔK in Eq. 11.17:

$$\frac{da}{dN} = C_0 \left[\frac{\Delta K}{(1 - R)^{1-\gamma}} \right]^m \tag{11.18}$$

This represents a family of da/dN versus ΔK curves, which, on a log–log plot, are all parallel straight lines of slope m. Some manipulation gives

$$\frac{da}{dN} = \frac{C_0}{(1 - R)^{m(1-\gamma)}} (\Delta K)^m \tag{11.19}$$

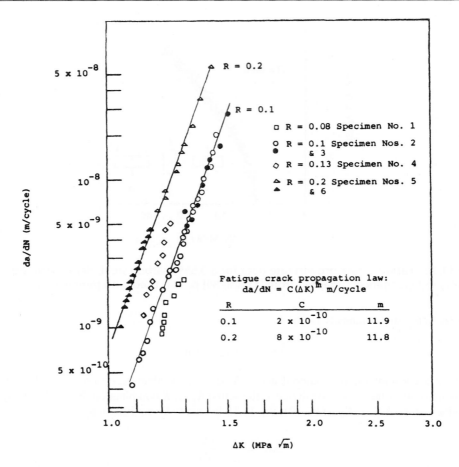

Figure 11.11   Effect of *R*-ratio on fatigue crack growth rates for Westerly granite, tested in the form of three-point bend specimens. (From [Kim 81]; copyright © ASTM; reprinted with permission.)

Comparing this with Eq. 11.10, we see that *m* is not expected to be affected by *R*, but *C* becomes a function of *R*.

$$C = \frac{C_0}{(1 - R)^{m(1-\gamma)}} \tag{11.20}$$

A useful interpretation arising from Eq. 11.18 is that $\overline{\Delta K}$, the equivalent zero-to-tension ($R = 0$) stress intensity, can be plotted versus da/dN, and a single straight line should result. The data of Fig. 11.4 are plotted in this manner in Fig. 11.12, with $\gamma = 0.42$. Since all of the data lie quite close to the single line, the equation is reasonably successful. However, it was necessary to handle loadings involving compression, $R < 0$, by assuming that the compressive portion of the

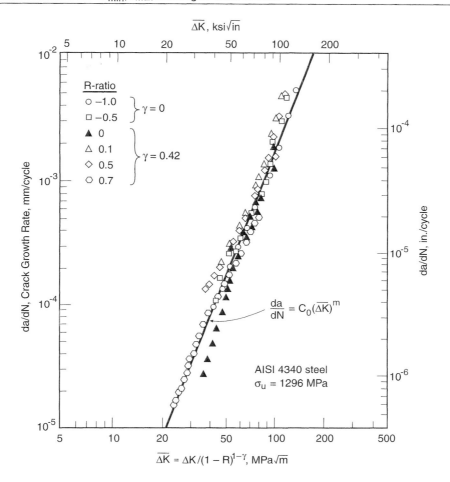

Figure 11.12   Representation of the data of Fig. 11.4 by a single relationship based on the Walker equation. (Data from [Dennis 86].)

cycle had no effect, which is accomplished by using $\gamma = 0$ where $R < 0$, so that $\overline{\Delta K} = K_{max}$. This is reasonable on the basis of the logic that the crack closes at zero load and no longer acts as a crack below this. In more ductile metals, the compressive portion of the loading may contribute to the growth, so this approach is not universally applicable.

Values of the constant γ for various metals are typically around 0.5, but vary from around 0.3 to nearly 1.0. A value of $\gamma = 1$ gives simply $\overline{\Delta K} = \Delta K$, corresponding to no effect of R. Decreasing values of γ imply a stronger effect of R. Constants for the Walker equation are given for several metals in Table 11.2, including the AISI 4340 steel of Fig. 11.12. Where data are available for $R < 0$, note that $\gamma = 0$ applies in three cases, but not for the very ductile Man-Ten steel, for which compressive loading does contribute to crack growth according to $\gamma = 0.22$.

Table 11.2 Constants for the Walker Equation for Several Metals

Material	Yield σ_o	Toughness K_{Ic}	Walker Equation C_0	C_0	m	γ	γ
	MPa (ksi)	MPa $\sqrt{\mathrm{m}}$ (ksi$\sqrt{\mathrm{in}}$)	mm/cycle $\overline{(\mathrm{MPa}\sqrt{\mathrm{m}})^m}$	in/cycle $\overline{(\mathrm{ksi}\sqrt{\mathrm{in}})^m}$		$(R \geq 0)$	$(R < 0)$
Man-Ten steel	363 (52.6)	200[1] (182)	3.28×10^{-9}	1.74×10^{-10}	3.13	0.928	0.220
RQC-100 steel	778 (113)	150[1] (136)	8.01×10^{-11}	4.71×10^{-12}	4.24	0.719	0
AISI 4340 steel ($\sigma_u = 1296$ MPa)	1255 (182)	130 (118)	5.11×10^{-10}	2.73×10^{-11}	3.24	0.420	0
17-4 PH steel (H1050, vac. melt)	1059 (154)	120[1] (109)	3.29×10^{-8}	1.63×10^{-9}	2.44	0.790	—
2024-T3 Al[2]	353 (51.2)	34 (31)	1.42×10^{-8}	7.85×10^{-10}	3.59	0.680	—
7075-T6 Al[2]	523 (75.9)	29 (26)	2.71×10^{-8}	1.51×10^{-9}	3.70	0.641	0

Notes: [1]Data not available; values given are estimates. [2]Values for C_0 include a modification for use in [Hudson 69] of k, where $K = k\sqrt{\pi}$.
Sources: Original data or fitted constants in [Crooker 75], [Dennis 86], [Dowling 79c], [Hudson 69], and [MILHDBK 94] pp. 3–10 and 3–11.

A value of γ can be obtained from data at various R values, the desired γ being the one that best consolidates the data along a single straight line or other curve on a plot of da/dN versus $\overline{\Delta K}$. Where a straight line on a log–log plot is expected, a good initial estimate of γ can be obtained by using the data for two different and contrasting R values, as illustrated in Example 11.3, presented next. However, a more rigorous procedure is to perform a multiple linear regression, starting by taking the logarithm of both sides of Eq. 11.19:

$$\log(da/dN) = m\log(\Delta K) - m(1 - \gamma)\log(1 - R) + \log C_0 \qquad (11.21)$$

The dependent variable is $y = \log(da/dN)$, and the independent ones are $x_1 = \log(\Delta K)$ and $x_2 = \log(1 - R)$. See Ex. 10.4 for a similar analysis.

The Walker $\overline{\Delta K}$ in the form of Eq. 11.15 or 11.16 can be used with any mathematical form for the da/dN versus ΔK equation. However, it is primarily employed for intermediate growth rates where Eq. 11.10 does apply.

Example 11.3
Obtain approximate values for the Walker equation constants for the AISI 4340 steel of Fig. 11.4.

Solution   Note that the Walker equation assumes that the same exponent m applies for all R-ratios, so that a family of parallel straight lines is formed on a log–log plot. Two such parallel lines for contrasting values of R are sufficient for obtaining approximate values of C_0, m, and γ. The line for $R = 0.1$ already determined in Ex. 11.1 can be used for one of these:

$$\frac{da}{dN} = 2.70 \times 10^{-10}(\Delta K)^{3.46} \qquad (R = 0.1)$$

In this equation and in what follows, units of MPa$\sqrt{\text{m}}$ and mm/cycle are employed. A second line parallel to this one and passing through the $R = 0.7$ data goes approximately through the point

$$\left(\Delta K, \frac{da}{dN}\right) = (11, 10^{-5})$$

The $R = 0.7$ data are roughly parallel to the $R = 0.1$ data, so it is reasonable to proceed with a common $m = 3.46$. The constant C for this second line may be obtained by substituting this m and the preceding point into Eq. 11.10:

$$10^{-5} = C(11)^{3.46}, \qquad C = 2.49 \times 10^{-9}$$

Hence, the equation of the line is

$$\frac{da}{dN} = 2.49 \times 10^{-9}(\Delta K)^{3.46} \qquad (R = 0.7)$$

We now have two values of C, both of which must obey Eq. 11.20.

$$C_{0.1} = \frac{C_0}{(1 - R)^{m(1-\gamma)}}, \qquad C_{0.7} = \frac{C_0}{(1 - R)^{m(1-\gamma)}}$$

Substituting the respective C and R values, along with the known m, gives two equations with unknowns C_0 and γ:

$$2.70 \times 10^{-10} = \frac{C_0}{(1 - 0.1)^{3.46(1-\gamma)}}, \qquad 2.49 \times 10^{-9} = \frac{C_0}{(1 - 0.7)^{3.46(1-\gamma)}}$$

Dividing the second equation into the first eliminates C_0:

$$\frac{2.70 \times 10^{-10}}{2.49 \times 10^{-9}} = \left(\frac{0.3}{0.9}\right)^{3.46(1-\gamma)}$$

Taking logarithms of both sides and solving for γ yields

$$\log \frac{2.70 \times 10^{-10}}{2.49 \times 10^{-9}} = 3.46\,(1-\gamma)\,\log \frac{0.3}{0.9}, \qquad \gamma = 0.415 \qquad \textbf{Ans.}$$

Substituting this γ back into either equation involving C_0 allows that constant to be determined:

$$C_0 = 2.70 \times 10^{-10}(0.9)^{3.46(1-0.415)} = 2.18 \times 10^{-10} \frac{\text{mm/cycle}}{(\text{MPa}\sqrt{\text{m}})^m} \qquad \textbf{Ans.}$$

The final constant is the m value used throughout, $m = 3.46$ (**Ans.**).

Comment   These approximate values of the constants agree only roughly with the ones in Table 11.2 for this material, as the latter were fitted by using the full set of data at several R values.

11.4.2 The Forman Equation

Another proposed generalization to include R effects is that of Forman:

$$\frac{da}{dN} = \frac{C_2\,(\Delta K)^{m_2}}{(1-R)\,K_c - \Delta K} = \frac{C_2\,(\Delta K)^{m_2}}{(1-R)\,(K_c - K_{max})} \qquad (11.22)$$

Here, K_c is the fracture toughness for the material and thickness of interest. The second form arises from the first simply by applying Eq. 9.4(a) to ΔK in the denominator. As K_{max} approaches K_c, the denominator approaches zero, and da/dN becomes large. In particular, there is an asymptote at $\Delta K/(1-R) = K_{max} = K_c$. The equation thus has the attractive feature of predicting accelerated growth near the final toughness failure, while approaching Eq. 11.10 at low ΔK. Hence, it can be used to fit data that cover both the intermediate and high growth rate regions.

Assuming that crack growth data are available for various R values, we can fit these to Eq. 11.22 by computing the following quantity for each data point:

$$Q = \frac{da}{dN}\,[(1-R)K_c - \Delta K] \qquad (11.23)$$

If these Q values are plotted versus the corresponding ΔK values on a log–log plot, a straight line is expected. This is illustrated for 7075-T6 aluminum in Fig. 11.13. The slope of the Q versus ΔK line on the log–log plot is given by m_2, and C_2 is the value of Q at $\Delta K = 1$.

For a given material, the success of the Forman equation can be judged by the extent to which data for various ΔK, R combinations all fall together on a straight line on a log–log plot of Q versus ΔK. For the data of Fig. 11.13(a), the consolidation onto a straight line in (b) is reasonably successful. Constants for the Forman equation corresponding to these data are given in Table 11.3, as are constants for three additional metals.

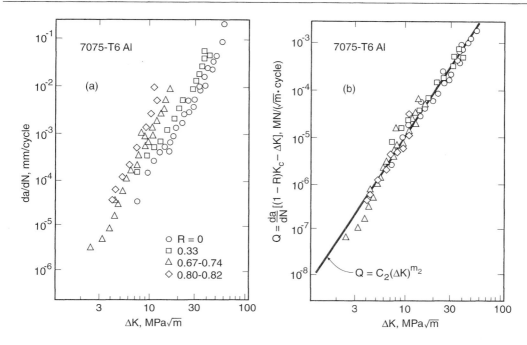

Figure 11.13   Effect of R-ratio on growth rates in 7075-T6 aluminum (a), and correlation of these data (b) on the basis of the Forman equation, with constants as listed in Table 11.3. (Data from [Hudson 69].)

11.4.3 Effects on ΔK_{th}

The R-ratio generally has a strong effect on the behavior at low growth rates, hence also on the threshold value ΔK_{th}. This occurs even for low-strength metals where there is little effect at intermediate growth rates. Some values of ΔK_{th} for various steels over a range of R-ratios are shown in Fig. 11.14. The lower limit of the scatter shown corresponds to ΔK_{th} as follows:

$$\Delta K_{th} = 7.0(1 - 0.85R) \text{ MPa}\sqrt{\text{m}}$$
$$(R \geq 0.1) \qquad (11.24)$$
$$\Delta K_{th} = 6.4(1 - 0.85R) \text{ ksi}\sqrt{\text{in}}$$

On the basis of the discussion in Barsom (1999), these equations appear to represent a reasonable worst-case estimate for a wide range of steels. However, lower values of ΔK_{th} may apply for highly strengthened steels, which will be illustrated later. Similar trends occur for other classes of metals.

The Walker equation in the form of Eq. 11.15 is sometimes employed to represent the effect of R-ratio on ΔK_{th} for a given material:

$$\Delta K_{th} = \overline{\Delta K}_{th}(1 - R)^{1 - \gamma_{th}} \qquad (11.25)$$

Table 11.3 Constants for the Forman Equation for Several Metals

Material	Yield σ_o MPa (ksi)	Toughness K_{Ic} MPa$\sqrt{\text{m}}$ (ksi$\sqrt{\text{in}}$)	Forman Equation			
			C_2 $\dfrac{\text{mm/cycle}}{(\text{MPa}\sqrt{\text{m}})^{m_2-1}}$	C_2 $\dfrac{\text{in/cycle}}{(\text{ksi}\sqrt{\text{in}})^{m_2-1}}$	m_2	K_c MPa$\sqrt{\text{m}}$ (ksi$\sqrt{\text{in}}$)
17-4 PH steel (H1025)	1145 (166)	—	1.40×10^{-6}	6.45×10^{-8}	2.65	132 (120)
Inconel 718 (Fe-Ni-base, aged)	1172 (170)	132 (120)	4.29×10^{-6}	2.00×10^{-7}	2.79	132 (120)
2024-T3 Al[1]	353 (51.2)	34 (31)	2.31×10^{-6}	1.14×10^{-7}	3.38	110 (100)
7075-T6 Al[1]	523 (75.9)	29 (26)	5.29×10^{-6}	2.56×10^{-7}	3.21	78.7 (71.6)

Notes: [1]Values for C_2 and K_c include a modification for use in [Hudson 69] of k, where $K = k\sqrt{\pi}$. The K_c values are for 2.3 mm thick sheet material; replace with K_{Ic} for thick material.
Sources: Values in [Hudson 69], [MILHDBK 94] pp. 2–198 and 6–59, and [Smith 82].

Here, $\overline{\Delta K}_{th}$ and γ_{th} are empirical constants fitted to test data of ΔK_{th} values for various R. Note that $\overline{\Delta K}_{th}$ corresponds to ΔK_{th} at $R = 0$. Values of γ_{th} will not generally agree with γ fitted to the Walker equation in the intermediate growth rate region. In particular, there is usually an increased sensitivity to R-ratio in the low growth rate and threshold region.

11.4.4 Discussion

A variety of other mathematical expressions, some of them quite complex, have been used to represent da/dN versus ΔK curves. Some of these are not merely empirical, but are based on attempts to include modeling of the closing of the crack and other physical phenomena that affect crack growth. Many give a curve shape similar to Fig. 11.3, where the curve steepens at both low and high growth rates. If R-ratio effects are included and the da/dN versus ΔK behavior ranges over the regions of low, intermediate, and high growth rates, as many as 10 empirical constants may be required to accurately represent the behavior of a given material.

An alternative to curve fitting with empirical constants is to use a *table lookup procedure*. In this case, numerical data of da/dN versus ΔK for various R-ratios are maintained in tabular form in a digital computer, and interpolation is employed to determine da/dN for a desired combination of ΔK and R. For additional detail on representing da/dN versus ΔK behavior, see Forman (2005), Grandt (2004), and Henkener (1993).

A simple, but approximate, approach to representing da/dN versus ΔK behavior is illustrated in Fig. 11.15. In the intermediate region, use the Walker relationship, Eq. 11.19, with appropriately fitted materials constants C_0, m, and γ. Then in the threshold region, assume that there is an abrupt

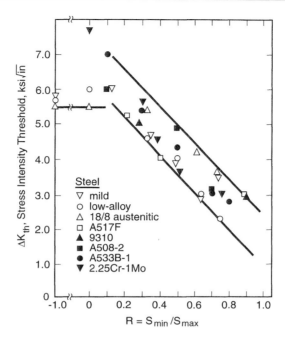

Figure 11.14   Effect of R-ratio on the threshold ΔK_{th} for various steels. For $R = -1$, the compressive portion of the loading cycle is here excluded from calculations of ΔK_{th}. (Adapted from [Barsom 87] p. 285; © 1987 by Prentice Hall, Upper Saddle River, NJ; reprinted with permission.)

transition to a vertical limit, ΔK_{th}, as given by Eq. 11.25 or other analogous relationship. Additional materials constants, such as $\overline{\Delta K}_{th}$ and γ_{th}, are then needed. However, it is conservative to simply ignore the threshold, as shown by the dashed line. Finally, represent the unstable rapid-growth-rate region as another vertical limit. This limit occurs upon reaching either the fracture toughness or the fully plastic limit load, the latter occurring due to the decreasing cross-sectional area of the cracked member. Either of these may occur first.

A situation often encountered is that data for a material of interest are available only for zero-to-tension or similar loading—that is, for R in the range 0 to 0.2. For engineering metals in the intermediate growth rate region, it is reasonable to employ such data with the Walker equation by assuming a value of $\gamma = 0.5$. This will generally provide a conservative estimate of the behavior at other positive R-ratios.

The use of a fracture toughness constant K_c in the Forman and other crack growth equations is necessary for accurate representation of behavior at high growth rates. However, some care is needed. First, K_c varies with thickness unless the behavior is plane strain, where K_{Ic} applies. In addition, the severe cyclic loading that occurs just prior to brittle fracture at the end of a crack growth test may alter K_c, increasing it for certain materials and decreasing it for others. Further, for ductile, high-toughness materials such as mild steel, fatigue crack growth tests may terminate due to gross yielding instead of brittle fracture. It is then not appropriate to obtain a K_c value from such data.

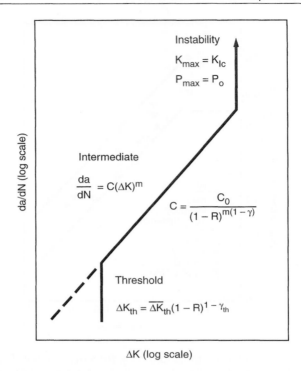

Figure 11.15 Approximate representation of da/dN versus ΔK behavior with R-ratio effects included. The Walker equation is used for the intermediate region, along with a possible threshold limit at low growth rates. There is also an instability limit at high growth rates, due to either brittle fracture or fully plastic yielding.

11.5 TRENDS IN FATIGUE CRACK GROWTH BEHAVIOR

Fatigue crack growth behavior differs considerably for different classes of material. It is also affected, sometimes to a large extent, by changes in the environment, such as temperature or hostile chemicals.

11.5.1 Trends with Material

The crack growth behavior in air at room temperature may vary only modestly within a narrowly defined class of materials. For example, data for $R \approx 0$ for several ferritic-pearlitic steels are shown in Fig. 11.16. An equation of the form of Eq. 11.10 is shown that represents the worst case for the several steels tested, with this equation corresponding to the constants given in Table 11.1. Recall from Chapter 3 that ferritic-pearlitic steels have low carbon contents and are relatively low-strength steels used for structural members, pressure vessels, and similar applications.

Worst-case da/dN versus ΔK equations are given in Barsom (1999) for two additional classes of steel, namely, martensitic steels and austenitic stainless steels. The constants have already been presented in Table 11.1. Martensitic steels are distinguished as being steels that are heat treated by

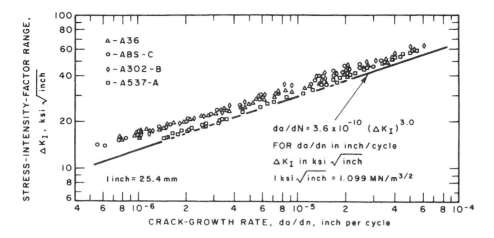

Figure 11.16   Fatigue crack growth rate data at $R \approx 0$ for four ferritic-pearlitic steels, and a line giving worst-case growth rates. Note that the axes are reversed, compared with the other da/dN versus ΔK plots given. (From [Barsom 71]; used with permission of ASME.)

quenching and tempering, so this group includes many low-alloy steels, and also those 400-series stainless steels with less than 15% Cr. Austenitic steels are primarily the 300-series stainless steels, which are used where corrosion resistance is critical. These equations apply for R values near zero, say, up to $R = 0.2$. For higher R-ratios, it is suggested that these constants be employed as C_0 and m in the Walker equation, along with an assumed value of $\gamma = 0.5$.

These general-purpose equations need to be used with some care, as exceptions do exist where they are not very accurate. For example, if the widely used martensitic steel AISI 4340 is heat treated to various strength levels, including very high strength levels, the crack growth rates may exceed the suggested worst-case trend. In addition, the ΔK_{th} values for high-strength steels may be considerably below the typical behavior of Fig. 11.14. Test data showing the trend of ΔK_{th} with strength level in AISI 4340 steel are given in Fig. 11.17. The decrease in ΔK_{th} with strength parallels the similar trend in fracture toughness for this material. (See Fig. 8.32.)

If various major classes of metals are considered, such as steels, aluminum alloys, and titanium alloys, crack growth rates differ considerably when compared on a da/dN versus ΔK plot. However, the ΔK values corresponding to a given growth rate scale roughly with the elastic modulus E. Hence, a plot of da/dN versus $\Delta K/E$ removes much of the difference among various metals, as shown in Fig. 11.18. Polymers exhibit a wide range of growth rates when compared on the basis of ΔK, as shown in Fig. 11.19. For any given ΔK level, the growth rates are considerably higher than for most metals.

One generalization that may be made is that the crack growth rate exponent m is higher for lower ductility (more brittle) materials. For ductile metals, m is typically in the range 2 to 4 and is often around 3. Higher exponents occur for more brittle cast metals, for short-fiber reinforced composites, and for ceramics, including concrete. For example, m is near 12 for the granite rock of Fig. 11.11.

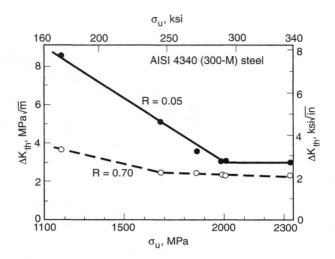

Figure 11.17 Effect of strength level of an alloy steel on ΔK_{th} at two R-ratios. (Adapted from [Ritchie 77]; used with permission of ASME.)

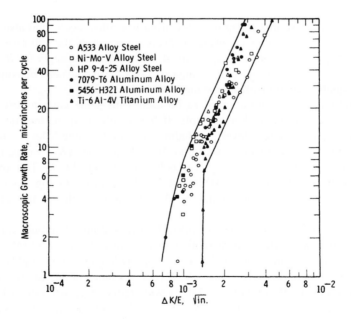

Figure 11.18 Fatigue crack growth trends for various metals correlated by plotting $\Delta K/E$. (From [Bates 69]; used with permission.)

Despite the generalizations that may be made as to similar behavior within classes of materials, surprisingly small differences can sometimes have a significant effect. For example, decreasing the grain size in steels has the detrimental effect of lowering ΔK_{th}, while the behavior outside of the low

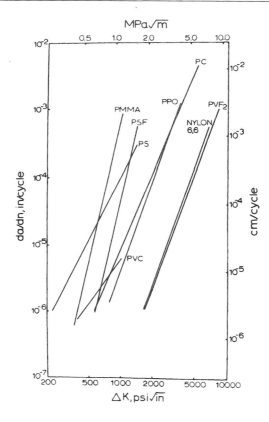

Figure 11.19 Fatigue crack growth trends for various crystalline and amorphous polymers. (From [Hertzberg 75]; used with permission.)

growth rate region is relatively unaffected. Also, as might be expected, variations in reinforcement often have a significant effect on crack growth in composites materials, an example of which is given in Fig. 11.20.

11.5.2 Trends with Temperature and Environment

Changing the temperature usually affects the fatigue crack growth rate, with higher temperature often causing faster growth. Data illustrating such behavior for the austenitic (FCC) stainless steel AISI 304 are shown in Fig. 11.21 (left). However, an opposite trend can occur in BCC metals due to the cleavage mechanism contributing to fatigue crack growth at low temperature. (See Section 8.6.) Such a trend for an Fe-21Cr-6Ni-9Mn alloy is illustrated in Fig. 11.21 (right). This alloy is austenitic at room temperature, but at low temperatures it is martensitic (BCC), and hence subject to cleavage, so that the more usual temperature effect is reversed. The effect of this cleavage contribution in BCC irons and steels can have a large effect on the fatigue crack growth exponent m, as shown in Fig. 11.22. Suppressing this effect by adding sufficient nickel avoids high growth rates at low temperature.

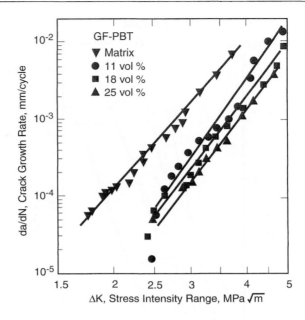

Figure 11.20 Effect on crack growth rates at $R = 0.2$ of various amounts of short glass fibers, in a matrix of the thermoplastic polymer PBT, with crack propagation perpendicular to the mold-fill direction. (Adapted from [Voss 88]; used with permission.)

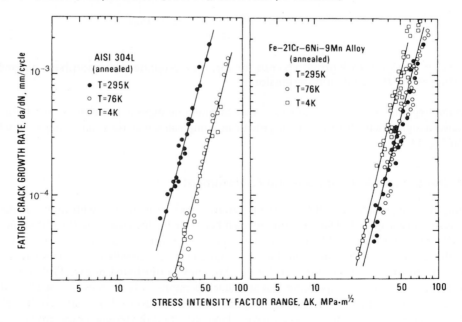

Figure 11.21 Effect of temperature on fatigue crack growth rates in two metals. (From [Tobler 78]; used with permission.)

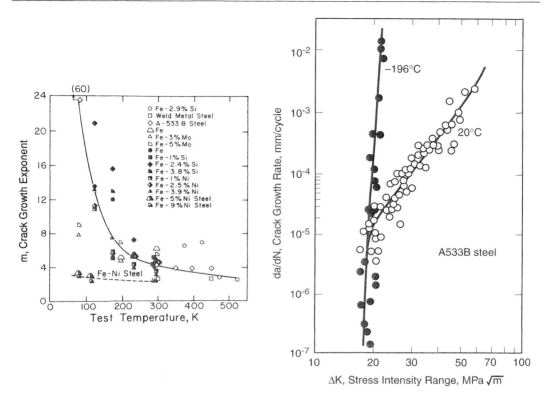

Figure 11.22   Variation (left) of the exponent *m* for the Paris equation with test temperature for iron and various steels at *R*-ratios near zero. Shown on the right is the associated drastic increase in growth rates at low temperature for A533B steel tested at $R = 0.1$. (Left from [Gerberich 79]; copyright © ASTM; reprinted with permission. Right adapted from [Campbell 82] p. 83, as based on data from [Stonesifer 76]; used with permission.)

Hostile chemical environments often increase fatigue crack growth rates, with certain combinations of material and environment causing especially large effects. The term *corrosion fatigue* is often used when the environment involved is a corrosive medium, such as seawater. Such behavior is illustrated in Fig. 11.23, which shows the effect of a saltwater solution similar to seawater on two strength levels of AISI 4340 steel. The effect is considerably greater for the higher strength level of this steel. The effect on growth rate per cycle, da/dN, of a given hostile environment is usually greater at slower frequencies of cycling, where the environment has more time to act. This trend is apparent in the data of Fig. 11.24.

Even the gases and moisture in air can act as a hostile environment, which can be demonstrated by comparing test data in vacuum or an inert gas with data in air. Such comparisons for a metal and a ceramic are shown in Fig. 11.25. This circumstance results in frequency effects occurring in ambient air for some materials. Since chemical activity increases with temperature, the general trend of increasing growth rate with temperature is explained, at least in part, by the ambient air having a hostile effect.

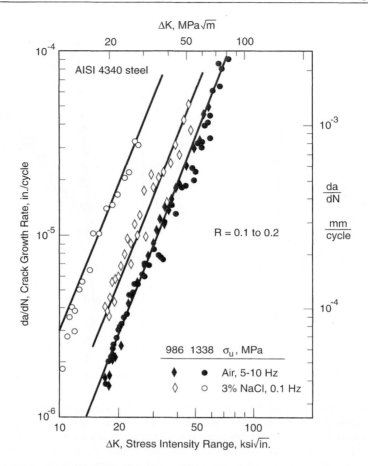

Figure 11.23   Contrasting sensitivity to corrosion fatigue crack growth of two strength levels of an alloy steel. (Adapted from [Imhof 73]; copyright © ASTM; reprinted with permission.)

11.6 LIFE ESTIMATES FOR CONSTANT AMPLITUDE LOADING

Since ΔK increases with crack length during constant amplitude stressing ΔS, and since the crack growth rate da/dN depends on ΔK, the growth rate is not constant, but increases with crack length. In other words, the crack accelerates as it grows, as for the data of Fig. 11.8. This situation of changing da/dN necessitates the use of an integration procedure to obtain the life required for crack growth.

Crack growth rates da/dN for a given combination of material and R-ratio are given as a function of ΔK by Eqs. 11.10, 11.18, and 11.22, and by other similar equations, which may be represented in general by

$$\frac{da}{dN} = f(\Delta K, R) \tag{11.26}$$

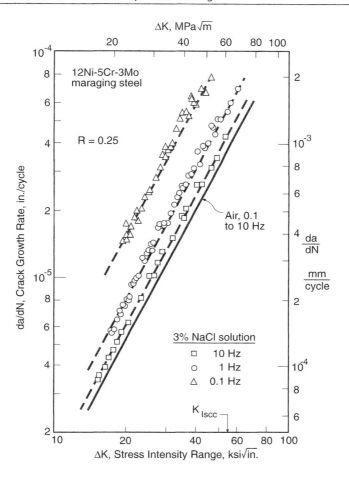

Figure 11.24   Frequency effects on corrosion fatigue crack growth rates in a maraging steel. (Adapted from [Imhof 73]; copyright © ASTM; reprinted with permission.)

where any effects of environment, frequency, etc., are assumed to be included in the material constants involved. The life in cycles required for crack growth may be calculated by solving this equation for dN and integrating both sides:

$$\int_{N_i}^{N_f} dN = N_f - N_i = N_{if} = \int_{a_i}^{a_f} \frac{da}{f(\Delta K, R)} \tag{11.27}$$

This integral gives the number of cycles required for the crack to grow from an initial size a_i at cycle number N_i to a final size a_f at cycle number N_f. It is convenient to use the symbol N_{if} to represent the number of elapsed cycles, $N_f - N_i$.

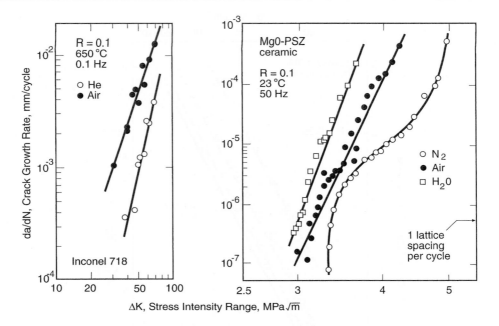

Figure 11.25 Faster fatigue crack growth in air than in inert gas (left) for the Ni-base alloy Inconel 718 at elevated temperature, and (right) for a magnesia, partially stabilized zirconia ceramic. (Left adapted from [Floreen 79]; used with permission. Right adapted from [Dauskardt 90]; reprinted by permission of the American Ceramic Society.)

The inverse of the growth rate, dN/da, is the rate of accumulation of cycles, N, per unit increase in crack length a. From Eq. 11.26, this is given by

$$\frac{dN}{da} = \frac{1}{da/dN} = \frac{1}{f(\Delta K, R)} \tag{11.28}$$

Note that Eq. 11.27 can also be written

$$N_{if} = \int_{a_i}^{a_f} \left(\frac{dN}{da}\right) da \tag{11.29}$$

Hence, if dN/da from Eq. 11.28 is plotted as a function of a, the life N_{if} is given by the area under this curve between a_i and a_f. This is illustrated in Fig. 11.26.

To perform the integration for a particular case, it is necessary to substitute the specific da/dN equation for the material and R of interest, and also the specific equation for ΔK for the geometry of interest. Some useful closed-form solutions exist, but numerical integration is necessary in many cases.

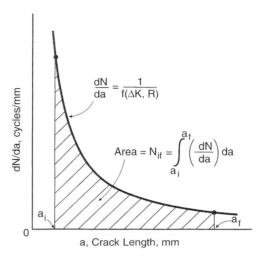

Figure 11.26 Area under the *dN/da* versus *a* curve used to estimate the number of cycles to grow a crack from initial size a_i to final size a_f.

11.6.1 Closed-Form Solutions

Consider a situation where growth rates are given by Eq. 11.10 and where $F = F(a/b)$ in Eq. 11.7 can be approximated as constant over the range of crack lengths a_i to a_f:

$$\frac{da}{dN} = f\,(\Delta K,\,R) = C\,(\Delta K)^m, \qquad \Delta K = F\,\Delta S\sqrt{\pi a} \qquad (11.30)$$

The value of C used can include the effect of the ratio $R = S_{\min}/S_{\max}$, as from the Walker approach using Eq. 11.20. Assume that $S_{\max}$ and $S_{\min}$ are constant, so that ΔS and R are also both constant. Substituting this particular $f(\Delta K,\,R)$ into Eq. 11.27 and then substituting for ΔK gives

$$N_{if} = \int_{a_i}^{a_f} \frac{da}{C\,(\Delta K)^m} = \int_{a_i}^{a_f} \frac{da}{C\left(F\,\Delta S\sqrt{\pi a}\right)^m} = \int_{a_i}^{a_f} \frac{1}{C\left(F\,\Delta S\sqrt{\pi}\right)^m}\frac{da}{a^{m/2}} \qquad (11.31)$$

Since C, F, ΔS, and m are all constant, the only variable is a, and integration is straightforward, giving

$$N_{if} = \frac{a_f^{\,1-m/2} - a_i^{\,1-m/2}}{C\left(F\,\Delta S\sqrt{\pi}\right)^m (1 - m/2)} \qquad (m \neq 2) \qquad (11.32)$$

If $m = 2$, this equation is mathematically indeterminate.

Where a_f is substantially larger than a_i and m is around 3 or greater, the a_i term dominates the numerator of Eq. 11.32, and the life is insensitive to the value of a_f. This trend is accentuated for larger values of m. With reference to Fig. 11.26, the area under the curve, N_{if}, is affected only a small amount by the exact choice of a_f. Also, since most of the area, and thus most of the cycles, are accumulated near a_i, the value of constant F chosen for Eq. 11.32 should be closer to the value

F_i corresponding to a_i than to the value F_f corresponding to a_f. Hence, either use F_i or a slightly higher intermediate value.

Additional closed-form solutions exist that may be useful, such as one for the case of $m = 2$, with derivations of some of these being included as Problems at the end of this chapter. However, where $F = F(a/b)$ must be treated as a variable, the variety of these is severely limited due to the appearance of m as an exponent on F in the denominator of Eq. 11.31.

The preceding equations assume constant amplitude loading, so the gross section nominal stresses $S_{\max}$ and $S_{\min}$ are constant during cycling. If these change, the integral of Eq. 11.27, and any equations obtained from it, can be used in separate calculations for periods of crack growth during which the load levels are constant. The cycle numbers for each of these periods can then be summed to obtain the total life. However, see the additional discussion of variable amplitude loading given later in Section 11.7.

11.6.2 Crack Length at Failure

In employing Eq. 11.27 to estimate crack growth life, the final crack length a_f is often unknown and must be determined before the equation can be applied. In addition, if F is taken as constant, as in Eq. 11.32, it is also necessary to determine $F_f = F(a_f/b)$, so that it can be confirmed that this value does not differ excessively from $F_i = F(a_i/b)$. If F_f and F_i differ by more than about 15 to 20%, the resulting error in N_{if} due to using a constant value will generally be unacceptably large. Numerical integration, as described in Section 11.6.3, is then usually needed.

Under constant amplitude cyclic loading, the value $K_{\max}$ corresponding to $S_{\max}$ increases as crack growth proceeds. When $K_{\max}$ reaches the fracture toughness K_c for the material and thickness of interest, failure is expected at the length a_c that is critical for brittle fracture:

$$a_c = \frac{1}{\pi} \left(\frac{K_c}{F S_{\max}} \right)^2 \tag{11.33}$$

Since F varies, a graphical or iterative solution as already illustrated by Example 8.1(c) is generally needed to obtain a_c.

In addition, crack growth causes a loss of cross-sectional area, and thus an increase in the stress on the remaining uncracked (net) area. Depending on the material and the member geometry and size, fully plastic yielding may be reached prior to $K_{\max} = K_c$. This is most likely for ductile materials with low strength and high fracture toughness. Hence, a_f is the smaller of two possibilities, a_c and a_o, where the latter is the crack length corresponding to fully plastic yielding. Values of a_o may be estimated on the basis of fully plastic behavior, as discussed in Appendix A, Section A.7.2. For some simple two-dimensional cases, useful equations for a_o obtained in this manner are given in Fig. A.16.

Use of linear-elastic fracture mechanics up to the crack length a_o corresponding to fully plastic yielding violates the plastic zone size limitations of LEFM, as discussed in Chapter 8. The effect of yielding just prior to reaching a_o will be to increase growth rates to higher values than those calculated, giving an actual life that is shorter than calculated. However, recall from Fig. 11.26 that cracks accelerate during their growth, so most cycles are exhausted while the crack is short, and few are spent while the crack is near its final length. The error in life from this source is thus usually small, so the suggested procedure of choosing the smaller of a_c and a_o is useful and appropriate as an approximation for engineering purposes.

Another source of possible error in life estimates is that the fracture toughness K_c at the end of cyclic loading may differ from standard values obtained in static tests. However, if a_f is significantly larger than a_i, the effect on life of an altered value of K_c may not be large, which also arises from the situation illustrated by Fig. 11.26.

Example 11.4

A center-cracked plate of the AISI 4340 steel ($\sigma_u = 1296$ MPa) of Table 11.2 has dimensions, as defined in Fig. 8.12(a), of $b = 38$ and $t = 6$ mm, and it contains an initial crack of length $a_i = 1$ mm. It is subjected to tension-to-tension cyclic loading between constant values of minimum and maximum force, $P_{min} = 80$ and $P_{max} = 240$ kN.

(a) At what crack length a_f is failure expected? Is the cause of failure yielding or brittle fracture?

(b) How many cycles can be applied before failure occurs?

(c) Assume that this member is an engineering component that is expected to be subjected to 150,000 cycles in its service life, and further assume that a safety factor of three on life is required. If $a_i = 1$ mm is the minimum detectable crack length a_d for inspection, are periodic inspections required? If so, at what interval?

(d) Consider the possibility of avoiding periodic inspections by improved initial inspection, such that a smaller a_i can be justified. What new $a_i = a_d$ would be required?

Solution   **(a)** The crack length at fully plastic yielding can be estimated from Fig. A.16(a):

$$a_o = b\left(1 - \frac{P_{max}}{2bt\sigma_o}\right) = (38 \text{ mm})\left(1 - \frac{240,000 \text{ N}}{2(38 \text{ mm})(6 \text{ mm})(1255 \text{ MPa})}\right) = 22.1 \text{ mm}$$

The yield strength (and also K_{Ic}) is obtained from Table 11.2.
The crack length a_c at brittle fracture is given by Eq. 11.33:

$$a_c = \frac{1}{\pi}\left(\frac{K_{Ic}}{F S_{max}}\right)^2$$

With reference to Fig. 8.12(a), an initial estimate of a_c may be made by assuming that $a_c/b \leq 0.4$, so that $F \approx 1$. We obtain

$$S_{max} = \frac{P_{max}}{2bt} = \frac{240,000 \text{ N}}{2(38 \text{ mm})(6 \text{ mm})} = 526 \text{ MPa}$$

$$a_c \approx \frac{1}{\pi}\left(\frac{K_{Ic}}{F S_{max}}\right)^2 = \frac{1}{\pi}\left(\frac{130 \text{ MPa}\sqrt{\text{m}}}{1(526 \text{ MPa})}\right)^2 = 0.0194 \text{ m} = 19.4 \text{ mm}$$

Table E11.4

Calc. No.	Trial a mm	$\alpha = a/b$	F	$K_{max} = FS_{max}\sqrt{\pi a}$ MPa$\sqrt{m}$
1	15	0.395	1.097	125.3
2	16	0.421	1.114	131.3
3	15.77	0.416	1.110	130.0

This corresponds to $a_c/b = 0.51$, which is beyond the region of 10% accuracy for $F \approx 1$. A trial and error solution, as in Ex. 8.1(c), is thus needed, with F taken from Fig. 8.12(a). This is shown in Table E11.4. The final K value is $K_{Ic} = 130$ MPa$\sqrt{m}$ so that $a_c = 15.8$ mm. Since this is smaller than a_o, brittle fracture determines the controlling value a_f, and

$$a_f = 15.8 \text{ mm} \qquad\qquad \textbf{Ans.}$$

(b) If F is approximately constant, Eq. 11.32 can be employed to calculate N_{if} by substituting either the initial F or an intermediate value that is biased toward the initial one:

$$N_{if} = \frac{a_f^{1-m/2} - a_i^{1-m/2}}{C\left(F\,\Delta S\sqrt{\pi}\right)^m (1 - m/2)}$$

In this case, the value increases from $F_i = 1.00$ to $F_f = 1.11$. So the variation is small enough that constant F is a reasonable assumption, and we can use $F = 1.00$ for the N_{if} calculation. If we note that Table 11.2 gives constants for the Walker equation, we see that the nonzero R-ratio for the applied load can be handled by calculating a C value from Eq. 11.20 as follows:

$$R = \frac{S_{min}}{S_{max}} = \frac{P_{min}}{P_{max}} = \frac{80}{240} = 0.333$$

$$C = \frac{C_0}{(1-R)^{m(1-\gamma)}} = \frac{5.11 \times 10^{-10}}{(1-0.333)^{3.24(1-0.42)}} = 1.095 \times 10^{-9} \frac{\text{mm/cycle}}{(\text{MPa}\sqrt{m})^m}$$

However, substitution into the equation for N_{if} is most convenient if all quantities have units consistent with MPa$\sqrt{m}$ as used for ΔK, requiring a units conversion for C as follows:

$$C = 1.095 \times 10^{-9} \frac{\text{mm/cycle}}{(\text{MPa}\sqrt{m})^m} \times \frac{1 \text{ m}}{1000 \text{ mm}} = 1.095 \times 10^{-12} \frac{\text{m/cycle}}{(\text{MPa}\sqrt{m})^m}$$

Two additional calculations are useful before computing N_{if}:

$$\Delta S = S_{max}(1 - R) = 526(0.667) = 351 \text{ MPa}$$

$$\left(1 - \frac{m}{2}\right) = \left(1 - \frac{3.24}{2}\right) = -0.62$$

Substituting the various numerical values finally gives N_{if}:

$$N_{if} = \frac{(0.0158\ \text{m})^{-0.62} - (0.001\ \text{m})^{-0.62}}{\left(1.095 \times 10^{-12} \dfrac{\text{m/cycle}}{(\text{MPa}\sqrt{\text{m}})^m}\right)(1.00 \times 351\ \text{MPa} \times \sqrt{\pi})^{3.24}(-0.62)}$$

$$N_{if} = 77{,}600\ \text{cycles} \qquad\qquad \textbf{Ans.}$$

In the preceding substitutions, note that all units are meters, MPa, or combinations of these. Careful checking indicates that these all cancel, leaving only "cycles."

(c) With no periodic inspections, the safety factor on life from Eq. 11.2 is

$$X_N = \frac{N_{if}}{\hat{N}} = \frac{77{,}600}{150{,}000} = 0.52$$

Hence, failure is expected before the end of the service life, so inspections are clearly needed. For the required $X_N = 3$, the inspection interval can be obtained from Eq. 11.5:

$$N_p = \frac{N_{if}}{X_N} = \frac{77{,}600}{3} = 25{,}900\ \text{cycles} \qquad\qquad \textbf{Ans.}$$

(d) To avoid periodic inspections and satisfy $X_N = 3$, we need a new, smaller $a_i = a_d$ such that N_{if} is

$$N_{if} = X_N \hat{N} = 3(150{,}000) = 450{,}000\ \text{cycles}$$

Equation 11.32 is needed again, but now with N_{if} known and a_i unknown. Noting that the same values of $a_f, C, m, F,$ and ΔS apply as in (b), and handling units as before, we have the following substitutions:

$$450{,}000 = \frac{(0.0158)^{-0.62} - a_i^{-0.62}}{(1.095 \times 10^{-12})(1.00 \times 351\sqrt{\pi})^{3.24}(-0.62)}$$

Solving for a_i gives

$$a_i = a_d = 7.63 \times 10^{-5}\ \text{m} = 0.0763\ \text{mm} \qquad\qquad \textbf{Ans.}$$

According to the earlier discussion in Section 11.2.1, this very small a_d is probably below the limits of any reasonable inspection. Hence, periodic inspection would be difficult to avoid in this case unless it is possible to lower the applied load through redesign or restrictions on the use of the component.

Comment   It would also be reasonable and more conservative to choose a slightly higher value of F for the N_{if} calculations. For example, choosing $F = 1.03$ gives $N_{if} = 70{,}500$ cycles for (b) and $a_i = 0.0657$ mm for (d).

11.6.3 Solutions by Numerical Integration

As already discussed, Eq. 11.32 and related equations that might be derived for calculating crack growth life assume that F is constant, so these cannot be used if F changes excessively between the initial and final crack lengths, a_i and a_f. Since closed-form integration of Eq. 11.27 is seldom possible if F is treated as a variable, numerical integration becomes necessary. Also, some elaborate mathematical forms used to fit da/dN versus ΔK curves lead to equations that cannot be integrated in closed form even for constant F, again necessitating numerical integration.

To perform a numerical integration, it is useful to employ Eq. 11.27 in the form of Eq. 11.29. First, pick a number of crack lengths between a_i and a_f:

$$a_i, a_1, a_2, a_3, \ldots a_f$$

For each of these, and for the material, geometry, and loading of interest, calculate ΔK, and then da/dN, inverting the latter to get dN/da. Finally, find N_{if} as the area under the dN/da versus a curve between a_i and a_f. This can be done for any mathematical form of the ΔK and da/dN equations. For example, for the forms of Eq. 11.30 with F allowed to vary, the dN/da for any given crack length a_j is

$$\left(\frac{dN}{da}\right)_j = \frac{1}{C\left(\Delta K_j\right)^m} = \frac{1}{C\left(F_j\,\Delta S\sqrt{\pi a_j}\right)^m} \tag{11.34}$$

where F_j needs to be specifically calculated for each a_j.

The intervals Δa between the a_j can be made equal, but this is not necessary. It is important that Δa be sufficiently small for accurate representation of the dN/da curve. This is most likely to be a problem for the shorter crack lengths where the curve is generally steepest. One alternative that gives small Δa only where needed is to increase a by a fixed percentage for each interval. A 10% (factor of 1.10) increase for each interval is sufficiently small for typical values of m:

$$a_{j+1} = r a_j, \qquad r \approx 1.10 \tag{11.35}$$

A manual solution for N_{if} may be done on graph paper. It is also straightforward to program an approximate area calculation on a digital computer. Standard methods and computer programs for numerical integration also apply.

A relatively simple method of numerical integration usually described in books on numerical analysis is Simpson's rule. To use this, consider three neighboring crack lengths a_j, a_{j+1}, and a_{j+2}, as shown in Fig. 11.27. Between a_j and a_{j+2}, an estimate of the area under the curve $y = dN/da$ can be made by assuming that a parabola passes through the three points (a_j, y_j), (a_{j+1}, y_{j+1}), and (a_{j+2}, y_{j+2}). If the points are equally spaced Δa apart, the area estimate is

$$\int_{a_j}^{a_{j+2}} y\, da = \frac{\Delta a}{3}\left(y_j + 4y_{j+1} + y_{j+2}\right) \tag{11.36}$$

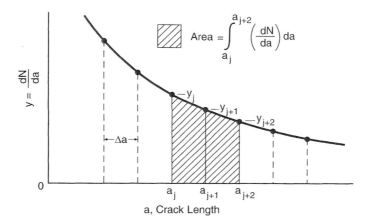

Figure 11.27   Area under the *dN/da* versus *a* curve over two intervals Δa as estimated by Simpson's rule.

This equation is applied for each of $j = 0, 2, 4, 6 \ldots (n-2)$, where n is even. Adding the contributions to the area from each calculation gives an approximate value of the total area under the curve between a_i and a_f, where $a_f = a_n$.

For crack growth analysis, the number of intervals can be kept reasonably small if the a values are not evenly spaced, but instead differ by a constant factor r, as in Eq. 11.35. Then

$$a_i, \qquad a_1 = ra_i, \qquad a_2 = r^2 a_i, \qquad \ldots a_n = r^n a_i = a_f \qquad (11.37)$$

The area for a parabola through three such points is given by

$$\int_{a_j}^{a_{j+2}} y \, da = \frac{a_j \left(r^2 - 1\right)}{6r} \left[y_j r(2 - r) + y_{j+1}(r + 1)^2 + y_{j+2}(2r - 1) \right] \qquad (11.38)$$

The integration up to a_n can be performed in a manner analogous to a Simpson's rule calculation, except for the use of the new area formula.

Example 11.5 _____

Refine the approximate life estimate of Ex. 11.4(b) by using numerical integration.

Solution   The modified Simpson's rule of Eq. 11.38 can be used. A factor for incrementing a is first chosen to be near $r = 1.1$, such that the integration will end at $a_f = 15.8$ mm, which is the a_f as determined in Ex. 11.4. From Eq. 11.37, we have $a_f = r^n a_i$, where $a_i = 1.0$ mm as given. Substituting a_f and a_i with $r = 1.10$ and solving gives $n = 28.96$. Thus, we need an even integer for n near this value. Choosing $n = 30$ and solving for r gives

$$r^n = \frac{a_f}{a_i}, \qquad r^{30} = \frac{15.8 \text{ mm}}{1.0 \text{ mm}}, \qquad r = 1.09637$$

The crack lengths for the $n = 30$ intervals can now be calculated by using this r with Eq. 11.35, starting with the first value as $a_0 = a_i = 0.001$ m. Some of the values are shown in Table E11.5 in units of meters.

Then, using F and S as appropriate for the center-cracked plate geometry from Fig. 8.12(a), we perform calculations as follows for each a_j, where $j = 0$ to 30:

$$\alpha = \frac{a}{b}, \qquad F = \frac{1 - 0.5\alpha + 0.326\alpha^2}{\sqrt{1-\alpha}}$$

$$\Delta K = F\,\Delta S\sqrt{\pi a} = F\frac{\Delta P}{2bt}\sqrt{\pi a}, \qquad y = \frac{dN}{da} = \frac{1}{C(\Delta K)^m}$$

Values from Ex. 11.4 are needed as follows: $b = 0.038$ m, $t = 0.006$ m, $\Delta P = 0.160$ MN, $m = 3.24$, and $C = 1.095 \times 10^{-12}$, where this C includes the effect of $R = 0.333$. Note that units of meters, MPa $=$ MN/m^2, and cycles, or combinations of these, are used for all quantities, including C. Some calculation results are shown in Table E11.5.

Next, numerical integration can proceed by applying Eq. 11.38 to each pair of intervals to obtain the number of cycles ΔN to grow the crack from a_j to a_{j+2}:

$$\Delta N_{j+2} = \int_{a_j}^{a_{j+2}} y\,da$$

Specifically, Eq. 11.38 is first applied for the two intervals from $j = 0$ to $j + 2 = 2$, then from $j = 2$ to $j + 2 = 4$, next from $j = 4$ to $j + 2 = 6$, etc., up to $j = 28$ to $j + 2 = 30$. The first

Table E11.5

j	a m	$\alpha = a/b$	$F = F(a/b)$	ΔK MPa$\sqrt{\text{m}}$	$y = dN/da$ cycles/m	ΔN cycles	$\Sigma(\Delta N)$ cycles
0	1.000×10^{-3}	0.0263	1.0003	19.67	5.869×10^7	0	0
1	1.096×10^{-3}	0.0289	1.0004	20.60	5.055×10^7	—	—
2	1.202×10^{-3}	0.0316	1.0005	21.57	4.354×10^7	10 203	10 203
3	1.318×10^{-3}	0.0347	1.0006	22.59	3.750×10^7	—	—
4	1.445×10^{-3}	0.0380	1.0007	23.66	3.229×10^7	9 098	19 300
5	1.584×10^{-3}	0.0417	1.0008	24.77	2.781×10^7	—	—
6	1.737×10^{-3}	0.0457	1.0010	25.94	2.395×10^7	8 110	27 410
⋮	⋮	⋮	⋮	⋮	⋮	⋮	⋮
26	1.094×10^{-2}	0.2878	1.0464	68.05	1.052×10^6	2 304	72 020
27	1.199×10^{-2}	0.3155	1.0572	71.99	8.770×10^5	—	—
28	1.314×10^{-2}	0.3459	1.0708	76.35	7.249×10^5	1 935	73 955
29	1.441×10^{-2}	0.3792	1.0881	81.23	5.931×10^5	—	—
30	1.580×10^{-2}	0.4158	1.1101	86.78	4.789×10^5	1 573	**75 528**

three calculations give

$$\Delta N_2 = \int_{a_0=a_i}^{a_2} y \, da = 10{,}203, \qquad \Delta N_4 = \int_{a_2}^{a_4} y \, da = 9098$$

$$\Delta N_6 = \int_{a_4}^{a_6} y \, da = 8110 \text{ cycles}$$

The cumulative sum of the ΔN values is also calculated as shown in the last column of the table. For example, the number of cycles to reach crack length a_6 is

$$\Sigma(\Delta N)_6 = 10{,}203 + 9098 + 8110 = 27{,}410 \text{ cycles}$$

The final such cumulative sum at $a_{30} = a_f$ is the calculated life for crack growth:

$$\Sigma(\Delta N)_{30} = N_{if} = 75{,}500 \text{ cycles} \qquad\qquad \textbf{Ans.}$$

Discussion   The life from this numerical integration is seen to be similar to the approximate result from Ex. 11.4 of $N_{if} = 77{,}600$ cycles, which is affected by the choice of $F = 1.00$. If Ex. 11.4 is redone with constant $F = 1.0085$, the same life is obtained as for Ex. 11.5.

11.7 LIFE ESTIMATES FOR VARIABLE AMPLITUDE LOADING

If the stress levels vary during crack growth, life estimates may still be made. One simple approach is to assume that growth for a given cycle is not affected by the prior history—that is, *sequence effects* are absent. Large sequence effects do occur in special situations, but it is often useful and sufficiently accurate to neglect these.

11.7.1 Summation of Crack Increments

The crack growth Δa in each individual cycle of variable amplitude loading can be estimated from the da/dN versus ΔK curve of the material. Summing these Δa, while keeping track of the number of cycles applied, leads to a life estimate. Such a procedure is equivalent to a numerical integration where a, rather than N, is the dependent variable.

Hence, if the current crack length is a_j and the increment is Δa_j, the new value of crack length a_{j+1} for the next cycle is

$$a_{j+1} = a_j + \Delta a_j = a_j + \left(\frac{da}{dN}\right)_j \tag{11.39}$$

where the Δa are numerically equal to da/dN, since $\Delta N = 1$ for one cycle. Denoting the initial crack length as a_i, we find that the crack length after N cycles is

$$a_N = a_i + \sum_{j=1}^{N} \left(\frac{da}{dN} \right)_j \tag{11.40}$$

Each da/dN is calculated from the ΔK and R for that particular cycle, where ΔK is obtained from the current crack length a_j and the ΔS for the particular cycle. Any form of expression for varying $F = F(a/b)$ and any form of a da/dN versus ΔK relationship can be readily used with this procedure. For highly irregular loading, rainflow cycle counting as described in Chapter 9 can be used to identify the cycles.

The summation is continued until a load peak is encountered that is sufficiently severe to cause either fully plastic yielding or brittle fracture. At this point, the calculation is terminated, and the number of cycles accumulated is the estimated crack growth life.

Note that the procedure just described can also be applied for constant amplitude loading as an alternative to the numerical integration approach of Section 11.6.3. In this case, the procedure can be modified to accommodate values of ΔN other than unity, so that cycles are taken in groups, such as $\Delta N = 100$. It is necessary only that ΔN be sufficiently small that da/dN does not change by more than a small amount, so that its value at the beginning of the interval is representative of the entire interval.

For a crack with a curved front, such as a portion of a circle or ellipse, as in Figs. 8.17 to 8.19, the stress intensity K varies around the periphery of the crack. This causes the growth rate to also vary around the periphery, so that the crack changes shape as it grows. This complexity can be handled by updating the crack shape and appropriately adjusting the geometry function F, as crack increments are summed. The needed details for F can be found in various References to Chapter 8, especially Newman (1986). Such a capability is included in the computer programs NASGRO and AFGROW; see LexTech (2010) and SWRI (2010).

11.7.2 Special Method for Repeating or Stationary Histories

In some cases, it may be reasonable to approximate the actual service load history by assuming that it is equivalent to repeated applications of a loading sequence of finite length. This can be useful where some repeated operation occurs, such as lift cycles for a crane, or flights of an aircraft, and also for random loading with characteristics that are constant with time, called *stationary* loading. The crack growth life can then be estimated by an alternative procedure that is equivalent to summing crack increments. The necessary mathematical derivation follows.

First, assume that the da/dN versus ΔK behavior obeys a power relationship of the form of Eq. 11.10. The increment in crack length for any cycle ($\Delta N = 1$) is then

$$\Delta a_j = C_0 \left(\overline{\Delta K}_j \right)^m \tag{11.41}$$

where different R-ratios are handled by calculating an equivalent zero-to-tension ($R = 0$) value $\overline{\Delta K}$, as in the Walker approach using Eq. 11.15. Note that the coefficient C_0 corresponding to $R = 0$ applies due to the use of $\overline{\Delta K}$. If the repeating load history contains N_B cycles, the increase in crack length during one repetition is obtained by summing:

$$\Delta a_B = \sum_{j=1}^{N_B} \Delta a_j = \sum_{j=1}^{N_B} C_0 \left(\overline{\Delta K}_j \right)^m \tag{11.42}$$

The average growth rate per cycle during one repetition of the history is thus

$$\left(\frac{da}{dN} \right)_{\text{avg.}} = \frac{\Delta a_B}{N_B} = \frac{C_0 \sum_{j=1}^{N_B} \left(\overline{\Delta K}_j \right)^m}{N_B} \tag{11.43}$$

Note that C_0 is constant and so can be factored from the summation. Manipulation gives

$$\left(\frac{da}{dN} \right)_{\text{avg.}} = C_0 \left(\left[\frac{\sum_{j=1}^{N_B} \left(\overline{\Delta K}_j \right)^m}{N_B} \right]^{1/m} \right)^m = C_0 \left(\Delta K_q \right)^m \tag{11.44}$$

where

$$\Delta K_q = \left[\frac{\sum_{j=1}^{N_B} \left(\overline{\Delta K}_j \right)^m}{N_B} \right]^{1/m} \tag{11.45}$$

The quantity ΔK_q can be interpreted as an equivalent zero-to-tension stress intensity range that is expected to cause the same crack growth as the variable amplitude history when applied for the same number of cycles N_B.

Since K and nominal stress S are proportional for any given crack length, an equivalent zero-to-tension stress level can also be defined:

$$\Delta S_q = \frac{\Delta K_q}{F \sqrt{\pi a}} = \left[\frac{\sum_{j=1}^{N_B} \left(\overline{\Delta S}_j \right)^m}{N_B} \right]^{1/m} \tag{11.46}$$

In this equation, the $\overline{\Delta S}$ for each cycle in the history is the equivalent zero-to-tension value corrected for R effect. If this is done on the basis of the Walker approach using Eq. 11.15, these values are obtained from

$$\overline{\Delta S} = S_{\max} (1 - R)^\gamma \tag{11.47}$$

where γ is the value for crack growth, as from Table 11.2.

Since ΔS_q is independent of crack length, it can be applied throughout the life as the crack grows. Hence, we can make a life estimate by using ΔS_q just as if it were a constant amplitude loading at $R = 0$, for example, by using Eq. 11.32. However, to determine the final crack length a_f as caused by either fully plastic yielding or brittle fracture, the actual peak stress $S_{\max}$ in one repetition of the history should be employed.

Such use of ΔS_q assumes that the load history of length N_B is repeated numerous times during the crack growth life. If the repeating history is so long that only a few repetitions occur, then special, detailed handling of the last repetition is needed to identify the load peak that causes failure and so determines a_f.

Note that Eq. 11.46 is very similar to Eq. 9.37, which is employed for calculating equivalent stress amplitudes for use with stress–life curves. If the latter is expressed in terms of stress range and equivalent zero-to-maximum stresses, the two become identical with the substitution $m = -1/b$.

Example 11.6

A center-cracked plate of the AISI 4340 steel of Table 11.2 has dimensions, as defined in Fig. 8.12(a), of $b = 38$ and $t = 6$ mm, and the initial crack length is $a_i = 1$ mm. It is repeatedly subjected to the axial force history of Fig. E11.6. How many repetitions of this history can be applied before fatigue failure is expected? (This is the same situation as Ex. 11.4, except for the load history.)

Solution   We will first calculate an equivalent zero-to-tension stress level for the load history from Eq. 11.46. This ΔS_q may then be employed in Eq. 11.32 to calculate the life N_{if} as if it were a simple zero-to-tension ($R = 0$) loading. However, a_f needs to correspond not to ΔS_q, but to the most severe force in the history, $P_{max} = 240$ kN. Since this P_{max} is the same as in Ex. 11.4, we need not repeat the calculation, but may employ the a_f value and corresponding approximate F from Ex. 11.4, which are

$$a_f = 15.8 \text{ mm}, \qquad F = 1.00$$

In addition, materials properties from Table 11.2 are needed:

$$C_0 = 5.11 \times 10^{-13} \frac{\text{m/cycle}}{(\text{MPa}\sqrt{\text{m}})^m}, \qquad m = 3.24, \qquad \gamma = 0.42$$

From rainflow counting of the given force history, we obtain the results presented in the first four columns of Table E11.6. The single cycle for $j = 4$ arises from rainflow cycle counting as the major cycle between the highest peak and lowest valley. (See Section 9.9.2).

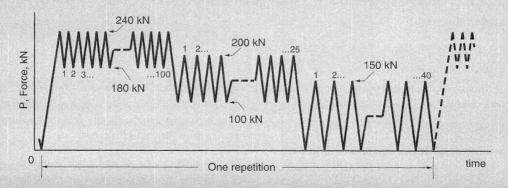

Figure E11.6

Table E11.6

j	N_j cycles	P_{max} kN	P_{min} kN	R	S_{max} MPa	$\overline{\Delta S}_j$ MPa	$N_j(\overline{\Delta S}_j)^m$
1	100	240	180	0.75	526.3	294.0	9.94×10^9
2	25	200	100	0.5	438.6	327.8	3.54×10^9
3	40	150	0	0	328.9	328.9	5.72×10^9
4	1	240	0	0	526.3	526.3	6.56×10^8
Σ	166						1.986×10^{10}

The following calculations are then needed for each load level j:

$$R = \frac{P_{min}}{P_{max}}, \qquad S_{max} = \frac{P_{max}}{2bt}, \qquad \overline{\Delta S} = S_{max}(1 - R)^\gamma$$

Here, S is defined as in Fig. 8.12(a).

Since multiple cycles occur at each of $k = 4$ load levels, the summation for Eq. 11.46 may be done in the form

$$\sum_{j=1}^{N_B} (\overline{\Delta S}_j)^m = \sum_{j=1}^{k} N_j(\overline{\Delta S}_j)^m$$

Details are given in Table E11.6, where the sum is shown at the bottom. Noting that $N_B = \Sigma N_j = 166$ cycles, we may now calculate ΔS_q:

$$\Delta S_q = \left[\frac{\sum_{j=1}^{k} N_j(\overline{\Delta S}_j)^m}{N_B} \right]^{1/m} = \left[\frac{1.986 \times 10^{10}}{166} \right]^{1/3.24} = 311.3 \, \text{MPa}$$

This value is then employed in Eq. 11.32 to obtain the number of cycles for crack growth:

$$N_{if} = \frac{a_f^{1-m/2} - a_i^{1-m/2}}{C_0(F \, \Delta S_q \sqrt{\pi})^m (1 - m/2)} = \frac{0.0158^{-0.62} - 0.001^{-0.62}}{5.11 \times 10^{-13}(1.00 \times 311.3\sqrt{\pi})^{3.24}(-0.62)}$$

$$N_{if} = 2.45 \times 10^5 \, \text{cycles}$$

Here, all quantities substituted correspond to units of meters and MPa, as in Ex. 11.4. Also, C_0 is the value for $R = 0$, as R-ratio effects are already included in the $\overline{\Delta S}$ values. Finally, the number of repetitions to failure is

$$B_{if} = \frac{N_{if}}{N_B} = \frac{2.45 \times 10^5}{166} = 1477 \, \text{repetitions} \qquad\qquad \textbf{Ans.}$$

11.7.3 Sequence Effects

In all of the treatment so far of variable amplitude loading, it has been assumed that the crack growth in a given cycle is unaffected by prior events in the load history. However, this assumption may sometimes lead to significant error. Consider the situation of Fig. 11.28. After a high tensile overload is applied, as in case C, the growth rate during the lower level cycles is decreased. Slower than normal growth continues for a large number of cycles until the crack grows beyond the region affected by the overload, where the size of the affected region is related to the size of the crack-tip plastic zone caused by the overload. For the case illustrated, the overall effect of only three overloads was to increase the life by about a factor of 10. This beneficial effect of tensile overloads is called *crack growth retardation*.

A tensile overload introduces a compressive residual stress around the crack tip in a manner similar to the notched member of Fig. 10.28. This compression tends to keep the crack tip closed during the subsequent lower level cycles, retarding crack growth. The magnitude of the effect is related to the ratio $S_{max\,2}/S_{max\,1}$, where $S_{max\,2}$ is the overload stress and $S_{max\,1}$ is the peak value of the lower level. For ratios greater than about 2.0, crack growth may be *arrested*—that is, stopped entirely. Conversely, if the ratio is less than about 1.4, the effect is small. Compressive overloads have an opposite, but lesser, effect. The effect is not as great because the crack tends to close during the overload, so the faces of the crack support much of the compressive load and shield the crack tip from its effect. Also, the effect of a tensile overload is much reduced if it is followed by a compressive one, as in case B of Fig. 11.28.

Several methods have been developed to incorporate sequence effects due to overloads into life calculations for crack growth. The general approach used is to base the life estimate on calculating crack growth increments for each cycle as previously described in connection with Eqs. 11.39 and 11.40. However, the da/dN values used are modified in a manner that is determined by the prior history of overloads. This is generally done by determining da/dN from an effective

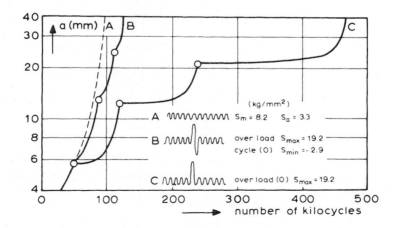

Figure 11.28 Effect of overloads on crack growth in center-cracked plates ($b = 80$, $t = 2$ mm) of 2024-T3 aluminum. (From [Broek 86] p. 273, based on data in [Schijve 62]; reprinted by permission of Kluwer Academic Publishers.)

ΔK that is modified on the basis of logic related to residual stress fields or crack closure levels. More detailed explanation can be found in Broek (1986) and (1988), Grandt (2004), and Suresh (1998).

Overload sequence effects are likely to be important where high overloads occur predominantly in one direction. This occurs in the service of some aircraft, where occasional severe wind gust loadings or maneuver loadings may introduce sequence effects. However, less effect is expected if overloads occur in both directions, if the history is highly irregular, or if the overloads are relatively mild. Noting that the effect is mainly to retard crack growth, we see that neglecting this sequence effect usually provides conservative estimates of crack growth life that will be sufficient for engineering purposes in many cases. Load histories that include severe compressive overloads then need to be handled with caution, due to the possibility of these causing faster crack growth than predicted.

11.8 DESIGN CONSIDERATIONS

It is becoming increasingly common to ensure adequate service life for components of machines, vehicles, and structures on the basis of crack growth calculations, as described in this chapter. This is appropriate for large structures subjected to cyclic loading, especially where personal safety or high costs are factors, and especially if cracks are commonly found in the type of hardware involved. Examples include bridge structure, large aircraft, space vehicles, and nuclear and other pressure vessels. Such a *damage-tolerant* approach is critically dependent on initial and sometimes periodic inspections for cracks.

Inspection for cracks, especially small ones, is an expensive process and is not generally feasible for inexpensive components that are made in large numbers. If the service stresses are relatively high, the cracks that would need to be found to use a damage-tolerant approach can be so small that the inspection would greatly increase the cost of the item. Periodic inspections would allow a larger crack to be tolerated initially, but the component may not be available for periodic inspection. Examples of parts that fall into this category are automobile engine, steering, and suspension parts, bicycle front forks and pedal cranks, and parts for home appliances. Here, fatigue life estimates are usually made on the basis of an *S-N* approach, or the related strain-based approach, neither of which specifically considers cracks. Where personal safety is involved, safety factors reflect this fact and are typically larger than if a damage-tolerant approach could be used. Failures are minimized by careful attention to design detail and to manufacturing quality control, including initial inspection to eliminate any obviously flawed parts.

Regardless of the approach used, a finite probability of failure always exists. For the damage-tolerant approach, this arises because the minimum detectable crack length a_d is difficult to establish and is never precisely known. For the *S-N* and related approaches, a finite probability of failure arises due to the possibility that a part passing inspection still contains a flaw that, though small, nevertheless leads to early failure. Also, all approaches to ensuring adequate life are subject to additional uncertainties, such as: (1) estimates of the service loading being too low, (2) accidental substitution during manufacturing of the wrong material, (3) undetected manufacturing quality control problems, and (4) hostile environmental effects that are more severe than forecast, with the latter including both ordinary corrosion and environmental crack growth.

Where a damage-tolerant approach is used, critical components must be designed so that they are accessible for inspection. For example, cracks at fastener (rivet or bolt) holes are of concern in aircraft structure, and access to the interior of the skin of the fuselage or wing structure may be needed for situations such as that illustrated in Fig. 11.29. If periodic inspections are required, then the design must accommodate disassembly when this is necessary for inspection. For example, in large aircraft, the passenger seats, interior panels, and even paint are removed, and some structural parts are disassembled, for costly, but necessary, periodic inspections.

Specific measures can also be taken by the designer to allow structures to function without sudden failure even if a large crack does develop. Some examples for aircraft structure are illustrated in Figs. 11.30 and 11.31. Stiffeners retard crack growth, and joints in skin panels may be

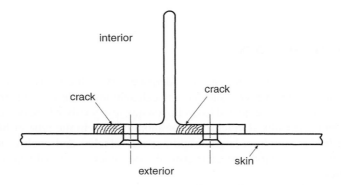

Figure 11.29 Cracks in the interior of an aircraft skin structure. (Adapted from [Chang 78].)

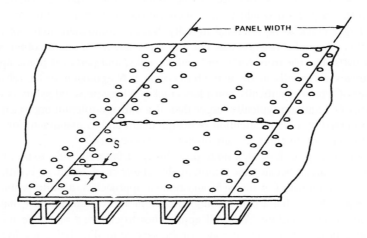

Figure 11.30 Stiffened panel in aircraft structure with a crack delayed before growing into adjacent panels. The rivet spacing dimensioned is 38 mm. (From the paper by J. P. Butler in [Wood 70] p. 41.)

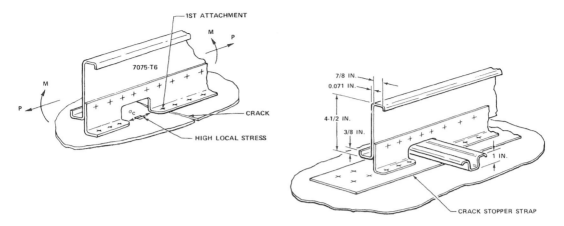

Figure 11.31   Crack (left) in a DC-10 fuselage in the longitudinal direction, due to cabin pressure loading, and (right) a crack stopper strap. Rivet locations are indicated by (+), and the longeron member with a hat-shaped cross section is omitted on the left for clarity. (From [Swift 71]; copyright © ASTM; reprinted with permission.)

intentionally introduced so that a crack in one panel has difficulty growing into the next. Similarly, a crack stopper strap may lower stresses in a critical area and provide some strength even if a crack does start.

Recall from the early part of this chapter and Eq. 11.2 that the safety factor on life X_N is the ratio of the failure life for crack growth N_{if} to the expected service life $\hat{N}$. The value of N_{if} depends not only on the detectable crack length a_d, but also on the stress level and the material. If the safety factor is insufficient, perhaps even less than unity, several different options exist to resolve the situation. Obviously, the design could be changed to lower the stress, thus increasing the calculated life N_{if} and X_N. Another possibility is to make a more careful initial inspection for cracks, decreasing a_d, and thus increasing the worst-case failure life N_{if}. Alternatively, the material could be changed to one with slower fatigue crack growth rates, as judged by comparing da/dN versus ΔK curves. Depending on whether failure occurs by brittle fracture or by yielding, increasing either the fracture toughness or the yield strength of the material also increases the life by increasing the final crack length a_f, but the effect is usually small, as the life is generally insensitive to the value of a_f.

If design changes or improved initial inspection do not suffice, it may be necessary to perform periodic inspections, making it permissible to calculate the safety factor from the inspection period N_p with the use of Eq. 11.5.

11.9 PLASTICITY ASPECTS AND LIMITATIONS OF LEFM FOR FATIGUE CRACK GROWTH

During cyclic loading, a region of reversed yielding exists at the crack tip, and the size of this region can be estimated by a procedure similar to that applied to static loading in Section 8.7. On this

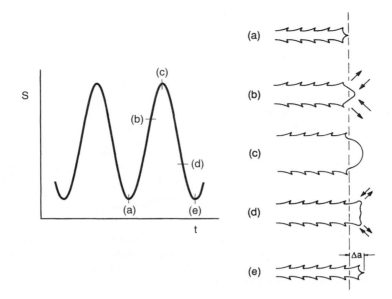

Figure 11.32 Hypothesized plastic deformation behavior at the tip of a growing fatigue crack during a loading cycle. Slip of crystal planes along directions of maximum shear occurs as indicated by arrows, and this plastic blunting process results in one striation (Δa) being formed for each cycle. (Adapted from the paper by J. C. Grosskreutz in [Wood 70] p. 55.)

basis, plasticity limitations on LEFM for fatigue crack growth can be explored. Limitations are also needed if the crack is so small that its size is comparable to that of the microstructural features of the material.

11.9.1 Plasticity at Crack Tips

In the immediate vicinity of the crack tip, there is a finite separation δ between the crack faces, as discussed in Chapter 8. Behavior on the size scale of δ determines how the crack advances through the material during cyclic loading. Details are not fully understood, they vary with material, and they even vary with the K level for a given material. In ductile metals, the process of crack advance during a cycle is thought to be similar to Fig. 11.32. Localized deformation by slip of crystal planes occurs and is most intense in bands above and below the crack plane. The crack tip moves ahead and becomes blunt as the maximum load is reached, and it is resharpened during decreasing load. This process results in striations on the fracture surface, as previously illustrated by Fig. 9.22.

Another mechanism is crack growth by small increments of brittle cleavage during each cycle. It is not uncommon in metals for the fracture surface to have regions of striation growth mixed with regions of cleavage, especially at high growth rates where K_{max} approaches K_c. In other cases, the boundaries between grains are the weakest regions in the material, so that the crack grows along grain boundaries. This is called *intergranular fracture*, to distinguish it from the more

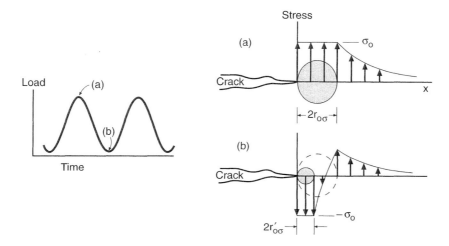

Figure 11.33   Monotonic (a) and cyclic (b) plastic zones. (Adapted from [Paris 64]; used with permission.)

usual *transgranular fracture* by striation formation or cleavage. For example, intergranular fatigue cracking occurred for the granite rock of Fig. 11.11. In metals, intergranular cracking is likely to occur if there is a hostile environmental influence.

If the material is relatively ductile, a crack-tip plastic zone will exist that is considerably larger than δ. The peak stress in the cyclic loading determines K_{max}, which can be substituted into Eq. 8.37 or 8.38 to estimate the extent of yielding ahead of the crack. For example, for plane stress,

$$2r_{o\sigma} = \frac{1}{\pi}\left(\frac{K_{max}}{\sigma_o}\right)^2 \tag{11.48}$$

This is called the *monotonic plastic zone*. As the minimum load in a cycle is approached, yielding in compression occurs in a region of smaller size, called the *cyclic plastic zone*, as illustrated in Fig. 11.33.

For an ideal elastic, perfectly plastic material, consider the behavior during unloading following $K = K_{max}$. For compressive yielding to occur as K changes by an amount ΔK, the stress of σ_o near the crack tip must change to $-\sigma_o$, which is a change of $2\sigma_o$, or twice the yield strength. In effect, for changes relative to K_{max}, the yield strength is doubled. The size of the cyclic plastic zone where yielding occurs not only in tension, but also in compression, can therefore be approximated by using ΔK for K and $2\sigma_o$ for σ_o in the monotonic plastic zone estimate:

$$2r'_{o\sigma} = \frac{1}{\pi}\left(\frac{\Delta K}{2\sigma_o}\right)^2 \tag{11.49}$$

For zero-to-tension ($R = 0$) loading, where $\Delta K = K_{max}$, the cyclic plastic zone is thus estimated to be one-fourth as large as the monotonic one. The cyclic plastic zone size may also be estimated for cases of plane strain. Using logic as in Section 8.7, we see that its size $r'_{o\varepsilon}$ is one-third as large as the corresponding plane stress zone.

We can further understand the monotonic and cyclic plastic zones by considering the stress–strain history at a point in the material as the crack approaches, as illustrated in Fig. 11.34. When the point being observed is still outside the monotonic plastic zone, no yielding occurs. Yielding begins, but only in the tensile direction, when the monotonic plastic zone boundary passes the point. Once the cyclic plastic zone boundary passes, yielding in both compression and tension occurs during each loading cycle.

11.9.2 Thickness Effects and Plasticity Limitations

If the monotonic plastic zone is not small compared with the thickness, then plane stress exists, and fatigue cracks may grow in a shear mode, with the fracture inclined about 45° to the surface. Since K and hence the plastic zone size increase with crack length, a transition to this behavior can occur during the growth of a crack, as illustrated in Fig. 11.35. Crack growth rates can be affected somewhat by member thickness as a result of different behavior in plane stress and plane strain. However, the effect is sufficiently small that it can generally be ignored, so crack growth data for one thickness can be used for any other thickness.

If large amounts of plasticity occur during cyclic loading, crack growth rates rapidly increase and exceed what would be expected from the da/dN versus ΔK curve. This circumstance arises from the fact that the theory supporting the use of K requires that the plasticity be limited to a

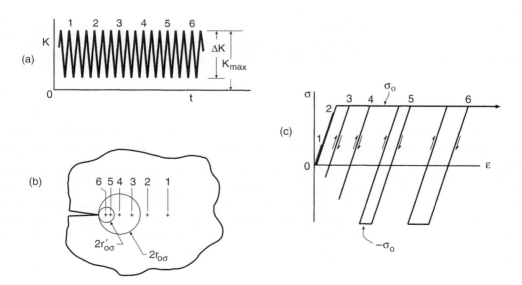

Figure 11.34 Stress–strain behavior at a point as the tip of a growing fatigue crack approaches. For selected cycles (a), relative positions of the point and the crack tip are shown in (b), and the stress–strain responses in (c). (Adapted from [Dowling 77]; copyright © ASTM; reprinted with permission.)

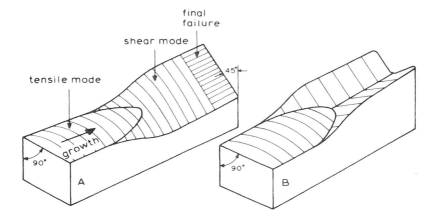

Figure 11.35   Schematic of surfaces of fatigue cracks showing transition from a flat tensile mode to an angular shear mode. The shear growth can (A) occur on a single sloping surface, or (B) form a *V*-shape. (From [Broek 86] p. 269; reprinted by permission of Kluwer Academic Publishers.)

region that is small compared with the planar dimensions of the member, as discussed previously in Section 8.7. Large effects occur only where the maximum load exceeds about 80% of fully plastic yielding, so this level represents a sufficient plasticity limitation in most cases. Modest effects may occur at somewhat lower levels. If a fairly strict limitation is desired, the limitation of Eq. 8.39 on the in-plane dimensions, as previously employed for static loading, can be applied to the peak stress:

$$a, (b-a), h \geq 8r_{o\sigma} = \frac{4}{\pi} \left(\frac{K_{\max}}{\sigma_o} \right)^2 \tag{11.50}$$

For fatigue crack growth, thickness effects and plasticity limitations are not generally issues of major importance, as they are for fracture toughness applications. This is because nominal stresses around or exceeding yielding are rare in engineering situations except near the very end of the life, when the fatigue crack growth phase is essentially complete. However, local yielding at stress raisers is fairly common, so difficulties may be encountered if it is necessary to use fracture mechanics for cracks growing from notches while they are still small, as they may be affected by local plasticity. Fortunately, a crack is under the influence of the local stress field of a notch only if its length is quite small, specifically less than about 10 to 20% of the notch radius. See Eq. 8.26 and Fig. 8.20.

11.9.3 Limitations for Small Cracks

Fracture mechanics in the form considered so far is based on stress analysis in an isotropic and homogeneous solid. The microstructural features of the material are, in effect, assumed to occur on such a small scale that only the average behavior needs to be considered. However, if a crack is sufficiently small, it can interact with the microstructure in ways that cause the behavior to differ from what would otherwise be expected. In engineering metals, small cracks tend to grow faster

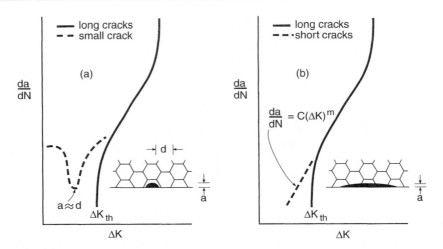

Figure 11.36 Behavior for a crack that is small in all dimensions (left) and also for a crack with one dimension that is large compared with the microstructure (right).

than estimated from the usual da/dN versus ΔK curves from test specimens with long cracks, as illustrated in Fig. 11.36.

It is useful to distinguish between *small cracks* and *short cracks*. For a small crack, all of its dimensions are similar to or smaller than the dimension of greatest microstructural significance, such as the average crystal grain size or the average reinforcement particle spacing. However, a short crack has one dimension that is large compared with the microstructure. The behavior of a small crack can be profoundly affected by the microstructure. For example, while the crack is within a single crystal grain in a metal, the growth rate is much higher than expected from the usual da/dN versus ΔK curve, as illustrated by Fig. 11.36(a). Upon encountering a grain boundary, the growth is temporarily retarded. Until the crack becomes several times larger than the grain size, the average growth rate, as affected by lattice planes within grains and grain boundaries, is considerably above the usual da/dN versus ΔK curve.

A less drastic effect occurs if the crack is merely short in one dimension and large compared with the microstructure in the other dimension, as illustrated by Fig. 11.36(b). Growth rates for such cracks in metals are similar to the da/dN versus ΔK curve, except at low ΔK, where a reasonable estimate of the behavior can be obtained by extrapolating Eq. 11.10 from the intermediate region of the curve. The cause of the special behavior in this case appears to be associated with the fact that the faces of a crack normally interfere behind the tip during part of the stress cycle. In particular, the crack opens and closes, and the portion of the stress cycle that occurs while the crack is closed does not contribute to its growth. Note that this cannot occur if there is insufficient length behind the tip for the interference to occur. Thus, for low ΔK where crack closure effects are especially important, short cracks grow faster than expected.

An approximate method for identifying crack sizes below which the usual da/dN versus ΔK curve may not apply is illustrated in Fig 11.37. Note that the unnotched-specimen fatigue limit is the stress level below which the small, naturally occurring flaws in the material will not grow, even with

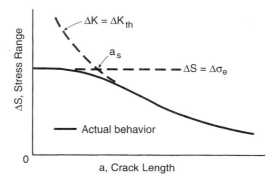

Figure 11.37 Fatigue limit stress as a function of crack length, and the transition length a_s, below which special small crack effects are expected.

their growth enhanced by the small crack effect, as just discussed. Considering members containing cracks of various sizes, we note that the fatigue limit decreases with crack length. For relatively long cracks, it follows the behavior expected from LEFM and the threshold, ΔK_{th}, from the long crack da/dN versus ΔK curve.

The crack length a_s, where the ΔK_{th} prediction exceeds the unnotched-specimen fatigue limit, is the intersection of the lines for the two equations

$$\Delta S = \Delta\sigma_e, \qquad \Delta K_{th} = \Delta S\sqrt{\pi a} \qquad (11.51)$$

where the completely reversed ($R = -1$) fatigue limit is given as a stress range $\Delta\sigma_e = 2\sigma_{er}$, where ΔK_{th} is the value for $R = -1$, and where the geometry factor is approximated as $F = 1$. Combining these and solving for a gives

$$a_s = \frac{1}{\pi}\left(\frac{\Delta K_{th}}{\Delta\sigma_e}\right)^2 \qquad (11.52)$$

For cracks larger than a_s in all dimensions, fracture mechanics based on long-crack data is expected to be reasonably accurate. For example, approximate values of $\Delta\sigma_e$ and ΔK_{th} for two steels with contrasting ultimate tensile strengths σ_u give a_s values as follows:

σ_u, MPa	$\Delta\sigma_e = 2\sigma_{er}$, MPa	ΔK_{th}, MPa$\sqrt{\text{m}}$	a_s, mm
500	500	12	0.18
1500	1400	9	0.013

For the lower strength steel, a_s is relatively large and could be within a range of crack sizes that is of engineering interest. The opposite is true for the higher strength steel, where a_s is so small that unusual short crack behavior would probably never affect the use of fracture mechanics for engineering applications.

Discussions of small crack effects, with references to additional literature, are given in Suresh (1998) and in Milne (2003, vol. 4).

11.10 ENVIRONMENTAL CRACK GROWTH

Similar considerations of inspection for cracks, and a similar need for life estimates, exist where crack growth is caused by a hostile chemical environment, a situation termed *environmentally assisted cracking* (EAC). There are several physical mechanisms that occur. One of these is *stress corrosion cracking*, where material removal by corrosion in water, salt water, or other liquid assists in growing the crack. In other cases, no corrosion is involved, as in cracking of steels due to *hydrogen embrittlement*, or cracking of aluminum alloys due to *liquid metal embrittlement* caused by mercury. In these cases, the embrittling substance appears to enhance the breaking of chemical bonds in the highly stressed region of the crack tip. Embrittlement, and hence crack growth, can occur even where the harmful substance is not present as an external environment, but is instead in solid solution in the material, which is sometimes the case for hydrogen cracking of metals. Also, even the moisture and gases in air can cause environmental crack growth in some materials—for example, in silica glass.

11.10.1 Life Estimates for Static Loading

In situations of environmental crack growth during an unchanging static load, the crack growth life can be estimated on the basis of fracture mechanics in a manner analogous to the procedures described previously for fatigue crack growth under constant amplitude loading. The parameter controlling crack growth is simply the static value K of the stress intensity factor, as determined from the applied static stress and the current crack length. Growth rates for the material are characterized by the use of a da/dt versus K curve, where da/dt is the time-based growth rate, or *crack velocity*, also denoted $\dot{a}$. For example, the $\dot{a}$ versus K relationship sometimes fits a straight line on a log–log plot, so that it has the form

$$\dot{a} = \frac{da}{dt} = AK^n \tag{11.53}$$

where A and n are material constants that depend on the particular environment and are affected by temperature. Data for two glasses that obey such a relationship are shown in Fig. 11.38.

Once the $\dot{a}$ versus K relationship is known, life estimates can proceed as for fatigue crack growth with the use of either closed-form expressions or numerical integration. For example, if $F = F(a/b)$ does not change substantially during crack growth, a relationship similar to Eq. 11.32 is obtained, due to the mathematical forms of Eqs. 11.10 and 11.53 being the same:

$$t_{if} = \frac{a_f^{1-n/2} - a_i^{1-n/2}}{A \left(F S \sqrt{\pi} \right)^n (1 - n/2)} \qquad (n \neq 2) \tag{11.54}$$

Here, t_{if} is the time required for a crack to grow from an initial size a_i to a final size a_f. As before, a_f can be estimated as the smaller of a_o due to fully plastic yielding or a_c due to brittle fracture.

Where the behavior follows Eq. 11.53, the exponent n may be quite high. For example, for silica glasses in various environments, it is usually at least 10 and may be considerably higher. A high value of n indicates that cracks accelerate rapidly, and also that growth rates da/dt are highly sensitive to the value of K, so that modest increases in stress can have a large effect.

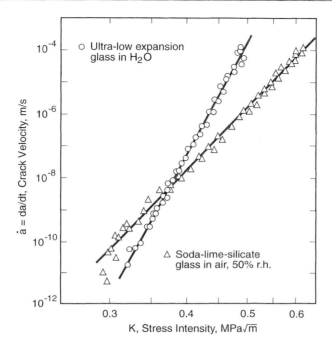

Figure 11.38   Crack velocity data for two silica glasses in room temperature environments as indicated. (Data from [Wiederhorn 77].)

A different behavior is sometimes observed where the growth rate is constant over a range of K values, as in Fig. 11.39. At low K, the growth rate may drop abruptly, so that the curve approaches an asymptote at the value K_{IEAC}, called the *environmentally assisted cracking threshold*, below which no crack growth occurs under static loading. (This quantity is also often denoted K_{Iscc}, especially in publications prior to about 1990.) A reasonable engineering approach in such cases is to approximate the curve with a constant rate $\dot{a}_{EAC}$, except that no growth occurs below K_{IEAC}. Life estimates are then given simply by

$$t_{if} = \frac{a_f - a_i}{\dot{a}_{EAC}} \qquad (K > K_{IEAC}) \qquad (11.55)$$

The value of $\dot{a}_{EAC}$ must, of course, be specific to the material, environment, and temperature of interest.

Values of K_{IEAC} are generally determined from long-term static loading tests. One approach is to hang weights on previously cracked cantilever beams, as shown in Fig. 11.40. A number of different initial values of K are obtained by using various weights. As also shown, the value of K below which no failure occurs after a long period of time is then identified as K_{IEAC}. Tests of this type are covered by ASTM Standard No. E1681.

More complex forms of an $\dot{a}$ versus K relationship that do not fit either Eq. 11.53 or constant $\dot{a}$ may be encountered.

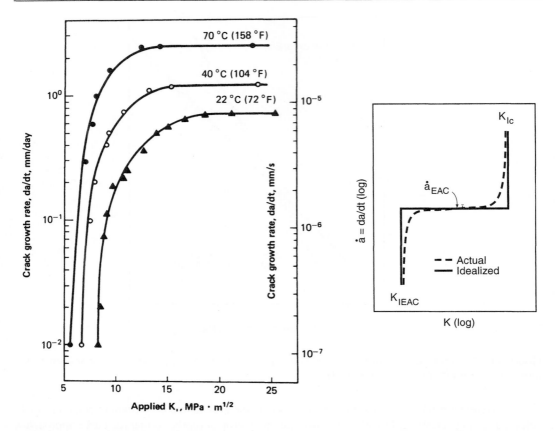

Figure 11.39   Crack velocity data (left) for 7075-T6 aluminum in a 3.5% NaCl solution similar to seawater, and approximation of such behavior (right) by use of a constant $\dot{a}$ between K_{IEAC} and K_{Ic}. (Left from [Campbell 82] p. 20; used with permission.)

11.10.2 Additional Comments

Environmental cracking problems occur for certain particular combinations of material and environment. Small changes in the processing or composition of a material, hence in its microstructure, may eliminate or introduce the problem. For example, AISI 4340 steel is susceptible to environmental cracking in H_2S gas, as illustrated by K_{IEAC} data in Fig. 11.41. The K_{IEAC} value is sensitive to the gas pressure and especially to the strength level (heat treatment) of the steel. Similar trends occur in this steel for other environments, such as seawater, and also in other alloy steels. In such cases, a modest decrease in strength may solve a cracking problem by increasing K_{IEAC}, despite the safety factor against yielding decreasing somewhat. Also, a seemingly small change in the environment can have a large effect. For example, alloy steels similar to AISI 4340 also crack in pure hydrogen gas, but the effect is considerably decreased if a small amount of oxygen is added to the hydrogen.

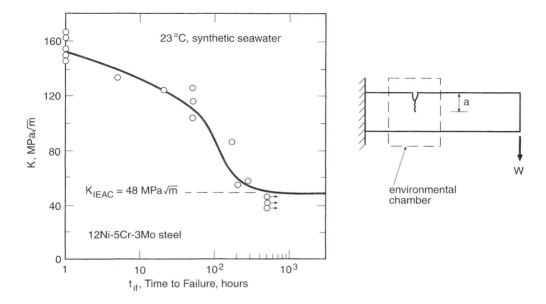

Figure 11.40   Determination of K_{IEAC} from cantilever beams loaded with dead weights. (Data from [Novak 69].)

As an additional example, grain boundary cracking and the resulting intergranular fracture surface from an actual pressure vessel cracking problem are shown in Fig. 11.42. The environment in the 2.25Cr-1Mo steel vessel contained hydrogen gas at a partial pressure of 10 MPa, and the temperature was 420°C. However, some of the welding rods used in fabricating the vessel were of the wrong type, resulting in some welds having much less Cr and Mo content than specified for this steel, in turn causing a loss of resistance to environmental cracking in the affected welds. Grain boundary cracking, as shown, then led to large cracks, necessitating a costly program of inspection and repair. Intergranular cracking is caused by the segregation of impurities at grain boundaries, or other metallurgical differences there, that make these boundaries susceptible to environmental attack. In this particular case, the Cr and Mo are needed to form carbides and thus limit the amount of iron carbide formed, and also to stabilize the iron carbides (such as Fe_3C) that do form. Note that iron carbides are the source of difficulty at the grain boundaries, probably by reacting with the hydrogen to form methane gas.

Opportunities thus exist for eliminating environmental cracking problems, making life estimates as previously described unnecessary. This is, of course, the preferred solution where it is feasible. As suggested by the preceding examples, a detailed knowledge of the material and environment combination involved is required to aid in choosing the correct course of action, so relevant literature or expert advice is needed. Some information along these lines can be found in Hertzberg (1996) and Milne (2003, vol. 6). Also, relevant materials data for $\dot{a}$ versus K and K_{IEAC} are sometimes available for commonly encountered environments, such as water and saltwater, as in Wachtman (2009) and Skinn (1994).

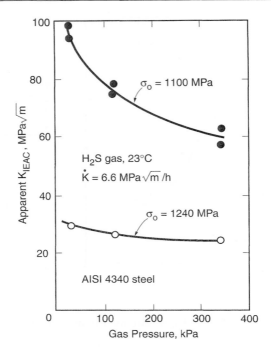

Figure 11.41   Effect of H_2S gas pressure on K_{IEAC} for two yield strength levels of AISI 4340 steel, tested as compact speciments with $b = 64.8$ mm and $h/b = 0.486$. (Adapted from [Clark 76]; copyright © ASTM; reprinted with permission.)

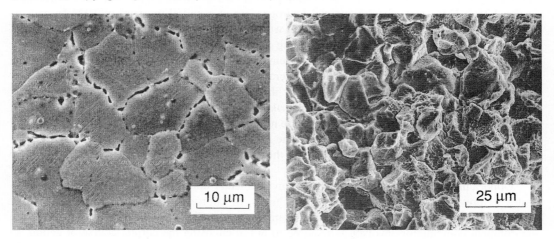

Figure 11.42   Grain boundary damage (left) and resulting intergranular fracture surface (right) in steel used in a pressure vessel containing H_2 gas at elevated temperature. (Photos courtesy of K. Rahka, Technical Research Center of Finland, Espoo, Finland. Published in [Rahka 86]; copyright © ASTM; reprinted with permission.)

Environmental and fatigue crack growth may occur in combination when cyclic loading is applied in a hostile environment, as in corrosion fatigue. A simple approach to making life estimates in such cases is to add the two contributions to crack growth by using both da/dN versus ΔK and da/dt versus K curves. However, this is not always sufficiently accurate, and a number of complexities exist that are difficult to incorporate into life estimates. Some discussion is given in Suresh (1998).

11.11 SUMMARY

The resistance of a material to fatigue crack growth under a given set of conditions can be characterized by a da/dN versus ΔK curve. At intermediate growth rates, the behavior can often be represented by the Paris equation,

$$\frac{da}{dN} = C\,(\Delta K)^m \tag{11.56}$$

Values of the exponent m are typically in the range 2 to 4 for ductile materials, but are higher for brittle materials, with values above 10 sometimes occurring.

Growth rates are affected by the value of the stress ratio $R = S_{\min}/S_{\max}$. For a given ΔK, increasing R increases da/dN in a manner analogous to the effect of mean stress on S-N curves. More general equations for da/dN have thus been developed that include this effect. For example, if the Walker equation is used, C in Eq. 11.56 depends on R as in Eq. 11.20. Hostile chemical environments may increase da/dN, especially at slow frequencies of cyclic loading. At low growth rates, da/dN versus ΔK curves generally exhibit a lower limiting or threshold value, ΔK_{th}, below which crack growth does not usually occur. The low growth rate region of the curve is especially sensitive to the effects of R-ratio and material variables, such as grain size and heat treatment in metals.

For a given applied stress, material, and component geometry, the crack growth life N_{if} depends on both the initial crack size a_i and the final crack size a_f. The life N_{if} is quite sensitive to the value of a_i and considerably less sensitive to a_f. To make a calculation of N_{if}, it is necessary to have an equation for the da/dN versus ΔK curve for the material. We also need a mathematical expression for the stress intensity for the geometry and loading case of interest, such as $K = FS\sqrt{\pi a}$. For example, where F is constant or approximately so, and for behavior according to Eq. 11.56, the life is

$$N_{if} = \frac{a_f^{1-m/2} - a_i^{1-m/2}}{C\left(F\,\Delta S\sqrt{\pi}\right)^m (1 - m/2)} \qquad (m \neq 2) \tag{11.57}$$

In design applications, the initial crack size a_i is often the minimum size a_d that can be reliably detected by inspection. The final crack size a_f is either a_c or a_o, whichever is smaller, as either brittle fracture or fully plastic yielding may occur first.

As F often varies, and as mathematical complexities may occur for certain forms of the da/dN versus ΔK equation, a closed-form expression for N_{if} may not be obtainable. It is then necessary to perform numerical integration by first evaluating ΔK and then da/dN for a number of different crack lengths. The crack growth life can be interpreted as the area under the dN/da versus a plot between a_i and a_f, as illustrated in Fig. 11.26. This area is given by the integral

$$N_{if} = \int_{a_i}^{a_f} \left(\frac{dN}{da} \right) da \tag{11.58}$$

For variable amplitude loading, the da/dN versus ΔK curve can be used to estimate increments in crack length Δa for each cycle. The end of the crack growth life occurs when the crack length increases such that a stress peak is expected to cause either brittle fracture or fully plastic yielding. An alternative procedure is to identify a representative sample of the load history and apply Eq. 11.46 to obtain an equivalent zero-to-maximum stress level ΔS_q. Then ΔS_q can be used to make a life estimate as for constant amplitude loading. If isolated severe overloads occur, these may cause sequence effects that need to be included in life estimates.

The estimated crack growth life from the minimum detectable crack length a_d must be longer than the expected actual service life by a sufficient safety factor X_N. If X_N is inadequate, it may be possible to resolve the situation by redesign that lowers stresses, by improving the initial inspection to decrease a_d, by changing materials, or by resorting to periodic inspections. Special crack-stopping design features as used in aircraft structure also contribute to safety.

Limitations on the use of LEFM due to excessive plasticity can be set on the basis of plastic zone sizes according to Eq. 11.50. However, the looser restriction of 80% of fully plastic yielding is generally sufficient. If a crack is so small that all of its dimensions are similar to or smaller than the microstructural features of the material, then its growth is likely to be significantly faster than expected from the usual da/dN versus ΔK curve. Equation 11.52 can be employed to estimate a crack length below which such behavior is expected.

For static loading in a hostile chemical environment, time-dependent crack growth may occur. Life estimates may be made by employing a da/dt versus K curve for the particular combination of material and environment. Since environmental cracking problems are sensitive to the exact combination of material and environment, it may be possible to make a modest change in the material or the environment that eliminates the problem.

NEW TERMS AND SYMBOLS

crack growth life, N_{if}

crack growth retardation

crack velocity, $\dot{a} = da/dt$

cyclic plastic zone size, $2r_o'$

damage-tolerant design

embrittlement

environmentally assisted cracking (EAC)

EAC threshold, K_{IEAC}

equivalent zero-to-maximum stress, ΔS_q

fatigue crack growth rate, da/dN

fatigue crack growth threshold, ΔK_{th}

Forman equation constants: C_2, m_2, K_c

initial and final crack lengths: a_i, a_f

inspection period, N_p

intergranular fracture

minimum detectable crack length, a_d

monotonic plastic zone size, $2r_o$

Paris equation constants: C, m

small crack; short crack

small crack transition length, a_s

stationary loading

stress corrosion cracking

stress intensity range, ΔK

transgranular fracture

Walker equation constants: C_0, m, γ

REFERENCES

(a) General References

ASTM. 2010. *Annual Book of ASTM Standards*, Vol. 03.01, ASTM International, West Conshohocken, PA. See No. E647, "Standard Test Method for Measurement of Fatigue Crack Growth Rates," and No. E1681, "Standard Test Method for Determining Threshold Stress Intensity Factor for Environment-Assisted Cracking of Metallic Materials."

BARSOM, J. M., and S. T. ROLFE. 1999. *Fracture and Fatigue Control in Structures*, 3d ed., ASTM International, West Conshohocken, PA.

BROEK, D. 1986. *Elementary Engineering Fracture Mechanics*, 4th ed., Kluwer Academic Pubs., Dordrecht, The Netherlands.

BROEK, D. 1988. *The Practical Use of Fracture Mechanics*, Kluwer Academic Pubs., Dordrecht, The Netherlands.

FISHER, J. W. 1984. *Fatigue and Fracture in Steel Bridges: Case Studies*, John Wiley, New York.

GRANDT, A. F. 2004. *Fundamentals of Structural Integrity: Damage Tolerant Design and Nondestructive Evaluation*, John Wiley, Hoboken, NJ.

HERTZBERG, R. W. 1996. *Deformation and Fracture Mechanics of Engineering Materials*, 4th ed., John Wiley, New York.

LAMPMAN, S. R., ed., 1996. *ASM Handbook, Vol. 19: Fatigue and Fracture*, ASM International, Materials Park, OH.

LEXTECH. 2010. *AFGROW: Fracture Mechanics and Fatigue Crack Growth Analysis Software Tool*, LexTech, Inc., AFGROW Training, Centerville, OH. (See *http://www.afgrow.net*.)

MIEDLAR, P. C., A. P. BERENS, A. GUNDERSON, and J. P. GALLAGHER. 2002. *USAF Damage Tolerant Design Handbook: Guidelines for the Analysis and Design of Damage Tolerant Aircraft Structures*, 3 vols., University of Dayton Research Institute, Dayton, OH.

MILNE, I., R. O. RITCHIE, and B. KARIHALOO, eds. 2003. *Comprehensive Structural Integrity: Fracture of Materials from Nano to Macro*, 10 vols., Elsevier Ltd., Oxford, UK. See vol. 4, *Cyclic Loading and Fatigue*, and vol. 6, *Environmentally Assisted Failure*.

RICE, R. C., ed. 1997. *Fatigue Design Handbook*, 3d ed., SAE Pub. No. AE-22, Soc. of Automotive Engineers, Warrendale, PA.

SCHIJVE, J. 2009. *Fatigue of Structures and Materials*, 2nd ed., Springer, New York.

SURESH, S. 1998. *Fatigue of Materials*, Cambridge University Press, 2d ed., Cambridge, UK.

SWRI. 2010. *NASGRO: Fracture Mechanics and Fatigue Crack Growth Analysis Software*, Southwest Research Institute, San Antonio, TX. (See *http://www.nasgro.swri.org*.)

TIFFANY, C. F., J. P. GALLAGHER, and C. A. BABISH, IV. 2010. "Threats To Aircraft Structural Safety, Including a Compendium of Selected Structural Accidents / Incidents," Report No. ASC-TR-2010-5002, Aeronautical Systems Center, U.S. Air Force, Wright-Patterson Air Force Base, OH.

WACHTMAN, J. B., W. R. Cannon, and M. J. Matthewson. 2009. *Mechanical Properties of Ceramics*, 2nd ed. John Wiley, Hoboken, NJ.

(b) Sources of Material Properties and Databases

CINDAS. 2010. *Aerospace Structural Metals Database (ASMD)*, CINDAS LLC, West Lafayette, IN. (See *https://cindasdata.com*.)

FORMAN, R. G., et al. 2005. "Fatigue Crack Growth Database for Damage Tolerance Analysis," Report No. DOT/FAA/AR-05/15, Office of Aviation Research, Federal Aviation Administration, U.S. Department of Transportation, Washington, DC.

HENKENER, J. A., V. B. LAWRENCE, and R. G. FORMAN. 1993. "An Evaluation of Fracture Mechanics Properties of Various Aerospace Materials," R. Chona, ed., *Fracture Mechanics: Twenty-third Symposium,* ASTM STP 1189, Am. Soc. for Testing and Materials, West Conshohocken, PA, pp. 474–497.

MMPDS. 2010. *Metallic Materials Properties Development and Standardization Handbook,* MMPDS-05, 5 vols., U.S. Federal Aviation Administration; distributed by Battelle Memorial Institute, Columbus, OH. (See *http://projects.battelle.org/mmpds*; replaces MIL-HDBK-5.)

SKINN, D. A., J. P. GALLAGHER, A. F. BERENS, P. D. HUBER, and J. SMITH, compilers. 1994. *Damage Tolerant Design Handbook,* 5 vols., CINDAS/USAF CRDA Handbooks Operation, Purdue University, West Lafayette, IN. (See *https://cindasdata.com*.)

TAYLOR, D. 1985. *A Compendium of Fatigue Thresholds and Growth Rates,* Engineering Materials Advisory Services Ltd., Cradley Heath, Warley, West Midlands, UK.

TAYLOR, D., and L. JIANCHUN. 1993. *Sourcebook on Fatigue Crack Propagation: Thresholds and Crack Closure,* Engineering Materials Advisory Services Ltd., Cradley Heath, Warley, West Midlands, UK.

PROBLEMS AND QUESTIONS

Section 11.2

11.1   Estimate the constants C and m for the straight line portion of the data of Fig. 11.3.

11.2   Look at Fig. 11.9, and determine your own values of constants C and m for the fitted line shown. Comment on the differences between your values and those given on the graph.

11.3   Look at Fig. 11.25 (right), and calculate constants C and m for crack growth of this MgO-PSZ ceramic material in air. Comment on the value of m obtained and its significance.

11.4   Look at Fig. 11.20, and determine constants C and m for crack growth of the PBT matrix material. Comment on the value of m obtained and its significance.

11.5   Representative data points are given in Table P11.5 from the results of tests at $R = 0.1$ on 2124-T851 aluminum.

      (a) Plot these points on log–log coordinates, and obtain approximate values of constants C and m for Eq. 11.10.

      (b) Use a log–log least-squares fit to obtain refined values of C and m.

Table P11.5

da/dN, mm/cycle	ΔK, MPa$\sqrt{\text{m}}$
1.26×10^{-6}	2.99
2.41×10^{-6}	3.64
4.84×10^{-6}	5.02
1.02×10^{-5}	6.04
1.99×10^{-5}	7.68
3.74×10^{-5}	9.95
6.69×10^{-5}	12.0
1.77×10^{-4}	15.9

Source: Data in [Ruschau 78].

11.6   Representative data points are given in Table P11.6 from the results of tests at $R = 0.0.032$ on a hard tool steel with $\sigma_u = 2200$ MPa. Proceed as in Prob. 11.5(a) and (b), except use these data.

Table P11.6

da/dN, mm/cycle	ΔK, MPa$\sqrt{m}$
4.23×10^{-6}	6.85
8.10×10^{-6}	8.39
1.77×10^{-5}	10.40
3.50×10^{-5}	13.42

11.7   Representative data points are given in Table P11.7 from the results of tests at $R = 0.5$ on 2124-T851 aluminum. Proceed as in Prob. 11.5(a) and (b), except use these data.

Table P11.7

da/dN, mm/cycle	ΔK, MPa$\sqrt{m}$
1.25×10^{-6}	2.18
2.00×10^{-6}	2.75
3.57×10^{-6}	3.53
6.62×10^{-6}	4.52
1.49×10^{-5}	5.48
3.38×10^{-5}	6.97
8.16×10^{-5}	9.20
1.65×10^{-4}	11.7

Source: Data in [Ruschau 78].

11.8   Representative data points are given in Table P11.8 from the results of tests at $R = 0.04$ on 17-4 PH stainless steel. Proceed as in Prob. 11.5(a) and (b), except use these data.

Table P11.8

da/dN, mm/cycle	ΔK, MPa$\sqrt{m}$
9.98×10^{-6}	11.2
2.84×10^{-5}	15.6
8.03×10^{-5}	22.4
1.83×10^{-4}	32.9
3.18×10^{-4}	42.3
7.92×10^{-4}	65.1
1.60×10^{-3}	90.8
3.68×10^{-3}	124

Source: Data in [Crooker 75].

Section 11.3

11.9 A center-cracked plate of 7075-T6 aluminum was tested as in Ex. 11.2. All details were the same, except that the force was cycled between $P_{min} = 48.1$ and $P_{max} = 96.2$ kN. The data obtained are listed in Table P11.9. Determine the da/dN and ΔK values from these data, make a da/dN versus ΔK plot of the results on log–log coordinates, and fit the data to Eq. 11.10 to obtain values of C and m. Does Eq. 11.10 appear to represent the data well?

Table P11.9

a, mm	N, 10^3 cycles	a, mm	N, 10^3 cycles
5.08	0	20.32	21.5
7.62	9.5	22.86	22.3
10.16	14.3	25.40	22.9
12.70	17.1	30.48	23.5
15.24	19.1	35.56	24.0
17.78	20.5		

Source: Data in [Hudson 69].

11.10 A center-cracked plate of 2024-T3 aluminum had dimensions, as defined in Fig. 8.12(a), of $b = 152.4$ and $t = 2.29$ mm. It was tested under cyclic loading between $P_{min} = 12.03$ and $P_{max} = 36.09$ kN. The crack length versus cycles data obtained are listed in Table P11.10.

    (a) Determine da/dN and ΔK values from these data, and make a da/dN versus ΔK plot of the results on log–log coordinates. Then fit the data to Eq. 11.10 to obtain values of C and m. Does Eq. 11.10 appear to represent the data well?

    (b) Change the ΔK scale on your plot to a linear one. Does this seem to be a better way to represent the data? Why or why not?

    (c) Change both the da/dN and ΔK scales to linear ones, and answer the same questions as in (b).

Table P11.10

a, mm	N, cycles	a, mm	N, cycles
5.08	0	22.86	600 000
7.62	230 000	25.40	620 000
10.16	350 000	30.48	670 000
12.70	450 000	35.56	690 000
15.24	500 000	40.64	710 000
17.78	540 000	45.72	720 000
20.32	570 000		

Source: Data in [Hudson 69].

11.11 Crack length versus cycles data are given in Table P11.11 from a test on a hard tool steel, with tensile properties 2200 MPa ultimate and 1.7% elongation. A standard compact specimen was used with dimensions, as defined in Fig. 8.16, of $b = 50.8$ and $t = 6.35$ mm. The force was cycled at a frequency of 30 Hz between $P_{min} = 44.5$ and $P_{max} = 1379$ N. Crack lengths a, measured from the centerline of the pin holes, are given in Table P11.11 with the corresponding cycle numbers. Determine the da/dN and ΔK values from these data, make a da/dN versus ΔK plot of the results on log–log coordinates, and fit the data to Eq. 11.10 to obtain values of C and m. Does Eq. 11.10 appear to represent the data well?

Table P11.11

a, mm	N, 10^3 cycles	a, mm	N, 10^3 cycles
19.86	0	27.43	1122
21.13	300	27.89	1148
22.15	508	28.32	1167
22.94	658	29.08	1191
23.80	792	29.85	1221
24.61	892	30.71	1241
25.37	976	31.01	1251
26.54	1070	31.29	1259

Source: Data in [Luken 87].

11.12 A compact specimen of AISI 4340 steel ($\sigma_u = 786$ MPa) had dimensions, as defined in Fig. 8.16, of $b = 50.8$ and $t = 9.525$ mm. It was tested under cyclic loading between $P_{min} = 211.5$ and $P_{max} = 4230$ N. The crack length versus cycles data obtained are listed in Table P11.12.

(a) Determine da/dN and ΔK values from these data, and make a da/dN versus ΔK plot of the results on log–log coordinates. Then fit the data to Eq. 11.10 to obtain values of C and m. Does Eq. 11.10 appear to represent the data well?

(b) Note that these data correspond to one of the tests for Figs. 11.8 and 11.9. How well does your fit agree with that of Fig. 11.9? Why might it differ?

Table P11.12

a, mm	N, cycles	a, mm	N, cycles	a, mm	N, cycles
25.78	0	30.81	100 680	35.89	135 000
26.16	12 560	31.37	106 620	36.42	136 430
26.67	24 000	31.88	112 830	36.91	137 720
27.56	41 250	32.33	115 730	37.36	138 800
28.07	52 900	32.89	119 590	37.97	139 780
28.45	61 410	33.35	122 650	38.48	140 740
28.83	70 610	33.99	125 530	38.99	141 400
29.21	80 000	34.29	128 310	39.37	142 000
29.72	87 580	34.87	130 660	39.88	142 460
30.30	95 500	35.31	133 000	40.26	142 820

Section 11.4

11.13 Consider 17-4 PH stainless steel with crack-growth constants for the Walker equation as in Table 11.2.

  (a) Determine da/dN versus ΔK equations of the form of Eq. 11.10 for $R = 0$, for $R = 0.5$, and for $R = 0.8$. Plot the three equations on the same log–log graph. (Suggestion: For each R, plot ΔK over the range 10 to 120 MPa$\sqrt{\text{m}}$.)

  (b) By what factor does da/dN increase for a given ΔK if R is increased from 0 to 0.5? From 0 to 0.8? Are these factors constant for different ΔK values?

11.14 Employ the results of Prob. 11.9 for 7075-T6 aluminum tested at $R = 0.5$ as follows: Plot the da/dN versus ΔK data on log–log coordinates, and also show the line corresponding to the Walker equation, with constants from Table 11.2. Do data and line agree?

11.15 Show that Eq. 11.18 can be expressed in the form $da/dN = C_0(\Delta K)^p (K_{\max})^q$, and give expressions for determining the new constants p and q from m and γ, that is, find $p = f(m, \gamma)$ and $q = g(m, \gamma)$.

11.16 For RQC-100 steel, three da/dN versus ΔK data points at two different contrasting R-ratios are given in Table P11.16.

  (a) Assume that the Walker equation applies, and employ these points to obtain estimates of the constants C_0, m, and γ.

  (b) On log–log coordinates, plot da/dN versus the equivalent values $\overline{\Delta K}$. Show values from the three data points and also the line $da/dN = C_0 \left(\overline{\Delta K}\right)^m$ based on your constants from (a). Do data and line agree?

Table P11.16

da/dN, mm/cycle	ΔK, MPa$\sqrt{\text{m}}$	R
4.87×10^{-2}	114	0.1
3.10×10^{-5}	20.1	0.1
1.64×10^{-4}	20.0	0.8

11.17 Proceed as in Prob. 11.16, but use the data for 17-4 PH stainless steel in Table P11.17.

Table P11.17

da/dN, mm/cycle	ΔK, MPa$\sqrt{\text{m}}$	R
3.68×10^{-3}	124	0.04
9.98×10^{-6}	11.2	0.04
2.46×10^{-4}	28.4	0.8

11.18 For RQC-100 steel, some da/dN versus ΔK data at three different positive R-ratios are given in Table P11.18.

  (a) Plot the given da/dN versus ΔK data on a log–log graph, and draw a set of parallel lines through the data, one for each R value. Is it reasonable to represent the data by such a set of parallel lines?

(b) If yes, then employ all of the data in a single multiple regression fit based on Eq. 11.21, to obtain values of the constants C_0, m, and γ for the Walker equation.

(c) On log–log coordinates, plot da/dN versus the equivalent values $\overline{\Delta K}$, showing both values from the data and the line from your fit. Are the data consolidated? Are they represented well by the line?

Table P11.18

ΔK MPa$\sqrt{\text{m}}$	da/dN mm/cycle	R	ΔK MPa$\sqrt{\text{m}}$	da/dN mm/cycle	R
20.1	3.10×10^{-5}	0.1	25.4	1.51×10^{-4}	0.5
25.2	7.54×10^{-5}	0.1	30.3	2.65×10^{-4}	0.5
30.2	1.68×10^{-4}	0.1	40.7	8.33×10^{-4}	0.5
40.5	5.02×10^{-4}	0.1	51.5	2.90×10^{-3}	0.5
49.8	1.56×10^{-3}	0.1	64.9	6.86×10^{-3}	0.5
65.7	5.08×10^{-3}	0.1	11.6	1.70×10^{-5}	0.8
81.4	1.27×10^{-2}	0.1	13.5	3.28×10^{-5}	0.8
99.0	2.34×10^{-2}	0.1	16.5	8.91×10^{-5}	0.8
114.0	4.87×10^{-2}	0.1	20.0	1.64×10^{-4}	0.8
11.2	8.72×10^{-6}	0.5	24.0	4.13×10^{-4}	0.8
15.2	2.78×10^{-5}	0.5	27.1	5.58×10^{-4}	0.8
19.5	4.94×10^{-5}	0.5			

Source: Data for [Dowling 79c].

11.19 Consider the data in Tables P11.5 and P11.7 from the results of tests at $R = 0.1$ and 0.5 on 2124-T851 aluminum. Combine these data all into a single set. Then proceed as in Prob. 11.18(a), (b), and (c), except use these data.

11.20 Representative data points are given in Table P11.20 from the results of tests on 17-4 PH stainless steel at $R = 0.67$ and 0.8. Combine these data and the data at $R = 0.04$ in Table P11.8 all into a single set. Then proceed as in Prob. 11.18(a), (b), and (c), except use these data.

Table P11.20

da/dN, mm/cycle	ΔK, MPa$\sqrt{\text{m}}$	R	da/dN, mm/cycle	ΔK, MPa$\sqrt{\text{m}}$	R
4.57×10^{-5}	15.8	0.67	2.45×10^{-5}	11.2	0.8
7.70×10^{-5}	20.1	0.67	5.23×10^{-5}	14.7	0.8
1.39×10^{-4}	25.4	0.67	7.75×10^{-5}	17.6	0.8
2.36×10^{-4}	32.6	0.67	1.30×10^{-4}	22.7	0.8
4.47×10^{-4}	41.1	0.67	2.46×10^{-4}	28.4	0.8
1.42×10^{-3}	53.6	0.67	4.67×10^{-4}	35.8	0.8
2.67×10^{-3}	66.2	0.67	9.14×10^{-4}	45.5	0.8

Source: Data in [Crooker 75].

11.21 Using the Forman equation and the constants in Table 11.3 for 2024-T3 aluminum:

   (a) Plot the da/dN versus ΔK curves that apply for both $R = 0$ and $R = 0.5$. Use log–log coordinates and include growth rates between 10^{-6} and 10^{-2} mm/cycle. Are the lines straight?

   (b) By about what factor is da/dN typically increased by changing R from 0 to 0.5? Its the factor constant for different ΔK values?

11.22 For a CrMoV forged steel (0.28C), having a yield strength of $\sigma_o = 661$ MPa, fatigue crack growth thresholds at various R-ratios are given in Table P11.22. Fit these data to Eq. 11.25, and compare data and fit on an appropriate plot. Does the resulting relationship provide a reasonable fit to the data?

Table P11.22

R	-1	0	0.27	0.46	0.54	0.63
ΔK_{th}, MPa$\sqrt{\text{m}}$	12.20	6.80	5.90	4.50	3.80	3.20

Source: Data in [Taylor 85] p. 131.

11.23 The SAE *Fatigue Design Handbook* (Rice, 1997) gives the following equation as being useful in fitting da/dN versus ΔK curves:

$$\frac{da}{dN} = \frac{C_4 \left(\Delta K - \Delta K_{th} \right)^{m_4}}{(1 - R) K_c - \Delta K}$$

The quantities C_4 and m_4 are new material constants, and K_c and ΔK_{th} are material constants as previously defined, with ΔK_{th} being a function of R.

   (a) Describe the shape of the resulting curve on a log–log plot of da/dN versus ΔK. Qualitatively, how is it affected by changing R? By changing ΔK_{th}? By changing K_c?

   (b) Assume that K_c is known, and also that ΔK_{th} is known for various R. How could values for C_4 and m_4 then be obtained by using a log–log plot of data from crack growth tests at several different R-ratios?

Section 11.5

11.24 Explain in your own words why hostile chemical environments have a greater effect on da/dN for slow frequencies of loading than for high frequencies. Is this related to the additional trend that growth rates usually increase with temperature if frequency is held constant? Explain why.

11.25 Consider the data on fracture toughness and crack-growth rate for AISI 4340 steel in Figs. 8.32 and 11.23. Further, note from Section 3.3 that the strength (yield and ultimate) of this and similar steels can be varied by changing the heat treatment. Write a paragraph that summarizes the trends seen in the data cited. Also comment on how the strength level chosen affects limitations on the use of this steel.

Section 11.6

11.26 Derive the equation for crack growth life N_{if} that is analogous to Eq. 11.32, but which is applicable to the special case of $m = 2$. The result should give N_{if} as a function of the remaining materials constant C, stress range ΔS, the approximately constant F, and initial and final crack lengths, a_i and a_f.

11.27 Consider da/dN versus ΔK behavior according to Eq. 11.10 with $K = P/(t\sqrt{\pi a})$, as for small a/b for prying loads in Fig. 8.15. Derive an equation for crack-growth life N_{if} as a function of material constants C and m, force range ΔP, geometric dimensions, and initial and final crack lengths, a_i and a_f.

11.28 From Fig. 8.23, note that the stress intensity factor for cases of cracks loaded on one side can be approximated over a range of crack lengths by $K = 0.89P/(t\sqrt{b})$. Consider crack growth behavior according to Eq. 11.10, and assume that the initial and final crack sizes, a_i and a_f, are both within the range where this K-expression applies. Then derive an equation giving the crack growth life N_{if} as a function of materials constants C and m, force range ΔP, geometric dimensions, and crack lengths a_i and a_f.

11.29 Derive an equation for calculating crack growth life N_{if} that is analogous to Eq. 11.32, where F is approximately constant, but where da/dN is given by the Forman equation, Eq. 11.22. The result should give N_{if} as a function of materials constants C_2, m_2, and K_c, stress range ΔS, stress ratio R, constant F, and initial and final crack lengths, a_i and a_f.

11.30 Consider an infinite collinear array of cracks under remote uniform stress S, which is the K_3 case of Fig. 8.23(b), so that K is given by

$$K = FS\sqrt{\pi a}, \quad F = \sqrt{\frac{2b}{\pi a} \tan \frac{\pi a}{2b}}$$

(a) Derive a closed-form expression for the number of cycles N_{if} to grow the cracks from initial lengths a_i to final lengths a_f, where the crack growth behavior obeys Eq. 11.10 with $m = 2$. The result should give N_{if} as a function of materials constants C and m, stress range ΔS, geometric dimensions, and crack lengths a_i and a_f.

(b) Are closed-form solutions possible for other values of m? If so, which ones? (Suggestion: Consult a table of integrals.)

11.31 A center-cracked plate made of 2024-T3 aluminum has dimensions, as defined in Fig. 8.12(a), of $b = 50$, $t = 4$ mm, and large h, and an initial crack length of $a_i = 2$ mm. How many cycles between $P_{min} = 18$ and $P_{max} = 60$ kN are required to grow the crack to failure by either fully plastic yielding or brittle fracture?

11.32 A bending member made of AISI 4340 steel ($\sigma_u = 1296$ MPa) has a rectangular cross section with dimensions, as defined in Fig. 8.13, of $b = 60$ and $t = 9$ mm. An initial edge crack of length $a = 0.5$ mm is present, and the member is subjected to cyclic bending between $M_{min} = 1.2$ and $M_{max} = 3.0$ kN·m. Estimate the number of cycles necessary to grow the crack to failure.

11.33 A double-edge-cracked plate made of RQC-100 steel has dimensions, as defined in Fig. 8.12(b), of $b = 100$ and $t = 8$ mm. The two edge cracks have equal lengths of $a = 1.0$ mm, and the member is subjected to cyclic loading between $P_{min} = -150$ and $P_{max} = 600$ kN. Estimate the number of cycles necessary to grow the cracks to failure.

11.34 A bending member made of 7075-T6 aluminum has a rectangular cross section with dimensions, as defined in Fig. 8.13, of $b = 40$ and $t = 10$ mm. Inspection can reliably find cracks only if they are larger than $a = 0.25$ mm, so it must be assumed that a through-thickness edge crack of this size may be present. A cyclic bending moment is applied with $M_{min} = -90$ and $M_{max} = 300$ N·m.

   (a) Estimate the number of cycles to grow the crack to failure.

   (b) What is the safety factor in life if the desired service life is 200,000 cycles?

   (c) A safety factor in life of 3.00 is required. Is periodic inspection necessary? If so, at what interval of cycles?

11.35 A circular shaft made of 17-4 PH stainless steel has a diameter of 60 mm and contains a half-circular surface crack, as in Fig. 8.17(d), of initial size $a_i = 0.5$ mm. A cyclic bending moment is applied between $M_{min} = 2.0$ and $M_{max} = 14.0$ kN·m. Estimate the number of cycles to grow the crack to failure. (Suggestion: Since Appendix A does not have a fully plastic yielding solution for this case, roughly estimate a_o from the solution of Fig. A.16(b), with the circular cross section analyzed as a rectangle, using the transformation $b, t \to d$.)

11.36 An aircraft structural member made of 7075-T6 aluminum has a cross section as shown in Fig. P11.36. A quarter circular corner crack of size $a = 0.5$ mm is present, and the member is subjected to a tension stress S. How many cycles between $S_{max} = 336$ and $S_{min} = -68$ MPa can be applied before failure is expected? (Comment: It is reasonable to assume that an approximately quarter-circular crack shape is maintained as the crack grows. Also, conservatively approximate the fully plastic limit force by assuming that the crack of depth a extends uniformly across the full 15 mm thickness of the member.)

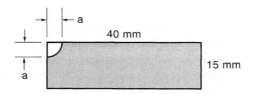

Figure P11.36

11.37 A bending member has a rectangular cross section of dimensions, as defined in Fig. 8.13, of depth $b = 60$ and thickness $t = 12$ mm. It is made of the AISI 4340 steel of Table 11.2 and is subjected to a cyclic moment between $M_{min} = 0.8$ and $M_{max} = 4.0$ kN·m. Failure occurred after 60,000 cycles of this loading by brittle fracture from a through-thickness edge crack extending 14 mm in the depth direction. Estimate the initial crack length present at the beginning of the cyclic loading.

11.38 A circular rod 80 mm in diameter contains a circumferential surface crack, as in Fig. 8.14. The material is the ferritic-pearlitic structural steel ASTM A572 with yield strength $\sigma_o = 345$ MPa and plane stress fracture toughness in this thickness of at least $K_c = 200$ MPa$\sqrt{m}$. What force range ΔP, applied at $R = 0.6$, will cause the crack to grow from $a_i = 0.5$ mm to $a_f = 10$ mm in two million cycles?

11.39 Consider the center-cracked plate of 2024-T3 aluminum and loading given in Prob. 11.31. The initial crack size of $a_i = 2$ mm gives a life of $N_{if} = 46{,}600$ cycles, where the life ends due to brittle fracture at $a_f = 14.8$ mm.

    (a) What is the largest initial crack size a_i that can be permitted to escape inspection if the part must withstand 100,000 cycles before it fails?

    (b) Assuming that inspection to find your a_i from (a) is possible, what inspection interval in cycles would give the plate a reasonable safety factor on life? Assume that the plate is a critical aircraft structural part.

11.40 A bending member made of 2024-T3 aluminum has a rectangular cross section with dimensions, as defined in Fig. 8.13, of $b = 40$ and $t = 5.0$ mm. The member is subjected to cyclic bending between $M_{min} = 46$ and $M_{max} = 184$ N·m.

    (a) If an initial edge crack of length $a_i = 1.0$ mm is present, estimate the number of cycles necessary to grow the crack to failure.

    (b) An inspection period of 50,000 cycles is planned, and a safety factor of 3.0 in life is required. What size crack a_d must be found in periodic inspections?

11.41 Consider the T-section of Prob. 8.21, which contains a crack of length $a = 1.5$ mm, as shown in Fig. P8.21. The member is subjected to cyclic bending about the x-axis between $M_{min} = 117$ and $M_{max} = 180$ N·m, with the crack on the tensile side of the bending axis. Estimate the number of cycles to grow this crack to failure. The 7075-T651 aluminum material may be assumed to have the same crack growth properties as the 7075-T6 alloy of Table 11.2.

11.42 A sheet of 2024-T3 aluminum 3.0 mm thick is fastened to a structural member with a row of rivets, as shown in Fig. 8.24. Cyclic stressing between $S_{min} = 8.5$ and $S_{max} = 28$ MPa is applied. The rivet holes are spaced $2b = 24$ mm apart, and the hole diameters are $d = 4.0$ mm. Most of the rivet holes have cracks starting from them, with the largest of these having a length of $l = 0.5$ mm. Estimate the number of cycles to grow the cracks to $l = 4.0$ mm, at which point the holes plus cracks occupy half of the sheet width. (Suggestion: Complete Prob. 11.28 before doing this one.)

Section 11.6.3

11.43 Consider the center-cracked plate of AISI 4340 steel of Ex. 11.4, with the same initial crack size of $a_i = 1$ mm, but let the cyclic forces be half as large—that is, $P_{min} = 40$ and $P_{max} = 120$ kN.

    (a) Estimate the crack length at failure.

    (b) Calculate the life using numerical integration.

11.44 For the situation of Prob. 11.31, estimate the number of cycles to failure, using numerical integration with F allowed to vary.

11.45 Check your a_i value from Prob. 11.37 by calculating N_{if} from numerical integration, with F allowed to vary. If the result is not close to 60,000 cycles, adjust the a_i value until $N_{if} = 60{,}000$ is obtained.

11.46 A single-edge-cracked plate is loaded in tension and has dimensions, as defined in Fig. 8.12(c), of $b = 75$, $t = 5$ mm, and large h, and it contains an initial crack of length

$a_i = 4$ mm. A zero-to-maximum cyclic load of 20 kN is applied, and the material is Man-Ten steel. How many cycles can be applied before fatigue failure is expected?

11.47 For the situation of Prob. 11.42, use numerical integration to estimate N_{if}, allowing K to vary with crack length according to the exact K_2 from Fig. 8.23(b).

11.48 A spherical pressure vessel has an inner radius of 0.6 m and a wall thickness of 50 mm. The material is an austenitic stainless steel with a fracture toughness of at least 200 MPa$\sqrt{m}$. Nondestructive inspection revealed a surface crack in the inner wall of length $2c = 8$ mm and depth $a = 2$ mm. Although the crack will change its $a/c = 0.5$ proportions somewhat if it grows, a reasonable approximation for preliminary analysis is to assume that a/c remains constant as the crack increases its depth a. In this case, F_D for Fig. 8.19(b) varies with the relative crack depth a/t, as given by Eq. 8.23.

  (a) How many times can the vessel be pressurized to 20 MPa and depressurized before failure occurs?

  (b) Does failure occur by leaking of the vessel or by brittle fracture? If the former, what is the safety factor against brittle fracture when the vessel leaks?

11.49 For the shaft of Prob. 10.36, assume that a number of small cracks 1 mm deep are present around the base of the fillet radius. Estimate the number of cycles (shaft rotations) to grow such cracks to failure. Use reasonable approximations where necessary to reach a solution. The steel has a ferritic-pearlitic microstructure (Table 11.1) and has yield and ultimate strengths roughly similar to those of Man-Ten steel (Tables 9.1 and 11.2).

Section 11.7

11.50 For the material and member of Prob. 11.31, replace the loading with repeated applications of the axial force history shown in Figure P11.50. How many repetitions are required to grow the crack from $a_i = 2$ mm to failure?

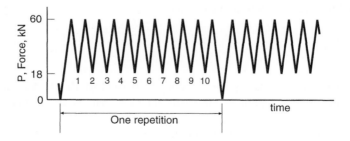

Figure P11.50

11.51 A double-edge-cracked member of 7075-T6 aluminum has dimensions, as defined in Fig. 8.12(b), of $b = 28.6$ and $t = 2.3$ mm, and it contains equal initial cracks on each side of length $a_i = 2.0$ mm. Estimate the number of repetitions of the load history shown in Fig. P11.51 necessary to grow the cracks to failure. Materials constants as in Table 11.2 apply, except that the fracture toughness for this thickness is $K_c = 78.7$ MPa$\sqrt{m}$.

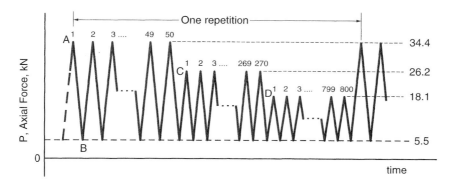

Figure P11.51

11.52 For the same material and member as in Prob. 11.37, the initial crack length is $a_i = 0.5\,\text{mm}$, and the load history is replaced by repeated applications of the sequence shown in Fig. P11.52. Estimate the number of repetitions to failure.

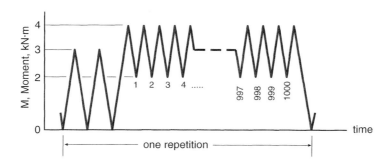

Figure P11.52

11.53 A beam with a rectangular cross section is made of Man-Ten steel and has dimensions, as defined in Fig. 8.13, of $b = 40$ and $t = 20\,\text{mm}$. Assume that a through-thickness, inspection-size crack of length $a_d = 1.00\,\text{mm}$ is initially present. How many repetitions of the bending moment history shown in Fig. P11.53 are required to grow the crack to failure?

11.54 A circular shaft of 7075-T6 aluminum has a diameter of 50 mm and contains a half-circular surface crack, as in Fig. 8.17(d), of initial length $a_i = 1.0\,\text{mm}$. How many repetitions of the bending moment history shown in Fig. P11.54 are required to grow the crack to failure? Failure occurs by brittle fracture, and it may be assumed that the crack maintains its shape as it grows.

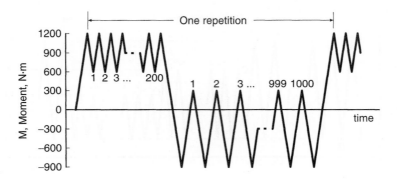

Figure P11.53

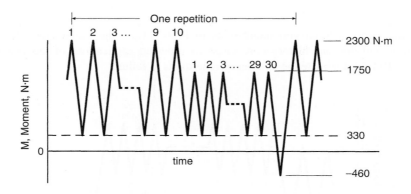

Figure P11.54

Section 11.8

11.55 Consider the center-cracked plate and AISI 4340 steel of Ex. 11.4. Assume that periodic inspections are done with $a_d = 1$ mm every 25,900 cycles, as determined in Ex. 11.4(c).

   (a) What are the safety factors against brittle fracture and against fully plastic yielding for the worst-case crack that might exist just prior to inspection?

   (b) Do these safety factors seem adequate, or should the inspection period be shortened or other action taken to ensure safety?

11.56 A plate of the AISI 4340 steel of Table 11.2 is loaded in tension and may contain an edge crack. It has dimensions, as defined in Fig. 8.12(c), of width $b = 250$ and thickness $t = 25$ mm. Cyclic loading occurs between loads of $P_{min} = 1.7$ and $P_{max} = 3.4$ MN.

   (a) Estimate the number of cycles required to grow a crack to failure, starting from a minimum detectable size of $a_d = 1.3$ mm.

   (b) The desired actual service life is 60,000 cycles, and a safety factor of 3.0 on life is required. Is the design adequate?

   (c) If not, what a_d would have to be found by improved inspection?

(d) If $a_d = 1.3$ mm cannot be improved, what interval of periodic inspections is required?

(e) If neither improved inspection nor periodic inspection is possible, how much must the stresses be lowered while maintaining $R = 0.5$?

11.57 A beam with a rectangular cross section has dimensions, as defined in Fig. 8.13, of $b = 40$ and $t = 20$ mm. Inspection can reliably find cracks only if they are larger than $a = 1.00$ mm, so it must be assumed that a through-thickness edge crack of this size may be present. A cyclic bending moment is applied with $M_{min} = 480$ and $M_{max} = 1200$ N·m, and the material is Man-Ten steel.

(a) Estimate the number of cycles to grow the crack to failure.

(b) What is the safety factor in life if the desired service life is 1,000,000 cycles?

(c) A safety factor in life of 3.00 is required. Is periodic inspection necessary? If so, at what interval of cycles?

(d) For your inspection period from (c), and where the inspection will reliably find any $a > 1.00$ mm, estimate the largest crack size that can be present just prior to inspection.

(e) For the (worst-case) crack size from (d), what are the safety factors against brittle fracture and against fully plastic yielding? Do these seem adequate?

Section 11.10

11.58 Obtain approximate values of the constants A and n of Eq. 11.53 for both sets of data in Fig. 11.38. Comment on the values of n obtained. In each case, by what factor is $\dot{a}$ increased if K is increased by 25%?

11.59 The constants A and n of Eq. 11.53 for soda-lime-silicate glass are approximately $A = 1.67$ and $n = 20.3$, where these values apply for K and $\dot{a}$ in units of MPa$\sqrt{m}$ and m/s, respectively. Assume that this glass contains initial cracks of length $a = 10\ \mu m$ and that these are half-circular surface cracks as in Fig. 8.17(b).

(a) Use Eq. 11.54 to derive a relationship between stress and time to failure for this situation. (Suggestion: Consider whether the life is likely to be significantly affected by a_f.)

(b) Develop similar equations for both $a_i = 5\mu m$ and $a_i = 20\ \mu m$. Then plot all three S versus *time* equations on log–log coordinates, and briefly discuss the dependence of life on stress level and initial crack length.

12

Plastic Deformation Behavior and Models for Materials

OBJECTIVES

- Become familiar with basic forms of stress–strain relationships, including fitting data to these and representing them with spring and slider rheological models.
- Employ deformation plasticity theory to explore the effects of multiaxial states of stress on stress–strain behavior.
- Analyze unloading and cyclic loading behavior for both rheological models and for real materials, including cyclic stress–strain curves, irregular variation of strain with time, and transient behavior such as mean stress relaxation.

12.1 INTRODUCTION

Deformation beyond the point of yielding that is not strongly time dependent, called *plastic deformation*, frequently occurs in engineering components and may need to be analyzed in design or in determining the cause of a failure. During plastic deformation, stresses and strains are no longer proportional, so relationships more general than Hooke's law (Eq. 5.26) are needed to provide an adequate description of the stress–strain behavior.

12.1.1 Significance of Plastic Deformation

Plastic deformation can impair the usefulness of an engineering component by causing large permanent deflections. Also, as already noted in Chapter 10, plastic deformation commonly causes residual stresses to remain after unloading. (See Fig. 10.28.) Residual stresses can either decrease or increase the subsequent resistance of a component to fatigue or environmental cracking, depending on whether the residual stress is tensile or compressive, respectively. Furthermore, the stress-based approach to fatigue, as in Chapter 10, is based primarily on elastic analysis. As a result of this limitation, traditional methods of estimating S-N curves and mean stress effects involve rough empirical adjustments to account for the influence of plastic deformation. The needed adjustments are especially large at short lives and at high mean stresses.

Improved understanding and analysis of permanent deflections, of residual stress, and of yielding during cyclic loading is made possible through a study of plastic deformation. In this chapter, we characterize the plastic deformation behavior of materials in more detail than is provided by the brief introduction in Chapter 5. The topic is extended in Chapter 13 to stress–strain analysis of beams, shafts, and notched members. Information from both this chapter and Chapter 13 is then used in Chapter 14 to present the strain-based approach to fatigue, which considers plasticity effects on fatigue in a fairly complete and rigorous manner.

Plastic deformation is generally considered to be time independent. This simplifying assumption is often a reasonable one for engineering purposes, as long as the always-present time-dependent (creep) deformations are relatively small. Further consideration of time-dependent behavior is postponed until Chapter 15.

12.1.2 Preview of Chapter

In characterizing the plastic deformation behavior of materials, the obvious starting point is to consider stress–strain curves for *monotonic* loading—that is, for loading that proceeds in only one direction, as in Fig. 12.1(a). Mathematical representation $\varepsilon = f(\sigma)$ of such curves is needed, as for later use in Chapter 13 for component analysis. Recalling from Chapter 7 that yielding is affected by

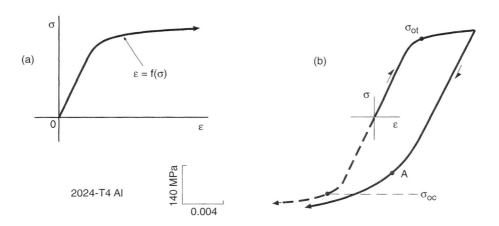

Figure 12.1 Monotonic stress–strain curve (a), and unloading stress–strain curve (b), where the Bauschinger effect causes yielding at A prior to the yield strength σ_{oc} from monotonic compression.

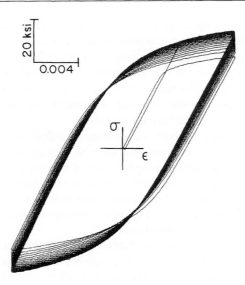

Figure 12.2   Stress–strain response in 2024-T4 aluminum for 20 cycles of completely reversed strain at $\varepsilon_a = 0.01$. (From [Dowling 72]; copyright © ASTM; reprinted with permission.)

the state of stress, we might expect that the stress–strain curve beyond yielding is also affected. This is indeed the case, and we will consider state-of-stress effects on stress–strain curves in some detail.

If the direction of straining is reversed after yielding has occurred, the stress–strain path that is followed differs from the initial monotonic one, as illustrated in Fig. 12.1(b). Yielding on unloading generally occurs prior to the stress reaching the yield strength σ_{oc} for monotonic compression, as at point A. This early yielding behavior is called the *Bauschinger effect*, after the German engineer who first studied it in the 1880s. Unloading stress–strain paths need to be described mathematically for use in predicting behavior after unloading from a severe load, as in estimating residual stresses.

Stress–strain behavior during cyclic loading exhibits a number of complexities. Some example test data are shown in Fig. 12.2. In this case, an aluminum alloy specimen under axial loading was subjected to cyclic straining between the levels $\varepsilon_{\max} = 0.01$ and $\varepsilon_{\min} = -0.01$. Yielding occurs on each half-cycle of loading, and the behavior is observed to gradually change with the number of applied cycles. At least approximate modeling of such behavior is needed in implementing the strain-based approach to fatigue. Rheological models composed of linear springs and frictional sliders, as introduced in Chapter 5, are found to be particularly useful for this purpose.

12.1.3 Additional Comments

Before proceeding in more detail, we note that the present chapter and the next are intended only as a brief introduction to the subject of *plasticity*. Furthermore, the emphasis on rheological modeling and cyclic loading is somewhat unconventional compared with the treatments found in traditional (graduate-level) textbooks on the subject, such as Mendelson (1968). But more recent textbooks, such as Khan (1995) and Skrzypek (1993), do tend to include increased coverage of cyclic loading.

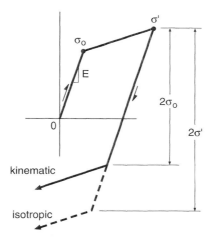

Figure 12.3 Differing unloading behavior for kinematic and isotropic hardening.

Here, we will consider primarily the total strain theory of plasticity, also called *deformation theory*, rather than the more advanced *incremental theory*. Also, the rheological models used are consistent with the behavior called *kinematic hardening*, the alternative choice of *isotropic hardening* not being employed, as it is a poor model for real materials.

These two hardening rules are illustrated for unloading behavior in Fig. 12.3. Kinematic hardening predicts that yielding in the reverse direction occurs when the stress change from the unloading point is twice the monotonic yield strength, $\Delta\sigma = 2\sigma_o$. In contrast, isotropic hardening predicts yielding later at $\Delta\sigma = 2\sigma'$, where σ' is the highest stress reached prior to unloading. Thus, kinematic hardening predicts a Bauschinger effect as observed in real materials, but isotropic hardening predicts the opposite.

12.2 STRESS–STRAIN CURVES

Two simple elasto-plastic stress–strain curves and the corresponding rheological models are shown in Fig. 12.4. Note that these rheological models follow the conventions introduced in Chapter 5, and they contain only linear springs and frictional sliders, there being no time-dependent dashpot elements. Forces on such models are proportional to stress in the material being modeled, and displacements are proportional to strains. Additional curves involving nonlinear hardening are shown in Fig. 12.5.

12.2.1 Elastic, Perfectly Plastic Relationship

An elastic, perfectly plastic stress–strain relationship is flat beyond yielding, as illustrated by Fig. 12.4(a) and the equations

$$\sigma = E\varepsilon \qquad (\sigma \le \sigma_o)$$
$$\sigma = \sigma_o \qquad \left(\varepsilon \ge \frac{\sigma_o}{E}\right) \tag{12.1}$$

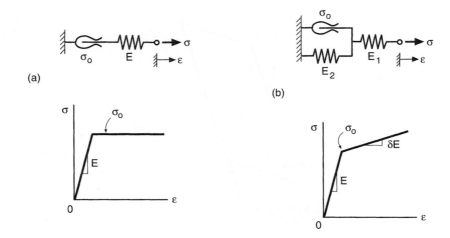

Figure 12.4 Stress–strain curves and rheological models for (a) elastic, perfectly plastic behavior and (b) elastic, linear-hardening behavior.

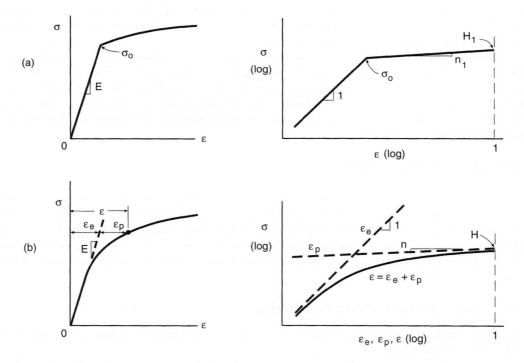

Figure 12.5 Stress–strain curves on linear and logarithmic coordinates for (a) an elastic, power-hardening relationship and (b) the Ramberg–Osgood relationship.

where σ_o is the yield strength. This form is a reasonable approximation for the initial yielding behavior of certain metals and other materials. Also, it is often used as a simple idealization to make rough estimates, even where the stress–strain curve has a more complex shape.

Beyond yielding, the strain is the sum of elastic and plastic parts:

$$\varepsilon = \varepsilon_e + \varepsilon_p = \frac{\sigma}{E} + \varepsilon_p \qquad \left(\varepsilon > \frac{\sigma_o}{E}\right) \tag{12.2}$$

In the rheological model, the elastic strain ε_e is analogous to the deflection of the linear spring of stiffness E, and the plastic strain ε_p is analogous to the movement of the frictional slider.

12.2.2 Elastic, Linear-Hardening Relationship

Elastic, linear-hardening behavior, Fig. 12.4(b), is useful as a rough approximation for stress–strain curves that rise appreciably following yielding. Such a relationship requires an additional constant, δ. This is the *reduction factor* for the slope following yielding, the slope before yielding being the elastic modulus E and the one after yielding being δE. The value of δ can vary from zero to unity, with smaller values giving flatter postyielding behavior. Also, $\delta = 0$ gives a special case that corresponds to the elastic, perfectly plastic relationship.

An equation for the postyield portion can be obtained by taking the slope between any point on this part of the curve and the yield point:

$$\delta E = \frac{\sigma - \sigma_o}{\varepsilon - \varepsilon_o} \tag{12.3}$$

Noting that the yield strain is given by $\varepsilon_o = \sigma_o/E$, and solving for stress, allows the entire relationship to be specified:

$$\begin{aligned}
\sigma &= E\varepsilon & (\sigma \le \sigma_o) \\
\sigma &= (1 - \delta)\,\sigma_o + \delta E\varepsilon & (\sigma \ge \sigma_o)
\end{aligned} \tag{12.4}$$

It is sometimes convenient to solve the second equation for strain:

$$\varepsilon = \frac{\sigma_o}{E} + \frac{(\sigma - \sigma_o)}{\delta E} \qquad (\sigma \ge \sigma_o) \tag{12.5}$$

The response of the rheological model is the sum of the elastic strain in spring E_1 and any plastic strain in the spring–slider (E_2, σ_o) parallel combination. No plastic strain occurs until the stress exceeds the slider yield strength σ_o, and beyond this point the deflection of spring E_2 is also equal to the plastic strain. Noting that, beyond yielding, spring E_2 is subjected to a stress of $(\sigma - \sigma_o)$, we can add the deflections in the two springs to obtain the total strain:

$$\varepsilon = \frac{\sigma}{E_1} + \frac{(\sigma - \sigma_o)}{E_2} \qquad (\sigma \ge \sigma_o) \tag{12.6}$$

Equations 12.5 and 12.6 are equivalent if the constants are related by

$$E = E_1, \qquad \delta E = \frac{E_1 E_2}{E_1 + E_2} \tag{12.7}$$

The slope δE corresponds to the stiffness of the two springs E_1 and E_2 in series.

12.2.3 Elastic, Power-Hardening Relationship

Reasonably accurate representation of the stress–strain curves of real materials generally requires a more complex mathematical relationship than those described so far. One form that is sometimes used assumes that stress is proportional to strain raised to a power, with this being applied only beyond a yield strength σ_o:

$$
\begin{aligned}
\sigma &= E\varepsilon & (\sigma \le \sigma_o) & \quad \text{(a)} \\
\sigma &= H_1 \varepsilon^{n_1} & (\sigma \ge \sigma_o) & \quad \text{(b)}
\end{aligned}
\tag{12.8}
$$

The term *strain hardening exponent* is used for n_1, and H_1 is an additional constant.

The most convenient means of fitting this relationship to a particular set of stress–strain data is to make a log–log plot of stress versus strain, where for the postyield portion a straight line is expected. This is illustrated on the right in Fig. 12.5(a). The value of σ at $\varepsilon = 1$ is H_1. Assuming that the logarithmic decades are the same length in both directions, we find that the slope of the line is n_1. On the same graph, the elastic region equation, $\sigma = E\varepsilon$, also forms a straight line, but with a slope of unity, and the two lines intersect at $\sigma = \sigma_o$. Values of the exponent n_1 are typically in the range 0.05 to 0.4 for metals where this equation fits well.

Equation 12.8(b) can be easily expressed in terms of strain:

$$\varepsilon = \left(\frac{\sigma}{H_1} \right)^{1/n_1} \qquad (\sigma \ge \sigma_o) \tag{12.9}$$

Also, the yield strength is not an independent constant, as any two of σ_o, H_1, and n_1 may be used to calculate the remaining one. An equation relating these can be obtained by applying both Eqs. 12.8(a) and (b) at the point $(\varepsilon_o, \sigma_o)$ and combining the results:

$$\sigma_o = E \left(\frac{H_1}{E} \right)^{1/(1-n_1)} \tag{12.10}$$

12.2.4 Ramberg–Osgood Relationship

A relationship similar to that proposed in a report by Ramberg and Osgood in 1943 is frequently used. Here, elastic and plastic strains, ε_e and ε_p, are considered separately and summed. An exponential relationship is used, but it is applied to the plastic strain, rather than to the total strain as before:

$$\sigma = H\varepsilon_p^n \tag{12.11}$$

This n is also called a *strain hardening exponent*, despite the fact that it is defined differently than the previous n_1.

Elastic strain is proportional to stress according to $\varepsilon_e = \sigma/E$, and plastic strain ε_p is the deviation from the slope E, as shown in Fig. 12.5(b). Solving Eq. 12.11 for plastic strain and adding the elastic and plastic strains gives an equation for total strain:

$$\varepsilon = \varepsilon_e + \varepsilon_p, \qquad \varepsilon = \frac{\sigma}{E} + \left(\frac{\sigma}{H}\right)^{1/n} \tag{12.12}$$

This relationship cannot be solved explicitly for stress. It provides a single smooth curve for all values of σ and does not exhibit a distinct yield point. Thus, it contrasts with the previously described elastic, power-hardening form, which is discontinuous at a distinct yield point σ_o. However, a yield strength may be defined as the stress corresponding to a given plastic strain offset, such as $\varepsilon_{po} = 0.002$, as in Fig. 4.11(a). Equation 12.11 then gives the offset yield strength:

$$\sigma_o = H(0.002)^n \tag{12.13}$$

Constants for Eq. 12.12 for a particular set of stress–strain data are obtained by making a log–log plot of stress versus *plastic* strain (σ versus ε_p), as illustrated on the right in Fig. 12.5(b). The constant H is the value of σ at $\varepsilon_p = 1$, and n is the slope on the log–log plot if the logarithmic decades in the two directions are of equal length. A plot of σ versus *total* strain ε is a curve on the log–log plot. At small strains, this curve approaches the line of unity slope corresponding to elastic strains; at large strains, it approaches the plastic strain line of slope n.

The Ramberg–Osgood equation and the power-hardening relationship are essentially equivalent if the strains are sufficiently large that the plastic portion dominates, so that the elastic portion can be considered to be negligible. The first term of Eq. 12.12 is then negligible, and values of H and n fitted to data at large strains for ductile materials will be similar to values of H_1 and n_1 fitted to the same data.

For tension tests, note that the Ramberg–Osgood form is often applied to true stresses and strains, as already discussed in connection with Eq. 4.25.

Example 12.1

Some test data points on the monotonic stress–strain curve of 7075-T651 aluminum for uniaxial stress are given in Table E12.1. Obtain values of the constants for a stress–strain curve of the Ramberg–Osgood form, Eq. 12.12, that fits these data.

Solution   The elastic modulus E is needed, as are the constants H and n. Prior to fitting, the strains given as percentages need to be converted to dimensionless values, $\varepsilon = \varepsilon_\%/100$. Then, plot all of the data on linear–linear coordinates as in Fig. E12.1(a), Curve 1. The overall trend is a continuous curve that gradually deviates from an elastic slope, so that attempting a fit to Eq. 12.12 is reasonable. The first three nonzero data points appear to form a straight line through the origin, which is confirmed by plotting these on a sensitive strain scale (Curve 2). Fitting a line $\sigma = E\varepsilon$ gives an elastic modulus value that is rounded to $E = 71,000\,\text{MPa}$.

We can now proceed to fit the constants H and n for the Eq. 12.11 relationship, $\sigma = H\varepsilon_p^n$. First, plastic strains ε_p are calculated for all of the data points where some nonlinearity is apparent in Curve 1 of Fig. E12.1(a), using

Table E12.1

Test Data		Calculations				Comment
σ, MPa	ε, %	ε	ε_p	$\log \sigma$	$\log \varepsilon_p$	
0	0	0	—	—	—	Used for E
135.3	0.191	0.00191	—	—	—	Used for E
270	0.381	0.00381	—	—	—	Used for E
362	0.509	0.00509	—	—	—	Used for E
406	0.576	0.00576	4.17×10^{-5}	—	—	Not used
433	0.740	0.00740	0.001301	2.636	−2.886	Used for H, n
451	0.895	0.00895	0.002598	2.654	−2.585	Used for H, n
469	1.280	0.01280	0.006194	2.671	−2.208	Used for H, n
487	2.290	0.02290	0.01604	2.688	−1.795	Used for H, n
505	4.570	0.04570	0.03859	2.703	−1.414	Used for H, n

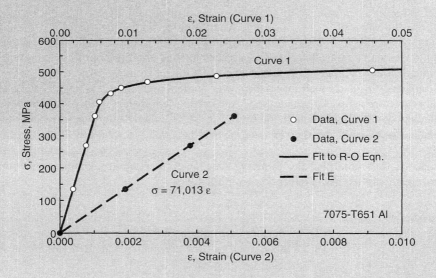

Figure E12.1(a)

$$\varepsilon_p = \varepsilon - \frac{\sigma}{E}$$

The resulting values are shown in Table E12.1. (Note that Eq. 12.12 implies that plastic strains exist at all stress values. But at low stresses these become so small that they cannot be readily measured in the laboratory, becoming essentially negligible.) Next, the stress versus plastic strain data are plotted on log–log coordinates as shown in Fig. E12.1(b). The smallest ε_p value departs from the linear trend of the other data and is so small that its accuracy is questionable; hence, this

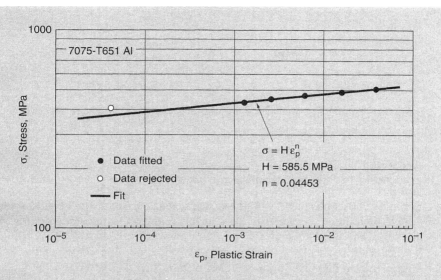

Figure E12.1(b)

data point is rejected from the fitting process. The remaining data are then fitted to Eq. 12.11. Taking logarithms of both sides of Eq. 12.11 gives

$$\log \sigma = n \log \varepsilon_p + \log H$$

This is a straight line on a log–log plot; that is,

$$y = mx + b$$

where

$$y = \log \sigma, \qquad x = \log \varepsilon_p, \qquad m = n, \qquad b = \log H$$

Performing a linear least-squares fit on this basis gives

$$m = n = 0.04453 \qquad\qquad\qquad \textbf{Ans.}$$

$$b = 2.7675, \qquad H = 10^b = 585.5 \text{ MPa} \qquad\qquad \textbf{Ans.}$$

Discussion   Equation 12.11 with the constants evaluated is thus

$$\sigma = 585.5 \varepsilon_p^{0.04453} \text{ MPa}$$

The resulting straight line on a log–log plot of σ versus ε_p is shown in Fig. E12.1(b). Substituting the constants obtained into Eq. 12.12 gives a relationship for the total strain:

$$\varepsilon = \frac{\sigma}{71,000} + \left(\frac{\sigma}{585.5}\right)^{1/0.04453}$$

Here, σ is in units of MPa. Entering a number of values of σ into this equation and calculating the corresponding total strains ε gives Curve 1 plotted in Fig. E12.1(a). The original data are in good agreement with the fitted curve.

12.2.5 Rheological Modeling of Nonlinear Hardening

A stress–strain curve of either the elastic, power-hardening, or Ramberg–Osgood types can be modeled by approximating it as a series of straight line segments, as illustrated in Fig. 12.6. The first segment ends at the yield strength for the elastic, power-hardening case and at a low stress where the plastic strain is small for the Ramberg–Osgood case. The corresponding rheological model has a linear spring that gives an initial elastic slope, and then a series of spring and slider parallel combinations that cause nonlinear behavior. The yield stresses for the various sliders have

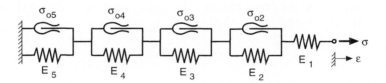

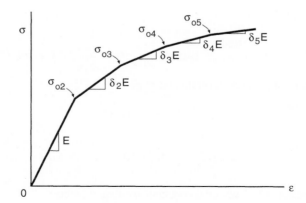

Figure 12.6 Multistage spring and slider model for nonlinear-hardening stress–strain curves.

increasingly higher values and correspond to the stresses at the ends of the straight line segments on the stress–strain curve. The slope of any segment corresponds to the stiffness of all the springs in series for which the associated sliders have yielded:

$$\delta_j E = \frac{1}{\dfrac{1}{E_1} + \dfrac{1}{E_2} + \dfrac{1}{E_3} + \cdots + \dfrac{1}{E_j}} \qquad (12.14)$$

Here, δ_j is the slope reduction factor for the segment that starts at σ_{oj}.

The strain in the model is the sum of the strains in each stage:

$$\varepsilon = \varepsilon_1 + \varepsilon_2 + \varepsilon_3 + \cdots + \varepsilon_j \qquad (12.15)$$

Until a slider yields, it absorbs all of the stress, and the associated spring absorbs none, as the strain in that stage is zero. Once a slider, say, the ith one, has moved, any stress in excess of that slider's yield stress must be resisted by the associated spring. Hence, the total stress is

$$\sigma = \sigma_{oi} + E_i \varepsilon_i \qquad (\sigma > \sigma_{oi}) \qquad (12.16)$$

Solving for strain gives

$$\varepsilon_i = \frac{\sigma - \sigma_{oi}}{E_i} \qquad (\sigma > \sigma_{oi}) \qquad (12.17)$$

This equation applies to each stage that has yielded, so that if all sliders up to the jth one have yielded, the strain is

$$\varepsilon = \frac{\sigma}{E_1} + \frac{\sigma - \sigma_{o2}}{E_2} + \frac{\sigma - \sigma_{o3}}{E_3} + \cdots + \frac{\sigma - \sigma_{oj}}{E_j} \qquad (12.18)$$

Evaluating $d\sigma/d\varepsilon$ to get the slope verifies Eq. 12.14.

12.3 THREE-DIMENSIONAL STRESS–STRAIN RELATIONSHIPS

From Chapters 5 and 7, the presence of stress components in more than one direction affects both a material's elastic stiffness and its yield strength. During plastic deformation, the state of stress continues to affect the behavior. Relationships between stress and strain are therefore needed for plastic deformation for the general three-dimensional case.

The generalized Hooke's law for elastic strains was previously developed in Chapter 5 as Eqs. 5.26 and 5.27. These relationships apply not only prior to yielding, but also after yielding, except that in the latter case they give only the elastic portions of the strains:

$$\varepsilon_{ex} = \frac{1}{E}\left[\sigma_x - \nu\left(\sigma_y + \sigma_z\right)\right] \qquad\qquad \text{(a)}$$

$$\varepsilon_{ey} = \frac{1}{E}\left[\sigma_y - \nu\left(\sigma_x + \sigma_z\right)\right] \qquad\qquad \text{(b)}$$

$$\text{(12.19)}$$

$$\varepsilon_{ez} = \frac{1}{E}\left[\sigma_z - \nu\left(\sigma_x + \sigma_y\right)\right] \qquad\qquad \text{(c)}$$

$$\gamma_{exy} = \frac{\tau_{xy}}{G}, \qquad \gamma_{eyz} = \frac{\tau_{yz}}{G}, \qquad \gamma_{ezx} = \frac{\tau_{zx}}{G} \qquad \text{(d)}$$

Subscripts e have been added to indicate that these are elastic strains, and the elastic constants E, ν, and G are defined in the usual manner.

The various strain components also include plastic portions that must be added to the elastic portions to obtain total strains:

$$\varepsilon_x = \varepsilon_{ex} + \varepsilon_{px}, \qquad\quad \varepsilon_y = \varepsilon_{ey} + \varepsilon_{py}, \qquad\quad \varepsilon_z = \varepsilon_{ez} + \varepsilon_{pz}$$

$$\gamma_{xy} = \gamma_{exy} + \gamma_{pxy}, \qquad \gamma_{yz} = \gamma_{eyz} + \gamma_{pyz}, \qquad \gamma_{zx} = \gamma_{ezx} + \gamma_{pzx} \qquad \text{(12.20)}$$

Shear strains, γ_{xy}, etc., are *engineering shear strains* as employed in Chapters 5 and 6 and in most elementary mechanics of materials textbooks. These values are twice the *tensor shear strains* often used in advanced textbooks.

12.3.1 Deformation Plasticity Theory

In Chapter 7, it was noted that yielding for a given material occurs at a value of *effective stress* $\bar{\sigma}$ that is approximately the same for all states of stress. Equation 7.35 gives $\bar{\sigma}$ as a function of the principal normal stresses:

$$\bar{\sigma} = \frac{1}{\sqrt{2}}\sqrt{(\sigma_1 - \sigma_2)^2 + (\sigma_2 - \sigma_3)^2 + (\sigma_3 - \sigma_1)^2} \qquad \text{(12.21)}$$

Recall that this particular $\bar{\sigma}$ is proportional to the octahedral shear stress and reduces to $\bar{\sigma} = \sigma_1$ for the uniaxial case.

Corresponding strain quantities are needed. The *effective plastic strain* is a function of the plastic strains in the principal directions and is given by

$$\bar{\varepsilon}_p = \frac{\sqrt{2}}{3}\sqrt{(\varepsilon_{p1} - \varepsilon_{p2})^2 + (\varepsilon_{p2} - \varepsilon_{p3})^2 + (\varepsilon_{p3} - \varepsilon_{p1})^2} \qquad \text{(12.22)}$$

where subscripts (1, 2, 3) indicate the (x, y, z) axes that are the principal stress directions. This $\bar{\varepsilon}_p$ is proportional to the plastic shear strain on the octahedral planes and reduces to $\bar{\varepsilon}_p = \varepsilon_{p1}$ for the uniaxial case. The *effective total strain* is the sum of elastic and plastic parts:

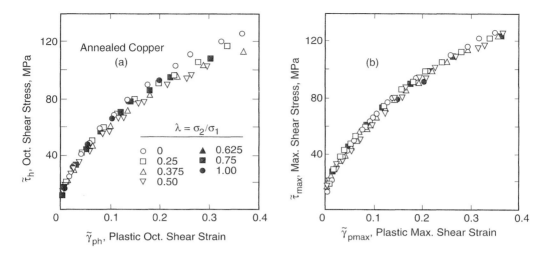

Figure 12.7   Correlation of true stresses and true plastic strains from combined axial and pressure loading of thin-walled copper tubes in terms of (a) octahedral shear stress and strain, and (b) maximum shear stress and strain. (Adapted from [Davis 43]; used with permission of ASME.)

$$\bar{\varepsilon} = \frac{\bar{\sigma}}{E} + \bar{\varepsilon}_p \tag{12.23}$$

Defined in this manner, $\bar{\varepsilon}$ reduces to ε_1 for the uniaxial case. A key feature of deformation theory is its prediction that a single curve relates $\bar{\sigma}$ and $\bar{\varepsilon}$ for all states of stress. Some test data on thin-walled copper tubes that approximately verify this are shown in Fig. 12.7(a). (Note that the octahedral shear stress τ_h is proportional to $\bar{\sigma}$, and the plastic octahedral shear strain γ_{ph} is proportional to $\bar{\varepsilon}_p$.)

Equations analogous to Hooke's law are used to relate stresses and plastic strains:

$$\varepsilon_{px} = \frac{1}{E_p} \left[\sigma_x - 0.5 \left(\sigma_y + \sigma_z \right) \right] \tag{a}$$

$$\varepsilon_{py} = \frac{1}{E_p} \left[\sigma_y - 0.5 \left(\sigma_x + \sigma_z \right) \right] \tag{b}$$

$$\varepsilon_{pz} = \frac{1}{E_p} \left[\sigma_z - 0.5 \left(\sigma_x + \sigma_y \right) \right] \tag{c}$$

$$\gamma_{pxy} = \frac{3}{E_p} \tau_{xy}, \qquad \gamma_{pyz} = \frac{3}{E_p} \tau_{yz}, \qquad \gamma_{pzx} = \frac{3}{E_p} \tau_{zx} \tag{d}$$

(12.24)

Comparing these with Hooke's law, Eq. 12.19, we replace the elastic modulus E by a *plastic modulus* E_p:

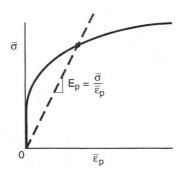

Figure 12.8 Definition of the plastic modulus as the secant modulus to a point on the effective stress versus effective plastic strain curve.

$$E_p = \frac{\bar{\sigma}}{\bar{\varepsilon}_p} \tag{12.25}$$

Graphically, E_p corresponds to a secant modulus drawn to a point on the $\bar{\sigma}$ versus $\bar{\varepsilon}_p$ curve, as shown in Fig. 12.8. Hence, E_p is a variable that decreases as plastic deformation progresses along the $\bar{\sigma}$ versus $\bar{\varepsilon}_p$ curve for the material.

12.3.2 Discussion

Poisson's ratio v in Hooke's law is replaced by 0.5 in Eq. 12.24, which is equivalent to the assumption that plastic strains do not contribute to volume change. This is supported by experimental evidence in metals, and is consistent with the physical mechanism of plastic strain being slip of crystal planes, as discussed in Chapter 2. Hence, the volumetric strain ε_v is given by Eq. 5.35 even in the presence of plastic strains. Further comparing Eqs. 12.19 and 12.24, we replace the elastic shear modulus G by $E_p/3$. This can be verified by using Eq. 12.24 to derive a plastic shear modulus G_p in a manner parallel to the derivation leading to $G = E/[2(1 + v)]$ in Section 5.3.3. The presence of 0.5 in place of v in the equation is seen to give $G_p = E_p/3$.

    Equations 12.19 and 12.24 can be combined to obtain expressions for the components of total strain that also have the form of Hooke's law. To derive these, add the elastic component from any one of Eq. 12.19(a) to (d) to the corresponding plastic component from Eq. 12.24(a) to (d). For the normal strains, using the x-direction as an example, we obtain

$$\varepsilon_x = \varepsilon_{ex} + \varepsilon_{px} = \frac{1}{E}[\sigma_x - v(\sigma_y + \sigma_z)] + \frac{1}{E_p}[\sigma_x - 0.5(\sigma_y + \sigma_z)] \tag{12.26}$$

Substituting $E_p = \bar{\sigma}/\bar{\varepsilon}_p$ and invoking Eq. 12.23 leads to the desired expression for the x-direction, and additional equations for the y- and z-directions are similarly obtained.

$$\varepsilon_x = \frac{1}{E_t} \, [\sigma_x - \tilde{\nu} \, (\sigma_y + \sigma_z)] \qquad \text{(a)}$$

$$\varepsilon_y = \frac{1}{E_t} \, [\sigma_y - \tilde{\nu} \, (\sigma_x + \sigma_z)] \qquad \text{(b)} \qquad (12.27)$$

$$\varepsilon_z = \frac{1}{E_t} \, [\sigma_z - \tilde{\nu} \, (\sigma_x + \sigma_y)] \qquad \text{(c)}$$

$$\text{where} \quad E_t = \frac{\bar{\sigma}}{\bar{\varepsilon}}, \quad \text{and} \quad \tilde{\nu} = \frac{\nu \bar{\sigma} + 0.5 E \bar{\varepsilon}_p}{E \bar{\varepsilon}} \qquad \text{(d, e)}$$

The variable E_t is the secant modulus to a point on the effective stress versus effective *total* strain curve. And the quantity $\tilde{\nu}$ can be viewed as a *generalized Poisson's ratio*, which turns out to be the weighted average between ν and 0.5, according to the split of the effective total strain $\bar{\varepsilon}$ into elastic and plastic components, $\bar{\sigma}/E$ and $\bar{\varepsilon}_p$. Hence, at small strains where the elastic component is dominant, we have $\tilde{\nu} = \nu$, with a continuous variation in $\tilde{\nu}$ as strain increases, approaching $\tilde{\nu} = 0.5$ at large strains where the plastic component is dominant.

Also, the effective total strain $\bar{\varepsilon}$ can be expressed directly in terms of the total strain components, providing an alternative to Eq. 12.23. First, let the x-y-z axes be the special case of the principal stress axes, 1-2-3. Then solve Eqs. 12.27(a), (b), and (c) for the principal stresses, σ_1, σ_2, and σ_3, to express these as functions of the total strains in the principal directions, ε_1, ε_2, and ε_3. Substituting these stresses and $E_t = \bar{\sigma}/\bar{\varepsilon}$ into Eq. 12.21, followed by algebraic manipulation, gives the desired result:

$$\bar{\varepsilon} = \frac{1}{\sqrt{2}\,(1 + \tilde{\nu})} \sqrt{(\varepsilon_1 - \varepsilon_2)^2 + (\varepsilon_2 - \varepsilon_3)^2 + (\varepsilon_3 - \varepsilon_1)^2} \qquad (12.28)$$

The preceding development derives from octahedral shear stress and plastic shear strain. However, a similar plasticity theory may be formulated on the basis of the maximum shear stress and plastic shear strain. The particular test results of Fig. 12.7 correlate even better on this basis, as shown in (b). But the use of $\bar{\sigma}$ and $\bar{\varepsilon}_p$ as described is more conventional and will be the only approach pursued here.

12.3.3 The Effective Stress–Strain Curve

Assume that the uniaxial stress–strain curve for a given material is known:

$$\varepsilon_1 = f\,(\sigma_1) \qquad (\sigma_2 = \sigma_3 = 0) \qquad (12.29)$$

For deformation plasticity theory in the form just given, the curve relating effective stress and effective strain is the same as the uniaxial one:

$$\bar{\varepsilon} = f(\bar{\sigma}) \qquad (12.30)$$

This can be verified by examining the uniaxial case, $\sigma_2 = \sigma_3 = 0$, for which Eq. 12.21 gives $\bar{\sigma} = \sigma_1$. Since the x-y-z axes are in this case the 1-2-3 principal axes, Eq. 12.24 gives plastic strains in the 2- and 3-directions that are negative and half as large as the plastic strain in the stress direction; that is, $\varepsilon_{p2} = \varepsilon_{p3} = -0.5\varepsilon_{p1}$. Substitution into Eq. 12.22 then gives $\bar{\varepsilon}_p = \varepsilon_{p1}$, so that the effective total strain from Eq. 12.23 is $\bar{\varepsilon} = \varepsilon_1$. Finally, Eq. 12.30 is verified by substituting $\bar{\sigma} = \sigma_1$ and $\bar{\varepsilon} = \varepsilon_1$ into Eq. 12.29.

Hence, if the uniaxial stress–strain curve for a given material is known, this can be taken as the effective stress–strain curve. This generalization then allows stress–strain curves to be obtained for other states of stress that might be of interest. Details for the particular case of plane stress follow.

12.3.4 Application to Plane Stress

Consider the case of plane stress where the coordinate axes chosen are the principal axes, for which the shear components are zero:

$$\sigma_x = \sigma_1, \qquad \sigma_y = \sigma_2 = \lambda\sigma_1, \qquad \sigma_z = \sigma_3 = 0 \tag{12.31}$$

Here, the ratio $\lambda = \sigma_2/\sigma_1$ is used as a convenience. Equation 12.21 gives the effective stress for this situation:

$$\bar{\sigma} = \sigma_1\sqrt{1 - \lambda + \lambda^2} \tag{12.32}$$

The total strain in the direction of σ_1 is composed of elastic and plastic parts:

$$\varepsilon_1 = \varepsilon_{e1} + \varepsilon_{p1} \tag{12.33}$$

The elastic part may be evaluated from Eq. 12.19(a), and the plastic part is obtained from Eq. 12.24(a), with $E_p = \bar{\sigma}/\bar{\varepsilon}_p$ substituted:

$$\varepsilon_{e1} = \frac{\sigma_1}{E}(1 - \nu\lambda), \qquad \varepsilon_{p1} = \frac{\sigma_1\bar{\varepsilon}_p}{\bar{\sigma}}(1 - 0.5\lambda) \tag{12.34}$$

Taking $\bar{\varepsilon} = f(\bar{\sigma})$ as any particular uniaxial curve, Eq. 12.23 gives

$$\bar{\varepsilon}_p = \bar{\varepsilon} - \frac{\bar{\sigma}}{E} = f(\bar{\sigma}) - \frac{\bar{\sigma}}{E} \tag{12.35}$$

Substituting this for $\bar{\varepsilon}_p$ and then combining Eq. 12.33 and 12.34 yields

$$\varepsilon_1 = \frac{1 - \nu\lambda}{E}\sigma_1 + \frac{(1 - 0.5\lambda)\,\sigma_1}{\bar{\sigma}}\left[f(\bar{\sigma}) - \frac{\bar{\sigma}}{E}\right] \tag{12.36}$$

where $\bar{\sigma}$ is obtained from Eq. 12.32.

Hence, for any particular uniaxial curve, $\bar{\varepsilon} = f(\bar{\sigma})$, and for any particular biaxial state of stress as given by λ, this equation provides a relationship between σ_1 and the strain ε_1 in the same direction. Equations can be similarly developed for the other strain components, ε_2 and ε_3, as functions of σ_1 and λ. More general equations for the case of nonzero σ_3 can also be developed by a similar procedure.

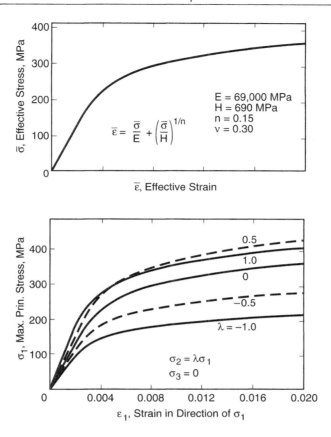

Figure 12.9   Estimated effect of biaxial stress on a Ramberg–Osgood stress–strain curve. (The constants correspond to a fictitious aluminum alloy.)

Equation 12.36 does not apply for an elastic, perfectly plastic material beyond yielding, as no $\bar{\varepsilon} = f(\bar{\sigma})$ can be defined. In this case, Eq. 12.19 applies up to yielding, and the new yield stress can be estimated by substituting $\bar{\sigma} = \sigma_o$ into Eq. 12.32, where σ_o is the uniaxial yield strength. This gives

$$\sigma_1 = \frac{E}{1 - \nu\lambda}\varepsilon_1 \qquad (\bar{\sigma} \leq \sigma_o) \qquad \text{(a)}$$

$$\sigma_1 = \frac{\sigma_o}{\sqrt{1 - \lambda + \lambda^2}} \qquad \left(\bar{\varepsilon} \geq \frac{\sigma_o}{E}\right) \qquad \text{(b)}$$

(12.37)

For other discontinuous stress–strain curves with a distinct yield point, apply Eq. 12.37(a) for the elastic portion; beyond this, employ Eq. 12.36 with the particular postyield $\bar{\varepsilon} = f(\bar{\sigma})$ that is of interest.

As an example of the use of Eq. 12.36, consider a uniaxial curve that fits the Ramberg–Osgood form, Eq. 12.12, so that

$$\bar{\varepsilon} = f(\bar{\sigma}) = \frac{\bar{\sigma}}{E} + \left(\frac{\bar{\sigma}}{H}\right)^{1/n} \tag{12.38}$$

Substituting this $\bar{\varepsilon} = f(\bar{\sigma})$ into Eq. 12.36, and applying the $\bar{\sigma}$ expression of Eq. 12.32, gives

$$\varepsilon_1 = (1 - \nu\lambda)\frac{\sigma_1}{E} + (1 - 0.5\lambda)\left(1 - \lambda + \lambda^2\right)^{(1-n)/(2n)}\left(\frac{\sigma_1}{H}\right)^{1/n} \tag{12.39}$$

An example of the use of Eq. 12.39 to estimate the effects of various transverse stresses on the σ_1 versus ε_1 curve is given in Fig. 12.9. Note that transverse tension, $\lambda > 0$, raises the stress–strain curve, whereas transverse compression, $\lambda < 0$, lowers it.

Example 12.2

A material has the Ramberg–Osgood uniaxial stress–strain curve given by the constants of Fig. 12.9. Write the equation relating the principal stress and strain σ_1 and ε_1 for the case of plane stress, $\sigma_3 = 0$, with $\lambda = \sigma_2/\sigma_1 = 1.0$.

Solution   Equation 12.39 applies. The following constants for the uniaxial (same as effective) stress–strain curve are given in Fig. 12.9:

$$E = 69,000\,\text{MPa}, \qquad H = 690\,\text{MPa}, \qquad n = 0.15, \qquad \nu = 0.3$$

Substituting these values and $\lambda = 1.0$ into Eq. 12.39 gives numerical factors preceding each term:

$$\varepsilon_1 = 0.700\frac{\sigma_1}{69,000} + 0.500\left(\frac{\sigma_1}{690}\right)^{1/0.15}$$

Consolidating the numerical constants then gives

$$\varepsilon_1 = \frac{\sigma_1}{98,570} + \left(\frac{\sigma_1}{765.6}\right)^{1/0.15} \qquad\qquad \textbf{Ans.}$$

A plot of this equation corresponds to the $\lambda = 1.0$ line in Fig. 12.9. Note that this equation has the same form as the original uniaxial one, Eq. 12.12, except that new values appear in place of E and H.

Example 12.3

A thin-walled tubular pressure vessel of radius r and wall thickness t has closed ends and is made of a material having a uniaxial stress–strain curve of the Ramberg–Osgood form, Eq. 12.12. If the internal pressure p is increased monotonically, derive an equation for the relative change in radius, $\Delta r/r$, as a function of p and the various constants involved.

Solution   The principal stresses are

$$\sigma_1 = \frac{pr}{t}, \qquad \sigma_2 = \frac{pr}{2t}, \qquad \sigma_3 \approx 0$$

where σ_1 is in the hoop direction and σ_2 is in the longitudinal direction. The strain ε_1 in the hoop direction is the ratio of the change in circumference to the original circumference, so that

$$\varepsilon_1 = \frac{\Delta\,(2\pi r)}{2\pi r} = \frac{\Delta r}{r}$$

Since we have plane stress, $\lambda = \sigma_2/\sigma_1 = 0.5$ can be substituted into Eq. 12.39, which gives

$$\frac{\Delta r}{r} = \varepsilon_1 = (1 - 0.5\nu)\,\frac{\sigma_1}{E} + (0.75)(0.75)^{(1-n)/(2n)}\left(\frac{\sigma_1}{H}\right)^{1/n}$$

Substitution of σ_1 and manipulation gives the desired result:

$$\frac{\Delta r}{r} = \left(1 - \frac{\nu}{2}\right)\frac{pr}{tE} + \frac{\sqrt{3}}{2}\left(\frac{\sqrt{3}\,pr}{2tH}\right)^{1/n} \qquad\qquad \textbf{Ans.}$$

Example 12.4

Consider the state of stress $\sigma_2 = \sigma_3 = 0.5\sigma_1$ applied to a material that follows the Ramberg–Osgood uniaxial stress–strain curve, Eq. 12.12. Derive an equation for the strain ε_1 in the direction of σ_1 as a function of σ_1 and material constants E, H, and n from the uniaxial curve.

Solution   Since this is not a case of plane stress, Eqs. 12.36 and 12.39 do not apply. However, by following a procedure parallel to that employed for deriving these in Section 12.3.4, we can proceed. First, apply Eqs. 12.19(a) and 12.24(a), letting the principal axes 1-2-3 be the x-y-z axes.

$$\varepsilon_{e1} = \frac{1}{E}[\sigma_1 - \nu(\sigma_2 + \sigma_3)] = \frac{1}{E}[\sigma_1 - \nu(0.5\sigma_1 + 0.5\sigma_1)] = \frac{(1 - \nu)\sigma_1}{E}$$

$$\varepsilon_{p1} = \frac{1}{E_p}[\sigma_1 - 0.5(\sigma_2 + \sigma_3)] = \frac{1}{E_p}[\sigma_1 - 0.5(0.5\sigma_1 + 0.5\sigma_1)] = \frac{\sigma_1}{2E_p}$$

To evaluate the variable $E_p = \bar{\sigma}/\bar{\varepsilon}_p$, we need an expression for $\bar{\varepsilon}_p$ for the Ramberg–Osgood form, which can be obtained from Eqs. 12.23 and 12.38.

$$\bar{\varepsilon}_p = \bar{\varepsilon} - \frac{\bar{\sigma}}{E} = \left(\frac{\bar{\sigma}}{H}\right)^{1/n}$$

Hence, we have

$$E_p = \frac{\bar{\sigma}}{\bar{\varepsilon}_p} = \frac{\bar{\sigma}}{(\bar{\sigma}/H)^{1/n}}$$

Then apply Eq. 12.21 to determine $\bar{\sigma}$ for this case, where $\sigma_2 = \sigma_3 = 0.5\sigma_1$.

$$\bar{\sigma} = \frac{1}{\sqrt{2}}\sqrt{(\sigma_1 - 0.5\sigma_1)^2 + (0.5\sigma_1 - 0.5\sigma_1)^2 + (0.5\sigma_1 - \sigma_1)^2} = 0.5\sigma_1$$

Substitute this into the expression for E_p, and then apply the result to the equation obtained for ε_{p1}.

$$E_p = \frac{0.5\sigma_1}{(0.5\sigma_1/H)^{1/n}}, \qquad \varepsilon_{p1} = \frac{\sigma_1}{2E_p} = \left(\frac{\sigma_1}{2H}\right)^{1/n}$$

Finally, the elastic and plastic components can be combined to obtain the total strain ε_1.

$$\varepsilon_1 = \varepsilon_{e1} + \varepsilon_{p1}, \qquad \varepsilon_1 = (1 - \nu)\frac{\sigma_1}{E} + \left(\frac{\sigma_1}{2H}\right)^{1/n} \qquad\qquad \textbf{Ans.}$$

Comment   For this three-dimensional state of stress, the ε_1 versus σ_1 curve is seen to have an elastic slope that is steeper than for the uniaxial case by a factor $1/(1 - \nu) \approx 1.4$. Further, at large plastic strains, the stresses are twice as high as for the uniaxial case.

12.3.5 Deformation versus Incremental Plasticity Theories

Experimental results indicate that plastic strains depend not only on the values of the stresses reached, but also on the history of stressing. For example, consider a thin-walled tube loaded to particular values of axial load $P = P'$ and torque $T = T'$, either of which is sufficient to cause yielding by itself. If the axial loading beyond yielding is applied first and then the torsion, the plastic strains that result differ from those which occur if the torsion is applied first. Also, a third result is obtained if the tension and torsion are increased proportionally, so that the ratio P/T remains constant until P' and T' are simultaneously reached.

These sequences of stressing correspond to variations in principal stresses as shown in Fig. 12.10. The lines shown are called *loading paths*, and any loading path that is a straight line through the origin is termed *proportional loading*. The situation of the plastic strains differing despite the final stresses being the same is said to represent *loading path dependence*. To analyze such path-dependent behavior, an *incremental plasticity theory* is needed, which is applied by following the loading path in small steps. The equations of incremental plasticity theory are similar to those previously given for deformation theory, Eqs. 12.21 to 12.25, except that all plastic strains, $\bar{\varepsilon}_p$, ε_{px}, etc., are replaced by the corresponding differential quantities, $d\bar{\varepsilon}_p$, $d\varepsilon_{px}$, etc.

However, if all stresses are applied so that their magnitudes are proportional, and if no unloading occurs, then incremental plasticity theory gives the same result as deformation theory. The previous discussion is thus restricted to cases of *monotonic proportional loading*. Proportional loading is defined mathematically at a given point in a deforming solid if the principal stresses maintain constant directions and constant ratios of their values as these increase. That is,

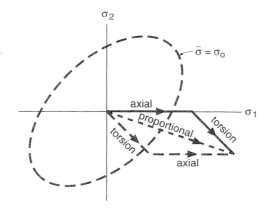

Figure 12.10   Three possible paths for combined axial and torsional loading of a thin-walled tube.

$$\frac{\sigma_2}{\sigma_1} = \lambda_2, \qquad \frac{\sigma_3}{\sigma_1} = \lambda_3 \qquad\qquad (12.40)$$

where λ_2 and λ_3 may vary from point to point in the deforming solid, but, for any given point, must not change.

As a practical matter, modest variations in λ_2 and λ_3 can occur without causing significant problems with deformation theory. Also, if proportionality is preserved, but unloading does occur, as in cyclic loading, deformation theory can still be used, as will be discussed later. However, some practical problems involve obviously nonproportional loading and thus require the use of incremental theory. Details on incremental theory and its application are given in textbooks on plasticity, such as those listed in the References.

12.4 UNLOADING AND CYCLIC LOADING BEHAVIOR FROM RHEOLOGICAL MODELS

Spring and slider rheological models do not include time-dependent effects, nor do they exhibit certain other complexities that are observed for real materials. They nevertheless provide a useful idealization, even for cyclic loading, as their behavior is basically similar to that of engineering metals and some other materials.

Some features of the behavior of these models are illustrated in Fig. 12.11. First consider the simple elastic, perfectly plastic model (a). If the direction of loading is reversed, the behavior may be elastic until yielding again occurs on reloading. However, if the strain excursion for the unloading–reloading event is sufficiently large, reversed yielding occurs. More specifically, reversed yielding occurs when the stress change since unloading reaches $\Delta\sigma = 2\sigma_o$. For completely reversed loading, the response for a $\Delta\varepsilon$ sufficient to cause reversed yielding is also shown. The behavior is symmetrical about the origin and repeats itself for each cycle of loading.

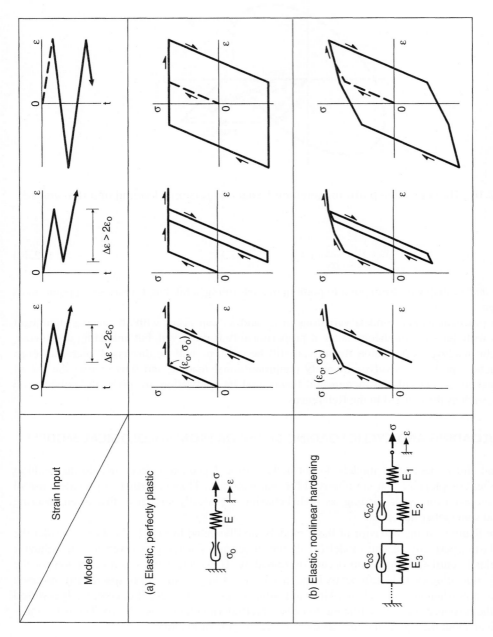

Figure 12.11 Unloading and reloading behavior for two rheological models. The first strain history causes only elastic deformation during unloading, but the second one is sufficiently large to cause compressive yielding. The third history is completely reversed and causes a hysteresis loop that is symmetrical about the origin.

If the model has one or more stages of parallel spring–slider combinations, then the behavior is analogous, but more complex, as shown in Fig. 12.11 by model (b). An unloading–reloading event similarly causes reversed yielding when $\Delta\sigma = 2\sigma_o$, which is similar to kinematic hardening as in Fig. 12.3. For the second strain history illustrated, reversed yielding occurs, causing a small loop to be formed, following which the stress–strain path rejoins the original path, then proceeding just as if the small loop had never occurred. This special behavior is called the *memory effect* and is similar to the behavior of real materials. For completely reversed straining, a loop symmetrical about the origin is formed that resembles the material behavior of Fig. 12.2.

We will now consider the behavior of multistage spring–slider models in more detail, starting with unloading behavior and then proceeding to cyclic loading behavior.

12.4.1 Unloading Behavior

Consider any one stage (no. i) of a multistage parallel spring–slider model as shown in Fig. 12.12. After this stage has yielded on monotonic loading, its stress and strain are related by Eq. 12.16. At a particular later stress–strain point (ε', σ'), we thus have

$$\sigma' = \sigma_{oi} + E_i \varepsilon_i' \tag{12.41}$$

where ε_i' is the strain in the ith stage only. If the direction of loading is reversed at the point (ε', σ'), no change in ε_i' occurs until the stress on the slider reaches $-\sigma_{oi}$. Hence, ε_i' at first remains

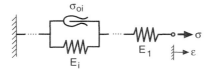

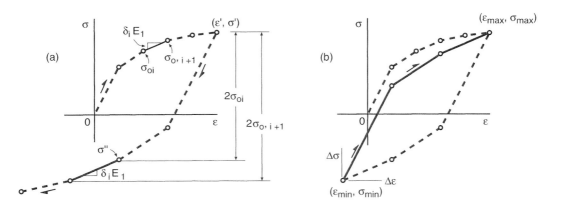

Figure 12.12 Unloading behavior of spring and slider rheological models showing (a) doubling of segment lengths with the slope unchanged, and (b) similar behavior on reloading.

unchanged, and thus so does the stress $E_i \varepsilon_i'$ in the spring, so that this stage can be said to be *locked* until the resistance of the slider is overcome. At the point of reversed yielding of this ith stage, the stress is thus

$$\sigma'' = -\sigma_{oi} + E_i \varepsilon_i' \qquad (12.42)$$

The change in stress necessary to cause reversed yielding in the ith stage is then

$$\Delta\sigma'' = \sigma' - \sigma'' = 2\sigma_{oi} \qquad (12.43)$$

Beyond the point of reversed yielding of the ith stage, the stress on the slider remains at $-\sigma_{oi}$, and the stress change beyond σ'', which is the difference $\Delta\sigma - 2\sigma_{oi}$, is applied to the spring and causes its elastic deflection. The contribution of the ith stage to the change in strain is thus

$$\Delta\varepsilon_i = \frac{\Delta\sigma - 2\sigma_{oi}}{E_i} \qquad (12.44)$$

The total change in strain is the sum for all yielded stages:

$$\Delta\varepsilon = \frac{\Delta\sigma}{E_1} + \frac{\Delta\sigma - 2\sigma_{o2}}{E_2} + \frac{\Delta\sigma - 2\sigma_{o3}}{E_3} + \cdots + \frac{\Delta\sigma - 2\sigma_{oj}}{E_j} \qquad (12.45)$$

Here, all sliders through the jth one have reverse yielded. The values of stress and strain relative to the original (σ, ε) axes are

$$\sigma = \sigma' - \Delta\sigma, \qquad \varepsilon = \varepsilon' - \Delta\varepsilon \qquad (12.46)$$

where (ε', σ') is the point of load reversal. Combining Eqs. 12.45 and 12.46 and evaluating the derivative $d\sigma/d\varepsilon$ gives the slope of the stress–strain response:

$$\frac{d\sigma}{d\varepsilon} = \frac{1}{\dfrac{1}{E_1} + \dfrac{1}{E_2} + \dfrac{1}{E_3} + \cdots + \dfrac{1}{E_j}} \qquad (12.47)$$

Thus, noting Eq. 12.14, we see that the slope is the same as for the interval in the monotonic response where the same number of sliders have yielded.

Furthermore, since Eq. 12.43 states that the $\Delta\sigma$ at each slider's point of reversed yielding is twice its monotonic yield stress, the intervals between reversed yielding events are twice as large as the intervals between the corresponding monotonic yieldings. In other words, the stress–strain path relative to a shifted origin at the point of unloading (ε', σ') has the same shape as the monotonic curve, differing in that it is expanded by a scale factor of two. Each straight-line segment of the unloading path has the same slope as the corresponding one in the monotonic response, but its length is doubled.

If the monotonic response of Eq. 12.18 is represented as

$$\varepsilon = f(\sigma) \tag{12.48}$$

then the unloading response of Eq. 12.45 is

$$\frac{\Delta\varepsilon}{2} = f\left(\frac{\Delta\sigma}{2}\right) \tag{12.49}$$

which can be verified from the two equations. The factor of two in the denominator is the mathematical expression of the factor-of-two expansion previously noted. In particular, half of the values $\Delta\sigma$ and $\Delta\varepsilon$ have the same functional relationship as σ and ε from the monotonic curve.

For initial loading in compression, followed by loading in the tensile direction, analogous behavior occurs. The initial loading in compression is given by $\varepsilon = -f(-\sigma)$, and Eq. 12.49 applies for the subsequent loading in the tensile direction.

12.4.2 Discussion of Unloading

Since the point of reversed yielding of the first slider stage must conform to Eq. 12.43, the first reversed yielding occurs at $\Delta\sigma = 2\sigma_o$, where $\sigma_o = \sigma_{o2}$ is the monotonic yield strength of the model.

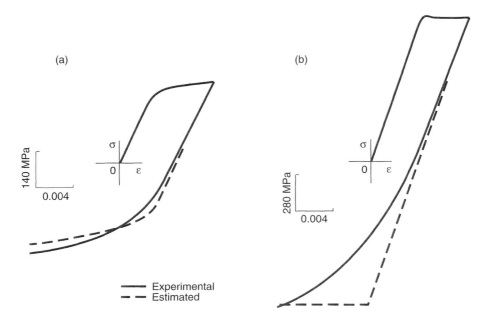

Figure 12.13 Monotonic tension followed by loading into compression for (a) aluminum alloy 2024-T4 and (b) quenched and tempered AISI 4340 steel. Unloading curves estimated from a factor-of-two expansion of the monotonic curve are also shown.

Hence, the first reversed yielding obeys kinematic hardening, as in Fig. 12.3. If unloading proceeds to such a degree that more sliders yield during unloading than previously yielded on loading, then Eq. 12.49 is followed until the stress–strain path joins the one that would be traced for monotonic compression. Beyond this point, the monotonic compression path is followed.

If the number of stages in the model is made relatively large, then its response approximates a smooth stress–strain curve. Equations 12.48 and 12.49 can thus be thought of as representing smooth curves.

Stress–strain paths for unloading are shown for laboratory tests of two engineering metals in Fig. 12.13. Also shown are estimated paths for unloading based on Eq. 12.49. Fair agreement is obtained for the aluminum alloy, but not for the steel. Materials that yield abruptly on monotonic loading seldom have similar behavior on unloading. A more gentle curve occurs instead, as for the steel in this case. For both experimental curves, note that yielding in compression begins at a lower absolute value of stress than the initial tensile yield strength; that is, a Bauschinger effect is observed. For the aluminum alloy, this is estimated reasonably well by the rheological model.

12.4.3 Cyclic Loading Behavior

As illustrated in Fig. 12.12(b), let unloading be terminated at a point $(\varepsilon_{min}, \sigma_{min})$, and then let reloading proceed in the tensile direction. The rheological model follows the same factor-of-two expanded curve as during unloading, with the origin now being at $(\varepsilon_{min}, \sigma_{min})$. This behavior persists until the original point of unloading (ε', σ') is reached, where a closed stress–strain loop is formed. Let this point be denoted $(\varepsilon_{max}, \sigma_{max})$, and let the strain be cycled between the two values ε_{max} and ε_{min}. During the resulting constant amplitude cycling, the stress–strain loop between ε_{max} and ε_{min}, called a *hysteresis loop*, is retraced for each cycle. This is further illustrated by Fig. 12.14.

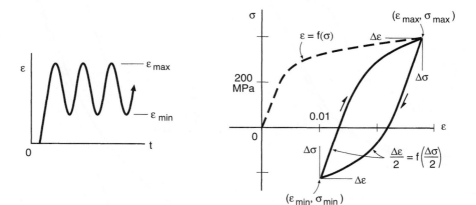

Figure 12.14 Stress–strain unloading and reloading behavior consistent with a spring and slider rheological model. The example curves plotted correspond to a Ramberg–Osgood stress–strain curve with constants as in Fig. 12.9.

In this case, it is assumed that there are a large number of model stages, so that smooth curves occur.

Relative to the original (σ, ε) coordinate axes, the stress–strain paths for the unloading and reloading branches of the hysteresis loop are given by

$$\varepsilon = \varepsilon_{max} - 2f\left(\frac{\sigma_{max} - \sigma}{2}\right), \qquad \varepsilon = \varepsilon_{min} + 2f\left(\frac{\sigma - \sigma_{min}}{2}\right) \qquad \text{(a, b)} \qquad (12.50)$$

Expression (a) for the unloading branch is obtained by combining $\varepsilon = \varepsilon_{max} - \Delta\varepsilon$ with Eq. 12.49, and (b) for the reloading branch is obtained by combining $\varepsilon = \varepsilon_{min} + \Delta\varepsilon$ with Eq. 12.49. For cyclic loading biased in the tensile direction, as in Fig. 12.14, the stress–strain path to the point (ε_{max}, σ_{max}) is given by $\varepsilon = f(\sigma)$, as shown. For cyclic loading biased in the compressive direction, initial loading to the point (ε_{min}, σ_{min}) is given by $\varepsilon = -f(-\sigma)$. Thus, the following apply:

$$\begin{array}{lll} \varepsilon_{max} = f(\sigma_{max}) & |\varepsilon_{max}| > |\varepsilon_{min}| & \text{(a)} \\[4pt] \varepsilon_{min} = -f(-\sigma_{min}) & |\varepsilon_{min}| > |\varepsilon_{max}| & \text{(b)} \end{array} \qquad (12.51)$$

Equation 12.50 gives the two branches of the hysteresis loop for either case.

Cyclic loading of engineering metals often follows a Ramberg–Osgood stress–strain relationship. Some constants for representative metals are given in Table 12.1, where the notation H' and n' is employed to denote curves that are specifically derived from cyclic loading, to distinguish these from curves from monotonic loading. Such *cyclic stress–strain curves* will be discussed in more detail in the next part of this chapter, Section 12.5.

Table 12.1   Constants for Cyclic Stress–Strain Curves for Four Engineering Metals

Material	Yield σ_o	Ultimate σ_u	Cyclic σ-ε curve		
			E	H'	n'
RQC-100 steel	683 (99)	758 (110)	200,000 (29,000)	903 (131)	0.0905
AISI 4340 steel	1103 (160)	1172 (170)	207,000 (30,000)	1655 (240)	0.131
2024-T351 Al	379 (55)	469 (68)	73,100 (10,600)	662 (96)	0.070
7075-T6 Al	469 (68)	578 (84)	71,000 (10,300)	977 (142)	0.106

Notes: Units are MPa (ksi), except for dimensionless n'. See Table 14.1 for additional properties and sources.

Example 12.5

A material has the uniaxial stress–strain curve given by the constants in Fig. 12.9. Assume that this curve also applies for cyclic loading and that the stress–strain behavior is similar to that of a multistage spring–slider model. Then estimate the stress–strain response for starting from zero and then cycling between $\varepsilon_{max} = 0.028$ and $\varepsilon_{min} = 0.01$.

Solution   The stress–strain response for this example is the one plotted in Fig. 12.14. For the initial monotonic loading from zero to ε_{max}, we use Eq. 12.12 with E, H, and n values as in Fig. 12.9:

$$\varepsilon = f(\sigma) = \frac{\sigma}{69,000} + \left(\frac{\sigma}{690}\right)^{1/0.15}$$

We first need to solve this equation for σ_{max}, given that $\varepsilon_{max} = 0.028$. A solution by trial and error or by an iterative procedure such as Newton's method is needed, giving

$$\sigma_{max} = 390.1 \, \text{MPa} \qquad\qquad\qquad \textbf{Ans.}$$

For unloading from the point $(\varepsilon_{max}, \sigma_{max})$, Eq. 12.49 applies:

$$\Delta\varepsilon = 2f\left(\frac{\Delta\sigma}{2}\right) = \frac{\Delta\sigma}{69,000} + 2\left(\frac{\Delta\sigma}{1380}\right)^{1/0.15}$$

This equation gives the unloading response relative to an origin at $(\varepsilon_{max}, \sigma_{max})$, as shown in Fig. 12.14. At $(\varepsilon_{min}, \sigma_{min})$, the direction of straining reverses, where

$$\Delta\varepsilon = \varepsilon_{max} - \varepsilon_{min} = 0.018, \qquad \Delta\sigma = \sigma_{max} - \sigma_{min}$$

Entering the preceding equation with $\Delta\varepsilon$ and performing a second iterative solution gives $\Delta\sigma$:

$$\Delta\sigma = 614.5 \, \text{MPa}$$

It then follows that

$$\sigma_{min} = \sigma_{max} - \Delta\sigma = 390.1 - 614.5 = -224.4 \, \text{MPa} \qquad\qquad \textbf{Ans.}$$

For reloading back to ε_{max}, the same Eq. 12.49 path is followed for the $\Delta\sigma$ versus $\Delta\varepsilon$ response relative to an origin at $(\varepsilon_{min}, \sigma_{min})$. Hence, the estimated curve reaches the same point $(\sigma_{max}, \varepsilon_{max})$ as before, and subsequent cycles are estimated to retrace the hysteresis loop thus formed.

Comment   If it is desired to plot the stress–strain response accurately, pick a number of values of σ between zero and σ_{max}, and plot these versus the corresponding strain values from $\varepsilon = f(\sigma)$ in the form of Eq. 12.12. Then, for a number of values of σ between σ_{max} and σ_{min}, calculate and plot the corresponding strain values for the two branches of the hysteresis loop from Eqs. 12.50(a) and (b). Since $\varepsilon = f(\sigma)$ is given by Eq. 12.12, the specific relationships needed are

$$\varepsilon = \varepsilon_{\max} - 2\left[\frac{\sigma_{\max} - \sigma}{2E} + \left(\frac{\sigma_{\max} - \sigma}{2H}\right)^{1/n}\right], \quad \varepsilon = \varepsilon_{\min} + 2\left[\frac{\sigma - \sigma_{\min}}{2E} + \left(\frac{\sigma - \sigma_{\min}}{2H}\right)^{1/n}\right]$$

12.4.4 Application to Irregular Strain versus Time Histories

The behavior of a multistage spring and slider rheological model (as in Fig. 12.6) can be summarized by a set of rules that apply to any irregular variation of strain with time. These rules are stated as follows in terms of the behavior of the straight-line segments that approximate the monotonic loading curve. The segments are numbered starting from the origin, as shown in Fig. 12.15(a):

1. Initially, and after each reversal of strain direction, segments are used in order, starting with the first.
2. Each segment may be used once in either direction with its original length. Thereafter, the length is twice the monotonic value and the segment retains the same slope.
3. An exception to rule (1) is that a segment (or portion thereof) must be skipped if its most recent use was not in the opposite direction of its impending use.

Figure 12.15 illustrates the application of these rules, the strain history of (b) resulting in the stress–strain response of (c). Segments 1 through 5 are each used once in reaching point A, and no additional segments are required by the example strain history, so that only double-length segments

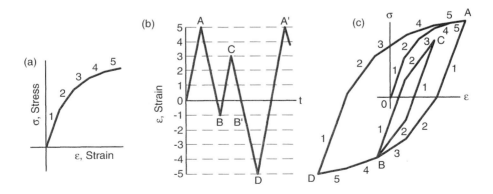

Figure 12.15 Behavior of a multistage spring–slider rheological model for an irregular strain history. A model having the monotonic stress–strain curve (a) is subjected to strain history (b), resulting in stress–strain response (c). (Adapted from [Dowling 79b]; used with permission of Elsevier Science Publishers.)

are used during the remainder of the history. At point B' in the strain history, segment 3 must be skipped, as its most recent use was not in the opposite direction of its impending use, so that the sequence of segments between C and D is 1-2-4-5.

Only double-length segments are used after the strain first reaches its largest absolute value. Thus, beyond this point, the model behaves such that all stress–strain curves follow a single shape, which is the monotonic curve expanded with a scale factor of two, according to Eq. 12.49. Rule (3) causes that memory effect to act, the skipping of segments (or portions thereof) resulting in a return to the stress–strain path previously established. The origins for the various $\Delta\sigma$ versus $\Delta\varepsilon$ curves are, of course, located at points where the direction of straining changes, and the particular origin that applies for a given section of curve is determined by the memory effect. The skipping of a portion of a segment does not occur in Fig. 12.15.

If the strain history subsequently returns to its largest absolute value, the stress–strain paths traced form a set of closed stress–strain hysteresis loops. This is the case in Fig. 12.15, where the loops correspond to events B-C-B' and A-D-A'. If the same strain history is applied again, the same loops are retraced.

12.5 CYCLIC STRESS–STRAIN BEHAVIOR OF REAL MATERIALS

A special laboratory test methodology has been developed for characterizing cyclic stress–strain behavior, which is done during low-cycle fatigue testing. This is described in ASTM Standard No. E606 and also in Landgraf (1969). As a result, considerable data are available for engineering metals, as are limited data from other materials.

12.5.1 Cyclic Stress–Strain Tests and Behavior

The most common test involves completely reversed $(R = -1)$ cycling between constant strain limits, as illustrated in Fig. 12.16. A strain amplitude, $\varepsilon_a = \Delta\varepsilon/2$, is selected, and an axial test specimen is loaded until the tensile strain reaches a value of $\varepsilon_{\max} = +\varepsilon_a$. Then the direction of loading is reversed until the strain reaches $\varepsilon_{\min} = -\varepsilon_a$, and the test is continued, with the direction of loading being reversed each time the strain reaches $+\varepsilon_a$ or $-\varepsilon_a$. The rate of straining between these limits may be held constant, or sometimes a fixed-frequency sinusoidal variation of strain with time is used. The rate or frequency of the test affects the behavior of materials that exhibit significant creep at the test temperature used. For engineering metals tested at room temperature, rate effects are generally small.

Such cyclic strain tests are continued until fatigue failure occurs. The stresses that are needed to enforce the strain limits usually change as the test progresses. Some materials exhibit *cycle-dependent hardening*, which means that the stresses increase, as shown in Fig. 12.16 (top). Others exhibit *cycle-dependent softening*, or a decrease in stress with increasing numbers of cycles, as also illustrated (bottom). In engineering metals, the cyclic hardening or softening is usually rapid at first, but the change from one cycle to the next decreases with increasing numbers of cycles. Often, the behavior becomes approximately stable in that further changes are small. These trends can be seen in Fig. 12.2, which shows hardening in an aluminum alloy.

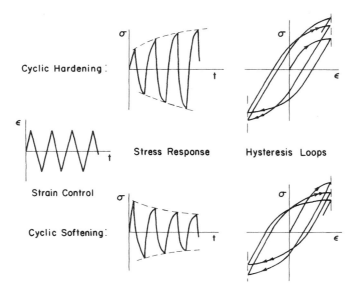

Figure 12.16   Completely reversed controlled strain test and two possible stress responses, cycle-dependent hardening and softening. (From [Landgraf 70]; copyright © ASTM; reprinted with permission.)

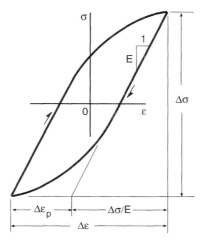

Figure 12.17   Stable stress–strain hysteresis loop.

If the stress–strain variation during stable behavior for one cycle is plotted, a closed hysteresis loop is formed on each cycle, as shown in Fig. 12.17. After the direction of loading changes at either the positive or the negative strain limit, the slope of the stress–strain path is at first constant and close to the elastic modulus, E, as from a tension test. Then the path gradually deviates from

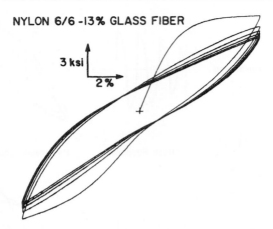

Figure 12.18   Cycle-dependent softening and asymmetric hysteresis loops in Nylon 6-6 reinforced with 13% glass fiber, which was cycled at a constant strain rate of $\dot{\varepsilon} = 0.01$ 1/s. (From [Beardmore 75]; used with permission.)

linearity as plastic strain occurs. We can think of each branch of the hysteresis loop as being a separate stress–strain curve which begins at an origin that is shifted to one of the loop tips, with the axes being inverted for the lower branch. Note that this hysteresis looping behavior is similar to that of the rheological models discussed earlier. Compare the completely reversed case in Fig. 12.11(b) with Fig. 12.17.

The maximum deviation from linearity reached during a cycle is the plastic strain range, labeled $\Delta\varepsilon_p$ in Fig. 12.17. The stress range is $\Delta\sigma$, and the elastic portion of the strain range is related to $\Delta\sigma$ by the elastic modulus E. Summing the elastic and plastic portions gives the total strain range, $\Delta\varepsilon$:

$$\Delta\varepsilon = \frac{\Delta\sigma}{E} + \Delta\varepsilon_p \tag{12.52}$$

It is often useful to work with the amplitudes—that is, half-ranges—of these quantities, $\varepsilon_a = \Delta\varepsilon/2$, $\sigma_a = \Delta\sigma/2$, and $\varepsilon_{pa} = \Delta\varepsilon_p/2$, so that

$$\varepsilon_a = \frac{\sigma_a}{E} + \varepsilon_{pa} \tag{12.53}$$

In most engineering metals, the stable hysteresis loops are nearly symmetrical with respect to tension and compression. One exception is gray cast iron, where the different behavior of graphite flakes in tension and compression causes asymmetric behavior. Ductile polymers and their composites also often have asymmetric hysteresis loops, with an example shown in Fig. 12.18.

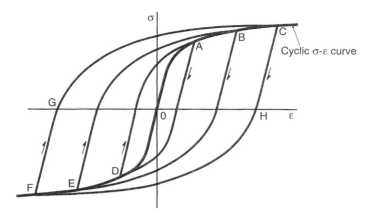

Figure 12.19 Cyclic stress–strain curve defined as the locus of tips of hysteresis loops. Three loops are shown, *A-D*, *B-E*, and *C-F*. The tensile branch of the cyclic stress–strain curve is *O-A-B-C*, and the compressive branch is *O-D-E-F*.

12.5.2 Cyclic Stress–Strain Curves and Trends

Hysteresis loops from near half the fatigue life are conventionally used to represent the approximately stable behavior. Such loops from tests at several different strain amplitudes can be plotted on one set of axes, as shown in Fig. 12.19. A line from the origin that passes through the tips of the loops, such as *O-A-B-C*, is called *cyclic stress–strain curve*. Where the branches in tension and compression do not differ greatly (which is often the case), their average is used. The cyclic stress–strain curve is thus the relationship between stress amplitude and strain amplitude for cyclic loading.

Cyclic stress–strain curves for several engineering metals are compared with monotonic tension curves in Fig. 12.20. Where the cyclic curve is above the monotonic one, the material is one that cyclically hardens, and vice versa. A mixed behavior may also occur, with crossing of the curves indicating softening at some strain levels and hardening at others. The cyclic curves virtually always deviate smoothly from linearity, even for materials where the monotonic curve has a distinct yield point or even a yield drop.

Equations of the Ramberg–Osgood form have this character and are thus commonly used to represent cyclic stress–strain curves:

$$\varepsilon_a = \frac{\sigma_a}{E} + \left(\frac{\sigma_a}{H'}\right)^{1/n'} \tag{12.54}$$

Here, primes are used to specify that the constants for the plastic term are from fitting cyclic rather than monotonic stress–strain data. An offset yield strength σ_o' for this cyclic curve may be obtained by employing Eq. 12.13 with H' and n'. For engineering metals, n' is often in the range of 0.1 to 0.2, so that 0.15, or about $\frac{1}{7}$, is a typical value. A low value of n from monotonic tension, say, 0.05,

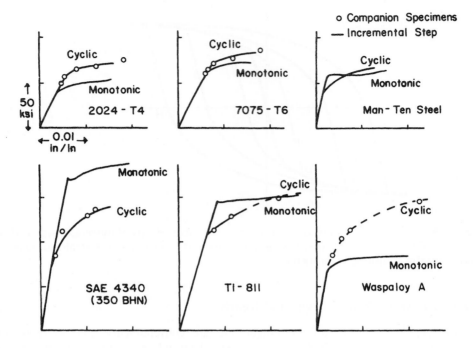

Figure 12.20   Cyclic and monotonic stress–strain curves for several engineering metals. (From [Landgraf 69]; copyright © ASTM; reprinted with permission.)

corresponds to a fairly flat stress–strain curve. A metal with low n is likely to cyclically soften to a lower, but steeper, curve, with the resulting n' generally being around 0.1 to 0.2. Conversely, a metal with a high n (steeply rising monotonic curve) is likely to harden to a higher, but flatter, curve, with n' again being around 0.1 to 0.2. Values of H' and n' for some engineering metals are given in Table 12.1, and more are given later in Chapter 14, specifically in Table 14.1.

The alloy composition and processing of engineering metals affects the cyclic stress–strain behavior, sometimes differently than it affects the monotonic tension properties. For example, strength achieved by cold working is often substantially reduced by cycle-dependent softening. Conversely, metals softened by annealing generally harden considerably. Hardening due to a fine precipitate, as in many aluminum alloys, is usually preserved and often increases under cyclic loading. This is the case for the two aluminum alloys included in Fig. 12.20. In medium-carbon steels that are hardened by heat treatment using quenching and tempering, some of the effect usually is lost if cyclic loading occurs. An example is provided by the curve for SAE 4340 steel in Fig. 12.20. For such steels, the average variation with hardness of the monotonic and cyclic yield strengths, σ_o and σ_o', is shown in Fig. 12.21. Cyclic softening, indicated by σ_o' being lower than σ_o, occurs, except at very high hardness.

Ductile polymers usually soften under cyclic loading. Recall from Section 7.6.4 that polymers have monotonic yield strengths that are typically 20% to 30% higher in compression than in tension,

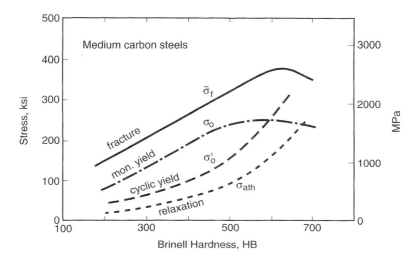

Figure 12.21 Average property trends for SAE 1045 steel and other medium-carbon steels as a function of hardness, including the true fracture strength, the monotonic and cyclic yield strengths, and the threshold stress amplitude for relaxation of mean stress. (Adapted from [Landgraf 88]; copyright © ASTM; reprinted with permission.)

indicating a sensitivity to hydrostatic stress. A similar ratio of compressive to tensile yield strengths is maintained in the cyclic stress–strain curves, such behavior being evident for polycarbonate in Fig. 12.22. The cyclic stress–strain curves for ductile polymers are affected by the strain rate, even at room temperature.

12.5.3 Hysteresis Loop Curve Shapes

One item of interest is the shape of hysteresis loop curves, such as C-H-F and F-G-C in Fig. 12.19. If the stable behavior obeys a multistage spring and slider rheological model of the type discussed earlier, the stress–strain path for the hysteresis loops should have the same shape as the cyclic stress–strain curve, except for expansion by a scale factor of two according to Eq. 12.49. Thus, for a cyclic stress–strain curve $\varepsilon = f(\sigma)$ of the Ramberg–Osgood form, Eq. 12.54, the equation of the loop curves obtained from $\Delta\varepsilon/2 = f(\Delta\sigma/2)$ is

$$\Delta\varepsilon = \frac{\Delta\sigma}{E} + 2\left(\frac{\Delta\sigma}{2H'}\right)^{1/n'} \tag{12.55}$$

Here, the variables $\Delta\sigma$ and $\Delta\varepsilon$ represent changes relative to coordinates axes at either loop tip.

This expected behavior can be compared with actual behavior by expanding the cyclic stress–strain curve with a scale factor of two and comparing the result with actual loop curves. Such a comparison for a steel is shown in Fig. 12.23. To enable this comparison, three actual hysteresis

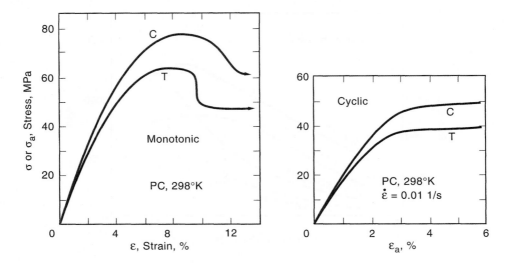

Figure 12.22   Monotonic (left) and cyclic (right) stress–strain curves for polycarbonate for both tension (T) and compression (C). (Adapted from [Beardmore 75]; used with permission.)

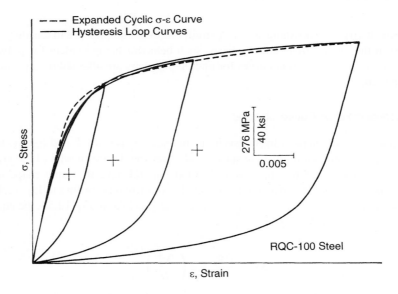

Figure 12.23   Stable hysteresis loops for a steel, plotted with shifted axes so that their compressive tips coincide. The loop curves fall near the dashed line, which is obtained by expanding the cyclic stress–strain curve with a scale factor of two, $\Delta\varepsilon/2 = f(\Delta\sigma/2)$. (From [Dowling 78]; used with permission of ASME.)

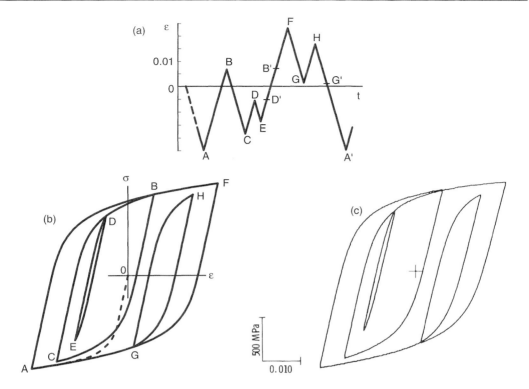

Figure 12.24   Stable stress–strain response of AISI 4340 steel ($\sigma_u = 1158\,\text{MPa}$) subjected to a repeatedly applied irregular strain history (a). The predicted response is shown in (b) and actual test data in (c). (Adapted from [Dowling 79b]; used with permission of Elsevier Science Publishers.)

loops from experimental data are plotted with shifted origins, so that their tips fall at the origin used to plot Eq. 12.55. Reasonably good agreement of the actual and estimated loop curves exists in this case. Similar behavior generally occurs for other engineering metals, but in some cases the agreement is not as good. Nevertheless, Eq. 12.55 provides a reasonable estimate, for engineering purposes, of loop shape in metals.

For irregular variations of strain with time, the hysteresis loop curves for stable behavior still generally follow shapes close to the cyclic stress–strain curve expanded with a scale factor of two, Eq. 12.55. Hence, the behavior is similar to that predicted by the spring–slider rheological model, as previously discussed and as illustrated in Fig. 12.15. Some supporting test data for an alloy steel are provided by Fig. 12.24. The stress–strain response for a short irregular history (a) is shown in (b) as predicted by the rheological model. The actual measured response for stable behavior shown in (c) is almost identical.

For nonuniaxial states of stress, Eq. 12.39 and related more general equations, that are not limited to plane stress, can be used to estimate cyclic stress–strain curves. The constants E, H', and

n' for the uniaxial cyclic stress–strain curve of the material of interest are, of course, employed. It is then reasonable to apply the same assumption that hysteresis loops have shapes following $\Delta\varepsilon/2 = f(\Delta\sigma/2)$, where $\varepsilon_a = f(\sigma_a)$ is now the cyclic stress–strain curve for a particular direction of the nonuniaxial state of stress. Such a procedure thus allows deformation plasticity theory to be used for cyclic loading, but the limitation of at least approximately proportional loading is still needed.

Example 12.6

Table E12.6(a) gives the strain history that is repeatedly applied for the stress–strain response example of Fig. 12.24. Estimate the stress response for stable behavior after cyclic softening in this material is complete. The AISI 4340 steel ($\sigma_u = 1158$ MPa) has fitting constants for its stable cyclic stress–strain curve, Eq. 12.54, of $E = 201{,}300$ MPa, $H' = 1620$ MPa, and $n' = 0.112$.

Solution Behavior similar to a spring and slider rheological model is expected. The starting point should be the peak or valley having the largest absolute value of strain, in this case, point A. To establish point A, assume that the loading follows the Eq. 12.54 cyclic stress–strain curve, $\varepsilon_a = f(\sigma_a)$, as if it were a monotonic curve. Use $\varepsilon = f(\sigma)$ for tension, or $\varepsilon = -f(-\sigma)$ for compression. Define a variable $\psi = +1$ if the direction is positive and $\psi = -1$ if the direction is negative, and employ Eq. 12.54 in the form

$$\varepsilon_A = \frac{\sigma_A}{E} + \psi \left(\frac{\psi \sigma_A}{H'} \right)^{1/n'}$$

In this case, $\psi = -1$. Then substituting $\varepsilon_A = -0.0248$ and solving iteratively gives $\sigma_A = -1043.0$ MPa, as listed in the first line of Table E12.6.

Stress–strain paths beyond A are then calculated by applying $\Delta\varepsilon/2 = f(\Delta\sigma/2)$, in the form of Eq. 12.55, to ranges X-Y that follow smooth hysteresis loop curves:

Table E12.6

(a) Strain History		(b) Calculated Values					
Point (Y)	Strain ε	Origin (X)	Origin Strain, ε	Direction ψ	$\Delta\varepsilon$ to Point	$\Delta\sigma$ MPa	Stress σ, MPa
A	-0.0248	—	—	-1	—	—	-1043.0
B	0.0067	A	-0.0248	$+1$	0.0315	1953.1	910.1
C	-0.0184	B	0.0067	-1	0.0251	1883.3	-973.1
D	-0.0056	C	-0.0184	$+1$	0.0128	1642.4	669.3
E	-0.0136	D	-0.0056	-1	0.0080	1394.2	-724.9
F	0.0232	A	-0.0248	$+1$	0.0480	2076.6	1033.6
G	0.0014	F	0.0232	-1	0.0218	1838.0	-804.4
H	0.0167	G	0.0014	$+1$	0.0153	1713.8	909.5

$$\Delta \varepsilon_{XY} = |\varepsilon_Y - \varepsilon_X|, \qquad \Delta \varepsilon_{XY} = \frac{\Delta \sigma_{XY}}{E} + 2 \left(\frac{\Delta \sigma_{XY}}{2H'} \right)^{1/n'}$$

Specifically, the X-Y are ranges for closed stress–strain hysteresis loops, in this case, D-E, B-C, G-H, and A-F, and also ranges that locate the starting points of loops, in this case, A-B, C-D, and F-G. To identify these ranges, a qualitative sketch of the stress–strain paths similar to Fig. 12.24(b) is helpful. Note that a hysteresis loop is closed where the strain next reaches the same value as a previous direction change, where the memory effect acts, and the stress–strain path continues on the curve established before the loop started. In this case, loops close at points D', B', G', and A'. (Such points can also be identified by applying rainflow cycle counting to the strain history, as they also correspond to points where rainflow cycles are completed.)

The calculations are organized as shown in Table E12.6(b). For each peak or valley (Y) in the history, the origin point (X) of the smooth hysteresis loop curve is tabulated, along with its strain value. (For example, to locate point F, range A-F is analyzed, as loop B-C closes at point B', so that the origin for the continuing curve to F is point A.) Next, ψ is listed as $+1$ if the strain is increasing during the range, or -1 if it is decreasing. Then, using the preceding equations, each strain range $\Delta \varepsilon_{XY}$ is calculated, and the value is employed to determine the corresponding stress range $\Delta \sigma_{XY}$. For example, the range from $\varepsilon_A = -0.0248$ to $\varepsilon_B = 0.0067$ is $\Delta \varepsilon_{AB} = 0.0315$. Entering this value into the second equation and solving iteratively gives $\Delta \sigma_{AB} = 1953.1$ MPa.

Analyzing the ranges for all loops and their starting points gives sufficient information to establish the stress values for all points in the strain history. This is done by starting from the initial point A and calculating the stress at each subsequent point by adding or subtracting the appropriate stress range. We employ

$$\sigma_Y = \sigma_X + \psi \Delta \sigma_{XY}$$

where the use of ψ causes $\Delta \sigma_{XY}$ to be added to or subtracted from σ_X to obtain σ_Y, depending on whether the strain is increasing or decreasing. For example, for points B and C,

$$\sigma_A = -1043.0, \qquad \Delta \sigma_{AB} = 1953.1, \qquad \psi = +1, \qquad \text{so that } \sigma_B = 910.1 \text{ MPa}$$

$$\sigma_B = 910.1, \qquad \Delta \sigma_{BC} = 1883.3, \qquad \psi = -1, \qquad \text{so that } \sigma_C = -973.1 \text{ MPa}$$

These and the remaining values for all peaks and valleys in the history are given Table E12.6.

Comment   If a quantitative plot of the stress–strain response is desired, Eq. 12.55 can be employed to calculate a number of points along each smooth curve connecting peak–valley points, while observing the memory effect. This can be implemented by applying the equations given at the end of Ex. 12.5 to each hysteresis loop, noting that these give Eq. 12.55 as referred to the original (σ, ε) coordinate axes.

12.5.4 Transient Behavior; Mean Stress Relaxation

The spring and slider rheological models exhibit only stable behavior for cyclic loading—that is, continuous repetition of an identical hysteresis loop for each cycle. Cycle-dependent hardening or softening thus represents a class of transient behavior that is not predicted by such models. Also, these models still exhibit stable behavior even if the mean stress is not zero—that is, if the loop is biased in either the tensile or compressive direction.

However, if a real material is subjected to loading with a nonzero mean stress, an additional class of transient behavior may be observed. Examples of such behavior for a steel are shown in Fig. 12.25. If biased strain limits are imposed, and if the strain range is sufficiently large to cause some cyclic plasticity, as on the left, the resulting mean stress will gradually shift toward zero as increasing numbers of cycles are applied. Sometimes a stable nonzero value is reached, or if the degree of plasticity is large, the mean stress may shift essentially to zero. This behavior is called *cycle-dependent relaxation*. Behavior of this type is further illustrated by Fig. 12.26.

If biased stress limits with a sufficiently large range are imposed, the mean strain will increase with cycles, as illustrated on the right in Fig. 12.25. The mean strain shift may decrease its rate and stop, it may establish an approximately constant rate, or it may accelerate and lead to a failure somewhat similar to that in a tension test. This behavior is called *cycle-dependent creep*

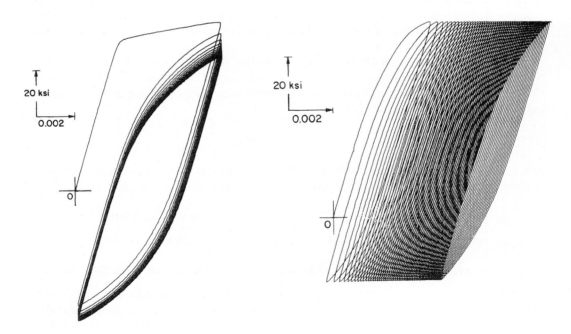

Figure 12.25 Cycle-dependent relaxation of mean stress (left) and cycle-dependent creep (right), both for an AISI 1045 steel. On the right, the specimen was previously yielded, so that the monotonic curve does not appear. (From [Landgraf 70]; copyright © ASTM; reprinted with permission.)

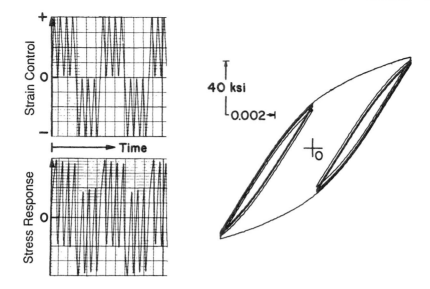

Figure 12.26   Cycle-dependent relaxation during controlled strain with an alternating mean value for the same steel as in Fig. 12.25. The stress–strain response is shown on the right for one typical repetition of the strain history. (Illustration courtesy of R. W. Landgraf, Howell, MI.)

or *ratchetting.* Cyclic creep and relaxation are a single phenomenon viewed under two different situations.

Cyclic creep–relaxation may occur at the same time as cyclic hardening or softening, and the two phenomena may interact. Relaxation effects are especially obvious when they are enhanced by cyclic softening occurring at the same time, which is the case for Fig. 12.25 (left). Cyclic creep–relaxation behavior occurs for combinations of material and temperature where time-dependent effects are usually considered small, as well as in situations where there is an obvious combination of cycle-dependent and time-dependent effects. However, subtle time dependency may play a role even where the behavior is thought to be mainly cycle dependent.

A paper by Martin (1971) describes a fairly straightforward approach of modifying the spring and slider model to handle cycle-dependent transient behavior. More general three-dimensional incremental plasticity models can also be devised that exhibit cycle-dependent transient behavior; see Skrzypek (1993).

A detailed study of cycle-dependent relaxation in SAE 1045 steel is described by Landgraf and Chernenkoff (1988). The following equation is used to determine the mean stress σ_{mN} after N cycles of relaxation:

$$\sigma_{mN} = \sigma_{mi} N^r \tag{12.56}$$

In this equation, σ_{mi} is the initial ($N = 1$) value of mean stress. The exponent r has values typically in the range 0 to -0.2 and varies with the level of cyclic strain and the material. For SAE 1045 steel heat treated to various strength levels, r was found to vary as follows:

$$r = 0.085 \left(1 - \frac{\varepsilon_a}{\varepsilon_{ath}} \right) \qquad (\varepsilon_a > \varepsilon_{ath})$$

$$r = 0 \qquad\qquad\qquad (\varepsilon_a \leq \varepsilon_{ath}) \qquad\qquad (12.57)$$

$$\varepsilon_{ath} = e^{-8.41 + 0.00536(HB)}$$

Here, ε_a is the applied strain amplitude, and ε_{ath} is a threshold value below which no relaxation occurs. Also, HB is the Brinell hardness in units of kg/mm^2. (See Section 4.7.). The stress value σ_{ath} corresponding to ε_{ath} on the cyclic stress–strain curve is somewhat lower than the cyclic yield strength. This trend is included in Fig. 12.21.

Equations 12.56 and 12.57 also provide reasonable estimates for mean stress relaxation in other heat-treated steels. For other engineering metals, similar equations may be useful if employed with numerical constants based on test data for the particular material.

Example 12.7
Let the strain history of Fig. 12.24(a) be replaced by that of Fig. E12.7, which differs only in that the cycle from G to H and return to G is now repeated 20 times. Simulate the stress response for this revised strain history (a) according to a spring and slider rheological model, and (b) including the transient effect of mean stress relaxation.

Solution (a) Behavior according to a spring and slider model predicts that hysteresis loop G-H in Fig. 12.24(b) is simply retraced 20 times. Thus, no new calculations are needed, and the results of Table E12.6(b) still apply, with $\sigma_G = -804.4$ and $\sigma_H = 909.5$ MPa for each of the 20 cycles.

(b) Some relaxation of mean stress during the 20 cycles is likely. The result of Ex. 12.6 is considered to provide only the initial value of the mean stress:

$$\sigma_{mi} = \frac{\sigma_G + \sigma_H}{2} = \frac{-804.4 + 909.5}{2} = 52.6 \text{ MPa}$$

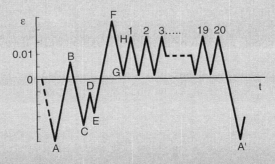

Figure E12.7

Subsequent values can then be calculated from Eqs. 12.56 and 12.57. For the latter, we need the Brinell hardness, HB, which can be estimated from Eq. 4.32 and the ultimate tensile strength given in Ex. 12.6:

$$HB = \frac{\sigma_u, \text{MPa}}{3.45} = \frac{1158\,\text{MPa}}{3.45} = 336\,\text{kg/mm}^2$$

From Table E12.6(b), we have $\varepsilon_a = \Delta\varepsilon_{GH}/2 = 0.0153/2 = 0.00765$, so that Eq. 12.57 gives

$$\varepsilon_{ath} = e^{-8.41+0.00536(HB)} = e^{-8.41+0.00536(336)} = 0.001346$$

$$r = 0.085\left(1 - \frac{\varepsilon_a}{\varepsilon_{ath}}\right) = 0.085\left(1 - \frac{0.00765}{0.001346}\right) = -0.398$$

Equation 12.56 then provides the specific relationship for mean stress relaxation in this case:

$$\sigma_{mN} = \sigma_{mi}N^r = 52.6N^{-0.398}$$

Employing this relationship for various numbers of cycles from the 20 that are applied gives the following:

N, cycles	1	2	5	10	15	20
σ_{mN}, MPa	52.6	39.9	27.7	21.0	17.9	15.9

Ans.

Hence, the mean stress decays to about 30% of its initial value over the 20 cycles. However, all of the mean stress values involved are relatively small, so the stress–strain response will be similar to Fig. 12.24, except that loop G-H drifts slightly downward during the 20 cycles.

12.6 SUMMARY

Some relationships commonly used to fit stress–strain curves involve linear-elastic behavior up to a distinct yield point σ_o. If the curve is flat beyond σ_o, the relationship is said to be elastic, perfectly plastic, and Eq. 12.1 applies. A rising linear behavior beyond σ_o is called an elastic, linear-hardening relationship, and this is given by Eq. 12.4. A power relationship beyond σ_o may also be used and is given by Eq. 12.8. The Ramberg–Osgood relationship differs from the others described in that there is no distinct yield point.

$$\varepsilon = \frac{\sigma}{E} + \left(\frac{\sigma}{H}\right)^{1/n} \tag{12.58}$$

At all values of stress, elastic and plastic strain are summed to obtain total strain, resulting in a smooth, continuous curve. The plastic (not total) strain and stress have a power relationship. Rheological models consisting of linear springs and frictional sliders can be used to model any of these stress–strain curves.

Considering three-dimensional states of stress, we note that Hooke's law still applies beyond yielding, but gives only the elastic portion of the strain. The plastic portion can be related to the stress by deformation plasticity theory, which employs equations analogous to Hooke's law:

$$\varepsilon_{px} = \frac{1}{E_p}[\sigma_x - 0.5(\sigma_y + \sigma_z)], \qquad \varepsilon_{py}, \varepsilon_{pz}, \text{ similarly}$$

$$\gamma_{pxy} = \frac{3}{E_p}\tau_{xy}, \qquad\qquad\qquad \gamma_{pyz}, \gamma_{pzx}, \text{ similarly}$$

$$(12.59)$$

Here, Poisson's ratio is replaced by 0.5, so that plastic strains do not contribute to volume change. The elastic modulus is replaced by the variable $E_p = \bar{\sigma}/\bar{\varepsilon}_p$, which is the secant modulus to a point on the effective stress versus plastic strain curve, $\bar{\sigma}$ versus $\bar{\varepsilon}_p$. These effective quantities are proportional to the corresponding octahedral shear stresses and strains and are related to the principal stresses and plastic strains by Eqs. 12.21 and 12.22. Total strains are obtained by adding elastic and plastic portions.

A key feature of deformation plasticity theory is that the $\bar{\sigma}$ versus $\bar{\varepsilon}_p$ curve is assumed to be independent of the state of stress, thus permitting a stress–strain curve from one state of stress to be used to estimate those for other states of stress. As employed here, the effective stress–strain curve, $\bar{\sigma} = f(\bar{\varepsilon})$, is identical to the uniaxial curve, $\sigma = f(\varepsilon)$. For plane stress, estimates of stress–strain curves as a function of $\lambda = \sigma_2/\sigma_1$ are given, in general, by Eq. 12.36, and more specific relationships for elastic, perfectly plastic and Ramberg–Osgood materials are given by Eqs. 12.37 and 12.39, respectively.

For unloading following yielding, and for cyclic loading, spring and frictional slider rheological models suggest that yielding should occur when the stress range reaches twice the yield stress from the monotonic stress–strain curve, $\Delta\sigma = 2\sigma_o$. Furthermore, stress–strain paths for these situations are predicted to follow a path that is given by a factor-of-two expansion of the monotonic stress–strain curve, namely,

$$\frac{\Delta\varepsilon}{2} = f\left(\frac{\Delta\sigma}{2}\right)$$

$$(12.60)$$

where $\varepsilon = f(\sigma)$ is the monotonic curve. In the preceding equation, $\Delta\sigma$ and $\Delta\varepsilon$ are measured from origins at points where the loading direction changes, resulting in symmetrical stress–strain hysteresis loops being formed. If the strain varies in an irregular manner with time, the stress–strain paths still form such hysteresis loops, obeying Eq. 12.60. After completion of a loop, the stress–strain behavior exhibits a memory effect in that it returns to the path previously established.

For stable cyclic loading following completion of most cycle-dependent hardening or softening, the behavior predicted by a multistage spring and slider rheological model is reasonably accurate for many engineering metals. It is necessary to replace the monotonic stress–strain curve with a special cyclic stress–strain curve, with the Ramberg–Osgood form often being used:

$$\varepsilon_a = \frac{\sigma_a}{E} + \left(\frac{\sigma_a}{H'}\right)^{1/n'}$$

$$(12.61)$$

In this equation, stress and strain amplitudes appear, and the constants H' and n' differ from those for the monotonic curve. In addition to hardening–softening, a second type of transient, cycle-dependent behavior occurs in engineering metals—namely, cyclic creep–relaxation.

NEW TERMS AND SYMBOLS

(a) Terms

Bauschinger effect	kinematic hardening
cycle-dependent creep (ratchetting)	memory effect
cycle-dependent hardening	monotonic loading
cycle-dependent relaxation	power-hardening σ-ε curve: σ_o, H_1, n_1
cycle-dependent softening	proportional loading
cyclic stress–strain curve	Ramberg–Osgood σ-ε curve
cyclic yield strength, σ_o'	monotonic: E, H, n
deformation plasticity theory	cyclic: E, H', n'
hysteresis loop	slope reduction factor, δ
incremental plasticity theory	strain-hardening exponent: n_1, n, n'
isotropic hardening	

(b) Nomenclature for Three-Dimensional Stresses and Strains

E_p	Plastic modulus
$\gamma_{xy}, \gamma_{yz}, \gamma_{zx}$	Total shear strains on orthogonal planes
$\gamma_{exy}, \gamma_{eyz}, \gamma_{ezx}$	Elastic shear strains
$\gamma_{pxy}, \gamma_{pyz}, \gamma_{pzx}$	Plastic shear strains
$\varepsilon_x, \varepsilon_y, \varepsilon_z$	Total normal strains in orthogonal directions
$\varepsilon_{ex}, \varepsilon_{ey}, \varepsilon_{ez}$	Elastic normal strains
$\varepsilon_{px}, \varepsilon_{py}, \varepsilon_{pz}$	Plastic normal strains
$\varepsilon_1, \varepsilon_2, \varepsilon_3$	Normal strains in the principal directions
$\varepsilon_{e1}, \varepsilon_{e2}, \varepsilon_{e3}$	Elastic strains in the principal directions
$\varepsilon_{p1}, \varepsilon_{p2}, \varepsilon_{p3}$	Plastic strains in the principal directions
$\bar{\varepsilon}$	Effective total strain
$\bar{\varepsilon}_p$	Effective plastic strain
λ	Ratio σ_2/σ_1 for plane stress ($\sigma_3 = 0$)
$\tilde{\nu}$	Generalized Poisson's ratio
$\sigma_x, \sigma_y, \sigma_z$	Normal stresses in orthogonal directions
$\sigma_1, \sigma_2, \sigma_3$	Principal normal stresses
$\bar{\sigma}$	Effective stress
$\tau_{xy}, \tau_{yz}, \tau_{zx}$	Shear stresses on orthogonal planes

REFERENCES

ASTM. 2010. *Annual Book of ASTM Standards*, Vol. 03.01, ASTM International, West Conshohocken, PA. See No. E606, "Standard Practice for Strain-Controlled Fatigue Testing."

CHEN, W. F., and D. J. HAN. 1988. *Plasticity for Structural Engineers*, Springer-Verlag, New York.

HILL, R. 1998. *The Mathematical Theory of Plasticity*, Oxford University Press, Oxford, UK.

KHAN, A. S., and S. HUANG. 1995. *Continuum Theory of Plasticity*, John Wiley, New York.

LANDGRAF, R. W., J. MORROW, and T. ENDO. 1969. "Determination of the Cyclic Stress–Strain Curve," *Journal of Materials*, ASTM, vol. 4, no. 1, Mar. 1969, pp. 176–188.

LANDGRAF, R. W., and R. A. CHERNENKOFF. 1988. "Residual Stress Effects on Fatigue of Surface Processed Steels," *Analytical and Experimental Methods for Residual Stress Effects in Fatigue*, ASTM STP 1004, R. L. Champous et al., eds., Am. Soc. for Testing and Materials, West Conshohocken, PA, pp. 1–12.

MARTIN, J. F., T. H. TOPPER, and G. M. SINCLAIR. 1971. "Computer Based Simulation of Cyclic Stress–Strain Behavior with Applications to Fatigue," *Materials Research and Standards*, ASTM, vol. 11, no. 2, Feb. 1971, pp. 23–29.

MENDELSON, A. 1968. *Plasticity: Theory and Applications*, Macmillan, New York. (Also reprinted by R. E. Krieger, Malabar, FL, 1983.)

NADAI, A. 1950. *Theory of Flow and Fracture of Solids*, McGraw-Hill, New York.

SKRZYPEK, J. J., and R. B. HETNARSKI. 1993. *Plasticity and Creep: Theory, Examples, and Problems*, CRC Press, Boca Raton, FL.

PROBLEMS AND QUESTIONS

Section 12.2

12.1   The monotonic stress–strain curve of RQC-100 steel under uniaxial stress can be approximated by an elastic, linear-hardening relationship. Two points on this curve are given in Table P12.1, with the first point corresponding to the beginning of yielding. Plot the curve and write its equation in the form of Eq. 12.4, with numerical values substituted for the constants E, δ, and σ_o.

Table P12.1

σ, MPa	ε
783	1.50×10^{-2}
810	$1.1 \ \times 10^{-2}$

12.2   Proceed as in Prob. 12.1, except use the two points in Table P12.2 for an AISI 4340 steel. Yielding begins at the first point.

Table P12.2

σ, MPa	ε
1200	4.00×10^{-2}
1310	3.50×10^{-2}

12.3   Consider the engineering stress–strain data in Table P4.8 for AISI 4140 steel tempered at 649°C. Make a stress–strain plot of the data for strains less than 2%. Of Eqs. 12.1, 12.4, 12.8, and 12.12, choose the one that will best represent the data, and perform a fit to evaluate the materials constants. Add your fitted curve to the plot of the data, and comment on how well it fits the data.

12.4 Engineering stress–strain data are given in Table P12.4 for the beginning of a tension test on AISI 4140 steel tempered at 427°C. Make a stress–strain plot of the data. Of Eqs. 12.1, 12.4, 12.8, and 12.12, choose the one that will best represent the data, and perform a fit to evaluate the materials constants. Add your fitted curve to the plot of the data, and comment on how well it fits the data.

Table P12.4

σ, MPa	ε, %	σ, MPa	ε, %
0	0	1399	0.781
402	0.197	1406	1.010
812	0.405	1445	1.386
1198	0.595	1466	1.823
1358	0.681	1483	2.502
1403	0.732	1492	3.278

12.5 Consider the engineering stress–strain data in Table P4.11 for near-γ titanium aluminide, Ti-48Al-2V-2Mn. Make a stress–strain plot of the data for strains less than 1.2%. Of Eqs. 12.1, 12.4, 12.8, and 12.12, choose the one that will best represent the data, and perform a fit to evaluate the materials constants. Add your fitted curve to the plot of the data, and comment on how well it fits the data.

12.6 Consider the engineering stress–strain data in Table P4.6 for 6061-T6 aluminum. Make a stress–strain plot of the data for strains less than 7.5%. Of Eqs. 12.1, 12.4, 12.8, and 12.12, choose the one that will best represent the data, and perform a fit to evaluate the materials constants. Add your fitted curve to the plot of the data, and comment on how well it fits the data.

12.7 Consider the engineering stress–strain data in Table P4.9 for AISI 4140 steel tempered at 204°C. Make a stress–strain plot of the data for strains less than 4%. Of Eqs. 12.1, 12.4, 12.8, and 12.12, choose the one that will best represent the data, and perform a fit to evaluate the materials constants. Add your fitted curve to the plot of the data, and comment on how well it fits the data.

12.8 Consider the engineering stress–strain data in Table P4.7 for gray cast iron. Make a stress–strain plot of these data. Of Eqs. 12.1, 12.4, 12.8, and 12.12, choose the one that will best represent the data, and perform a fit to evaluate the materials constants. Or if none of these seems to fit very well, suggest another form of equation yourself, and fit it. Add your fitted curve to the plot of the data, and comment on how well it fits the data.

12.9 Consider the engineering stress–strain data in Table P4.14 for a tension test on PMMA polymer. Make a stress–strain plot of these data. Of Eqs. 12.1, 12.4, 12.8, and 12.12, choose the one that will best represent the data, and perform a fit to evaluate the materials constants. Or if none of these seems to fit very well, suggest another form of equation yourself, and fit it. Add your fitted curve to the plot of the data, and comment on how well it fits the data.

Section 12.3

12.10 Consider Eqs. 12.26 and 12.27 and proceed as follows: Starting with Eq. 12.26, derive Eq. 12.27(a), verifying in the process that the expressions of Eq. 12.27(d) and (e) for E_t and $\tilde{\nu}$ appear in the modulus and Poisson's ratio positions in the equation.

12.11 Proceed as in Ex. 12.3, except change the pressure vessel to a thin-walled spherical one of radius r and wall thickness t.

12.12 A thin-walled tubular pressure vessel of radius r, wall thickness t, and length L has closed ends and is made of a material having a uniaxial stress–strain curve of the Ramberg–Osgood form, Eq. 12.12. If the internal pressure p is increased monotonically, derive an equation for the relative change in the enclosed volume, dV_e/V_e, as a function of the pressure p and the various constants involved. (Suggestion: See Prob. 5.21.)

12.13 Consider stress with principal normal stresses $\sigma_2 = \sigma_3 = \sigma_{1/2}$, and a material with a uniaxial stress–strain curve of the Ramberg–Osgood form. Develop an equation for ε_1 as a function of σ_1 and λ as well as materials constants E, H_1, n_1, and ν.

12.14 Consider plane stress with principal normal stresses σ_1, $\sigma_2 = \lambda\sigma_1$, and $\sigma_3 = 0$. Assuming a Ramberg–Osgood form of stress–strain curve, derive relationships analogous to Eq. 12.39 for the other two principal strains, ε_2 and ε_3, each as a function of σ_1 and λ and materials constants.

12.15 For a given material, assume that constants E, H, and n are known for its uniaxial stress–strain curve of the Ramberg–Osgood form, Eq. 12.12. An estimate is needed of the stress–strain curve $\gamma = f_\tau(\tau)$ for a state of pure planar shear stress.

(a) Show that the appropriate estimate is

$$\gamma = \frac{\tau}{G} + \left(\frac{\tau}{H_\tau}\right)^{1/n}$$

where $G = E/[2(1+\nu)]$ and $H_\tau = H/3^{(n+1)/2}$. Note that the principal stresses and strains for pure shear are given in Fig. 4.41.

(b) For the Fig 12.9 material, calculate a number of points on both the uniaxial and the pure shear stress–strain curves, covering strains from zero to 0.04. Then plot the two curves on the same graph and comment on the comparison.

12.16 For a given material, assume that constants E, σ_o, and δ are known for its uniaxial stress–strain curve of the elastic, linear-hardening form, Eq. 12.5.

(a) Develop an equation for estimating the stress–strain curve $\gamma = f_\tau(\tau)$ for a state of pure planar shear stress. (See Fig. 4.41.) The materials constants in your equation should be G, δ, ν, and the yield strength in shear, τ_o.

(b) Does the new equation still exhibit linear hardening? What is its slope $d\tau/d\gamma$? If the new slope is denoted $\delta_\tau G$, where G is the shear modulus, is δ_τ the same as δ for the uniaxial curve?

12.17 Consider a material with a uniaxial stress–strain curve of the Ramberg–Osgood form, Eq. 12.12, subjected to the state of stress

$$\sigma_1 = \sigma_2, \qquad \sigma_3 = \alpha\sigma_1 \qquad (-1 \leq \alpha \leq 1)$$

where σ_1, σ_2, and σ_3 are the principal normal stresses and α is a constant.

     (a) Derive an equation for the principal normal strain ε_1 as a function of σ_1, α, and materials constants.

     (b) Assume that the material is the 7075-T651 aluminum of Ex. 12.1, with Poisson's ratio $\nu = 0.33$. Plot the family of curves resulting from $\alpha = -1, -0.5, 0, 0.5$, and 1, covering strains from zero to 0.04. Then comment on the trends observed.

12.18 Consider a situation of plane stress, $\sigma_3 = 0$, with an applied stress σ_1, where deformation is prevented in the other in-plane direction, so that $\varepsilon_2 = 0$. (For example, this occurs in a sample of material loaded and constrained as in Fig. E5.3.)

     (a) Letting the x-y-z axes be the principal stress axes, 1-2-3, apply Eq. 12.27 to develop expressions as follows: (1) σ_2 as a function of σ_1 and the generalized Poisson's ratio $\tilde{\nu}$, (2) σ_1 as a function of effective stress $\bar{\sigma}$ and $\tilde{\nu}$, for which Eq. 12.21 is also needed, and (3) ε_1 as a function of effective strain $\bar{\varepsilon}$ and $\tilde{\nu}$.

     (b) Let the effective (same as uniaxial) stress–strain curve be the Ramberg–Osgood one from Ex. 12.1, with Poisson's ratio $\nu = 0.33$. Then calculate a number of values of σ_1 and ε_1 for $\bar{\varepsilon}$ ranging from zero to 0.04.

     (c) Plot the $\bar{\sigma}$ versus $\bar{\varepsilon}$ curve, and on the same graph, plot a second curve for σ_1 versus ε_1. Comment on the comparison of the two curves. Explain the cause of the trend observed.

12.19 Consider the state of strain $\varepsilon_2 = \varepsilon_3 = 0$, with a stress σ_1 applied, and note that symmetry requires $\sigma_2 = \sigma_3$. Proceed as in Prob. 12.18(a), (b), and (c), except do so for the $\varepsilon_2 = \varepsilon_3 = 0$ case.

Section 12.4

12.20 For a titanium alloy, assume that the stress–strain relationship is an elastic, perfectly plastic one, with constants $E = 120\,\text{GPa}$ and $\sigma_o = 600\,\text{MPa}$, and also assume that the behavior follows a spring and slider rheological model of the type shown in Fig. 12.4(a).

     (a) Determine and plot the stress–strain response if the material is loaded from zero stress and strain to $\varepsilon_{max} = 0.009$ and then cycled between this ε_{max} and $\varepsilon_{min} = -0.009$.

     (b) Proceed as in (a) for $\varepsilon_{max} = 0.009$ and $\varepsilon_{min} = 0.002$.

     (c) Proceed as in (a) for $\varepsilon_{max} = 0.009$ and $\varepsilon_{min} = -0.003$.

12.21 An elastic, linear-hardening material has elastic modulus $E = 200\,\text{GPa}$, yield strength $\sigma_o = 500\,\text{MPa}$, and a value of $\delta = 0.1$ for Eq. 12.4. Assuming that the behavior follows the rheological model of Fig. 12.4(b), estimate and plot the stress–strain response for the following:

     (a) Completely reversed cyclic straining at $\varepsilon_a = 0.006$.

     (b) Straining from zero to $\varepsilon = 0.012$, followed by decreasing strain to $\varepsilon = 0.005$, and then increasing strain to $\varepsilon = 0.015$.

12.22 Assume that a steel behaves according to the rheological model of Fig. 12.4(b), with the elastic, linear-hardening stress–strain curve, Eq. 12.4, having constants $E = 208$ GPa, $\sigma_o = 523$ MPa, and $\delta = 0.0535$.

     (a) Determine and plot the stress–strain response if the material is loaded from zero stress and strain to $\varepsilon_{max} = 0.012$ and then cycled between this ε_{max} and $\varepsilon_{min} = 0.008$.

     (b) Proceed as in (a) for $\varepsilon_{max} = 0.012$ and $\varepsilon_{min} = 0.005$.

12.23 A multistage spring–slider rheological model as in Fig. 12.6 has a spring in series with three parallel spring–slider combinations. For model constants as given in the table that follows, determine and plot the stress–strain response as the strain increases from zero to $\varepsilon = 0.016$ and then returns to zero.

Stage No.	1	2	3	4
E_i, GPa	200	120	150	50
σ_{oi}, MPa	0	800	1100	1300

12.24 The rheological model of Prob. 12.23 is started from zero, strained to $\varepsilon_{max} = 0.016$, and then cycled between this ε_{max} and $\varepsilon_{min} = 0$. Determine and plot the stress–strain response.

12.25 For the rheological model of Prob. 12.23, determine and plot the stress–strain response for starting at zero and then following the sequence of strains given in the accompanying table.

Peak or Valley	A	B	C	D	A'
ε, Strain	0.016	−0.008	0.008	0	0.016

12.26 Aluminum alloy 2024-T351 is loaded from zero stress and strain to $\varepsilon_{max} = 0.016$ and then cycled between this ε_{max} and $\varepsilon_{min} = 0.004$. Assume that the stress–strain behavior is similar to a multistage spring–slider model that follows the stable cyclic stress–strain curve of Ramberg–Osgood form given by constants in Table 12.1. Estimate the maximum and minimum stresses σ_{max} and σ_{min} for this cyclic loading. Then plot the stress–strain response during the cyclic loading.

12.27 Proceed as in Prob. 12.26, but let the material be loaded from zero stress and strain to $\varepsilon_{min} = -0.016$ and then cycled between this ε_{min} and $\varepsilon_{max} = -0.004$. Note that the loading to ε_{min} should follow Eq. 12.51(b).

12.28 The steel AISI 4340 steel ($\sigma_u = 1172\,\text{MPa}$) is loaded from zero stress and strain to $\varepsilon_{max} = 0.012$ and then cycled between this ε_{max} and $\varepsilon_{min} = 0.003$. Assume that the stress–strain behavior is similar to a multistage spring–slider model that follows the stable cyclic stress–strain curve of Ramberg–Osgood form given by constants in Table 12.1. Estimate the maximum and minimum stresses σ_{max} and σ_{min} for this cyclic loading. Then plot the stress–strain response during the cyclic loading.

12.29 Aluminum alloy 7075-T6 is loaded from zero stress and strain to $\varepsilon_{max} = 0.035$ and then cycled between this ε_{max} and $\varepsilon_{min} = 0.005$. Assume that the stress–strain behavior is similar to a multistage spring–slider model that follows the stable cyclic stress–strain curve of Ramberg–Osgood form given by constants in Table 12.1. Estimate the maximum and minimum stresses, σ_{max} and σ_{min}, for this cyclic loading. Then plot the stress–strain response during the cyclic loading.

Section 12.5

12.30 For aluminum alloy 2024-T351, the monotonic and cyclic stress–strain curves both fit Ramberg–Osgood forms, Eqs. 12.12 and 12.54, respectively. Constants for the monotonic curve are $E = 73.1\,\text{GPa}$, $H = 662\,\text{MPa}$, and $n = 0.070$, and those for the cyclic curve are given in Table 12.1.

    (a) Plot both of these curves on the same linear–linear axes out to a strain of $\varepsilon = 0.01$.

    (b) Does this material harden or soften cyclically? How do the yield strengths from the two curves compare?

12.31 Various properties are given in Chapter 14, specifically Table 14.1, for four strength levels of SAE 4142 steel, including E, H', and n' for Eq. 12.54.

    (a) Plot all four cyclic stress–strain curves on the same graph, covering strain amplitudes from zero to 0.04.

    (b) Then comment on the trends in these curves and how they correlate with the strength and ductility from tension tests. Include in your comparison the monotonic yield strength versus the 0.2% offset yield strength from the cyclic curves.

12.32 For completely reversed strain cycling ($\sigma_m \approx 0$) of 7075-T6 Al alloy,. This alloy has tensile properties of yield strength 469 MPa, ultimate strength 578 MPa, and 51% reduction in area.

    (a) Make a stress–strain plot of these data. Then fit the data to obtain a cyclic stress–strain curve of the Ramberg–Osgood form, Eq. 12.54, for which $E = 710\,\text{GPa}$. Add your fitted curve to the plot of the data, and comment on how well it fits the data.

    (b) Representative points from a typical monotonic stress–strain curve for this material are given in Table P12.32(b). Add these data to the stress–strain plot from (a) and comment on the behavior of the material.

Table P12.32(a)

ε_a	σ_a, MPa	ε_{pa}	N_f, cycles
0.0200	524	0.01741	257
0.0100	459	0.00774	1 494
0.0060	410	0.00398	6 749
0.0040	352	0.00227	19 090
0.0030	315	0.00144	36 930
0.0020	270	0.00067	321 500
0.0015	241	0.00031	2 451 000

Source: Data in [Leese 85].

Table P12.32(b)

ε	σ, MPa
0	0
0.00218	441
0.00218	379
0.01200	379
0.01400	402
0.01600	422
0.01800	433
0.02000	438

12.33 For completely reversed strain cycling ($\sigma m \approx 0$) of 2024-T351 Al with $\sigma_u = 469\,\text{MPa}$ and $\sigma_0 = 379\,\text{MPa}$, Table P12.33(a) gives strain amplitudes and the corresponding cyclically stable amplitudes of stress and plastic strain, as well as fatigue lives.

    (a) Make a stress–strain plot of these data. Then fit the data to obtain a cyclic stress–strain curve of the Ramberg–Osgood form, Eq. 12.54, for which $E = 73,100\,\text{MPa}$. Add your fitted curve to the plot of the data, and comment on how well it fits the data.

(b) Representative points from a typical monotonic stress–strain curve for this material are given in Table P12.33(b). Add these data to the stress–strain plot from (a) and comment on the behavior of the material.

Table P12.33(a)

ε_a	σ_a, MPa	ε_{pa}	N_f, cycles
0.02000	948	0.01495	222
0.01000	834	0.00570	992
0.00500	703	0.00150	6 004
0.00400	631	0.00085	14 130
0.00318	579	0.00036	43 860
0.00270	524	0.00015	132 150

Note: Last three prestrained 10 cycles at $\varepsilon_a = 0.01$.
Source: Data in [Dowling 73].

Table P12.33(b)

ε	σ, MPa
0	0
0.00495	1025
0.00520	1070
0.00556	1109
0.00625	1097
0.00675	1091
0.01000	1091
0.02000	1148

12.34 For quenched and tempered RQC-100 steel with ultimate tensile strength $\sigma_u = 758$ MPa and $E = 200$ GPa, Table P12.34 gives strain amplitudes and the corresponding cyclically stable amplitudes of stress, plastic strain, and mean stress, as well as fatigue lives. Make a stress–strain plot of these data. Then fit the data to obtain a cyclic stress–strain curve of the Ramberg–Osgood form, Eq. 12.54, for which $E = 206.7$ GPa. Add your fitted curve to the plot of the data, and comment on how well it fits the data.

Table P12.34

ε_a	σ_a, MPa	σ_m, MPa	ε_{pa}	N_f, cycles
0.0177	2089	−55	0.00720	20
0.0150	1972	0	0.00490	40
0.0125	1931	−34	0.00300	91
0.0095	1751	28	0.00110	245
0.0090	1586	76	0.00070	476
0.0075	1524	0	0.00020	1 130
0.0072	1379	138	—	800
0.0050	1034	0	—	18 950
0.0040	827	0	—	386 500

Source: Data in [Landgraf 66] and [Landgraf 68].

12.35 From strain-controlled cyclic torsion tests on thin-walled tubes of hot-rolled and normalized SAE 1045 steel, the applied shear strain amplitudes γ_a, as well as the resulting amplitudes of shear stress τ_a and plastic shear strain γ_{pa}, are given in Table P12.35. (The τ_a and γ_{pa} values are for cyclically stable behavior near half of the fatigue life, N_f.)

    (a) Make a shear stress–strain plot of these data. Then fit the data to a cyclic stress–strain curve of the Ramberg–Osgood form. Use $G = 79.1\,\text{GPa}$, and obtain H_{τ}' and n' from fitting $\tau_a = H_{\tau}' \gamma_{pa}^{n'}$. Then add your fitted curve to the plot of the data, and comment on how well it fits.

    (b) For this material under uniaxial stress, constants E, H', and n' for the cyclic stress–strain curve are given in Table 14.1. On the basis of Prob. 12.15, use these uniaxial constants to estimate the cyclic stress–strain for shear. Poisson's ratio is $\nu = 0.277$. Compare this estimate to the data on the stress–strain plot from (a), and comment on the success of the estimate.

Table P12.35

γ_a	τ_a, MPa	γ_{pa}	N_f, cycles
0.0250	267	0.0217	502
0.0150	234	0.0120	1 372
0.0082	197	0.0057	6 998
0.0050	165	0.0029	33 840
0.0040	158	0.0020	70 020
0.0030	148	0.0012	546 000

Source: Data in [Leese 85].

12.36 The steel RQC-100 of Table 12.1 is loaded from zero stress and strain to $\varepsilon_{\max} = 0.010$ and then cycled between this $\varepsilon_{\max}$ and $\varepsilon_{\min} = 0.006$.

    (a) Estimate the maximum and minimum stresses, $\sigma_{\max}$ and $\sigma_{\min}$, for this cyclic loading, and plot the stress–strain response.

    (b) Consider cyclic relaxation of mean stress. Estimate and plot the variation of mean stress with cycles out to $N = 5 \times 10^4$ cycles, and comment on the trend observed.

12.37 The steel SAE 1045, when heat treated to a hardness of $HB = 500$, has constants for its cyclic stress–strain curve (Eq. 12.54) of $E = 206\,\text{GPa}$, $H' = 2636\,\text{MPa}$, and $n' = 0.12$. An axially loaded member of this material is cycled between $\varepsilon_{\min} = 0$ and $\varepsilon_{\max} = 0.008$.

    (a) Estimate and plot the stress–strain response for behavior that is cyclically stable.

    (b) Consider cyclic relaxation of mean stress. Estimate and plot the variation of mean stress with cycles out to $N = 10^4$ cycles, and comment on the trend observed.

12.38 Aluminum alloy 2024-T351 is loaded from zero stress and strain and is then subjected to the strain sequence given in the accompanying table and also shown in Fig. P12.38. Note that valley A occurs 11 times and peak B occurs 10 times. Estimate and plot the stress–strain response. Assume that the stress–strain behavior is stable (cyclic hardening or softening already complete), and use the Ramberg–Osgood cyclic stress–strain curve given by the constants in Table 12.1.

Peak or Valley	A_1	B_1	A-B	A_{10}	B_{10}	A_{11}	C	A'
ε, Strain	-0.016	-0.005	repeats	-0.016	-0.005	-0.016	-0.002	-0.016

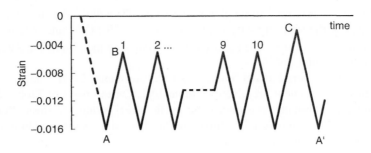

Figure P12.38

12.39 Aluminum alloy 2024-T351 is loaded from zero stress and strain and is then subjected to the strain sequence given in the accompanying table. Note that valley B occurs 11 times and peak C occurs 10 times. Estimate and plot the stress–strain response. Assume stable stress–strain behavior (cyclic hardening or softening already complete) and use the Ramberg–Osgood cyclic stress–strain curve given by the constants in Table 12.1.

Peak or Valley	A	B_1	C_1	B-C	B_{10}	C_{10}	B_{11}	A'
ε, Strain	0.020	0.004	0.016	repeats	0.004	0.016	0.004	0.020

12.40 Aluminum alloy 7075-T6 is loaded from zero stress and strain and is then subjected to the strain sequence given in the accompanying table. Note that valley B and peak C each occur 50 times. Estimate and plot the stress–strain response. Assume that the stress–strain behavior is stable (cyclic hardening or softening already complete), and use the Ramberg–Osgood cyclic stress–strain curve given by the constants in Table 12.1.

Peak or Valley	A	B_1	C_1	B-C	B_{50}	C_{50}	D	A'
ε, Strain	0.010	0.035	0.025	repeats	0.01	0.025	0.005	0.035

12.41 The steel AISI 4340 steel ($\sigma_u = 1172\,\mathrm{MPa}$) is loaded from zero stress and strain and is then subjected to the strain sequence in the accompanying table. Note that peak C and valley D each occur 5 times. Estimate and plot the stress–strain response. Assume stable stress–strain behavior (cyclic hardening or softening already complete) and use the Ramberg–Osgood cyclic stress–strain curve given by the constants in Table 12.1.

Peak or Valley	A	B_1	C_1	D_1	C-D	C_5	D_5	A'
ε, Strain	0.015	−0.003	0.005	0.002	repeats	0.007	0.003	0.015

13

Stress–Strain Analysis of Plastically Deforming Members

OBJECTIVES

- Perform elasto-plastic stress–strain analysis for simple cases of bending and torsion, considering various forms of stress–strain curve.
- Employ approximate methods, such as Neuber's rule, to estimate stresses and strains at notches where there is local plastic deformation.
- Extend the analysis of bending, torsion, and notched members to unloading, for determining residual stresses and strains, and further to cyclic loading, including irregular load versus time histories.

13.1 INTRODUCTION

It is often useful for engineering purposes to analyze plastic deformation in components of machines, vehicles, or structures. This occurs in two types of situations. First, it may be desirable to know the load necessary to cause gross plastic deformation, sometimes called *plastic collapse*. The safety factor for failure due to accidental overload can then be calculated by comparing the failure load with the loads expected during service of the component. Second, the stresses and strains that accompany plastic deformation in localized areas, as at the edge of a beam or at a stress raiser, are of interest. Such deformations introduce residual stresses, perhaps intentional ones, that can be evaluated by analysis of the plastic deformation. Localized plastic deformation caused by cyclic loading is of considerable importance, as this is often associated with fatigue cracking.

693

Local plasticity at stress raisers (notches) can be analyzed by applying an approximate method such as *Neuber's rule*. In some cases that are frequently of practical interest, such as bending of beams and torsion of circular shafts, plastic deformation can be analyzed in a fairly straightforward manner by a mechanics-of-materials type of approach. Three steps are needed: (1) Assume a strain distribution. (2) Apply equilibrium of forces. (3) Choose a particular stress–strain relationship, and use this to complete the analysis.

We will apply such approaches not only to static loading, but also to unloading and to cyclic loading. The application to cyclic loading will be employed in the next chapter for the strain-based approach to fatigue. Detailed analysis of many complex situations of loading and geometry is not possible with the relatively simple methods of this chapter. Analysis by *finite elements* or another numerical method may be needed. (See the SAE *Fatigue Design Handbook* (Rice, 1997) for a chapter-length introduction to numerical stress–strain analysis.) The treatment given here nevertheless provides an introduction and some useful engineering tools. In what follows, it is assumed that the reader is familiar with portions of Chapter 12.

13.2 PLASTICITY IN BENDING

Bending of beams where the material deforms in a linear-elastic manner is quite thoroughly covered in elementary and advanced textbooks on mechanics of materials. Plastic bending is also often introduced, but typically is limited to elastic, perfectly plastic behavior. In this portion of the chapter, bending involving plastic deformation will be considered for various stress–strain curves. Procedures for developing closed-form solutions are described, and some completed solutions are given. We will consider only cases where the applied loads lie in a plane of symmetry of the cross section.

13.2.1 Review of Elastic Bending

As a brief review of linear-elastic bending, consider the simple case of three-point bending of a beam having a rectangular cross section, as illustrated in Fig. 13.1. The applied loads lie in the x-y plane, which is a plane of symmetry of the beam. Elastic stress distributions in the beam involve a zero stress or *neutral axis*, N-N, that coincides with a centroidal axis of the cross-sectional area.

Normal stresses for linear-elastic bending are given by

$$\sigma = \frac{My}{I_z} \tag{13.1}$$

where M is the bending moment at the cross section of interest, such as $M = Px/2$ for the cross section illustrated in Fig. 13.1. The quantity I_z is the moment of inertia of the cross-sectional area about the neutral axis, and the distance y is measured from the neutral axis. The positive direction for y is chosen as the direction that gives positive σ on the side of the neutral axis where tensile stresses occur. The equation gives a linear distribution of the normal stress, $\sigma = \sigma_x$, with distance y from the neutral axis, which arises from two key assumptions: (1) linear-elastic stress–strain behavior and (2) plane sections remaining plane after deformation—which combine to require a linear stress

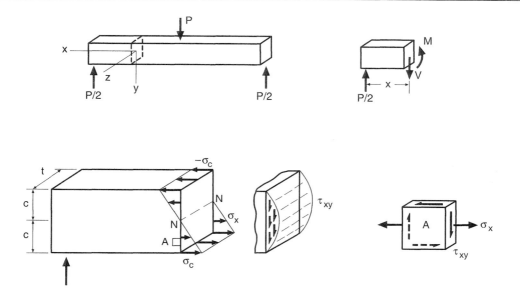

Figure 13.1   Elastic bending and shear in a rectangular beam. For a cross section as indicated above, the stresses are distributed as shown below.

distribution. For rectangular cross sections of thickness t and depth $2c$, Eq. 13.1 gives the maximum tensile stress as

$$\sigma_c = \frac{3M}{2tc^2} \tag{13.2}$$

where the subscript indicates that this stress occurs at $y = c$. Since in this case the cross section is symmetrical above and below the neutral axis, an equal compressive stress $-\sigma_c$ occurs at $y = -c$.

Except for cases of pure bending, these normal stresses are accompanied by shear stresses that can be computed as described in Appendix A, Section A.2. For a rectangular cross section, the shear stress $\tau = \tau_{xy}$ for elastic deformation varies as a parabola with a maximum value at the neutral axis:

$$\tau = \frac{3V\left(c^2 - y^2\right)}{4tc^3} \tag{13.3}$$

Here, V is the shear force, such as $V = P/2$ for the cross section illustrated in Fig. 13.1.

Equation 13.1 applies even if the cross-sectional area is not symmetrical about the neutral axis, provided that the requirement of symmetry about the plane of loading is still met. Such a case is illustrated in Fig. 13.2(a). However, if symmetry about the plane of loading does not exist, then the stresses can still be determined by considering bending about two axes, as for Fig. 13.2(b). In addition, if the plane of unsymmetrical bending does not pass through the *shear center* of the cross-sectional area, torsional stresses must be considered.

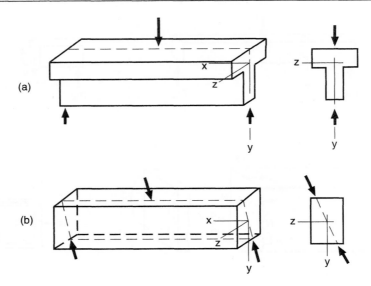

Figure 13.2   Bending due to loads in a plane of symmetry of the cross section (a), and bending due to loads not in a plane of symmetry (b).

13.2.2 Plastic Bending Analysis by Integration

Let us restrict our attention to cases of bending in a plane of symmetry of the beam and generalize the problem to permit plastic deformation. Also, assume that shear stresses are absent, or if present, that their effects are small. Under these circumstances, a reasonably accurate physical assumption, even for plastic deformation, is that originally plane cross sections remain plane. This results in a linear variation of strain with distance from the neutral axis, given by

$$\frac{\varepsilon}{y} = \frac{\varepsilon_c}{c} \tag{13.4}$$

where ε is strain in the longitudinal (x) direction and ε_c is its value at $y = c$, the edge of the beam. Hence, if yielding occurs, the nonlinear stress–strain curve causes the stress distribution to become nonlinear, as illustrated in Fig. 13.3. Due to the linear strain distribution, the stress distribution has the same shape as the portion of the stress–strain curve up to $\varepsilon = \varepsilon_c$.

We can derive the bending moment by considering the contribution of a differential element of area, as shown in Fig. 13.4:

$$dM = (\text{stress})(\text{area})(\text{distance}) = (\sigma)(t\,dy)(y) \tag{13.5}$$

Here, the thickness t can vary with y. Integrating to obtain the moment gives

$$M = \int_{-c_2}^{c_1} \sigma t y\,dy \tag{13.6}$$

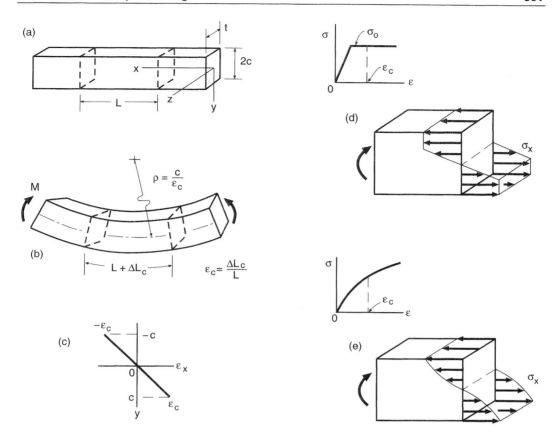

Figure 13.3 A rectangular beam (a) subjected to pure bending (b), which causes yielding. Plane sections remaining plane results in a linear strain distribution (c), but the stress distribution is nonlinear as in (d) or (e), having the same shape as that portion of the stress–strain curve up to ε_c.

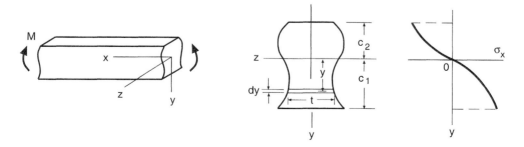

Figure 13.4 Area element ($t\,dy$) and stress distribution needed for integration to relate bending moment M to stresses and strains.

The cross-sectional area may not be symmetrical above and below the x-axis, and the stress–strain curve may not be symmetrical with respect to tension and compression. If either of these asymmetries exists, then the neutral axis shifts somewhat from the centroid of the cross-sectional area as plastic deformation progresses, so it needs to be located before the integration can proceed. The principle to be followed in doing so is that the volumes under the tensile and compressive portions of the stress distribution must give equal and opposite forces—that is, a sum of zero—corresponding to an axial force P of zero:

$$P = \int_{-c_2}^{c_1} \sigma t \, dy = 0 \tag{13.7}$$

Equations 13.4, 13.6, and 13.7, and a stress–strain curve $\varepsilon = f(\sigma)$, are needed to solve any specific problem.

13.2.3 Rectangular Cross Sections

Consider the simple case of a rectangular cross section and a material with a symmetrical stress–strain curve. Hence, t is constant, $c_1 = c_2 = c$, and the neutral axis remains at the centroid. The symmetry that exists is such that the integral can be computed for one side of the neutral axis and then doubled:

$$M = 2t \int_0^c \sigma y \, dy \tag{13.8}$$

This equation may be integrated for various forms of stress–strain curve. Stress σ first needs to be written as a function of y for integration to proceed.

For example, let $\varepsilon = f(\sigma)$ be a simple power-hardening stress–strain curve with no elastic region; that is,

$$\sigma = H_2 \varepsilon^{n_2} \tag{13.9}$$

Substituting the strain ε from Eq. 13.4 gives

$$\sigma = H_2 \left(\frac{y \varepsilon_c}{c} \right)^{n_2} \tag{13.10}$$

This is the equation of the positive part of a nonlinear stress distribution, as illustrated in Fig. 13.3(e). We then substitute this σ into Eq. 13.8 and perform the integration, obtaining

$$M = \frac{2tc^2 H_2 \varepsilon_c^{n_2}}{n_2 + 2} = \frac{2tc^2 \sigma_c}{n_2 + 2} \tag{13.11}$$

Since the stress–strain curve holds for the edge of the beam where $\sigma = \sigma_c$ and $\varepsilon = \varepsilon_c$, Eq. 13.9 permits the result to be expressed in terms of stress, giving the second form. The special case of $n_2 = 1$ corresponds to the linear-elastic case with $H_2 = E$, so that Eq. 13.11 then gives the same result as Eq. 13.2.

13.2.4 Discontinuous Stress–Strain Curves

Consider a stress–strain curve that is discontinuous, in that the mathematical relationship changes at the end of a distinct linear-elastic region. Three such relationships are described in Chapter 12, specifically, behavior that is perfectly plastic, linear hardening, or power hardening. A beam made of such a material has a distinct elastic-plastic boundary and a region on each side of the neutral axis where only elastic deformation occurs. For example, for perfectly plastic behavior beyond yielding, the stress distribution is similar to Fig. 13.3(d).

As a result of the discontinuity, integration must be performed in two steps. For a symmetrical stress–strain curve and a rectangular cross section, Eq. 13.8 applies. The integration step occurs at y_b, the distance from the neutral axis to the point where yielding begins:

$$M = 2t \left[\int_0^{y_b} \sigma y \, dy + \int_{y_b}^{c} \sigma y \, dy \right] \tag{13.12}$$

To evaluate the integral, y_b must first be found by applying Eq. 13.4 at $y = y_b$:

$$\frac{\varepsilon_o}{y_b} = \frac{\varepsilon_c}{c} \tag{13.13}$$

Noting that the yield stress and strain are related by $\sigma_o = E\varepsilon_o$ gives

$$y_b = \frac{\sigma_o c}{E \varepsilon_c} \tag{13.14}$$

Between $y = 0$ and $y = y_b$, the stress distribution is linear as a consequence of the linear-elastic stress–strain relationship, $\varepsilon = \sigma/E$. To obtain σ as a function of y in this interval, apply Eq. 13.4 at any $y < y_b$:

$$\frac{\sigma/E}{y} = \frac{\varepsilon_c}{c} \qquad (0 \le y \le y_b) \tag{13.15}$$

Then combine this with Eq. 13.13 and solve for σ:

$$\sigma = \frac{E \varepsilon_o y}{y_b} \qquad (0 \le y \le y_b) \tag{13.16}$$

The second step of the integration is affected by the type of hardening beyond yielding. As an example, consider an elastic, perfectly plastic stress–strain curve. In this case, the stress beyond $y = y_b$ is simply equal to the yield strength:

$$\sigma = \sigma_o \qquad (y_b \le y \le c) \tag{13.17}$$

To obtain a solution, first substitute Eqs. 13.16 and 13.17 into the first and second terms, respectively, of Eq. 13.12, perform the integration, and then use Eq. 13.14 to eliminate y_b from the equation. After some manipulation, the result is

$$M = tc^2 \sigma_o \left[1 - \frac{1}{3} \left(\frac{\sigma_o}{E \varepsilon_c} \right)^2 \right] \qquad (\varepsilon_c \ge \sigma_o/E) \tag{13.18}$$

If yielding is just beginning at the edge of the beam, we have $\varepsilon_c = \sigma_o/E$. Equation 13.18 then gives the same result as the elastic solution, Eq. 13.2, namely,

$$M_i = \frac{2tc^2\sigma_o}{3} \qquad (\varepsilon_c = \sigma_o/E) \tag{13.19}$$

which is called the *initial yielding moment*. For smaller values of M, the elastic solution applies in the form of Eq. 13.2, with $\sigma_c = E\varepsilon_c$. For large values of the maximum strain, Eq. 13.18 approaches a limiting value called the *fully plastic moment*:

$$M_o = tc^2\sigma_o \qquad (\varepsilon_c \gg \sigma_o/E) \tag{13.20}$$

Note that $M_o/M_i = 1.5$, which ratio changes if the cross-sectional shape is other than a rectangle. The variation of moment with strain, according to Eq. 13.18, and also the accompanying changes in the stress distribution, are shown in Fig. 13.5. As the fully plastic moment is approached, large deformations occur and a *plastic hinge* is said to develop. This corresponds to the elastic region of the beam, $y \leq y_b$, shrinking and approaching zero. The development of increased plastic deformation and, finally, a plastic hinge in three-point bending is illustrated in Fig. 13.6.

Additional analysis similar to that just given can be done for various other combinations of stress–strain curve and cross-sectional shape, some of which are in the exercises at the end

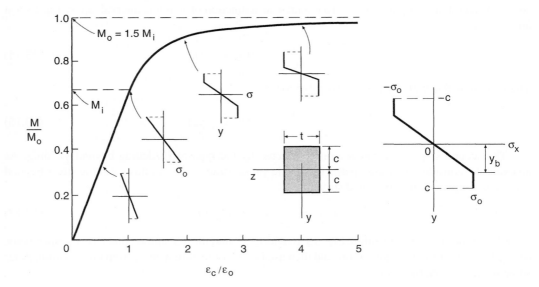

Figure 13.5 Moment versus strain behavior for a rectangular beam of an elastic, perfectly plastic material. As loading progresses, the stress distribution changes as shown.

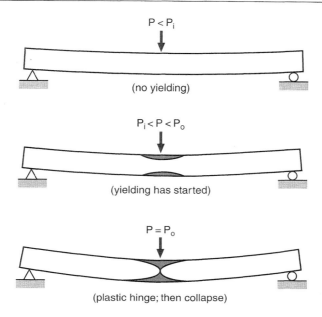

Figure 13.6 Development of a plastic hinge in three-point bending. The initial yield load P_i and the fully plastic load P_o correspond to moments M_i and M_o, respectively. Large deflections occur when P_o is reached.

of this chapter. It is not always possible to perform the integration analytically; sometimes numerical integration is needed. Also, Appendix A gives fully plastic loads for additional cases.

13.2.5 Ramberg–Osgood Stress–Strain Curve

The Ramberg–Osgood stress–strain curve, Eq. 12.12, has the advantage that it can be used to accurately represent the stress–strain curves of many materials:

$$\varepsilon = \frac{\sigma}{E} + \left(\frac{\sigma}{H}\right)^{1/n} \tag{13.21}$$

Although this relationship is not explicitly solvable for stress, closed-form integration can still be performed in certain cases by changing the variable of integration from y to σ. This is demonstrated next for a rectangular cross section.

To begin, use the linear strain distribution, Eq. 13.4, to obtain y in terms of strain, and differentiate to obtain dy:

$$y = \frac{c}{\varepsilon_c}\varepsilon, \qquad dy = \frac{c}{\varepsilon_c}\,d\varepsilon \tag{13.22}$$

Substitute these into Eq. 13.8 to express M in terms of an integral with both stress and strain as variables:

$$M = 2t \left(\frac{c}{\varepsilon_c}\right)^2 \int_0^{\varepsilon_c} \sigma \varepsilon \, d\varepsilon \tag{13.23}$$

Strain ε is given as a function of stress by Eq. 13.21, and $d\varepsilon$ can be obtained from this by differentiation and manipulation as

$$d\varepsilon = \left[\frac{1}{E} + \frac{1}{n\sigma}\left(\frac{\sigma}{H}\right)^{1/n}\right] d\sigma \tag{13.24}$$

Substituting both Eqs. 13.21 and 13.24 into the integral of Eq. 13.23 gives

$$M = 2t \left(\frac{c}{\varepsilon_c}\right)^2 \int_0^{\sigma_c} \sigma \left[\frac{\sigma}{E} + \left(\frac{\sigma}{H}\right)^{1/n}\right]\left[\frac{1}{E} + \frac{1}{n\sigma}\left(\frac{\sigma}{H}\right)^{1/n}\right] d\sigma \tag{13.25}$$

This integral can be evaluated in a straightforward manner by first obtaining the product of the two quantities in brackets. Doing so and performing some manipulation gives

$$M = 2t\sigma_c \left(\frac{c}{\varepsilon_c}\right)^2 \left[\frac{1}{3}\left(\frac{\sigma_c}{E}\right)^2 + \frac{n+1}{2n+1}\left(\frac{\sigma_c}{E}\right)\left(\frac{\sigma_c}{H}\right)^{1/n} + \frac{1}{n+2}\left(\frac{\sigma_c}{H}\right)^{2/n}\right] \tag{13.26}$$

This result may be written with the beam-edge stress σ_c as the only variable by substituting $\varepsilon_c = f(\sigma_c)$ as Eq. 13.21. A useful form obtained after some manipulation is

$$M = \frac{2tc^2\sigma_c}{3}\left[\frac{1 + \dfrac{3n+3}{2n+1}\beta + \dfrac{3}{n+2}\beta^2}{(1+\beta)^2}\right] \tag{13.27}$$

$$\text{where} \quad \beta = \frac{\varepsilon_{pc}}{\varepsilon_{ec}}, \quad \varepsilon_{pc} = \left(\frac{\sigma_c}{H}\right)^{1/n}, \quad \varepsilon_{ec} = \frac{\sigma_c}{E}, \quad \varepsilon_c = \varepsilon_{ec} + \varepsilon_{pc}$$

The quantities ε_{pc} and ε_{ec} are the edge-of-beam values of plastic and elastic strain, respectively, and β is their ratio. Using the preceding quantities, we can relate the moment to either stress or strain, with the relationship with strain being implicit.

Equation 13.27 gives a smooth variation of moment with strain, as shown in Fig. 13.7. Also shown for comparison are the trends for elastic analysis, Eq. 13.2, and for Eq. 13.11, which is the

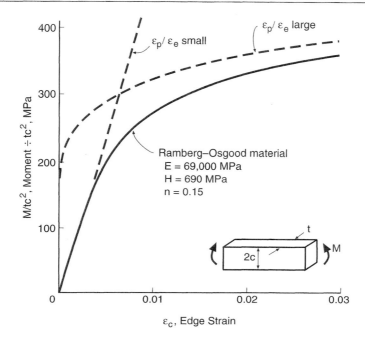

Figure 13.7   Moment vs. strain relationship for a material having a particular Ramberg–Osgood stress–strain curve. The curve approaches the limiting case of the elastic solution for small strains, and another limiting case corresponding to simple power hardening for large strains.

result derived with the use of a simple power-hardening stress–strain curve having $H_2 = H$ and $n_2 = n$. If the ratio of plastic to elastic strain β is small, Eq. 13.27 reduces to the elastic solution. Conversely, if β is large, Eq. 13.27 approaches the solution for the simple power-hardening case, Eq. 13.11.

13.3 RESIDUAL STRESSES AND STRAINS FOR BENDING

A beam that is plastically deformed and then has the bending moment removed is illustrated in Fig. 13.8. Let the material exhibit not only plastic deformation, but also elastic deformation that is recovered during unloading. Upon unloading of the beam, the strains will decrease, but not to zero, so that a permanent deflection remains in the beam. Locked-in or *residual* stresses will also exist in the beam.

Since plane sections are still expected to remain plane during unloading, the greatest changes in strain are at the edge of the beam. Here, the residual stress is opposite in sign to the stress previously present at the maximum load. What happens is that the material at the beam-edge that was permanently stretched in tension is forced into compression as the beam springs back upon removal of the load. Conversely, the material at the beam-edge subjected to compressive yielding is

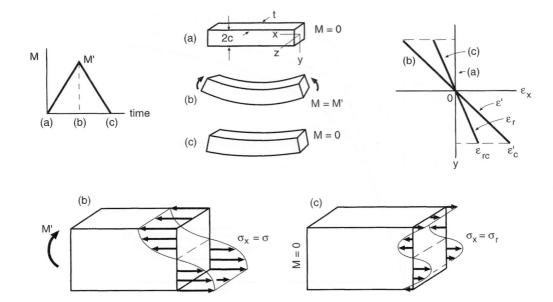

Figure 13.8 Loading of a rectangular beam beyond the point of yielding, followed by unloading. Loading starts from zero moment at time (a) and proceeds to the maximum moment M' at time (b). When unloading is complete at time (c), residual strains ε_r having a linear distribution remain, and residual stresses σ_r are distributed as shown.

forced into tension upon unloading. Closer to the neutral axis, there are regions where the residual stresses have the same sign as the previously applied stress.

13.3.1 Rectangular Beam of Elastic, Perfectly Plastic Material

Consider an elastic, perfectly plastic material and the case of a rectangular cross section that has been loaded beyond yielding. This situation is illustrated in Fig. 13.9. At the highest moment reached, M', the stress distribution is similar to Fig. 13.9(a). The moment M' is related to the strain at the edge of the beam, ε'_c, by Eq. 13.18.

$$M' = tc^2\sigma_o \left[1 - \frac{1}{3}\left(\frac{\sigma_o}{E\varepsilon'_c}\right)^2 \right] \tag{13.28}$$

Let us proceed by assuming that there is no yielding on unloading, corresponding to linear-elastic behavior, and then later check this assumption. In this case, the change in moment on unloading, ΔM, is related to the change in stress at the edge of the beam, $\Delta\sigma_c$, by the elastic solution, Eq. 13.2:

$$\Delta M = \frac{2tc^2\Delta\sigma_c}{3} \tag{13.29}$$

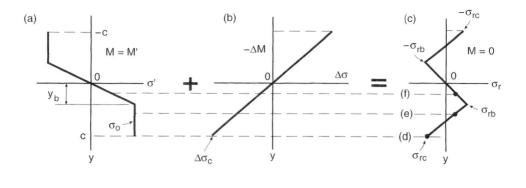

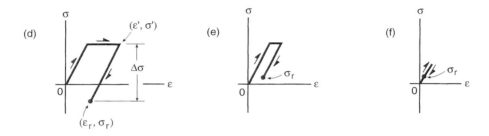

Figure 13.9 For a rectangular beam of an elastic, perfectly plastic material, stresses at the maximum moment are shown in (a), stress changes during unloading in (b), and residual stresses in (c). Depending on the location, residual stresses may be opposite in sign to the maximum stress (d) or of the same sign (e, f). The particular case illustrated corresponds to $M' = 0.95M_o$.

Since the beam is unloaded to zero moment, $M' - \Delta M = 0$. Combining the previous two equations on this basis and solving for $\Delta\sigma_c$ gives

$$\Delta\sigma_c = \frac{\sigma_o}{2}\left[3 - \left(\frac{\sigma_o}{E\varepsilon_c'}\right)^2\right] \tag{13.30}$$

The residual stress and strain at $y = c$ are the values at M' minus the changes on unloading, where the change in strain is $\Delta\varepsilon_c = \Delta\sigma_c/E$ due to the assumed elastic unloading behavior.

$$\sigma_{rc} = \sigma_c' - \Delta\sigma_c, \qquad \varepsilon_{rc} = \varepsilon_c' - \Delta\sigma_c/E \qquad \text{(a, b)} \tag{13.31}$$

Noting that $\sigma_c' = \sigma_o$, since the beam has yielded at M', and combining (a) with Eq. 13.30, we get the residual stress at $y = c$:

$$\sigma_{rc} = -\frac{\sigma_o}{2}\left[1 - \left(\frac{\sigma_o}{E\varepsilon_c'}\right)^2\right] \tag{13.32}$$

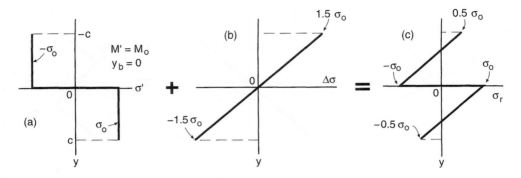

Figure 13.10   For the special case of fully plastic yielding of a rectangular beam, maximum stresses prior to unloading are shown in (a), stress changes during unloading in (b), and residual stresses in (c).

In a similar manner, (b) gives the residual strain at $y = c$:

$$\varepsilon_{rc} = \frac{\sigma_o}{2E}\left[-3 + 2\left(\frac{E\varepsilon'_c}{\sigma_o}\right) + \left(\frac{\sigma_o}{E\varepsilon'_c}\right)^2\right] \tag{13.33}$$

The quantity $E\varepsilon'_c/\sigma_o = \varepsilon'_c/\varepsilon_o$ is the ratio of the highest strain reached to the yield strain, which must be greater than unity for an initially yielded beam. Noting that this ratio and its inverse appear in both Eqs. 13.32 and 13.33, we readily conclude that σ_{rc} is negative and ε_{rc} is positive at $y = +c$, corresponding to the edge of the beam that was yielded in tension. Appropriate sign changes give values equal in magnitude, but opposite in sign, for $y = -c$.

For the extreme case where the highest strain reached is large compared with the yield strain, Eq. 13.32 gives a residual stress of magnitude half the yield strength, and Eq. 13.33 indicates that essentially none of the strain is lost upon unloading:

$$\sigma_{rc} = -\frac{\sigma_o}{2}, \qquad \varepsilon_{rc} = \varepsilon'_c \qquad (\varepsilon'_c/\varepsilon_o \gg 1) \tag{13.34}$$

The corresponding stress distributions are shown in Fig. 13.10. Conversely, if the edge of the beam just reaches the yield stress, $\varepsilon'_c/\varepsilon_o = 1$, these equations give $\sigma_{rc} = \varepsilon_{rc} = 0$, as expected. Equations 13.32 and 13.33 give a smooth variation between the two limiting cases. Note that the initial assumption of no yielding in compression is confirmed for the most extreme case by Eq. 13.34, so the analysis is valid.

13.3.2 Analysis Extended to the Interior of the Beam

Now consider interior locations in the beam. The residual stress distribution consists of straight-line segments with slope changes at $y = \pm y_b$, as shown in Fig. 13.9(c). This arises from the fact that the residual stress distribution is the sum of the distributions for σ' and $\Delta\sigma$. Since the σ' distribution has slope changes at $y = \pm y_b$, and the $\Delta\sigma$ distribution has none, their sum σ_r has slope changes at $\pm y_b$ only. Comparing Figs. 13.9(a) and (c), it is seen that points in the beam that were yielded, $y > y_b$, follow a stress–strain path similar to either (d) or (e), depending on the sign of the residual stress. Points not yielded, $y < y_b$, deform only along the elastic line, but the stresses do not return to zero, as for (f).

The residual stress distribution can thus be completely described if its value at the elastic-plastic boundary, σ_{rb}, is determined in addition to σ_{rc}. Recall that the location of the elastic-plastic boundary y_b is related to the maximum strain reached by Eq. 13.14. Since σ_{rb} has reached, but not exceeded, the yield stress, it is related to the corresponding residual strain by the elastic modulus, $\sigma_{rb} = E \varepsilon_{rb}$. Plane sections remaining plane requires that the distribution of residual strain be linear:

$$\frac{\varepsilon_{rb}}{y_b} = \frac{\varepsilon_{rc}}{c}, \qquad \frac{\sigma_{rb}/E}{y_b} = \frac{\varepsilon_{rc}}{c} \qquad \text{(a, b)} \qquad\qquad (13.35)$$

Substituting y_b from Eq. 13.14 with $\varepsilon_c = \varepsilon_c'$ into (b) yields

$$\sigma_{rb} = \frac{\sigma_o \varepsilon_{rc}}{\varepsilon_c'} \qquad\qquad (13.36)$$

Hence, σ_{rb} can be easily obtained from ε_{rc}, which is given by Eq. 13.33, so that the entire residual stress distribution can be plotted as in Fig. 13.9(c). As the strain ε_c' increases from $\varepsilon_c'/\varepsilon_o = 1$ to a large value, $\varepsilon_c'/\varepsilon_o \gg 1$, the value of σ_{rb} is seen to increase from zero to σ_o. The latter case of $\sigma_{rb} = \sigma_o$ corresponds to fully plastic yielding, $y_b = 0$, as in Fig. 13.10.

Analogous residual stress distributions occur for other cross-sectional shapes and types of elasto-plastic stress–strain curve. Closed-form analysis similar to that just described can be performed in some cases, and in other cases numerical analysis is required.

13.4 PLASTICITY OF CIRCULAR SHAFTS IN TORSION

Circular shafts loaded beyond the point of yielding in torsion, either solid or hollow, can be analyzed with procedures similar to those previously applied for bending. The assumption that plane sections remain plane is again employed. (For noncircular sections, this assumption is violated, and more sophisticated analysis is needed that is not covered here.) Analysis of torsion of circular shafts requires stress–strain curves for a state of pure shear. These are not generally known, but can be estimated from the more commonly available uniaxial stress–strain curves. We thus need to discuss estimation of stress–strain curves for shear before proceeding with analysis of circular shafts.

13.4.1 Stress–Strain Curves for Shear

Circular shafts in torsion are stressed at all points in pure planar shear. In this state of stress, the only nonzero component of stress is τ_{xy}, the x-y plane being taken to be tangent to the surface of the shaft, and the z-axis normal to the surface, as illustrated in Fig. 13.11(a). To estimate stress–strain curves for this case from uniaxial ones, the principal stresses and strains can be evaluated and used with equations based on deformation theory of plasticity, as described in the previous chapter.

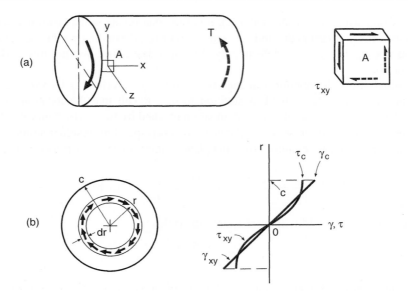

Figure 13.11   Circular shaft subjected to pure torsion. A state of pure shear stress occurs, with its magnitude varying with radius r as determined by a linear distribution of shear strain.

For such a pure shear τ_{xy}, one of the principal axes is the z-axis, and the other two lie in the x-y plane and are rotated $45°$ with respect to the x-y axes. The principal normal stresses are related to τ_{xy} by

$$\sigma_1 = -\sigma_2 = \tau_{xy}, \qquad \sigma_3 = 0 \tag{13.37}$$

which was previously illustrated in Fig. 4.41. For an isotropic, homogeneous material subjected to such a τ_{xy}, the only nonzero component of strain is γ_{xy}. The strains along the principal axes are

$$\varepsilon_1 = -\varepsilon_2 = \frac{\gamma_{xy}}{2}, \qquad \varepsilon_3 = 0 \tag{13.38}$$

These principal stresses, strains, and directions can be verified by applying transformation equations or Mohr's circle, as described in Sections 6.2 and 6.6.

Since pure shear is a special case of plane stress, any desired stress–strain curve for shear can be obtained from Eq. 12.36 used with $\lambda = \sigma_2/\sigma_1 = -1$. Substitution of this λ, along with the preceding σ_1 and ε_1, gives the τ-γ relationship corresponding to any chosen form of uniaxial (same as effective) stress–strain curve.

For example, for a uniaxial curve of the Ramberg–Osgood form, Eq. 12.12, we may use Eq. 12.36 in the specific form of Eq. 12.39, which gives

$$\gamma_{xy} = \frac{\tau_{xy}}{G} + \left(\frac{\tau_{xy}}{H_\tau}\right)^{1/n}, \qquad H_\tau = \frac{H}{3^{(n+1)/2}} \tag{13.39}$$

Here, n is the same as for the uniaxial case, and the new constant H_τ is related to H from the uniaxial curve as indicated. Also, G is the shear modulus, which may be estimated from Eq. 5.28.

For an elastic, perfectly plastic stress–strain curve, the yield strength τ_o for pure shear can be related to the uniaxial value by applying Eq. 12.32 with $\lambda = -1$. At yielding, $\bar{\sigma} = \sigma_o$ and $\sigma_1 = \tau_{xy} = \tau_o$, so that $\tau_o = \sigma_o/\sqrt{3}$. Hence, the relationship is

$$\tau_{xy} = G\gamma_{xy} \qquad \left(\tau_{xy} \leq \tau_o\right) \qquad \text{(a)}$$

$$\tau_{xy} = \tau_o = \frac{\sigma_o}{\sqrt{3}} \qquad \left(\gamma_{xy} \geq \frac{\tau_o}{G}\right) \qquad \text{(b)}$$

(13.40)

For other discontinuous stress–strain curves with a distinct yield point, $\tau_o = \sigma_o/\sqrt{3}$ and Eq. 13.40(a) still apply, but Eq. 13.40(b) must be replaced by an appropriate expression derived from Eq. 12.36.

13.4.2 Analysis of Circular Shafts

Analysis of circular shafts loaded beyond yielding in torsion proceeds in a manner similar to that previously described for bending. Consider the cross section of a shaft as shown in Fig. 13.11(b). Due to the radial symmetry, the shear stress $\tau_{xy} = \tau$ is constant for all points at a distance r from the shaft axis. The contribution to the torque of an annular element of area as shown is

$$dT = (\text{stress})(\text{area})(\text{distance}) = (\tau)(2\pi r\, dr)(r) \tag{13.41}$$

Integrating from $r = 0$ to the outer surface, $r = c$, gives the torque:

$$T = 2\pi \int_0^c \tau r^2\, dr \tag{13.42}$$

For a hollow shaft with inner radius c_1 and outer radius c_2, Eq. 13.42 needs to be modified to

$$T = 2\pi \int_{c_1}^{c_2} \tau r^2\, dr \tag{13.43}$$

To evaluate either integral, a particular stress–strain curve for shear, $\gamma = f_\tau(\tau)$, is needed, along with the assumption that plane sections remain plane during twisting. This requires a linear distribution of shear strain, $\gamma_{xy} = \gamma$, or

$$\frac{\gamma}{r} = \frac{\gamma_c}{c} \tag{13.44}$$

where γ_c is the shear strain at $r = c$.

Consider a case of simple power hardening with no distinct yield point; that is,

$$\tau = H_3\gamma^{n_3} \tag{13.45}$$

Substituting Eqs. 13.44 and 13.45 into Eq. 13.42 and evaluating the integral for a solid shaft gives

$$T = \frac{2\pi c^3 \tau_c}{n_3 + 3} = \frac{2\pi c^3 H_3 \gamma_c^{n_3}}{n_3 + 3} \tag{13.46}$$

For a solid shaft and an elastic, perfectly plastic stress–strain curve, Eq. 13.40, the analysis parallels that leading to Eq. 13.18 for bending with a similar σ-ε curve. The result is

$$T = \frac{\pi c^3 \tau_c}{2} \qquad\qquad (\tau_c \le \tau_o)$$

$$T = \frac{\pi c^3 \tau_o}{6}\left[4 - \left(\frac{\tau_o}{G\gamma_c}\right)^3 \right] \qquad (\gamma_c \ge \tau_o/G) \tag{13.47}$$

As a final case, for a solid shaft and a Ramberg–Osgood type stress–strain curve, Eq. 13.39, analysis similar to that used for bending to obtain Eq. 13.27 gives

$$T = 2\pi c^3 \tau_c \left[\frac{\dfrac{1}{4} + \dfrac{2n+1}{3n+1}\beta_\tau + \dfrac{n+2}{2n+2}\beta_\tau^2 + \dfrac{1}{n+3}\beta_\tau^3}{(1+\beta_\tau)^3} \right] \tag{13.48}$$

where β_τ is the ratio of the plastic to elastic shear strain at the shaft surface, $r = c$:

$$\beta_\tau = \frac{\gamma_{pc}}{\gamma_{ec}}, \qquad \gamma_{pc} = \left(\frac{\tau_c}{H_\tau}\right)^{1/n}, \qquad \gamma_{ec} = \frac{\tau_c}{G}, \qquad \gamma_c = \gamma_{ec} + \gamma_{pc}$$

Equation 13.48 thus constitutes a relationship between torque and surface shear stress that can be written explicitly, and also an implicit relationship between torque and surface shear strain.

Residual shear stresses for torsion behave in an analogous manner to those for bending and can be analyzed by a similar procedure.

13.5 NOTCHED MEMBERS

Notched engineering members are often subjected to loads in service that cause localized yielding. The resulting plastic strains are of special interest in estimating fatigue lives with the strain-based approach, which is the subject of the next chapter. Gross plastic deformation in notched members must also be avoided in engineering design by providing a sufficient safety factor against overload. This portion of the chapter provides engineering tools that address these needs. Before proceeding, the reader may wish to review the topics of elastic stress concentration factors and fully plastic yielding loads in Appendix A, Sections A.6 and A.7.

Consider the behavior of notched members over a wide range of applied loads, as illustrated in Fig. 13.12. At low loads, the behavior is everywhere elastic and a simple linear relationship prevails. Localized plastic deformation begins when the stress at the notch exceeds the yield strength of the material. Plastic deformation then spreads over a region of increasing size for increasing load, until the entire cross section of the member has yielded. The behavior of load versus local notch strain is similar to the curve shown. Such a curve exhibits three regions corresponding to the three types of behavior: (a) no yielding, (b) local yielding, and (c) fully plastic yielding. Some plastic zones for local yielding at a notch in polycarbonate plastic are shown in Fig. 13.13.

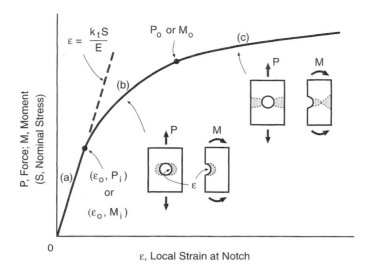

Figure 13.12   Load versus local strain behavior of a notched member showing three regions of behavior: (a) no yielding, (b) local yielding, and (c) fully plastic yielding. The applied load may be represented by a quantity such as a force P, moment M, or nominal stress S.

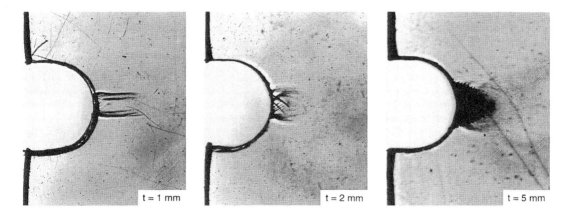

Figure 13.13   Plastic zones at notches in polycarbonate plastic. The notches are 3 mm deep and have radii of $\rho = 2$ mm, and the thickness varies from 1 mm (left) and 2 mm (center) to 5 mm (right). Thickness affects the development of the plastic zone, as the state of stress is altered by different degrees of transverse constraint. (Photos courtesy of Prof. H. Nisitani, Kyushu Sangyo University, Fukuoka, Japan. Published in [Nisitani 85]; reprinted with permission from *Engineering Fracture Mechanics*, Pergamon Press, Oxford, UK.)

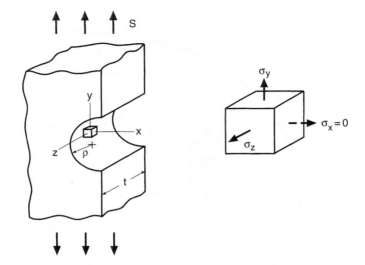

Figure 13.14 Coordinate system for the local stresses and strains at a notch.

13.5.1 Elastic Behavior and Initial Yielding

For elastic behavior, the notch stress σ can be determined from the nominal stress S and the elastic stress concentration factor k_t:

$$\sigma = k_t S \qquad (\sigma \le \sigma_o) \tag{13.49}$$

For axial or bending loads, this σ is the stress at the bottom of the notch in a direction parallel to S, specifically σ_y as shown in Fig. 13.14. Values of k_t may be obtained from Figs. A.11 and A.12 and from various handbooks, as noted in Appendix A. Except where the notch radius ρ is small compared with the thickness t, the stress σ_z in the thickness direction will be small compared with σ_y. Also, $\sigma_x = 0$ due to the free surface normal to the x direction, so that the state of stress is approximately uniaxial with $\sigma_y = \sigma$. The corresponding strain is then simply

$$\varepsilon = \frac{k_t S}{E} \qquad \left(\varepsilon \le \frac{\sigma_o}{E}\right) \tag{13.50}$$

Noting that S/E can be considered to be a nominal (average) strain, k_t is not only a stress concentration factor, but is also a strain concentration factor. Equations 13.49 and 13.50 apply only until σ reaches the yield strength σ_o, beyond which they are not valid. For cases of shear loading, τ, γ, and G are similarly used with an appropriate k_t value, provided, of course, that the yield strength in shear is not exceeded.

Consider a plate with a central hole, with dimensions as defined in Fig. 13.15(a), loaded with an axial force P. Assuming that k_t is defined on the basis of net section nominal stresses, we have

$$S = \frac{P}{2(b-a)t} \tag{13.51}$$

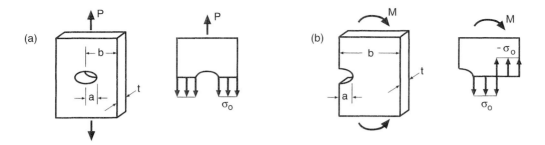

Figure 13.15 Geometries and stress distributions corresponding to fully plastic yielding for two cases of notched members.

where the nomenclature a and b parallels that previously used for cracked members in Chapter 8, but is here applied for notches with blunt ends of some definite radius ρ. Yielding first occurs at the force denoted P_i, where $k_t S = \sigma_o$, for which Eq. 13.51 gives

$$P_i = \frac{2(b-a)t}{k_t}\sigma_o \tag{13.52}$$

which is called the *initial yielding force*.

For notched bending members, nominal stress is generally defined by applying the elastic bending formula to the cross section of depth $(b-a)$ remaining after removal of the notch. For a rectangular bending member with a single edge notch, as in Fig. 13.15(b), we thus have

$$S = \frac{6M}{(b-a)^2 t} \tag{13.53}$$

which can be obtained by substituting $c = (b-a)/2$ into Eq. 13.2. The *initial yielding moment* occurs when $k_t S = \sigma_o$, so that

$$M_i = \frac{(b-a)^2 t}{6k_t}\sigma_o \tag{13.54}$$

Similar equations based on the particular definition of nominal stress being used can be obtained for any other case.

13.5.2 Fully Plastic Yielding

Beyond the point of yielding, the local notch strains are larger than would be estimated from elastic analysis. (Compare the solid and dashed lines in Fig. 13.12.) Yielding is initially confined to a relatively small volume of material, but a larger volume yields as loads increase. When yielding spreads to the entire cross-sectional area, the situation is described as *fully plastic yielding*. Beyond this point, small increases in load cause large increases in notch strain. The overall displacement, which up to this point has been nearly linear, also begins to increase rapidly with load. For an elastic, perfectly plastic material, no further increase in load is possible, and the load versus strain curve becomes flat.

Rough estimates of fully plastic yielding forces or moments can be easily made on the basis of stress distributions for a perfectly plastic material, as shown in Fig. 13.15. For the particular cases illustrated, the fully plastic force P_o for (a), and the fully plastic moment M_o for (b), are, respectively,

$$P_o = 2(b - a)t\sigma_o, \qquad M_o = \frac{(b - a)^2 t\sigma_o}{4} \qquad \text{(a, b)} \qquad (13.55)$$

These equations are derived in Section A.7, where results are also given for additional cases. Estimates of fully plastic load of this type are lower bounds, as actual failure loads for notched members are somewhat higher. As noted in Section A.7.3, this situation arises from two causes: (1) strain hardening beyond yielding in most actual stress–strain curves, and (2) geometric constraint at notches effectively elevating the yield strength.

13.5.3 Estimates of Notch Stress and Strain for Local Yielding

Few closed-form solutions exist for determining notch strains during plastic deformation. Numerical analysis, as by finite elements, can be used, but nonlinear elasto-plastic stress–strain relationships complicate such analysis and increase costs compared with linear-elastic analysis. Although nonlinear numerical analysis is sometimes necessary, various approximate methods for estimating notch stresses and strains have also been developed. Of these, *Neuber's rule* is the most widely used and will now be described.

Consider monotonic loading of a notched member having an elasto-plastic stress–strain curve, as shown in Fig. 13.16(a). The maximum stress σ_y and the corresponding strain ε_y at the notch are of interest, where these will be denoted simply as σ and ε. Once plastic deformation begins at the notch, the ratio of the notch stress to the nominal stress falls below the value k_t that applies for linear-elastic behavior. As already noted and illustrated in Fig. 13.12, strains show the opposite trend, exceeding values corresponding to elastic behavior. It therefore becomes necessary to define separate stress and strain concentration factors as

$$k_\sigma = \frac{\sigma}{S}, \qquad k_\varepsilon = \frac{\varepsilon}{e} \qquad (13.56)$$

where e is nominal strain—in particular, the value from the material's stress–strain curve corresponding to S. The trends of these quantities with increasing notch strain are illustrated in Fig. 13.16(b).

Neuber's rule states simply that the geometric mean of the stress and strain concentration factors remains equal to k_t during plastic deformation:

$$\sqrt{k_\sigma k_\varepsilon} = k_t \qquad (13.57)$$

For axial loading with bilateral symmetry, the approximately uniform stress distribution during fully plastic yielding causes both σ and S to have similar values. Hence, k_σ tends toward unity for large strains, so the preceding equation suggests that k_ε is limited to the value k_t^2.

If fully plastic yielding does not occur, $e = S/E$ applies. This permits a useful equation for local yielding to be obtained from Neuber's rule by substituting Eq. 13.56, along with $e = S/E$,

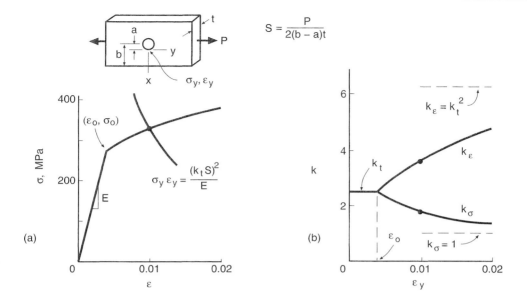

Figure 13.16   For a given notched member and stress–strain curve (a), Neuber's rule may be used to estimate local notch stresses and strains, σ and ε, corresponding to a particular value of nominal stress S. Stress and strain concentration factors vary as in (b).

into Eq. 13.57. After simple manipulation, we obtain

$$\sigma\varepsilon = \frac{(k_t S)^2}{E} \tag{13.58}$$

For a given material, geometry, and applied load, hence, for known E, k_t, and S, the product of stress and strain is thus a known constant. Since stress and strain are also related by the stress–strain curve of the material, a solution can be obtained for their values. Noting that $\sigma\varepsilon = constant$ is simply a hyperbola, a graphical solution is quite easy, as illustrated in Fig. 13.16(a). If the local notch stress does not exceed the yield strength, Eq. 13.58 still gives the correct solution consistent with linear-elastic behavior. The use of Eq. 13.58 for a number of different values of S gives a trend with ε as in Fig. 13.12, regions (a) and (b). If there is fully plastic yielding, region (c), Eq. 13.58 does not apply, and will in fact underestimate the strains. Note that plotting nominal stress S versus strain ε gives the same curve, except for a scale factor, as plotting force or moment, P or M. This occurs because S is proportional to P or M, or other applied load quantity, as from Eq. 13.51 or 13.53. In fact, nominal stress S should be regarded as merely a convenient means of representing applied load.

For an elastic, perfectly plastic material beyond the point of yielding, strains are easily calculated by substituting $\sigma = \sigma_o$ into Eq. 13.58:

$$\varepsilon = \frac{(k_t S)^2}{\sigma_o E} \qquad (\varepsilon \geq \sigma_o/E) \tag{13.59}$$

Useful closed-form equations may also be obtained for a material with power-hardening beyond yielding by substituting either stress or strain from Eq. 12.8(b) into Eq. 13.58 and solving for the other quantity:

$$\sigma = H_1 \left[\frac{(k_t S)^2}{E H_1} \right]^{n_1/(n_1+1)} \quad , \qquad \varepsilon = \left[\frac{(k_t S)^2}{E H_1} \right]^{1/(n_1+1)} \qquad (\sigma \geq \sigma_o) \qquad (13.60)$$

If a Ramberg–Osgood stress–strain curve is used, no closed-form solution for stresses and strains is possible. Elimination of ε between Eq. 12.12 and 13.58 gives an equation involving S and σ that can be solved for σ by trial and error or some other numerical procedure:

$$S = \frac{1}{k_t} \sqrt{\sigma^2 + \sigma E \left(\frac{\sigma}{H} \right)^{1/n}}, \qquad k_t S = \sqrt{\sigma^2 + \sigma E \left(\frac{\sigma}{H} \right)^{1/n}} \qquad (a, b) \qquad (13.61)$$

Substitution of σ into Eq. 12.12 then gives ε. Form (b) is useful where the local stress for elastic behavior, $\sigma_{elas} = k_t S$, is calculated directly, as by finite elements.

Cases of loading in the compressive (negative) direction may be handled by replacing (σ, ε, S) with $(-\sigma, -\varepsilon, -S)$ in any of 13.58 to 13.61, with the material's stress–strain curve, $\varepsilon = f(\sigma)$, similarly modified to become $\varepsilon = -f(-\sigma)$.

Example 13.1

The notched member of Fig. 13.16 has an elastic stress concentration factor of $k_t = 2.5$, and its material has an elastic, power-hardening stress–strain curve, Eq. 12.8, with constants $E = 69\,\text{GPa}$, $H_1 = 834\,\text{MPa}$, and $n_1 = 0.200$. Estimate the stress and strain at the notch in the y-direction if the member is loaded to a nominal stress of $S = 200\,\text{MPa}$.

Solution   We first need to determine whether yielding occurs at the notch by comparing $k_t S = 2.5 \times 200 = 500\,\text{MPa}$ with the yield strength, which, from Eq. 12.10, is

$$\sigma_o = E \left(\frac{H_1}{E} \right)^{1/(1-n_1)} = (69{,}000\,\text{MPa}) \left(\frac{834\,\text{MPa}}{69{,}000\,\text{MPa}} \right)^{1/(1-0.200)} = 276.5\,\text{MPa}$$

As $k_t S$ exceeds this value, the notch stress is not equal to $k_t S$, and an estimate that considers yielding is required, as from Neuber's rule. Thus, stress and strain values are needed that satisfy both the elasto-plastic part of the stress–strain curve and Neuber's rule:

$$\sigma = H_1 \varepsilon^{n_1}, \qquad \sigma = 834 \varepsilon^{0.200}\,\text{MPa}$$

$$\sigma \varepsilon = \frac{(k_t S)^2}{E}, \qquad \sigma \varepsilon = \frac{(2.5 \times 200)^2}{69{,}000} = 3.623\,\text{MPa}$$

Substitute σ from the first equation into the second equation, and solve the expression obtained for ε. Then calculate σ from the first equation. The resulting values are

$$\varepsilon = 0.01075, \qquad \sigma = 336.9\,\text{MPa} \qquad\qquad \textbf{Ans.}$$

> **Discussion**   These values could also be obtained directly from Eq. 13.60, which is derived from the same two equations that are employed in this example. Also, a graphical solution could be implemented as in Fig. 13.16 by a plot of the hyperbola $\sigma\varepsilon = 3.623\,\text{MPa}$ on the same axes as the stress–strain curve, where the intersection with the stress–strain curve gives the desired values.

13.5.4 Discussion

Stresses are often calculated from finite element analysis or other numerical methods, usually assuming elastic materials behavior. Such analytical results are thus said to provide *elastically calculated stresses*, σ_{elas}, which can be interpreted as $k_t S$ values and used directly with Neuber's rule. In numerical analysis to obtain local (elastically calculated) stresses, it is important to ensure that the geometric detail is analyzed at a sufficiently high spatial resolution to capture the maximum stresses at locations of interest.

It is reasonable to use Neuber's rule in the form of Eq. 13.58 for all loads except those approaching fully plastic yielding. This is the case despite the fact that S values may exceed σ_o. For example, for bending of a rectangular section, fully plastic yielding does not occur until $S = 1.5\sigma_o$. (Substitute M_o from Eq. 13.55(b) into Eq. 13.53 to verify this.) Where fully plastic yielding does occur, a special version of Neuber's rule may be used. See the paper by Seeger (1980) for details.

Neuber's rule may also be employed for shear stresses and strains, as in torsionally loaded notched shafts. Equation 13.58 applies, where σ and ε are replaced with τ and γ, and k_t and S are defined as appropriate for the particular case. For more complex situations, such as combined bending and torsion or other multiaxial loading, Neuber's rule or related methods may still be applied. However, for nonproportional loading with principal stress axes that vary in direction during stressing, the application is difficult. See the papers by Hoffmann (1989), Chu (1995), and Reinhardt (1997) for more information.

It is important to keep in mind in all uses of Neuber's rule that it is an approximation. Estimated strains generally tend to be reasonably accurate or somewhat larger than those from more precise nonlinear numerical analysis or from careful strain measurements. See the paper by Harkegard (2003) for a study of the accuracy of Neuber's rule.

Another approximate procedure that can be used in a manner similar to Neuber's rule is the *strain energy density method* as described by Glinka (1985). The strain energy density is the area under the stress–strain curve up to the stress and strain values that are present, specifically, W_p in Fig. 13.17. In this method, W_p is postulated to be equal to the energy density W_e that would occur in the absence of yielding, $W_e = W_p$. This method gives estimates of local notch stress and strain, σ and ε, in a manner generally similar to the application of Neuber's rule.

13.5.5 Effects of Geometric Constraint at Notches

In Fig. 13.14, if the notch radius ρ is small compared with the thickness t, deformation at the notch in the thickness (z) direction is difficult. The physical cause of this geometric constraint on

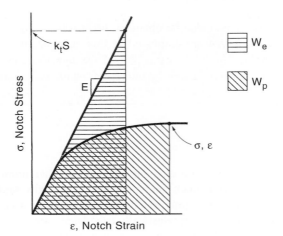

Figure 13.17   Method of notch strain estimation of Glinka, where $W_e = W_p$ gives estimates of notch stress and strain, σ and ε.

transverse deformation is the same as for a cracked member, as explained in Section 8.7.2. Hence, the state of stress will not be uniaxial, as previously assumed, but will approach plane strain, $\varepsilon_z = 0$. A similar circumstance occurs in axisymmetric geometries with notches, such as grooved shafts, if ρ is small compared with the diameter.

For such plane strain at a notch surface, we still have $\sigma_x = 0$ due to the free surface—that is, y-z plane stress—but now also $\varepsilon_z = 0$. In this case, Eq. 12.27(c) shows that a tensile stress σ_z develops:

$$\sigma_z = \tilde{\nu}\sigma_y, \qquad \text{where} \quad \tilde{\nu} = \frac{\nu\bar{\sigma} + 0.5E\bar{\varepsilon}_p}{E\bar{\varepsilon}} \tag{13.62}$$

Note that $\tilde{\nu}$ is the generalized Poisson's ratio of Eq. 12.27(e). For loading that causes a nominal tension stress S in the region of the notch, there are no shear stresses on the x-y-z axes of Fig. 13.14, so the stresses in these directions are principal normal stresses. Hence, let $\sigma_1 = \sigma_y$, $\sigma_2 = \sigma_z$, and $\sigma_3 = \sigma_x = 0$, and note that $\tilde{\nu} = \sigma_2/\sigma_1 = \lambda$, as in Eq. 12.31. Then, applying Eq. 12.32, and also Eq. 12.27(b), we obtain

$$\sigma_1 = \sigma_y = \frac{\bar{\sigma}}{\sqrt{1 - \tilde{\nu} + \tilde{\nu}^2}}, \qquad \varepsilon_1 = \varepsilon_y = \frac{\bar{\varepsilon}(1 - \tilde{\nu}^2)}{\sqrt{1 - \tilde{\nu} + \tilde{\nu}^2}} \tag{13.63}$$

Thus, we can pick a number of points $(\bar{\sigma}, \bar{\varepsilon})$ on the effective (same as uniaxial) stress–strain curve of the material, evaluate $\tilde{\nu}$, and then calculate corresponding points on the stress–strain curve $(\sigma_1, \varepsilon_1)$ for the notch surface material. This modified stress–strain curve may then be used with Neuber's rule to estimate the stresses and strains at the notch.

Cases intermediate between plane stress and plane strain can also be handled as described by Hoffman (1989).

13.5.6 Residual Stresses and Strains at Notches

If a notched member is loaded sufficiently for local yielding to occur, and then the load is removed, residual stresses will remain. This is illustrated for an overload in tension in Fig. 13.18. As the nominal stress S is increased to (a) and then to (b), local yielding occurs at the notch. When the load is removed (c), a tensile residual strain and a compressive residual stress remain as shown. Stress distributions are also shown for the three situations (a), (b), and (c). If the overload is compressive, analogous behavior occurs with a tensile residual stress resulting.

This behavior is similar to that already discussed for bending. As before, the elastic recovery of the material upon unloading results in the most intensely deformed regions having a residual stress that is opposite in sign to the peak stress previously reached. Since equilibrium of forces requires that the integral sum of the stresses must be zero after the load is removed, some interior regions retain stresses of the same sign as the overload.

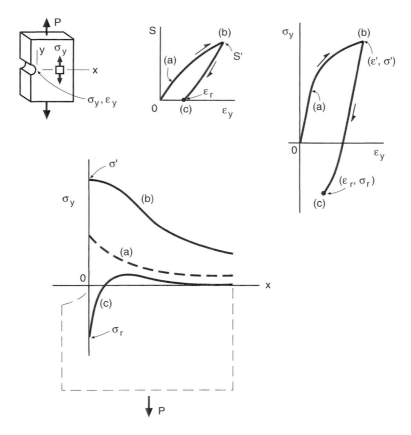

Figure 13.18 Residual stress and strain remaining after local yielding in a notched member. For loading to (a) there is no yielding, but at (b) there is, causing the stress distribution to flatten. After unloading (c), a tensile residual strain and a compressive residual stress remain at the notch surface.

Residual stresses and strains at notches can be estimated by extending the application of Neuber's rule to the unloading event. Specifically, Neuber's rule is applied to the changes $\Delta\sigma$, $\Delta\varepsilon$, and ΔS that occur during unloading:

$$\Delta\sigma\,\Delta\varepsilon = \frac{(k_t\,\Delta S)^2}{E} \tag{13.64}$$

When combined with the stress–strain curve for unloading, $\Delta\sigma$ and $\Delta\varepsilon$ can thus be determined. These quantities are then subtracted from the maximum stress and strain reached, σ' and ε', giving the residuals, σ_r and ε_r:

$$\sigma_r = \sigma' - \Delta\sigma, \qquad \varepsilon_r = \varepsilon' - \Delta\sigma \tag{13.65}$$

If the initial loading is in the compressive direction, σ' and ε' will have negative values, and $\Delta\sigma$ and $\Delta\varepsilon$ should instead be added to obtain the residuals; the behavior is analogous to that of Fig. 13.18 with (σ, ε, S) replaced by $(-\sigma, -\varepsilon, -S)$.

Example 13.2

The notched member of Fig. 13.16 has an elastic stress concentration factor of $k_t = 2.5$, and its material has an elastic, power-hardening stress–strain curve, Eq. 12.8, with constants $E = 69\,\text{GPa}$, $H_1 = 834\,\text{MPa}$, and $n_1 = 0.200$. Estimate the residual stress and strain at the notch if the member is loaded to a nominal stress S', and then unloaded, for (a) $S' = 200\,\text{MPa}$ and (b) $S' = 260\,\text{MPa}$.

Solution (a) A stress–strain response qualitatively similar to Fig. 13.18(b) is expected. For the initial loading, the stress and strain at $S' = 200\,\text{MPa}$ have already been estimated in Ex. 13.1.

$$\sigma' = 336.9\,\text{MPa}, \qquad \varepsilon' = 0.01075$$

Since no specific stress–strain path is given for unloading, we will approximate this as $\Delta\varepsilon/2 = f(\Delta\sigma/2)$, where the monotonic stress–strain curve is denoted $\varepsilon = f(\sigma)$. As discussed in Section 12.4, this corresponds to a factor-of-two expansion of the monotonic curve. Thus, yielding on unloading will occur only if the stress changes by more than $2\sigma_o$, where the monotonic yield strength is $\sigma_o = 276.5\,\text{MPa}$ from Ex. 13.1. If we note that $\Delta S = 200\,\text{MPa}$ for unloading, we see that the change in notch stress during unloading, as calculated under the assumption of elastic behavior, needs to be compared with $2\sigma_o$:

$$k_t\,\Delta S = 2.5 \times 200 = 500\,\text{MPa}, \qquad 2\sigma_o = 2 \times 276.5 = 553.1\,\text{MPa}, \qquad k_t\,\Delta S < 2\sigma_o$$

Hence, the change is less than $2\sigma_o$, and no plastic deformation occurs on unloading, so the changes in stress and strain are given by elastic behavior:

$$\Delta\sigma = k_t\,\Delta S = 500\,\text{MPa}, \qquad \Delta\varepsilon = \Delta\sigma/E = 500/69{,}000 = 0.00725$$

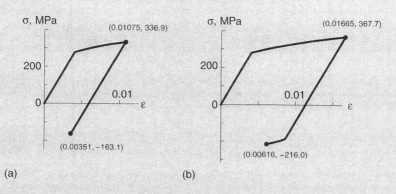

Figure E13.2

The residuals then follow from Eq. 13.65:

$$\sigma_r = \sigma' - \Delta\sigma = 336.9 - 500, \qquad \sigma_r = -163.1\,\text{MPa}$$

Ans.

$$\varepsilon_r = \varepsilon' - \Delta\varepsilon = 0.01075 - 0.00725, \qquad \varepsilon_r = 0.00351$$

The stress–strain response is shown in Fig. E13.2(a). Note that yielding occurs at σ_o during the initial loading, but the unloading simply follows the elastic modulus slope E.

(b) The stress and strain for the initial loading to $S' = 260\,\text{MPa}$ may be determined by the same procedure as in Ex. 13.1. The values for loading to this higher S' are

$$\sigma' = 367.7\,\text{MPa}, \qquad \varepsilon' = 0.01665$$

For unloading with the new value $\Delta S = 260\,\text{MPa}$, the assumption of elastic behavior gives $k_t \Delta S = 650\,\text{MPa}$, which is greater than $2\sigma_o$. Hence, plastic deformation occurs during unloading, and Neuber's rule in the form of Eq. 13.64 needs to be solved with the unloading stress–strain path, $\Delta\varepsilon/2 = f(\Delta\sigma/2)$:

$$\frac{\Delta\sigma}{2} = H_1\left(\frac{\Delta\varepsilon}{2}\right)^{n_1}, \qquad \Delta\sigma = 2 \times 834\left(\frac{\Delta\varepsilon}{2}\right)^{0.200}\,\text{MPa}$$

$$\Delta\sigma\,\Delta\varepsilon = \frac{(k_t \Delta S)^2}{E}, \qquad \Delta\sigma\,\Delta\varepsilon = \frac{(2.5 \times 260)^2}{69{,}000} = 6.123\,\text{MPa}$$

Substitute $\Delta\sigma$ from the first equation into the second equation, and then solve the expression obtained for $\Delta\varepsilon$. Then calculate $\Delta\sigma$ from the first equation. The resulting values are

$$\Delta\varepsilon = 0.01049, \qquad \Delta\sigma = 583.7\,\text{MPa}$$

Finally, the residuals follow from Eq. 13.65.

$$\sigma_r = \sigma' - \Delta\sigma = 367.7 - 583.7, \qquad \sigma_r = -216.0\,\text{MPa}$$

$$\varepsilon_r = \varepsilon' - \Delta\varepsilon = 0.01665 - 0.01049, \qquad \varepsilon_r = 0.00616$$

Ans.

The stress–strain response is shown in Fig. E13.2(b). As before, yielding occurs at σ_o during the initial loading. Unloading follows the elastic modulus slope E until compressive yielding occurs, where the change in stress exceeds $2\sigma_o$.

13.6 CYCLIC LOADING

Analysis of stresses and strains for cyclic loading is needed for dealing with such engineering situations as vibratory loading, earthquake loading, and fatigue. The preceding analysis of plastic deformation can be extended to cyclic loading by idealizing the stress–strain behavior of the material according to the spring and slider rheological models of the previous chapter. In particular, cycle-dependent hardening or softening and creep–relaxation behavior are assumed to be absent. Such an idealized material has identical cyclic and monotonic stress–strain curves, $\varepsilon = f(\sigma)$, and hysteresis loop curves that obey the factor-of-two assumption, $\Delta\varepsilon/2 = f(\Delta\sigma/2)$. In applications, the stable cyclic stress–strain curve is used for $\varepsilon = f(\sigma)$. Both constant amplitude cyclic loading and irregular variation of load with time can be considered on this basis.

13.6.1 Bending

To develop a methodology for dealing with cyclic loading, first consider the example of cyclic loading of a beam due to loads that all lie in a plane of symmetry of the beam. For simplicity, assume that the cross section is symmetrical about the neutral axis. Let the moment vary cyclically between two values, $M_{\max}$ and $M_{\min}$, as illustrated in Fig. 13.19. Assuming that inertial effects are small, equilibrium of forces exists at any given time and requires that the integral of Eq. 13.6 must always be satisfied. Equation 13.6 therefore applies in the following form at times corresponding to $M_{\max}$ and $M_{\min}$:

$$M_{\max} = 2\int_0^c \sigma_{\max} t y \, dy, \qquad M_{\min} = 2\int_0^c \sigma_{\min} t y \, dy \qquad \text{(a, b)} \qquad (13.66)$$

Here, $\sigma_{\max}$ is a function of y and constitutes the stress distribution that exists at a time corresponding to $M = M_{\max}$, and similarly, $\sigma_{\min}$ is the stress distribution at $M = M_{\min}$. Such distributions are illustrated in Fig. 13.19(b). Since plane sections are expected to remain plane even during cyclic loading, linear strain distributions as in Fig. 13.19(c) are expected at $M_{\max}$ and $M_{\min}$, so that the distribution of strain range $\Delta\varepsilon$ is also linear.

Considering the range of moment ΔM, the properties of integrals give:

$$\Delta M = M_{\max} - M_{\min} = 2\int_0^c \Delta\sigma \, t y \, dy \qquad (13.67)$$

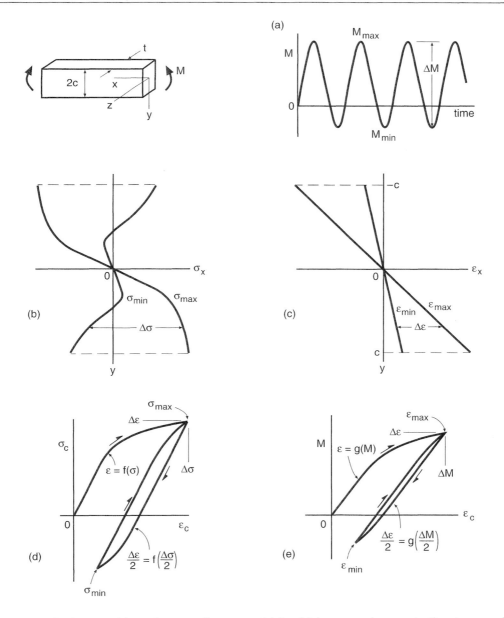

Figure 13.19   Beam subjected to a cyclic moment (a), which causes changes in the stress and strain distributions as in (b) and (c). The stress versus strain behavior is illustrated in (d), and the moment versus strain behavior in (e).

where $\Delta\sigma = \sigma_{max} - \sigma_{min}$ is the distribution of stress range with y. Dividing by two, and also noting that amplitude quantities are given by $M_a = \Delta M/2$ and $\sigma_a = \Delta\sigma/2$, we obtain two additional and equivalent forms:

$$\frac{\Delta M}{2} = 2 \int_0^c \frac{\Delta\sigma}{2} \, ty \, dy, \qquad M_a = 2 \int_0^c \sigma_a \, ty \, dy \qquad \text{(a, b)} \qquad (13.68)$$

These indicate that stress–strain analysis for ranges and amplitudes during cyclic loading may proceed in a straightforward manner that is similar to the analysis for static loading.

Let the material behavior be idealized as following stable behavior according to a spring and slider rhelogical model. As discussed in Section 12.4, such a material has a monotonic stress–strain curve $\varepsilon = f(\sigma)$ that is the same as its cyclic stress–strain curve, expressed as $\Delta\varepsilon/2 = f(\Delta\sigma/2)$, or equivalently as $\varepsilon_a = f(\sigma_a)$. Combining this stress–strain curve with Eq. 13.68, and invoking the linear variation of strain with y, a (sometimes implicit) relationship $\varepsilon = g(M)$ is obtained that applies to cyclic loading as $\Delta\varepsilon/2 = g(\Delta M/2)$, or as $\varepsilon_a = g(M_a)$. The analysis differs from one for static loading only in the use of the cyclic stress–strain curve.

Given such a static analysis that uses the cyclic stress–strain curve, the stresses and strains at the edge of the beam ($y = c$) corresponding to M_{max} and M_{min} can be obtained as follows:

$$\varepsilon_{c\,max} = g(M_{max}), \qquad \varepsilon_{c\,max} = f(\sigma_{c\,max}) \qquad \text{(a)}$$

$$\Delta\varepsilon_c/2 = g(\Delta M/2), \qquad \Delta\varepsilon_c/2 = f(\Delta\sigma_c/2) \qquad \text{(b)} \qquad (13.69)$$

$$\varepsilon_{c\,min} = \varepsilon_{c\,max} - \Delta\varepsilon_c, \qquad \sigma_{c\,min} = \sigma_{c\,max} - \Delta\sigma_c \qquad \text{(c)}$$

Note that (a) gives the initial loading to M_{max}; next, (b) gives the half-ranges (amplitudes) for the cyclic loading; and then (c) is the subtraction of ranges from the maximum values to obtain the minimum values. If it is desired to work directly with amplitude quantities, substitutions may be made as follows: $M_a = \Delta M/2$, $\varepsilon_{ca} = \Delta\varepsilon_c/2$, and $\sigma_{ca} = \Delta\sigma_c/2$.

Example 13.3

Consider cyclic loading of a rectangular beam made of an elastic, perfectly plastic material. Assuming that the initial loading is sufficiently severe to cause yielding, write the equations that give the maximums, amplitudes, and minimums of stress and strain at $y = c$ for cyclic loading.

Solution   An explicit relationship $\varepsilon = g(M)$ is available from the combined use of the elastic solution of Eq. 13.2 and the postyield solution of Eq. 13.18. In the former, the substitution $\sigma_c = E\varepsilon_c$ is made, and both are solved for ε_c:

$$\varepsilon_c = \frac{3M}{2tc^2 E}, \qquad \varepsilon_c = \frac{\sigma_o}{E}\sqrt{\frac{tc^2\sigma_o}{3(tc^2\sigma_o - M)}} \qquad \text{(a, b)}$$

In this equation, (a) applies for $\varepsilon_c \leq \sigma_o/E$, and (b) for $\varepsilon_c \geq \sigma_o/E$. Since we have yielding for the initial loading, (b) is employed for Eq. 13.69(a), giving

$$\sigma_{c\,\text{max}} = \sigma_o, \qquad \varepsilon_{c\,\text{max}} = \frac{\sigma_o}{E}\sqrt{\frac{M_o}{3(M_o - M_\text{max})}} \qquad (\varepsilon_{c\,\text{max}} \geq \sigma_o/E) \qquad \textbf{Ans.}$$

where the fully plastic moment $M_o = tc^2\sigma_o$ from Eq. 13.20 is introduced as a convenience.

There may or may not be cyclic yielding. Considering either possibility, and applying Eq. 13.69(b) to amplitude quantities, we obtain

$$\sigma_{ca} = E\varepsilon_{ca}, \qquad \varepsilon_{ca} = \frac{3M_a}{2tc^2 E} \qquad (\varepsilon_{ca} \leq \sigma_o/E)$$

$$\qquad \qquad \qquad \qquad \qquad \qquad \qquad \qquad \qquad \qquad \qquad \qquad \qquad \textbf{Ans.}$$

$$\sigma_{ca} = \sigma_o, \qquad \varepsilon_{ca} = \frac{\sigma_o}{E}\sqrt{\frac{M_o}{3(M_o - M_a)}} \qquad (\varepsilon_{ca} \geq \sigma_o/E)$$

If there is no cyclic yielding, the first relationship applies, and if there is cyclic yielding, the second one applies. In either case, the values at M_min are then obtained from Eq. 13.69(c):

$$\varepsilon_{c\,\text{min}} = \varepsilon_{c\,\text{max}} - 2\varepsilon_{ca}, \qquad \sigma_{c\,\text{min}} = \sigma_{c\,\text{max}} - 2\sigma_{ca} \qquad \textbf{Ans.}$$

The stress–strain response at $y = c$ is similar to Fig. E13.3(a) if there is no cyclic yielding and similar to (b) if there is cyclic yielding.

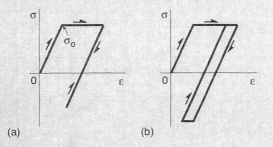

(a)   (b)

Figure E13.3

13.6.2 Generalized Methodology for Other Cases

The procedure just described for analyzing cyclic bending uses the results of analysis performed in the same manner as for monotonic loading. Such a methodology is applicable to other geometries and modes of loading, and relevant theoretical discussion and proofs from the viewpoint of plasticity theory are given in the papers by Mroz (1967, 1973). The following restrictions and comments apply: The same idealizations of the stress–strain behavior must be retained, namely, stable behavior always following the cyclic stress–strain curve and hysteresis loop curves obeying $\Delta\varepsilon/2 = f(\Delta\sigma/2)$. Also, if there are multiple applied loads, they must not result in significantly nonproportional loading in regions of yielding; that is, the ratios of the principal stresses must remain at least approximately constant. States of stress other than uniaxial can be handled by applying deformation plasticity theory to the cyclic stress–strain curve in the same manner as done in Chapter 12 for monotonic curves.

Consider the strain at some location of interest, such as the edge of a beam in bending, but now also include other cases, such as the surface of a circular shaft, or the notch surface in a notched member. Assume that this strain, denoted ε, can be related explicitly or implicitly to the applied load by stress–strain analysis that considers plastic deformation, perhaps employing some of the equations given earlier in this chapter. Then

$$\varepsilon = g(S) \tag{13.70}$$

where the applied load, such as an axial force, bending moment, torque, pressure, or a combination of these, is represented generically as a nominal stress S.

Cyclic loading with a maximum value S_{max} and an amplitude $S_a = \Delta S/2$ can be analyzed with the use of this $\varepsilon = g(S)$. Analysis to obtain $\varepsilon = g(S)$ is done just as for monotonic loading, by using a stress–strain curve $\varepsilon = f(\sigma)$ that is already adjusted to correspond to the particular state of stress involved. The specific curve used is the same as the stable (half-life) cyclic stress–strain curve for the material and state of stress of interest. The monotonic-loading analytical result $\varepsilon = g(S)$ can then be used for cyclic loading to obtain peak values and cyclic variations of stresses and strains. Assuming that the mean load during cycling is positive (tensile), $R > -1$, we have

$$\varepsilon_{max} = g(S_{max}) = f(\sigma_{max}) \qquad \text{(a)}$$

$$\varepsilon_a = g(S_a) = f(\sigma_a) \qquad \text{(b)} \tag{13.71}$$

$$\frac{\Delta\varepsilon}{2} = g\left(\frac{\Delta S}{2}\right) = f\left(\frac{\Delta\sigma}{2}\right) \qquad \text{(c)}$$

where (b) and (c) are equivalent, but are both given to indicate that either amplitudes or ranges can be obtained, where all amplitudes are half the corresponding ranges. Values at S_{min} are obtained by subtracting the ranges from the values at S_{max}:

$$\varepsilon_{min} = \varepsilon_{max} - \Delta\varepsilon, \qquad \sigma_{min} = \sigma_{max} - \Delta\sigma \tag{13.72}$$

The procedure represented by Eqs. 13.71 and 13.72, and the corresponding stress–strain and load–strain paths, are illustrated for the bending example by Fig. 13.19(d) and (e).

If the loading is completely reversed ($R = -1$), the amplitude and maximum values are identical, so that Eqs. 13.71(a) and (b) give the same result. If the cyclic loading extends farther into the negative (compressive) direction than into tension, $R < -1$, Eq. 13.71(a) needs to be replaced by

$$\varepsilon_{min} = -g(-S_{min}) = -f(-\sigma_{min}) \tag{13.73}$$

Ranges are then added to these minimum values to compute maximum values.

   Consider a notched member and approximate analysis for notch stress and strain that uses Neuber's rule. If the cyclic stress–strain curve obeys the Ramberg–Osgood form, $\varepsilon = g(S)$ is given implicitly by Neuber's rule and the stress–strain curve, Eqs. 13.58 and 12.54. For a numerical solution, the combination of Eqs. 13.58 and 12.54 given by Eq. 13.61 is convenient. Substituting $S = S_{max}$ into Eq. 13.61 and solving iteratively gives $\sigma = \sigma_{max}$, which then gives $\varepsilon = \varepsilon_{max}$ from Eq. 12.54. Similarly, substituting $S = S_a$ into Eq. 13.61 and solving iteratively gives $\sigma = \sigma_a$, which then gives $\varepsilon = \varepsilon_a$ from Eq. 12.54. If a more exact analysis is desired, $\varepsilon = g(S)$ could be obtained by finite element analysis of the plastic deformation, which would be performed just as for monotonic loading, except for use of the cyclic stress–strain curve.

Example 13.4

A notched plate made of the AISI 4340 steel of Table 12.1 has an elastic stress concentration factor of $k_t = 2.80$. The nominal stress is cycled between $S_{max} = 750$ and $S_{min} = 50$ MPa. Assume that the stress–strain behavior can be approximated with the stable cyclic stress–strain curve and that the behavior is similar to a spring and slider rheological model. Then estimate the stress–strain response.

Solution   Use Neuber's rule and the cyclic stress–strain curve as in Eq. 13.71 to estimate both the maximums and amplitudes of the local notch stress and strain. For the initial monotonic response, assumed to follow the cyclic stress–strain curve, Eqs. 12.54 and 13.61 are employed for Eq. 13.71(a):

$$\varepsilon_{max} = \frac{\sigma_{max}}{E} + \left(\frac{\sigma_{max}}{H'}\right)^{1/n'}, \qquad \varepsilon_{max} = \frac{\sigma_{max}}{207{,}000} + \left(\frac{\sigma_{max}}{1655}\right)^{1/0.131}$$

$$S_{max} = \frac{1}{k_t}\sqrt{\sigma_{max}^2 + \sigma_{max}E\left(\frac{\sigma_{max}}{H'}\right)^{1/n'}}, \qquad 750 = \frac{1}{2.80}\sqrt{\sigma_{max}^2 + 207{,}000\,\sigma_{max}\left(\frac{\sigma_{max}}{1655}\right)^{1/0.131}}$$

Here, E, H', σ_{max}, and S_{max} are all in MPa units. Solve the second equation iteratively to obtain σ_{max}. Then calculate ε_{max} from the first equation. The resulting values are

$$\sigma_{max} = 972 \text{ MPa}, \qquad \varepsilon_{max} = 0.02192 \qquad\qquad \textbf{Ans.}$$

For the cyclic loading, we need the amplitude of the nominal stress:

$$S_a = \frac{S_{max} - S_{min}}{2} = 350 \text{ MPa}$$

Amplitude quantities in Eqs. 12.54 and 13.61 are then employed for Eq. 13.71(b):

$$\varepsilon_a = \frac{\sigma_a}{E} + \left(\frac{\sigma_a}{H'}\right)^{1/n'}, \qquad \varepsilon_a = \frac{\sigma_a}{207{,}000} + \left(\frac{\sigma_a}{1655}\right)^{1/0.131}$$

$$S_a = \frac{1}{k_t}\sqrt{\sigma_a^2 + \sigma_a E\left(\frac{\sigma_a}{H'}\right)^{1/n'}}, \qquad 350 = \frac{1}{2.80}\sqrt{\sigma_a^2 + 207{,}000\,\sigma_a\left(\frac{\sigma_a}{1655}\right)^{1/0.131}}$$

Solving in the same manner as previously gives

$$\sigma_a = 755\,\text{MPa}, \qquad \varepsilon_a = 0.00615 \qquad\qquad \textbf{Ans.}$$

Finally, the minimum values for cyclic loading are

$$\sigma_{\min} = \sigma_{\max} - 2\sigma_a = -538\,\text{MPa}$$
$$\varepsilon_{\min} = \varepsilon_{\max} - 2\varepsilon_a = 0.00962 \qquad\qquad \textbf{Ans.}$$

where cycle-dependent relaxation and creep are assumed not to occur.

The estimated stress–strain response is shown in Fig. E13.4. This was plotted as $\varepsilon = f(\sigma)$ for the monotonic portion and $\Delta\varepsilon = 2f(\Delta\sigma/2)$ for both branches of the hysteresis loop. The mean stress σ_m during the cyclic loading, which will be of interest in the next chapter for fatigue, is also shown. Its value is

$$\sigma_m = \sigma_{\max} - \sigma_a = 972 - 755 = 217\,\text{MPa}$$

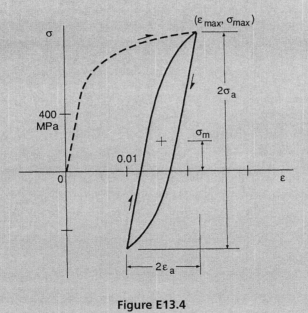

Figure E13.4

13.6.3 Application to Irregular Load Versus Time Histories

Estimates of stress–strain response for cyclic loading, as just described, can be extended to irregular variations of load with time. A stress–strain analysis done as for monotonic loading, but using the cyclic stress–strain curve, is still needed. This analysis can be applied in the form $\Delta\varepsilon/2 = g(\Delta S/2)$

during irregular loading histories—specifically, to all load excursions that correspond to stress–strain paths following the curve shape $\Delta\varepsilon/2 = f(\Delta\sigma/2)$.

Consider the example of Fig. 13.20. A notched member as in (a) is made of a material having a cyclic stress–strain curve, $\varepsilon_a = f(\sigma_a)$, as shown in (b). The load–strain curve, $\varepsilon_a = g(S_a)$, from Neuber's rule for this case is also shown. The load history of (c) is repeatedly applied, resulting in the load versus notch strain response of (d) and the local notch stress–strain response of (e). As a convenience, the load history has already been ordered to start at the largest absolute value

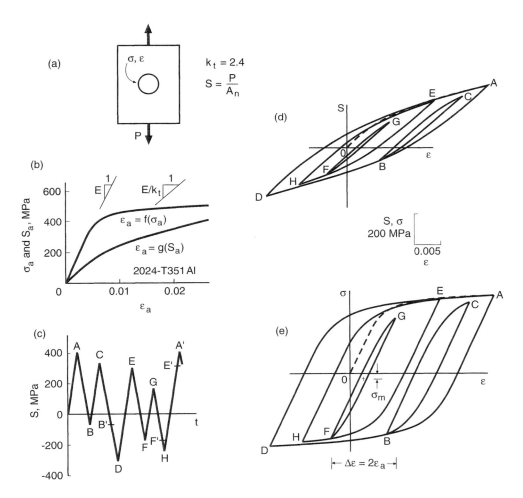

Figure 13.20 Analysis of a notched member subjected to an irregular load versus time history. Notched member (a), having cyclic stress–strain and load–strain curves as in (b), is subjected to load history (c). The resulting load versus notch strain response is shown in (d), and the local stress–strain response at the notch in (e). (Adapted from [Dowling 89]; copyright © ASTM; reprinted with permission.)

of load. Recalling the behavior of the rheological model from Chapter 12, this results in all subsequent stress–strain paths following $\Delta\varepsilon/2 = f(\Delta\sigma/2)$, with origins at their respective hysteresis loop tips.

Analysis proceeds as follows: First, the stress and strain for point A are found from S_A by applying Eq. 13.71(a) or 13.73:

$$\varepsilon_A = g(S_A) = f(\sigma_A) \qquad\qquad (S_A > 0)$$

$$\varepsilon_A = -g(-S_A) = -f(-\sigma_A) \qquad (S_A < 0)$$

(13.74)

Then Eq. 13.71(c) is applied to load ranges from the given history as

$$\frac{\Delta\varepsilon_{AB}}{2} = g\left(\frac{\Delta S_{AB}}{2}\right) = f\left(\frac{\Delta\sigma_{AB}}{2}\right), \qquad \frac{\Delta\varepsilon_{BC}}{2} = g\left(\frac{\Delta S_{BC}}{2}\right) = f\left(\frac{\Delta\sigma_{BC}}{2}\right) \qquad (13.75)$$

and similarly for the following additional ranges: $\Delta S_{AD}, \Delta S_{DE}, \Delta S_{EF}, \Delta S_{FG}$, and ΔS_{EH}. Events $\Delta S_{CB'}, \Delta S_{GF'}, \Delta S_{HE'}$, and $\Delta S_{DA'}$ do not need to be analyzed, as the results are the same as for the other branches of the corresponding hysteresis loops. The results of this analysis are sufficient to establish stress and strain values for all peaks and valleys in the load history, and also all of the intervening σ-ε paths. Overall ranges similar to ΔS_{AD} can be analyzed by ignoring the included minor load excursion, in this case event B-C-B'. This is the case because the *memory effect* causes the stress–strain path beyond B' to be the same as it would have been if event B-C-B' had not occurred. The memory effect similarly acts at points F' and E'. However, the equations used do not apply to events such as ΔS_{CD}, since the stress–strain path involves portions of more than one hysteresis loop and so does not obey $\Delta\varepsilon/2 = f(\Delta\sigma/2)$.

The same logic can be applied to completely analyze load histories of any length, as long as the underlying assumptions of stable material behavior, and of at least approximately proportional loading, are satisfied. Beginning the analysis at the most extreme value of load is merely a convenience. Any starting point can be used if a more general logic based on spring and slider rheological models is employed.

Analysis of irregular load histories as just described is needed when the strain-based approach is used to make fatigue life estimates. This topic is considered in the next chapter.

Example 13.5

Table E13.5(a) gives the history of nominal stress S for Fig. 13.20. Estimate the local notch stress–strain response for stable behavior. Note that the value of stress concentration factor is $k_t = 2.40$ and the material is 2024-T351 aluminum.

Solution   Constants for the material's cyclic stress–strain curve $\varepsilon_a = f(\sigma_a)$ in the form of Eq. 12.54 are available from Table 12.1 as $E = 73,100$ MPa, $H' = 662$ MPa, and $n' = 0.070$. Assume that the materials behavior is similar to that of a spring and slider rheological model. Use Neuber's rule to approximate the load–strain function $\varepsilon_a = g(S_a)$, specifically, by the combination of Eqs. 12.54 and 13.61. To analyze point A, assume loading that follows the

Table E13.5

(a) Load History			(b) Calculated Values						
Point (Y)	S MPa	Origin (X)	Origin S MPa	Direction ψ	ΔS to Point	$\Delta \sigma$ MPa	$\Delta \varepsilon$	Stress σ, MPa	Strain ε
A	414	—	—	+1	—	—	—	503.3	0.02683
B	−69	A	414	−1	483	900.3	0.02042	−397.0	0.00642
C	345	B	−69	+1	414	857.3	0.01575	460.3	0.02217
D	−310	A	414	−1	724	983.4	0.04200	−480.0	−0.01517
E	310	D	−310	+1	620	954.6	0.03173	474.5	0.01656
F	−172	E	310	−1	482	899.8	0.02034	−425.3	−0.00378
G	172	F	−172	+1	344	784.9	0.01188	359.6	0.00810
H	−241	E	310	−1	551	930.6	0.02571	−456.0	−0.00915

cyclic stress–strain curve as if it were a monotonic one, and employ Eq. 13.61 in the same manner, to obtain

$$S_A = \psi \frac{1}{k_t} \sqrt{\sigma_A^2 + \psi \sigma_A E \left(\frac{\psi \sigma_A}{H'}\right)^{1/n'}}, \qquad \varepsilon_A = \frac{\sigma_A}{E} + \psi \left(\frac{\psi \sigma_A}{H'}\right)^{1/n'}$$

where $\psi = +1$ if the direction is positive (as is the case here), or $\psi = -1$ if the direction is negative. Substitute $S_A = 414$ MPa into the first equation, solve iteratively to obtain $\sigma_A = 503.3$ MPa, and then substitute this value into the second equation to obtain $\varepsilon_A = 0.02683$.

Analysis beyond point A can now be done by applying Eqs. 12.54 and 13.61 to ranges that correspond to smooth hysteresis loop curves, employing these in the forms $\Delta \varepsilon / 2 = g(\Delta S / 2)$ and $\Delta \varepsilon / 2 = f(\Delta \sigma / 2)$. First, identify points in the history where the memory effect acts and stress–strain hysteresis loops are closed, which are also points where rainflow cycles are completed, here at points B', F', E', and A'. Then apply Eqs. 12.54 and 13.61 for each closed loop, B-C, F-G, E-H, and A-D, and also for ranges locating the starting points of loops, A-B, D-E, and E-F.

The calculations are organized as shown in Table E13.5(b). For each peak or valley (Y) in the history, the origin point (X) of the smooth hysteresis loop curve is tabulated, along with its S value. (For example, when loop B-C closes at point B', the origin for the continuing curve is point A, so that range A-D is analyzed to locate point D.) Next, ψ is listed as $+1$ if the strain is increasing during the range, or -1 if it is decreasing. Then each load range ΔS_{XY} is calculated, from which each corresponding stress and strain range, $\Delta \sigma_{XY}$ and $\Delta \varepsilon_{XY}$, can be determined:

$$\Delta S_{XY} = |S_Y - S_X|$$

$$\frac{\Delta S_{XY}}{2} = \frac{1}{k_t} \sqrt{\left(\frac{\Delta \sigma_{XY}}{2}\right)^2 + \frac{\Delta \sigma_{XY} E}{2} \left(\frac{\Delta \sigma_{XY}}{2H'}\right)^{1/n'}}$$

$$\frac{\Delta \varepsilon_{XY}}{2} = \frac{\Delta \sigma_{XY}}{2E} + \left(\frac{\Delta \sigma_{XY}}{2H'}\right)^{1/n'}$$

For example, the range from $S_A = 414$ to $S_B = -69$ is $\Delta S_{AB} = 483\,\text{MPa}$. Entering this value into the second equation just given and solving iteratively yields $\Delta \sigma_{AB} = 900.3\,\text{MPa}$. Substituting the latter value into the third equation then gives $\Delta \varepsilon_{AB} = 0.02042$.

Finally, determine the stress and strain values for all peaks and valleys in the history by starting from the initial point A and calculating the stress and strain at each subsequent point. Do so by adding or subtracting the appropriate ranges, using the equations

$$\sigma_Y = \sigma_X + \psi\,\Delta\sigma_{XY}, \qquad \varepsilon_Y = \varepsilon_X + \psi\,\Delta\varepsilon_{XY}$$

where the use of ψ causes $\Delta\sigma_{XY}$ to be added to or subtracted from σ_X to obtain σ_Y, and similarly for the strains, depending on whether the S is increasing or decreasing. For example, for points B and C,

$$
\begin{aligned}
&\sigma_A = 503.3, & &\Delta\sigma_{AB} = 900.3, & &\psi = -1, & &\text{so that } \sigma_B = -397.0\,\text{MPa}\\
&\varepsilon_A = 0.02683, & &\Delta\varepsilon_{AB} = 0.02042, & &\psi = -1, & &\text{so that } \varepsilon_B = 0.00642\\[6pt]
&\sigma_B = -397.0, & &\Delta\sigma_{BC} = 857.3, & &\psi = +1, & &\text{so that } \sigma_C = 460.3\,\text{MPa}\\
&\varepsilon_B = 0.00642, & &\Delta\varepsilon_{BC} = 0.01575, & &\psi = +1, & &\text{so that } \varepsilon_C = 0.02217
\end{aligned}
$$

Comments   The stress and strain values for the peaks and valleys in the load history, A, B, C, etc., can be plotted on stress–strain coordinates as in Fig. 13.20(e). Equation 12.54 in the form $\Delta\varepsilon/2 = f(\Delta\sigma/2)$ can be employed to calculate a number of points along each smooth curve connecting peak–valley points, while observing the memory effect. (The equations at the end of Ex. 12.5 apply.) Or the peak–valley points can be used as a guide to sketch the curves by hand, noting that only one curve shape is needed.

13.6.4 Discussion

The methodology just described for cyclic loading is consistent with the analysis of residual stresses presented earlier. Consider starting from zero and applying a particular load, as described by a nominal stress S', and then returning to zero. Analysis of this event is identical to that for the first cycle of constant amplitude loading with $S_{\max} = S'$ at $R = 0$, so that $S_{\min} = 0$. The resulting values of $\sigma_{\min}$ and $\varepsilon_{\min}$ are the residual stress and strain, σ_r and ε_r.

The procedure described clearly involves idealized materials behavior. Cycle-dependent hardening or softening is at least roughly included by the use of the stable cyclic stress–strain curve. However, the approach does not include cycle-dependent creep–relaxation or the details of the hardening or softening behavior. The degree of approximation involved with omitting these transient behaviors is not expected to be a problem except in unusual cases. The ease of application of the approach described makes it a useful engineering tool, as in its use for the strain-based approach to fatigue in Chapter 14.

More serious limitations may be encountered if multiple applied loads cause significantly nonproportional loading during plastic deformation. Time-dependent creep–relaxation behavior, as for metals at high temperature, is, of course, also beyond the scope of the method described. If such complexities need to be analyzed, a number of computer programs are available that incorporate sophisticated models of material behavior into analysis by finite elements. However, caution is needed to ensure that the stress–strain modeling is appropriate and specific to the material and situation of interest. Computer programs sometimes employ stress–strain models that are mathematically convenient, but which represent the behavior of real materials poorly.

13.7 SUMMARY

For symmetrical bending of beams, and for torsion of solid or hollow circular shafts, stresses and strains can be readily analyzed for situations where plastic deformation occurs. Plane sections are assumed to remain plane, and an integral must be evaluated for the particular form of stress–strain curve of interest. Analysis of this type can be extended to determine residual stresses and strains. For members containing notches, stresses and strains at the notch may be estimated by using Neuber's rule in the form of Eq. 13.58. Satisfying both Neuber's rule and the particular stress–strain curve of interest provides a solution. Also, this procedure may be extended to estimating residual stresses and strains at notches.

Plastic deformation in bending or torsion, and also localized plastic deformation at notches, causes strains to occur that exceed those from elastic analysis for the given loads. The specific analytical results presented are listed in Table 13.1, and additional cases are suggested as exercises.

Cyclic loading is readily analyzed if the behavior of the material is idealized to follow the stable (half-life) cyclic stress–strain curve. For this curve in the form $\varepsilon = f(\sigma)$, hysteresis loop curves can be approximated as obeying $\Delta\varepsilon/2 = f(\Delta\sigma/2)$. A useful expediency is to ignore the transient cycle-dependent stress–strain behavior, namely, creep–relaxation and hardening or softening.

On this basis, stress–strain analysis may be performed just as for monotonic loading, except for the use of the stable cyclic stress–strain curve. For applied loading characterized by a nominal stress S that cycles between S_{max} and S_{min}, let the strain of interest be functionally related to S by an analytical result expressed in the form $\varepsilon = g(S)$. For cyclic loading that is completely reversed or

Table 13.1   Cases Analyzed

Case	Equation No.
Bending of Rectangular Beams	
(a) Simple power-hardening material	13.11
(b) Elastic, perfectly plastic material	13.18
(c) Ramberg–Osgood material	13.27
(d) Residual stress–strain for case (b)	13.32, 13.33
Torsion of Solid Circular Shafts	
(e) Simple power-hardening material	13.46
(f) Elastic, perfectly plastic material	13.47
(g) Ramberg–Osgood material	13.48
Local σ-ε in Notched Members	
(h) Elastic, perfectly plastic material	13.59
(i) Elastic, power-hardening material	13.60
(j) Ramberg–Osgood material	13.61

which has a tensile (positive) mean level, $R \geq 1$, maximums and amplitudes (half-ranges) of stress and strain can be determined by applying this result as follows:

$$\varepsilon_{\max} = g(S_{\max}) = f(\sigma_{\max}), \qquad \varepsilon_a = g(S_a) = f(\sigma_a) \tag{13.76}$$

Minimums of stress and strain are obtained by subtracting ranges from maximum values. Similar analysis can also be applied for loading that is biased in the compressive direction, $R < -1$.

Analysis of cyclic loading can be extended to irregular variation of load with time by applying $\Delta\varepsilon/2 = g(\Delta S/2)$ to all load excursions that correspond to stress–strain paths following $\Delta\varepsilon/2 = f(\Delta\sigma/2)$. The memory effect is invoked at points where stress–strain hysteresis loops close, after which the stress and strain return to the path established prior to starting the loop.

NEW TERMS AND SYMBOLS

elastically calculated stress, σ_{elas}

finite element method

fully plastic force or moment: P_o, M_o

fully plastic yielding

initial yielding

initial yield force or moment: P_i, M_i

local notch stress and strain

local yielding

Neuber's rule

residual stress and strain, σ_r and ε_r

stress and strain concentration factors, k_σ and k_ε

REFERENCES

CHU, C.-C. 1995. *Incremental Multiaxial Neuber Correction for Fatigue Analysis*, Paper No. 950705, Soc. of Automotive Engineers, SAE International Congress and Exposition, Detroit, MI, Feb. 1995.

CRANDALL, S. H., N. C. DAHL, and T. J. Lardner, eds. 1978. *An Introduction to the Mechanics of Solids: SI Units*, 2nd ed., McGraw-Hill, New York.

GLINKA, G. 1985. "Energy Density Approach to Calculation of Inelastic Stress–Strain Near Notches and Cracks," *Engineering Fracture Mechanics*, vol. 22, no. 3, pp. 485–508. See also vol. 22, no. 5, pp. 839–854.

HARKEGARD, G., and T. MANN. 2003. "Neuber Prediction of Elastic-Plastic Strain Concentration in Notched Tensile Specimens Under Large-Scale Yielding," *Journal of Strain Analysis*, IMechE, vol. 38, no. 1, pp. 79–94.

HILL, R. 1998. *The Mathematical Theory of Plasticity*, Oxford University Press, Oxford, UK.

HOFFMANN, M., and T. SEEGER. 1989. "Stress–Strain Analysis and Life Predictions of a Notched Shaft Under Multiaxial Loading," G. E. Leese and D. Socie, eds., *Multiaxial Fatigue: Analysis and Experiments*, AE-14, Soc. of Automotive Engineers, Warrendale, PA.

MROZ, Z. 1967. "On the Description of Anisotropic Workhardening," *Jnl. of the Mechanics and Physics of Solids*, vol. 15, May 1967, pp. 163–175.

MROZ, Z. 1973. "Boundary-Value Problems in Cyclic Plasticity," *Second Int. Conf. on Structural Mechanics in Reactor Technology*, W. Berlin, Germany, Vol. 6B, Part L, Paper L7/6.

REINHARDT, W., A. MOFTAKHAR, and G. GLINKA. 1997. "An Efficient Method for Calculating Multiaxial Elasto-Plastic Notch Tip Strains and Stresses Under Proportional Loading," R. S. Piascik, J. C. Newman, and N. E. Dowling, eds., *Fatigue and Fracture Mechanics: 27th Volume*, ASTM STP 1296, Am. Soc. for Testing and Materials, West Conshohocken, PA.

RICE, R. C., ed. 1997. *Fatigue Design Handbook*, 3d ed., SAE Pub. No. AE-22, Society of Automotive Engineers, Warrendale, PA.

SEEGER, T., and P. HEULER. 1980. "Generalized Application of Neuber's Rule," *Jnl. of Testing and Evaluation*, ASTM, vol. 8, no. 4, pp. 199–204.

SKRZYPEK, J. J., and R. B. Hetnarski. 1993. *Plasticity and Creep: Theory, Examples, and Problems*, CRC Press, Boca Raton, FL.

PROBLEMS AND QUESTIONS

Section 13.2

13.1 A beam has a symmetrical diamond-shaped cross section, as shown in Fig. P13.1, and the material obeys a simple power-hardening stress–strain curve, Eq. 13.9. For pure bending with the z-axis as the neutral axis, derive an equation giving the bending moment M as a function of ε_c, the strain at $y = c$, and also constants H_2, n_2, b, and c.

13.2 A beam has an I-shaped cross section, as shown in Fig. P13.2, and the material obeys a simple power-hardening stress–strain curve, Eq. 13.9.

    (a) For pure bending with the z-axis as the neutral axis, derive an equation giving the bending moment M as a function of ε_{c2}, the strain at $y = c_2$, and also constants H_2, n_2, t_1, t_2, c_1, and c_2.

    (b) Adapt your equation from (a) to the nomenclature of Fig. A.2(d), employing dimensions h_1, h_2 and b_1, b_2. Does the result also apply to a box section?

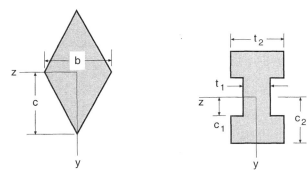

Figure P13.1　　　　　　　　**Figure P13.2**

13.3 A rectangular beam of depth $2c$ and thickness t is subjected to pure bending and is made of a material with an elastic, power-hardening stress–strain curve, Eq. 12.8. Show that the bending moment M is related to the edge strain ε_c, beam dimensions, and constants for the stress–strain curve, by

$$M = \frac{2tc^2\sigma_c}{3}, \qquad M = \frac{2tc^2}{n_1+2}\left[\frac{E\varepsilon_o^3(n_1-1)}{3\varepsilon_c^2} + H_1\varepsilon_c^{n_1}\right] \qquad \text{(a, b)}$$

where (a) applies for ($\varepsilon_c \leq \varepsilon_o$), and (b) applies for ($\varepsilon_c \geq \varepsilon_o$), with $\varepsilon_o = \sigma_o/E$ being the yield strain. Does the post-yield solution (b) reduce to the elastic case for incipient yielding at the beam edge? Does it reduce to Eq. 13.11 for large values of ε_c?

13.4 For the situation of Prob. 13.3, assume that the beam has cross-sectional dimensions of depth $2c = 48$ mm and thickness $t = 18$ mm, and let the material be an aluminum alloy with $E = 70$ GPa, $H_1 = 600$ MPa, and $n_1 = 0.200$.

    (a) Calculate bending moments M for a range of edge strain values up to approximately $\varepsilon_c = 0.03$, and then plot M as a function of ε_c on linear–linear coordinates.

    (b) Concisely discuss the M versus ε_c behavior observed. Is a distinct yielding event seen in the M versus ε_c trend? Why or why not? What is the limiting case of the post-yield solution for large strains? Does your curve approach this case as you might expect?

13.5 A beam with a circular cross section of radius c is subjected to pure bending, and it is made of a material with an elastic, perfectly plastic stress–strain curve, Eq. 12.1. Show that the moment M is related to ε_c, the strain at $y = c$, by

$$M = \frac{\pi c^3 E \varepsilon_c}{4}, \qquad M = \frac{c^3 \sigma_o}{6}\left[2\left(1 - \frac{1}{\alpha^2}\right)^{3/2} + 3\sqrt{1 - \frac{1}{\alpha^2}} + 3\alpha \sin^{-1}\frac{1}{\alpha}\right] \qquad \text{(a, b)}$$

where (a) applies for ($\varepsilon_c \leq \varepsilon_o$), and (b) applies for ($\varepsilon_c \geq \varepsilon_o$), with $\varepsilon_o = \sigma_o/E$ being the yield strain, and $\alpha = \varepsilon_c/\varepsilon_o$.

13.6 For the situation of Prob. 13.5, assume that the cross section radius is $c = 20$ mm, and let the material be an alloy steel with $E = 120,000$ MPa and $\sigma_o = 600$ MPa.

    (a) Calculate bending moments M for a range of edge strain values up to approximately $\varepsilon_c = 0.03$, and then plot M as a function of ε_c on linear–linear coordinates.

    (b) Concisely discuss the M versus ε_c behavior observed. Is a distinct yielding event seen in the M versus ε_c trend? Why or why not? What is the limiting case of the post yield solution for large strains? Does your curve approach this case as you might expect?

13.7 Consider a material with a simple power-hardening stress–strain curve, Eq. 13.9.

    (a) For a beam with a circular cross section of radius c, derive an equation for the bending moment M as a function of ε_c, the strain at $y = c$, and also constants H_2, n_2, and c. (Suggestion: Consult the *definite integrals* section of a table of integrals, and note that a closed-form solution can be obtained in terms of the standard Gamma function, more specifically, the Beta function.)

    (b) Extend the result from (a) to the more general case of a tubular cross section with inner radius c_1 and outer radius c_2.

Section 13.3

13.8 Consider three identical rectangular beams, of depth $2c = 60$ and thickness $t = 30$ mm, loaded in symmetrical pure bending. All are made of an elastic, perfectly plastic material with yield strength $\sigma_o = 400$ MPa and elastic modulus $E = 300$ GPa. The first beam is loaded to an edge strain of $\varepsilon_c^1 = 0.003$ and then unloaded, the second to $\varepsilon_c^1 = 0.006$, and the third to $\varepsilon_c^1 = 0009$. For each of the three beams, complete the following tasks:

    (a) Calculate the moment M^1 required to reach ε_c^1 and the residual stress and residual strain, σ_{rc} and ε_{rc}, remaining after unloading.

    (b) Determine and plot the stress distribution, both at the maximum moment M^1 and after removal of M'.

    (c) Comment on the differences among the three cases analyzed.

13.9 A rectangular beam has depth $2c = 40$ and thickness $t = 20\,\text{mm}$, and is made of an aluminum alloy having elastic, perfectly plastic stress–strain behavior, with $E = 70\,\text{GPa}$ and $\sigma_o = 350\,\text{MPa}$. A bending moment of $750\,\text{N·m}$ is applied and then removed.

    (a) Determine the residual stresses, and plot their distribution versus the distance y from the neutral axis. On the same plot, also show the stress distribution at the maximum moment.

    (b) Plot the stress–strain paths for each edge of the beam—that is, for both $y = c$ and $y = -c$.

Section 13.4

13.10 Derive Eq. 13.47.

13.11 Derive Eq. 13.48, and show that it reduces to the correct elastic case for small plastic strains and to Eq. 13.46 for large plastic strains.

13.12 For a simple power-hardening stress–strain curve, Eq. 13.45, and for a thick-walled tube with inner radius c_1 and outer radius c_2, complete the following:

    (a) Derive an equation for torque T as a function of the maximum shear strain γ_c.

    (b) Check your result to be sure that it reduces to Eq. 13.46 as c_1 approaches zero.

13.13 A thick-walled tube subjected to simple torsion has inner radius c_1 and outer radius c_2. The material has an elastic, perfectly plastic stress–strain relationship with shear modulus G and yield strength in shear τ_o.

    (a) Assume that the elastic-plastic boundary occurs between c_1 and c_2, and derive an equation for the torque T as a function of the shear strain γ_{c2} at $r = c_2$, material constants G and τ_o, and c_1 and c_2.

    (b) For the no yielding case, employ elastic analysis, Fig. A.1(c), to obtain the applicable equation relating T and γ_{c2}.

    (c) For fully plastic yielding, obtain the equation for T that applies. (Suggestion: In Fig. A.15(e), subtract the torque that is missing due to the tube being hollow.)

    (d) Verify that your results for (b) and (c) are consistent with limiting cases of your equation from (a).

13.14 Aluminum alloy 2024-T351 has a uniaxial stress–strain curve for monotonic loading of Ramberg–Osgood form, Eq. 12.12, with $E = 73.1\,\text{GPa}$, $H = 527\,\text{MPa}$, and $n = 0.0663$, and also a value of Poisson's ratio of $\nu = 0.33$.

    (a) Estimate the shear stress–strain curve for this material.

    (b) A solid round shaft of this material of radius $c = 9.53\,\text{mm}$ is loaded in torsion. Estimate and plot the curve relating torque T and surface shear strain out to $\gamma_c = 0.1$.

(Problem continues)

(c) For a gage length of $L = 152.4\,\text{mm}$, corresponding torque versus angle of twist data are given in Table P13.14. Plot these points on the curve from (b), and comment on the comparison. (Hint: Angle of twist θ in radians is related to shear strain by $\theta = \gamma_c L / c$.)

Table P13.14

T, N·m	θ, degrees
0	0
82.5	2
164	4
229	6
297	10
339	15
377	25
407	40
438	60
467	90

13.15 A circular shaft of radius c is subjected to torsion, and the material has an elastic, power-hardening curve for shear stress versus shear strain. In particular, $\tau = G\gamma$ for $(\tau \leq \tau_o)$, and $\tau = H_4 \gamma^{n_4}$ for $(\tau \geq \tau_o)$. Show that the torque T is related to γ_c, the strain at $r = c$, by

$$T = \frac{\pi c^3 G \gamma_c}{2}, \qquad T = \frac{2\pi c^3}{n_4 + 3}\left[\frac{G\gamma_o^4(n_4 - 1)}{4\gamma_c^3} + H_4 \gamma_c^{n_4}\right] \qquad \text{(a, b)}$$

where (a) applies for $(\gamma_c \leq \gamma_o)$, and (b) applies for $(\gamma_c \geq \gamma_o)$, with $\gamma_o = \tau_o / G$ being the yield strain. Does the postyield solution (b) reduce to the elastic case for incipient yielding at the beam edge? Does it reduce to Eq. 13.46 for large strains?

13.16 For the situation of Prob. 13.15, assume that the shaft radius is $c = 50\,\text{mm}$ and that the material is an aluminum alloy with $G = 120\,\text{GPa}$, $H_4 = 375\,\text{MPa}$, and $n_4 = 0.100$.

   (a) Calculate torques T for a range of maximum strain values up to approximately $\gamma_c = 0.05$, and then plot T as a function of γ_c on linear–linear coordinates.

   (b) Briefly discuss the T versus γ_c behavior observed. Is a distinct yielding event seen in the T versus γ_c trend? Why or why not? What is the limiting case of the post-yield solution for large strains? Does your curve approach this case as you might expect?

Section 13.5

13.17 Consider the notched member and stress–strain curve of Fig. 13.16. Using stress and strain values estimated with Neuber's rule in Examples 13.1 and 13.2, calculate the stress and strain concentration factors, k_σ and k_ε, for loading to (a) $S = 240$ and (b) $S = 280\,\text{MPa}$. Are your values consistent with the graph of Fig. 13.16(b) ?

13.18 A notched member has an elastic stress concentration factor of $k_t = 3$, and it is made of an elastic, perfectly plastic material having an elastic modulus $E = 120\,\text{GPa}$ and a yield strength $\sigma_o = 280\,\text{MPa}$. Estimate the stress and strain at the notch if the member is loaded to a nominal stress S^l of (a) 120, (b) 140, and (c) 160 MPa. For each case, plot the stress–strain path, and calculate the stress and strain concentration factors, k_σ and k_ε. Also, (d) briefly discuss the behavior seen.

13.19 A notched member has an elastic stress concentration factor of $k_t = 2.80$, and it is made of an elastic, perfectly plastic material having an elastic modulus $E = 240$ GPa and a yield strength $\sigma_o = 1400$ MPa. Estimate the stress and strain at the notch if the member is loaded to a nominal stress S' of (a) 400, (b) 800, and (c) 1200 MPa. For each case, plot the stress–strain path, and calculate the stress and strain concentration factors, k_σ and k_ε. Also, (d) briefly discuss the behavior seen.

13.20 A notched member has an elastic stress concentration factor of $k_t = 3.20$, and it is made of an elastic, power-hardening material with $E = 140$ GPa, $H_1 = 1600$ MPa, and $n_1 = 0.20$. Estimate the stress and strain at the notch if the member is loaded to a nominal stress S^l of (a) 200, (b) 400, and (c) 600 MPa. For each case, plot the stress–strain path, and calculate the stress and strain concentration factors, k_σ and k_ε. Also, (d) briefly discuss the behavior seen.

13.21 Consider an elastic, linear-hardening material with an Eq. 12.4 stress–strain curve having constants σ_o, E, and δ. A notched member made of such a material has an elastic stress concentration factor k_t and is subjected to a nominal stress S.

   (a) Assuming that local yielding occurs at the notch, and on the basis of Neuber's rule, derive expressions for the local stress and strain at the notch, σ and ε, as functions of k_t, S, σ_o, E, and δ.

   (b) Confirm that your result reduces to Eq. 13.59 for $\delta = 0$.

   (c) Assume that $E = 400$ GPa, $\sigma_o = 700$ MPa, and $\delta = 0.200$ for the material, and that $k_t = 3.0$ for the notched member. If $S = 250$ MPa is applied, estimate σ and ε, and then $k\sigma$ and $k\varepsilon$.

13.22 A notched plate having an elastic stress concentration of $k_t = 4.0$ is made of 7075-T651 aluminum, and a nominal stress $S = 350$ MPa is applied. The material's Ramberg–Osgood stress–strain curve has constants E, H, and n as in Ex. 12.1, with Poisson's ratio $\nu = 0.33$. The member thickness is several times larger than the notch radius, so that the strain in the transverse direction, ε_z in Fig. 13.14, is expected to be close to zero. Estimate the notch surface stress and strain in the y-direction of Fig. 13.14. (Comments: The situation described in Section 13.5.5 applies, and an iterative solution is required. Pick a point $(\bar\varepsilon, \bar\sigma)$ on the effective (same as uniaxial) stress–strain curve. Then calculate $(\varepsilon_1, \sigma_1) = (\varepsilon_y, \sigma_y)$, and use Neuber's rule with these values. Vary the $(\bar\varepsilon, \bar\sigma)$ choice until the desired S is obtained.)

13.23 Aluminum alloy 7075-T651 has a monotonic stress–strain curve for uniaxial stress of the Ramberg–Osgood form, Eq. 12.12, with constants E, H, and n as in Ex 12.1. With reference to Fig. A.11(a), a plate of this material with a central round hole had dimensions of width $w = 76.2$, hole diameter $d = 19.05$, and thickness $t = 6.35$ mm, giving an elastic stress concentration factor of $k_t = 2.42$. A strain gage was mounted inside the hole to measure the strain ε_y as in Fig. 13.16. Values ε_y are given in Table P13.23 for various levels of force P during monotonic loading of the plate. Estimate the P versus ε_y curve expected from Neuber's rule, plot this curve along with the test data, and comment on the comparison.

Table P13.23

P, Force, kN	ε_y, Notch Strain
0	0
44.5	0.0042
66.7	0.0064
89.0	0.0087
111.2	0.0121
133.4	0.0174
155.7	0.0251
177.9	0.0366

13.24 Proceed as in Prob. 13.23, except approximate the stress–strain curve as an elastic, perfectly plastic one, with σ_o corresponding to the 0.2% offset yield strength.

13.25 On the basis of the method of Glinka as described in Section 13.5.4 and Fig. 13.17, perform the following tasks:

    (a) Develop an alternative relationship analogous to Eq. 13.59 for estimating notch strain for an elastic, perfectly plastic material.

    (b) Develop an alternative relationship analogous to Eq. 13.61 that gives S as a function of notch stress for a Ramberg–Osgood material.

    (c) Apply your result (b) to the notch strain data of Prob. 13.23, plotting the estimated P versus ε_y curve along with the test data. How well do curve and data agree?

13.26 A notched member has a stress concentration factor of $k_t = 3.0$, and it is made of a material having an elastic, linear hardening stress–strain relationship, Eq. 12.4, with constants $E = 70\,\text{GPa}$, $\sigma_o = 800\,\text{MPa}$, and $\delta = 0.18$.

    (a) Estimate the stress and strain at the notch if a nominal stress $S' = 300\,\text{MPa}$ is applied.

    (b) What residual stress and strain, σ_r and ε_r, remain after this S' is removed?

    (c) Plot the stress–strain response for loading to S' and then unloading.

13.27 A notched member has an elastic stress concentration of $k_t = 3.50$ and is made of a material and has an elastic, power-hardening stress–strain curve, Eq. 12.8, with constants $E = 69\,\text{GPa}$, $H_1 = 834\,\text{MPa}$, and $n_1 = 0.200$. The member is loaded from zero to a nominal stress S^1 and then unloaded. Determine the local notch residual stress and strain that remain for (a) $S^1 = 250$, (b) $S^1 = -250$, and (c) $S^1 = 300\,\text{MPa}$. Also, plot the stress–strain paths for each case. Also (d) briefly discuss the different types of behavior that occur.

13.28 A notched member has an elastic stress concentration factor of $k_t = 3.30$, and it is made of a material and has an elastic, power-hardening stress–strain curve, Eq. 12.8, with constants $E = 73100\,\text{MPa}$, $H_1 = 622\,\text{MPa}$, and $n_1 = 0.070$. Estimate the residual stress and strain at the notch if the member is loaded to a nominal stress S^1, and then unloaded, for (a) $S^1 = -280$ and (b) $S^1 = 280\,\text{MPa}$. For each case, plot the stress–strain path for loading and unloading. Also, (c) briefly discuss the relationship between the signs of S^1 and σ_r and why the observed trend occurs.

13.29 A plate with around hole is loaded in tension. As defined in Fig. A.11(a), the dimensions are $w = 50$, $d = 15$, and $t = 5.0\,\text{mm}$. The plate is made of 7075-T651 aluminum, which has a

Ramberg–Osgood stress–strain curve, with constants E, H, and n, as in Ex. 12.1. Verify from Fig. A.11(a) that $k_t = 2.35$. Then estimate the residual stress and strain at the notch if the member is loaded to a force P', and then unloaded, for (a) $P' = 54$ and (b) $P' = 70\,\text{kN}$. For each case, plot the stress–strain path for loading and unloading. Also, (c) concisely discuss the behavior that occurs.

Section 13.6

13.30 A notched member has an elastic stress concentration factor of $k_t = 3.00$ and is made of a material with an elastic, perfectly plastic stress–strain relationship, where $E = 200\,\text{GPa}$ and $\sigma_o = 400\,\text{MPa}$. Estimate and plot the local notch stress–strain response for cyclic loading with nominal stresses of (a) $S_{\max} = 100$ and $S_{\min} = -20\,\text{MPa}$, (b) $S_{\max} = 200$ and $S_{\min} = -40\,\text{MPa}$, (c) $S_{\max} = 200$ and $S_{\min} = -100\,\text{MPa}$, and (d) $S_{\max} = 200$ and $S_{\min} = -200\,\text{MPa}$. Also, (e) concisely discuss the different types of behavior that occur.

13.31 A notched member has an elastic stress concentration factor of $k_t = 3.50$ and is made of the AISI 4340 steel ($\sigma_u = 1468\,\text{MPa}$) of Table 14.1, where constants are given for the stable cyclic stress–strain curve, Eq. 12.54. Estimate and plot the local notch stress–strain response for cyclic loading between nominal stresses $S_{\max} = 500$ and $S_{\min} = -400\,\text{MPa}$.

13.32 A notched plate is loaded axially, as in Fig. A.11(b), and has a stress concentration factor of $k_t = 2.5$. It is made of the Al-T6-V4 of Table 12.1, where constants are given for the stable cyclic stress–strain curve, Eq. 12.54 with $E = 69\,\text{GPa}$, $H_1 = 834$ and $n_1 = 0.2$. Estimate and plot the local notch stress–strain response if the nominal stress is cycled between $S_{\max} = 100$ and $S_{\min} = -40\,\text{MPa}$.

13.33 A notched plate is loaded axially, as in Fig. A.11(b), and has a stress concentration factor of $k_t = 2.5$. It is made of the 2024-T351 aluminum of Table 12.1, where constants are given for the stable cyclic stress–strain curve, Eq. 12.54. The member and material as in Prob. 13.32 is subjected to constant amplitude cyclic loading between $S_{\min} = -250$ and $S_{\max} = 100\,\text{MPa}$. Estimate and plot the local notch stress–strain response.

13.34 A plate with a round hole is made of the RQC-100 steel of Table 12.1. The dimensions, as defined in Fig. A.11(a), are $w = 150$, $d = 12$, and $t = 2.5\,\text{mm}$. Confirm that $k_t = 2.8$. Then estimate and plot the local notch stress–strain response for cyclic loading between $P_{\max} = 130$ and $P_{\min} = 35\,\text{kN}$.

13.35 The same member and material as in Prob. 13.34 is subjected to constant amplitude cyclic loading between $P_{\min} = -100$ and $P_{\max} = 5\,\text{kN}$. Estimate and plot the local notch stress–strain response.

13.36 A member is made of the titanium 6Al-4V alloy of Table 14.1, where constants are given for the cyclic stress–strain curve, Eq. 12.54. It is a flat plate with a width reduction and is subjected to in-plane bending. The dimensions, as defined in Fig. A.11(d), are $w_2 = 75$, $w_1 = 50$, fillet radius $\rho = 1.75$, and thickness $t = 6.5\,\text{mm}$. Confirm that $k_t = 2.5$. Then estimate and plot the local notch stress–strain response for cyclic loading between $M_{\max} = 1500$ and $M_{\min} = -200\,\text{N·m}$.

13.37 Some rectangular beams made of the RQC-100 steel of Table 12.1 had a depth of $2c = 6.35$ and a thickness of $t = 12.7\,\text{mm}$. Five of these beams were subjected to completely reversed cyclic pure bending under controlled edge strains. Bending moment and edge strain amplitudes from these tests are given in Table P13.37. (The M_a values are for cyclically stable behavior near $N_f/2$, that is, half of the fatigue life, N_f.) Make a plot of M_a versus ε_{ca}, and compare these data with the curve from Eq. 13.27 applied to cyclic loading.

Table P13.37

No.	M_a, Moment Amplitude, N·m	ε_{ca}, Edge Strain Amplitude	N_f, cycles
1	39.0	0.0022	240 000
2	46.4	0.0030	32 990
3	58.6	0.0050	4 882
4	68.9	0.0100	1 335
5	79.0	0.0180	438

Source: Data courtesy of R. W. Landgraf; see [Dowling 78].

13.38 Bluntly notched compact specimens, as shown in Fig. P13.38, were made of AISI 4340 steel ($\sigma_u = 1158$ MPa). These were subjected to various amplitudes of completely reversed cyclic force, P_a. Small strain gages were applied parallel to the force direction on the curved surface at the end of the notch, giving measurements of strain amplitude ε_a for stable (near half the fatigue life) behavior as listed in Table P13.38. Also, elasto-plastic finite element analysis (FEA) was done, as for static loading, but with the stable cyclic stress–strain curve, represented by the elastic, power-hardening form, Eq. 12.8, with constants $E = 206.9$ GPa, $H_1' = 1924$ MPa, and $n_1' = 0.167$. This analysis gave an elastic stress concentration factor of $k_t = 2.62$ and notch strain values as also listed in the table. To define k_t, nominal stress S was calculated from tension and bending on the net section, giving the equation for S in Fig. P13.38.

 (a) Calculate a number of points on the P_a versus ε_a curve estimated from Neuber's rule. Plot this curve and the strain gage data points on the same graph.

 (b) Add the curve from the FEA results to the plot from (a), and then comment on the success of Neuber's rule and the FEA.

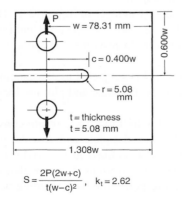

$$S = \frac{2P(2w+c)}{t(w-c)^2}, \quad k_t = 2.62$$

Figure P13.38

Table P13.38

P_a, kN	ε_a (gages)	ε_a (FEA)
7.03	—	0.00298
8.54	0.00354	0.00362
10.23	—	0.00444
12.01	—	0.00547
14.03	0.00630	0.00685
15.57	—	0.00792
17.35	—	0.00934
19.19	0.01015	0.01092
24.02	0.01455	0.01598
26.02	0.01730	0.01850
27.58	0.01850	0.02064
32.03	0.02615	0.02746
34.92	0.02970	0.03282

Source: Data for [Dowling 79b].

13.39 A rotating annular disc has inner radius $r_1 = 105$, outer radius $r_2 = 525$, and thickness $t = 50$ mm. It is made of the AISI 4340 steel ($\sigma_u = 1172$ MPa) of Table 12.1 and rotates at a frequency of $f = 120$ revolutions/second. (See Fig. A.9 and the accompanying text.)

    (a) Calculate radial and tangential stresses, σ_r and σ_t, for a number of values of variable radius R between r_1 and r_2. Then plot these stresses as a function of R.

    (b) Does the peak stress exceed the 0.2% offset cyclic yield strength? Over what range of R?

    (c) Estimate and plot the local stress–strain response at the inner radius for the cyclic loading that results from starting and stopping the rotation. The inner radius acts as a stress raiser, so Neuber's rule should provide a reasonable estimate, with the Fig. A.9 equations giving stresses for elastic behavior, σ_{elas}.

13.40 A notched member has an elastic stress concentration factor of $k_t = 2.50$ and is made of the titanium 6Al-4V alloy of Table 14.1, where constants are given for the cyclic stress–strain curve, Eq. 12.54. Estimate and plot the local notch stress–strain response for repeated applications of the nominal stress history given in the table that follows. In each repetition, note that valley B and peak C each occur 1000 times.

Peak or Valley	A	B_1	C_1	B-C	B_{1000}	C_{1000}	D	A'
S, Nom. Stress, MPa	600	-100	300	repeats	-100	300	-200	600

13.41 A notched bending member has an elastic stress concentration factor of $k_t = 2.40$. It is made of the 2024-T351 aluminum of Table 12.1, where constants are given for the stable cyclic stress–strain curve, Eq. 12.54. Estimate and plot the local notch stress–strain response for repeated applications of the nominal stress history given in the accompanying table. In each repetition, note that peak C and valley D each occur 200 times.

Peak or Valley	A	B	C_1	D_1	C-D	C_{200}	D_{200}	A'
S, Nom. Stress, MPa	360	-100	260	60	repeats	260	60	360

13.42 A notched member has an elastic stress concentration of $k_t = 3.00$. It is made of the SAE 1045 steel (hot-rolled and normalized) of Table 14.1, where constants are given for the stable cyclic stress–strain curve, Eq. 12.54. Estimate and plot the local notch stress–strain response for repeated applications of the nominal stress history given in the accompanying table. In each repetition, note that peak C and valley D each occur 50 times.

Peak or Valley	A	B	C_1	D_1	C-D	C_{50}	D_{50}	E	F	A'
S, Nom. Stress, MPa	350	-160	160	-80	repeats	160	-80	240	-250	350

13.43 A notched member has an elastic stress concentration factor of $k_t = 3.00$ and is made of RQC-100 steel. Determine and plot the local notch stress–strain response for repeated applications of the nominal stress history given in the accompanying table. In each repetition, note that valley D and peak E each occur 2000 times.

Peak or Valley	A	B	C	D_1	E_1	D-E	D_{2000}	E_{2000}	F	A'
S, Nom. Stress, MPa	380	-170	260	-90	170	repeats	-90	170	-260	380

14

Strain-Based Approach to Fatigue

OBJECTIVES

- Explore strain versus fatigue life curves and equations, including trends with material and adjustments for surface finish and size.
- Extend strain–life curves to cases of nonzero mean stress and multiaxial stress.
- Apply the strain-based method to make life estimates for engineering components, especially members with geometric notches, including cases of irregular variation of load with time.

14.1 INTRODUCTION

The strain-based approach to fatigue considers the plastic deformation that may occur in localized regions where fatigue cracks begin, as at edges of beams and at stress raisers. Stresses and strains in such regions are analyzed and used as a basis for life estimates. This procedure permits detailed consideration of fatigue situations where local yielding is involved, which is often the case for ductile metals at relatively short lives. However, the approach also applies where there is little plasticity at long lives, so that it is a comprehensive approach that can be used in place of the stress-based approach.

The strain-based approach differs significantly from the stress-based approach, which is described in Chapters 9 and 10. Its features are highlighted in Fig. 14.1. Recall that the stress-based approach emphasizes nominal (average) stresses, rather than local stresses and strains, and it employs elastic stress concentration factors and empirical modifications thereof. Employment of the

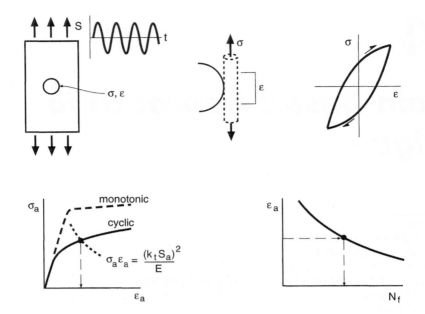

Figure 14.1   The strain-based approach to fatigue, in which local stress and strain, σ and ε, are estimated for the location where cracking is most likely. The effects of local yielding are included, and the material's cyclic stress–strain and strain–life curves from smooth axial test specimens are employed.

cyclic stress–strain curve is a unique feature of the strain-based approach, as is the use of a *strain versus life curve*, instead of a nominal stress versus life (*S-N*) curve. As a result of the more detailed analysis of local yielding, the strain-based method gives improved estimates for intermediate and especially short fatigue lives. Also, the method permits a more rational and accurate handling of mean stress effects by employing the local mean stress at the notch, rather than the mean nominal stress. A similarity between the stress-based and strain-based approaches is that neither includes specific analysis of crack growth, as in the fracture mechanics approach of Chapter 11.

The strain-based approach was initially developed in the late 1950s and early 1960s in response to the need to analyze fatigue problems involving fairly short fatigue lives. The particular applications were nuclear reactors and jet engines—specifically, cyclic loading associated with their operating cycles, especially cyclic thermal stresses. Subsequently, it became clear that the service loadings of many machines, vehicles, and structures include occasional severe events that can best be evaluated with a strain-based approach. One example is the loading on automotive suspension parts caused by potholes, high-speed turns, or unusually rough roads. Another is the transient disturbance of electrical power systems, in some cases caused by lightning strikes, which can produce large mechanical vibrations in the turbines and generators of a power plant. Additional examples include loadings on aircraft due to gusts of wind in storms, and loads due to combat maneuvers of fighter aircraft.

Figure 14.2 Test specimen, extensometer, and grips for strain-controlled fatigue testing. (Photo by G. K. McCauley, Virginia Tech.)

In this chapter, we will use the definitions and nomenclature given early in Chapter 9. Since the strain-based approach has some similarities to the stress-based approach, certain concepts employed will be related to those introduced in Chapters 9 and 10. Also, we will draw upon the information in Chapters 12 and 13 on plastic deformation. Of particular relevance is the cyclic stress–strain curve, Eq. 12.54:

$$\varepsilon_a = \frac{\sigma_a}{E} + \left(\frac{\sigma_a}{H'}\right)^{1/n'} \tag{14.1}$$

Other material from Section 12.5 will be used, as will Neuber's rule from Section 13.5 and the general procedure for analyzing cyclic loads, Section 13.6.

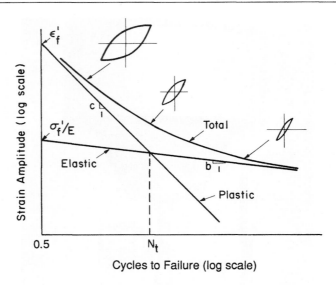

Figure 14.3   Elastic, plastic, and total strain versus life curves. (Adapted from [Landgraf 70]; copyright © ASTM; reprinted with permission.)

14.2 STRAIN VERSUS LIFE CURVES

A strain versus life curve is a plot of strain amplitude versus cycles to failure. Such a curve is employed in the strain-based approach for making life estimates in a manner analogous to the use of the *S-N* curve in the stress-based approach.

14.2.1 Strain–Life Tests and Equations

Strain–life curves are derived from fatigue tests under completely reversed ($R = -1$) cyclic loading between constant strain limits, with stress also measured, as described in ASTM Standard No. E606. Recall that the behavior of metal samples during such tests has already been discussed in Section 12.5 in connection with the cyclic stress–strain curve, which is determined from the same set of data as the strain–life curve. In these tests, axial loading is usually applied to specimens with straight, cylindrical test sections, as illustrated in Fig. 14.2. At long lives where there is little plastic deformation, tests may be run under stress control, which is then essentially equivalent to strain control. The number of cycles to failure N_f is usually defined as occurring when there is substantial cracking of the specimen. A schematic diagram of a strain–life curve on log–log coordinates is shown by the curve labeled *total* in Fig. 14.3, and a curve fitted to actual data is shown in Fig. 14.4.

For each test, amplitudes of stress, strain, and plastic strain, σ_a, ε_a, and ε_{pa}, are measured from a hysteresis loop, as in Fig. 12.17. As for the cyclic stress–strain curve, the particular hysteresis loop chosen is one taken at a cycle number near half of the fatigue life, which is considered to represent the approximately stable behavior after most cycle-dependent hardening or softening is complete.

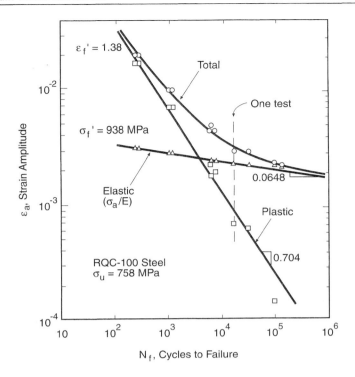

Figure 14.4 Strain versus life curves for RQC-100 steel. For each of several tests, elastic, plastic, and total strain data points are plotted versus life, and fitted lines are also shown. (From the author's data on the ASTM Committee E9 material.)

Note that the strain amplitude can be divided into elastic and plastic parts as

$$\varepsilon_a = \varepsilon_{ea} + \varepsilon_{pa} \qquad (14.2)$$

where the elastic strain amplitude is related to the stress amplitude by $\varepsilon_{ea} = \sigma_a/E$. The plastic strain amplitude ε_{pa} is a measure of the half-width of the stress–strain hysteresis loop. In addition to the total strain ε_a, it is also useful to plot the elastic strain ε_{ea} and the plastic strain ε_{pa} separately versus life N_f. Thus, for each test, three points are plotted, as shown by the vertical dashed line in Fig. 14.4.

If data from several tests are plotted, the elastic strains often give a straight line of shallow slope on a log–log plot, and the plastic strains give a straight line of steeper slope. Equations can then be fitted to these lines.

$$\varepsilon_{ea} = \frac{\sigma_a}{E} = \frac{\sigma_f'}{E}(2N_f)^b, \qquad \varepsilon_{pa} = \varepsilon_f'(2N_f)^c \qquad \text{(a, b)} \qquad (14.3)$$

In these equations, b and c are slopes on the log–log plot, assuming, of course, that the decades on the logarithmic scales in the two directions are equal in length. The intercept constants σ_f'/E and ε_f'

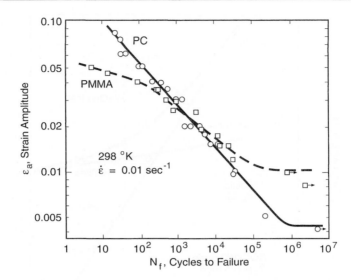

Figure 14.5 Strain–life curves for polycarbonate and polymethyl methacrylate. The shallow slope for PMMA at short lives is associated with crazing. (Data from [Beardmore 75].)

are, by convention, evaluated at $N_f = 0.5$ and so require use of the quantity $(2N_f)$ in the equations. The four constants needed are illustrated in Fig. 14.3.

Combining Eqs. 14.2 and 14.3 gives a relationship between the total strain amplitude ε_a and life:

$$\varepsilon_a = \frac{\sigma_f'}{E}(2N_f)^b + \varepsilon_f'(2N_f)^c \tag{14.4}$$

The quantities σ_f', b, ε_f', and c are considered to be material properties. This equation corresponds to the curves labeled *total* in Figs. 14.3 and 14.4. To obtain N_f for a given value of ε_a, the mathematical form of this equation requires either a graphical or numerical solution. An equation of this form is generally called the Coffin–Manson relationship, which name arises from the separate development of related equations in the late 1950s by both L. F. Coffin and S. S. Manson.

Note that Eq. 14.3(a) provides the stress–life relationship previously presented as Eq. 9.7:

$$\sigma_a = \sigma_f'(2N_f)^b \tag{14.5}$$

Hence, if data over a wide range of lives are used to evaluate the strain–life constants, Eq. 14.4 includes a stress–life curve as its limiting case for small plastic strains. Equations 14.4 and 14.5 can thus be used up to quite long lives, at which point the slope b generally decreases, apparently approaching zero for materials with a distinct fatigue limit. (See Chapter 9.)

Strain–life data are available for a variety of engineering metals, as are values of the constants for the strain–life and cyclic stress–strain curves. Published collections of such information are

Table 14.1   Cyclic Stress–Strain and Strain–Life Constants for Selected Engineering Metals.[1]

Material	Source	Tensile Properties				Cyclic σ-ε Curve			Strain–Life Curve			
		σ_o	σ_u	$\tilde{\sigma}_{fB}$	% RA	E	H'	n'	σ'_f	b	ε'_f	c
(a) Steels												
SAE 1015	(8)	228	415	726	68	207,000	1349	0.282	1020	−0.138	0.439	−0.513
(normalized)		(33.0)	(60.2)	(105)		(30,000)	(196)		(148)			
Man-Ten[2]	(7)	322	557	990	67	203,000	1096	0.187	1089	−0.115	0.912	−0.606
(hot rolled)		(46.7)	(80.8)	(144)		(29,500)	(159)		(158)			
RQC-100	(2)	683	758	1186	64	200,000	903	0.0905	938	−0.0648	1.38	−0.704
(roller Q & T)		(99.0)	(110)	(172)		(29,000)	(131)		(136)			
SAE 1045	(6)	382	621	985	51	202,000	1258	0.208	948	−0.092	0.260	−0.445
(HR & norm.)		(55.4)	(90.1)	(143)		(29,400)	(182)		(137)			
SAE 4142	(1)	1619	2450	2580	6	200,000	2810	0.040	2550	−0.0778	0.0032	−0.436
(As Q, 670 HB)		(235)	(355)	(375)		(29,000)	(407)		(370)			
SAE 4142	(1)	1688	2240	2650	27	207,000	4140	0.126	3410	−0.121	0.0732	−0.805
(Q & T, 560 HB)		(245)	(325)	(385)		(30,000)	(600)		(494)			
SAE 4142	(1)	1584	1757	1998	42	207,000	2080	0.093	1937	−0.0762	0.706	−0.869
(Q & T, 450 HB)		(230)	(255)	(290)		(30,000)	(302)		(281)			
SAE 4142	(1)	1378	1413	1826	48	207,000	2210	0.133	2140	−0.0944	0.637	−0.761
(Q & T, 380 HB)		(200)	(205)	(265)		(30,000)	(321)		(311)			
AISI 4340[2]	(3)	1103	1172	1634	56	207,000	1655	0.131	1758	−0.0977	2.12	−0.774
(Aircraft Qual.)		(160)	(170)	(237)		(30,000)	(240)		(255)			
AISI 4340	(1)	1371	1468	1557	38	200,000	1910	0.123	1879	−0.0859	0.640	−0.636
(409 HB)		(199)	(213)	(226)		(29,000)	(277)		(273)			
Ausformed H-11	(1)	2030	2580	3170	33	207,000	3475	0.059	3810	−0.0928	0.0743	−0.7144
(660 HB)		(295)	(375)	(460)		(30,000)	(504)		(553)			
(b) Other Metals												
2024-T351 Al	(1)	379	469	558	25	73,100	662	0.070	927	−0.113	0.409	−0.713
		(55.0)	(68.0)	(81.0)		(10,600)	(96.0)		(134)			
2024-T4 Al[3]	(4)	303	476	631	35	73,100	738	0.080	1294	−0.142	0.327	−0.645
(Prestrained)		(44.0)	(69.0)	(91.5)		(10,600)	(107)		(188)			
7075-T6 Al	(5)	469	578	744	33	71,000	977	0.106	1466	−0.143	0.262	−0.619
		(68.0)	(84)	(108)		(10,300)	(142)		(213)			
Ti-6Al-4V	(1)	1185	1233	1717	41	117,000	1772	0.106	2030	−0.104	0.841	−0.688
(soln. tr. & age)		(172)	(179)	(249)		(17,000)	(257)		(295)			
Inconel X	(1)	703	1213	1309	20	214,000	1855	0.120	2255	−0.117	1.16	−0.749
(Ni base, annl.)		(102)	(176)	(190)		(31,000)	(269)		(327)			

Notes: [1]The tabulated values either have units of MPa (ksi), or they are dimensionless. [2]Test specimens prestrained, except at short lives, also periodically overstrained at long lives. [3]For nonprestrained tests, use same constants, except $\sigma'_f = 900(131)$ and $b = -0.102$.

Sources: Data in (1) [Conle 84]; (2) author's data on the ASTM Committee E9 material; (3) [Dowling 73]; (4) [Dowling 89] and [Topper 70]; (5) [Endo 69] and [Raske 72]; (6) [Leese 85]; (7) [Wetzel 77] pp. 41 and 66; (8) [Keshavan 67] and [Smith 70].

referenced at the end of this chapter, and values of the constants for some representative metals are given in Table 14.1. Strain–life data are also available for some polymers, curves for two ductile polymers being shown in Fig. 14.5. Note that forms different than Eq. 14.4 would be needed to fit these data.

Example 14.1

Data are given in Table E14.1 for completely reversed strain-controlled fatigue tests on RQC-100 steel. The elastic modulus is $E = 200$ GPa, and σ_a and ε_{pa} are measured near $N_f/2$. Determine constants for the strain–life curve.

Solution   Two least-squares fits are needed to obtain the constants σ_f', b, ε_f', and c, one for Eq. 14.5 and one for Eq. 14.3(b). Both fits proceed in a manner similar to Ex. 9.1(b). For the first, solve Eq. 14.5 for the dependent variable $2N_f$, and take logarithms of both sides:

$$2N_f = \left(\frac{\sigma_a}{\sigma_f'}\right)^{1/b}, \qquad \log(2N_f) = \frac{1}{b}\log\sigma_a - \frac{1}{b}\log\sigma_f'$$

This has the form $y = mx + d$, where

$$y = \log(2N_f), \qquad x = \log\sigma_a, \qquad m = \frac{1}{b}, \qquad d = -\frac{1}{b}\log\sigma_f'$$

Performing a linear least-squares fit on this basis gives

$$m = -17.096, \qquad d = 50.513$$

so that the needed constants are

$$b = \frac{1}{m} = -0.0585, \qquad \sigma_f' = 10^{-db} = 901 \text{ MPa} \qquad\qquad \textbf{Ans.}$$

Table E14.1

ε_a	σ_a, MPa	ε_{pa}	N_f, cycles
0.0202	631	0.01695	227
0.0100	574	0.00705	1 030
0.0045	505	0.00193	6 450
0.0030	472	0.00064	22 250
0.0023	455	(0.00010)	110 000

Source: The author's data on the ASTM
Committee E9 material.

To obtain the remaining two constants, proceed similarly, solving Eq. 14.3(b) for $2N_f$ and taking logarithms of both sides to obtain the form $y = mx + d$:

$$2N_f = \left(\frac{\varepsilon_{pa}}{\varepsilon_f'}\right)^{1/c}, \qquad \log(2N_f) = \frac{1}{c}\log \varepsilon_{pa} - \frac{1}{c}\log \varepsilon_f'$$

$$y = \log(2N_f), \qquad x = \log \varepsilon_{pa}, \qquad m = \frac{1}{c}, \qquad d = -\frac{1}{c}\log \varepsilon_f'$$

However, the last ε_{pa} value, shown in parentheses in Table E14.1, is judged to be so small that its accuracy of measurement is likely to be poor. Moreover, this point does not lie along the linear trend of the other ε_{pa} vs. N_f data on a plot similar to Fig. 14.4. Hence, the fit is done with only the first four ε_{pa} values, giving

$$m = -1.3456, \qquad d = 0.39690$$

$$c = \frac{1}{m} = -0.743, \qquad \varepsilon_f' = 10^{-dc} = 1.972 \qquad\qquad \textbf{Ans.}$$

Employing $E = 200{,}000\,\text{MPa}$ as given, the strain–life curve of the form of Eq. 14.4 can finally be written:

$$\varepsilon_a = 0.004505\,(2N_f)^{-0.0585} + 1.972\,(2N_f)^{-0.743}$$

Comments   The constants obtained differ somewhat from those in Fig. 14.4 due to the use of an abbreviated set of data. The given σ_a and ε_{pa} data may also be employed to fit the cyclic stress–strain curve, with the procedure being the same as in Ex. 12.1, except for the use of amplitude quantities. Again excluding the last point, the results are $H' = 900\,\text{MPa}$, $n' = 0.0896$.

14.2.2 Comments on Strain–Life Equations and Curves

At long lives, the first (elastic strain) term of Eq. 14.4 is dominant, as the plastic strains are relatively small, and the curve approaches the elastic strain line. This corresponds to a thin hysteresis loop, as shown in Fig. 14.3. Conversely, at short lives, the plastic strains are large compared with the elastic strains, the curve approaches the plastic strain line, and the hysteresis loops are fat. At intermediate lives, near the crossing point of the elastic and plastic strain lines, the two types of strain are of similar magnitude. The crossing point is identified as the *transition fatigue life*, N_t. An equation relating N_t to the other constants can be obtained by using the substitution $\varepsilon_{ea} = \varepsilon_{pa}$ to combine Eqs. 14.3(a) and (b), which gives

$$N_t = \frac{1}{2}\left(\frac{\sigma_f'}{\varepsilon_f' E}\right)^{1/(c-b)} \tag{14.6}$$

For a given material, the transition fatigue life N_t locates a boundary between fatigue behavior involving substantial plasticity and behavior involving little plasticity. The value of N_t is thus the most logical point for separating low-cycle and high-cycle fatigue. Special analysis of plasticity effects by the strain-based approach may be needed if lives around or less than N_t are of interest. Conversely, the S-N approach, which is based primarily on elastic analysis, may suffice at lives longer than N_t.

From Eqs. 12.11 and 12.12, the plastic strain term of the cyclic stress–strain curve gives

$$\sigma_a = H' \varepsilon_{pa}^{n'} \tag{14.7}$$

If N_f is eliminated between Eqs. 14.3(b) and 14.5 and the result compared with this equation, the constants for the strain–life curve can be related to those for the cyclic stress–strain curve:

$$n' = \frac{b}{c}, \qquad H' = \frac{\sigma_f'}{(\varepsilon_f')^{b/c}} \tag{14.8}$$

Thus, of the six constants H', n', σ_f', b, ε_f', and c, only four are independent. However, it is common practice to make three separate fits of data, using Eqs. 14.3(b), 14.5, and 14.7, so that the preceding relationships among the constants are satisfied only approximately. In other words, reported values for the six constants may not be exactly mutually consistent as implied by Eq. 14.8.

In a few cases, there may be fairly large inconsistencies among the six constants. This arises in situations where the data do not fit the assumed mathematical forms very well. In particular, data points of σ_a versus N_f or ε_{pa} versus N_f may depart somewhat from log–log straight lines. In such cases, it should be ensured that the strain–life constants σ_f', b, ε_f', and c used for Eq. 14.4 still give a reasonable representation of the total strain data, ε_a versus N_f. Also, the H' and n' values used should be the ones actually fitted to the σ_a versus ε_{pa} data, not values calculated from Eq. 14.8.

For ductile materials at very short lives, the strain may be sufficiently large that true stresses and strains, as defined in Section 4.5, differ significantly from the more usual engineering values. In such cases, σ_a, ε_{pa}, and ε_a in the preceding equations should be replaced by true stress and strain values, $\tilde{\sigma}_a$, $\tilde{\varepsilon}_{pa}$, $\tilde{\varepsilon}_a$. If this is done, these equations often give a reasonable representation of fatigue data over a wide range that includes very short lives. Also, if a tension test is interpreted as a fatigue test where failure occurs at $N_f = 0.5$ cycles, then the intercept constants σ_f' and ε_f' should be the same as the true fracture stress and strain from a tension test, $\tilde{\sigma}_f$ and $\tilde{\varepsilon}_f$. Although values of σ_f' and ε_f' are best obtained from fitting actual fatigue data, there is often reasonable agreement with $\tilde{\sigma}_f$ and $\tilde{\varepsilon}_f$. Note that the convenience of such a direct comparison explains why σ_f' and ε_f' are defined as intercepts at $N_f = 0.5$.

14.2.3 Trends for Engineering Metals

The large amount of data available for engineering metals permits some generalizations and trends to be stated concerning strain–life curves for this class of materials. Details follow.

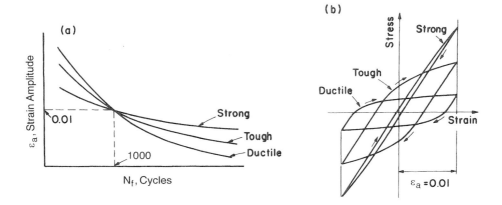

Figure 14.6 Trends in strain–life curves for strong, tough, and ductile metals. (Adapted from [Landgraf 70]; copyright © ASTM; reprinted with permission.)

As just explained, the intercept constants for the strain–life curve are expected to be similar to the true fracture stress and strain from a tension test:

$$\sigma_f' \approx \tilde{\sigma}_f, \qquad \varepsilon_f' \approx \tilde{\varepsilon}_f \qquad\qquad (14.9)$$

A ductile metal has a high value of $\tilde{\varepsilon}_f$ and a low value of $\tilde{\sigma}_f$. Hence, the plastic strain line, as in Fig. 14.3, tends to be high, and the elastic strain line low. This results in a steep strain–life curve, as illustrated in Fig. 14.6. Also, the transition fatigue life N_t will be relatively long. The opposite trend generally occurs for a strong but relatively brittle metal, for which a high $\tilde{\sigma}_f$ and a low $\tilde{\varepsilon}_f$ correspond to a flatter strain–life curve and a relatively low value of N_t. A *tough* material, which has intermediate values of both $\tilde{\sigma}_f$ and $\tilde{\varepsilon}_f$, tends to have a strain–life curve and N_t value between the two extremes. It is noteworthy that the strain–life curves for a wide variety of engineering metals tend to all pass near the strain $\varepsilon_a = 0.01$ for a life of $N_f = 1000$ cycles.

Strain–life curves for various steels that exhibit the trends just discussed are shown in Fig. 14.7. The variation of N_t with mechanical properties is illustrated by plotting its value versus hardness for various steels in Fig. 14.8. Hardness, of course, varies inversely with ductility, so that N_t decreases as hardness is increased.

Some generalizations may also be made concerning the strain–life slope constants b and c. Values around $c = -0.6$ are common, and the relatively narrow range of $c = -0.5$ to -0.8 appears to include most engineering metals. A typical value of the elastic strain slope is $b = -0.085$. Relatively steep elastic slopes, around $b = -0.12$, are common for soft metals, such as annealed metals; shallow slopes, nearer $b = -0.05$, are common for highly hardened metals. This trend contributes to the overall trend already noted of steep versus shallow strain–life curves for ductile versus brittle metals, respectively.

For steels with ultimate tensile strengths below about $\sigma_u = 1400$ MPa, recall from Section 9.6.1 that a fatigue limit occurs near 10^6 cycles at a stress amplitude around $\sigma_a = \sigma_u/2$. This establishes

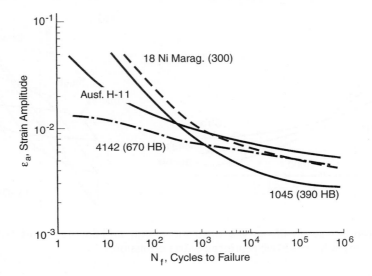

Figure 14.7 Strain–life curves for four representative hardened steels. (Adapted from [Landgraf 68]; used with permission.)

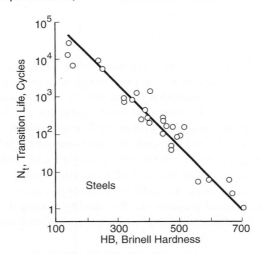

Figure 14.8 Transition fatigue life versus hardness for a wide range of steels. (Adapted from [Landgraf 70]; copyright © ASTM; reprinted with permission.)

one point that must satisfy the stress–life relationship, Eq. 14.5. If the estimate $\sigma'_f \approx \tilde{\sigma}_f$ is also applied, Eq. 14.5 gives

$$b = -\frac{1}{6.3} \log \frac{2\tilde{\sigma}_f}{\sigma_u} \tag{14.10}$$

In other cases, where the fatigue limit (or long-life fatigue strength) at N_e cycles is given by $\sigma_a = m_e \sigma_u$, the estimate becomes

$$b = -\frac{\log \dfrac{\tilde{\sigma}_f}{m_e \sigma_u}}{\log (2N_e)} \tag{14.11}$$

where some approximate m_e and N_e values for various classes of engineering metals are given in Table 10.1. Higher ratios $\tilde{\sigma}_f / \sigma_u$ apply for more ductile metals, so that Eqs. 14.10 and 14.11 are consistent with the aforementioned trends noted for b.

14.2.4 Factors Affecting Strain–Life Curves; Surface Finish and Size

If a hostile chemical environment or elevated temperature is present, smaller numbers of cycles to failure are expected, especially for lower frequencies where the environment has more time to act. At temperatures exceeding about half of the absolute melting temperature of a given material, nonlinear deformations due to time-dependent creep–relaxation behavior generally become significant. Strain–life and cyclic stress–strain curves then become dependent on test frequency. Hence, such effects will occur at a sufficiently elevated temperature for any structural engineering metal, and they occur at room temperature for low-melting-temperature metals, such as lead and tin, and also for most polymers. Analysis of creep–relaxation and its effect on life, where this occurs in combination with cyclic loading, involves the problem area called *creep–fatigue interaction*. Some additional comments on this topic are given in Chapter 15.

In contrast to S-N curves at long lives, strain–life curves at relatively short lives are not highly sensitive to such factors as surface finish and residual stress. Residual stresses that are initially present are quickly removed by cycle-dependent relaxation if cyclic plastic strains are present, and so these have only limited effect at lives around and below N_t. Surface finish is important in high-cycle fatigue, because most of the life at the low stresses involved is spent initiating a crack. However, if significant plastic strains are present, a small crack (or cracklike damage) starts relatively early in the life, even if the surface is smooth. Most of the life is thus spent in growing small cracks into the material at some depth, where the surface finish cannot have an effect. The importance of crack growth effects at relatively short lives was previously illustrated by Fig. 9.19, and it is further illustrated by strain–life data in Fig. 14.9.

A reasonable method of modifying the strain–life curve to include the effect of surface finish is to change only the elastic slope b. This can be done by lowering the stress–life curve at the number of cycles N_e usually associated with the fatigue limit, such as $N_e = 10^6$ cycles for steel, while leaving σ_f' unchanged. In particular, the stress amplitude at $N_f = N_e$, which is $\sigma_e = \sigma_f'(2N_e)^b$, is replaced by $m_s \sigma_e$ to obtain the new slope. Here, m_s is a surface effect factor, as in Chapter 10. This gives a new slope constant b_s that replaces the original b in making life estimates:

$$b_s = -\frac{\log \dfrac{\sigma_f'}{m_s \sigma_e}}{\log (2N_e)} = b + \frac{\log m_s}{\log (2N_e)} \tag{14.12}$$

Here, substitution for σ_e leads to the second form.

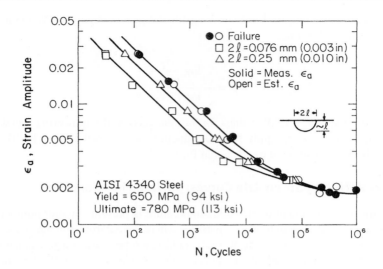

Figure 14.9 Strain–life curves for failure, and for two specific crack sizes, in an alloy steel. (Adapted from [Dowling 79a]; used with permission.)

Size effects, as discussed in Chapter 10, are also a concern in applying a strain-based approach to large-size members, but experimental data are limited. In one study of shafts up to 250 mm in diameter that included data on low-carbon and low-alloy (turbine-generator rotor) steels, the size reduction factor was found to vary with shaft diameter, d, as

$$m_d = \left(\frac{d}{25.4\,\text{mm}} \right)^{-0.093} \tag{14.13}$$

where d is interpreted as the minimum diameter for shafts containing fillet radii or circumferential grooves. Further, the study suggested lowering the entire strain–life curve by this factor, so that the intercept constants σ_f' and ε_f' are replaced by reduced values and σ_{fd}' and ε_{fd}':

$$\sigma_{fd}' = m_d \sigma_f', \qquad \varepsilon_{fd}' = m_d \varepsilon_f' \tag{14.14}$$

The slope constants b and c are not altered. (Equations 14.13 and 14.14 are based on [Placek 84].)

Adjusted values of materials constants from Eq. 14.12 or 14.14 should in no case be used with Eq. 14.8 to obtain H' and n' for the cyclic stress–strain curve. As already noted, H' and n' should always be based on fitting stress–strain data.

14.3 MEAN STRESS EFFECTS

Mean stress effects, as discussed in Chapters 9 and 10, need to be evaluated in applying the strain-based approach. In particular, the strain–life curve for completely reversed loading needs to be modified if a mean stress is present. It is useful to think of a family of strain–life curves, where the

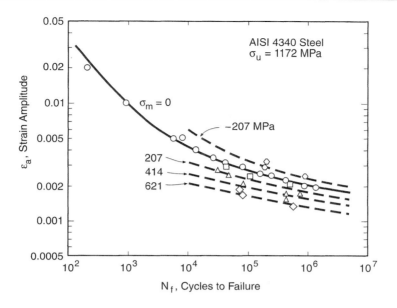

Figure 14.10 Mean stress effect on the strain–life curve of an alloy steel, with dashed curves from the mean stress equation of Morrow. Most test specimens were overstrained prior to testing, and most with $N_f > 10^5$ cycles were also periodically overstrained. (Data from [Dowling 73].)

particular one to be used depends on the mean stress. Test data illustrating this situation for an alloy steel are shown in Fig. 14.10.

14.3.1 Mean Stress Tests

For a cyclic strain test conducted with a nonzero mean strain, cycle-dependent relaxation of the mean stress is likely, as described in Chapter 12 and illustrated by Fig. 12.25. If the plastic strain amplitude is not large, some of the mean stress will remain. The life will then be affected by this mean stress. Other than this influence of an accompanying mean stress, there is little effect on fatigue life of mean strain itself, unless the value is so large that it is a significant fraction of the tensile ductility.

Alternatively, controlled stress tests can be run. In this case, there can be no relaxation of the mean stress, but cycle-dependent creep can occur. Large amounts of this type of deformation may accumulate and result in a failure similar to that from a tension test. However, the situation of primary interest here is plasticity in localized regions, in which large cyclic creep deformations are generally prevented by the stiffness of the surrounding elastic material. Hence, results from controlled stress tests are of present interest only if the failure is not dominated by cycle-dependent creep.

Regardless of the test procedure used, data can be obtained for evaluating the effect of mean stress on life. Discussion follows of various alternative methods of quantifying this mean stress effect in the context of strain–life curves.

14.3.2 Including Mean Stress Effects in Strain–Life Equations

As was done in Chapter 9, let us define the special case of stress amplitude where the mean stress is zero as σ_{ar}. Since the fitting constants σ'_f and b for Eq. 14.5 are obtained from tests with zero mean stress, this relationship should be stated for cases of nonzero mean stress as Eq. 9.22, which is repeated here:

$$\sigma_{ar} = \sigma'_f (2N_f)^b \tag{14.15}$$

To obtain the estimated fatigue life N_f, an additional equation is needed to calculate σ_{ar} for the mean stress situation of interest.

$$\sigma_{ar} = f(\sigma_a, \sigma_m) \tag{14.16}$$

In this context, σ_{ar} can be thought of as an *equivalent completely reversed stress amplitude*. Some of the more widely applied mean stress methods, which may be expressed as particular equations $\sigma_{ar} = f(\sigma_a, \sigma_m)$, are given as Eqs. 9.15 to 9.19.

To include mean stress effects in the strain–life relationship, first combine Eqs. 14.15 and 14.16 as follows:

$$\sigma_{ar} = f(\sigma_a, \sigma_m) = \sigma_a \frac{f(\sigma_a, \sigma_m)}{\sigma_a} = \sigma'_f (2N_f)^b \tag{14.17}$$

Then solve for the stress amplitude σ_a that is in the numerator after the second equals sign, and manipulate the remaining stress quantities to be within brackets with N_f, allowing us to define a *zero-mean-stress-equivalent life, N^**.

$$\sigma_a = \sigma'_f \left[2N_f \left(\frac{\sigma_a}{f(\sigma_a, \sigma_m)} \right)^{1/b} \right]^b = \sigma'_f (2N^*)^b \qquad \text{(a)}$$

$$\text{where } N^* = N_f \left(\frac{\sigma_a}{f(\sigma_a, \sigma_m)} \right)^{1/b} \qquad \text{(b)} \tag{14.18}$$

Hence, one can determine the life N^* that is expected for a given stress amplitude σ_a under zero mean stress, and then solve Eq. 14.18(b) to obtain the life N_f as affected by a nonzero mean stress.

$$N_f = N^* \left(\frac{\sigma_a}{f(\sigma_a, \sigma_m)} \right)^{-1/b} \tag{14.19}$$

The effect on life should be the same regardless of whether one employs a stress–life or a strain–life curve. This permits Eq. 14.4 to be generalized to

$$\varepsilon_a = \frac{\sigma'_f}{E} (2N^*)^b + \varepsilon'_f (2N^*)^c \tag{14.20}$$

Here, N^* is the life calculated from the strain amplitude ε_a as if the mean stress were zero, and then N_f as affected by the nonzero mean stress is obtained from Eq. 14.19. Also, on a strain–life plot, data plotted as ε_a versus the equivalent life N^* are expected to all fall together along the curve for zero mean stress, Eq. 14.4. This is demonstrated in Fig. 14.11 for the same set of steel data as in Fig. 14.10, where the particular $f(\sigma_a, \sigma_m)$ is in this case based on the Morrow mean stress expression of Eq. 9.17(b).

As noted in Section 9.7.3, the Goodman and the Gerber mean stress relationships are less accurate than the Morrow, SWT, and Walker methods. As a result of the general recognition of this situation, only the latter three are commonly applied to strain–life curves.

14.3.3 Mean Stress Equation of Morrow

The approach suggested by J. Morrow can be expressed as an equation giving the equivalent completely reversed stress amplitude, σ_{ar}, which is expected to produce the same life as a given combination of amplitude σ_a and mean σ_m:

$$\sigma_{ar} = \frac{\sigma_a}{1 - \dfrac{\sigma_m}{\sigma'_f}} \tag{14.21}$$

Here, the constant σ'_f is the same as for the stress–life curve. This expression arises from Eq. 9.17(b) and was previously introduced as Eq. 9.21. Substituting this particular σ_{ar} into Eqs. 14.18(b) and 14.19, we obtain

$$N^*_{mi} = N_f \left(1 - \frac{\sigma_m}{\sigma'_f}\right)^{1/b} \tag{14.22}$$

$$N_f = N^*_{mi} \left(1 - \frac{\sigma_m}{\sigma'_f}\right)^{-1/b} \tag{14.23}$$

Subscripts mi have been added to N^* to indicate the particular case of the *Morrow* mean stress equation using the stress–life *intercept* constant σ'_f.

Substituting N^*_{mi} into Eq. 14.20 gives a single equation for a family of strain–life curves:

$$\varepsilon_a = \frac{\sigma'_f}{E}\left(1 - \frac{\sigma_m}{\sigma'_f}\right)(2N_f)^b + \varepsilon'_f \left(1 - \frac{\sigma_m}{\sigma'_f}\right)^{c/b}(2N_f)^c \tag{14.24}$$

This expression is similar to the original strain–life equation, except that the intercept constants are, in effect, modified for any particular nonzero value of mean stress. It was used to plot the family of curves shown in Fig. 14.10. Also, plotting the data of Fig. 14.10 versus N^*_{mi} from Eq. 14.22 consolidates the data along the curve for $\sigma_m = 0$ as seen in Fig. 14.11. The success of the Morrow equation for this set of data is quite good, as judged by the agreement of the data points for nonzero mean stress with the curve.

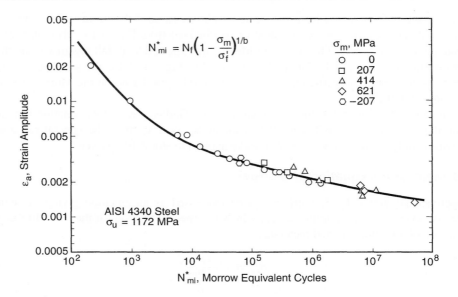

Figure 14.11   Mean stress data of Fig. 14.10 plotted versus N^* according to the Morrow equation.

As noted in Section 9.7.3, the Morrow mean stress expression of Eq. 9.17(a) employing the true fracture strength $\tilde{\sigma}_{fB}$ is sometimes useful, especially for aluminum alloys where the σ'_f form gives poor results. In this case, the σ_{ar} and N^* expressions that apply are

$$\sigma_{ar} = \frac{\sigma_a}{1 - \dfrac{\sigma_m}{\tilde{\sigma}_{fB}}} \tag{14.25}$$

$$N^*_{mf} = N_f \left(1 - \frac{\sigma_m}{\tilde{\sigma}_{fB}}\right)^{1/b} \tag{14.26}$$

Subscripts *mf* are added to N^* to specify the *Morrow* equation based on the true *fracture* strength.

14.3.4 Modified Morrow Approach

The following modification of Eq. 14.24 is often used:

$$\varepsilon_a = \frac{\sigma'_f}{E} \left(1 - \frac{\sigma_m}{\sigma'_f}\right) (2N_f)^b + \varepsilon'_f (2N_f)^c \tag{14.27}$$

The first (elastic strain) term is the same, but the mean stress dependence has been removed from the second (plastic strain) term. This has the effect of reducing the estimated effect of mean stress at relatively short lives.

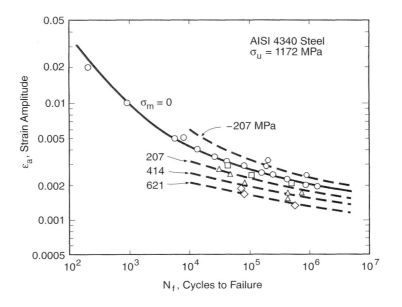

Figure 14.12 Family of strain–life curves given by the modified Morrow approach, and comparison with the data of Fig. 14.10.

Members of the family of strain–life curves corresponding to Eq. 14.27 are compared with the alloy steel test data of Fig. 14.10 in Fig. 14.12. The trend of a smaller predicted effect of mean stress at relatively short lives is evident from comparison with Fig. 14.10. Nevertheless, the agreement with the test data is still reasonable. Equation 14.27 does not lend itself to any graphical presentation other than plotting several members of the family of curves.

14.3.5 Smith, Watson, and Topper (SWT) Parameter

The SWT method was previously introduced, in the context of stress–life curves, as Eq. 9.18. An analogous application to strain–life curves, which reduces to Eq. 9.18 if the plastic strains are small, is often employed. Specifically, this approach assumes that the life for any situation of mean stress depends on the product

$$\sigma_{\max}\varepsilon_a = h''(N_f) \tag{14.28}$$

By definition, $\sigma_{\max} = \sigma_m + \sigma_a$, and $h''(N_f)$ indicates a function of fatigue life N_f. Hence, the life is expected to be the same as for completely reversed ($\sigma_m = 0$) loading where this product has the same value.

Let σ_{ar} and ε_{ar} be the completely reversed stress and strain amplitudes that result in the same life N_f as the ($\sigma_{\max}, \varepsilon_a$) combination. Noting that, for $\sigma_m = 0$, we have $\sigma_{\max} = \sigma_{ar}$, we find that the function of life $h''(N_f)$ becomes $\sigma_{\max}\varepsilon_a = \sigma_{ar}\varepsilon_{ar}$. If the stress–life and strain–life curves for

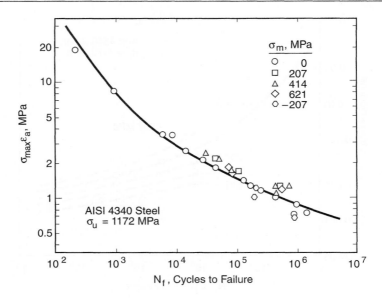

Figure 14.13 Plot of the Smith, Watson, and Topper parameter versus life for the data of Fig. 14.10.

completely reversed loading are given by Eqs. 14.5 and 14.4, the function $h''(N_f)$ can be obtained by substituting these equations for σ_{ar} and ε_{ar} to produce

$$\sigma_{\max}\varepsilon_a = \sigma'_f(2N_f)^b \left[\frac{\sigma'_f}{E}(2N_f)^b + \varepsilon'_f(2N_f)^c \right] \tag{14.29}$$

which can be rearranged to obtain

$$\sigma_{\max}\varepsilon_a = \frac{\left(\sigma'_f\right)^2}{E}(2N_f)^{2b} + \sigma'_f\varepsilon'_f(2N_f)^{b+c} \tag{14.30}$$

A convenient graphical presentation is to make a plot of the quantity $\sigma_{\max}\varepsilon_a$ versus N_f by using Eq. 14.30, which requires only the constants from $\sigma_m = 0$ test data. Then, for any situation involving a nonzero mean stress, enter this plot with the value of the product $\sigma_{\max}\varepsilon_a$ to obtain N_f. Such a plot for the alloy steel of Fig. 14.10 is shown in Fig. 14.13. The success of the SWT parameter for this particular case can be judged by the extent to which the data for nonzero mean stress agree with the curve. The agreement is reasonable, but not as good as for the Morrow equation in Fig. 14.11.

14.3.6 Walker Mean Stress Equation

Recall the two equivalent forms of the Walker mean stress relationship previously presented as Eq. 9.19.

$$\sigma_{ar} = \sigma_{\max}^{1-\gamma}\sigma_a^{\gamma}, \quad \sigma_{ar} = \sigma_{\max}\left(\frac{1-R}{2}\right)^{\gamma} \qquad \text{(a, b)} \qquad (14.31)$$

where either of these can be derived from the other by noting the definition $R = \sigma_{\min}/\sigma_{\max}$. Substituting each of these in turn into Eq. 14.18(b) gives corresponding alternate expressions for N^*, denoted N_w^*.

$$N_w^* = N_f \left(\frac{\sigma_a}{\sigma_{\max}}\right)^{(1-\gamma)/b} \qquad N_w^* = N_f \left(\frac{1-R}{2}\right)^{(1-\gamma)/b}, \qquad \text{(a, b)} \qquad (14.32)$$

Substituting N_w^* into Eq. 14.20 gives a family of strain–life curves; the one for form (b) is

$$\varepsilon_a = \frac{\sigma_f'}{E}\left(\frac{1-R}{2}\right)^{(1-\gamma)}(2N_f)^b + \varepsilon_f'\left(\frac{1-R}{2}\right)^{c(1-\gamma)/b}(2N_f)^c \qquad (14.33)$$

Note that employing $\gamma = 0.5$ in this equation corresponds to the stress-based SWT relationship, Eq. 9.18, but this is not the same as the usual application of the SWT relationship of Eq. 14.30.

Plotting ε_a versus N_w^* is of course expected to consolidate strain–life data at various mean stresses all onto a single curve, as for the analogous plot based on N_{mi}^* of Fig. 14.11. Such comparisons for a number of steels, aluminum alloys, and one titanium alloy gave excellent results as reported in the recent study of Dowling (2009).

Applying the Walker method of course requires a value of γ. Recall that γ for steels can be estimated from Eq. 9.20. Where data at various mean stresses are available, the procedure of Section 10.6.4 can be applied to all of the data, in a single fitting procedure, to obtain values of σ_f', b, and γ. Corresponding ε_f' and c are then obtained by fitting N_w^* and plastic strain amplitudes, ε_{pa}, as described in Dowling (2009).

14.3.7 Discussion

The unmodified Morrow method works quite well for steels, but it is often inaccurate for aluminum alloys. The latter difficulty is associated with the fact that the fitted stress–life constant σ_f' is typically considerably larger than the true fracture strength $\tilde{\sigma}_{fB}$, as a result of the stress–life data not fitting the form of Eq. 14.5 very well. In such cases, better agreement with test data is obtained by employing N^* from Eq. 14.26 with Eq. 14.20.

One justification for using the modified Morrow approach is that the resulting reduced effect of σ_m at short lives may offset a bias in estimated life that arises from neglecting the transient relaxation of mean stress in notched members. The SWT equation gives acceptable results for a wide range of materials. It is generally as accurate for steels as the Morrow approach, and it is quite good for aluminum alloys.

In general, if a single method is desired, the SWT life relationship, Eq. 14.30, can be chosen. The Morrow approach is a good choice for steels. But it should not be used for aluminum alloys, or for other metals where σ_f' and $\tilde{\sigma}_{fB}$ differ by a large amount, unless N^* is obtained from Eq. 14.26. Where γ is known or can be estimated, the Walker relationship is likely to be the most accurate of all of the possibilities discussed.

Example 14.2

The RQC-100 steel of Table 14.1 is subjected to cycling with a strain amplitude of $\varepsilon_a = 0.004$ and a tensile mean stress of $\sigma_m = 100\,\text{MPa}$. How many cycles can be applied before fatigue cracking is expected?

First Solution   Of the various methods given, we will first apply the Morrow equation. Substituting the constants E, σ_f', b, ε_f', and c from Table 14.1 for RQC-100 steel into Eq. 14.20, we have

$$\varepsilon_a = \frac{938}{200,000}(2N^*)^{-0.0648} + 1.38(2N^*)^{-0.704}$$

Using the given $\varepsilon_a = 0.004$ and solving numerically for N^* gives

$$N^* = 8124 \text{ cycles}$$

Since N^* does not include the effect of mean stress, its value must be employed along with $\sigma_m = 100\,\text{MPa}$ to obtain an N_f value that does include this effect. Hence, we apply N^* in Eq. 14.23, specifically as N_{mi}^*.

$$N_f = N_{mi}^*\left(1 - \frac{\sigma_m}{\sigma_f'}\right)^{-1/b} = 8124\left(1 - \frac{100}{938}\right)^{1/0.0648} = 1426 \text{ cycles} \qquad \textbf{Ans.}$$

Second Solution   To apply the modified Morrow approach, simply substitute the same material constants into Eq. 14.27:

$$\varepsilon_a = \frac{938}{200,000}\left(1 - \frac{\sigma_m}{938}\right)(2N_f)^{-0.0648} + 1.38(N_f)^{-0.704}$$

Substituting $\sigma_m = 100\,\text{MPa}$ and simplifying gives

$$\varepsilon_a = \frac{838}{200,000}(2N_f)^{-0.0648} + 1.38(2N_f)^{-0.704}$$

We then enter this equation with $\varepsilon_a = 0.004$ and solve numerically for N_f, obtaining

$$N_f = 6597 \text{ cycles} \qquad \textbf{Ans.}$$

Third Solution   For the SWT approach, Eq. 14.30, we need the product $\sigma_{max}\varepsilon_a$. Thus, first apply the cyclic stress–strain curve with constants from Table 14.1 to obtain σ_a:

$$\varepsilon_a = \frac{\sigma_a}{E} + \left(\frac{\sigma_a}{H'}\right)^{1/n'} = \frac{\sigma_a}{200,000} + \left(\frac{\sigma_a}{903}\right)^{1/0.0905}$$

Entering this equation with $\varepsilon_a = 0.004$ and solving numerically for σ_a gives

$$\sigma_a = 501.2\,\text{MPa}, \qquad \sigma_{\max} = \sigma_m + \sigma_a = 100 + 501.2 = 601.2\,\text{MPa}$$

$$\sigma_{\max}\varepsilon_a = 601.2(0.004) = 2.4046\,\text{MPa}$$

Next, we substitute material constants into Eq. 14.30.

$$\sigma_{\max}\varepsilon_a = \frac{(938)^2}{200,000}\left(2N_f\right)^{2(-0.0648)} + (938)(1.38)(2N_f)^{-0.0648-0.704}$$

$$\sigma_{\max}\varepsilon_a = 4.399(2N_f)^{-0.1296} + 1294\left(2N_f\right)^{-0.7688}$$

Entering this equation with $\sigma_{\max}\varepsilon_a = 2.4046\,\text{MPa}$ and solving numerically yields N_f:

$$N_f = 5088\,\text{cycles} \qquad\qquad \textbf{Ans.}$$

Fourth Solution   For the Walker method, the constant γ can be estimated for this steel from Eq. 9.20. With σ_u from Table 14.1, we obtain

$$\gamma = -0.000200\,\sigma_u + 0.8818 = -0.000200\,(758\,\text{MPa}) + 0.8818 = 0.7302$$

Then apply N^* from the first solution, but now specifically as N_w^*. Since σ_a and $\sigma_{\max}$ are available from the third solution, form (a) of Eq. 14.32 is convenient. Solving for N_f and substituting the needed values gives

$$N_f = N_w^*\left(\frac{\sigma_a}{\sigma_{\max}}\right)^{-(1-\gamma)/b} = 8124\left(\frac{501.2}{601.2}\right)^{-(1-0.7302)/(-0.0648)} = 3809\,\text{cycles} \qquad \textbf{Ans.}$$

Comment   In this example, the Morrow and modified Morrow calculations give values that differ considerably due to the relatively short life involved. The values from the SWT and Walker methods lie between the two Morrow estimates, with the Walker estimate likely being the most accurate of the four.

14.4 MULTIAXIAL STRESS EFFECTS

Fatigue under multiaxial loading where plastic deformations occur is currently an area of active research. Reasonable estimates are possible for relatively simple situations, but some uncertainty exists as to the best procedure for complex nonproportional loadings, where the ratios of the principal stresses change, and where the principal axes may also rotate. Given this situation, the discussion that follows first considers some simple, but limited methods. Then an introductory discussion is given of possible approaches for more complex loadings.

14.4.1 Effective Strain Approach

Consider situations where all cyclic loadings have the same frequency and are either in-phase or 180° out-of-phase. It is then reasonable to define an effective strain amplitude that is proportional to the cyclic amplitude of the octahedral shear strain:

$$\bar{\varepsilon}_a = \frac{\bar{\sigma}_a}{E} + \bar{\varepsilon}_{pa} \tag{14.34}$$

The quantities $\bar{\sigma}_a$ and $\bar{\varepsilon}_{pa}$ are obtained from Eqs. 12.21 and 12.22 by substituting amplitudes of the principal stresses and plastic strains. A negative sign is employed for amplitude quantities that are 180° out-of-phase with amplitudes selected as positive.

The fatigue life for multiaxial loading is postulated to depend on the value of this effective strain amplitude. For uniaxial loading, $\sigma_2 = \sigma_3 = 0$, its value reduces to the uniaxial strain amplitude, $\bar{\varepsilon}_a = \varepsilon_{1a}$. Since the latter is related to life by Eq. 14.4, we can write

$$\bar{\varepsilon}_a = \frac{\sigma'_f}{E}(2N_f)^b + \varepsilon'_f(2N_f)^c \tag{14.35}$$

where the first and second terms correspond to elastic and plastic components of the effective strain, so that

$$\bar{\sigma}_a = \sigma'_f(2N_f)^b, \qquad \bar{\varepsilon}_{pa} = \varepsilon'_f(2N_f)^c \qquad \text{(a, b)} \tag{14.36}$$

Consider the special case of plane stress, namely,

$$\sigma_{2a} = \lambda\sigma_{1a}, \qquad \sigma_{3a} = 0, \qquad \varepsilon_{1a} = \varepsilon_{e1a} + \varepsilon_{p1a} \tag{14.37}$$

where the notation of Chapter 12 is used, except for the added subscript a, to indicate amplitude quantities. Letting the (x, y, z) axes be the principal $(1, 2, 3)$ axes, we can combine Eqs. 12.19, 12.24, and 12.32 with Eqs. 14.35 to 14.37 to obtain an equation for the strain–life curve in terms of the first principal strain:

$$\varepsilon_{1a} = \frac{\dfrac{\sigma'_f}{E}(1 - \nu\lambda)(2N_f)^b + \varepsilon'_f(1 - 0.5\lambda)(2N_f)^c}{\sqrt{1 - \lambda + \lambda^2}} \tag{14.38}$$

This equation can be used along with the Ramberg–Osgood type stress–strain curve for biaxial loading, Eq. 12.39, where all stresses and strains are interpreted as amplitude quantities.

For the special state of plane stress that is pure shear, Eqs. 13.37 and 13.38 apply, and $\lambda = -1$. The preceding equation then reduces to

$$\gamma_{xya} = \frac{\sigma'_f}{\sqrt{3}G}(2N_f)^b + \sqrt{3}\varepsilon'_f(2N_f)^c \tag{14.39}$$

where γ_{xya} is the shear strain amplitude and G is the shear modulus. The corresponding Ramberg–Osgood type of stress–strain curve has already been derived as Eq. 13.39.

14.4.2 Discussion of the Effective Strain Approach

The cyclic amplitude of the hydrostatic stress appears to have an additional effect not accounted for by the octahedral shear strain. This quantity is the average of the amplitudes of the principal normal stresses:

$$\sigma_{ha} = \frac{\sigma_{1a} + \sigma_{2a} + \sigma_{3a}}{3} \tag{14.40}$$

To quantify this effect, the relative value of σ_{ha} may be expressed as a *triaxiality factor*, $T = 3\sigma_{ha}/\bar{\sigma}_a$. For plane stress ($\sigma_3 = 0$) with $\lambda = \sigma_{2a}/\sigma_{1a}$, the triaxiality factor is

$$T = \frac{1 + \lambda}{\sqrt{1 - \lambda + \lambda^2}} \tag{14.41}$$

Three notable special cases are (a) pure planar shear, $\lambda = -1$, $T = 0$, (b) uniaxial stress, $\lambda = 0$, $T = 1$, and (c) equal biaxial stresses, $\lambda = 1$, $T = 2$. The specific trend observed is that, for a given value of $\bar{\varepsilon}_a$, the life is shorter for larger values of T.

Several modifications of the strain–life equation have been proposed that include this effect. For example, the paper by Marloff (1985) suggests that

$$\bar{\varepsilon}_a = \frac{\sigma'_f}{E}(2N_f)^b + 2^{1-T}\varepsilon'_f(2N_f)^c \tag{14.42}$$

Note that this is the same as Eq. 14.35, except that ε'_f is replaced by the quantity $2^{1-T}\varepsilon'_f$. The same modification also applies to Eqs. 14.38 and 14.39. Compared with the uniaxial case, note that the additional effect amounts to multiplying ε'_f by 2.0 for pure shear or by 0.5 for equal biaxial stresses.

So far, we have not considered the mean stress effect in the context of an effective strain approach. This could be done, for example, by assuming that the controlling mean stress variable is the noncyclic component of the hydrostatic stress, as previously applied for the stress-based approach in Section 9.8. Equation 14.35 or 14.42 can then be generalized in a manner similar to Eq. 14.24, 14.27, 14.30, or 14.33.

However, the effective strain approach is severely limited in its applicability to combined loading. It is reasonable to apply it for combined loadings that are in-phase or 180° out-of-phase, provided that there are no steady (mean) loadings which cause substantial rotation of the principal stress axes during cyclic loading, as in the situation of Fig. 9.41. Such rotation of the principal axes causes nonproportional loading, as discussed previously in Section 12.3.5.

14.4.3 Critical Plane Approaches

Where the loading is nonproportional to a significant degree, a *critical plane approach* is needed. In such an approach, stresses and strains during cyclic loading are determined for various orientations (planes) in the material, and the stresses and strains acting on the most severely loaded plane are used to predict fatigue failure.

Cracks virtually always have irregular shapes, due to growth through the grain structure of the material. Thus, growth due to a shear stress alone tends to be difficult due to mechanical interlocking and friction effects involving irregularities on the faces of cracks, as shown in Fig. 14.14. Stresses and strains normal to the crack plane may have a major effect on the behavior, accelerating the

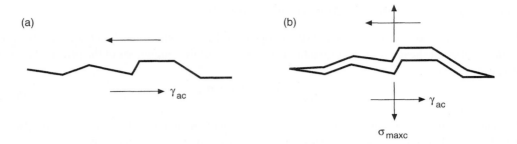

Figure 14.14 Crack under pure shear (a), where irregularities retard growth, compared with a situation (b) where a normal stress acts to open the crack, enhancing its growth. (Adapted from [Socie 87]; used with permission of ASME.)

growth if they tend to open the crack. This situation has led to a number of proposals for critical plane approaches. For example, Fatemi and Socie suggest a relationship similar to

$$\gamma_{ac}\left(1 + \frac{\alpha\sigma_{\max c}}{\sigma_o'}\right) = \frac{\tau_f'}{G}(2N_f)^b + \gamma_f'(2N_f)^c \tag{14.43}$$

where γ_{ac} is the largest amplitude of shear strain for any plane, and $\sigma_{\max c}$ is the peak tensile stress normal to the plane of γ_{ac}, occurring at any time during the γ_{ac} cycle. Also, α is an empirical constant, $\alpha = 0.6$ to 1.0, depending on the material, and σ_o' is the yield strength for the cyclic stress–strain curve. The quantities γ_{ac} and $\sigma_{\max c}$ are illustrated in Fig. 14.14. The constants τ_f', b, γ_f', and c give the strain–life curve from completely reversed tests in pure shear, specifically, torsion tests on thin-walled tubes. If not known, these constants can be estimated from the ones from uniaxial loading with the use of Eq. 14.39. Implementation of this type of an approach for complex variable amplitude loading requires considering the possibility of failure on a number of different planes.

An additional complexity is that there are two distinct modes of crack initiation and early growth, namely, growth on planes of high shear stress (mode II) or growth on planes of high tensile stress (mode I). Shear cracking is most likely at high strains, but may occur even at low strains for pure shear loading. Tensile cracking is most likely for equal biaxial stresses ($\lambda = 1$), but is also common for uniaxial loading. The occurrence of a given mode depends on the type of loading and the magnitude of the strain, and the details vary for different materials. Shear dominated cracking is addressed by Eq. 14.43 or other analogous relationship. A reasonable approach for tensile stress dominated cracking is to employ the Smith, Watson, and Topper parameter, Eq. 14.30. The quantity ε_a is interpreted as the largest amplitude of normal strain for any plane, and $\sigma_{\max}$ is the maximum normal stress on the same plane as ε_a, specifically, the peak value during the ε_a cycle. The shortest life estimated from either the SWT parameter used in this way or Eq. 14.43 is the final life estimate. The necessity of making two calculations reflects the two possible modes of cracking.

A single multiaxial fatigue criterion that considers both the shear and normal stress cracking modes is that of Chu (1995):

$$2\tau_{\max}\gamma_a + \sigma_{\max}\varepsilon_a = f(N_f) \tag{14.44}$$

Here, each term involves the product of the maximum stress in a cycle and the corresponding strain amplitude, with the first term involving shear stress and strain, and the second, normal stress and strain. The critical plane is simply the plane where the left-hand side of Eq. 14.44 is largest, and $f(N_f)$ can be obtained from uniaxial test data. Note that this criterion can be thought of as a generalization of the SWT parameter, Eq. 14.28.

A number of other critical plane approaches have been proposed, and research is currently active in this area. For complex nonproportional loadings, determining the stresses and strains of interest for critical-plane fatigue life estimates for an engineering component will generally require the use of fairly sophisticated analysis that employs incremental plasticity theory.

14.5 LIFE ESTIMATES FOR STRUCTURAL COMPONENTS

So far in this chapter, we have considered only relationships between stresses and strains and life. To use these for given cyclic loadings on a structural component, such as a beam, a shaft, or a notched member, stresses and strains need to be first determined from applied loads. Thus, stress–strain analysis from Chapter 13 needs to be combined with the fatigue life relationships from the earlier portions of this chapter. Sections 13.5 and 13.6, which consider notched members and cyclic loading, are especially needed.

We will use the same simplifying assumptions for the behavior of the material as in Chapters 12 and 13. The transient effects of cycle-dependent hardening or softening and creep–relaxation are thus not generally considered. In particular, the stress–strain behavior is idealized to always follow the stable cyclic stress–strain curve according to a multistage spring and slider rheological model. Such a material has identical monotonic and cyclic stress–strain curves. Where there are multiple applied loads, we will consider only cases with at least approximately proportional loading in regions of yielding—that is, cases where the directions and ratios of the principal stresses remain at least approximately constant. The strain-based approach can be extended to handle more complex cases by employing a critical-plane approach, as previously described, but we will not pursue the topic that far here.

14.5.1 Constant Amplitude Loading

Assuming idealized behavior for the material as just described, we note that the monotonic and cyclic stress–strain curves are the same:

$$\varepsilon = f(\sigma), \qquad \varepsilon_a = f(\sigma_a) \tag{14.45}$$

The specific function used is often the Ramberg–Osgood form, Eq. 14.1, and the constants for this curve are evaluated from stable behavior in cyclic strain tests. As in the rheological model, unloading and reloading during cycling is approximated as following stress–strain paths that are expanded with a scale factor of two relative to the preceding curve:

$$\frac{\Delta\varepsilon}{2} = f\left(\frac{\Delta\sigma}{2}\right) \tag{14.46}$$

Recall that origins for the $\Delta\sigma$ versus $\Delta\varepsilon$ curves are the points where the direction of straining changes, as illustrated in Fig. 12.14.

A stress–strain analysis of the component of interest is needed, which is done just as for monotonic loading but with the use of the cyclic stress–strain curve. Let this result be expressed as an equation, which may be explicit or implicit, giving the strain as a function of a generic variable S that denotes load, moment, nominal stress, etc., as applicable in the particular case:

$$\varepsilon = g(S) \tag{14.47}$$

As discussed in Section 13.6, the material behavior assumed permits this analysis to be applied to cyclic loading. For constant amplitude loading that is biased in the tensile direction, the maximum stress and strain can be estimated from

$$\varepsilon_{\max} = g(S_{\max}) = f(\sigma_{\max}) \qquad (R \geq -1) \tag{14.48}$$

Also, the amplitudes or ranges can be estimated from

$$\varepsilon_a = g(S_a) = f(\sigma_a), \qquad \frac{\Delta\varepsilon}{2} = g\left(\frac{\Delta S}{2}\right) = f\left(\frac{\Delta\sigma}{2}\right) \tag{14.49}$$

where these two equivalent equations are both given merely as a convenience. For loading that is biased in compression, $R < -1$, Eq. 13.73 replaces Eq. 14.48.

Once $\sigma_{\max}$, $\varepsilon_{\max}$, $\sigma_a = \Delta\sigma/2$, and $\varepsilon_a = \Delta\varepsilon/2$ are known, other quantities of interest follow easily. The local notch mean stress is of special interest for fatigue life prediction:

$$\sigma_m = \sigma_{\max} - \sigma_a \tag{14.50}$$

The values of ε_a and σ_m or $\sigma_{\max}$ then allow the fatigue life N_f to be estimated from one of the methods of Section 14.3. Such a procedure can be applied for bending, torsional, or notched members by using analytical results $\varepsilon = g(S)$, such as those given in Chapter 13.

As an example, consider using Neuber's rule to analyze a notched member, followed by a fatigue life estimate. If Eq. 14.1 is used for the cyclic stress–strain curve, the function $\varepsilon = g(S)$ is the implicit one obtained by using this σ-ε relation with Neuber's rule, Eq. 13.58. For cyclic loading with a nonzero mean level, Neuber's rule can be used twice with the cyclic (same as monotonic) stress–strain curve, once for $S_{\max}$ and once for S_a. Thus, two equations need to be solved simultaneously to obtain $\sigma_{\max}$ and $\varepsilon_{\max}$:

$$\varepsilon_{\max} = \frac{\sigma_{\max}}{E} + \left(\frac{\sigma_{\max}}{H'}\right)^{1/n'}, \qquad \frac{(k_t S_{\max})^2}{E} = \sigma_{\max}\varepsilon_{\max} \tag{14.51}$$

Similarly, for σ_a and ε_a, we need to simultaneously solve

$$\varepsilon_a = \frac{\sigma_a}{E} + \left(\frac{\sigma_a}{H'}\right)^{1/n'}, \qquad \frac{(k_t S_a)^2}{E} = \sigma_a\varepsilon_a \tag{14.52}$$

Such calculations have already been illustrated in Ex. 13.4, where the combination of the preceding expressions given by Eq. 13.61 was found to be useful.

The fatigue notch factor k_f, as discussed in Chapter 10, is often employed in place of k_t in these equations. Use of the empirically based parameter k_f improves the accuracy of life prediction for

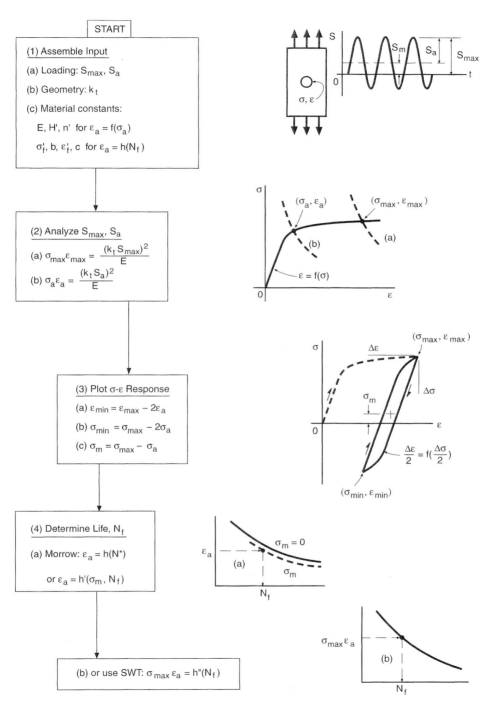

Figure 14.15 Steps required in strain-based life prediction for a notched member under constant amplitude loading.

sharp notches. However, see the discussion on crack growth effects near the end of this chapter for another viewpoint, which suggests that k_t should be retained.

The steps necessary to perform a life estimate for constant amplitude loading of a notched member are summarized by Fig. 14.15. Step (1) is to assemble the needed input information related to the loading, geometry, and material involved. Then (2) the values of $(\varepsilon_{max}, \sigma_{max})$ and $(\varepsilon_a, \sigma_a)$ are obtained from Eqs. 14.51 and 14.52, corresponding to a graphical solution as illustrated. The estimated stress–strain response can then be plotted, and the local notch mean stress σ_m determined, which is shown as step (3). Finally, (4) the life is obtained by using either ε_a and σ_m, or ε_a and σ_{max}.

Example 14.3

A notched plate made of the AISI 4340 (aircraft quality) steel of Table 14.1 has an elastic stress concentration factor of $k_t = 2.80$. If the nominal stress is cycled between $S_{max} = 750$ and $S_{min} = 50\,\text{MPa}$, how many cycles can be applied before fatigue cracking is expected?

Solution The identical situation has already been analyzed in Ex. 13.4 to estimate the local notch stresses and strains. In particular, the cyclic stress–strain curve and Neuber's rule were used, as in Eqs. 14.51 and 14.52, to obtain both the maximums and amplitudes of stress and strain. The resulting values are

$$\sigma_{max} = 972\,\text{MPa}, \qquad \varepsilon_{max} = 0.02192$$

$$\sigma_a = 755\,\text{MPa}, \qquad \varepsilon_a = 0.00615$$

Note that the steps followed in Ex. 13.4 correspond to (1) and (2) in Fig. 14.15. Plotting the stress–strain response as in step (3) gives the result shown previously as Fig. E13.4. Also, the mean stress during cycling is

$$\sigma_m = \sigma_{max} - \sigma_a = 972 - 755 = 217\,\text{MPa}$$

where cycle-dependent relaxation is assumed not to occur.

The life can now be estimated. If the Morrow mean stress method is chosen, ε_a and σ_m are needed, and we substitute material constants from Table 14.1 into Eq. 14.20 to obtain

$$\varepsilon_a = \frac{1758}{207,000}(2N^*)^{-0.0977} + 2.12(2N^*)^{-0.774}$$

Substituting the value we found for ε_a and solving numerically for N^* gives

$$N^* = 3011 \text{ cycles}$$

The life N_f with the σ_m effect included is then obtained from Eq. 14.23, for which $N_{mi}^* = N^*$.

$$N_f = N_{mi}^* \left(1 - \frac{\sigma_m}{\sigma_f'}\right)^{-1/b} = 3011\left(1 - \frac{217}{1758}\right)^{1/0.0977} = 781 \text{ cycles} \qquad \textbf{Ans.}$$

We could also choose a different mean stress method, such as the SWT parameter, in which case ε_a and σ_{max} are employed with Eq. 14.30, giving $N_f = 1800$ cycles (**Ans.**).

14.5.2 Irregular Load Versus Time Histories

The methodology just described can be extended to irregular variations of load with time. This requires applying stress–strain analysis for irregular load versus time histories, as described in Section 13.6.3 and illustrated by Fig. 13.20 and Ex. 13.5. Once such an analysis is done, a fatigue life estimate may be readily made by means of the Palmgren–Miner rule from Chapter 9.

The strain amplitude and mean stress of each closed stress–strain hysteresis loop are needed. Consider Fig. 14.16, which is the example load history and local notch stress–strain response from Fig. 13.20. There are four closed loops as shown in (c), specifically corresponding to load excursions B-C-B', F-G-F', E-H-E', and A-D-A'. The strain amplitude ε_a and mean stress σ_m for each are calculated from the (ε, σ) coordinates of the loop tips. For example, these quantities are labeled in (c) for loop F-G-F'. The life to failure N_f corresponding to each hysteresis loop can then be determined from its combination of strain amplitude and mean stress. If the SWT parameter is used, σ_{max} is simply the highest stress for a given loop, such as σ_G for loop F-G-F'. Having obtained the N_f value for each loop, we can apply the Palmgren–Miner rule, where each closed stress–strain hysteresis loop is considered to represent a cycle.

Note that the cycle counting condition of Fig. 9.46 is satisfied at the same points in the load history where the memory effect acts and the stress–strain path returns to one previously established. These are also the points where segments are skipped in the rheological model, as described in Section 12.4. Thus, the use of closed stress–strain hysteresis loops to identify cycles is equivalent

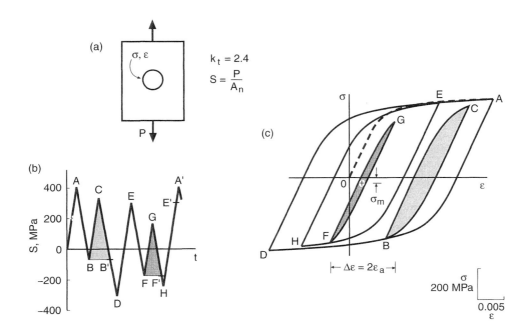

Figure 14.16 Analysis of a notched member subjected to an irregular load versus time history. Notched member (a), made of 2024-T351 aluminum, is subjected to load history (b). The resulting local stress–strain response at the notch is shown in (c).

to rainflow cycle counting. Furthermore, rainflow cycle counting is now seen to possess a physical justification based on this correspondence with elasto-plastic stress–strain behavior.

The full procedure for estimating the stress–strain response and then the fatigue life can be summarized for a repeating history by steps as follows: (1) Assemble the following input information: (a) materials constants for the cyclic stress–strain and strain–life curves, Eqs. 14.1 and 14.4, (b) component analysis results, such as the elastic stress concentration factor k_t and Neuber's rule, or other component analysis $\varepsilon = g(S)$, done with the cyclic stress–strain curve as for monotonic loading, and (c) the load (S) versus time history. (2) Reorder the load–time history to start and return to the peak or valley having the largest absolute value of load. (3) Perform rainflow cycle counting on the load history, noting that the cycles identified also correspond to closed stress–strain hysteresis loops. (4) Estimate the local stress–strain response, as at a notch or a beam edge, as described in Section 13.6.3, applying Eqs. 13.74 and 13.75, while observing the memory effect at points where hysteresis loops close. (5) For each closed hysteresis loop (cycle), identify the strain amplitude ε_a and either the mean or maximum stress, σ_m or $\sigma_{\max}$, and use these to determine the corresponding fatigue life N_f, as affected by mean stress, from one of the mean stress equations of Section 14.3. (6) Apply the Palmgren–Miner rule in the form of Eq. 9.34 to estimate the number of repetitions of the load history to fatigue cracking, B_f.

Example 14.4

A shaft made of hot-rolled and normalized SAE 1045 steel is loaded in bending and has a diameter change, as in Fig. A.12(b) of Appendix A. The stress concentration factor for the fillet radius is $k_t = 3.00$, and the member is repeatedly subjected to the history of net section nominal stress shown in Fig. E14.4(a).[1] How many times can this loading history be applied before fatigue cracking is expected?

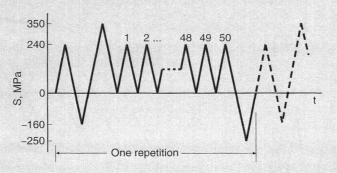

Figure E14.4(a)

---

[1] Note: The peak nominal stress in this history is close to the yield strength of the material. However, with reference to Fig. A.15(c), gross yielding will not occur, as $M_o/M_i = 1.7$ indicates that the fully plastic bending moment M_o is 70% above the moment M_i that corresponds to $S = \sigma_o$.

Solution   The constants for this material's cyclic stress–strain and strain–life curves, Eqs. 14.1 and 14.4, are listed in Table 14.1. We will employ k_t with Neuber's rule and the cyclic stress–strain curve to estimate the stress–strain response for the given load history and, on this basis, make the life estimate.

To begin, the first peak and valley in the history are moved to the end, and the second peak is repeated at the end, so that the highest absolute value of S occurs first and last. This is shown on the left in Fig. E14.4(b), as is rainflow cycle counting of the history according to the procedure of Section 9.9.2. There are 50 cycles B-C, one cycle E-F, and the major cycle A-D. Since these cycles correspond to closed stress–strain hysteresis loops, the stress–strain response is as shown on the right in Fig. E14.4(b). The stress and strain values for each peak and valley are calculated in a manner similar to Ex. 13.5, with the details given in Table E14.4(a).

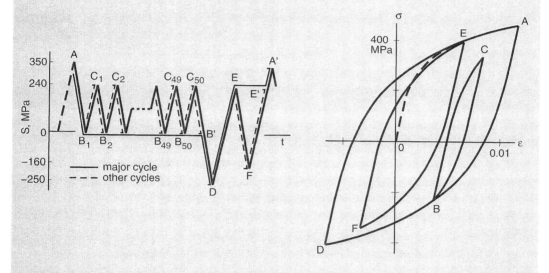

Figure E14.4(b)

Table E14.4(a)

Load History				Calculated Values				
Point (Y)	S MPa	Origin (X)	Origin S MPa	Direction ψ	ΔS to Point	$\Delta\sigma$ MPa	$\Delta\varepsilon$	Stress σ, MPa	Strain ε
A	350	—	—	$+1$	—	—	—	474.0	0.011513
B	0	A	350	-1	350	701.5	0.007780	-227.4	0.003733
C	240	B	0	$+1$	240	573.5	0.004475	346.1	0.008208
D	-250	A	350	-1	600	890.9	0.018004	-416.9	-0.006490
E	240	D	-250	$+1$	490	818.1	0.013075	401.3	0.006585
F	-160	E	240	-1	400	747.3	0.009539	-346.0	-0.002954

For peak A, the value of S_A is substituted into Eq. 13.61, and the equation is solved iteratively for stress σ_A. Then σ_A is substituted into the cyclic stress–strain curve, Eq. 14.1, to calculate ε_A. The specific forms used are

$$S_A = \psi \frac{1}{k_t} \sqrt{\sigma_A^2 + \psi \sigma_A E \left(\frac{\psi \sigma_A}{H'}\right)^{1/n'}}, \qquad \varepsilon_A = \frac{\sigma_A}{E} + \psi \left(\frac{\psi \sigma_A}{H'}\right)^{1/n'}$$

where ψ allows either tensile or compressive initial loading to be handled. Note that the cyclic stress–strain curve is assumed to give the initial monotonic stress–strain path, $\varepsilon = f(\sigma)$.

Next, stress and strain ranges $\Delta \sigma_{XY}$ and $\Delta \varepsilon_{XY}$ are calculated from nominal stress ranges ΔS_{XY} corresponding to smooth hysteresis loop curves that follow $\Delta \varepsilon / 2 = f(\Delta \sigma / 2)$. In particular, this is done for the closed stress–strain hysteresis loops, B-C, E-F, and A-D, and also for ranges A-B and D-E that locate starting points for closed loops. Equations 13.61 and 14.1 are again employed, now for half-ranges as follows:

$$\Delta S_{XY} = |S_Y - S_X|, \qquad \frac{\Delta S_{XY}}{2} = \frac{1}{k_t} \sqrt{\left(\frac{\Delta \sigma_{XY}}{2}\right)^2 + \frac{\Delta \sigma_{XY} E}{2} \left(\frac{\Delta \sigma_{XY}}{2H'}\right)^{1/n'}}$$

$$\frac{\Delta \varepsilon_{XY}}{2} = \frac{\Delta \sigma_{XY}}{2E} + \left(\frac{\Delta \sigma_{XY}}{2H'}\right)^{1/n'}$$

The value of the range ΔS_{XY} is first calculated. Then $\Delta S_{XY}/2$ is substituted into the second equation, allowing $\Delta \sigma_{XY}/2$ to be obtained from an iterative calculation, after which the result is substituted into the third equation to give $\Delta \varepsilon_{XY}/2$. In Table E14.4(a), the resulting full ranges ΔS_{XY}, $\Delta \sigma_{XY}$, and $\Delta \varepsilon_{XY}$ are tabulated.

The stress–strain response calculations are completed by starting from the initial point A and computing the stress and strain at each subsequent point by adding or subtracting the appropriate ranges:

$$\sigma_Y = \sigma_X + \psi \, \Delta \sigma_{XY}, \qquad \varepsilon_Y = \varepsilon_X + \psi \, \Delta \varepsilon_{XY}$$

Here, ψ causes addition or subtraction, depending on whether S is increasing or decreasing. In these calculations, the memory effect is observed. For example, we locate point D relative to its origin point A by subtracting ranges A-D, with cycles B-C not affecting the calculation.

As stress and strain values are now available for each peak and valley in the load history, a life calculation based on the Palmgren–Miner rule can proceed in a straightforward manner. If the Morrow equation is used for the mean stress effect, values are needed for the strain amplitude and mean stress, ε_a and σ_m, the quantity N^*, and finally the life N_f. This is done for each cycle, B-C, E-F, and A-D. Thus, Eqs. 14.20 and 14.23 are needed and are applied as follows, with $N_{mi}^* = N^*$:

$$\varepsilon_a = \frac{\Delta \varepsilon}{2}, \qquad \sigma_m = \frac{\sigma_{\max} + \sigma_{\min}}{2}$$

$$\varepsilon_a = \frac{\sigma_f'}{E} \left(2N^*\right)^b + \varepsilon_f' \left(2N^*\right)^c, \qquad N_f = N_{mi}^* \left(1 - \frac{\sigma_m}{\sigma_f'}\right)^{-1/b}$$

Table E14.4(b) gives the results of these calculations. Each ε_a is obtained from the corresponding $\Delta\varepsilon$ in Table E14.4(a), and each σ_m from the two appropriate stress values in the same table. For example, for cycle B-C, the value of ε_a is half of the $\Delta\varepsilon$ on the third line of Table E14.4(a)—that is, the line for point C with origin B. For calculating σ_m for cycle B-C, our σ_{max} is the σ value from the third (point C) line of Table E14.4(a), and σ_{min} is the σ value from the second (point B) line. Note that an iterative calculation is needed to calculate N^* from ε_a, and then N_f as affected by σ_m follows.

Table E14.4(b)

Cycle	N_j	ε_a	σ_m, MPa	N^*	Morrow N_{fj}	N_j/N_{fj}
B-C	50	0.002237	59.3	2.127×10^5	1.054×10^5	4.745×10^{-4}
E-F	1	0.004770	27.6	1.207×10^4	8.751×10^3	1.143×10^{-4}
A-D	1	0.009002	28.6	1.803×10^3	1.293×10^3	7.736×10^{-4}

$$\Sigma = 1.362 \times 10^{-3}$$

In Table E14.4(a), the N_j and N_{fj} values are employed to calculate cycle ratios N_j/N_{fj}, and the sum of these is computed. Finally, the estimated number of repetitions to failure is obtained by substituting this sum into the Palmgren–Miner rule in the form of Eq. 9.34, with the result being

$$B_f = 1 \bigg/ \left[\sum \frac{N_j}{N_{fj}}\right]_{\text{one rep.}} = 1/1.362 \times 10^{-3} = 734 \text{ repetitions} \qquad \textbf{Ans.}$$

Another option is to use the SWT equation. In this case, the ε_a and σ_{max} values for each cycle give the product $\sigma_{max}\varepsilon_a$, which is then substituted into Eq. 14.30 to obtain the N_f value. Details are given in Table E14.4(c).

Table E14.4(c)

Cycle	N_j	ε_a	σ_{max}	$\sigma_{max}\varepsilon_a$	SWT N_{fj}	N_j/N_{fj}
B-C	50	0.002237	346.1	0.7743	1.196×10^5	4.181×10^{-4}
E-F	1	0.004770	401.3	1.9140	1.017×10^4	9.829×10^{-5}
A-D	1	0.009002	474.0	4.2673	1.577×10^3	6.339×10^{-4}

$$\Sigma = 1.150 \times 10^{-3}$$
$$B_f = 1/\Sigma = 869 \text{ repetitions} \qquad \textbf{Ans.}$$

14.5.3 Discussion

Computer programs for accomplishing the procedure described in the previous subsection are given in Wetzel (1977), specifically in the papers therein by Landgraf and by Brose, and also in Socie (1980). The programming strategy used to follow the σ-ε paths can employ the rules corresponding to the behavior of the rheological model, as given in Section 12.4. These rules are applied not only for the σ-ε response, but also for the S-ε response, where the curve $\varepsilon = g(S)$ is used just as if it were a stress–strain curve, as in Fig. 13.20(d). One strategy that has been successfully employed is to make prior calculations of a number of points along the smooth curves, storing these in an array to be drawn upon while actually performing the S-ε and σ-ε modeling.

The procedure described can be used for multiaxial loading. Adjustments as described in Chapter 12 and earlier in this chapter must, of course, be made to the cyclic stress–strain and strain–life relationships, and mean stress effects need to be handled appropriately. Also, the analysis employed for relating load and strain, such as Neuber's rule, must include a consideration of the multiaxiality, as discussed in Sections 13.5.4 and 13.5.5. If multiple external loads cause significantly nonproportional loading in regions of yielding, more sophisticated analysis using incremental plasticity theory is needed, perhaps combined with finite element analysis on a digital computer.

14.5.4 Simplified Procedure for Irregular Histories

A simplification of the procedure described is often employed that does not require a detailed knowledge of the loading sequence. It becomes necessary to have only a summary of the load history in the form of a matrix (as in Fig. 9.48) giving the numbers of rainflow-counted cycles at various combinations of load range and mean load. The procedure is illustrated in Fig. 14.17 for one of the cycles, specifically F-G, of the example of Figs. 13.20 and 14.16. Consistent with the assumption that only the cycle counting result for the load history is known, the values of S_F and S_G are considered to be known. However, the exact location of this cycle within the loading sequence is assumed to be unknown, and this affects the local notch mean stress for the cycle, and hence also its N_f value. The result of a similar situation occurring for all cycles except the largest one is that the analysis does not provide a single answer, but rather places generally narrow bounds on the calculated life.

Using F-G as a typical cycle, the key to making the simplified life estimate is to note that both load–strain loop F-G and stress–strain loop F-G must lie within the corresponding loop for the major (largest) cycle in the history, in this case cycle A-D. Since the loads S_F and S_G are known, this places limits on the mean strain of cycle F-G. In particular, in Fig. 14.17(a), load–strain loop F-G could be so far to the right that it is attached to the lower branch of loop A-D at P, or so far to the left that it is attached to the upper branch at Q.

These limits on the strains for loop F-G confine the corresponding stress–strain loop as shown in (b). We can place bounds σ_{mP} and σ_{mQ} on the mean stress of loop F-G by calculating the peak and valley stresses and strains for the two extreme possibilities. We do this by applying Eq. 13.74 to S_A, and then applying Eq. 13.75 for load ranges A-P, A-D, D-Q, and F-G. Knowing the bounds on the mean stress for cycle F-G then allows us to calculate bounds for the corresponding number of cycles to failure, N_{fFG}.

The upper bound values on N_f are similarly obtained for all cycles in the history, and these are employed with the Palmgren–Miner rule to obtain the upper bound on calculated life for the irregular load history. The lower bound N_f values are similarly used to obtain the lower bound on the life. Such a procedure was applied to the transmission load history of Fig. 9.48 for the case of a notched member and material combination for which test data are available. Estimated bounds

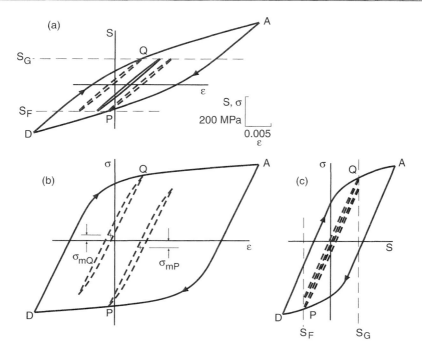

Figure 14.17 Simplified procedure that places bounds on the mean stress effect. For cycle *F-G* of Fig. 14.16, the mean stress must lie between the values σ_{mP} and σ_{mQ}. (Adapted from [Dowling 89]; copyright © ASTM; reprinted with permission.)

on the life are compared with these test data in Fig. 14.18. The agreement obtained is reasonable, considering the degree of scatter in the data.

Note that summarizing the load history as its rainflow matrix results in a loss of detail relative to the original ordered list of peaks and valleys. A number of different sequences of peaks and valleys have this same matrix, and each potentially results in a different calculated life. This explains the situation of a bounded life calculation, where the bounds are the extremes from all possible sequences that give the rainflow matrix used.

14.6 DISCUSSION

Additional discussion is useful. This will include noting some relationships and contrasts between the methodology presented in this chapter and that from earlier chapters describing other approaches to fatigue.

14.6.1 Strain-Based Versus Stress-Based Approaches

The strain-based approach handles local plasticity effects in a more rational and detailed manner than does the stress-based approach of Chapters 9 and 10. Hence, it is generally the preferred

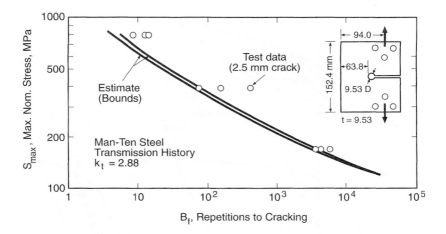

Figure 14.18 Maximum nominal stress vs. the number of repetitions to cracking, for repeated application of the SAE transmission history of Fig. 9.48 to the notched member and material indicated. (Adapted from [Dowling 87]; used with permission; © Society of Automotive Engineers. See [Wetzel 77] for data.)

approach for analyzing short fatigue lives, as judged by the transition fatigue life of the material. The strain-based approach can also be used at long lives where elastic strains dominate, in which case it becomes equivalent to a stress-based approach.

In some cases, *S-N* curves may be available from testing of members very similar to the actual component of interest. Examples might be welded joints, built-up riveted beams, or vehicle axles, of a specific design and material. *S-N* curves from such members automatically include the effects of various complexities that are difficult to evaluate, such as the complex metallurgy and geometry of welds, fretting effects, or effects of surface hardening processes. Where such *S-N* curves are available, it may be advantageous to use these with a nominal-stress-based approach as described in Chapter 10. Although the advantages of detailed analysis of local yielding effects by the strain-based approach are lost, the advantage gained by automatic inclusion of other complexities will sometimes outweigh this loss. The choice of an approach in such cases will be dictated by the details of the particular situation. It may even be useful to perform design or analysis by using more than one approach and compare the results.

14.6.2 Mean Stresses and Plasticity Effects

A key feature of the strain-based approach is that fatigue life estimates are made on the basis of local stresses and strains in the region where fatigue cracking is expected to start, as at the edge of a beam or in the bottom of a notch. Hence, the manner of accounting for mean stress effects is fundamentally different than applying relationships such as Eqs. 10.21 or 10.28 directly to nominal stress *S*. In particular, the mean stress used is the one that occurs locally, and its value is obtained by specifically analyzing the local plastic deformation.

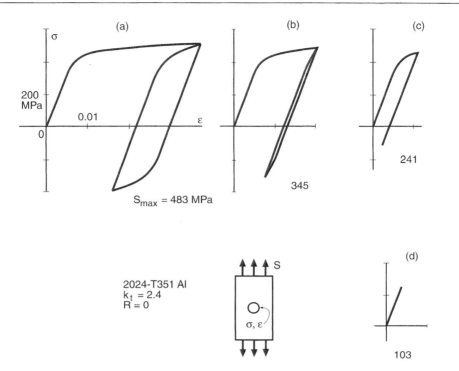

Figure 14.19   Estimated stress–strain responses for an aluminum alloy, for various levels of zero-to-maximum loading on plates with central round holes. (Adapted from [Dowling 87]; used with permission; © Society of Automotive Engineers.)

An example of analysis by the strain-based approach involving mean stresses is provided by Figs. 14.19 and 14.20. The procedure previously described for constant amplitude loading (Fig. 14.15) is applied to zero-to-maximum ($R = 0$) loading of notched plates of 2024-T351 aluminum. Stress–strain paths for four different load levels are shown in Fig. 14.19, and life calculations made on this basis are in reasonable agreement with test data as shown in Fig. 14.20. For the highest loads in this example, the mean stresses are near zero, as in Fig. 14.19(a). For decreasing load, the ratio $k_{fm} = \sigma_m/S_m$ of local to nominal mean stress increases. It becomes equal to k_t where the load is sufficiently low that no yielding occurs, as in (d). The overall trend is similar to that discussed in connection with the stress-based approach; see Fig. 10.15. Also, the ratio $k_f' = \sigma_a/S_a$ varies in a manner similar to Fig. 10.12. Thus, in contrast to the estimation procedures for S-N curves in Chapter 10, it is apparent that the strain-based approach provides a rational basis for specifically evaluating the effect of plastic deformation on S-N curves.

It is noteworthy that the procedure described for estimating local mean stresses does not consider cycle-dependent creep–relaxation effects. Actual stress–strain responses at notches are expected to be similar to Fig. 14.21. Both creep and relaxation occur simultaneously, and these may interact with the cycle-dependent hardening or softening that is also occurring. More detailed modeling of the stress–strain response, as already discussed to an extent in Section 12.5, is a

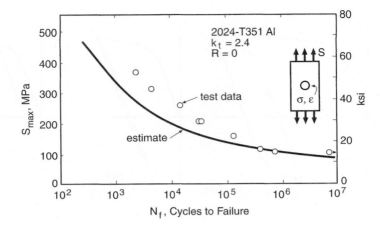

Figure 14.20   Life estimates for the situation of Fig. 14.19 using the SWT parameter, and also corresponding test data. (Data from [Wetzel 68].)

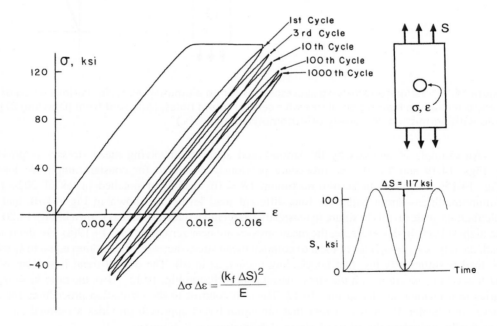

Figure 14.21   Simulation of the stress–strain behavior at a notch, for zero-to-maximum loading of Ti-811 with $k_f = 1.75$. A smooth specimen was subjected to cyclic loading, with the direction of straining reversed whenever Neuber's rule using k_f was satisfied. (Adapted from [Stadnick 72]; copyright © ASTM; reprinted with permission.)

possibility. In particular, values of mean stress could be revised to reflect relaxation according to Eq. 12.56 or another analogous relationship. The improved accuracy of fatigue life prediction resulting from this may, in a few cases, justify the increased complexity of the analysis. However, an impediment to such more refined analysis is the necessity of obtaining additional material constants to describe the transient behavior. Note that the overall effect of lowered mean stress due to local yielding is considered even by the analysis based on stable behavior, as in Fig. 14.19.

14.6.3 Sequence Effects Related to Local Mean Stress

The rational handling of mean stress effects by the strain-based approach is especially important for irregular load versus time histories. Consider the two load histories of Fig. 14.22. They differ only in that the initial severe loading cycle has two different sequences. No difference in these two situations would be predicted by the stress-based approach, as the mean nominal stress for the subsequent lower level cycles is zero in both cases.

   Stress–strain responses for the two load histories as shown were estimated from the procedure of Section 14.5.2. Mean stresses are present for the lower level cycles, and these differ in sign as a result of the sequence of the initial severe cycle. Large differences in the fatigue life can occur in such situations, and these are predicted with reasonable accuracy by the strain-based approach. It is, of course, of special concern that the stress-based approach, as usually applied, does not predict the detrimental effect of history (a).

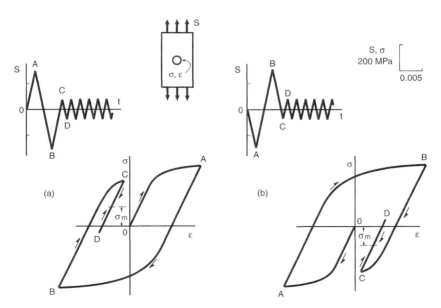

Figure 14.22   Two load histories applied to a notched member ($k_t = 2.4$), and the estimated notch stress–strain responses for 2024-T4 aluminum. The high–low overload in (a) produces a tensile mean stress, and the low–high overload in (b) produces the opposite. (Adapted from [Dowling 82]; used with permission of ASME.)

14.6.4 Sequence Effects Related to Physical Damage to the Material

Any situation where the order of loading affects the life is called a *sequence effect*. In addition to sequence effects related to local mean stress, as just described, sequence effects also occur that are associated with physical damage to the material caused by occasional severe cycles. Small cracks, and also the preceding slip band damage, etc., usually occur at shorter fractions of the total life at higher strain levels. This is evident in the strain–life curves of Fig. 14.9, and also in the stress–life curves of Fig. 9.19. Such behavior causes a sequence effect and a resulting difficulty in applying the Palmgren–Miner rule.

Note that a physical measure of the damage D caused by fatigue loading, such as the size of the dominant microcrack, usually increases in a nonlinear manner with life fraction, as illustrated in Fig. 14.23(a). Let the life fraction for N_j cycles, applied at a particular stress level S_j, be termed U_j. Then

$$U_j = \frac{N_j}{N_{fj}} \tag{14.53}$$

If the stress level is changed from S_1 to S_2 during the life, the Palmgren–Miner rule requires that

$$U_1 + U_2 = 1 \tag{14.54}$$

This is obeyed for Fig. 14.23(a), but not for (b). In the latter case, the damage curves differ for the two different stress levels, with the result that the summation of life fractions at failure is not unity. If the damage proceeds at a higher rate for S_1 than for S_2, the summation is less than unity, which is the particular case illustrated. Hence, the Palmgren–Miner rule can accurately predict the life where there is only nonlinearity in the D versus U curve as in (a), but nonuniqueness as in (b) causes the rule to be in error.

This is precisely the situation that occurs if a relatively small number of cycles at a high stress level are followed by, or mixed with, cycling at a lower stress level. Thus, summations of life fractions can be less than unity as a result of the same degree of physical damage occurring at shorter fractions of the life at higher stress levels. A reasonable engineering approach to this problem

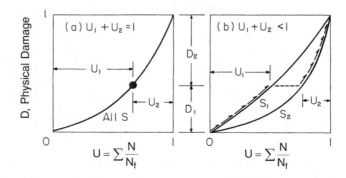

Figure 14.23 Physical damage versus life fraction, where the relationship is (a) unique and (b) nonunique. (From [Dowling 87]; used with permission; © Society of Automotive Engineers.)

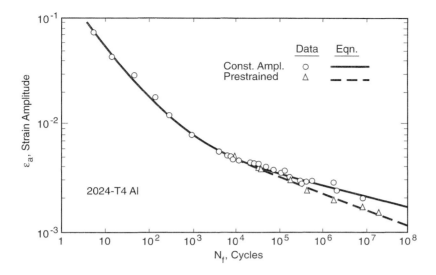

Figure 14.24   Effect of initial overstrain (10 cycles at $\varepsilon_a = 0.02$) on the strain–life curve of an aluminum alloy. (Adapted from [Dowling 89] as based on data from [Topper 70]; copyright © ASTM; reprinted with permission.)

is to obtain strain–life or *S-N* curves by applying a few high-level cycles prior to each test, so as to predamage the material. A life fraction of around 0.01 or 0.02 appears, in general, to be sufficient to lower the strain–life curve so that nonconservative life estimates are avoided. An example of such a strain–life curve for prestrained material is shown in Fig. 14.24.

In steels that have a distinct fatigue limit, effects of this sort extend to stresses below the fatigue limit. Periodic overstrains have an especially severe effect and appear to essentially eliminate the fatigue limit, as shown in Fig. 14.25 and previously in Fig. 9.33. Therefore, for irregular loading where some stress levels substantially exceed the fatigue limit, infinite life should not be assumed for cycles below this level. Limited data, as in Fig. 14.25, suggest that extrapolation below the fatigue limit of the strain–life curve obtained at shorter lives could be used to deal with this situation. As discussed in Sections 9.6.5 and 9.9.1, such extrapolation should extend at least as low as half of the fatigue limit from constant amplitude test data, at which stress it may be reasonable to assume that a true fatigue limit exists.

14.6.5 Crack Growth Effects

In the usual manner of obtaining strain–life curves, the N_f values correspond to failure or to substantial cracking in small (typically 5 to 10 mm diameter) axial test specimens. It is generally observed that life predictions made on this basis correspond to an *engineering size crack* that is easily visible with the naked eye, hence of size on the order of 1 to 5 mm. The existence of such a crack is often considered to constitute failure of the component. However, this rather loose definition

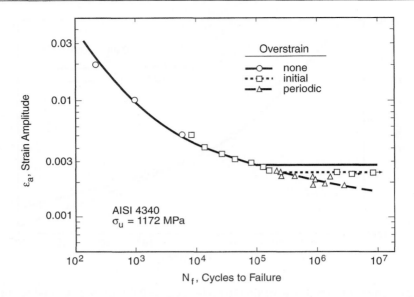

Figure 14.25 Effects of both initial and periodic overstrains on the strain–life curve for an alloy steel. The fatigue limit for the no-overstrain case is estimated from test data on similar material. (Data from [Dowling 73].)

of failure is not always sufficient. For example, it may be desired to predict the life required to develop a crack of a definite size, so that the remaining life required to grow this crack to failure can be estimated from fracture mechanics, as described in Chapter 11. Strain–life curves corresponding to specific small crack sizes, as in Fig. 14.9, are needed if this is to be done in a rigorous manner.

On this basis, the strain-based approach provides the *crack initiation life* N_i to a crack size a_i, and the fracture mechanics approach provides the life N_{if} to grow the crack from a_i to the failure size a_f. Hence, the total life to failure, N_f, is

$$N_i + N_{if} = N_f \tag{14.55}$$

If a_i is chosen to be too short, then the behavior of the crack may be affected by local notch plasticity or other complexities affecting small cracks, so that the use of linear-elastic fracture mechanics is compromised. On the other hand, a_i cannot be too long, as the notch surface strains used in the strain-based approach do not apply at too great a distance from the notch. A reasonable choice as an initiation size is the crack length l' defined by Eq. 8.26. The length l' varies with geometry and is generally around 0.1ρ to 0.2ρ, where ρ is the notch tip radius. However, this degree of rigor is not always needed. Additional discussion is provided in Dowling (1979) and Socie (1984).

From Section 10.2, recall that the principal reason that an empirical fatigue notch factor k_f is needed appears to be related to the growth of cracks near the notch. The initiation of small cracks at notches appears to be governed by k_t, not by k_f. Hence, if the life is separated into crack initiation and growth phases, as previously described, it is reasonable to use k_t rather than

k_f with the strain-based approach to estimate N_i. For sharp notches, this procedure will predict early initiation of cracks that are then expected from fracture mechanics to grow slowly or not at all. Such *nonpropagating cracks* are indeed commonly observed.

14.7 SUMMARY

The strain-based approach employs estimates for the stresses and strains that occur at locations where fatigue cracking is likely to start, such as edges of beams and notches. The behavior of the material is characterized with the use of the stable cyclic stress–strain curve and the strain–life curve from uniaxial loading:

$$\varepsilon_a = \frac{\sigma_a}{E} + \left(\frac{\sigma_a}{H'}\right)^{1/n'}, \qquad \varepsilon_a = \frac{\sigma'_f}{E}(2N_f)^b + \varepsilon'_f(2N_f)^c \qquad (14.56)$$

Mean stress also affects the fatigue life, so that the strain–life curve often needs to be generalized to include this effect according to one of the methods of Section 14.3.

Strain–life and cyclic stress–strain curves vary for different engineering metals and processing histories in a manner that can generally be correlated with other mechanical properties. For example, very ductile metals usually have good resistance to fatigue at high strains corresponding to short lives, but poor resistance at long lives, and vice versa for highly strengthened metals. Elevated temperature and hostile chemical environments affect strain–life curves, and time-dependent creep–relaxation behavior may complicate analysis at high temperatures.

If multiaxial loading occurs, then the cyclic stress–strain and strain–life curves need to be used in more general form. For biaxial loading that is proportional or approximately so, the relationships needed are Eqs. 12.39 and 14.38, with the latter perhaps being modified on the basis of Eq. 14.42. For nonproportional loading, the more advanced incremental plasticity theory is needed for relating stresses and strains, and a critical plane approach is appropriate for estimating fatigue life.

To apply the strain-based approach to an engineering component, such as a beam or a notched member, an analysis relating applied load and strain at the expected failure location is needed. In uncomplicated cases, proportional loading is assumed, as is stable stress–strain behavior without cycle- or time-dependent creep–relaxation. A stress–strain analysis is needed that is done just as for monotonic loading, except that the cyclic stress–strain curve is used. For example, Neuber's rule can be used for notched members with a stress–strain curve $\varepsilon = f(\sigma)$, where $\varepsilon_a = f(\sigma_a)$ is the cyclic stress-strain curve. The result of this analysis is given by a (perhaps implicit) load–strain relationship, $\varepsilon = g(S)$, such as the combination of Eqs. 13.61 and 14.1, where S quantifies the applied load.

A starting point for analyzing cyclic loading may be established by applying monotonic loading to the highest absolute value of S. Where this S is positive, we use $\varepsilon_{\max} = g(S_{\max}) = f(\sigma_{\max})$. Load–strain and stress–strain paths for cyclic loading are then estimated by $\Delta\varepsilon/2 = g(\Delta S/2) = f(\Delta\sigma/2)$. For irregular variation of load with time, cycle counting and the stress–strain memory effect are employed as detailed in Section 13.6.3. Once the stress and strain values have been estimated for all peaks and valleys in the load history, the quantities needed to estimate the fatigue life N_f for each cycle, such as the strain amplitude ε_a and the mean stress σ_m, are readily determined.

Application of the Palmgren–Miner rule can then follow to estimate the life for an irregular loading history.

Use of the local notch mean stress, rather than the nominal (average) mean stress, provides a rational basis for analyzing the effects of local plastic deformation, including the effects of loading sequence for irregular load versus time histories. Additional sequence effects are caused by physical damage to the material during occasional severe loading cycles. These can be handled by using strain–life curves for test specimens that have been subjected to plastic deformation before testing or periodically during testing. The strain-based approach can also be used in combination with crack growth life estimates by fracture mechanics to obtain total fatigue lives for crack initiation plus growth.

NEW TERMS AND SYMBOLS

crack initiation life, N_i

critical plane approach

effective strain approach

engineering size crack

modified Morrow approach

sequence effect

Smith, Watson, and Topper (SWT)
parameter, $\sigma_{max}\varepsilon_a$

strain-based approach

strain–life (Coffin–Manson) curve:
σ_f', b, ε_f', c

transition fatigue life, N_t

zero-mean-stress-equivalent life, N^*

REFERENCES

(a) General References

ASTM. 2010. *Annual Book of ASTM Standards*, Vol. 03.01, ASTM International, West Conshohocken, PA. See No. E606, "Standard Practice for Strain-Controlled Fatigue Testing."

CHU, C.-C. 1995. "Fatigue Damage Calculation Using the Critical Plane Approach," *Jnl. of Engineering Materials and Technology*, ASME, vol. 117, pp. 41–49.

CORDES, T., and K. LEASE, eds. 1999. *Multiaxial Fatigue of an Induction Hardened Shaft*, SAE Pub. AE-28, Society of Automotive Engineers, Warrendale, PA.

DOWLING, N. E. 1979. "Notched Member Fatigue Life Predictions Combining Crack Initiation and Propagation," *Fatigue of Engineering Materials and Structures*, vol. 2, no. 2, pp. 129–138.

DOWLING, N. E., December 2009 "Mean Stress Effects in Strain-Life Fatigue," *Fatigue and Fracture of Engineering Materials and Structures*, vol. 32, no. 12, December 2009, pp. 1004–1019.

DRAPER, JOHN. 2008. *Modern Metal Fatigue Analysis*, Engineering Materials Advisory Services, Cradley Heath, West Midlands, England.

HBM. 2010. *nCode DesignLife*, fatigue analysis software, HBM, Inc. (HBM-nCode), Southfield, MI. (See *http://www.ncode.com.*)

LANDGRAF, R. W. 1970. "The Resistance of Metals to Cyclic Deformation," *Achievement of High Fatigue Resistance in Metals and Alloys*, ASTM STP 467, Am. Soc. for Testing and Materials, West Conshohocken, PA, pp. 3–36.

LEE, Y.-L., M. E. BARKEY, and H.-T. KANG. 2012. *Metal Fatigue Analysis Handbook: Practical Problem-Solving Techniques for Computer-Aided Engineering*, Elsevier Butterworth-Heinemann, Oxford, UK.

LEE, Y.-L., J. PAN, R. B. HATHAWAY, and M. E. BARKEY. 2005. *Fatigue Testing and Analysis: Theory and Practice*, Elsevier Butterworth-Heinemann, Oxford, UK.

LEESE, G. E., and D. SOCIE, eds. 1989. *Multiaxial Fatigue: Analysis and Experiments*, SAE Pub. No. AE-14, Society of Automotive Engineers, Warrendale, PA.

MARLOFF, R. H., R. L. JOHNSON, and W. K. WILSON. 1985. "Biaxial Low-Cycle Fatigue of Cr-Mo-V Steel at 538°C by Use of Triaxiality Factors," K. J. Miller and M. W. Brown, eds., *Multiaxial Fatigue*, ASTM STP 853, Am. Soc. for Testing and Materials, West Conshohocken, PA.

RICE, R. C., ed. 1997. *Fatigue Design Handbook*, 3d ed., SAE Pub. No. AE-22, Soc. of Automotive Engineers, Warrendale, PA.

SAFE TECHNOLOGY. 2010. *fe-safe* and *safe4fatigue*, fatigue analysis software, Safe Technology Limited, Sheffield, UK. (See: *http://www.safetechnology.com.*)

SOCIE, D. F., N. E. DOWLING, and P. KURATH. 1984. "Fatigue Life Estimation of Notched Members," *Fracture Mechanics: Fifteenth Symposium*, ASTM STP 833, Am. Soc. for Testing and Materials, West Conshohocken, PA, pp. 284–299.

SOCIE, D. F., and G. B. MARQUIS. 2000. *Multiaxial Fatigue*, Society of Automotive Engineers, Warrendale, PA.

SOCIE, D. F., and J. MORROW. 1980. "Review of Contemporary Approaches to Fatigue Damage Analysis," *Risk and Failure Analysis for Improved Performance and Reliability*, J. J. Burke and V. Weiss, eds., Plenum Pub. Corp., New York, pp. 141–194.

WETZEL, R. M., ed. 1977. *Fatigue Under Complex Loading: Analyses and Experiments*, SAE Pub. No. AE-6, Society of Automotive Engineers, Warrendale, PA.

(b) Sources for Material Properties and Databases

BOLLER, C., and T. SEEGER. 1987. *Materials Data for Cyclic Loading*, 5 vols., Elsevier Science Pubs., Amsterdam. See also *Supplement 1*, 1990, by A. Baumel and T. Seeger.

NIMS. 2010. *Fatigue Data Sheets*, periodically updated database, National Institute of Materials Science, Tsukuba, Ibaraki, Japan. (See *http://mits.nims.go.jp/index_en.html.*)

SAE. 2002. *Technical Report on Low Cycle Fatigue Properties: Ferrous and Non-Ferrous Materials*, Document No. J1099, Soc. of Automotive Engineers, Warrendale, PA.

PROBLEMS AND QUESTIONS

Section 14.2

14.1 Using the two straight lines plotted for RQC-100 steel in Fig. 14.4, estimate your own values of the constants σ_f', b, ε_f', and c for the strain–life curve. The elastic modulus is $E = 200\,GPa$. Do your values agree reasonably well with those given?

14.2 Plot strain–life curves for the four heat treatments of SAE 4142 steel in Table 14.1 all together on one graph. Employ log–log coordinates and cover lives from 1 to 10^6 cycles. Comment on any trends that you observe and how these correlate with the tensile properties and hardness. (Suggestion: Include the transition fatigue life N_t in your discussion.)

14.3 How do the strain–life curves for the two ductile polymers in Fig. 14.5 differ from those typical of engineering metals? Consider both qualitative trends, such as the shape of the curves, and quantitative trends, such as the life corresponding to $\varepsilon_a = 0.01$.

14.4 For hot-rolled and normalized SAE 1045 steel with an elastic modulus of $E = 202\,GPa$, some fatigue data for completely reversed loading are given in Table P12.32(a). The stress and strain values listed correspond to stable (near $N_f/2$) behavior.

   (a) Determine constants for the strain–life curve. Compare the results with those listed in Table 14.1, which were obtained from a larger set of data.

   (b) Plot both the data and the fitted curves for elastic, plastic, and total strain. Do your constants provide a good representation of the data?

14.5 For AISI 4340 steel with $\sigma_u = 1172$ MPa, data of stress, strain, and fatigue life from completely reversed tests are given in Table P12.33(a). The elastic modulus is $E = 207$ GPa. Proceed as in Prob. 14.4(a) and (b), except use these data.

14.6 For quenched and tempered SAE 1045 steel with ultimate tensile strength $\sigma_u = 2248$ MPa and hardness $HB = 595$, data of stress, strain, and fatigue life from completely reversed tests are given in Table P12.34. The elastic modulus is $E = 206.7$ GPa. Proceed as in Prob. 14.4(a) and (b), except use these data, and omit the comparison with Table 14.1. (For now, ignore the relatively small values of mean stress, σ_m.)

14.7 Based on the constants in Table 14.1:

   (a) Plot strain–life curves for steels SAE 1015 and SAE 4142 (380 HB). Employ log–log coordinates and cover lives from 1 to 10^6 cycles.

   (b) Noting that these curves are from polished test specimens, also plot the curves for both materials that include the effect of a typical machined surface finish. How do the effects of surface finish differ for the two steels?

14.8 Hot-rolled and normalized SAE 1045 steel, as in Table 14.1, is made into a large shaft. There is a change in the shaft diameter from $d_1 = 222$ to $d_2 = 343$ mm, with a fillet of radius $\rho = 11.1$ mm having a machined surface. Adjust the constants for the strain–life curve so that it is appropriate for making life estimates for this shaft. Then plot both the original and modified strain–life curves, and comment on how they differ.

14.9 For all materials in Table 14.1, complete the following tasks:

   (a) Plot σ_f' versus the $\tilde{\sigma}_{fB}$ on linear–linear coordinates. How good is the correlation, and what trends are evident?

   (b) Plot ε_f' versus the true fracture strain $\tilde{\varepsilon}_f$ on log–log coordinates, and answer the same questions. (Hint: Calculate $\tilde{\varepsilon}_f$ from $\%RA$.)

14.10 Use the strain–life constants given for each material in Table 14.1 to calculate the strain amplitude ε_a corresponding to $N_f = 1000$ cycles. Then prepare a histogram of the frequency of occurrence of various ε_a values, and comment on the result obtained.

Section 14.3

14.11 Estimate the fatigue life for SAE 4142 steel (560 HB) for a strain amplitude of $\varepsilon_a = 0.0040$ with a mean stress of $\sigma_m = 150$ MPa. Employ each of the following methods: (a) Morrow, (b) modified Morrow, (c) SWT, and (d) Walker with γ estimated from Eq. 9.20.

14.12 Proceed as in Prob. 14.11, except change the mean stress to $\sigma_m = -150$ MPa. Also calculate the fatigue life for a strain amplitude of $\varepsilon_a = 0.0040$ with a mean stress of zero.

14.13 Estimate the fatigue life for 2024 – T4 aluminum for a strain amplitude of $\varepsilon_a = 0.0050$ with a mean stress of $\sigma_m = 200$ MPa. Employ each of the following methods: (a) Morrow, (b) modified Morrow, (c) SWT, and (d) Walker with an estimate of $\gamma = 0.50$.

14.14 Proceed as in Prob. 14.13, except change the mean stress to $\sigma_m = -200\,\text{MPa}$. Also calculate the fatigue life for a strain amplitude of $\varepsilon_a = 0.0050$ with a mean stress of zero.

14.15 Estimate the fatigue life for SAE 1015 steel for a strain amplitude of $\varepsilon_a = 0.0030$ with a mean stress of $\sigma_m = 175\,\text{MPa}$. Employ each of the following methods: (a) Morrow, (b) modified Morrow, (c) SWT, and (d) Walker with γ estimated from Eq. 9.20.

14.16 Proceed as in Prob. 14.15, except change the mean stress to $\sigma_m = -175\,\text{MPa}$. Also calculate the fatigue life for a strain amplitude of $\varepsilon_a = 0.0030$ with a mean stress of zero.

14.17 Estimate the fatigue life for the material AISI 4340 (aircraft qual.) with mean stress $\sigma_m = 100\,\text{MPa}$ and strain amplitude $\varepsilon_a = 0.0040$ using: (a) Morrow, and (b) SWT approach.

14.18 Estimate the fatigue life for the material 2024 – T351 aluminum alloy with mean stress $\sigma_m = 150\,\text{MPa}$ and strain amplitude $\varepsilon_a = 0.0030$ using: (a) Morrow, and (b) SWT approach.

14.19 Proceed as in Prob 14.17, except use (a) modified Morrow, and (b) Walker approach.

14.20 Proceed as in Prob 14.18, except use (a) modified Morrow, and (b) Walker approach.

14.21 Compare Figs. 14.11 and 14.13. Does either the Morrow approach or the SWT approach appear to be superior for this material? Are there any specific trends of disagreement with the data in either case, and if so, what are these trends?

14.22 Some strain–life data at nonzero mean stresses are given in Table P14.22 for prestrained 2024-T4 aluminum.

Table P14.22

ε_a	σ_a, MPa	σ_m, MPa	N_f, cycles
0.00345	245	71.7	37 800
0.00232	165	71.7	244 600
0.00172	122	71.7	760 000
0.00410	291	142	11 000
0.00303	215	141	30 000
0.00254	181	144	58 500
0.00198	143	143	158 000
0.00148	105	142	437 100
0.00121	85.5	144	820 000
0.00250	178	292	27 700
0.00149	106	292	200 000
0.00109	76.5	287	747 000

Source: Data in [Topper 70].

(a) Plot data points of the SWT parameter, $\sigma_{max}\varepsilon_a$, versus N_f on log–log coordinates. Also plot the curve expected from the constants in Table 14.1, and comment on the success of the SWT parameter for this material.

(b) Using the modified Morrow approach, Eq. 14.27, plot the members of the family of strain–life curves that correspond to mean stresses of $\sigma_m = 0$, 72, 142, and 290 MPa. Then plot the test data and comment on the agreement with the curves.

14.23 Using the data for prestrained 2024-T4 aluminum from Prob. 14.22, complete the following:

(a) Plot ε_a versus N^*_{mi} from Eq. 14.22 on log–log coordinates. Also plot the strain–life curve from the material constants in Table 14.1, and comment on the success of the Morrow equation for this data.

(b) Repeat (a) with N^*_{mf} calculated using the true fracture strength, Eq. 14.26. Is the agreement improved?

14.24 Additional data for the SAE 1045 steel of Prob. 12.34 are given in Table P14.24. These are stress-controlled tests with mean stresses imposed. Cyclic stress–strain and strain–life constants fitted to the Prob. 12.34 data are as follows:

E, MPa	H', MPa	n'	σ'_f, MPa	b	ε'_f	c
206,700	3246	0.0918	3149	−0.1014	0.251	−0.891

(a) For the combined data from Tables P12.34 and P14.24, plot data points of strain amplitude ε_a versus N^*_{mi}, where the latter is from the Morrow relationship, Eq. 14.22. Where ε_a is not given, estimate the value from σ_a and the cyclic stress–strain curve, Eq. 14.1. On the same graph, also plot the strain–life curve from the given constants.

(b) On a second graph, plot the SWT parameter $\sigma_{max}\varepsilon_a$ versus N_f, showing both the combined data and the curve expected from the given constants.

(c) Comment on the success of both the Morrow and SWT methods in correlating the mean stress data for this material. Is either significantly better than the other?

Table P14.24

σ_a, MPa	σ_m, MPa	N_f, cycles
1379	−345	3 750
1207	−345	19 500
1207	690	135
1034	690	2 270
896	690	4 850
724	690	22 750
621	690	572 000

Source: Data in [Landgraf 66].

14.25 Consider the data of Tables P12.33(a) and E9.5 for AISI 4340 steel with $\sigma_u = 1172$ MPa. A stress–life fit to these combined data, using $\sigma_{ar} = \sigma'_f(2N_f)^b$ with the Walker relationship,

Eq. 9.19, gives constants $\sigma'_f = 1951\,\text{MPa}$, $b = -0.1074$, and $\gamma = 0.652$. (See Section 10.6.4.)

(a) For the combined data from Tables P12.33(a) and E9.5, plot data points of strain amplitude ε_a versus N^*_w, where the latter is from the Walker relationship, Eq. 14.32. On the same graph, also plot the strain–life curve, using the constants for this material from Table 14.1, except replace σ'_f and b with the values given in this problem. Where ε_a is not given, estimate the value from σ_a and the cyclic stress–strain curve, Eq. 14.1.

(b) Compare the success of the data correlation from (a) with that for other mean stress equations in Figs. 14.11 to 14.13.

Section 14.4

14.26 Some shear strain versus life data from completely reversed torsion of thin-walled tubes are given in Table P12.35 for hot-rolled and normalized SAE 1045 steel. The shear strain amplitude γ_a was constant in each test, and the shear stress and plastic shear strain amplitudes, τ_a and γ_{pa}, were measured near $N_f/2$. Some properties of this steel are listed in Table 14.1, and the shear modulus is $G = 79.1\,\text{GPa}$.

(a) Plot the γ_a versus N_f data on log–log coordinates, compare them with the curve predicted by Eq. 14.39, and comment on the success of this equation.

(b) Add the γ_a versus N_f equation to your plot that is obtained by using the hydrostatic stress adjustment of Eq. 14.42. Does this improve the agreement with the data?

14.27 For the hot-rolled and normalized SAE 1045 steel of Table 14.1, plot a family of estimated strain–life curves, ε_{1a} versus N_f, for biaxial loadings specified by $\lambda = -1.0, -0.5, 0, 0.5$, and 1.0. Use Poisson's ratio $\nu = 0.277$, employ log–log coordinates, and cover lives from 10 to 10^6 cycles. Then comment on the trends in the curves.

14.28 Derive an equation analogous to Eq. 14.38 for ε_{1a} versus N_f for the case of axisymmetric loading, where $\sigma_{2a} = \sigma_{3a} = \beta\sigma_{1a}$. Also, for the hot-rolled and normalized SAE 1045 steel of Table 14.1, plot the particular curve that applies for $\beta = 0.5$, along with the one for uniaxial loading. Use Poisson's ratio $\nu = 0.277$, employ log–log coordinates, and cover lives from 10 to 10^6 cycles. Then comment on the comparison.

Section 14.5.1

14.29 Plates with round holes of 2024-T351 aluminum are axially loaded and have an elastic stress concentration factor from Fig. A.11(a) of $k_t = 2.4$. Make estimates of the life to fatigue cracking, and also plot the estimated stress–strain response, for cycling at $R = 0$ with (a) $S_{max} = 240\,\text{MPa}$, and (b) $S_{max} = 345\,\text{MPa}$. Your results should be similar to those of Figs. 14.19 and 14.20.

14.30 Estimate the number of cycles to cause fatigue cracking for the notched member and cyclic loading of Prob. 13.32.

14.31 A notched plate of 2024-T351 aluminum is loaded axially, as in Fig. A.11(b), and has a stress concentration factor of $k_t = 2.5$. Estimate the number of cycles to cause fatigue cracking for the cyclic loading of Prob. 13.33.

14.32 Estimate the number of cycles to cause fatigue cracking for the notched member and cyclic loading of Prob. 13.31.

14.33 A plate with a round hole, Fig. A.11(a), made of RQC-100 steel, is loaded in tension and has a stress concentration factor of $k_t = 2.8$. Estimate the number of cycles to cause fatigue cracking for the cyclic loading of Prob. 13.35.

14.34 For the rotating annular disc of Prob. 13.39, estimate the number of stop–start cycles necessary to cause fatigue cracking.

14.35 Consider the test data in Prob. 10.22 for axially loaded plates with double-edge notches, having $k_t = 4$, made of 7075-T6 aluminum. Estimate the *S-N* curve for $S_m = 0$ loading from the strain-based approach, employing materials constants from Table 14.1. (Suggestion: Calculate the life for several different values of S_{max}.) Then plot your estimated curve along with the $S_m = 0$ test data, and comment on the success of the estimate.

14.36 Consider the data for bending of rectangular beams of RQC-100 steel in Prob. 13.37.
- **(a)** Use the strain-based approach to estimate moment amplitudes corresponding to several fatigue lives over the range $N_f = 10^2$ to 10^6 cycles. Then plot the estimated curve of M_a versus N_f, along with the test data, and comment on the comparison.
- **(b)** Also, plot the strain amplitude versus life data, ε_a versus N_f, along with the curve from axial specimen data given by constants in Table 14.1. Do data and curve agree?

14.37 Consider the bluntly notched compact specimen of Prob. 13.38 made of AISI 4340 steel ($\sigma_u = 1158$ MPa). Fatigue life data for completely reversed loading are given in Table P14.37. Note that fatigue lives are listed both for failure and for the initiation in the end of the notch of a small surface crack of length $2c = 0.5$ mm, corresponding to a crack depth around half this length, $a \approx 0.25$ mm.
- **(a)** Make a load amplitude versus fatigue life plot, P_a versus both N_i and N_f, of these data.
- **(b)** On this life plot, add a curve calculated from strains estimated by Neuber's rule. The constants for the strain–life curve are $E = 206.9$ GPa, $\sigma'_f = 1544$ MPa, $b = -0.0767$, $\varepsilon'_f = 0.526$, and $c = -0.655$.
- **(c)** Also add a curve for lives estimated from the FEA strain values of Table P13.38.
- **(d)** Concisely discuss the success of the two different estimates, considering both N_i and N_f.

Table P14.37

P_a kN	N_i, cycles $a \approx 0.25$ mm	N_f, cycles failure
35.58	60	103
24.46	150	474
16.01	874	4 150
11.12	5 000	23 200
8.45	24 900	75 700
7.12	73 800	154 700
6.67	3 340 000	3 400 000
6.23	1 800 000	2 070 000
6.23	2 900 000	3 100 000

Source: Data for [Dowling 82].

14.38 Round shafts with a diameter transition having a fillet radius were made of ASTM A470 (Ni-Cr-Mo-V) steel with $\sigma_u = 724$ MPa. The smaller and larger diameters and the fillet radius were $d_1 = 25.4$, $d_2 = 57.15$, and $\rho = 1.575$ mm, giving an elastic concentration factor for shear stress due to torsion of $k_t = 1.56$. Nominal stress is defined as for the related case of Fig. A.12(d). These shafts were subjected to completely reversed torsional loading, with torque amplitudes T_a and numbers of cycles N_f to fatigue cracking being given in Table P14.38. From axial loading tests on similar material, constants for the cyclic stress–strain and strain–life curves, Eqs. 14.1 and 14.4, are given as follows, as is Poisson's ratio, ν:

E, GPa	H', MPa	n'	σ'_f, MPa	b	ε'_f	c	ν
206.9	710	0.0640	748	−0.0490	1.74	−0.738	0.300

(a) Estimate the cyclic stress–strain and strain–life equations for a state of planar shear stress.

(b) Using Neuber's rule applied to shear stress and strain, along with your equations from (a), estimate the curve relating torque amplitude and cycles to failure over the range $N_f = 10^2$ to 10^7 cycles. Add the given data to the curve and comment on the success of the estimated curve.

Table P14.38

T_a kN·m	N_f, cycles to cracking
1.1718	950
1.0080	2 000
0.7548	20 000
0.6492	80 100
0.5995	118 000
0.5995	567 000
0.5283	1 000 000

Source: Data in [Placek 84].

Section 14.5.2

14.39 AISI 4340 steel with $\sigma_u = 1468$ MPa is made into a notched shaft that is loaded in bending and has an elastic stress concentration factor of $k_t = 3.0$. This shaft is a part in a helicopter, and the nominal bending stress history for each flight in simplified form is shown in Fig. P14.39. Estimate the number of flights necessary to develop a crack in this part if $S_{a2} = 70$ MPa for (a) $S_{max} = 275$ MPa, and (b) $S_{max} = 480$ MPa. Make a qualitative sketch of the local stress–strain response to guide your solution.

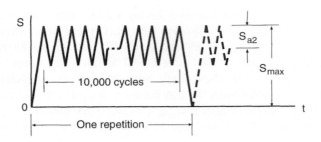

Figure P14.39

14.40 The nominal stress history shown in Fig. P14.40 is repeatedly applied to a notched member made of the Ti-6Al-4V alloy of Table 14.1. The elastic stress concentration factor is $k_t = 2.50$, the value of $S_{max} = 600$ MPa, and $N_2 = 3000$ cycles. Estimate the number of repetitions required to cause fatigue cracking. Make a qualitative sketch of the local stress-strain response to guide your solution.

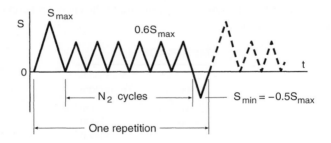

Figure P14.40

14.41 Estimate the number of repetitions to cause fatigue cracking for the notched member and load history of Fig. 13.20, starting from the results of Ex. 13.5.

14.42 For the material and strain history of Prob. 12.38, assume that the history is repeatedly applied, and estimate the number of repetitions to cause fatigue cracking.

14.43 For the material and strain history of Prob. 12.41, assume that the history is repeatedly applied, and estimate the number of repetitions to cause fatigue cracking.

14.44 For the notched member and repeatedly applied nominal stress history of Prob. 13.40, estimate the number of repetitions to cause fatigue cracking.

14.45 For the notched member and repeatedly applied nominal stress history of Prob. 13.41, estimate the number of repetitions to cause fatigue cracking.

14.46 For the notched member and repeatedly applied nominal stress history of Prob. 13.42, estimate the number of repetitions to cause fatigue cracking.

14.47 For the notched member and repeatedly applied nominal stress history of Prob. 13.43, estimate the number of repetitions to cause fatigue cracking.

14.48 A member made of 2024-T351 aluminum has a notch with an elastic stress concentration factor of $k_t = 2.50$. It is repeatedly subjected to the variable amplitude loading history shown in Fig. P14.48. Qualitatively sketch the local notch stress–strain response, and then estimate the number of repetitions to cause fatigue cracking.

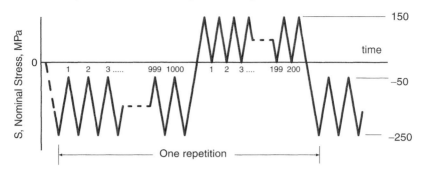

Figure P14.48

14.49 Make the life estimate of Ex. 10.6 by the strain-based method. Use properties for 2024-T351 aluminum as likely to be similar to those for the given 2024-T3 alloy. Then compare and briefly discuss the two calculations as to the life obtained, the nature of the input information required, and the complexity of the calculation.

14.50 Problem 10.40 gives a nominal stress history that was repeatedly applied to axially loaded, double-edge-notched plates of 7075-T6 aluminum, with $k_t = 4.00$. Fatigue lives from six identical tests are given in Table P10.40(b). The plate dimensions are the same as in Prob. 10.22.

    (a) Qualitatively sketch the local notch stress–strain response, and then use the strain-based method to estimate the number of repetitions to cause fatigue cracking. Compare your calculated life with the test data and comment on the success of your estimate.

    (b) Consider the notches on each side of the member to be collapsed to sharp cracks of the same length a as the notch depth. On this approximate basis, estimate the number of repetitions of the history required to grow the cracks from initiation to failure. Add this life to that from (a) to obtain the total life to failure, and again compare with the test results. (Materials properties for crack growth are given in Table 11.2. Note that K_c from Table 11.3 applies for $t = 2.3$ mm.)

14.51 Problem 10.41 gives a nominal stress history that was repeatedly applied to axially loaded, double-edge-notched plates of 7075-T6 aluminum, with $k_t = 4.00$. Fatigue lives from six identical tests are given in Table P10.40(b). The plate dimensions are the same as in Prob. 10.22. Proceed as in Prob. 14.50(a) and (b).

Section 14.6

14.52 Rework Ex. 10.3, using the strain-based approach. Then discuss the differences between your calculation and that of Ex. 10.3.

14.53 Chain with an average static breaking strength of $P_u = 106.8\,\text{kN}$ has links as shown in Fig. P14.53(a). The links are made from SAE 8622H steel bar of diameter $d = 10\,\text{mm}$, which is cut to length and cold formed to the needed shape, then welded into solid links, and finally heat treated by quenching and tempering. Tensile properties are yield 1014 MPa, ultimate 1117 MPa, and 62% reduction in area. Fatigue properties were estimated from data on similar material and adjusted to obtain agreement with fatigue data on chain links, giving the following values:

E, MPa	H', MPa	n'	σ'_f, MPa	b	ε'_f	c
213,700	1386	0.0985	1517	−0.10	1.00	−0.55

Elastic finite element analysis found the highest stresses at points such as F and G, where similar values of $k_t = 5.8$ were obtained. This k_t is based on nominal stress defined as $S = P/(2A)$, where P is the force on the chain and $A = \pi d^2/4$. (Source: Data from [Tipton 92].)

  (a) Estimate the fatigue life for chain that is subject to a load amplitude of 8% of P_u about a mean level of 16% of P_u.
  (b) Chain is normally proof tested before use by applying a high load, such as O-A-B in Fig. P14.53(b). (This eliminates defective links and introduces beneficial residual stresses.) Revise your life estimate from (a) to include an initial proof test at 60% of P_u.
  (c) Compare your results from (a) and (b) as to both the life and the local mean stress during use of the chain, and comment on the expected effectiveness of the proof loading.

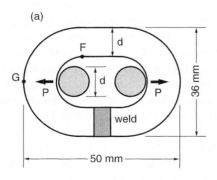 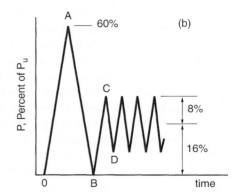

Figure P14.53

14.54 A shaft that supports cable pulleys used to lift coal from a mine is loaded in rotating bending in a situation similar to that of Prob. 10.36, but the shaft is larger, due to higher loads. A fillet radius analogous to that labeled in Fig. P10.36 is the most severely stressed location,

Table P14.54

Situation	No. of Rotations per Hoist Cycle	Nominal Stress S, MPa
Accelerating	9	92
Up with coal	45	86
Down empty	54	60

where the diameter in this case increases from $d_1 = 222$ to $d_2 = 343$ mm, with a fillet radius of $\rho = 11.1$ mm, having a machined surface. The shaft material is hot-rolled and normalized SAE 1045 steel with tensile properties of yield 306 MPa, ultimate 569 MPa, and 48% area reduction. In each lift and return cycle of the hoist, the shaft rotates 108 times, and there are approximately 32,000 hoist cycles in a typical year of operation. The coal skip (bucket) is first loaded with coal in the mine 515 m below the pulley shaft. It then accelerates upward, next moves upward at constant speed, stops at the top of its travel and dumps the coal, and finally returns empty to the bottom of its travel. Details are given in Table P14.54. Combinations of nominal (without k_t) bending stress and numbers of stress cycles are given, where the stress cycles correspond to shaft rotations, totaling 108 per hoist cycle. These stresses assume smooth operation of the equipment; no impact factor is included. They result from the weights of shaft and attached pulleys, coal, skip, and cables.

(a) Evaluate the shaft design for resistance to fatigue failure. Is the design adequate?

(b) Approximately three years after installation, the shaft failed from a large crack that had started at the fillet radius. Fifteen months prior to the failure, an accident occurred in which the skip went out of control while moving upward and crashed into the structure below the shaft, causing a nominal stress that may have been as high as $S = 200$ MPa at the instant of impact. Did the accident contribute to the failure?

(c) After the failure, the shaft was replaced by a similar one made of SAE 4340 steel having an ultimate tensile strength of 700 MPa. Was this a reasonable solution to the problem? What additional design changes would you suggest?

15

Time-Dependent Behavior: Creep and Damping

15.1 **INTRODUCTION**
15.2 **CREEP TESTING**
15.3 **PHYSICAL MECHANISMS OF CREEP**
15.4 **TIME–TEMPERATURE PARAMETERS AND LIFE ESTIMATES**
15.5 **CREEP FAILURE UNDER VARYING STRESS**
15.6 **STRESS–STRAIN–TIME RELATIONSHIPS**
15.7 **CREEP DEFORMATION UNDER VARYING STRESS**
15.8 **CREEP DEFORMATION UNDER MULTIAXIAL STRESS**
15.9 **COMPONENT STRESS–STRAIN ANALYSIS**
15.10 **ENERGY DISSIPATION (DAMPING) IN MATERIALS**
15.11 **SUMMARY**

OBJECTIVES

- Explore time-dependent behavior and physical mechanisms for creep and damping.
- Apply time–temperature parameters to estimate creep–rupture life.
- Review stress–strain–time models and relationships for engineering materials, and apply these to analysis of simple components.

15.1 INTRODUCTION

Elastic and plastic strains are commonly idealized as appearing instantly upon the application of stress. Further deformation that occurs gradually with time is called *creep strain*. Creep is often important in engineering design, as in applications involving high temperature, such as steam turbines in power plants, jet and rocket engines, and nuclear reactors. Some other examples of creep are the failure of lightbulb filaments, the gradual loosening of plastic eyeglass frames, slow deformation leading to rupture of plastic pipe, and the movement of ice in glaciers.

For metals and crystalline ceramics, creep deformation is sufficiently large to be of importance in a given material only above a temperature that is generally in the range of 30 to 60% of its absolute melting temperature. Large creep strains can occur in polymers and glasses above the particular

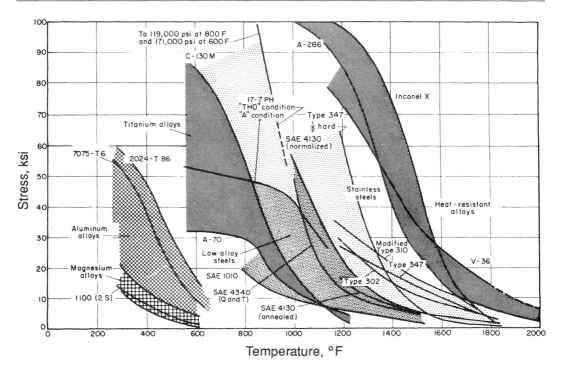

Figure 15.1   Stress versus temperature for 3% total deformation in 10 min for various engineering metals. (From [van Echo 58]; used with permission.)

material's glass transition temperature T_g, as discussed in Chapters 2 and 3. Thus, polymers that are in a leathery or rubbery state are susceptible to creep, and this is often the case even at room temperature. Concrete creeps at room temperature, but the process becomes slower with time, so that only small additional strains occur after the first year or so.

Selection of an appropriate material is likely to be a critical factor in a creep-sensitive design. Engineering metals used in high-temperature service generally contain alloying elements such as chromium, nickel, and cobalt, with the percentages of these expensive materials increasing with temperature resistance. The large differences that exist in temperature resistance among various classes of engineering metals are illustrated by short-time creep data in Figure 15.1. New tough ceramic materials offer opportunities for greater temperature resistance than even the best metal alloys. Conversely, polymers are severely limited in their temperature resistance.

Other environmental effects, such as oxidation and environmental cracking, are also likely to cause difficulty as chemical activity increases with temperature. For example, the resistance to oxidation in air and creep-related failure are compared for various classes of heat-resisting metals in Fig. 15.2. Although such other environmental factors are not treated in this chapter, they nevertheless also need to be considered in design for high-temperature service. Another complexity that often occurs in engineering situations is cyclic loading combined with time-dependent deformation. A harmful creep–fatigue interaction that accelerates the fatigue process can then occur.

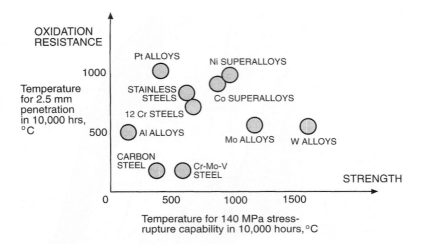

Figure 15.2 Relative creep and oxidation resistance of various classes of engineering metals. (Adapted from [Sims 78]; used with permission.)

The engineering methods that have been developed for analyzing and predicting creep behavior provide tools that can be used in design to avoid failure due to creep. One concern is excessive deformation. Another is *creep rupture*, which is a separation (fracture) of the material that can occur as a result of the creep process. In what follows, we will first consider creep testing and physical mechanisms, which topics provide needed introductory information prior to emphasizing engineering methods in the remainder of the chapter.

An additional topic covered near the end of this chapter is *materials damping*, which is the dissipation of energy resulting from cyclic loading. Since the deformations involved are often time dependent, the topic is included in this chapter. Note that the amount of materials damping affects the severity of mechanical vibrations.

15.2 CREEP TESTING

The most common method of creep testing is simply to apply a constant axial force, either in tension or compression, to a bar or cylinder of the material of interest. Since the force is to be held constant for long periods of time, simple dead weights and a lever system may be used, as shown in Fig. 15.3. The creep strain is measured with time, and the time at rupture is recorded if this occurs during the test. Tests on a given material are generally done at various stresses and temperatures, and test durations can range from less than one minute to several years.

15.2.1 Behavior Observed in Creep Tests

The behavior observed on a graph of strain versus time is usually similar to Fig. 15.4. There is an initial nearly instantaneous occurrence of elastic and perhaps also plastic strain, followed by the gradual accumulation of creep strain. The strain rate, $\dot{\varepsilon} = d\varepsilon/dt$, hence the slope of the ε versus t

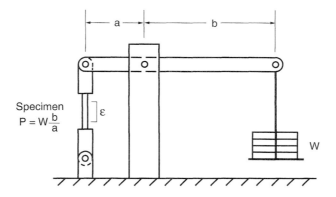

Figure 15.3 Schematic of a creep testing machine.

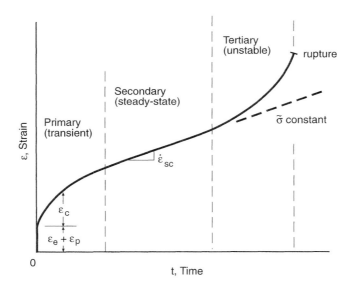

Figure 15.4 Strain versus time behavior during creep under constant force, hence constant engineering stress, and the three stages of creep.

plot, is at first relatively high. However, $\dot{\varepsilon}$ decreases and often becomes approximately constant, at which point the *primary* or *transient* stage of creep is said to end, and the *secondary* or *steady-state* stage to begin. At the end of the secondary stage, $\dot{\varepsilon}$ increases in an unstable manner as rupture failure approaches, with this portion being called the *tertiary* stage. In this final stage, the deformation becomes localized by the formation of a neck as in a tension test, or voids may form inside the material, or both may occur.

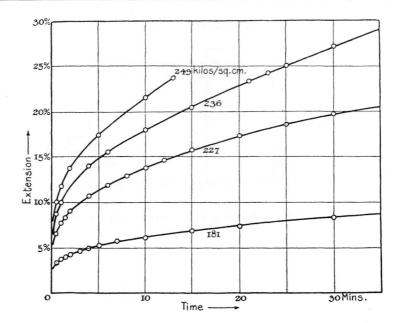

Figure 15.5   Creep curves for lead at 17°C from the early work of Andrade, where $1\,kg/cm^2 = 0.0981\,MPa$. (From [Andrade 14]; used with permission.)

Some creep data for a metal in the form of strain versus time records are shown in Fig. 15.5. As might be expected, higher strain rates occur for higher stresses. These data are from the work of Andrade, a notable early investigator of creep who was active around 1910, and were obtained under constant true stress, rather than constant force, with the use of the apparatus shown in Fig. 15.6. No tertiary stage occurs in the data of Fig. 15.5, probably as a result of the constant true stress. Note that the usual tertiary acceleration of creep is, in at least some cases, due not to any change in the behavior of the material itself, but rather to the decreasing cross-sectional area under constant force. This causes the true stress to increase, which in turn causes $\dot{\varepsilon}$ to increase.

15.2.2 Representing Creep Test Results

The results of a single creep test can be summarized by giving the following four quantities: stress σ, temperature T, steady-state creep rate $\dot{\varepsilon}_{sc}$, and time to rupture t_r. A variety of alternatives exist for presenting the data from a series of tests at various stresses and temperatures. For example, stress versus strain rate, σ versus $\dot{\varepsilon}_{sc}$, can be plotted for each of several temperatures, as illustrated in Fig. 15.7. Another useful presentation is to plot stress versus life, σ versus t_r, for various temperatures, as illustrated by Fig. 15.8. As seen in these examples, logarithmic scales are generally used. A σ versus t_r plot is analogous to an S-N curve for fatigue, except that the life is a rupture time rather than a number of cycles. Stress–life plots for three values of strain, and also for rupture, all for a single temperature, are shown for a polymer in Fig. 15.9.

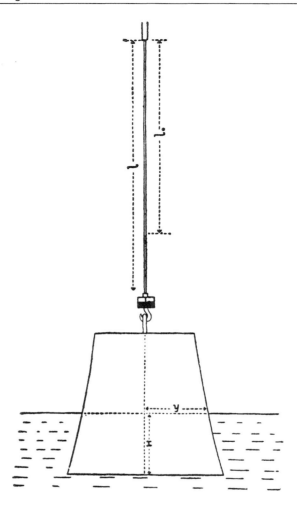

Figure 15.6 Apparatus used by Andrade for creep testing under constant true stress. The mass M is shaped according to $y = \frac{1}{l_o + x}\sqrt{\frac{Ml_o}{\rho\pi}}$ and is suspended in a liquid of mass density ρ, so that the force decreases with strain to maintain constant true stress during uniform elongation. (From [Andrade 10]; used with permission.)

Stress–life data are also often represented by plotting σ versus T, with lines for different times to failure t_r. This is, of course, simply an alternative means of representing the same information as a plot similar to Fig. 15.8. Such a representation for nickel metal is shown in Fig. 15.10. This particular plot covers a wide range of the variables, and it also indicates some details of the nature of the creep fractures that occur for various stresses and temperatures. Such a comprehensive representation is said to be a *fracture mechanism map*.

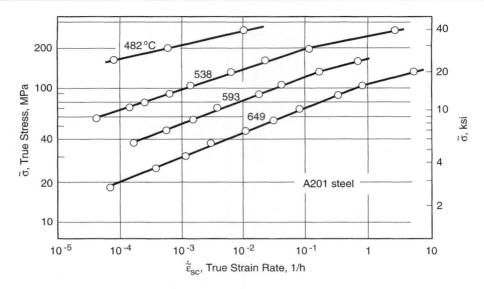

Figure 15.7   Stress versus steady-state strain rate at various temperatures for a carbon steel used for pressure vessels. (Adapted from [Randall 57]; copyright © ASTM; reprinted with permission.)

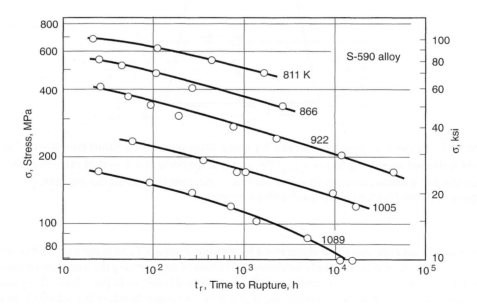

Figure 15.8   Stress versus rupture life curves for S-590, an iron-based, heat-resisting alloy. (Data from [Goldhoff 59a].)

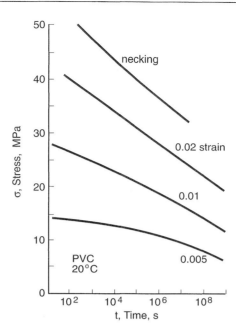

Figure 15.9 Stress–life curves for unplasticized polyvinyl chloride for three values of strain, and also for the onset of rupture by necking. (Adapted from [EVC 89]; used with permission.)

Stress–strain curves for various constant values of time, called *isochronous stress–strain curves*, are often needed. These are constructed from strain versus time data for several stress levels, as shown in Figs. 15.11(a) and (b). Strains corresponding to a particular time, such as $t = t_1$, are obtained as shown in (a). These are then plotted versus the corresponding stress values, as in (b), forming the isochronous stress–strain curve for time t_1. Similar curves can be constructed for other values of time, such as t_2 and t_3, so that a family of stress–strain curves is obtained. For polymers, it is a common practice to use isochronous stress–strain curves to determine secant moduli, E_s, corresponding to specific values of strain, as shown for strain $\varepsilon = \varepsilon'$ in (c). Such E_s values are then plotted versus time to characterize the behavior of the material, as in (d). Secant modulus versus time curves for more than one value of strain may be obtained and plotted as a family of curves.

Of particular significance are plots of $\dot{\varepsilon}_{sc}$ versus $1/T$, the reciprocal of absolute temperature, where a log scale is used for $\dot{\varepsilon}_{sc}$, and a linear scale for $1/T$. Such a plot with lines for various stresses is shown for a ceramic in Fig. 15.12. Also useful is a similar plot with t_r replacing $\dot{\varepsilon}_{sc}$. Slopes on these plots give apparent *activation energies*, a subject that will be discussed in the next section.

15.3 PHYSICAL MECHANISMS OF CREEP

The physical mechanisms causing creep differ markedly for different classes of materials. In addition, even for a given material, different mechanisms act at various combinations of stress and temperature. Motions of atoms, vacancies, dislocations, or molecules within a solid material occur in

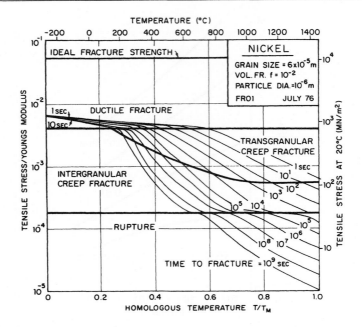

Figure 15.10 Fracture mechanism map showing stress versus temperature for various times to creep rupture for nickel with the indicated grain size. Stresses σ are normalized with the elastic modulus E, which varies with temperature. (From [Ashby 77]; used with permission.)

a time-dependent manner, and they occur more rapidly at higher temperatures. Such motions are important in explaining creep behavior and fall within the broad category of behavior called *diffusion*.

15.3.1 Viscous Creep

The viscosity of a liquid, as employed in fluid mechanics, is the ratio of the applied shear stress to the resulting rate of shear strain. That is,

$$\eta_\tau = \frac{\tau}{\dot{\gamma}} \tag{15.1}$$

where η_τ is the shear viscosity. Similarly, a tensile viscosity can be defined as

$$\eta = \frac{\sigma}{\dot{\varepsilon}} \tag{15.2}$$

For an ideal viscous substance that is incompressible, $\eta = 3\eta_\tau$. Also, a constant value of η corresponds to the behavior of an ideal dashpot with force–displacement behavior of the form $P = c\dot{x}$, where the constant c is analogous to η. (See Section 5.2).

Some nominally solid materials behave in a manner similar to a liquid with a very high viscosity. This is generally the case for amorphous solids such as silica glass and some polymers. In response to a stress applied to the material, molecules or groups of molecules move relative to one another in a time-dependent manner, resulting in creep deformation. Such molecular

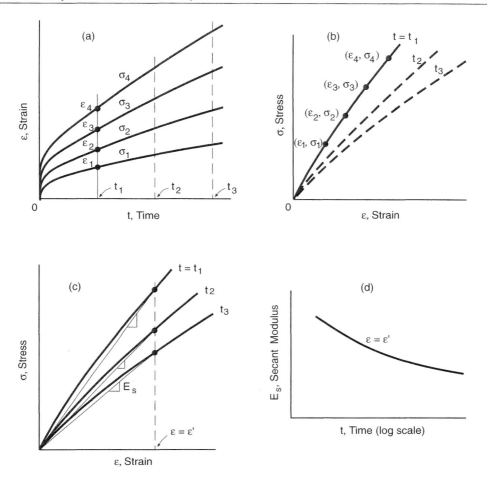

Figure 15.11   Construction of isochronous stress–strain curves and secant modulus curves. Strain–time data (a) for several stress levels can be used to obtain isochronous σ-ε curves, as in (b). Secant moduli E_s can then be obtained from the isochronous σ-ε curves, as shown in (c), and E_s is often plotted versus time, as in (d).

motions constitute a diffusion process that is enhanced if the temperature is increased. This occurs because a temperature increase is related to an increase of the average oscillations of atoms about their equilibrium positions. Greater oscillations result in more frequent stress-driven molecular rearrangements that contribute to creep deformation.

Such a situation is a case of *thermal activation*. From the physics involved, the rate of a thermally activated process is expected to be governed by an equation of the following form, which is called the *Arrhenius equation*:

$$\dot{\varepsilon} = Ae^{\frac{-Q}{RT}} \tag{15.3}$$

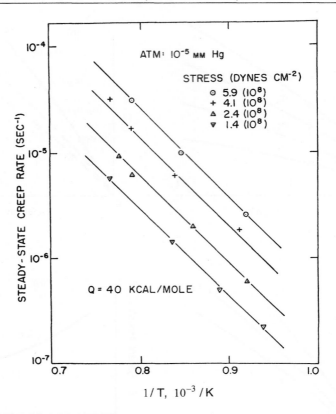

Figure 15.12   Steady-state creep rate versus reciprocal of absolute temperature for single crystals of titanium oxide ceramic, TiO$_2$, also called *rutile*, tested under compression in a vacuum, where 1 dyne/cm^2 = 10^{-7} MPa. (Adapted from [Hirthe 63]; reprinted by permission of the American Ceramic Society.)

The rate here is the strain rate $\dot\varepsilon$, and Q is a special physical constant called the *activation energy*. It is a measure of the energy barrier that must be overcome for molecular motion to occur. Temperature T is the absolute temperature in units of kelvins (K). And R is the universal gas constant, the value of which depends on the choice of units for Q, such as calories/mole or joules/mole. The corresponding values and their units are

$$R = 1.987 \text{ cal/(mole·K)} \qquad \text{(for } Q \text{ in cal/mole)}$$
$$R = 8.314 \text{ J/(mole·K)} \qquad \text{(for } Q \text{ in J/mole)} \tag{15.4}$$

The coefficient A depends, at a minimum, on stress. For a creep process that is similar to viscous flow obeying Eq. 15.2, the stress dependence can be included in the rate equation as follows:

$$\dot\varepsilon = A_1 \sigma e^{\frac{-Q}{RT}} \tag{15.5}$$

The new coefficient A_1 depends mainly on the material, but its value and Q may both change if the physical mechanism is altered due to a sufficient shift in temperature or stress.

15.3.2 Creep in Polymers

At temperatures below the glass transition temperature T_g of a given polymer, creep effects are relatively small. Above T_g, creep effects rapidly become significant. As T_g for common polymers is often in the range -100 to $+200°C$, this temperature may be exceeded around or even below room temperature. For a primarily crystalline thermoplastic such as polyethylene, viscous flow occurs at temperatures substantially above T_g, especially upon approaching the melting temperature. Note that the secondary (hydrogen and van der Waals) bonds that hold the carbon-based molecular chains to one another below T_g are less effective above T_g. Thus, creep can occur by the molecular chains sliding past one another in a viscous manner. The process is made easier in linear polymers if the molecular chains are shorter, and it is enhanced by the absence of obstacles to sliding, such as branching or cross-linking in the chainlike molecules. The stress and temperature dependence of this type of viscous flow at least roughly obey Eq. 15.5.

However, the behavior is more complicated at intermediate temperatures, only modestly above T_g, where the behavior is leathery or rubbery. Here, sliding of the molecular chains is more difficult, and they are more easily entangled with one another, particularly if the chains are long. Such entanglements give the material an increasing resistance as deformation proceeds, so that the rate of creep decreases as deformation progresses. Other obstacles to sliding, such as branching or cross-linking, have a similar effect, so that these also tend to limit creep if they are present.

Obstacles to sliding of the molecules also give the material a memory of its before-deformation shape. In particular, after removal of the applied stress, the stretched and distorted chain segments between entanglement or cross-link points act somewhat like springs that tend to cause the prior creep deformation to disappear (recover) with time. This self-limiting creep and recovery behavior is a departure from simple viscous behavior that is similar to that of the transient creep rheological model of Fig. 5.5(b). In a real polymer, some nonrecoverable viscous deformation occurs in addition to the recoverable portion. The simplest rheological model that has behavior even roughly similar to that of a polymer is thus one that combines elastic, steady-state creep, and transient creep elements, as shown in Fig. 15.13.

15.3.3 Creep in Crystalline Materials

Crystalline materials commonly used in engineering include metals and their alloys and the engineering ceramics. Some ceramics contain a crystalline phase in combination with a glassy phase, such as porcelain and fired clay brick. As a result of their similarities in structure, crystalline materials (or phases) have roughly similar physical mechanisms for creep deformation. A variety of physical mechanisms occur, which may be separated into two broad classes, termed *diffusional flow* and *dislocation creep*. Some authors also consider *grain boundary sliding* to be a distinct mechanism.

A general equation for the steady-state creep rate in *crystalline* materials is

$$\dot{\varepsilon} = \frac{A_2 \sigma^m}{d^q T} e^{\frac{-Q}{RT}} \tag{15.6}$$

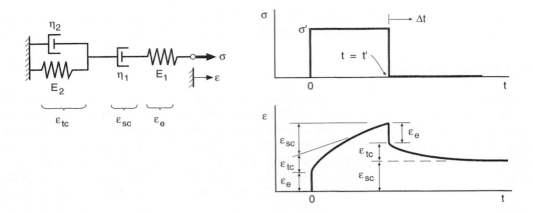

Figure 15.13 Creep and recovery behavior in a rheological model that combines elastic, steady-state creep, and transient creep elements. The elastic strain ε_e in spring E_1 is recovered immediately upon unloading, whereas the transient creep strain ε_{tc} in parallel combination (E_2, η_2) is recovered slowly with time. The steady-state creep strain ε_{sc} in dashpot η_1 is never recovered.

Table 15.1 Creep Exponents for Various Physical Mechanisms

Name of Mechanism	m	q	Description
Diffusional flow (Nabarro–Herring creep)	1	2	Vacancy diffusion through the crystal lattice
Diffusional flow (Coble creep)	1	3	Vacancy diffusion along grain boundaries
Grain boundary sliding	2	2 or 3	Sliding accommodated by vacancy diffusion through the crystal lattice ($q = 2$) or along grain boundaries ($q = 3$)
Dislocation creep (Power law creep)	3 to 8	0	Dislocation motion, with climb over microstructural obstacles

In this equation, the variables that affect the strain rate $\dot{\varepsilon}$ are stress σ, average grain diameter d, and absolute temperature T. The coefficient A_2, the exponents m and q, and the activation energy Q have values that depend on the material and the particular creep mechanism that is acting. Values of m and q are summarized in Table 15.1. The temperature dependence is similar to Eq. 15.3, indicating that all creep mechanisms are thermally activated. However, there is an additional (relatively weak) inverse temperature dependence; that is, A in Eq. 15.3 is affected somewhat by temperature.

Diffusional flow can occur at low stress, but requires relatively high temperature. This mechanism involves the movement of vacancies (holes) in the crystal lattice, as previously illustrated by Fig. 2.26. It occurs as a result of the spontaneous formation of vacancies being favored near grain boundaries that are approximately normal to the applied stress. The uneven distribution thus created results in movement (diffusion) of vacancies to regions of lower concentration. Hence, there is a transfer of material that causes an overall deformation of the polycrystalline material.

If the vacancies move through the crystal lattice, the behavior is called *Nabarro–Herring creep*. Also, the resulting strain rate is approximately proportional to the stress, $m = 1$, and inversely proportional to the square of the average grain diameter, $q = 2$. However, if the vacancies instead move along grain boundaries, the behavior is termed *Coble creep*. The dependence on stress is similar, but the dependence on grain size is altered to $q = 3$. The proportionality of strain rate to stress indicates that both types of diffusional flow are essentially viscous processes. The activation energy Q is similar to either Q_v for self-diffusion of the material in its own crystal lattice or Q_b for diffusion along grain boundaries, as applicable.

Dislocation creep, also called *power-law creep*, involves the more drastic motion of dislocations, which are line defects, rather than only vacancies, which are point defects. Consequently, high stresses are required, but the effect can occur at intermediate temperatures where diffusional flow is small. The mechanisms are complex and not fully understood, but *dislocation climb* is thought to be important.

Consider Fig. 15.14. Due to the effect of an applied stress, an edge dislocation moves along a crystal lattice plane by the stepwise slip process described in Chapter 2, which is also called *glide*. On encountering an obstacle, such as a precipitate particle or an immobile entanglement of other dislocations, further deformation requires that the dislocation move to another lattice plane. Such a motion is termed *climb* and requires a rearrangement of atoms, again by vacancy diffusion. The cumulative effect of a large number of such climb events is to permit more glide, hence more macroscopic deformation, than could otherwise occur. The deformation is time dependent because the climb process is time dependent. As grain boundaries are not a major factor, the strain rate is not significantly affected by grain size, but the resistance to the climb process is such that there is a strong stress dependence. Values of m vary with material and test conditions, being typically

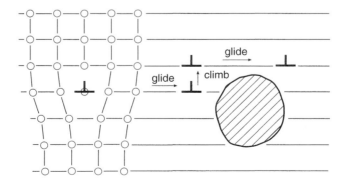

Figure 15.14 Climb of an edge dislocation, permitting continued glide past an obstacle, and enabling deformation to proceed.

around 5, and usually within the range 3 to 8. The process appears to be diffusion controlled, which is supported by the fact that Q for dislocation creep generally agrees with that for self-diffusion of the material in its own crystal lattice.

15.3.4 Discussion

If a given material, grain size, and temperature are of interest, it may be convenient to restate Eq. 15.6 as

$$\dot{\varepsilon} = B\sigma^m, \qquad \text{where } B = \frac{A_2}{d^q T} e^{\frac{-Q}{RT}} \qquad \text{(a, b)} \tag{15.7}$$

The quantity B then becomes a constant. If the applied stress σ does not vary with time, then the creep strain accumulates linearly with time t according to

$$\varepsilon_{sc} = B\sigma^m t \tag{15.8}$$

where the subscript sc is included to indicate that this is the strain resulting from steady-state creep. Since elastic strain corresponding to an elastic modulus E occurs in all materials, the total strain will be at least the sum of the elastic and creep strains:

$$\varepsilon = \varepsilon_e + \varepsilon_{sc} = \frac{\sigma}{E} + B\sigma^m t \tag{15.9}$$

If plastic strains also occur, then this additional strain component needs to be added as well, perhaps based on Eq. 12.11.

15.3.5 Evaluation of Activation Energies

Activation energies for creep can be determined by fitting slopes of straight lines on plots of $\log \dot{\varepsilon}$ versus $1/T$ for constant stress, such as the lines in Fig. 15.12. Assume that the simple form of Eq. 15.3 applies, and take logarithms to the base 10 of both sides. Then

$$\log \dot{\varepsilon} = \log A - \frac{Q}{RT} \log e = \log A - 0.434 \frac{Q}{R} \left(\frac{1}{T} \right) \tag{15.10}$$

The gas constant R takes a value from Eq. 15.4, depending on the units desired for Q. In the second form, $\log_{10} e$ is evaluated, and T continues to be absolute temperature in kelvins.

If Eq. 15.3 is indeed obeyed, the activation energy Q will be the same for all values of stress. Hence, data of $\log \dot{\varepsilon}$ versus $1/T$ for various stresses should form parallel straight lines. This is seen to be at least approximately the case in Fig. 15.12. An analogous procedure may be applied to find activation energies where the behavior obeys Eq. 15.6. In particular, for a given material and grain size d, a plot of the quantity $\log (\dot{\varepsilon} T)$ versus $1/T$ produces straight lines, all having the same slope proportional to Q, but with intercepts depending on stress σ. Alternatively, if the constant m is known, a plot of $\log (\dot{\varepsilon} T / \sigma^m)$ versus $1/T$ can be made. This produces a single line of slope proportional to Q for all stresses.

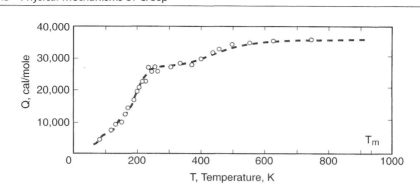

Figure 15.15 Activation energy for creep of pure aluminum as a function of the absolute temperature. (Adapted from [Sherby 57]; reprinted with permission from *Acta Metallurgica*; © 1957 Elsevier, Oxford, UK.)

Care is needed in employing values of activation energy Q, as large shifts in temperature or stress may change the mechanism sufficiently to alter Q. This is demonstrated by some data for high-purity aluminum shown in Fig. 15.15. In this case, Q for creep at relatively high temperature is found to be independent of both stress and strain, and it is constant and close to the self-diffusion value. However, below about half the absolute melting temperature, Q decreases and becomes variable, as a result of other mechanisms occurring that are not controlled by the same activation energy.

15.3.6 Deformation Mechanism Maps

For a given material, a *deformation mechanism map* can be drawn that shows what deformation mechanism is dominant for any given combination of stress and temperature. Examples for nickel metal and a nickel-base superalloy are shown in Fig. 15.16. Lines of constant shear strain rate $\dot{\gamma}$ are shown, and the behavior may be considered to be essentially elastic below the lowest one of these. The diffusional flow region is subdivided, depending on the type of vacancy diffusion, and two types of power-law creep occur for nickel, low-temperature (LT) creep and high-temperature (HT) creep. Above the yield stress, plastic deformation by dislocation glide is the dominant type of deformation. A theoretical limit on the strength is also shown, this corresponding to the theoretical shear strength, $\tau_b \approx G/10$, that can cause shear of crystal planes even if no dislocation motion occurs. (See Section 2.4.)

Details of the map of course differ with the material and its processing. For example, in crystalline materials, diffusional flow is more likely to be an important factor if the grain size is small. This results from the inverse dependence of strain rate on grain size, as in Eq. 15.6 with $q = 2$ or 3. Hence, where this mechanism is dominant, large grain size is beneficial.

In the deformation mechanism maps of Fig. 15.16, the stresses plotted are shear stresses τ, and these are normalized with respect to the shear modulus G, so that the vertical axis is τ/G. Since G decreases with temperature, its value is needed to use the map. The following relationship applies:

$$G = G_{300} - h(T - 300) \tag{15.11}$$

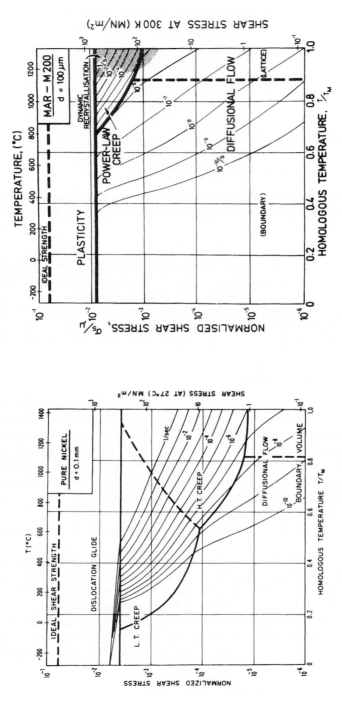

Figure 15.16 Deformation mechanism maps giving shear strain rates $\dot{\gamma}$ for nickel (left) and a nickel-base superalloy (right), both having the same grain size. Shear stresses τ are normalized to the temperature-varying shear modulus G, so that the left-hand vertical axis is τ/G. For the homologous temperature scale T/T_m, the quantity T_m is the melting temperature, and absolute temperatures in degrees K are used. (From [Ashby 77] and [Frost 82] p. 57, respectively; used with permission).

In this equation, G_{300} is the value at $T = 300$ K, the quantity h is a material constant, and T is the absolute temperature in degrees K. These values and the melting temperature T_m are given in the following table for the materials of these two maps:

Material	G_{300}, MPa	h, MPa/K	T_m, K
Nickel	78,900	29.3	1726
MAR-M200	80,000	25.0	1600

Source: Data in [Frost 82] p. 54.

For creep under uniaxial tension, stress σ and strain rate $\dot{\varepsilon}$ are related to the shear quantities τ and $\dot{\gamma}$ of the map by

$$\sigma = \sqrt{3}\tau, \qquad \dot{\varepsilon} = \dot{\gamma}/\sqrt{3} \tag{15.12}$$

Additional similar maps are given for various metals and ceramics in Frost (1982). In that book, materials constants are also listed for each region of the maps on the basis of relationships similar to Eq. 15.6.

Example 15.1

Consider nickel with the same grain size and processing as the material of Fig. 15.16. This material is subjected to a tensile stress of 6 MPa at a temperature of 900°C. What is the approximate strain rate, and what creep mechanism is dominant?

Solution   To enter the map, we need τ and G from Eqs. 15.12 and 15.11, which give the normalized shear stress τ/G. We have

$$\tau = \frac{\sigma}{\sqrt{3}} = \frac{6\,\text{MPa}}{\sqrt{3}} = 3.464\,\text{MPa}$$

$$G = G_{300} - h(T - 300) = 78,900 - 29.3(1173 - 300) = 53,320\,\text{MPa}$$

$$\tau/G = 6.50 \times 10^{-5}$$

where $T = 900 + 273 = 1173$ K is substituted for obtaining G.

For the temperature, either use the upper scale and enter the graph directly with $T = 900$°C, or enter the lower scale with $T/T_m = 1173/1726 = 0.680$. To enter the τ/G scale, it may be useful to calculate $\log{(\tau/G)} = -4.19$, allowing linear scaling between $\tau/G = 10^{-4}$ and 10^{-5} (that is, between $\log{(\tau/G)} = -4$ and -5). Entering the map with these values and interpolating between curves gives a strain rate of approximately

$$\dot{\gamma} \approx 10^{-6.7} = 2.0 \times 10^{-7}\,\text{s}^{-1}, \qquad \dot{\varepsilon} = \dot{\gamma}/\sqrt{3} = 1.2 \times 10^{-7}\,\text{s}^{-1} \qquad \textbf{Ans.}$$

This point falls within the region of dominance of the high-temperature type of power law creep.

Comment   The value calculated actually represents quite a high strain rate for any practical application. For example, in one day, the accumulated strain would be

$$\varepsilon = \dot{\varepsilon}t = (1.2 \times 10^{-7} \text{ s}^{-1})(3600 \text{ s/h})(24 \text{ h}) = 0.010 = 1.0\%$$

15.3.7 Creep in Concrete

Although concrete can be described in general terms as a crystalline ceramic, its complex structure results in distinctive creep mechanisms and behavior. Concrete contains cement paste that has been chemically combined with water in the hydration reaction that hardens the concrete. Unhydrated paste is also present that is slowly converted by the hydration reaction as time passes. Additional unreacted water is present in pores, between microlayers of the hydrated cement, and chemically adsorbed (weakly attached by secondary chemical bonds) to the hydrated paste. Finally, there is aggregate (sand and stone) in a gradation of sizes.

Creep in concrete occurs mostly in the cement paste, with the aggregate acting to limit the deformation. Thus, elastic strains build up in the aggregate and oppose the creep in the paste, causing the creep rate to decrease. Data illustrating this trend are shown in Fig. 15.17. The detailed mechanisms of creep in the cement paste are complex and not completely understood. One possibility is that an applied stress squeezes the unreacted water in some voids and causes it to move by viscous flow to another location, permitting a time-dependent distortion of the microstructure. Another is that adsorbed water lubricates layers and particles of hydrated cement and allows them to slide relative to one another. Microcracking at interfaces between aggregate and paste also progresses with time and contributes to creep. In addition, at high stresses, mechanisms similar to those in more ordinary crystalline ceramics may be significant.

Since creep occurs primarily in the cement paste, the elastic deformations that build up in the aggregate reverse the creep strain when the load is removed. This recovery behavior, and also the

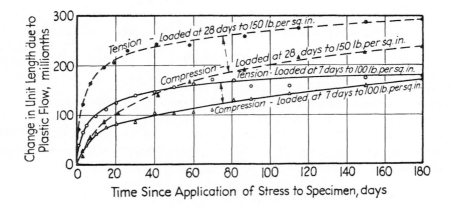

Figure 15.17 Creep strain in μm/m for concrete in tension and compression for two different times of curing. (From [Davis 37]; copyright © ASTM; reprinted with permission.)

decreasing creep rate under load, is similar to the behavior of the transient creep rheological model of Fig. 5.5(b). However, as the creep strain due to microcracking is not recovered on unloading, the behavior is represented better by the rheological model of Fig. 15.13. More complex models with additional stages, and special nonlinear springs and dashpots, are also used.

15.4 TIME–TEMPERATURE PARAMETERS AND LIFE ESTIMATES

Creep deformation can proceed to the point of rupture of the material by the development of cracking, crazing, or other damage, which results from the intense strain. For example, in crystalline materials, voids may appear along grain boundaries or at other points of localized stress concentration, such as precipitate particles, by a process called *creep cavitation*. An example is shown in Fig. 15.18. The enlarging and joining of grain boundary or other voids then causes cracks, which can progress to the point of fracture, called *creep rupture*. However, if the temperature is sufficiently high in a ductile and relatively pure metal, the process of *dynamic recrystallization* can occur, in which these voids are essentially repaired as they try to form. Large deformations are then possible, and failure eventually occurs by necking. Creep rupture of ductile polymers is generally preceded by large uniform or necking deformations.

In engineering design where creep occurs, there must be neither excessive deformation nor rupture within the desired service life, which is likely to be lengthy, perhaps 20 years or more. However, test-time limitations result in creep data generally being available only out to 1000 hours (42 days), or sometimes 10,000 h (14 months), but seldom to 100,000 h (11 years). For estimating the behavior at low strain rates and long times, one possible approach is to estimate creep strains for the service temperature of interest by extrapolating the appropriate σ versus $\dot{\varepsilon}$ curve, such as

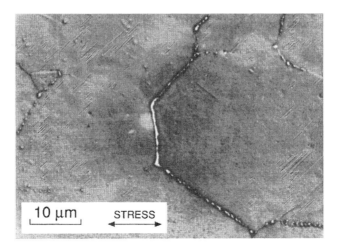

Figure 15.18   Grain boundary cavitation and cracking due to creep in a tantalum alloy (T-111), tested under creep–fatigue interaction with temperature variation between 200 and 1150°C. (Adapted from [Sheffler 72].)

one of those in Fig. 15.7, back to low $\dot{\varepsilon}$ values. Similarly, rupture lives, or lives to a particular strain value, could be estimated by extrapolating stress–life plots, such as Figs. 15.8 or 15.9, to long lives. However, such extrapolations do not work very well, as the slopes of fitted lines on log–linear or log–log plots of σ versus $\dot{\varepsilon}$ or σ versus t_r may not be constant, or they may be constant over only limited ranges of these variables. Abrupt slope changes may occur due to a shift in the creep mechanism, so that extrapolation is not valid. In other words, one cannot extrapolate across the boundaries for various creep mechanisms on a deformation mechanism map.

A more successful approach is to use data from relatively short time tests, but at temperatures above the service temperature of interest, to estimate the behavior for the longer time at the service temperature. Under these circumstances, a common physical mechanism for tests and service is more likely than for extrapolation at a constant temperature. Such an approach involves the use of a *time–temperature parameter*. We will consider two approaches of this type, namely the Sherby–Dorn parameter and the Larson–Miller parameter.

15.4.1 Sherby–Dorn (*S-D*) Parameter

The Arrhenius rate equation is the basis of the Sherby–Dorn (*S-D*) time–temperature parameter. A key assumption is that the activation energy for creep is constant. First, write Eq. 15.3 in differential form and note that the coefficient is a function of stress, $A = A(\sigma)$:

$$d\varepsilon = A(\sigma)e^{\frac{-Q}{RT}}\, dt \tag{15.13}$$

Then integrate both sides of the equation, and discard the constant of integration so that only the steady-state creep strain appears:

$$\varepsilon_{sc} = A(\sigma)te^{\frac{-Q}{RT}} \tag{15.14}$$

This equation suggests that creep strains for a given stress form a unique curve if plotted versus the quantity

$$\theta = te^{\frac{-Q}{RT}} \tag{15.15}$$

which is termed the *temperature-compensated time*. Some supporting test data for aluminum alloys are shown in Fig. 15.19.

To formally define the *S-D* parameter, we use logic as follows: The creep strain at rupture is observed to be fairly constant for a given value of temperature-compensated time to rupture, θ_r, as for the data for any one material in Fig. 15.19. Hence, θ_r depends only on stress, so for a given material, there should be a single curve relating θ_r and stress for various combinations of temperature T and rupture time t_r. Rather than working directly with θ_r, we find it convenient to define the *S-D* parameter as $P_{SD} = \log\theta_r$. Thus, take logarithms to the base 10 of both sides of Eq. 15.15, note that $t = t_r$ at $\theta = \theta_r$, and substitute $\log_{10} e = 0.434$ and $R \approx 2.0$ cal/(mole·K), to obtain

$$P_{SD} = \log t_r - \frac{0.217Q}{T} \tag{15.16}$$

Units of hours for t_r, cal/mole for Q, and kelvins for T are employed.

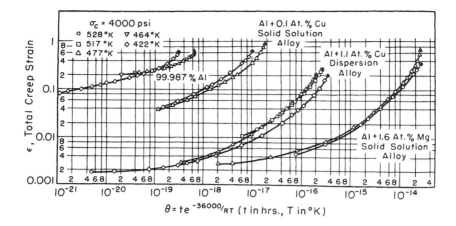

Figure 15.19 Creep strain versus temperature-compensated time for aluminum and dilute alloys tested at $\sigma = 27.6$ MPa at various temperatures. (From [Orr 54]; used with permission.)

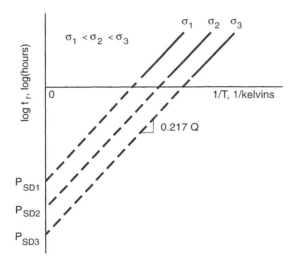

Figure 15.20 Graphical interpretation for the Sherby–Dorn parameter, with constant slope proportional to the activation energy Q.

Values of the activation energy Q for use with the S-D parameter can be obtained by plotting creep–rupture data on coordinate axes of $\log t_r$ versus $1/T$, as illustrated in Fig. 15.20. A family of parallel straight lines is expected, one for each value of stress. These lines all have slopes given by $0.217Q$, and each intercept at $1/T = 0$ can be interpreted as the P_{SD} value for that stress. Some typical values of Q are 90,000 cal/mole for various steels and stainless steels, and 36,000 cal/mole for pure aluminum and dilute alloys. A few additional values for specific engineering metals are listed in Table 15.2.

Table 15.2   Activation Energies for the Sherby–Dorn Parameter

Material	1Cr-1Mo-0.25V steel	A-286 Fe-Ni-Cr alloy	S-590 Fe-Cr-Ni-Co alloy	Nimonic 80A Ni-base alloy
Q, cal/mole	110,000	91,000	85,000	91,000

Source: Data in [Conway 69], [Goldhoff 59a], and [Goldhoff 59b].

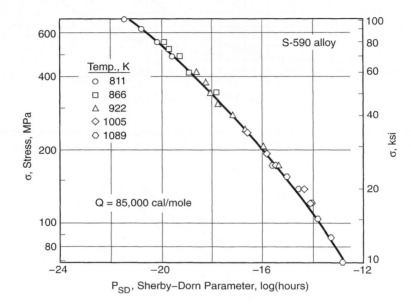

Figure 15.21   Correlation using the Sherby–Dorn parameter of creep–rupture data for S-590 alloy. (Data from [Goldhoff 59a].)

Once Q is known, stress–life data can be employed to make a plot of P_{SD} versus stress, as shown for a heat-resisting iron-base alloy in Fig. 15.21. The data for all stresses and temperatures should fall together along a single curve, with the correlation of the data being a measure of the success of the parameter for any particular set of data. Using such a plot and Eq. 15.16, we can determine rupture times t_r for particular values of stress and temperature. The test data used to obtain the P_{SD} versus σ plot generally involve shorter rupture times than the service lives of interest. Hence, test data at relatively short t_r and high temperature are being used to predict the behavior at longer t_r and lower temperature.

Service lives in creep situations may be limited by excess deformation rather than by rupture. It is then useful to identify a particular value of creep strain, such as 1% or 2%, that is considered to represent failure. The $S\text{-}D$ parameter can be used in this situation also, by simple replacement of the rupture life t_r in Eq. 15.16 by t_f, the time to reach the strain of interest. The values of P_{SD} used, of course, need to be obtained from data for t_f rather than t_r.

Example 15.2

An engineering component made of the heat-resisting Fe-Cr-Ni-Co alloy S-590 is subjected in service to a static stress of 200 MPa at a temperature of 600°C. What creep–rupture life in days is expected?

Solution   Figure 15.21 provides the needed stress versus P_{SD} curve and value of $Q = 85,000$ cal/mole for this material. Entering the curve with $\sigma = 200$ MPa gives $P_{SD} \approx -16.0$. Temperature must be in kelvins for Eq. 15.16; that is, $T = 600°\text{C} + 273 = 873$ K. Equation 15.16 then gives

$$\log t_r = P_{SD} + \frac{0.217Q}{T} = -16.0 + \frac{0.217(85,000 \text{ cal/mole})}{873 \text{ K}} = 5.128$$

$$t_r = 10^{\log t_r} = 10^{5.128} = 134,400 \text{ hours} = 5600 \text{ days} \qquad \textbf{Ans.}$$

15.4.2 Larson–Miller (L-M) Parameter

The time–temperature parameter of Larson and Miller is an analogous approach to that of Sherby and Dorn, but different assumptions, and therefore different equations, are used. The L-M parameter can also be derived starting from Eq. 15.15, substituting $\theta = \theta_r$ and $t = t_r$, and similarly taking logarithms to the base 10 of both sides. However, Q is assumed to vary, and θ_r to be constant. The parameter is in this case defined as $P_{LM} = 0.217Q$, and a constant $C = -\log \theta_r$ is employed. Proceeding on this basis and solving for P_{LM} gives

$$P_{LM} = T(\log t_r + C) \tag{15.17}$$

Units of kelvins (K) for T and hours for t_r will be used here. However, in much of the literature related to the L-M parameter, the temperature is in degrees Fahrenheit, here denoted T_F. The parameter is then given by

$$P'_{LM} = (T_F + 460)(\log t_r + C) \tag{15.18}$$

so that $P'_{LM} = 1.8 P_{LM}$. The units for C are unaffected, as t_r is in units of hours in all cases.

The value of C can be interpreted as an extrapolated intercept on a plot of $\log t_r$ versus $1/T$, as shown in Fig. 15.22. A family of straight lines is expected for various stress values, with all of these lines having a common intercept of $\log t_r = -C$ at $1/T = 0$. The slopes are the values of P_{LM} corresponding to each stress. Note that this approach has the same theoretical basis as the S-D parameter, differing in that the activation energy is assumed not to be constant, but to vary with stress. Also, θ_r is assumed not to vary with stress, but instead to be a material constant as given by C.

Once the constant C is known, values of P_{LM} from stress–life data can be plotted against stress, as shown in Fig. 15.23. Such a plot is used in a manner similar to a P_{SD} versus σ curve to estimate

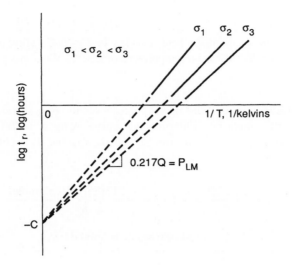

Figure 15.22   Graphical interpretation for the Larson–Miller parameter, with $-C$ being the common intercept of lines of varying slope.

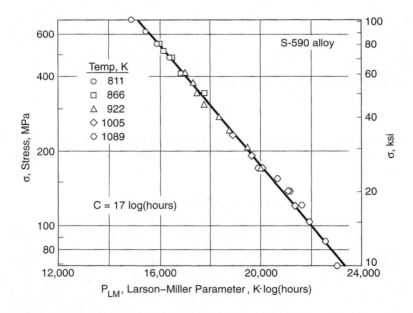

Figure 15.23   Correlation using the Larson–Miller parameter of creep–rupture data for S-590 alloy. (Data from [Goldhoff 59a].)

Table 15.3   Constants for the Larson–Miller Parameter

Material	C log (hours)	Polynomial Fit (units of hours, K, and MPa)				Range of L-M Fit	
		b_0	b_1	b_2	b_3	σ, MPa	T, K
1Cr-1Mo-0.25V steel	22	128,200	−141,500	64,380	−9,960	69–621	755–1005
AISI 310 stainless steel	10	20,470	−4,655	0	0	3.4–31	1255–1366
A-286 (Fe-Ni-Cr alloy)	20	116,400	−120,500	53,460	−8,188	69–758	811–1089
S-590 (Fe-Cr-Ni-Co alloy)	17	38,405	−8,206	0	0	69–690	811–1089
Nimonic 80A (Ni-base alloy)	18	16,510	11,040	−4,856	403	54–486	923–1089

Source: Values and data in [Conway 69], [Goldhoff 59a], [Goldhoff 59b], [Larson 52], [Orr 54], and [van Echo 67].

rupture times. Values of the constant C for rupture of various steels and other structural engineering metals are often near 20. Table 15.3 gives some values for specific metals. The L-M parameter may also be used to estimate times t_f corresponding to a limiting creep strain prior to rupture, provided, of course, that the needed t_f data are available. Another use of the L-M parameter, or of any other time–temperature parameter, is in comparing and ranking materials. Such a comparison for several materials is shown in Fig. 15.24. Higher curves indicate more resistant materials.

Example 15.3
Consider again Example 15.2, using the Larson–Miller parameter.

Solution   The logic is the same as before, except that now P_{LM} from Eq. 15.17 is employed. Figure 15.23 provides the needed stress versus P_{LM} curve and value of $C = 17 \log(\text{hours})$ for this material. Entering the curve with $\sigma = 200$ MPa gives $P_{LM} \approx 19{,}500$. Equation 15.17 with temperature in kelvins, $T = 600°\text{C} + 273 = 873$ K, then gives

$$\log t_r = \frac{P_{LM}}{T} - C = \frac{19{,}500}{873 \text{ K}} - 17 = 5.337$$

$$t_r = 10^{\log t_r} = 10^{5.337} = 217{,}200 \text{ hours} = 9050 \text{ days} \qquad \textbf{Ans.}$$

The result is seen to differ somewhat from that of Ex. 15.2 using P_{SD}.

15.4.3 Discussion

The two time–temperature parameters discussed seem to differ considerably from one another, and neither is consistent with the creep rate equation that is currently the most widely accepted, namely, Eq. 15.6, which includes the added (but weak) dependence on the inverse of temperature. Nevertheless, they seem to often give reasonable results. For example, note that both have a similar and reasonable ability to correlate the same set of data in Figs. 15.21 and 15.23. A number of other time–temperature parameters have been proposed. See Conway (1971) and Penny (1995) for more detail.

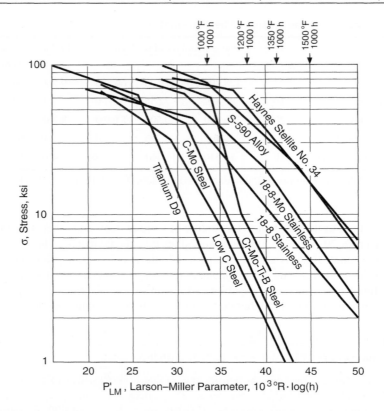

Figure 15.24 Comparison of several metals by means of the Larson–Miller parameter. Note that the absolute temperature is in Rankine units, °R = °F + 460. (Adapted from [Larson 52]; used with permission of ASME.)

The success of any time–temperature parameter approach depends on a similar physical mechanism of creep occurring in the relatively short-time, high-temperature tests as in the typically longer-time, lower-temperature service situation. Thus, the test data should involve times as close to the service application as possible, so that the extrapolation involved is not so extreme that an entirely new mechanism is encountered. A good general rule is that the test data should extend to about 10% of the desired service life, such as tests out to 17,500 hours = 2 years for a 20-year service life. Caution is advised where this must be compromised. Also, curves fitted to stress versus parameter data should not be extrapolated to stresses very far beyond the range of the data.

The utility of time–temperature parameters is aided by fitting equations to stress versus parameter curves, as in Figs. 15.21, 15.23, and 15.24. For example, for the S-D parameter, solve Eq. 15.16 for the dependent variable $\log t_r$, and then fit a polynomial to P_{SD} versus x, where $x = \log \sigma$:

$$\log t_r = P_{SD} + \frac{0.217Q}{T} \qquad \text{(a)}$$

$$P_{SD} = a_0 + a_1 x + a_2 x^2 + a_3 x^3 \qquad \text{(b)}$$

$$(15.19)$$

A similar polynomial fit can be applied to the L-M parameter of Eq. 15.17, where again $x = \log \sigma$:

$$\log t_r = \frac{P_{LM}}{T} - C \qquad \text{(a)}$$

$$P_{LM} = b_0 + b_1 x + b_2 x^2 + b_3 x^3 \qquad \text{(b)}$$

(15.20)

In these equations, a linear fit will sometimes be sufficient; that is, $a_2 = a_3 = 0$, or $b_2 = b_3 = 0$. Also, a polynomial of order higher than three may be employed, with the order preferably being an odd number. Coefficients fitted to Eq. 15.20(b) are given in Table 15.3 for several metals. Note that the equation from a parameter versus stress fit, such as Eq. 15.19 or 15.20, can be used to obtain a family of stress–life curves for various temperatures, as in Fig. 15.8.

Rather than separately determining Q and then fitting P_{SD} by means of Eq. 15.19, we can choose another option, which is to determine Q as part of the data fitting procedure. To accomplish this, we again employ $x = \log \sigma$ and combine Eqs. 15.19(a) and (b), with $y = \log t_r$ considered to be the dependent variable:

$$\log t_r = a_0 + a_1 x + a_2 x^2 + a_3 x^3 + 0.217 Q \, (1/T) \qquad \text{(a)}$$

$$y = a_0 + a_1 z_1 + a_2 z_2 + a_3 z_3 + a_4 z_4 \qquad \text{(b)}$$

(15.21)

A multiple linear regression can then be done with independent variables $z_1 = x$, $z_2 = x^2$, $z_3 = x^3$, and $z_4 = 1/T$, which yields values for fitting constants a_0, a_1, a_2, a_3, and $a_4 = 0.217Q$. Of course, the values for a_0 to a_3 will differ somewhat from those obtained from fitting Eq. 15.19(b) with a predetermined Q.

For P_{LM}, the determination of C can be similarly included in a multiple linear regression by combining Eqs. 15.20(a) and (b) to obtain a different form for $y = \log t_r$:

$$\log t_r = -C + b_0(1/T) + b_1(x/T) + b_2(x^2/T) + b_3(x^3/T) \qquad \text{(a)}$$

$$y = d + b_0 z_1 + b_1 z_2 + b_2 z_3 + b_3 z_4 \qquad \text{(b)}$$

(15.22)

In this case, the independent variables are $z_1 = 1/T$, $z_2 = x/T$, $z_3 = x^2/T$, and $z_4 = x^3/T$, and the fitting constants obtained are $d = -C$, and b_0, b_1, b_2, and b_3.

Example 15.4

The creep–rupture data for alloy S-590 plotted in Fig. 15.8 are given in Table E15.4(a), where, for each test, the temperature T, stress σ, and rupture time t_r are listed. Employ these data as follows:

(a) On the basis of Eq. 15.19, obtain a fitted equation relating the Sherby–Dorn parameter to stress. Consider $Q = 85,000$ cal/mole from Table 15.2 to be given.

(b) Similarly, use Eq. 15.20 to obtain a fitted equation relating the Larson–Miller parameter to stress, with $C = 17 \log$ (h) from Table 15.3 given.

Table E15.4(a)

| T | σ | t_r | T | σ | t_r | T | σ | t_r |
K	MPa	hours	K	MPa	hours	K	MPa	hours
811	690	22	922	345	93	1005	121	16 964
811	621	109	922	310	192	1089	172	25
811	552	433	922	276	756	1089	155	88
811	483	1 677	922	241	2 243	1089	138	267
866	552	25	922	207	11 937	1089	121	719
866	517	44	922	172	43 978	1089	103	1 354
866	483	109	1005	234	59	1089	86	5 052
866	414	264	1005	193	342	1089	69	15 335
866	345	3 149	1005	172	809	1089	69	11 257
922	414	26	1005	172	1 028	—	—	—
922	379	63	1005	138	9 529	—	—	—

Source: Data in [Goldhoff 59a].

Solution   (a) First calculate $x = \log \sigma$ and P_{SD} for each data point—that is, for each $T, \sigma,$ t_r combination in Table E15.4(a). The P_{SD} values are obtained by substituting t_r and T into Eq. 15.16, with the first few calculation results shown in Table E15.4(b). Then employ the full set of data to fit $P_{SD} = f(x)$ to the cubic polynomial of Eq. 15.19(b). The result is

$$P_{SD} = -12.35 + 4.42x - 2.287x^2 - 0.1292x^3, \qquad x = \log \sigma \qquad \text{(units: h, K, MPa)} \quad \textbf{Ans.}$$

A reasonable fit to the data is obtained, with the curve plotted in Fig. 15.21 corresponding to this equation.

   (b) The fit for the Larson–Miller parameter proceeds similarly, and the first few values of P_{LM} from Eq. 15.17 are also shown in Table E15.4(b). However, in Fig. 15.23, where P_{LM} is plotted against σ on a log scale, the data appear to lie along a straight line. It was thus assumed that $b_3 = b_4 = 0$ in Eq. 15.20(b), resulting in a simple linear equation for the fit.

$$P_{LM} = 38,405 - 8206x, \qquad x = \log \sigma \qquad \text{(units: h, K, MPa)} \qquad \textbf{Ans.}$$

This line is the one plotted in Fig. 15.23, where it is seen to represent the data well.

Table E15.4(b)

| T | σ | t_r | $x = \log \sigma$ | $y_1 = P_{SD}$ | $y_2 = P_{LM}$ |
K	MPa	hours	log (MPa)	log (h)	K·log (h)
811	690	22	2.839	−21.40	14 876
811	621	109	2.793	−20.71	15 439
811	552	433	2.742	−20.11	15 925
...	...	...	...	...	...

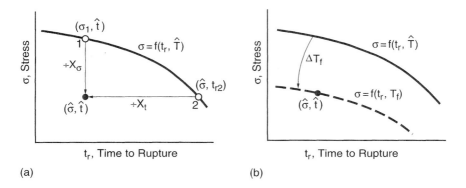

Figure 15.25 Stress versus time to creep rupture curves, showing (a) safety factors in stress and in life, and (b) safety margin in temperature.

15.4.4 Safety Factors for Creep Rupture

Safety factors in stress and in life for creep rupture, X_σ and X_t, may be defined as illustrated in Fig. 15.25. The logic is parallel to that employed for fatigue stress–life curves in Section 9.2.4.

Consider a combination of stress $\hat{\sigma}$, time $\hat{t}$, and temperature $\hat{T}$ that are expected to occur in actual service. As shown in Fig. 15.25(a), the point $(\hat{\sigma}, \hat{t})$ must fall below the stress–life curve for failure at the service temperature, $\sigma = f(t_r, \hat{T})$. Point (1) on the failure curve corresponds to failure at the desired service life $\hat{t}$, so that comparing the stress σ_1 with the service stress $\hat{\sigma}$ provides the safety factor in stress:

$$X_\sigma = \frac{\sigma_1}{\hat{\sigma}} \qquad (t_r = \hat{t}) \tag{15.23}$$

Also, Point (2) corresponds to failure at the service stress $\hat{\sigma}$, and comparing rupture time t_{r2} with the service life $\hat{t}$ gives the safety factor in life:

$$X_t = \frac{t_{r2}}{\hat{t}} \qquad (\sigma = \hat{\sigma}) \tag{15.24}$$

As for fatigue, rather large safety factors in life are needed to achieve reasonable safety factors in stress, which should generally be around 1.5 or larger.

Also of interest is the temperature increase above $\hat{T}$ that will cause failure at the service stress and time, $\hat{\sigma}$ and $\hat{t}$, as illustrated by Fig. 15.25(b). The failure temperature T_f is the temperature that lowers the stress–life curve so that it passes through the point $(\hat{\sigma}, \hat{t})$. The increase ΔT_f that is required to reach T_f can be regarded as the *safety margin in temperature*:

$$\Delta T_f = T_f - \hat{T} \qquad (\sigma = \hat{\sigma}, \ t_r = \hat{t}) \tag{15.25}$$

Example 15.5

Consider the situation of Ex. 15.2 and 15.3, where a component made of alloy S-590 is subjected to a stress of 200 MPa at a temperature of 600°C.

(a) Repeat the rupture life calculation of Ex. 15.3, using the Eq. 15.20 fit for P_{LM}.

(b) If the desired service life is 1.5 years, what are the safety factors in life and in stress?

(c) What is the safety margin in temperature?

Solution   (a) From Table 15.3, the S-590 alloy constants for Eq. 15.20 are $C = 17$, $b_0 = 38,405$, $b_1 = -8206$, and $b_2 = b_3 = 0$. Noting that $x = \log \sigma$, substituting these values gives P_{LM} from Eq. 15.20(b), and then t_r follows from Eq. 15.20(a) with substitution of $T = 600°C + 273 = 873$ K:

$$P_{LM} = b_0 + b_1 x = 38,405 - 8,206 \log (200 \text{ MPa}) = 19,523$$

$$\log t_r = \frac{P_{LM}}{T} - C = \frac{19,523}{873 \text{ K}} - 17 = 5.363, \qquad t_r = 230,583 \text{ h} = 9608 \text{ days} \quad \textbf{Ans.}$$

(b) The safety factor in life is calculated by comparing t_r from (a) with the service life $\hat{t}$:

$$\hat{t} = (1.5 \text{ years})(365.25 \text{ days/year})(24 \text{ h/day}) = 13,149 \text{ h}$$

$$X_t = \frac{t_{r2}}{\hat{t}} = \frac{230,583 \text{ h}}{13,149 \text{ h}} = 17.5 \qquad\qquad \textbf{Ans.}$$

For the safety factor in stress, we need to determine the σ_1 that causes failure at $t_r = \hat{t}$, which depends on the value of P_{LM} corresponding to $t_r = \hat{t}$ at temperature $T = \hat{T}$. The needed P_{LM} value can be calculated from Eq. 15.17:

$$P_{LM} = T(\log t_r + C) = \hat{T}(\log \hat{t} + C) = (873 \text{ K})[\log (13,149 \text{ h}) + 17] = 18,437$$

Substituting this P_{LM} into Eq. 15.20(b) and solving gives $\sigma = \sigma_1$, and then Eq. 15.23 gives X_σ:

$$P_{LM} = b_0 + b_1 x, \qquad 18,437 = 38,405 - 8,206 \log \sigma_1$$

$$\log \sigma_1 = 2.433, \qquad \sigma_1 = 271.2 \text{ MPa}$$

$$X_\sigma = \frac{\sigma_1}{\hat{\sigma}} = \frac{271.2}{200} = 1.36 \qquad\qquad \textbf{Ans.}$$

(c) To obtain the temperature increase, $\Delta T_f = T_f - \hat{T}$, that causes failure at $(\sigma, t_r) = (\hat{\sigma}, \hat{t})$, solve Eq. 15.17 for T. Then calculate T_f by substituting $t_r = \hat{t}$ along with P_{LM} from (a), as this value corresponds to $\hat{\sigma}$. The result of these two operations is

$$T = \frac{P_{LM}}{\log t_r + C}, \qquad T_f = \frac{19{,}523}{\log{(13{,}149\,\mathrm{h})} + 17} = 924.4\,\mathrm{K}$$

$$\Delta T_f = T_f - \hat{T} = 924.4 - 873 = 51.4\,\mathrm{K} \qquad\qquad \textbf{Ans.}$$

Comments   Solving Eq. 15.20(b) for σ, as in (b) of this example, requires an iterative solution if this polynomial is of order 3 (or 5, etc.). But a closed-form calculation is possible in this case, due to $b_2 = b_3 = 0$ giving a linear relationship. Note that the safety factor in stress of $X_\sigma = 1.36$ is rather low. A higher value would require a safety factor in life even larger than the $X_t = 17.5$ that is calculated.

15.4.5 Creep Rupture under Multiaxial Stress

For multiaxial loading, it is logical to use stress–life curves or time–temperature parameters by simply replacing the uniaxial stress with the effective stress $\bar{\sigma}$ of Eq. 12.21. However, creep rupture under multiaxial loading is also affected to an extent by the maximum principal stress σ_1. One approach is to use the following effective stress for creep rupture:

$$\bar{\sigma}_c = \alpha \sigma_1 + (1 - \alpha)\bar{\sigma} \tag{15.26}$$

Here, $\bar{\sigma}$ is from Eq. 12.21, and α is a material constant with a value between zero and unity that must be evaluated from multiaxial testing. The quantity $\bar{\sigma}_c$ is then considered to be equivalent to a uniaxial stress. If a value of α is unavailable, another possibility is to take the worst possible case for α between zero and unity, which corresponds to $\bar{\sigma}_c = \mathrm{MAX}\,(\sigma_1, \bar{\sigma})$. For additional discussion, see Gooch (1986), Penny (1995), and Skrzypek (1993).

15.5 CREEP FAILURE UNDER VARYING STRESS

If stresses change infrequently, stress–life curves and time–temperature parameters can still be employed to make life estimates. However, if stress changes occur so often that the cyclic loading begins to cause fatigue damage, a more complex situation exists that requires special analysis.

15.5.1 Creep Rupture under Step Loading

Rough estimates of life to creep rupture can be made by applying a *time-fraction rule* to stress–life plots in the same manner that the Palmgren–Miner rule is used with cyclic lives for fatigue:

$$\sum \frac{\Delta t_i}{t_{ri}} = 1, \qquad B_f \left(\sum \frac{\Delta t_i}{t_{ri}}\right)_{\text{one rep.}} = 1 \tag{15.27}$$

In this case, life is expressed in terms of time, and stress versus rupture life curves similar to those in Fig. 15.8 are used. The quantity Δt_i is the time spent at stress level σ_i, and t_{ri} is the corresponding rupture life. For the second version, the summation is done for one repetition of a loading sequence that occurs a number of times, and B_f is the number of repetitions to failure. If the temperature also changes, then the appropriate stress–life curve is used for each temperature step. A similar procedure can be employed where failure is considered to be the accumulation of a particular amount of creep strain. Stress–life curves for the particular strain value are, of course, used.

Failure lives for use with these equations also can be obtained from time–temperature parameters. Each stress level σ_i is used to obtain a parameter value P_i, which is then solved for t_{ri} by employing the appropriate temperature.

15.5.2 Creep–Fatigue Interaction

Practical applications at high temperature often involve both creep and fatigue, and these phenomena may act together in a synergistic manner. For example, various components of aircraft jet engines experience periods of both fluctuating and steady stress, due to the complex situation of thermal stresses caused by large temperature variations combined with cyclic loading, as the aircraft flies at constant speed, changes speed, lands, and shuts down the engines, etc. High-temperature components in nuclear reactors and various pressure vessels are also subjected to combined creep and fatigue.

One simple approach is to sum the life fractions due to both creep and fatigue, and thus combine the Palmgren–Miner rule, Eq. 9.33, and the time-fraction rule of Eq. 15.27:

$$\sum \frac{\Delta t_i}{t_{ri}} + \sum \frac{N_i}{N_{fi}} = 1 \tag{15.28}$$

However, this approach is very rough, because the physical processes of creep and fatigue are distinct, so a simple addition of effects cannot be expected to be accurate. In particular, in engineering metals, creep damage may involve grain boundary cracking, whereas the damage due to the fatigue portion of the loading may be concentrated in slip bands within the crystal grains.

Where creep and fatigue interact, the frequency of cycling is important, as slow frequencies give creep more time to contribute to the damage. One approach developed with such effects in mind is the *frequency-modified fatigue* approach of L. F. Coffin. The cyclic stress–strain and strain–life relationships are generalized so that the various material constants become functions of temperature and frequency.

Even the details of the time variation of stress and strain can be important. This is illustrated by some high-temperature test data on an engineering metal in Fig. 15.26. When compared on the basis of equal inelastic (creep plus plastic) strain ranges, the different waveforms can have very different cyclic lives. This results from the complexities of the physical process of damage in the material. For example, the loading with creep in compression only, called PC, is sometimes (but not always) the most severe. This can occur where an oxidizing environment, perhaps only air, causes an oxide surface layer to form during the compressive creep loading. Subsequent rapid loading into tension cracks this oxide, leading to early cracking of the metal beneath. Data of the type in Fig. 15.26 form the basis of the *strain-range partitioning* approach developed by S. S. Manson and co-workers.

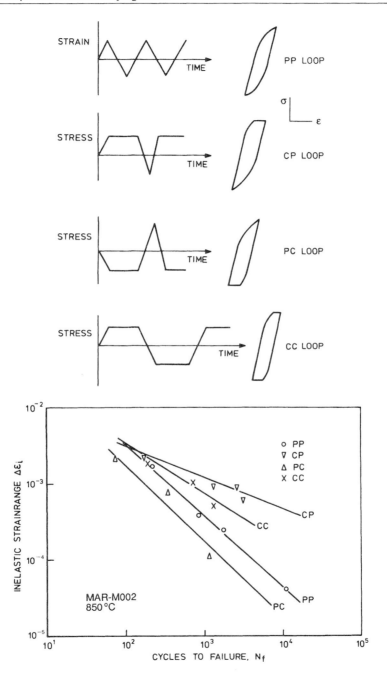

Figure 15.26   Effect on life of intermittent creep in tension, compression, or both, during cyclic loading of the cast Ni-base alloy MAR-M002 at 850°C. Stress–strain hysteresis loops have the shapes shown. (Adapted from [Antunes 78]; used with permission; first published by AGARD/NATO.)

Four types of test are run, namely, tests involving mainly plastic deformation and little creep (PP), creep mainly in tension (CP), creep mainly in compression (PC), and creep in both tension and compression (CC). Life predictions are then made for engineering components on the basis of the life fractions spent in each of the four types of loading.

No consensus currently exists as to the best approach to creep–fatigue interaction, and this is an active area of current research. See Penny (1995) and Saxena (2003) for more detail.

15.6 STRESS–STRAIN–TIME RELATIONSHIPS

To analyze the stresses and strains in engineering components subject to creep, it is necessary to have stress–strain relationships that include the time dependency. Relationships suggested by simple linear rheological models are often useful for polymers, but more complex behavior also occurs in these materials, and especially in metals, that requires special consideration.

15.6.1 Linear Viscoelasticity

Strain–time equations for a constant applied stress are given for various rheological models in Fig. 15.27. The equations for (a), (b), and (c) are developed in Section 5.2.2. The relationship for (c) is the same as for (b), except that the elastic displacement of spring E_1 is added. Since (d) is simply the series combination of (a) and (b), the strains from these two simply add to give the relationship for (d):

$$\varepsilon = \frac{\sigma}{E_1} + \frac{\sigma t}{\eta_1} + \frac{\sigma}{E_2}\left(1 - e^{-E_2 t/\eta_2}\right) \tag{15.29}$$

The three terms in this equation correspond respectively to the instantaneous elastic strain in spring E_1, the steady-state creep strain in dashpot η_1, and the transient creep strain in the (E_2, η_2) parallel combination:

$$\varepsilon_e = \frac{\sigma}{E_1}, \qquad \varepsilon_{sc} = \frac{\sigma t}{\eta_1}, \qquad \varepsilon_{tc} = \frac{\sigma}{E_2}\left(1 - e^{-E_2 t/\eta_2}\right) \tag{15.30}$$

Strain rates from differentiation with respect to time are also of interest.

$$\dot{\varepsilon}_e = 0, \qquad \dot{\varepsilon}_{sc} = \frac{\sigma}{\eta_1}, \qquad \dot{\varepsilon}_{tc} = \frac{\sigma}{\eta_2} e^{-E_2 t/\eta_2} \tag{15.31}$$

Hence, the steady-state creep strain has a constant rate, as it should, and the transient creep strain proceeds at a decreasing rate, approaching the limiting value $\varepsilon_{tc} = \sigma/E_2$ for large t. For a given stress, such a trend of strain with time is similar to that observed in real materials, except that no tertiary creep stage occurs in the model.

From examining the preceding equations and Fig. 15.27, it is apparent, for any of these models, that for a given time t there is a simple proportionality between stress and strain, and also between stress and strain rate. A similar proportionality applies for any model constructed from combinations of linear springs and dashpots, so that such models are said to exhibit *linear viscoelasticity*. As a result of this situation, the stress–strain relationships for given values of time—that is, the

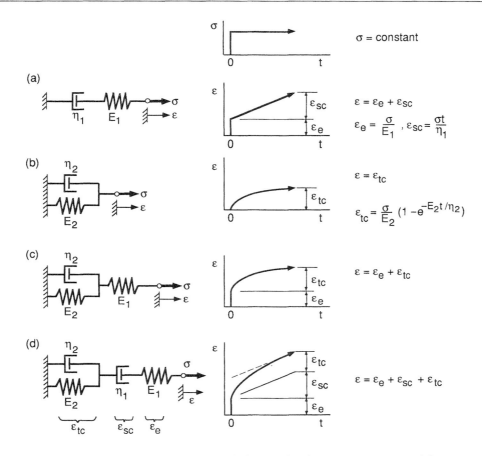

Figure 15.27   Strain versus time behavior for four viscoelastic models.

isochronous stress–strain curves—are all straight lines. This is illustrated in Fig. 15.28 for two of the models. For the transient-creep-plus-elastic model (a), only spring E_1 deforms for small t; but for large t, the dashpot has no effect, and the stiffness is that corresponding to E_1 and E_2 in series:

$$E_e = \frac{E_1 E_2}{E_1 + E_2} \tag{15.32}$$

For (b), the slope is again E_1 for short times, but zero at long times, due to the deformation of dashpot η_1 not being constrained. For design applications with polymers, it is common practice to assume that the behavior follows linear viscoelasticity, with the time-dependent elastic modulus being taken as the secant modulus E_s to mildly nonlinear isochronous stress–strain curves as in Fig. 15.11(c).

In crystalline materials that behave according to Eq. 15.6, note that steady-state creep by either type of diffusional flow gives $m = 1$, so that Eq. 15.7(a) becomes $\dot{\varepsilon} = B\sigma$, and Eq. 15.7(b) still

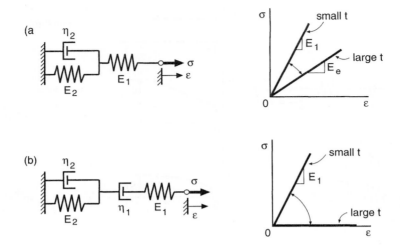

Figure 15.28   Limits on the linear isochronous stress–strain curves for two linear viscoelastic models.

applies. In such cases, we thus have linear viscoelastic behavior, with the viscosity, $\eta = \sigma/\dot{\varepsilon} = 1/B$, depending on material, temperature, and grain size. As elastic strains also occur, the behavior is that of the steady-state creep model of Fig. 15.27(a), with the elastic modulus at the temperature of interest being $E = E_1$.

15.6.2 Nonlinear Creep Equations

From the discussion on mechanisms of creep strain in crystalline materials in Section 15.3.3, it is apparent that nonlinear behavior, $m \neq 1$, is not unusual. For example, for dislocation creep in crystalline materials, strain rates are not proportional to stress, as there is instead a strong power dependence with $m \approx 5$. Polymers and concrete may behave in a linear viscoelastic manner at low stresses, but not generally at high stresses. Isochronous stress–strain curves for a polymer and a concrete are shown in Figs. 15.29 and 15.30. These materials are clearly nonlinear at the relatively high stresses involved.

Thus, more general stress–strain–time relationships than those provided by linear viscoelastic models are often needed. This situation has led to a wide variety of nonlinear relationships that employ expressions involving powers of σ, such as

$$\varepsilon = \varepsilon_i + B\sigma^m t + D\sigma^\alpha \left(1 - e^{-\beta t}\right) \tag{15.33}$$

The quantities B, m, D, α, and β are empirical constants from creep data for a given material and temperature. The instantaneous strain ε_i can include both elastic and plastic parts, $\varepsilon_i = \varepsilon_e + \varepsilon_p$. In a manner similar to Eq. 15.29, the second term of Eq. 15.33 is the steady-state (secondary) creep strain, and the third is the transient (primary) creep strain. In Marin (1962), a useful form of Eq. 15.33 is employed that is the special case where plastic strain is given by $\varepsilon_p = B_1\sigma^{1/n}$, with $1/n = \alpha = m$:

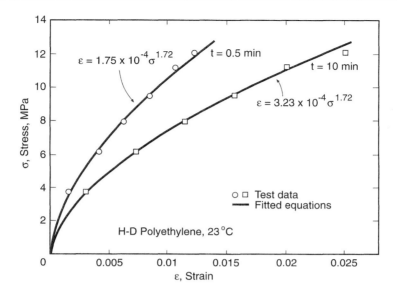

Figure 15.29   Two isochronous stress–strain curves for high-density polyethylene in tension.

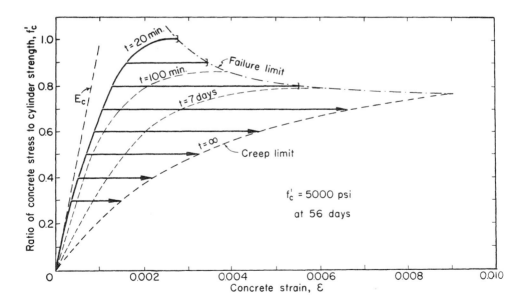

Figure 15.30   Isochronous stress–strain curves (dashed lines) for a concrete tested in compression after curing 56 days, where f_c' is the ultimate strength in compression. As the strain rates decrease with time and appear to approach zero, a creep limit curve can be drawn. (From [Rusch 60]; used with permission.)

$$\varepsilon = \frac{\sigma}{E} + \left[B_1 + B_2 t + B_3 \left(1 - e^{-\beta t}\right)\right]\sigma^m \tag{15.34}$$

Since the Ramberg–Osgood relationship, Eq. 12.12, is widely used for elasto-plastic stress–strain curves, it is convenient to employ stress–strain–time relationships that can be put into the same form. Thus, we have

$$\varepsilon = \frac{\sigma}{E} + \left(\frac{\sigma}{H_c}\right)^{1/n_c} \tag{15.35}$$

where n_c is an appropriate value for creep and H_c includes a time dependence. For example, Eq. 15.34 is equivalent to employing Eq. 15.35 with

$$n_c = \frac{1}{m}, \qquad H_c = \left[B_1 + B_2 t + B_3(1 - e^{-\beta t})\right]^{-1/m} \tag{15.36}$$

At times sufficiently large for the transient straining to be essentially complete, Eq. 15.33 gives a simplified expression for steady-state creep:

$$\varepsilon = \varepsilon_i + B\sigma^m t + D\sigma^\alpha, \qquad \dot{\varepsilon}_{sc} = B\sigma^m \qquad \text{(a, b)} \tag{15.37}$$

In this pair of equations, the third term of (a) is the limiting value of transient creep strain. The temperature dependence of the steady-state creep rate can be estimated from an activation energy, as described earlier. For example, for power-law creep according to Eq. 15.7, noting that $q = 0$, the constant B is given in temperature-dependent form by

$$B = \frac{A_2}{T} e^{\frac{-Q}{RT}} \tag{15.38}$$

Creep equations having an exponent applied to time t are sometimes employed, such as

$$\varepsilon = \varepsilon_i + D_3 \sigma^\delta t^\phi, \qquad \varepsilon = \frac{\sigma}{E} + D_3 \sigma^\delta t^\phi \qquad \text{(a, b)} \tag{15.39}$$

where the exponent ϕ is in the range zero to unity, and a power-type stress dependence is seen to be included. In the second form, the instantaneous strain ε_i is assumed to consist of elastic strain only. For some engineering metals at specific temperatures, values of constants for Eq. 15.39(b) are given in Table 15.4. Also, Eq. 15.39(b) has the form of Eq. 15.35, where

$$n_c = \frac{1}{\delta}, \qquad H_c = \frac{1}{\left(D_3 t^\phi\right)^{1/\delta}} \tag{15.40}$$

Other relationships that are used feature a time function that is logarithmic or hyperbolic:

$$\varepsilon = \varepsilon_i + D_4 \log\left(1 + \beta_4 t\right), \qquad \varepsilon = \varepsilon_i + \frac{D_5 t}{1 + \beta_5 t} \qquad \text{(a, b)} \tag{15.41}$$

These relationships, and modifications and extensions of them, are used for transient creep, as is Eq. 15.33 with $B = 0$. They are especially useful for materials where the behavior is dominated

Table 15.4　Some Constants for Eq. 15.39(b)

Material	Temperature	E	D_3	δ	ϕ
	°C	MPa (ksi)	for MPa, hours (for ksi, hours)		
SAE 1035 steel[1]	524	161,000 (23,300)	1.58×10^{-11} (4.78×10^{-8})	4.15	0.40
Copper alloy 360[1]	371	85,500 (12,400)	4.26×10^{-9} (1.06×10^{-5})	4.05	0.87
Pure nickel[2]	700	150,000 (21,700)	2.42×10^{-6} (3.02×10^{-4})	2.50	0.28
7075-T6 Al[2]	316	36,500 (5,300)	1.35×10^{-13} (1.00×10^{-7})	7.00	0.33
Cr-Mo-V steel[2]	538	152,000 (22,000)	1.15×10^{-9} (1.07×10^{-7})	2.35	0.34

Notes: [1]Constants from [Chu 70] based on 1-hour creep tests. [2]From [Lubahn 61] pp. 159, 255, and 574, based on creep data extending to 300, 18, and 10^4 hours, respectively.

by transient creep, such as concrete. Note that Eq. 15.41(b) approaches a limiting value for infinite time, as does Eq. 15.33 with $B = 0$. All the other expressions presented give unlimited strains for large t.

Constants for nonlinear stress–strain–time equations, as just described, are not generally available in comprehensive tabular or similar form for various materials. This is due to the lack of a consensus as to which of the many equations to use, and also due to the constants changing, not only with material, but also with stress and temperature. Hence, it is generally necessary in engineering applications to obtain the needed constants from creep data for the material and conditions of interest, either from the literature or from new laboratory tests. An exception is that steady-state creep constants for a wide range of stresses and temperatures are given in Frost (1982) for representative metals and ceramics, some of which are engineering materials.

15.7 CREEP DEFORMATION UNDER VARYING STRESS

Up to this point, we have considered creep deformation where the stress and temperature are held constant. However, many engineering applications involve situations where one or both of these vary. An introduction that emphasizes creep under varying stress follows. For more detail, see the books by Neville (1983), Penny (1995), and Skrzypek (1993).

15.7.1 Recovery of Creep Strain

The time-dependent disappearance of creep strain after the removal of some or all of the applied stress is called *recovery*. Such behavior was previously illustrated for simple rheological models in Fig. 5.5. There is no recovery of creep strain for the steady-state creep model (a), but in the transient creep model (b), all creep strain is recovered in the spring and slider parallel combination after infinite time. For the combined rheological model of Fig. 15.13, the transient creep strain ε_{tc} in the parallel combination is recovered slowly with time, but the steady-state creep strain ε_{sc} in the dashpot remains.

To explore the recovery behavior of the model of Fig. 15.13 in detail, let a constant stress σ' be maintained for a time t'. From Fig. 15.27(b), the strain in the transient creep element at t' is

$$\varepsilon_2' = \varepsilon_{tc} = \frac{\sigma'}{E_2}\left(1 - e^{-E_2 t'/\eta_2}\right) \tag{15.42}$$

After removal of the stress, it is easily shown (see Prob. 15.38) that this strain decreases and approaches zero at infinite time according to

$$\varepsilon_2 = \varepsilon_2' e^{-E_2 \Delta t/\eta_2} \tag{15.43}$$

where $\Delta t = t - t'$ is the time elapsed since removal of the stress. Now consider recovery for the entire model. The elastic strain in spring E_1 is recovered instantly, but the strain in the steady-state creep element, dashpot η_1, remains unchanged:

$$\varepsilon_1 = \varepsilon_{sc} = \frac{\sigma' t'}{\eta_1} \tag{15.44}$$

The strain–time response of the entire model after removal of σ' can now be obtained by combining ε_1 and ε_2, with ε_2' from Eq. 15.42 also being substituted:

$$\varepsilon = \frac{\sigma' t'}{\eta_1} + \frac{\sigma'}{E_2}\left(1 - e^{-E_2 t'/\eta_2}\right) e^{-E_2 \Delta t/\eta_2} \tag{15.45}$$

This equation corresponds to the decreasing strain curve after unloading at $t = t'$ in Fig. 15.13.

Analogous, but more complex, behavior occurs in real materials. In particular, the governing equations are not generally linear with stress, and strains initially classified as transient may not be recovered fully. In polymers and concrete, considerable portions of the creep strain are often recovered. However, for metals or for cases of simple viscous flow in polymers or glass, there is generally only a relatively small amount of recovery. In modeling real materials, additional transient creep elements in series or special nonlinear springs and dashpots are sometimes used.

15.7.2 Stress Relaxation

Consider a material and temperature combination such that creep occurs under constant applied stress. But employ a new type of test in which the specimen is quickly loaded to some given strain and then held. The stress will decrease with time, and this loss of stress is called *relaxation*. Equations for the stress variation with time in two simple rheological models are given in Fig. 15.31. (The equation for (a) was previously derived in Example 5.1, and that for (b) is requested as Prob. 15.39.) In a relaxation test, the stress appears to approach a stable value after a long time, which value may be only a little below the initial stress, or it may be much lower, depending on the

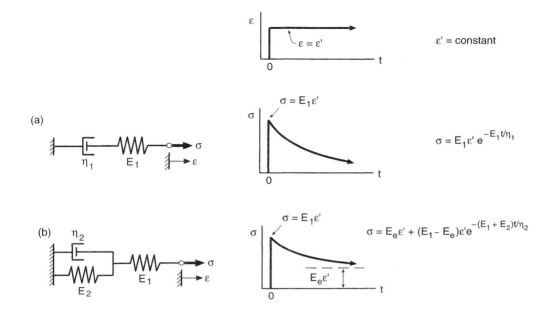

Figure 15.31 Relaxation under constant strain for two linear viscoelastic models.

material, temperature, and strain level involved. What occurs during relaxation is that some of the elastic strain that appears on initial rapid loading is slowly replaced by creep strain, with the total of the two being constant according to the constraint of the test.

Real materials, of course, behave in a more complex manner than do simple linear viscoelastic models. For example, consider stress relaxation during constant strain in a material for which the plastic strain and the transient creep strain are small, so that the behavior is dominated by elastic strain and steady-state creep strain. Assume that the rate of creep strain is related to stress by a power relationship, as in Eq. 15.7(a). Further assume that this applies even during the decreasing stress situation of relaxation. Then let the total strain be held constant at a value ε', so that

$$\varepsilon_e + \varepsilon_c = \varepsilon', \qquad \dot{\varepsilon}_e + \dot{\varepsilon}_c = 0 \tag{15.46}$$

where $\varepsilon_e = \sigma/E$ is the elastic strain, ε_c is the creep strain, and the second equation is obtained by differentiating the first with respect to time.

Since $\dot{\varepsilon}_e = \dot{\sigma}/E$, the previous equations, ε_c is the creep strain, and $\dot{\varepsilon}_c = B\sigma^m$ from Eq. 15.7(a) combine to give

$$\frac{1}{E}\frac{d\sigma}{dt} + B\sigma^m = 0 \tag{15.47}$$

This differential equation is easily solved by integration:

$$\int_0^t dt = -\frac{1}{BE}\int_{\sigma_i}^{\sigma}\frac{d\sigma}{\sigma^m} \tag{15.48}$$

Since only elastic strain occurs on the rapid initial loading, the initial stress at the beginning of relaxation, $t = 0$, is $\sigma_i = E\varepsilon'$. After integration and then some manipulation, the following equations are obtained for the variation of stress with time:

$$\sigma = \frac{\sigma_i}{\left[tBE(m-1)\,\sigma_i^{m-1} + 1\right]^{1/(m-1)}} \qquad (m \neq 1)$$

$$\sigma = \sigma_i e^{-BEt} \qquad\qquad\qquad (m = 1)$$

(15.49)

This analysis, in effect, generalizes the case of Fig. 15.31(a) so that the dashpot has a nonlinear response according to

$$\eta_1 = \frac{\sigma}{\dot{\varepsilon}} = \frac{1}{B\sigma^{m-1}} \tag{15.50}$$

The special case of $m = 1$ is seen to be equivalent to the original linear model with $\eta_1 = 1/B$.

Equation 15.49, with m as appropriate, can be used to approximate the behavior of crystalline materials in the power-law (dislocation creep) and viscous (diffusional flow) regions of the deformation mechanism map. However, caution is advised, as it needs to be remembered that transient creep strain effects are neglected in doing so.

15.7.3 Step Loading of Linear Viscoelastic Models

Consider a series of loading steps as shown in Fig. 15.32(a). An increase in stress causes additional instantaneous (elastic plus plastic) strain, additional transient creep strain, and an increased steady-state strain rate. A decrease in stress causes instantaneous loss of some of the elastic strain and a decrease in strain rate, and perhaps even some recovery of transient creep strain if the resulting stress is low. A number of approaches exist for predicting strain versus time behavior under these conditions.

First, consider the behavior of any linear viscoelastic rheological model—that is, any combination of standard linear springs and dashpots. Any such model can be shown to obey the *superposition principle*. This principle states simply that the creep strain at any time is the sum of the strains due to each change in stress, $\Delta\sigma$, that has occurred, where each $\Delta\sigma$ is considered to act continuously as an applied stress, starting from the time it occurs to any later time. An application is illustrated in Fig. 15.32. Stress σ_1 is applied at time t_1, but at time t_2 the stress changes to σ_2. After this change, the creep strain due to $\Delta\sigma_1 = \sigma_1$ continues to accumulate, but an additional creep strain must be added due to the additional stress $\Delta\sigma_2 = \sigma_2 - \sigma_1$. The amount of this additional creep strain is the same as that due to a stress equal to $\Delta\sigma_2$ applied by itself, starting at time t_2. Similarly, following t_3, the creep strains due to $\Delta\sigma_1$ and $\Delta\sigma_2$ continue, but the strain for $\Delta\sigma_3$ must now be added. In this particular example, the $\Delta\sigma_3 = \sigma_3 - \sigma_2$ to be added is negative, so subtraction occurs.

In general, the stress change to reach the ith load step from the previous level is

$$\Delta\sigma_i = \sigma_i - \sigma_{i-1} \tag{15.51}$$

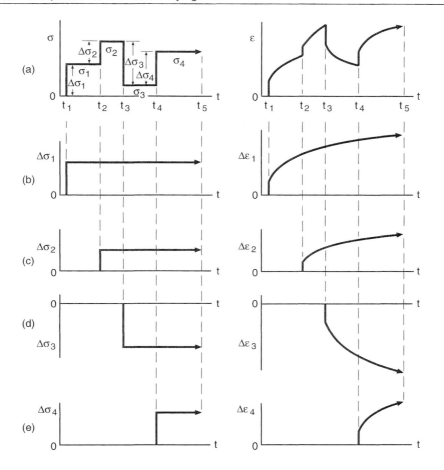

Figure 15.32 The superposition principle for linear viscoelastic models and materials. An applied stress history and the resulting strain response are shown in (a), and the stress changes and resulting strains that are superimposed to obtain this response are shown in (b–e).

The stress during the ith step is the sum of all changes that have occurred so far. That is,

$$\sigma_i = \sum \Delta\sigma_i \tag{15.52}$$

Let the linear strain–time relationship for the model be represented by $\varepsilon = \sigma f(t)$, where various examples of $f(t)$ are available from Fig. 15.27. The strain at any later time t due to $\Delta\sigma_i$ acting as an applied stress starting at time t_i is thus

$$\Delta\varepsilon_i = \Delta\sigma_i \, f(t - t_i) \tag{15.53}$$

Note that $(t - t_i)$ is the time since the stress change $\Delta\sigma_i$. According to the superposition principle, the total strain is the sum of all of the strains $\Delta\varepsilon_i$ due to each $\Delta\sigma_i$ that has occurred:

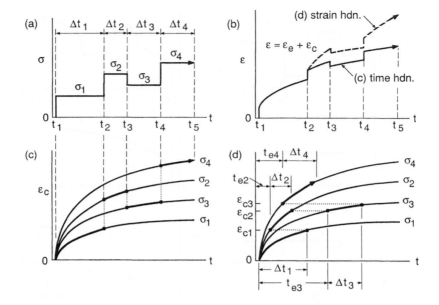

Figure 15.33 A step stress history (a) and estimated strain responses (b), based on time hardening (c) and strain hardening (d).

$$\varepsilon = \sum \Delta \varepsilon_i = \sum \Delta \sigma_i \, f(t - t_i) \tag{15.54}$$

This summation is equivalent to the graphical procedure of simply adding the strains due to each $\Delta \sigma$ at any desired time, as illustrated by Fig. 15.32(b–e).

The behavior of real materials is often too complex to be represented by linear viscoelasticity. Hence, nonlinear extensions of this approach are sometimes used. For materials such as metals, where recovery behavior is relatively unimportant, it may be reasonable to use certain approaches that neglect recovery behavior entirely, such as *time hardening* and *strain hardening*, as discussed next.

15.7.4 Time-Hardening and Strain-Hardening Rules

These methods are illustrated in Fig. 15.33 for the stress history shown in (a). Estimated strains are shown in (b) for the two approaches. For *time hardening*, creep (not total) strain versus time curves are first plotted for all stress levels involved, as shown in (c). Whenever the stress changes, the deformation is assumed to proceed according to the curve for the new stress, starting at the point on this curve corresponding to the actual value of time. For example, after the stress changes to σ_2 at time t_2, the strain–time curve for σ_2 is used to estimate the behavior until the stress changes again. These segments of strain–time response for each stress level are then combined to estimate the overall strain response as shown in (b). Changes in the elastic and plastic strain may also need to be included. In this example, instantaneous changes in elastic strain are shown in (b), along with the segments of creep strain versus time response from (c).

Assume that the creep strain versus time curves are given by

$$\varepsilon_c = f_2(\sigma, t) \tag{15.55}$$

The change in creep strain $\Delta\varepsilon_{ci}$ during the ith stress level is obtained from the curve for σ_i and is the difference between the creep strains corresponding to times t_i and t_{i+1}. Also, the accumulated creep strain ε_c is the sum of the changes. Thus,

$$\Delta\varepsilon_{ci} = f_2(\sigma_i, t_{i+1}) - f_2(\sigma_i, t_i), \qquad \varepsilon_c = \sum \Delta\varepsilon_{ci} \tag{15.56}$$

For example, consider creep according to Eq. 15.39(b). Summing the elastic strain due to the current value of stress and the accumulated creep strain, we obtain the total strain:

$$\varepsilon = \varepsilon_e + \varepsilon_c = \frac{\sigma}{E} + D_3 \sum \sigma_i^\delta \left(t_{i+1}^\phi - t_i^\phi \right) \tag{15.57}$$

Strain hardening assumes that the deformation after a stress change starts at a point on the new creep strain versus time curve that corresponds to the actual value of creep strain, as illustrated in Fig. 15.33(d). At time t_2, the stress changes to σ_2, and the curve for σ_2 is used for a time period $\Delta t_2 = t_3 - t_2$. The starting point on the σ_2 curve corresponds to the creep strain ε_{c1} reached at the end of the σ_1 step. Hence, it corresponds not to the real time t_2 but rather to a fictitious time t_{e2}. Similarly, at time t_3, the curve for σ_3 is used for the time period $\Delta t_3 = t_4 - t_3$, starting at the fictitious time t_{e3} corresponding to the creep strain ε_{c2} at the end of the previous step. For each step, such as the ith one, the t_{ei} value must be calculated from the creep strain reached at the end of the previous step by solving Eq. 15.55 for t_{ei}, that is

$$\varepsilon_{c(i-1)} = f_2(\sigma_i, t_{ei}) \tag{15.58}$$

The creep strain occurring during the ith step and the accumulated strain can then be computed:

$$\Delta\varepsilon_{ci} = f_2(\sigma_i, t_{ei} + \Delta t_i) - f_2(\sigma_i, t_{ei}), \qquad \varepsilon_c = \sum \Delta\varepsilon_{ci} \tag{15.59}$$

For example, for creep according to Eq. 15.39(b), the previous equations give

$$t_{ei} = \left(\frac{\varepsilon_{c(i-1)}}{D_3\sigma_i^\delta} \right)^{1/\phi}, \qquad \varepsilon = \frac{\sigma}{E} + D_3 \sum \sigma_i^\delta \left[(t_{ei} + \Delta t_i)^\phi - t_{ei}^\phi \right] \tag{15.60}$$

Strain hardening and time hardening give different results, except for creep strain versus time curves that are linear—that is, for steady-state creep. Although neither procedure can be regarded as anything other than a rough approximation, strain hardening does appear to be more accurate for engineering metals than time hardening. Such a trend might be expected, as it is logical to assume that the effect of prior deformation is more closely related to the amount of strain that has occurred than simply to the amount of time elapsed. If step changes in temperature occur instead of, or in addition to, stress changes, then time hardening and strain hardening can still be used by introducing strain–time curves for more than one temperature.

15.8 CREEP DEFORMATION UNDER MULTIAXIAL STRESS

Multiaxial stresses, of course, often occur in engineering components, but creep data and constants are generally based on uniaxial tests. Thus, special methodology is needed for generalizing uniaxial data to handle multiaxial situations.

Consider an ideal linear viscous fluid that is incompressible, called a Newtonian fluid. Incompressibility requires that the volumetric strain be zero, hence also that the volumetric strain rate be zero. Thus, Eq. 5.34 gives

$$\dot{\varepsilon}_x + \dot{\varepsilon}_y + \dot{\varepsilon}_z = 0 \tag{15.61}$$

Now consider a uniaxial stress σ_x and the resulting strain rate:

$$\dot{\varepsilon}_x = \frac{\sigma_x}{\eta} \qquad (\sigma_y = \sigma_z = 0) \tag{15.62}$$

Here, η is the tensile viscosity of Eq. 15.2. Equal strain rates occur in the other two directions, so that these can be obtained by invoking Eq. 15.61:

$$\dot{\varepsilon}_y = \dot{\varepsilon}_z = -\frac{\dot{\varepsilon}_x}{2} = -\frac{1}{2}\left(\frac{\sigma_x}{\eta}\right) \qquad (\sigma_y = \sigma_z = 0) \tag{15.63}$$

If stresses also occur in the other directions, these produce additional strains in a similar manner, so that strain rates are given by

$$\dot{\varepsilon}_x = \frac{1}{\eta}\left[\sigma_x - 0.5\left(\sigma_y + \sigma_z\right)\right] \qquad \text{(a)}$$

$$\dot{\varepsilon}_y = \frac{1}{\eta}\left[\sigma_y - 0.5\left(\sigma_x + \sigma_z\right)\right] \qquad \text{(b)} \tag{15.64}$$

$$\dot{\varepsilon}_z = \frac{1}{\eta}\left[\sigma_z - 0.5\left(\sigma_x + \sigma_y\right)\right] \qquad \text{(c)}$$

Shear stresses and strains may also be present, for which the shear viscosity η_τ of Eq. 15.1 applies. Pursuing logic similar to that leading to Eq. 5.28 gives $\eta_\tau = \eta/3$, so that the only independent constant is η, and the equations for shear strain rates can be written as

$$\dot{\gamma}_{xy} = \frac{3}{\eta}\tau_{xy}, \qquad \dot{\gamma}_{yz} = \frac{3}{\eta}\tau_{yz}, \qquad \dot{\gamma}_{zx} = \frac{3}{\eta}\tau_{zx} \tag{15.65}$$

These relationships are analogous to Hooke's law, Eqs. 5.26 and 5.27, except that they involve strain rates. Poisson's ratio ν is replaced by 0.5, also E by η, and G by $\eta/3$.

The preceding equations can be extended to cases where the stress versus strain rate relationship is nonlinear by interpreting η as a secant modulus on a stress versus strain rate plot. That is,

$$\eta = \frac{\bar{\sigma}}{\bar{\dot{\varepsilon}}} \tag{15.66}$$

Here, $\bar{\sigma}$ and $\bar{\dot{\varepsilon}}$ are respectively the *effective stress* and the *effective strain rate*, which, in terms of principal stresses and corresponding strain rates, are

$$\bar{\sigma} = \frac{1}{\sqrt{2}} \sqrt{(\sigma_1 - \sigma_2)^2 + (\sigma_2 - \sigma_3)^2 + (\sigma_3 - \sigma_1)^2} \qquad \text{(a)}$$

$$\tag{15.67}$$

$$\bar{\dot{\varepsilon}} = \frac{\sqrt{2}}{3} \sqrt{(\dot{\varepsilon}_1 - \dot{\varepsilon}_2)^2 + (\dot{\varepsilon}_2 - \dot{\varepsilon}_3)^2 + (\dot{\varepsilon}_3 - \dot{\varepsilon}_1)^2} \qquad \text{(b)}$$

Note that $\bar{\sigma}$ is the same as Eq. 12.21 and $\bar{\dot{\varepsilon}}$ is analogous to Eq. 12.22. We now have a situation analogous to deformation plasticity theory, as described in Section 12.3, except for strain rates replacing strains. In a similar manner, the effective stress versus strain rate relationship is the same as the uniaxial one. Thus, if $\dot{\varepsilon} = g(\sigma)$ is the uniaxial relationship, then $\bar{\dot{\varepsilon}} = g(\bar{\sigma})$.

Example 15.6

For a given material and temperature, the uniaxial creep behavior follows Eq. 15.39(b). A thin-walled tubular pressure vessel of radius r and wall thickness b has closed ends and is made of this material. Develop an equation for the relative change in radius, $\Delta r / r$, as a function of time t and a constant pressure p in the vessel.

Solution   We first generalize the uniaxial stress–strain curve to an effective stress–strain curve:

$$\bar{\varepsilon} = \frac{\bar{\sigma}}{E} + D_3 \bar{\sigma}^\delta t^\phi, \qquad \bar{\dot{\varepsilon}} = D_3 \phi \bar{\sigma}^\delta t^{\phi-1}$$

The viscosity is thus both stress and time dependent:

$$\frac{1}{\eta} = \frac{\bar{\dot{\varepsilon}}}{\bar{\sigma}} = D_3 \phi \bar{\sigma}^{\delta-1} t^{\phi-1}$$

This relationship can now be used with Eq. 15.64 to solve our particular problem, which involves stresses and strains as follows:

$$\sigma_1 = \frac{pr}{b}, \qquad \sigma_2 = \frac{pr}{2b}, \qquad \sigma_3 \approx 0, \qquad \varepsilon_1 = \frac{\Delta(2\pi r)}{2\pi r} = \frac{\Delta r}{r}$$

Here, σ_1 and ε_1 are in the hoop direction, σ_2 is in the longitudinal direction, and these stresses are noted to be principal stresses.

Letting the (x, y, z) directions be the principal $(1, 2, 3)$ directions, Eq. 15.64(a) gives

$$\dot{\varepsilon}_1 = \frac{1}{\eta}[\sigma_1 - 0.5(\sigma_2 + \sigma_3)] = D_3 \phi \bar{\sigma}^{\delta-1} t^{\phi-1}\left[\frac{pr}{b} - 0.5\left(\frac{pr}{2b}\right)\right]$$

Also, $\bar{\sigma}$ is given by Eq. 15.67(a):

$$\bar{\sigma} = \frac{1}{\sqrt{2}}\sqrt{\left(\frac{pr}{b} - \frac{pr}{2b}\right)^2 + \left(\frac{pr}{2b}\right)^2 + \left(-\frac{pr}{b}\right)^2} = \frac{\sqrt{3}\,pr}{2b}$$

Substituting this $\bar{\sigma}$ into the expression for $\dot{\varepsilon}_1$ and simplifying gives

$$\dot{\varepsilon}_1 = \frac{\sqrt{3}}{2}D_3\phi t^{\phi-1}\left(\frac{\sqrt{3}\,pr}{2b}\right)^{\delta}$$

Since the pressure p is constant, we can integrate with respect to time to obtain the creep strain:

$$\varepsilon_{c1} = \int_0^t \dot{\varepsilon}_1\,dt = \frac{\sqrt{3}}{2}D_3 t^{\phi}\left(\frac{\sqrt{3}\,pr}{2b}\right)^{\delta}$$

We now need the elastic strain from Eq. 5.26. This is

$$\varepsilon_{e1} = \frac{1}{E}[\sigma_1 - \nu(\sigma_2 + \sigma_3)] = \left(1 - \frac{\nu}{2}\right)\left(\frac{pr}{bE}\right)$$

Adding the elastic and creep strains finally gives the desired result:

$$\frac{\Delta r}{r} = \varepsilon_{e1} + \varepsilon_{c1}, \qquad \frac{\Delta r}{r} = \left(1 - \frac{\nu}{2}\right)\left(\frac{pr}{bE}\right) + \frac{\sqrt{3}}{2}D_3 t^{\phi}\left(\frac{\sqrt{3}\,pr}{2b}\right)^{\delta} \qquad \textbf{Ans.}$$

15.9 COMPONENT STRESS–STRAIN ANALYSIS

Stress–strain analysis of engineering components subject to time-dependent deformation can be performed for simple cases using isochronous stress–strain curves. If these curves are approximately linear, corresponding to linear viscoelastic behavior, only linear-elastic stress analysis is needed. For nonlinear isochronous σ-ε curves, analysis is done in the same manner as for elasto-plastic stress–strain curves that are not time dependent. Hence, various analytical results from Chapter 13 can be adapted to creep situations.

15.9.1 Linear Viscoelastic Behavior

Assume that it is reasonable to represent the behavior of a given material by a rheological model built up of combinations of linear springs and dashpots. As already explained in Section 15.6.1, the isochronous stress–strain curves are then all straight lines, which can be represented by $\varepsilon = \sigma f(t)$,

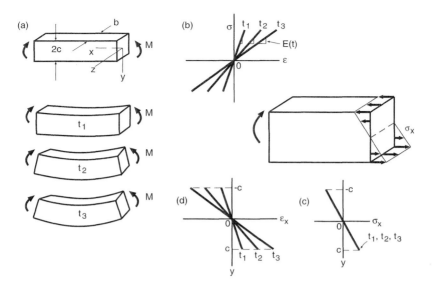

Figure 15.34 Behavior under constant applied moment of a beam (a) made of a linear viscoelastic material (b). The stress distribution is linear and constant with time (c), while the strain maintains a linear distribution as it increases (d).

where the particular time function $f(t)$ that applies depends on the model. A time-dependent modulus

$$E(t) = \frac{1}{f(t)} = \frac{\sigma}{\varepsilon} \tag{15.68}$$

where $E(t)$ is simply the slope of the isochronous stress–strain curve, is often used. Since the stress–strain relationship is linear, component stress–strain analysis for any particular time t can be done by a stress analysis performed on the basis of linear-elastic behavior. The analysis is unaffected, except that the elastic modulus varies with time.

The situation for a rectangular beam under pure bending is illustrated in Fig. 15.34. For all values of time, the stress distribution is linear and unchanging, according to the bending formula from linear-elastic analysis. Thus,

$$\sigma = \frac{My}{I_z} = \frac{3My}{2bc^3} \tag{15.69}$$

The strain for any position y in the beam at any time t is then obtained by combining Eqs. 15.68 and 15.69:

$$\varepsilon = \frac{\sigma}{E(t)} = \frac{3My}{2bc^3} \frac{1}{E(t)} \tag{15.70}$$

Analysis of linear-elastic behavior can be similarly applied to other situations, such as more complex bending problems, shafts in torsion, pressure vessels, geometries containing stress raisers, etc.

The stress distributions from linear-elastic analysis apply in all cases. To determine strains where nonuniaxial stress states occur, it is necessary to apply both Hooke's law, Eq. 5.26, and the equations for multiaxial viscous flow, Eq. 15.64.

If the isochronous stress–strain curves are nonlinear, but not grossly so, it may still be reasonable to employ linear-elastic analysis as just described. Values of $E(t)$ are replaced by values of the secant modulus, $E_s(t)$, as defined in Fig. 15.11.

Example 15.7

A beam is simply supported over a length of $L = 100$ mm and is loaded at its center with a transverse load of $P = 50$ N. Its cross section has width $b = 15$ mm and depth $2c = 10$ mm. The material has linear viscoelastic behavior with elastic and steady-state creep strains, similar to the model of Fig. 15.27(a), with the constants being $E_1 = 3$ GPa and $\eta_1 = 10^5$ GPa·s. Determine (a) the maximum stress in the beam, (b) the initial elastic deflection when the load is applied, and (c) the deflection after one week.

Solution   Due to the linear viscoelastic behavior, stresses may be obtained from the ordinary elastic bending formula:

$$\sigma = \frac{Mc}{I}, \qquad I = \frac{2bc^3}{3}$$

Here, I is from Fig. A.2(a) in Appendix A. The maximum stress is at the midlength, where the moment is $M = PL/4$ from Fig. A.4(a). Hence, substituting for M and I gives

$$\sigma = \frac{3PL}{8bc^2} = \frac{3(50 \text{ N})(100 \text{ mm})}{8(15 \text{ mm})(5 \text{ mm})^2} = 5.00 \text{ MPa} \qquad \textbf{Ans.}$$

Using the equation from Fig. A.4(a), we find that the initial elastic deflection is controlled by E_1, as the creep strain is initially zero:

$$v = \frac{PL^3}{48E_1 I} = \frac{(50 \text{ N})(100 \text{ mm})^3}{48(3000 \text{ MPa})(1250 \text{ mm}^3)} = 0.278 \text{ mm} \qquad \textbf{Ans.}$$

To obtain the deflection as affected by creep, note that the strain–time behavior is given by the equation from Fig. 15.27(a):

$$\varepsilon = \frac{\sigma}{E_1} + \frac{\sigma t}{\eta_1}$$

Hence, the time-dependent modulus for $t = 1$ week $= 604{,}800$ seconds is

$$E(t) = \frac{\sigma}{\varepsilon} = \frac{1}{\dfrac{1}{E_1} + \dfrac{t}{\eta_1}} = \frac{1}{\dfrac{1}{3000 \text{ MPa}} + \dfrac{604{,}800 \text{ s}}{10^8 \text{ MPa·s}}} = 156.7 \text{ MPa}$$

Repeating the deflection calculation with this lower value $E(t)$ finally gives the deflection after one week:

$$v = \frac{PL^3}{48E(t)I} = \frac{(50\ \text{N})(100\ \text{mm})^3}{48(156.7\ \text{MPa})(1250\ \text{mm}^3)} = 5.32\ \text{mm} \qquad \textbf{Ans.}$$

15.9.2 Analysis with Nonlinear Isochronous Stress–Strain Curves

If the isochronous stress–strain curves are markedly nonlinear, then analysis similar to that described in Chapter 13 for plastic deformation is needed. The isochronous stress–strain curve for any particular time is used just as if it were an elasto-plastic stress–strain curve. This is illustrated in Fig. 15.35 for a rectangular beam under static pure bending. The stress distribution must resist a bending moment that does not vary with time; however, the shape of the stress distribution may change as a result of a changing shape of the isochronous stress–strain curve. A linear strain

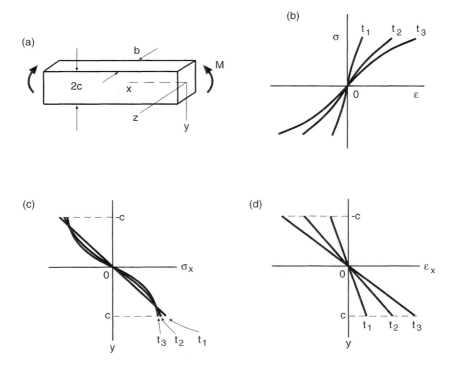

Figure 15.35   Behavior under constant moment of a beam (a) made of a material with nonlinear isochronous stress–strain curves (b). The stress distribution may change its shape with time (c), while the strain distributions remain linear as the strain increases (d).

distribution is a reasonable assumption for all values of time, but the magnitude of the strain increases.

For example, assume, for the beam material in Fig. 15.35, that all strains except the steady-state creep strains are small and that these are given by

$$\varepsilon = B\sigma^m t \tag{15.71}$$

For any particular time t, this equation represents simple power hardening, as in Eq. 13.9, with constants as follows:

$$n_2 = \frac{1}{m}, \qquad H_2 = \frac{1}{(Bt)^{1/m}} \tag{15.72}$$

The analytical result of Eq. 13.11 can now be employed by making these substitutions. Denoting the beam thickness as b to avoid confusion with time t, we get

$$M = \frac{2mbc^2\sigma_c}{1+2m} = \frac{2mbc^2}{1+2m}\left(\frac{\varepsilon_c}{Bt}\right)^{1/m} \tag{15.73}$$

where σ_c, ε_c are the stress and strain at the edge of the beam. The relationship between strain and moment depends on time, as expected. In this particular case, the stress distribution is nonlinear, but does not adjust with time unless m differs for the various isochronous curves.

Other analytical results from Chapter 13 can be applied to creep problems in a similar manner if the isochronous stress–strain curves are represented by equations of the same mathematical form as those used in each case. The power-law form of many of the stress–strain–time equations for creep makes the simple power-hardening and Ramberg–Osgood forms particularly convenient to use. For the Ramberg–Osgood case, Eq. 15.35 applies, where H_c specifies the time dependence, as from Eq. 15.36 or 15.40.

In stress–strain analysis for creep situations, it may be useful to perform multiple analyses by using several members of the family of isochronous stress–strain curves, each corresponding to a different value of time, to determine how the component behavior evolves with time. Also, if the combination of geometry and loading is complex, then it may be appropriate to employ numerical analysis, as by finite elements.

Example 15.8

A rectangular beam made of S-590 alloy has depth $2c = 50$ mm and thickness $b = 20$ mm. It is loaded with a moment of $M = 1.50$ kN·m at a temperature of $725°C$. At this temperature, and for stresses in the range 100 to 400 MPa, constants for Eq. 15.71 are $m = 10.74$ and $B = 3.91 \times 10^{-29}$, where t is in units of hours. (From data in [Grant 50].) Estimate the stress in the beam, the creep strain after 16,000 hours, and the life to creep rupture.

Solution   The stress at the edge of the beam is obtained directly from Eq. 15.73. Retaining units of mm for b and c, and substituting $M = 1.50 \times 10^6$ N·mm, we obtain

$$\sigma_c = \frac{M(1 + 2m)}{2mbc^2} = 125.6 \text{ MPa} \qquad \text{**Ans.**}$$

After 16,000 hours, the creep strain at the edge of the beam is

$$\varepsilon_c = B\sigma_c^m t = 3.91 \times 10^{-29} (125.6 \text{ MPa})^{10.74} (16{,}000 \text{ h}) = 0.0218 \qquad \text{**Ans.**}$$

From constants C, b_1, and b_2 in Table 15.3, the Larson–Miller parameter and the estimated life to rupture from Eq. 15.20 are

$$P_{LM} = 38{,}405 - 8206 \log \sigma = 38{,}405 - 8206 \log (125.6 \text{ MPa}) = 21{,}181 \text{ K·log (h)}$$

$$\log t_r = \frac{P_{LM}}{T} - C = \frac{21{,}181}{(725 + 273) \text{ K}} - 17 = 4.224, \qquad t_r = 16{,}730 \text{ hours} \qquad \text{**Ans.**}$$

It is assumed in this calculation that the steady-state creep strain is large compared with both the elastic and the transient creep strain, so that Eq. 15.71 applies on an approximate basis.

15.10 ENERGY DISSIPATION (DAMPING) IN MATERIALS

Materials subjected to cyclic loading absorb energy, some of which may be stored as potential energy within the structure of the material, but most of which is dissipated as heat to the surroundings. Such energy dissipation may be small, and even difficult to measure, but it is nevertheless always present. Otherwise, vibrations (say, in a tuning fork of the material) would never decay, and the physically impossible situation of a perpetual motion machine would exist. Energy dissipation in materials, termed *damping* or *internal friction*, is caused by a wide range of physical mechanisms, depending on the material, temperature, and frequency of cyclic loading involved. Any physical mechanism that causes creep can cause damping, but other mechanisms that act at low stresses are not associated with macroscopic creep effects. The small strains associated with such low-stress damping phenomena are recoverable or *anelastic strains*, as defined in Section 5.2.4, and low-stress damping itself is called *anelastic damping*. Damping also occurs as a result of plastic deformation.

Damping in materials is of practical importance, as the degree of damping affects the behavior under vibratory loading. In particular, higher damping results in lower stresses under forced vibration near resonance, and also in more rapid decay of free vibration. Damping behavior may thus affect the choice of materials in vibration-sensitive applications, such as turbine blades.

15.10.1 Damping Behavior of Rheological Models

The transient-creep-plus-elastic rheological model exhibits behavior similar to low-stress (anelastic) damping, as summarized in Fig. 15.36. A sinusoidal stress is assumed to be applied. That is,

$$\sigma = \sigma_a \sin \omega t \qquad (15.74)$$

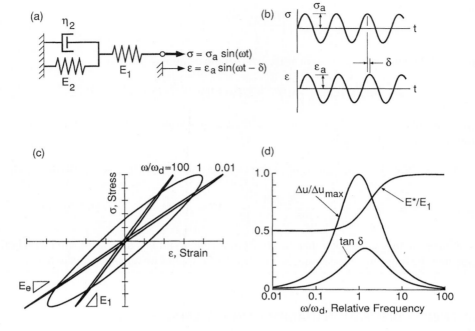

Figure 15.36 Behavior of a transient-creep-plus-elastic rheological model under a sinusoidal stress. The curves shown correspond to $E_1/E_2 = 1$.

where σ_a is the stress amplitude and ω is the angular frequency. The strain response of the model at any frequency is sinusoidal, but there is a phase shift, as specified by a phase angle δ, relative to the sine wave of the stress:

$$\varepsilon = \varepsilon_a \sin(\omega t - \delta) \tag{15.75}$$

The preceding two equations are the parametric equations for an ellipse. Hence, the stress–strain response forms an elliptical hysteresis loop, as shown in Fig. 15.36(c).

The area inside this loop is the energy absorbed in each cycle per unit volume of material, which is called the *unit damping energy*, Δu. Evaluating the loop area gives an equation for Δu:

$$\Delta u = \pi \sigma_a \varepsilon_a \sin \delta \tag{15.76}$$

Both δ and Δu exhibit maxima when plotted versus the angular frequency ω. For this particular model, the Δu maximum occurs at the frequency $\omega_d = E_2/\eta_2$. The quantity ($\varepsilon_a \sin \delta$) is the strain from Eq. 15.75 when σ is zero. Hence, it is the half-width of the elliptical hysteresis loop and is a measure of the nonlinearity in strain, as shown in Fig. 15.37. This quantity, sometimes called the *remnant displacement*, is roughly analogous to the plastic strain amplitude, $\varepsilon_{pa} = \Delta \varepsilon_p/2$, of Fig. 12.17. Since ($\varepsilon_a \sin \delta$) is proportional to Δu, it exhibits the same type of frequency dependence as Δu.

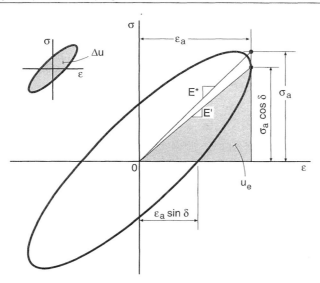

Figure 15.37   Definitions for an elliptical hysteresis loop.

At frequencies that are high compared with ω_d, the dashpot is essentially rigid. Deformation is thus prevented in spring E_2 and occurs only in E_1, so that the response is linear with stiffness E_1. Conversely, at frequencies that are low compared with ω_d, there is sufficient time for free movement of the dashpot, so that it has little effect. The elliptical loop again reduces to a straight line, but in this case with the lower stiffness E_e corresponding to E_1 and E_2 in series. (See Eq. 15.32.) The stiffness is an elastic modulus, called E^*, defined as shown in Fig. 15.37. Its value varies with frequency, increasing from E_e at low frequency to E_1 at high frequency. The transition between the two occurs in the neighborhood of the energy dissipation peak.

For any rheological model composed of linear springs and dashpots—that is, for any linear viscoelastic model—elliptical hysteresis loops are formed, and the strain response is proportional to the applied stress. Hence, the strain amplitude ε_a is proportional to the stress amplitude σ_a. Also, the phase shift δ does not depend on σ_a, but only on ω. Hence, the elliptical hysteresis loops for various σ_a at a given frequency all have the same proportions and differ only in size. From Eq. 15.76, this results in the unit damping energy being proportional to the square of the stress amplitude:

$$\Delta u = J\sigma_a^2 \tag{15.77}$$

In this equation, J is a constant for a given set of model constants and frequency. More complex rheological models that are useful for damping include series combinations of several transient creep elements with differing constants. Such a model exhibits several peaks on a plot of δ or Δu versus ω, one for each transient creep element. Also, elements having more complex nonlinear behavior are sometimes used.

15.10.2 Definitions of Variables Describing Damping

A number of different definitions are in use for describing the damping behavior of any model or material. The *unit damping energy* Δu, also often denoted D, has already been defined, as have the *phase angle* δ and the *remnant displacement*. The *loss coefficient* Q^{-1} is defined as

$$Q^{-1} = \tan \delta \tag{15.78}$$

The variable Q itself is called the *quality factor*.

The ratio of the stress amplitude to the strain amplitude, $E^* = \sigma_a/\varepsilon_a$, as shown in Fig. 15.37, is called the *dynamic modulus* or the *absolute modulus*. Another frequently used measure of stiffness is the *storage modulus*, E', which is the slope of a line from the origin to the maximum strain point on the elliptical hysteresis loop, which occurs at the stress $\sigma = \sigma_a \cos \delta$ as shown. The storage modulus is conventionally used to define the elastic strain energy at the peak strain, u_e, as also shown in Fig. 15.37. The loss coefficient is related to the energies Δu and u_e by

$$Q^{-1} = \frac{\Delta u}{2\pi u_e} \tag{15.79}$$

One additional definition that is often used is the *log decrement*, $\Delta_t = \pi Q^{-1}$. Where Δu is small compared with u_e, such that $Q^{-1} = 0.1$ or less, the damping is considerd to be relatively low.

15.10.3 Low-Stress Mechanisms in Metals

At low stresses in engineering metals, a variety of damping mechanisms occur, each of which behaves in a manner similar to the linear viscoelastic model previously discussed. This results in a number of different peaks in energy dissipation that occur as the frequency or temperature is changed, as illustrated in Fig. 15.38.

An example of such a mechanism is the *Snoek effect*. This involves interstitial solute atoms in a body-centered-cubic (BCC) metal, such as carbon or nitrogen in iron, as illustrated in Fig. 15.39. Such interstitial atoms are small compared with iron atoms, so they can occupy the normally unoccupied positions in the middle of the cube edges of the BCC iron crystal structure, somewhat distorting the structure in doing so. If a tensile stress is applied as shown, interstitial atoms along cube edges that are approximately normal to the applied stress are further squeezed by the Poisson contraction that occurs. They tend to jump to cube edges that are more parallel to the applied stress, where the tensile strain provides added space to accommodate them.

If the frequency of loading is very high, the interstitials have insufficient time to move, so the effect does not occur. Conversely, if the frequency is very low, the interstitials can move freely. In both cases, the strain in the material is in phase with the stress, but for the lower frequency, the material deforms more and thus has a slightly lower elastic modulus. However, at intermediate cyclic loading frequencies corresponding to the time required for a jump to occur, the strain response is slower than the applied stress, a phase lag occurs, and the dissipation of energy is at a maximum. The applied stress can then be said to be in resonance with the jumping of the interstitials. Since the jumping process is thermally activated, a peak in energy dissipation can also be observed by varying the temperature at a constant frequency.

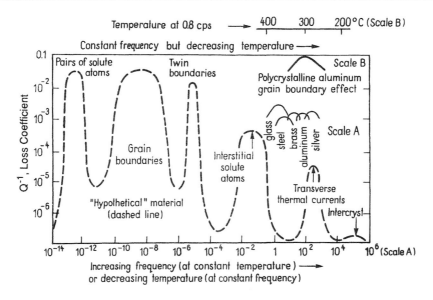

Figure 15.38 Damping peaks for a hypothetical metal and several real metals, and the associated microstructural mechanisms. (Adapted from [Lazan 68] p. 39; used with permission.)

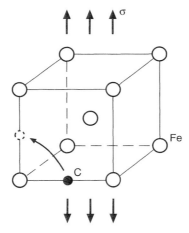

Figure 15.39 Mechanism of the Snoek effect, involving motion of interstitial atoms in a BCC metal structure.

Another example is the *thermoelastic effect*, also called thermal current damping. As Poisson's ratio is usually somewhat less than the value of $\nu = 0.5$ corresponding to the volume being constant, the volume of a stressed solid increases during the tensile portion of cyclic loading. If the loading is so rapid that heat exchange with the surroundings does not have time to occur, the increased volume results in a temperature decrease, hence also in a thermal contraction. Conversely, for rapid loading under compression, there is decreased volume, increased temperature, and thermal expansion. Hence, rapid cyclic loading is accompanied by thermal strains that are in the opposite direction of the mechanical strains, resulting in an apparent stiffening of the material. The elastic modulus that occurs is referred to as the *adiabatic* (meaning constant heat) value. But under slow cycling, where heat exchange with the surroundings can occur freely, there are no thermal strains opposing the mechanical strains. The elastic modulus then takes on the lower *isothermal* value. At intermediate frequencies that correspond to the time required for heat flow, the strain response exhibits a phase lag and there is a relative maximum in energy dissipation.

15.10.4 Additional Mechanisms and Trends

Other damping mechanisms involve various time-dependent movements of impurity atoms or vacancies (point defects), movements of dislocations (line defects), and sliding of grain boundaries. In ferromagnetic materials, an effect called *magnetoelastic damping* is important, in which energy dissipation results from rotations in the directions of the microscopic magnetic domains that occur in such a material. This effect is unusual in that it is independent of frequency and is more strongly dependent on stress amplitude than is expected from the ideal model discussed previously. In particular, Δu is proportional to the cube of stress, rather than the square. In addition, the effect may saturate and become independent of stress above a critical level, and it may be sensitive to mean stress.

The gross dislocation motions that result in slip of crystal planes, and hence in plastic deformation, can cause large amounts of energy dissipation called *plastic strain damping*. Such effects are inactive at low stresses, but for engineering metals at temperatures where creep effects are small, they become the dominant mechanism of damping at high stresses. The behavior is dramatically different from that of the linear viscoelastic model, being insensitive to frequency and very sensitive to stress. Hysteresis loops due to plastic deformation are not elliptical; rather, they are pointed as in Fig. 12.17. According to the approximation for the shape of hysteresis loop curves discussed in Chapter 12, plastic strain damping can be calculated from the area inside the stress–strain hysteresis loop. For a cyclic stress–strain curve of Ramberg–Osgood form, Eq. 12.55 applies on an approximate basis, giving

$$\Delta u = 4 \left(\frac{1 - n'}{1 + n'} \right) \sigma_a \varepsilon_{pa} = \frac{4 \left(1 - n' \right) \sigma_a^{1 + 1/n'}}{(1 + n') (H')^{1/n'}} \tag{15.80}$$

where Eq. 12.11 is used to obtain the second form, and H' and n' are the constants for the cyclic stress–strain curve. Let Eq. 15.77 be generalized to

$$\Delta u = J \sigma_a^d \tag{15.81}$$

Noting that $n' = \frac{1}{7}$ is typical, we find that the exponent on stress from Eq. 15.80 is

$$d = 1 + \frac{1}{n'} \approx 8 \tag{15.82}$$

This indicates a very strong dependence on stress, in contrast to $d = 2$ for ideal anelastic damping.

Polymers and elastomers are likely to exhibit behavior similar to ideal linear viscoelasticity ($d = 2$) if the stress levels are not excessively high. Some of the mechanisms that operate to cause peaks in energy dissipation involve chain molecule motions, such as rotations, translations, or coiling and uncoiling, of interior or end segments of chains. The segments involved can be long or short, and motions of side groups can also cause damping. In general, larger moving entities cause damping peaks at lower frequencies for a given temperature, or at higher temperatures for a given frequency.

At stresses where metals are used for engineering purposes, the damping is generally quite low, involving loss coefficients around $Q^{-1} = 0.01$ or less. In contrast, the values for polymers at service stresses may be much larger, such as $Q^{-1} = 0.1$ or more. Correspondingly large phase angles and variations in the elastic modulus (E^* or E') then also occur. Such large damping may be disadvantageous if excessive heat is generated, but it is often beneficial in quickly damping any vibrations that develop. High damping is, of course, often intentionally employed to mitigate sound or vibration by the use of polymers, especially elastomers.

Some trend curves for damping energy in engineering metals at room temperature are suggested by Lazan (1968) and are shown in Fig. 15.40. For nonmagnetic metals, the stress exponent for the

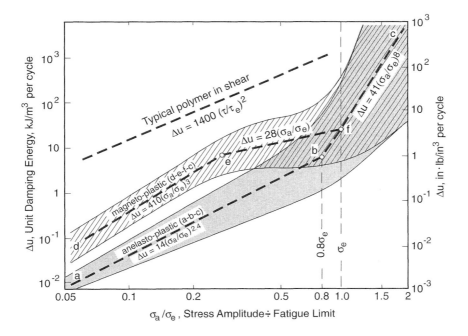

Figure 15.40   Trends for damping in ferromagnetic and nonferromagnetic metals, and also for a typical viscoelastic polymer. For the two classes of metals, ranges of behavior and idealized relations are given, with the equations being for Δu in kJ/m³. (Adapted from [Lazan 68] p. 139; used with permission.)

middle of the data trend is a little larger than the ideal viscoelastic value of $d = 2$, up to about 80% of the fatigue limit σ_e, where the slope of about $d = 8$ begins due to plastic strain damping. Ferromagnetic metals have higher damping at low stresses and a value of $d \approx 3$, followed by a region of $d \approx 1$, which prevails until $d \approx 8$ begins around the fatigue limit.

15.10.5 Damping in Engineering Components

The discussion so far of damping has considered only the behavior of uniformly stressed samples of material, rather than engineering components, such as beams, shafts, etc., that contain nonuniform distributions of stress. For ideal viscoelastic behavior, $d = 2$, the loss coefficient Q^{-1} for a component is the same as for the material. Otherwise, Q^{-1} depends on the geometry and so is not the same as for a uniformly stressed material.

The total damping energy ΔU for a component can be obtained by integrating over its volume. A second integration over the volume yields the elastic energy for the component, and the ratio of these is the loss factor for the component, giving

$$\Delta U = \int \Delta u \, dV, \qquad U_e = \int u_e \, dV, \qquad Q_v^{-1} = \frac{\Delta U}{2\pi U_e} \tag{15.83}$$

Such analysis is considered in Lazan (1968) and Marin (1962) for cases where it is reasonable to assume linear-elastic behavior, that is, behavior where the nonlinear strains due to damping are small compared with the elastic strains. If large plastic deformations occur, the methods of Chapter 13 for beams and shafts can be extended to calculate damping energies, with Δu given by Eq. 15.80. Numerical analysis, as by finite elements, may be employed for complex geometries and loadings.

Example 15.9
Consider a rectangular beam of depth $2c$, thickness b, and length L, that is subjected to a cyclic pure bending moment M_a about zero mean. The strains are sufficiently large that a nonlinear stress distribution occurs, and the material follows a cyclic stress–strain curve of the Ramberg–Osgood form, Eq. 12.54. Obtain an equation for the total energy ΔU dissipated in each cycle of loading as a function of the stresses and strains at the beam edge.

Solution   The damping energy in the member is obtained by combining Eq. 15.81 with the integral for ΔU of Eq. 15.83. We obtain

$$\Delta U = \int \Delta u \, dV = \int J\sigma_a^d \, dV$$

where J and d from Eq. 15.80 apply:

$$J = \frac{4\left(1 - n'\right)}{(1 + n')\,(H')^{1/n'}}, \qquad d = 1 + \frac{1}{n'}$$

Since we have pure bending, the stress amplitude varies with distance y from the neutral axis, but not with position x along the beam length. (The coordinate axes of Fig. 13.3 are being used.) Hence, a suitable volume element is

$$dV = Lb \, dy$$

Symmetry permits the integral to be evaluated on only one side of the beam, so that it becomes

$$\Delta U = 2JLb \int_0^c \sigma_a^d \, dy$$

This integral can be evaluated by a procedure similar to that leading to the bending analysis of Eq. 13.27. We first make the reasonable physical assumption that plane sections remain plane even during the cyclic plastic deformation. Thus, Eq. 13.22 applies to the strain amplitudes:

$$y = \frac{c}{\varepsilon_{ca}} \varepsilon_a, \qquad dy = \frac{c}{\varepsilon_{ca}} d\varepsilon_a$$

Here, ε_a is strain amplitude and ε_{ca} is the particular value at the beam edge, $y = c$. The cyclic stress–strain curve (Eq. 12.54) and its differential are also needed:

$$\varepsilon_a = \frac{\sigma_a}{E} + \left(\frac{\sigma_a}{H'}\right)^{1/n'}, \qquad d\varepsilon_a = \left[\frac{1}{E} + \frac{1}{n'\sigma_a}\left(\frac{\sigma_a}{H'}\right)^{1/n'}\right] d\sigma_a$$

Substituting $d\varepsilon_a$ into the expression for dy, and then substituting the result into the integral for ΔU, gives a form with stress as the only variable:

$$\Delta U = \frac{2JLbc}{\varepsilon_{ca}} \int_0^{\sigma_{ca}} \sigma_a^{1+1/n'} \left[\frac{1}{E} + \frac{1}{n'\sigma_a}\left(\frac{\sigma_a}{H'}\right)^{1/n'}\right] d\sigma_a$$

In this equation, σ_{ca} is the stress amplitude at $y = c$, and the expression involving n' has been substituted for d.

The integral is now readily evaluated. After doing so, substituting for J, and performing some manipulation, we obtain

$$\Delta U = \frac{8Lbc}{(H')^{1/n'}} \left(\frac{1-n'}{1+n'}\right) \sigma_{ca}^{1+1/n'} \left[\frac{\dfrac{n'}{2n'+1} + \dfrac{1}{2+n'}\beta}{1+\beta}\right] \qquad \textbf{Ans.}$$

where $\quad \beta = \dfrac{\varepsilon_{pca}}{\varepsilon_{eca}}, \qquad \varepsilon_{pca} = \left(\dfrac{\sigma_{ca}}{H'}\right)^{1/n'}, \qquad \varepsilon_{eca} = \dfrac{\sigma_{ca}}{E}, \qquad \varepsilon_{ca} = \varepsilon_{eca} + \varepsilon_{pca}$

Here, ε_{pca} and ε_{eca} are plastic and elastic strain amplitudes, respectively, at $y = c$.

15.11 SUMMARY

15.11.1 Creep: Introductory Aspects

Creep tests of materials are most commonly performed by applying various levels of constant stress to uniaxial specimens. Data can be obtained on strains, strain rates, and rupture lives. In addition to strain versus time plots, the data may be used to construct stress versus life plots, where life is the time to rupture or to a particular value of strain. Stress–strain curves corresponding to given times, called isochronous stress–strain curves, are also useful.

The physical mechanisms associated with creep deformation vary widely with the material and with the combination of stress and temperature involved. Behavior similar to simple viscous flow, where stress and strain rate are proportional, may occur. This is the case for glasses, for polymers at temperatures significantly above T_g, and for crystalline materials (metals and ceramics) at high temperature, but low stress. For the latter, the mechanism of viscous flow is often diffusional flow involving movement of vacancies through the crystal lattice or along grain boundaries. At relatively high stresses in crystalline materials, the dominant creep mechanisms involve movement of dislocations, which process is highly sensitive to stress, so that strain rates are proportional to stress raised to a power on the order of five. Steady-state creep rates in crystalline materials may be described by

$$\dot{\varepsilon} = \frac{A_2\sigma^m}{d^qT}e^{\frac{-Q}{RT}} \tag{15.84}$$

where the trends for the exponents m on stress and q on average grain diameter are summarized in Table 15.1. The dependence on absolute temperature T follows an Arrhenius relationship with an activation energy Q that depends on the creep mechanism.

Creep mechanisms in polymers around and above T_g, but not very close to the melting temperature, involve various relatively complex motions and interactions of the long chainlike molecules. Effects such as entanglement of the chains can cause increased resistance as deformation proceeds, and also a tendency for much of the creep deformation to be recovered if the load is removed. Creep in concrete involves distinctive mechanisms associated with time-dependent deformation in the cement paste and movement of water in pores. Elastic strains in the aggregate oppose and limit the creep strain, and also cause a strong recovery behavior to occur.

15.11.2 Creep: Engineering Analysis

For making life estimates, time–temperature parameters are generally used, rather than more direct extrapolation of stress–life curves. For example, creep–rupture lives for various combinations of stress and temperature can be employed with a material constant C to calculate values of the Larson–Miller parameter:

$$P_{LM} = T\left(\log t_r + C\right) \tag{15.85}$$

A plot or fitted equation of P_{LM} versus stress can then be used to estimate times to rupture t_r for situations not represented in the original data. Extrapolation beyond the data by up to a factor of 10 in life is reasonable, as long as a new creep mechanism is not encountered. Other time–temperature parameters are available, including the Sherby–Dorn parameter, Eq. 15.16. Where stress levels vary, a time-fraction rule, used similarly to the Palmgren–Miner rule for fatigue, provides rough life estimates. If creep is combined with cyclic loading, life fractions for creep may be combined with those for fatigue from the Palmgren–Miner rule to roughly estimate the combined effect.

A variety of stress–strain–time relationships have been proposed that can be used for making engineering estimates of behavior. For example, for steady-state creep, the power-law dependence of Eq. 15.84 has the form $\dot{\varepsilon} = B\sigma^m$ for a given material and temperature. Additional terms, or an altered mathematical form, are used to describe transient creep, for which $\dot{\varepsilon}$ varies with time. Situations of varying stress are also of interest, including recovery of creep strain after removal of stress, relaxation of stress under constant strain, and step loading. Various alternatives exist for handling step loading. Where linear viscoelastic behavior is a reasonable approximation, a superposition procedure can be used, as in Fig. 15.32. Time hardening or strain hardening (Fig. 15.33) is often employed for step loading of metals, with the latter preferred.

For multiaxial stresses, creep strains can be estimated by means of equations similar to those of plasticity theory, but applied to strain rates:

$$\dot{\varepsilon}_x = \frac{1}{\eta}\left[\sigma_x - 0.5\left(\sigma_y + \sigma_z\right)\right], \text{etc.} \tag{15.86}$$

The tensile viscosity η appears, and since creep strains cause little volume change, 0.5 replaces Poisson's ratio. For linear viscoelastic behavior, η may vary with time, but not with stress. However, η may be treated as a stress-dependent variable to handle cases of nonlinear isochronous stress–strain curves. Rupture lives for multiaxial states of stress can be estimated by assuming that the effective stress $\bar{\sigma}$ has the same effect as a numerically equal uniaxial stress. A secondary dependence on the maximum principal stress can also be added according to Eq. 15.26.

For engineering components, ordinary linear-elastic stress analysis can be applied if the material behavior can be approximated as following linear viscoelasticity. Strains at various times are then obtained from the time-dependent elastic modulus $E(t)$ of the material. Where the isochronous stress–strain curves are nonlinear, analysis is done just as for an elasto-plastic stress–strain curve, with several repetitions of the analysis for various values of time often being needed. Nonlinear isochronous stress–strain curves sometimes have the Ramberg–Osgood form, as for Eq. 15.35 combined with either Eq. 15.36 or 15.40, allowing stress–strain analysis for this form to be used in a straightforward manner for creep.

15.11.3 Materials Damping

Energy dissipation during cyclic loading, called *damping*, can occur as a result of various low stress (anelastic) damping mechanisms in metals, such as the Snoek effect and thermoelastic coupling. In general, the damping energy per cycle, per unit volume, varies with stress amplitude according to

$$\Delta u = J\sigma_a^d \tag{15.87}$$

where the exponent d depends on the material and the mechanism that is dominant for a given stress, temperature, and frequency. The damping behavior of metals at low stresses, and also of polymers in general, is often similar to the behavior of linear viscoelastic models that contain transient creep elements. As a result, peaks in energy dissipation occur at certain frequencies for constant temperature, and the energy dissipated in each cycle is approximately proportional to the square of stress, $d \approx 2$. At stresses around and above the fatigue limit in metals, the energy dissipation is insensitive to frequency and is dominated by plastic deformation. The energy dissipated in each cycle is then highly sensitive to stress, typically being proportional to the eighth power of stress, $d \approx 8$.

NEW TERMS AND SYMBOLS

(a) Creep
activation energy, Q
Coble creep
creep cavitation
creep exponent, m
creep–fatigue interaction
creep recovery
creep rupture
deformation mechanism map
diffusional flow
dislocation (power-law) creep
effective strain rate, $\bar{\dot{\varepsilon}}$
isochronous stress–strain curve
Larson–Miller constant, C
linear viscoelasticity
Nabarro–Herring creep
primary (transient) creep
safety factors: X_σ, X_t

safety margin in temperature, ΔT_f
secondary (steady-state) creep
strain-hardening rule
stress relaxation
superposition principle
temperature compensated time, θ
tertiary creep
thickness, b
time-dependent elastic modulus, $E(t)$
time-fraction rule
time-hardening rule
time–temperature parameters:
    Larson–Miller, P_{LM}
    Sherby–Dorn, P_{SD}
time to rupture, t_r
universal gas constant, R
viscosity: η_τ, η

(b) Damping
anelastic damping
component energies: ΔU, U_e
damping exponent, d
dynamic modulus, E^*
elastic strain energy, u_e
loss coefficient: $Q^{-1} = \tan\delta$
magnetoelastic damping

materials damping (internal friction)
phase shift, δ
plastic strain damping
remnant displacement
Snoek effect
thermoelastic effect
unit damping energy, Δu

REFERENCES

(a) General References

ASTM. 2010. *Annual Book of ASTM Standards*, ASTM International, West Conshohocken, PA. See Vol. 03.01: No. E139, "Standard Test Methods for Conducting Creep, Creep-Rupture, and Stress-Rupture Tests of Metallic Materials", No. E328, "Standard Test Methods for Stress Relaxation for Materials and Structures." Vol. 04.02: No. C512, "Standard Test Method for Creep of Concrete in Compression." Vol. 08.01: No. D2990, "Standard Test Methods for Tensile, Compressive, and Flexural Creep and Creep-Rupture of Plastics."

BRINSON, H. F., and L. C. BRINSON. 2008. *Polymer Engineering Science and Viscoelasticity: An Introduction*, Springer, New York.

CONWAY, J. B., and P. N. FLAGELLA. 1971. *Creep-Rupture Data for the Refactory Metals to High Temperatures*, Gordon and Breach, New York.

ENO, D. R., G. A. YOUNG, and T.-L. SHAM. 2008. "A Unified View of Engineering Creep Parameters," ASME Paper No. PVP2008-61129, *ASME 2008 Pressure Vessels and Piping Conference (PVP2008), Proceedings, Volume 6: Materials and Fabrication, Parts A and B*, pp. 777–792.

EVANS, R. W., and B. WILSHIRE. 1993. *Introduction to Creep*, The Institute of Materials, London.

GOOCH, D. J., and I. M. HOW. 1986. *Techniques for Multiaxial Creep Testing*, Elsevier Applied Science Pubs., London.

KASSNER, M. E., and M. T. PÉREZ-PRADO. 2009. *Fundamentals of Creep in Metals and Alloys*, 2nd ed., Elsevier, Amsterdam.

KRAUS, H. 1980. *Creep Analysis*, John Wiley, New York.

LAZAN, B. J., 1968. *Damping of Materials and Members in Structural Mechanics*, Pergamon Press, Oxford, UK.

MARIN, J. 1962. *Mechanical Behavior of Engineering Materials*, Prentice-Hall, Englewood Cliffs, NJ.

NEVILLE, A. M., W. H. DILGER, and J. J. BROOKS. 1983. *Creep of Plain and Structural Concrete*, Construction Press, New York.

PENNY, R. K., and D. L. MARRIOTT. 1995. *Design for Creep*, 2d ed., Chapman and Hall, London.

SAXENA, A., ed. 2003. *Creep and High-Temperature Failure*, vol. 5 of *Comprehensive Structural Integrity: Fracture of Materials from Nano to Macro*, I. Milne, R. O. Ritchie, and B. Karihaloo, eds., Elsevier Ltd., Oxford, UK.

SKRZYPEK, J. J., and R. B. HETNARSKI. 1993. *Plasticity and Creep: Theory, Examples, and Problems*, CRC Press, Boca Raton, FL.

WACHTMAN, J. B., W. R. CANNON, and M. J. MATTHEWSON. 2009. *Mechanical Properties of Ceramics*, 2nd ed., John Wiley, Hoboken, NJ.

(b) Sources for Materials Properties and Databases

ABE, F., and W. MARTIENSSEN. 2004. *Creep Properties of Heat Resistant Steels and Superalloys, 2: Advanced Materials and Technologies*, Springer, New York.

CINDAS. 2010. *Aerospace Structural Metals Database (ASMD)*, CINDAS LLC, West Lafayette, IN. (See *https://cindasdata.com*.)

DAVIS, J. R., ed. 1997. *ASM Specialty Handbook: Heat Resistant Materials*, ASM International, Materials Park, OH.

FROST, H. J., and M. F. ASHBY. 1982. *Deformation Mechanism Maps: The Plasticity and Creep of Metals and Ceramics*, Pergamon Press, Oxford, UK.

KAUFMAN, J. G. 2008. *Parametric Analyses of High-Temperature Data for Aluminum Alloys*, ASM International, Materials Park, OH.

NIMS. 2010. *Creep Data Sheets*, periodically updated database, National Institute of Materials Science, Tsukuba, Ibaraki, Japan. (See *http://mits.nims.go.jp/index_en.html*.)

PDL. 1991. *The Effect of Creep and Other Time Related Factors on Plastics*, Plastics Design Library, Norwich, NY. See also: E-book Edition 2001, Knovel Corp., Norwich, NY, www.knovel.com.

PROBLEMS AND QUESTIONS

Section 15.2

15.1 A 40% tin, 60% lead alloy solder wire of diameter 3.15 mm is subjected to creep by hanging weights from lengths of the wire. Length changes measured over a 254 mm gage length after various elapsed times are given in Table P15.1 for three different weights.

Table P15.1

| | Length change, mm | | |
Time, min	4.54 kg	6.80 kg	9.07 kg
0	0	0	0
0.25	0.28	0.46	0.69
0.5	0.36	0.66	0.94
1	0.48	0.91	1.45
2	0.71	1.40	2.36
4	1.09	2.24	4.09
6	1.47	3.00	5.72
8	1.83	3.38	7.26
12	2.54	4.90	10.41
16	3.23	6.38	13.64
20	3.91	7.82	16.74

(a) Plot the family of strain versus time curves that results. Is the behavior dominated by either transient or steady-state creep, or do significant amounts of both occur?

(b) Determine the steady-state creep rate, $\dot{\varepsilon}_{sc}$, for each value of weight, and plot these on log–log coordinates versus the corresponding stresses. Does a straight line provide a reasonable fit? If so, find values of B and m for the relationship $\dot{\varepsilon}_{sc} = B\sigma^m$.

15.2 From the data in Fig. 15.8, construct an approximate plot with curves of stress versus temperature for various times to failure. In particular, plot three curves, one corresponding to each of the three rupture times 10^2, 10^3, and 10^4 hours.

15.3 Plot isochronous stress–strain curves for lead–tin solder from the data in Table P15.1, doing so for times of $t = 4$, 12, and 20 min. Are the curves linear?

Section 15.3

15.4 Consider metals, polymers, and concrete. Which of these classes of materials typically exhibit strong recovery of creep strain after unloading, and which do not? Briefly explain in terms of the physical mechanisms of creep why the strains are generally recovered, or why they are not recovered, for each class of materials.

15.5   Compare the diffusional flow and dislocation creep mechanisms of crystalline materials. In particular, considering the effects of grain size, stress, and temperature, how do the trends in behavior differ?

15.6   For AISI 304 stainless steel with a grain size of $200 \, \mu$m, constants for Eq. 15.6 follow for the power-law region of the deformation mechanism map. These apply for stress σ in units of MPa, temperature T in kelvins (K), and strain rates $\dot{\varepsilon}$ in s^{-1}. (Constants based on [Frost 82] p. 62.)

$$m = 7.5, \qquad q = 0, \qquad Q/R = 33{,}700 \text{ K}$$

$$A_2 = \frac{1.04 \times 10^{27}}{G^{m-1}}, \qquad G_{300} = 81{,}000 \text{ MPa}, \qquad h = 38 \text{ MPa/K}$$

Here, A_2 depends on the shear modulus G as it varies with temperature according to Eq. 15.11. Make a log–log plot of σ versus $\dot{\varepsilon}$, showing lines for $T = 900$, 1200, and 1450 K, and covering strain rates in the range 10^{-2} to 10^{-8} s^{-1}.

15.7   Using the constants from the previous problem for 304 SS at 1200 K, plot isochronous stress–strain curves for times of 1 minute, 1 hour, and 1 week. Consider stresses such that the strains extend to about $\varepsilon = 0.02$ in each case. Assume that only elastic strains need to be added to creep strains from Eq. 15.6. The elastic modulus E may be estimated from the shear modulus G by approximating Poisson's ratio as $\nu = 0.3$.

15.8   For the AISI 304 stainless steel of Prob. 15.6, assume that only elastic strains need to be added to creep strains, and approximate Poisson's ratio as $\nu = 0.3$. Then answer the following:

   (a) For a stress of 42 MPa applied at a temperature of 950 K for one year, what is the resulting strain?

   (b) If the strain at 950 K cannot exceed 0.0015 in one year, what is the highest value of stress that can be permitted?

   (c) If the strain at 42 MPa cannot exceed 0.0015 in one year, what is the highest temperature that can be permitted?

   (d) Compare the results of the calculations for (a), (b), and (c), and comment on the trends seen.

15.9   Approximately confirm the value of activation energy Q shown on Fig. 15.12.

15.10 Consider a situation where creep strain rate data are available for a given material for various values of stress, grain size, and temperature, all for the same creep mechanism. Develop an equation that can be used as the basis of multiple linear regression to evaluate the constants A_2, m, q, and Q in Eq. 15.6.

15.11 Several creep tests were conducted on 40% tin, 60% lead solder wire. Table P15.11 gives steady-state creep rates for the various combinations of stress and temperature that were investigated. Since all of the data are for one batch of material, only a single grain size is represented, and a constant $A_3 = A_2/d^q$ can be employed for Eq. 15.6. Also, it is useful to isolate the quantity $(\dot{\varepsilon} \, T)$ on one side of the equation and then take the natural logarithm of both sides:

$$\dot{\varepsilon} \, T = A_3 \sigma^m e^{\frac{-Q}{RT}}, \qquad \ln{(\dot{\varepsilon} \, T)} = m \ln \sigma - \frac{Q}{R}\left(\frac{1}{T}\right) + \ln A_3$$

(a) On the basis of these equations, fit the data using multiple linear regression to obtain values of the constants A_3, m, and Q.

(b) Graphically compare the test data and fitted equation, and comment on the success of the fit.

Table P15.11

T, °C	σ, MPa	$\dot{\varepsilon}$, 1/s
25	2.80	6.00×10^{-6}
25	7.20	1.49×10^{-5}
25	12.70	5.48×10^{-5}
43	2.80	9.58×10^{-6}
66	2.80	2.69×10^{-5}
79	2.80	5.32×10^{-5}

Source: Data in [Arthur 10].

15.12 A bar of the MAR-M200 alloy of Fig. 15.16 (right) with grain size $d = 100\,\mu$m is 40 mm long. It is subjected to a tensile stress of 110 MPa at a temperature of 687°C.

(a) What is the initial elastic length change of the bar? (Suggestions: Use the constants that follow Eq. 15.11; assume Poisson's ratio $\nu = 0.30$.)

(b) Using Fig. 15.16, estimate the length change due to the combination of creep and elastic strain after one day, and also after one year.

(c) Check your result for (b), using Eq. 15.6. Some constants (from [Frost 82] p. 54) for this material for grain boundary diffusion (Coble) creep are as follows:

$$Q/R = 13{,}800 \text{ K}, \qquad A_2 = 9.81 \times 10^{-14} \frac{\text{K} \cdot \text{m}^5}{\text{MN} \cdot \text{s}}$$

(d) Repeat (c), except assume that the grain size is 10 times larger, $d = 1000\,\mu$m. Why might this difference be important in an actual application?

15.13 The blades in one stage of a gas turbine engine are subjected to normal stresses up to 150 MPa and temperatures that range from 450 to 650°C. To avoid excessive deformation, the creep strain should nowhere exceed 2% in 2000 hours. Consider the two materials of Fig. 15.16 as candidates for these turbine blades.

(a) What is the maximum strain rate, and what is the creep mechanism, for nickel material? Is it suitable for this use?

(b) What is the maximum strain rate, and what is the creep mechanism, for MAR-M200, and is it suitable?

(c) Either material can be differently processed to achieve a grain size anywhere in the range $10\,\mu$m to 1 cm. Should this be done? What would be your final choice of a material and a grain size?

Sections 15.4 and 15.5

15.14 For the alloy Fe-Cr-Ni-Co alloy S-590 of Table 15.3, do the following:

(a) Estimate the creep rupture life for the following four combinations of stress and temperature: (1) $\sigma = 80$ MPa, $T = 600$°C; (2) $\sigma = 80$ MPa, $T = 750$°C; (3) $\sigma = 160$ MPa, $T = 600$°C; and (4) $\sigma = 160$ MPa, $T = 750$°C.

(b) Comment on the trends in rupture life with stress and temperature. Is the life very sensitive to these variables?

15.15 The stainless steel AISI 310 is used in a high-temperature application with an applied stress of 10 MPa. The planned actual service life is 1000 hours, and a safety factor of 1.5 on stress is required.

(a) What is the highest operating temperature that is permissible while satisfying the safety factor of 1.5 on stress?

(b) Assuming operation at the temperature that you found in (a), what safety factor on life is achieved by using the safety factor of 1.5 on stress?

15.16 Alloy S-590 is required to withstand one year of service at a temperature of 600°C.

(a) What stress is expected to cause creep rupture in one year?

(b) What stress can be allowed in actual service if a safety factor of 1.4 on stress is required?

(c) What safety factor on life is achieved by the safety factor of 1.4 on stress?

15.17 A pipe in a spacecraft, made of AISI 310 stainless steel, is near the rocket engine, causing it to be subjected to temperatures as high as 1200°C. The stress applied to the pipe in actual service is expected to be 10 MPa.

(a) How long would you allow the pipe to be subjected to the given temperature and stress if a safety factor of 10 on life is required?

(b) What safety factor on stress is achieved by the safety factor of 10 on life? Does the resulting safety factor on stress seem reasonable and adequate?

15.18 Alloy A-286 is subjected in service to a stress of 200 MPa at a temperature of 750°C.

(a) Estimate the creep rupture life at these service conditions.

(b) If a safety factor of 2.0 on stress is required, what is the maximum service life that can be allowed?

(c) What is the safety margin in temperature?

15.19 An engineering component made of alloy S-590 will be subjected in actual service to temperatures as high as 800°C at a stress of 100 MPa.

(a) What life to creep rupture is expected for the given service conditions?

(b) It has been suggested that components of this type should be replaced after they have reached half the expected life. What safety factor on stress would be provided by this replacement policy?

(c) Do you agree with the suggestion of replacement at half the expected life? Why or why not?

15.20 The Cr-Mo-V steel of Table 15.3 is used in an application where the applied stress is 100 MPa. The planned actual service life is 10,000 hours, and a safety factor of 1.5 on stress is required.

(a) What is the highest permissible operating temperature?

(b) What safety factor on life is achieved by using the factor of 1.5 on stress?

(c) What safety margin in temperature corresponds to the factor of 1.5 on stress?

15.21 The Cr-Mo-V steel of Table 15.3 is used in an application where the applied stress is 300 MPa. The planned actual service life is 20,000 hours, and a safety factor of 1.5 on stress is required.

(a) What is the highest permissible operating temperature?

(b) What safety factor on life is achieved by using the factor of 1.5 on stress?

(c) What safety margin in temperature corresponds to the factor of 1.5 on stress?

15.22 Nimonic 80A is required to withstand one year of service at a temperature of 700°C.

(a) What stress is expected to cause creep rupture in one year?

(b) What stress can be allowed in actual service if a safety factor of 1.75 on stress is required?

(c) What safety factor on life is achieved by the safety factor of 1.75 on stress?

15.23 A gas turbine aircraft engine has blades made of alloy A-286. One critical row of blades has stress σ (bending plus axial) and temperature T that vary with location according to Table P15.23, where x is the distance beyond the base of the blade, as shown in Fig. P15.23. For larger x, the stress continues to decease toward a value of zero at the end of the blade, but the temperature remains near 680°C. These values correspond to the most severe operating condition encountered in normal use of the aircraft.

(a) Estimate the life of the blades, as limited by creep rupture.

(b) The maintenance schedule specifies replacing these blades every 5000 flight hours. What safety factor in stress is provided by this retirement life?

(c) What safety margin in temperature is provided by the 5000-hour retirement life?

(d) Do you agree with the 5000-hour retirement life? Should it be shorter or longer?

Table P15.23

x, mm	0	15	30	45	60	75	90
σ, MPa	170	168	164	155	142	120	90
T, °C	560	597	630	657	675	680	680

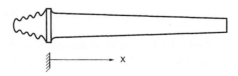

Figure P15.23

15.24 Creep-rupture data are given in Table P15.24 for the nickel-base alloy Nimonic 80A. Note that temperature, stress, and rupture time are given for a number of different tests.

(a) Fit these data to a Larsen–Miller parameter versus stress relationship of the form of Eq. 15.20, that is, obtain your own values of b_0, b_1, b_2, and b_3. Consider the C

value from Table 15.3 to be given. Then plot P_{LM} versus σ for both data and fit, and comment on the success of the fit.

(b) Similarly fit and plot these data for a Sherby–Dorn parameter versus stress relationship of the form of Eq. 15.19, that is, obtain your own values of a_0, a_1, a_2, and a_3. Consider the Q value from Table 15.2 to be given.

Table P15.24

T, °C	σ, MPa	t_r, hours	T, °C	σ, MPa	t_r, hours	T, °C	σ, MPa	t_r, hours
650	486	300	700	247	1 735	750	132	3 000
650	417	1 000	700	232	3 000	750	123	4 450
650	352	3 000	700	201	4 836	750	92	13 089
650	339	2 655	700	171	10 000	750	85	10 000
650	309	5 270	700	154	10 893	750	62	22 657
650	281	10 000	700	113	30 000	750	54	30 000
650	278	8 171	700	108	34 065	816	154	100
650	247	13 386	750	276	100	816	122	300
650	216	30 000	750	228	300	816	87	1 000
700	350	300	750	178	1 000	816	56	3 000
700	283	1 000	750	154	1 857	—	—	—

Source: Data in [Goldhoff 59b].

15.25 Creep–rupture data are given in Table P15.25 for 1Cr-1Mo-0.25V steel. Note that temperature, stress, and rupture time are given for a number of different tests. Proceed as in Prob.15.24(a) and (b), except use these data.

Table P15.25

T °C	σ MPa	t_r hours	T °C	σ MPa	t_r hours	T °C	σ MPa	t_r hours
482	621	37	538	338	5 108	649	276	19
482	565	975	538	262	10 447	649	207	102
482	538	3 581	593	417	18	649	172	125
482	483	9 878	593	345	167	649	138	331
538	552	7.0	593	276	615	732	138	3.7
538	469	213	593	200	2 200	732	103	8.9
538	414	1 493	593	152	6 637	732	69	31.8

Source: Data in [Goldhoff 59b].

15.26 An engineering component made of the heat-resisting Nimonic 80A alloy is subjected in service to a static stress of 400 MPa at a temperature of 400°C. What creep–rupture life is expected?

15.27 Using the creep–rupture data for alloy S-590 of Ex. 15.4, perform a new P_{SD} fit on the basis of Eq. 15.21, where a new value of Q is obtained from fitting, along with new values of a_0 to a_3. Plot P_{SD} versus σ for both data and fit, and comment on the success of the fit.

15.28 Creep–rupture data are given in Table P15.28 for ruthenium, a platinum group metal. Note that test temperature T, stress σ, and rupture time t_r are given for each test.

    (a) Perform a Larson–Miller parameter fit on the basis of Eq. 15.22, where C and b_0 to b_3 are obtained from fitting. Plot P_{LM} versus σ for both data and fit, and comment on the success of the fit.

    (b) Similarly fit and plot these data for a Sherby–Dorn parameter relationship of the form of Eq. 15.21, where Q and a_0 to a_3 are obtained from fitting.

Table P15.28

T °C	σ MPa	t_r minutes	T °C	σ MPa	t_r minutes
1000	327	137	1250	131	78
1000	322	1427	1250	115	283
1000	312	1835	1500	86.2	13
1250	198	8	1500	65.5	55
1250	165	33	1500	50.3	159

Source: Data in [Douglass 62].

15.29 A thin-walled tube with closed ends has an inner diameter of 160 mm and a wall thickness of 2.5 mm, and it is loaded with an internal pressure of 7.0 MPa. The material is the Cr-Mo-V steel of Table 15.3, and the temperature is 550°C. Estimate the life to creep rupture.

15.30 A beam is simply supported over a length of $L = 140$ mm and is loaded at its center with a transverse load of $P = 70$ N. Its cross section has width $b = 14$ mm and depth $2c = 12$ mm. The material has linear viscoelastic behavior with elastic and steady-state creep strains, similar to the model of Fig. 15.27(a), with the constants being $E_1 = 3$ GPa and $\eta_1 = 105$ GPa·s. Determine (a) the maximum stress in the beam, (b) the initial elastic deflection when the load is applied, and (c) the deflection after one week.

15.31 For 21 hours of each day, an engineering component made of alloy S-590 is subjected to a stress of 250 MPa at a temperature of 550°C. For the remaining 3 hours of each day, the stress is 200 MPa, and the temperature is 600°C. Estimate the number of years to creep rupture.

15.32 A rectangular beam made of S-590 alloy has depth $2c = 50$ mm and thickness $b = 20$ mm. It is loaded with a moment of $M = 1.65$ kN·m at a temperature of 800°C. At this temperature, and for stresses in the range 100 to 400 MPa, constants for Eq. 15.73 are $m = 10.74$ and $B = 3.91 \times 10^{-29}$, where t is in units of hours. (From data in [Grant 50].) Estimate the stress in the beam, the creep strain after 20,000 hours, and the life to creep rupture.

Section 15.6

15.33 Using the constants in Table 15.4 for SAE 1035 steel at 524°C, complete the following:

    (a) Plot isochronous stress–strain curves for times of 1, 10, 10^2, 10^3, and 10^4 hours, considering stresses up to 100 MPa. Comment on the trends seen in these curves.

    (b) Plot strain–time curves out to 1000 hours for stresses of 50, 70, and 90 MPa. Comment on the trends in these curves, also.

15.34 Strain versus time data obtained by hanging weights from strips of high-density polyethylene are given in Table P15.34, where the stress is listed for each test, along with strain values for times, $t = 30$, 200, and 600 seconds.

    (a) Fit these data to an equation of the form $\varepsilon = D\sigma^{\delta}t^{\phi}$, obtaining values of the fitting constants D, δ, and ϕ. (This is Eq. 15.39(b) with elastic strains neglected.)

    (b) On a stress–strain plot, which may be a log–log plot if desired, verify that your fitted constants provide a reasonable representation of the data.

Table P15.34

Stress σ, MPa	Strain, ε, for time t =		
	30 s	200 s	600 s
3.71	0.0016	0.0024	0.0030
6.17	0.0042	0.0059	0.0072
7.91	0.0063	0.0090	0.0113
9.43	0.0085	0.0125	0.0156
11.15	0.0107	0.0157	0.0201
12.08	0.0123	0.0190	0.0251

15.35 Data from creep tests on polycarbonate plastic are given in Table P15.35. Specifically, for three values of uniaxial stress, strains are given for various times in seconds.

    (a) Fit these data to Eq. 15.39(b). First, subtract elastic strains to calculate creep strains $\varepsilon_c = \varepsilon - \sigma/E$, with $E = 2400\,\text{MPa}$ from Table 4.3. Then perform a multiple regression fit based on $\varepsilon_c = D_3\sigma^{\delta}t^{\phi}$.

    (b) Graphically compare the test data and fitted equation, and comment on the success of the fit.

Table P15.35

Stress σ, MPa	Total Strain ε in %, for time t =						
	10 s	30 s	100 s	300 s	600 s	1200 s	1800 s
35.5	1.667	1.692	1.723	1.757	1.779	1.808	1.826
45.2	2.216	2.289	2.373	2.460	2.522	2.590	2.633
52.7	3.266	3.457	3.682	3.915	4.086	4.282	4.413

Source: Data in [Welker 10].

Section 15.7

15.36 A material behaves according to Eq. 15.39(b), and the strain rate from this equation is assumed to apply even during stress relaxation.

    (a) For a strain ε' that is quickly applied and held constant, develop an equation for the stress versus time behavior during relaxation.

    (b) Does your result reduce to Eq. 15.49 for the special case of $\phi = 1$?

15.37 A bolt used at 550°C is made of 304 stainless steel with a grain size of $d = 50\,\mu m$. The bolt is tightened to a preload stress of 60 MPa. Loss of this preload may occur due to creep dominated by diffusional flow along grain boundaries—that is, Eq. 15.6 with $m = 1$ and $q = 3$. Constants (from [Frost 82] p. 62) that apply are

$$Q_b/R = 20,100 \text{ K}, \qquad A_2 = 7.73 \times 10^{-12} \frac{\text{K·m}^5}{\text{MN·s}}$$

$$G_{300} = 81,000 \text{ MPa}, \qquad h = 38 \text{ MPa/K}$$

where the last two items and Eq. 15.11 give the shear modulus G as it varies with temperature. The elastic modulus E may be estimated from G by approximating Poisson's ratio as $\nu = 0.3$.

(a) After what time period is half the bolt preload lost due to creep?

(b) What grain size is needed to avoid losing more than half the preload in one year?

(c) What reduced temperature with the original grain size would avoid loss of half the preload in one year?

15.38 For the transient creep model of Fig. 15.27(b), perform the following tasks:

(a) Show that the recovery of creep strain after removal of a constant stress is given by Eq. 15.43. (Hint: During recovery, stresses $E_2\varepsilon$ in the spring and $\eta_2\dot{\varepsilon}$ in the dashpot must sum to the value of zero for the parallel combination.)

(b) A spring E_1 is added in series to form an elastic, transient creep model, as in Fig. 15.27(c). The constants are $E_1 = 6$ GPa, $E_2 = 3$ GPa, and $\eta_2 = 10^5$ GPa·s. Determine and plot the strain–time response of this model if a stress of $\sigma = 15$ MPa is quickly applied, held constant for one day, and then removed, with the strain allowed to recover for one additional day.

15.39 Consider a step strain ε' that is applied to the elastic, transient creep model, and held constant, as in Fig. 15.31(b).

(a) Derive the equation shown for the stress–time response during relaxation. (Hint: The stress applied to the parallel combination is the sum of stresses $E_2\varepsilon_2$ in the spring and $\eta_2\dot{\varepsilon}_2$ in the dashpot.)

(b) Let the model constants be $E_1 = 6$ GPa, $E_2 = 3$ GPa, and $\eta_2 = 10^5$ GPa·s. Determine and plot the stress–time response if a strain of $\varepsilon' = 0.008$ is applied and held constant for one day.

15.40 Verify Eq. 15.45 by using the superposition principle.

Section 15.8

15.41 A thin-walled spherical pressure vessel has an inner diameter of 250 mm and wall thickness of 8 mm, and it contains a liquid at a pressure of 0.40 MPa. It is made of a borosilicate glass and is used at a temperature of 500°C, where the shear viscosity of the glass is $\eta_\tau = 10^{14}$ Pa·s.

(a) What is the rate of creep strain in the vessel wall?

(b) How much does the vessel diameter increase in one month?

15.42 Show that the shear viscosity, $\eta_\tau = \tau/\dot{\gamma}$, and the tensile viscosity are expected to be related by $\eta = 3\eta_\tau$. (Hint: Follow a procedure parallel to that used to verify Eq. 5.28.)

15.43 For a given material and temperature, the uniaxial creep behavior follows Eq. 15.39(b). Develop a corresponding equation $\gamma = f(\tau)$ for creep in pure planar shear, where the constants are expressed in terms of D_3, δ, and ϕ from uniaxial test data.

15.44 Proceed as in Ex. 15.6, except change the pressure vessel to a thin-walled spherical one of radius r and wall thickness b.

15.45 A stainless steel pressure vessel is a cylindrical tube with closed ends, wall thickness 10 mm, and an inner diameter of 300 mm. It is loaded with an internal pressure of 4 MPa and an axial force in tension of 150 kN. The operating temperature is 900 K, and the material has constants as given in Prob.15.6.

   (a) What is the effective (uniaxial equivalent) strain rate $\bar{\dot{\varepsilon}}$?

   (b) What are the percentage increases in the vessel length and diameter in 10 years?

   (c) Does the design seem to be reasonable from the standpoint of creep deformation?

Section 15.9

15.46 Consider the simply supported beam over a length of $L = 100$ mm and is loaded at its center with a transverse load of $P = 50$ N. Its cross section has width $b = 15$ mm and depth $2c = 10$ mm., except change the beam material to one with elastic plus transient creep behavior, as in Fig. 15.27(c). Let the material constants be $E_1 = 4$ GPa, $E_2 = 0.5$ GPa, and $\eta_2 = 10^6$ GPa·s. Similarly determine (a) the maximum stress, (b) the initial elastic deflection, and (c) the deflection after one week.

15.47 A pipe of length 200 mm, made of 304 stainless steel, is fixed at one end and free at the other. It is loaded as a cantilever beam with a force of $P = 100$ N at the free end. The inner and outer diameters of the cross section are $d_1 = 24$ and $d_2 = 30$ mm, and the temperature is 625°C. The material deforms by the combination of steady-state creep strain from Eq. 15.6 and elastic strain. Materials constants and grain size are the same as in Prob. 15.37. Determine: (a) the maximum stress in the pipe, (b) the initial elastic deflection at the free end, and (c) the total deflection after one year.

15.48 A solid circular shaft for a high speed rotor is made of the MAR-M200 alloy of Fig. 15.16 (right) with grain size $d = 100\mu$m. The shaft has a diameter of 60 mm and a length of 1.00 m, and it is used in service at a temperature of 687°C. The shaft is supported by bearings at each end, similar to the support of a simple beam, Fig. A.4(b). The weight of the shaft itself and the rotor mounted on it total 2500 N, which may be assumed to be distributed uniformly along the shaft length. The material deforms by the combination of elastic strain and steady-state creep strain of the Coble (boundary diffusion) type from Eq. 15.6. Materials constants are the same as in Prob.15.12 and following Eq. 15.11, and Poisson's ratio can be approximated as $\nu = 0.30$. Determine (a) the initial elastic deflection of the shaft, and (b) the deflection if the shaft sits idle at the service temperature for one week. Also, (c) would you recommend restarting the operation of the rotor after this delay? Why or why not?

15.49 An annular disc rotates at a frequency of 50 revolutions/second at a temperature of 700°C. It has inner radius $r_1 = 40$, outer radius $r_2 = 130$, and thickness $t = 50$ mm. The disc is made of the nickel-base superalloy MAR-M200, with grain size $d = 100\,\mu$m, as in Fig. 15.16 (right). The material deforms by the combination of elastic strain and steady-state creep strain, due to grain boundary diffusion (Coble creep). Materials constants for Eq. 15.6 are the same as in Prob. 15.12 and following Eq. 15.11.

   (a) Calculate radial and tangential stresses, σ_r and σ_t, for a number of values of variable radius R between r_1 and r_2. Then plot these stresses as a function of R. (See Fig. A.9 and the accompanying text.)

   (b) How much does the inner radius increase due to creep after one day, and also after one year?

   (c) Proceed as in (b) for the outer radius.

15.50 A rectangular beam of depth $2c$ and thickness b is subjected to pure bending due to a moment M that is held constant with time. Develop an equation giving the maximum strain as a function of M, time t, and geometry and materials constants, for creep behavior according to (a) $\varepsilon_c = B\sigma^m t$, and (b) $\varepsilon_c = D_3 \sigma^\delta t^\phi$. In both cases, assume that the instantaneous elastic and plastic strains are small.

15.51 A solid circular shaft of radius c is subjected to a torque T that is held constant with time. Develop equations giving the surface shear strain as a function of torque T, time t, and geometry and materials constants, for materials that have uniaxial creep behavior according to (a) and (b) of Prob. 15.50. Assume that the instantaneous elastic and plastic strains are small.

15.52 A hollow circular shaft has inner radius c_1 and outer radius c_2. The material has a shear stress–strain–time relationship $\gamma = D_2 \tau^\delta t^\phi$. Obtain an equation for the maximum shear strain γ_{c2} in the shaft as a function of the applied torque T, the time t, and the various constants involved, c_1, c_2, D_2, δ, and ϕ.

15.53 A high-density polyethylene material is made into a cantilever beam of depth $2c = 10$ mm and thickness $b = 6.2$ mm, and a 1.2 kg weight is applied to the end of the beam. What strain is expected at a point on the edge of the beam ($y = c$), which is 90 mm from the weight, after (a) 30 seconds and (b) 10 minutes? You may use the isochronous stress–strain curves of Fig. 15.29.

15.54 Consider pure bending about the z-axis of a beam with a box or I-shaped cross section, as shown in Fig. A.2(d). The material and temperature combination are such that creep is expected to occur according to $\dot{\varepsilon} = B\sigma^m$, where m is in the range 3 to 8, and elastic and plastic strains can be assumed to be small compared to creep strains. Obtain an equation for the maximum strain as a function of the bending moment M, time t, materials constants B and m, and geometric variables b_1, b_2, h_1, and h_2.

15.55 A beam of 7075-T6 aluminum has a rectangular cross section and is used at a temperature of 316°C. The material has stress–strain constants as given in Table 15.4. A moment of 2.7 kN·m is applied, a safety factor of 1.5 on moment is required, and the creep strain cannot exceed 1% in 100 hours. Select a beam size such that the depth $2c$ is twice the thickness b, that is, find $b = c$. Obtain solutions, (a) assuming that elastic deformation is negligible, and (b) including elastic deformation.

15.56 A rectangular beam made of AISI 310 stainless steel has depth $2c = 60$ mm and thickness $b = 40$ mm. It is loaded with a moment of $M = 1.70$ kN·m at a temperature of 725°C. At this temperature, and for stresses in the range 3.4 to 31 MPa, constants for Eq. 15.71 are $m = 4.06$ and $B = 9.45 \times 10^{-9}$, where t is in units of hours. Estimate the stress in the beam, the creep strain after 16,000 hours, and the life to creep rupture.

Section 15.10

15.57 Use Eq. 12.55 to verify Eq. 15.80.

15.58 Consider a rectangular beam of depth $2c$, thickness b, and length L that is subjected to a uniform cyclic moment of amplitude M_a about zero mean. Assume that the energy dissipation of the material is given by Eq. 15.77, and that the damping is small, so that the distribution of stress over the beam depth is approximately linear. Proceed as follows, expressing results as functions of stress amplitude, geometry, and materials constants:

    (a) Obtain an equation giving the energy ΔU dissipated in each cycle of loading.

    (b) Evaluate the loss coefficient Q^{-1}. How is the value related to that for uniaxial loading of the material?

    (c) Use your result from (a) to obtain ΔU for a cantilever beam with one end fixed and a cyclic load P_a at the free end.

15.59 Proceed as in (a) and (b) of the previous problem, but consider the more general situation of small damping where the exponent $d \neq 2$, as in Eq. 15.81.

15.60 Consider completely reversed cyclic loading at a strain amplitude ε_a of an elastic, perfectly plastic material having yield strength σ_o and elastic modulus E.

    (a) Write an expression for the unit damping energy Δu as a function of ε_a and materials constants.

    (b) Use (a) to obtain the energy ΔU dissipated by cyclic pure bending of a rectangular beam of depth $2c$, thickness b, and length L. Express the result as a function of the strain amplitude ε_{ca} at the beam edge, where ε_{ca} exceeds σ_o/E, and also geometry and materials constants.

15.61 A solid circular shaft of radius c is subjected to a completely reversed cyclic torque T_a that is sufficiently large to cause cyclic yielding. The material obeys a Ramberg–Osgood type of cyclic stress–strain behavior, so that the cyclic stress–strain curve for pure shear has the form of Eq. 13.39. As a result, the unit damping energy is given by a relationship analogous to Eq. 15.80, that is

$$\Delta u = 4 \left(\frac{1 - n'}{1 + n'} \right) \tau_a \gamma_{pa}$$

where τ_a and γ_{pa} are the amplitudes of shear stress and plastic shear strain, respectively. Develop an equation for the energy ΔU, dissipated by the shaft in each cycle of loading, that is similar to the relationship for bending from Example 15.9. In particular, express the energy ΔU as an implicit function of the shear strain γ_{ca} at the shaft surface, and also geometry and materials constants.

A

Review of Selected Topics from Mechanics of Materials

A.1 INTRODUCTION

Presented in this Appendix is review and reference material that is related to elementary mechanics of materials. Basic stress and deflection formulas are given, as are selected properties of areas, beam deflections, and stress concentration factors for notched members. In addition, fully plastic yielding is considered in more detail than is usual for elementary treatments. The presentation consists of pictorial charts with equations, accompanied by brief explanation.

The information given here provides useful input to various topics covered in the main body of this text. For additional details of theory and derivations of equations, the reader is referred to the References at the end of this Appendix.

A.2 BASIC FORMULAS FOR STRESSES AND DEFLECTIONS

Assume that the material is isotropic and exhibits linear-elastic behavior. In particular, stress and strain are related by $\varepsilon = \sigma/E$ for the uniaxial case, where E is the elastic modulus of the material, or by Eqs. 5.26 and 5.27 for more complex states of stress. Stresses and deflections for various situations of prismatic (constant cross section) members are then given by the equations shown in Fig. A.1. In these equations, A is the cross-sectional area, L is length, and I_z is the area moment of inertia about the z-axis through the centroid of the cross-sectional area. Also, J is the centroidal polar moment of inertia of the cross-sectional area, and G is the shear modulus of the material.

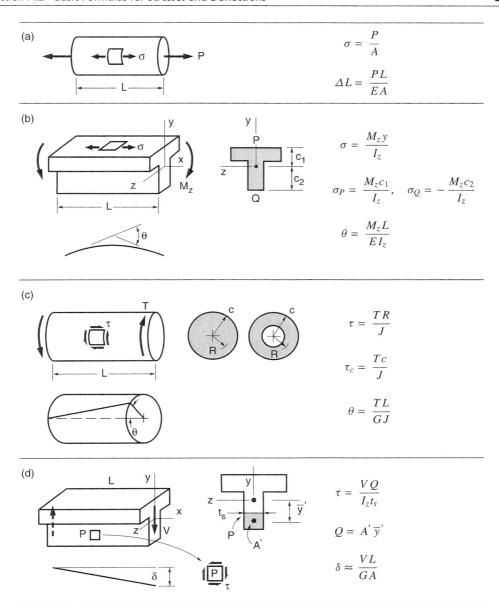

Figure A.1   Equations for calculating stresses and deflections for (a) centric axial loading, (b) symmetric bending, (c) torsion of circular shafts and tubes, and (d) transverse shear.

The simple relationships in (a) apply for a uniaxial tensile or compressive force P applied along the centroid of the cross-sectional area. For eccentric loading, the equivalent force system, of axial force at the centroid plus bending moment, is needed, and bending stresses must be added. In (b), formulas for bending stress and angular deflection are given that apply where there is symmetry about an x-y plane normal to the z-axis, as shown. The quantity M_z is a moment about the centroidal z-axis. For torsion of solid or hollow circular shafts, the equations in (c) give shear stress and angle of twist. The torque T is a moment about the shaft axis.

In (d), a transverse shear force V is applied in the y-direction along a line through the centroid of the cross section. Symmetry about an x-y plane normal to the z-axis is again assumed to exist. Consider a point P that is of interest. The area A' is identified that is outside of a line through P, parallel to the z-axis. Also needed is the distance $\overline{y}'$ from the centroid of A' to the centroid of the overall cross-sectional area. The quantity $Q = A'\overline{y}'$ is then the first moment of area A' about the overall centroidal z-axis. Also, t_s is the thickness of material cut to isolate A'. The shear stress τ calculated is actually an average across the cut t_s.

Cases where loadings of the preceding types occur together, called *combined loading*, can be handled by simply superimposing the stresses and deflections from each individual loading component. This includes situations of bending (b) where there are moments about both the y- and z-axes, provided there are two planes of symmetry, as for rectangular or circular cross sections. Where the required symmetry does not exist for bending or transverse shear, and for torsion of noncircular cross sections, additional analysis is needed, as described in elementary and advanced textbooks on mechanics of materials, theory of elasticity, and related topics. See the References listed at the end of this Appendix.

A.3 PROPERTIES OF AREAS

Some areas, A, and area moments of inertia about centroidal axes, I_z, are given for simple shapes in Fig. A.2. Both I_z and polar moments of inertia, J, are given for circular and hollow circular cross sections, including an approximation for thin-walled tubes. For these, $J = I_y + I_z = 2I_z$, due to the symmetry.

Centroids are given for half- and quarter-circular areas, and similarly for portions of tubular cross sections, in Fig. A.3. Noting Fig. A.1(d), we find that these centroids are useful in analyzing the maximum transverse shear for circular and tubular cross sections.

For more complex shapes, areas and moments of inertia may often be obtained by adding or subtracting those for simple shapes. For example, subtraction of values for a smaller circular area from those for a larger one gives A, I_z, and J for the tubular cross section in Fig. A.2(c). Similarly, subtraction involving two rectangular areas gives A and I_z for box and I-sections in Fig. A.2(d).

In general, the centroid of the cross-sectional area may not be known from symmetry, so it must be located. For example, this is the case for the T-section of Fig. A.1(b). The centroidal I_z for the overall shape may then be obtained by determining the individual centroidal I_z of each of its parts and then applying the *parallax axis theorem* to transfer each to the overall centroidal axis. See any elementary mechanics of materials textbook for details and examples.

For standard structural steel shapes, such as I-sections, T-sections, channels, angles, and tubing, properties of cross-sectional areas are given in the *AISC Steel Construction Manual*. Materials manufacturers' handbooks and other handbooks also often contain such information.

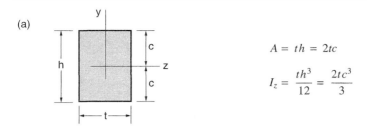

(a)

$$A = th = 2tc$$

$$I_z = \frac{th^3}{12} = \frac{2tc^3}{3}$$

(b)

$$A = \pi r^2 = \frac{\pi d^2}{4}$$

$$I_z = \frac{\pi r^4}{4} = \frac{\pi d^4}{64}, \qquad J = \frac{\pi r^4}{2} = \frac{\pi d^4}{32}$$

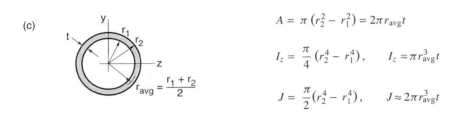

(c)

$$A = \pi \left(r_2^2 - r_1^2 \right) = 2\pi r_{avg} t$$

$$I_z = \frac{\pi}{4} \left(r_2^4 - r_1^4 \right), \qquad I_z \approx \pi r_{avg}^3 t$$

$$J = \frac{\pi}{2} (r_2^4 - r_1^4), \qquad J \approx 2\pi r_{avg}^3 t$$

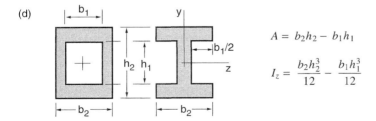

(d)

$$A = b_2 h_2 - b_1 h_1$$

$$I_z = \frac{b_2 h_2^3}{12} - \frac{b_1 h_1^3}{12}$$

Figure A.2   Selected shapes and their areas A and centroidal area moments of intertia I_z. Centroidal polar moments of inertia J are also given for (b) and (c). For (c), the second, approximate equations for I_z and J are within 1% for $t/r_1 < 0.2$, and 5% for $t/r_1 < 0.6$.

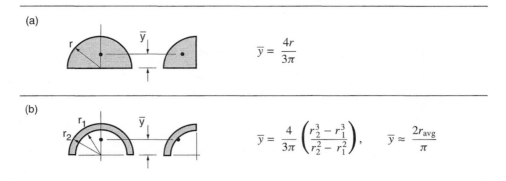

Figure A.3 Centroids for (a) half-circular and quarter-circular areas and (b) half-circular and quarter-circular sections of tubes. For (b), the second, approximate equation for $\bar{y}$ is within 1% for $t/r_1 < 0.4$, and 5% for $t/r_1 < 1.3$, where $t = r_2 - r_1$.

A.4 SHEARS, MOMENTS, AND DEFLECTIONS IN BEAMS

Simply supported and cantilever beams with concentrated and uniformly distributed forces are shown in Fig. A.4. The variations with position along the length of the beam of the internal shear and bending moment are plotted, and the maximum bending moments are given. Equations for the maximum deflections are also given for linear-elastic behavior. If symmetry about an x-y plane exists, as in Fig. A.1(b), the deflection will be in this plane in the y-direction. The equations given include deflection due to bending but neglect deflection due to shear, such as δ in Fig. A.1(d), as the latter is a relatively small effect in most beams.

Three- and four-point bending situations as in Fig. 4.40 are common in materials testing. Figure A.4(a) corresponds to the three-point bending case, and corresponding information is given for four-point bending in Fig. A.5.

Additional information of this type can be found in various textbooks and handbooks, including the *AISC Steel Construction Manual*.

A.5 STRESSES IN PRESSURE VESSELS, TUBES, AND DISCS

Useful equations are available for various cases of tubular and spherical pressure vessels, for other loadings on tubes, and for rotating discs. Some of these are described in this section, with linear-elastic behavior being assumed in all cases. Most of what follows is derived in Timoshenko (1970).

Consider loading by internal pressure p of tubular and hollow spherical vessels, as shown in Fig. A.6. Let the inner and outer radii be r_1 and r_2, respectively, and also let R be any radial distance between r_1 and r_2. For a tubular pressure vessel, a cylindrical coordinate system is convenient, so that radial, tangential, and longitudinal directions, r-t-x, are employed. Closed-form equations for the stresses σ_r, σ_t, and σ_x due to the pressure loading are given in Fig. A.6(a). The radial stress σ_r is always compressive, varying smoothly with R from $\sigma_r = -p$ at the inner radius to zero at the

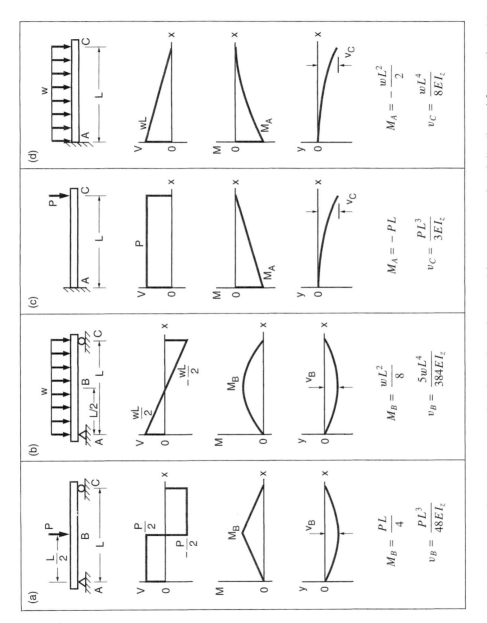

Figure A.4 Various cases of simply supported and cantilever beams with concentrated and distributed forces. Shear V, and moment M, diagrams are shown, along with maximum deflection, v.

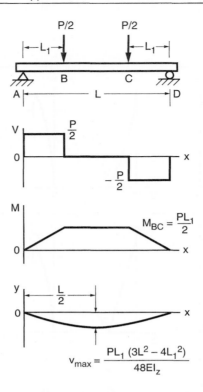

Figure A.5 Shear and moment diagrams and maximum deflection for a four-point bend test with total applied force P.

outer radius. The tangential stress σ_t is always tensile, decreasing with R from a maximum value at the inner wall to a smaller value at the outer wall. The longitudinal stress σ_x is zero for open-end tubes; and for closed-end tubes it is uniform, as given by the equation shown. If the tubular vessel is also subjected to torsion, a shear stress $\tau_{tx} = TR/J$ is present. Note that τ_{tx} increases linearly with R, and so has a maximum value at the outer wall. These equations do not consider the local stress raiser effects of the end closure of the vessel, nozzles, etc.

Similar equations for a hollow spherical pressure vessel are given in Fig. A.6(b). The stresses σ_r and σ_t vary with R in a qualitatively similar manner as for the tubular vessel, but the values, of course, differ. Due to the symmetry of the sphere, the x-direction is replaced by a second t-direction, with the tangential stress σ_t at any given R being the same for any direction normal to a radius of the sphere.

For internal pressure loading of thin-walled tubular and spherical vessels, the equations of Fig. A.6 still apply, but may be replaced by simpler expressions, as shown in Fig. A.7. Stresses from these approximate equations should be considered to be uniform through the wall thickness. Limits on t/r_1 for 5% and 10% accuracy are given in the figure caption.

Figure A.8 gives some useful approximations for stresses in thin-walled tubes due to torsion and/or bending. For torsion, applying $\tau_{tx} = TR/J$ at the middle of the wall thickness, $R = r_{\text{avg}}$,

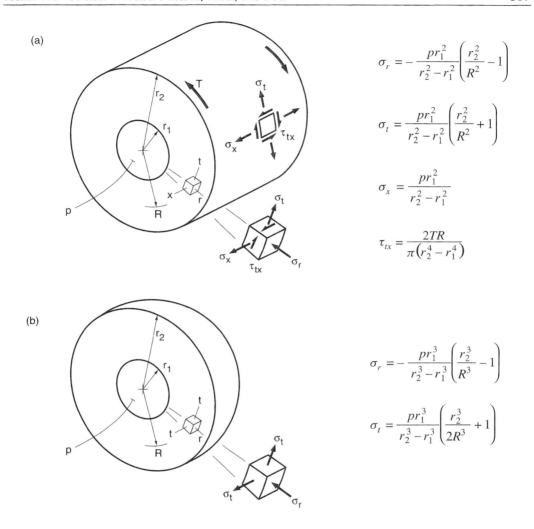

Figure A.6   Stresses in thick-walled pressure vessels, (a) tubular and (b) spherical.

along with the approximate J from Fig. A.2(c), gives the first equation shown. Similarly, for bending, applying $\sigma_x = My/I_z$ at any point C in the middle of the wall thickness, along with the approximate I_z from Fig. A.2(c), gives the second equation shown. The third equation given is the maximum value σ_{xA} of this approximate bending stress, which occurs at $y = r_{\text{avg}}$, that is, at point A along the y-axis. The bending stress is, of course, zero along the neutral axis, which is the z-axis. Stresses from these approximate equations should be considered to be uniform through the wall thickness, and limits on t/r_1 for 5% and 10% accuracy are given in the figure caption.

Stresses in a rotating annular disc are given in Fig. A.9. Normalized variables $\alpha = r_1/r_2$ and $z = R/r_2$ are employed as a convenience. Further, ρ is mass density, ω is angular

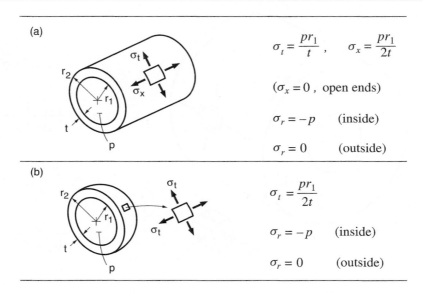

$$\sigma_t = \frac{pr_1}{t}, \qquad \sigma_x = \frac{pr_1}{2t}$$

$$(\sigma_x = 0, \text{ open ends})$$

$$\sigma_r = -p \qquad \text{(inside)}$$

$$\sigma_r = 0 \qquad \text{(outside)}$$

$$\sigma_t = \frac{pr_1}{2t}$$

$$\sigma_r = -p \qquad \text{(inside)}$$

$$\sigma_r = 0 \qquad \text{(outside)}$$

Figure A.7 Approximate stresses in thin-walled pressure vessels, (a) tubular and (b) spherical. For (a), the approximations are within 5% for $t/r_1 < 0.1$, and 10% for $t/r_1 < 0.2$. For (b), they are within 5% for $t/r_1 < 0.3$, and 10% for $t/r_1 < 0.45$.

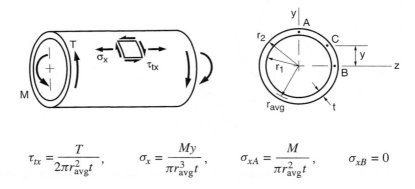

$$\tau_{tx} = \frac{T}{2\pi r_{avg}^2 t}, \qquad \sigma_x = \frac{My}{\pi r_{avg}^3 t}, \qquad \sigma_{xA} = \frac{M}{\pi r_{avg}^2 t}, \qquad \sigma_{xB} = 0$$

Figure A.8 Approximate stresses in thin-walled tubes due to torsion and/or bending. These approximations are within 5% for $t/r_1 < 0.1$, and 10% for $t/r_1 < 0.25$.

velocity (as in radians per second), and ν is Poisson's ratio. Note that $\omega = 2\pi f$, where f is the rotational frequency, as in revolutions per second. The radial stress σ_r is zero at both the inner and outer radii, and elsewhere tensile, with a maximum value at $R = \sqrt{r_1 r_2}$. The tangential stress σ_t is tensile for all R and has its highest value at the inner radius, with the bore of the disc essentially acting as a stress raiser. To apply the equations given, it is useful to express the quantity $\rho \omega^2 r_2^2$ in units of stress, such as MPa.

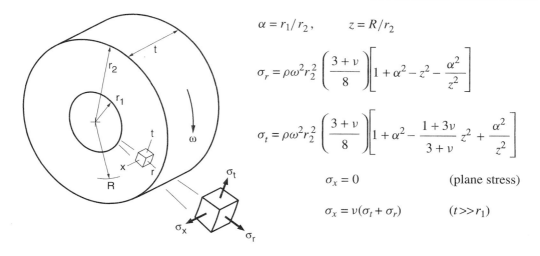

$$\alpha = r_1/r_2, \qquad z = R/r_2$$

$$\sigma_r = \rho\omega^2 r_2^2 \left(\frac{3+v}{8}\right)\left[1 + \alpha^2 - z^2 - \frac{\alpha^2}{z^2}\right]$$

$$\sigma_t = \rho\omega^2 r_2^2 \left(\frac{3+v}{8}\right)\left[1 + \alpha^2 - \frac{1+3v}{3+v}z^2 + \frac{\alpha^2}{z^2}\right]$$

$$\sigma_x = 0 \qquad\qquad \text{(plane stress)}$$

$$\sigma_x = v(\sigma_t + \sigma_r) \qquad (t \gg r_1)$$

Figure A.9   Stresses due to rotation of an annular disc, where ρ is mass density, ω is angular velocity, and v is Poisson's ratio.

For example, assume that $\rho = 7.9$ g/cm^3, $f = 120$ rev/s, and $r_2 = 200$ mm. To aid with units, note that g/cm^3 = Mg/m^3, N = kg·m/s^2, and MPa = 10^6 N/m^2. Hence, we obtain

$$\rho\omega^2 r_2^2 = \left(7.9\frac{\text{Mg}}{\text{m}^3} \times \frac{1000\text{ kg}}{\text{Mg}} \times \frac{\text{N}}{\text{kg·m/s}^2}\right)\left(120\frac{\text{rev}}{\text{s}} \times 2\pi\frac{\text{rad}}{\text{rev}}\right)^2 (0.200\text{m})^2 = 179.6 \times 10^6 \frac{\text{N}}{\text{m}^2}$$

$$\rho\omega^2 r_2^2 = 179.6 \text{ MPa}$$

For a solid disc, $r_1 = 0$, the equations in Fig. A.9 need to be modified before use by substituting $\alpha = 0$. In this case, it is found that $\sigma_r = \sigma_t$ at the center, $R = 0$, with σ_t decreasing to a lower value at the outer radius, and σ_r decreasing to zero.

A.6 ELASTIC STRESS CONCENTRATION FACTORS FOR NOTCHES

Geometric discontinuities, such as holes, fillets, grooves, and keyways, are unavoidable in design. They cause the stress to be locally elevated and so are called *stress raisers*, or *notches*. Such a situation is illustrated by Fig. A.10(a) and (b). The stress concentration factor k_t for linear-elastic materials behavior is used to characterize notches, where $k_t = \sigma/S$ is the ratio of the local notch (point) stress σ to the nominal (average) stress S. Curves giving k_t for some typical cases are provided in Figs. A.11 and A.12.

Values of k_t are widely available in various textbooks, handbooks, and papers, such as Peterson (1974) and the additional sources in Section (b) of the References. As analysis methods have improved with time, values of k_t found in older publications do not always agree with more accurate values from recent work.

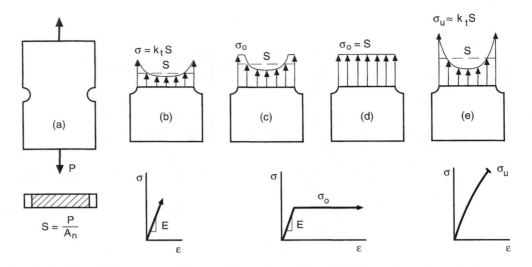

Figure A.10 Component with a stress raiser (a) and stress distributions for various cases: (b) linear-elastic deformation, (c) local yielding for a ductile material, (d) full yielding for a ductile material, and (e) brittle material at fracture.

Any particular definition of S is arbitrary, and the choice made affects the value of k_t. Hence, it is important to be consistent with the definition of S being used when employing k_t values. The most common convention is to define S in terms of the net area, which is the area after the notch has been removed. Note that this convention is observed for each example in Figs. A.11 and A.12. Also, the equality $\sigma = k_t S$ holds at the notch only if there is no yielding of the material—that is, only if $k_t S$ is less than the yield strength σ_o.

A.7 FULLY PLASTIC YIELDING LOADS

All of the stresses and deflections considered so far in this Appendix assume linear-elastic materials behavior. However, situations may be encountered where the stresses and strains exceed the linear-elastic range of the material. We may identify such a situation by noting whether or not stresses calculated under the assumption that the behavior is linear-elastic exceed the material's yield strength. If they do, the results of the calculation are invalid, and analysis that specifically considers yielding effects is needed.

If yielding spreads across the full cross section of a member, a situation of *fully plastic yielding* is said to occur. The applied load necessary to cause this is called the *fully plastic load*. Fully plastic loads correspond to the onset of large and unstably increasing strains and deflections in engineering members, so that they are estimates of the final failure load of the member.

In this Appendix, we will make the simplifying assumption that the material's stress–strain curve can be approximated as being elastic, perfectly plastic, as shown in Fig. A.13. For the uniaxial case, E is the elastic modulus and σ_o is the yield strength; for pure shear, G is the shear modulus and τ_o is the yield strength in shear. The value of τ_o can be estimated from σ_o by using

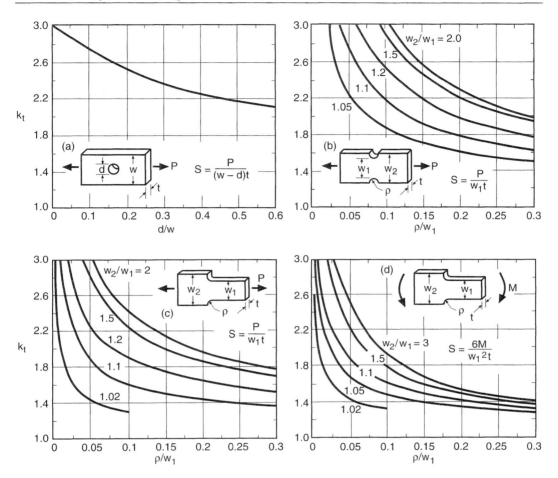

Figure A.11 Elastic stress concentration factors for various cases of notched plates. (Values from [Peterson 74] pp. 35, 89, 98, and 150.)

the octahedral shear stress yield criterion of Section 7.5, which gives $\tau_o = \sigma_o/\sqrt{3} = 0.577\sigma_o$. An alternative estimate is $\tau_o = 0.5\sigma_o$ from the maximum shear stress criterion of Section 7.4.

Thus, the discussion here will have only the limited objective of analyzing fully plastic loads for elastic, perfectly plastic stress–strain behavior. More detailed analysis of engineering members for stresses and strains beyond yielding is considered in Chapter 13.

A.7.1 Fully Plastic Bending and Torsion

Consider pure bending of a beam with a rectangular cross section, as shown in Fig. A.14. At low values of moment M, the stresses are given by the elastic bending formula of Fig. A.1(b). Note that the stress varies linearly with distance y from the neutral (z) axis. If the moment is increased,

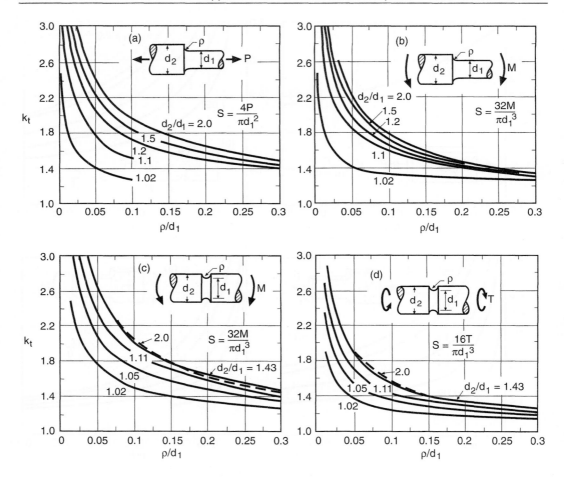

Figure A.12 Elastic stress concentration factors for various cases of notched circular shafts. (Values from [Peterson 74] pp. 96 and 103 for (a) and (b), [Nisitani 84] for (c) and (d).)

Figure A.13 Elastic, perfectly plastic stress–strain assumptions for the uniaxial (σ-ε) and pure shear (τ-γ) cases.

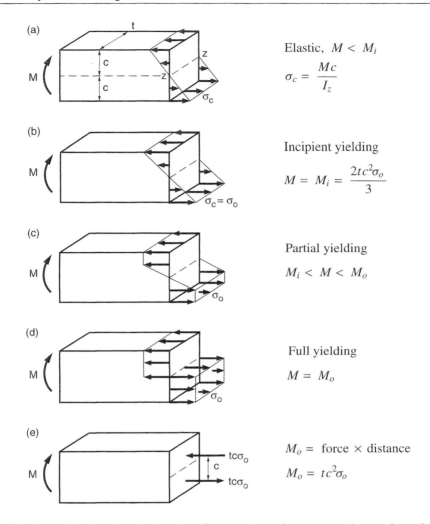

Figure A.14   Stress distributions in bending for a rectangular cross section and an elastic, perfectly plastic stress–strain curve. Proceeding from (a) to (d), the moment is increased beyond elastic behavior to fully plastic yielding.

a value of $M = M_i$ is reached where the maximum stress is at the yield value σ_o. We thus have a case of *incipient yielding*. Substituting I_z from Fig. A.2(a) and solving for M in the bending stress formula gives the expression for M_i of Fig. A.14(b). We will call M_i the *initial yielding moment*.

    If the moment is increased beyond M_i, yielding progresses from the outer edges of the beam toward the neutral axis, as shown in (c). Note that a portion of the stress distribution is now flat, as the idealized material cannot support a stress higher than σ_o. (Strains exceeding $\varepsilon_o = \sigma_o / E$, of course, occur.) As yielding approaches the neutral axis as in (d), the entire stress distribution becomes flat at σ_o on the tension side and $-\sigma_o$ on the compression side. No further increase in M

is possible, and the limiting value is denoted M_o, the *fully plastic moment*. An equation for M_o can be obtained by replacing the stress distributions above and below the neutral axis with concentrated forces located at their centroids, as shown in (e). The resulting M_o is an estimate of the moment where large, unstable deflections begin, as illustrated in Fig. 13.6.

Comparing the equations of Fig. A.14(b) and (e), we obtain a ratio $M_o/M_i = 1.50$. Thus, the moment may increase by a factor of 1.5 beyond initial yielding before the beam collapses completely. This contrasts with the situation for simple tension, as shown in Fig. A.15(a). Here, the initial and fully plastic yielding forces, P_i and P_o, are the same, due to the idealized, flat stress–strain curve, so that initial yielding and final failure are predicted to occur at the same force. Similar results for additional cases are shown in Fig. A.15, specifically for bending of solid circular cross sections and thin-walled tubes, and also for torsion of the same geometries. Note that the ratio M_o/M_i decreases if more of the cross-sectional area is concentrated away from the neutral axis. For bending, standard I-beams are rather extreme in this regard, having values around $M_o/M_i = 1.1$.

Analysis of flat stress distributions, as in Fig. A.14, may be readily applied to obtain fully plastic moments for other cross-sectional shapes. If the section is not symmetrical about the x-z plane, as in Fig. A.1(b), a new neutral axis is needed. In particular, the neutral axis for fully plastic bending is the line parallel to the centroidal z-axis that has equal areas above and below. (This gives a zero sum of forces in the longitudinal direction, as required by equilibrium.) The moment of the stress distribution about this neutral axis then gives M_o.

The equations in Fig. A.15(b), (c), and (e) may also be extended to some related cases. For example, consider a box beam having outside dimensions of half-depth c_2 and width t_2, and analogous inside dimensions, c_1 and t_1. Subtracting the moment due to the missing central portion gives

$$M_o = t_2 c_2^2 \sigma_o - t_1 c_1^2 \sigma_o, \qquad M_o = \frac{\sigma_o}{4}\left(b_2 h_2^2 - b_1 h_1^2\right) \qquad \text{(a, b)} \qquad \text{(A.1)}$$

where the second form has been converted to the nomenclature of Fig. A.2(d), and also applies to the I-section. Similar logic gives M_o and T_o for thick-walled tubes, providing a more general result than the approximations of Fig. A.15(d) and (f):

$$M_o = \frac{4\sigma_o}{3}\left(r_2^3 - r_1^3\right), \qquad T_o = \frac{2\pi\tau_o}{3}\left(r_2^3 - r_1^3\right) \qquad \text{(a, b)} \qquad \text{(A.2)}$$

Additional results of fully plastic analysis may be found in books on advanced mechanics of materials, plasticity, and related topics.

A.7.2 Fully Plastic Behavior in Notched and Cracked Members

If a notched member is made of a ductile material, yielding occurs first in a small region near the notch, as shown in Fig. A.10(c). Increased loading causes yielding to spread over the entire cross section, as shown in (d). As a result, the final strength of the notched member is similar to that for an unnotched member with the same net cross-sectional area. However, if the material is a brittle one that does not yield prior to fracture, the locally elevated stress situation prevails up to the point of fracture, as shown in (e), and the strength is considerably lower than for an unnotched member.

Case	Initial Yielding	Fully Plastic Yielding	$\dfrac{P_o}{P_i}, \dfrac{M_o}{M_i}$, or $\dfrac{T_o}{T_i}$
(a)	$P_i = A\sigma_o$	$P_o = A\sigma_o$	1.00
(b) 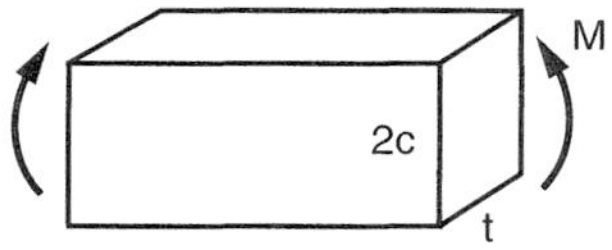	$M_i = \dfrac{2tc^2\sigma_o}{3}$	$M_o = tc^2\sigma_o$	1.50
(c) 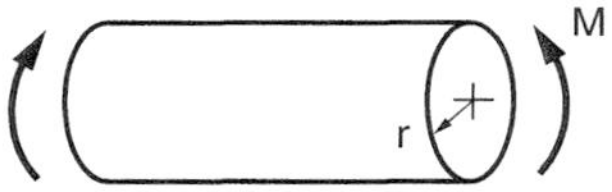	$M_i = \dfrac{\pi r^3 \sigma_o}{4}$	$M_o = \dfrac{4r^3\sigma_o}{3}$	1.70
(d) 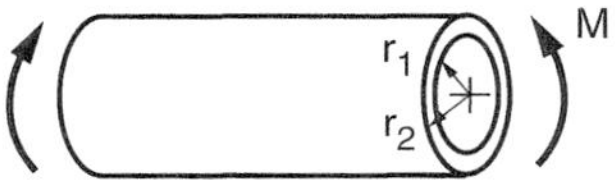	$M_i \approx \dfrac{\pi r_{\mathrm{avg}}^3 t\sigma_o}{r_2}$	$M_o \approx 4r_{\mathrm{avg}}^2 t\sigma_o$	$\dfrac{4r_2}{\pi r_{\mathrm{avg}}} \approx 1.35$
(e) 	$T_i = \dfrac{\pi r^3 \tau_o}{2}$	$T_o = \dfrac{2\pi r^3 \tau_o}{3}$	1.33
(f) 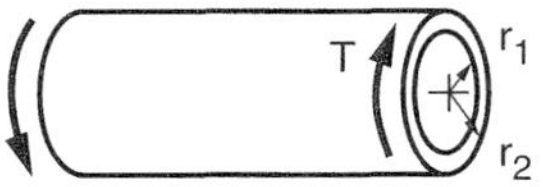	$T_i \approx \dfrac{2\pi r_{\mathrm{avg}}^3 t\tau_o}{r_2}$	$T_o \approx 2\pi r_{\mathrm{avg}}^2 t\tau_o$	$\dfrac{r_2}{r_{\mathrm{avg}}} \approx 1.1$

Figure A.15 Initial yielding and fully plastic yielding forces, moments, or torques, for simple cross-sectional shapes. Cases (d) and (f) represent approximations for thin-walled tubes, both accurate within 5% for $t/r_1 < 1.3$.

Fully plastic loads for notched members of ductile materials may be estimated by again assuming elastic, perfectly plastic behavior as in Fig. A.13. A uniform stress distribution at σ_o or $-\sigma_o$, as in Fig. A.10(d), is employed to evaluate the fully plastic load. Results of some analyses of this type are given in Fig. A.16.

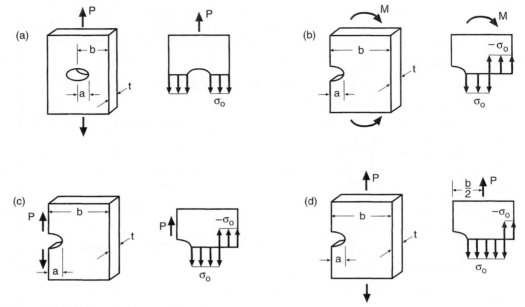

Fully plastic force or moment for given $\alpha = a/b$:

(a) $P_o = 2bt\sigma_o \, (1 - \alpha)$

(b) $M_o = \dfrac{b^2 t \sigma_o}{4} \, (1 - \alpha)^2$

(c) $P_o = bt\sigma_o \left[-\alpha - 1 + \sqrt{2\left(1 + \alpha^2\right)} \, \right]$

(d) $P_o = bt\sigma_o \left[-\alpha + \sqrt{2\alpha^2 - 2\alpha + 1} \, \right]$

Crack length at fully plastic yielding for given load, where, for (c) and (d), $P' = P/(bt\sigma_o)$:

(a) $a_o = b \left[1 - \dfrac{P}{2bt\sigma_o} \right]$

(b) $a_o = b \left[1 - \dfrac{2}{b}\sqrt{\dfrac{M}{t\sigma_o}} \right]$

(c) $a_o = b \left[P' + 1 - \sqrt{2P'(P' + 2)} \, \right]$

(d) $a_o = b \left[P' + 1 - \sqrt{2P'(P' + 1)} \, \right]$

Figure A.16 Freebody diagrams and resulting equations for fully plastic forces or moments, P_o or M_o, for various two-dimensional cases of notched or cracked members. The same equations solved for notch or crack length, a_o, are shown at the bottom. Diagrams and equations labeled (a) all correspond to the same case, and similarly for (b), (c), and (d).

In Fig. A.16, the notch of dimension a, defined as shown in each case, may also represent a crack. Equations are given for the fully plastic force or moment, P_o or M_o, as a function of the geometric ratio $\alpha = a/b$, where b is a width dimension, as also shown for each case. In addition, the P_o or $M_o = f(\alpha)$ equations for each case are solved for the notch or crack dimension a_o that corresponds to fully plastic yielding for a given force or moment, producing the $a_o = g(P \text{ or } M)$ equations also shown.

For each case in Fig. A.16, the freebody diagram is shown that is used to evaluate P_o or M_o. For example, for case (a), summing forces gives

$$P_o = \text{stress} \times \text{area} = [\sigma_o][2(b-a)t]$$
$$P_o = 2bt\sigma_o(1 - a/b) = 2bt\sigma_o(1 - \alpha) \tag{A.3}$$

Also, solving Eq. A.3 for a gives

$$a_o = b\left[1 - \frac{P}{2bt\sigma_o}\right] \tag{A.4}$$

where a_o is the notch or crack length corresponding to fully plastic yielding for a given force P. Equations A.3 and A.4 also apply to a double-edge-notched member, as in Fig. A.10 or 8.12(b), where a and b are defined as in the latter.

The pure bending case (b) may be verified by applying the equation $M_o = tc^2\sigma_o$ of Fig. A.15(b) to the net section of width $2c = b - a$, that is, by substituting $c = (b - a)/2$. Cases (c) and (d) involve a more lengthy analysis as a result of each representing a situation of combined bending and tension. In the course of the analysis, both forces and moments must be summed, and the unknown location of the neutral axis found.

Example A.1
Verify the equation for P_o for case (d) of Fig. A.16.

Solution   A detailed freebody diagram is shown as Fig. A.17. The location Q of the neutral axis is unknown. Let x represent the distance from Q to the right edge, so $c = b - a - x$ is the distance from the end of the notch to Q. Next, sum forces, noting that the freebody is of uniform thickness t. Choosing upward as positive, we have

$$\Sigma F = 0, \quad P_o + \sigma_o xt - \sigma_o ct = 0$$

Substitute $c = b - a - x$ and solve for x

$$x = \frac{1}{2}\left(b - a - \frac{P_o}{\sigma_o t}\right)$$

Next, sum moments about Q. Choosing clockwise as positive, we have

$$\Sigma M_Q = 0, \quad P_o\left(\frac{b}{2} - x\right) - \sigma_o xt\left(\frac{x}{2}\right) - \sigma_o ct\left(\frac{c}{2}\right) = 0$$

Substitute for c, expand the c^2 term that is present, and collect terms:

$$\frac{P_o}{\sigma_o t}(b - 2x) - 2x^2 + 2x(b - a) - (b - a)^2 = 0$$

Then substitute x as found previously, and again collect terms:

$$\left(\frac{P_o}{\sigma_o t}\right)^2 + 2a\left(\frac{P_o}{\sigma_o t}\right) - (b - a)^2 = 0$$

We now have a quadratic equation in the variable $P_o/\sigma_o t$. Apply the standard quadratic formula and discard the negative root, as it does not permit positive P_o:

$$\frac{P_o}{\sigma_o t} = -a + \sqrt{2a^2 - 2ab + b^2}$$

Letting $\alpha = a/b$ finally gives the desired result:

$$P_o = bt\sigma_o\left[-\alpha + \sqrt{2\alpha^2 - 2\alpha + 1}\right]$$ **Ans.**

The quadratic equation can be solved for notch or crack length a rather than for force P, giving the expression for a_o that is shown in Fig. A.16 for case (d).

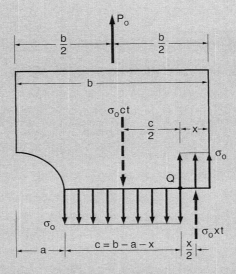

Figure A.17   Geometric detail for verifying the result of Fig. A.16(d).

A.7.3 Discussion

The fully plastic forces, moments, and torques of Figs. A.15 and A.16 represent lower bound estimates, so that actual values of the load at member failure may be somewhat higher. There are two factors that contribute to this situation. First, strain hardening in actual stress–strain curves will increase the value somewhat, for the following reason: At the point of failure in a component made of a real material, the stresses on some portions of the cross-sectional area will exceed the yield strength σ_o and approach the higher ultimate strength σ_u. Hence, the actual load exceeds that for uniform stress at σ_o. The second contributing factor is that the yield strength is, in effect, increased if constrained deformation causes a triaxial state of stress to develop. This effect is especially prevalent for sharp notches or cracks if the thickness of the member is sufficient for a state of *plane strain* to exist. For example, for a center-notched plate, Fig. A.16(a), this second effect can increase P_o by as much as 15%. And for bending of a notched member, Fig. A.16(b), the increase in M_o can reach 45%.

REFERENCES

(a) General References
AISC. 2006. *Steel Construction Manual*, 13th ed., Am. Institute of Steel Construction, Chicago, IL.

BEER, F. P., E. R. JOHNSTON, Jr., J. T. DEWOLF, and D. MAZUREK. 2012. *Mechanics of Materials*, 6th ed., McGraw-Hill, New York.

BORESI, A. P., and R. J. SCHMIDT. 2003. *Advanced Mechanics of Materials*, 6th ed., John Wiley, Hoboken, NJ. (See also the 2d ed. of this book, same title, 1952, by F. B. Seely and J. O. Smith.)

PILKEY, W. D. 2004. *Formulas for Stress, Strain, and Structural Matrices*, 2d ed., John Wiley, New York.

TIMOSHENKO, S. P. and J. N. GOODIER. 1970. *Theory of Elasticity*, 3d ed., McGraw-Hill, New York.

TIMOSHENKO, S. P. 1984. *Strength of Materials, Part I, and Part II*, 3d ed., Robert E. Krieger Pub. Co., Malabar, FL.

YOUNG, W. C., R. G. BUDYNAS, and A. SADEGH. 2011. *Roark's Formulas for Stress and Strain*, 8th ed., McGraw-Hill, New York.

(b) Sources for Stress Concentration Factors
HARDY, S. J., and N. H. MALIK. 1992. "A Survey of Post-Peterson Stress Concentration Factor Data," *Int. Jnl. of Fatigue*, vol. 14, no. 3, pp. 147–153.

NODA, N.-A., and Y. TAKASE. 2003. "Stress Concentration Formula Useful for Any Dimensions of Shoulder Fillet in a Round Bar Under Tension and Bending," *Fatigue and Fracture of Engineering Materials and Structures*, vol. 26, no. 3, pp. 245–255. See also earlier papers by Noda et al. referenced within.

NODA, N.-A., and Y. TAKASE. 2006. "Stress Concentration Formula Useful for all Notch Shape in a Round Bar (Comparison Between Torsion, Tension and Bending)," *Int. Jnl. of Fatigue*, vol. 28, no. 2, pp. 151–163. See also earlier papers by Noda et al. referenced within.

PETERSON, R. E. 1974. *Stress Concentration Factors*, John Wiley & Sons, New York.

PILKEY, W. D., and D. F. PILKEY. 2008. *Peterson's Stress Concentration Factors*, 3d ed., John Wiley, Hoboken, NJ.

ROLOVIC, R., S. M. TIPTON, and J. R. SOREM, Jr,. 2001. "Multiaxial Stress Concentration in Filleted Shafts," *Jnl. of Mechanical Design, Trans. ASME*, vol. 123, pp. 300–303.

TIPTON, S. M., J. R. SOREM, Jr., and R. D. ROLOVIC, 1996. "Updated Stress Concentration Factors for Filleted Shafts in Bending and Tension," *Jnl. of Mechanical Design, Trans. ASME*, vol. 118, pp. 321–327.

B

Statistical Variation in Materials Properties

B.1 INTRODUCTION

Laboratory measurements of materials properties, such as yield strength or fracture toughness, contain random error due to such causes as minor calibration errors, imperfect test specimen geometry and testing machine alignment, and noise in electronic components. The properties will also vary with location in a plate or bar of material that is large enough to remove multiple test specimens. Furthermore, a material of a given nominal type, such as 2024-T351 aluminum alloy, polycarbonate plastic, or 99.5% dense Al_2O_3, will vary to some extent as to chemical composition, level of impurities, size and number of microscopic defects, and the exact details of processing. Such differences among batches of similar material are a major source of variation in materials properties. It is simply a fact of life that no two measurements or samples of material are identical.

This variation in materials properties can be subjected to analysis by *statistics* to permit estimates of the *probability* associated with variation of a given magnitude. This Appendix provides a brief introduction to the statistical treatment of variations in materials properties.

B.2 MEAN AND STANDARD DEVIATION

Consider a variable x that has statistical variation. Repeated observations could be made and the variation plotted as a *histogram*, as shown in Fig. B.1. A histogram is simply a bar chart showing the number of observations of x as a function of the value of x. The values are usually concentrated

900

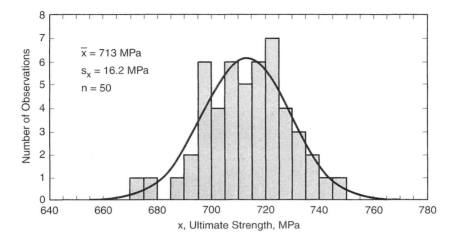

Figure B.1   Histogram showing variations in the ultimate tensile strength of cold-drawn and annealed SAE 4340 steel wire. The corresponding curve for a normal distribution is also shown. (Data from [Haugen 80] p. 5.)

near the *sample mean*, or average value, given by

$$\bar{x} = \frac{1}{n} \sum_{i=1}^{n} x_i \tag{B.1}$$

where n is the total number of observations, called the *sample size*, and the x_i are the individual observations.

The variability of x may be small, with most values being quite close to $\bar{x}$, or it may be large, with values ranging widely. The *sample standard deviation* s_x is a measure of the magnitude of the variation:

$$s_x = \sqrt{\frac{\sum_{i=1}^{n}(x_i - \bar{x})^2}{n-1}} = \sqrt{\frac{\sum_{i=1}^{n}x_i^2 - n\bar{x}^2}{n-1}} \tag{B.2}$$

The two forms of this equation are mathematically equivalent, with the second being more convenient for manual computation.

Another useful measure of the variation is the *sample coefficient of variation*,

$$\delta_x = \frac{s_x}{\bar{x}} \tag{B.3}$$

The coefficient of variation is a dimensionless measure of the uncertainty in the value of x. Values of δ_x are often expressed as percentages—for example, $\delta_x = 0.083 = 8.3\%$. This measure is particularly convenient, as its value for a given property tends to be relatively constant over a range

Table B.1   Fracture Toughness Data for Dolomitic Limestone

Test No.	K_{Ic}, MPa$\sqrt{m}$	Test No.	K_{Ic}, MPa$\sqrt{m}$
1	1.305	7	1.197
2	1.341	8	1.334
3	1.355	9	1.306
4	1.437	10	1.300
5	1.192	11	1.183
6	1.353		

Source: Data from [Karfakis 90].

of mean values. For example, yield strengths of steels have a value of roughly $\delta_x = 7\%$, despite the mean values ranging over a factor of 10, from 200 to 2000 MPa.

Note that the sample mean $\bar{x}$ and the sample standard deviation s_x are merely estimates, based on a limited number of observations, of the true values of these quantities from an infinite number of observations. The *true mean* is denoted μ, and the *true standard deviation* is denoted σ.

Example B.1

The results of a number of fracture toughness tests on dolomitic limestone are given in Table B.1. Determine the sample values of the mean, standard deviation, and coefficient of variation.

Solution   Equations B.1 to B.3 are needed, for which $n = 11$, and the x_i are the various K_{Ic} values. Performing these computations gives

$$\bar{x} = 1.300 \text{ MPa}\sqrt{m}, \qquad s_x = 0.0797 \text{ MPa}\sqrt{m} \qquad \textbf{Ans.}$$

$$\delta_x = s_x/\bar{x} = 0.0613 = 6.13\% \qquad \textbf{Ans.}$$

B.3 NORMAL OR GAUSSIAN DISTRIBUTION

If the variation is approximately symmetrical about the mean, it may be reasonable to assume that the mathematical form known as the *normal* or *Gaussian* distribution applies. This distribution forms a bell-shaped curve, as shown in Fig. B.1.

To work with the normal distribution, it is convenient to transform the original variable x to the *standard normal variable*, z:

$$z = \frac{x - \mu}{\sigma} \tag{B.4}$$

Thus, z has zero mean relative to the true mean μ. Also, its magnitude is normalized with respect to the true standard deviation σ, so that z is in units of numbers of standard deviations. On this basis, the bell-shaped curve of the normal distribution has the equation

$$f(z) = \frac{1}{\sqrt{2\pi}} e^{-z^2/2} \tag{B.5}$$

which is called the *probability density function.*

The area under the $f(z)$ curve between minus infinity and plus infinity is unity. Let us assume that a large number of observations were employed to determine $\bar{x}$ and s_x, so that these values are close to the true mean and standard deviation, μ and σ, and also that a normal distribution gives a good representation of the data. It can then be said that any portion of the area under $f(z)$ gives the probability that z lies within the values that bound the area. Partial areas bounded by integer z values are shown in Fig. B.2. From these areas, it is seen that approximately 68% of the observations are expected to fall within one standard deviation of the mean—that is, within $\mu \pm \sigma$. Furthermore, 95.5% are expected to be within two standard deviations, and 99.7% within three. These bounds and probabilities for large samples are summarized in Table B.2.

In applying materials property values in engineering design, it is of particular concern that values of the property, such as yield strength or fracture toughness, may vary considerably below the mean. For a large sample size and a normal distribution, areas under $f(z)$ may also be employed to estimate the probability that the property will be less than a particular value. For example, from Fig. B.2, the probability P that x is less than $(\mu - 3\sigma)$ is the area between $z = -\infty$ (negative infinity) and $z = -3$, so that $P = 0.00135$, or 0.135%. Since $1/P \approx 740$, we would expect, on the average, one sample out of 740 to be below this limit. Additional probabilities for various numbers of standard deviations below the mean are given in Table B.3(a).

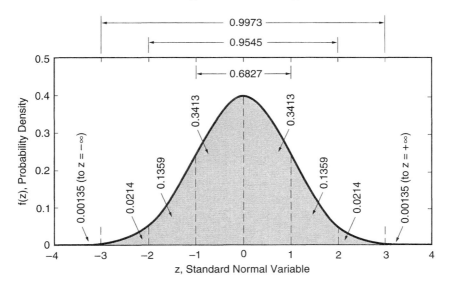

Figure B.2   Probability density function for the normal distribution. The total area under the curve from $z = -\infty$ to $+\infty$ is unity, and portions of the area bounded by various numbers of standard deviations are shown.

Table B.2   Probabilities for
Various Bounds About the Mean

Bounds	Percent Within Bounds
$\mu \pm \sigma$	68.27
$\mu \pm 2\sigma$	95.45
$\mu \pm 3\sigma$	99.73
$\mu \pm 4\sigma$	99.994

Table B.3   Probabilities for Various Values Below the Mean

Limiting Value of x	Percent Less Than Limit, P	Fraction Less Than Limit	Percent More Than Limit, R
(a) For integer numbers of standard deviations			
μ	50	1/2	50
$\mu - \sigma$	15.9	1/6	84.1
$\mu - 2\sigma$	2.28	1/44	97.72
$\mu - 3\sigma$	0.135	1/740	99.865
$\mu - 4\sigma$	0.00317	1/31,600	99.99683
(b) For particular values of probability			
$\mu - 1.28\sigma$	10	1/10	90
$\mu - 2.33\sigma$	1	1/100	99
$\mu - 3.09\sigma$	0.1	1/1000	99.9
$\mu - 3.72\sigma$	0.01	1/10,000	99.99

It is also useful to identify limits that correspond to particular probabilities of failure, such as $P = 0.001 = 0.1\%$, corresponding to one value out of a thousand. Limits of this type are given in Table B.3(b). Note that the *reliability* is $R = 1 - P$. For example, a probability of failure of $P = 0.001 = 0.1\%$ corresponds to a reliability of $R = 0.999 = 99.9\%$.

Textbooks and handbooks on probability and statistics give detailed numerical tables for the normal distribution that provide more complete information similar to that in Tables B.2 and B.3.

Example B.2

From tension tests on 121 samples of ASTM A514 structural steel, the mean yield strength is 794 MPa and the standard deviation is 38.6 MPa. Assume that a normal distribution applies, and estimate the yield strength value for a reliability of 99%. (Data from [Kulak 72].)

Solution   A reliability of 99% corresponds to a strength such that only 1%, or one out of 100, values are expected to be lower. From Table B.3(b), this limit corresponds to $\mu - 2.33\sigma$. If $\bar{x}$ and s_x are employed as estimates of μ and σ, respectively, the 99% reliability value is

$$x_{99} = \bar{x} - 2.33 s_x = 794 - 2.33 \times 38.6 = 704 \text{ MPa} \qquad \textbf{Ans.}$$

Table B.4   Typical Coefficients of Variation

Variable x	Typical δ_x, %
Yield strength of metals	7
Ultimate strength of metals	5
Modulus of elasticity of metals	5
Fracture toughness of metals	15
Tensile strength of welds	10
Compressive strength of concrete	15
Strength of wood	15
Cycles to failure in fatigue	50
Crack growth rate in fatigue	50
Strength for a given life in fatigue	10

Source: Values in [Wirsching 96] p. 18.2.

B.4 TYPICAL VARIATION IN MATERIALS PROPERTIES

For materials property data, such as yield strength, hardness, and fracture toughness, coefficients of variation δ_x are generally in the range 0.05 to 0.20, that is, 5% to 20%. Some typical values for particular materials property variables are given in Table B.4. These coefficients are suggested by P. H. Wirsching as default values for use where more specific information is not available. Specific data from fracture toughness tests on various materials are given in Table B.5. Note that sample sizes n are given in addition to $\bar{x}$, s_x, and δ_x. The δ_x values for metals are noted to vary considerably, and some exceed the typical value of 15% from Table B.4.

The coefficient of variation has particular intuitive appeal as a measure of variation that is normalized to the mean value. For example, consider the typical $\delta_x = 15\%$ for fracture toughness of metals, and assume that the mean value is known from a large sample. From Table B.3(b), there is a 10% chance that a value will be more than $1.28\sigma_x$ below the mean. Hence, there is a 10% chance that the value will be $1.28 \times 15\% = 19.2\%$ below the mean. Similarly, there is a 1% chance that the value will be $2.33 \times 15\% = 35.0\%$ below, and a 0.1% chance that it will be $3.09 \times 15\% = 46.3\%$ below.

B.5 ONE-SIDED TOLERANCE LIMITS

Direct use of the normal distribution to estimate probability limits on materials properties is inaccurate unless the sample size n used to establish the mean and standard deviation is indeed quite large. This arises from the fact that $\bar{x}$ and s_x from Eqs. B.1 and B.2 are only estimates, and not the true values μ and σ for an infinite number of observations, so that these values themselves contain random error. This additional source of statistical error can be included by using *tolerance limits* for normally distributed variables. It is necessary to specify a *confidence level*, such as 90%, 95%, or 99%, to make a specific estimate.

The value of x that is exceeded R percent of the time at a confidence level C is

$$x_{R,C} = \bar{x} - k_{R,C}\, s_x \tag{B.6}$$

Table B.5 Statistical Variation of Fracture Toughness

Material	Strength[1] σ_o or σ_{uc}, MPa	Number of K_{Ic} Tests n	Fracture Toughness, $x = K_{Ic}$		
			Mean $\bar{x}$, MPa$\sqrt{\text{m}}$	Standard Deviation s_x, MPa$\sqrt{\text{m}}$	Coefficient of Variation δ_x, %
(a) Metals[2]					
D6AC steel 540°C temper	1496	103	70.3	13.3	18.9
9Ni-4Co-0.20C steel, Q & T	1300	27	141.8	11.8	8.3
2024-T351 Al	325	11	34.1	5.6	16.5
7075-T651 Al	505	99	28.6	2.2	7.6
7475-T7351 Al	435	151	51.6	5.4	10.4
Ti-6Al-4V annealed	925	43	65.9	6.9	10.5
(b) Rock and Concrete					
Dolomitic limestone (Hokie stone)	283	11	1.300	0.080	6.1
Westerly granite	233	9	0.885	0.031	3.5
Concrete beams 1.14 m span	54.4	16	1.191	0.156	13.1

Notes: [1]Yield strength, σ_o, is tabulated for metals, and ultimate compressive strength, σ_{uc}, for rock and concrete. [2]All metals data are for the L-T orientation.
Sources: Data in [Boyer 85] p. 6.35, [Karfakis 90], [MILHDBK 94] pp. 2.4, 3.11, and 3.12, and [Shah 95] p. 176.

where k is the *one-sided tolerance limit factor*. The factor k depends on the sample size n, and on both R and C. Values for various R and C combinations are tabulated in some handbooks of statistical tables. A few values for reliabilities $R = 90$, 99, and 99.9%, and for a confidence level $C = 95\%$, are given in Table B.6. The confidence level of $C = 95\%$ means that there is a 95% chance that the reliability R is satisfied. For an infinite number of observations, note that these k values give the same limits as Table B.3(b). However, for sample sizes around $n = 100$ or less, the tolerance limits are significantly farther from the mean—that is, k is significantly larger—than for $n = \infty$.

Convenient formulas for the one-sided tolerance limit factor are given in the handbook MMPDS-05 (2010), specifically for reliabilities of $R = 90\%$ and 99%, with confidence $C = 95\%$:

$$k_{90,95} = 1.282 + \exp\left[0.958 - 0.520 \ln n + 3.19/n\right] \quad \text{(a)}$$

$$k_{99,95} = 2.326 + \exp\left[1.34 - 0.522 \ln n + 3.87/n\right] \quad \text{(b)}$$

$$(n \geq 16) \quad \text{(B.7)}$$

Table B.6   One-Sided Tolerance Limit Factors
for Normally Distributed Variables and 95%
Confidence

Number of Observations	Reliability Level		
	90%	99%	99.9%
n	k_{90}	k_{99}	$k_{99.9}$
5	3.41	5.74	7.50
10	2.35	3.98	5.20
20	1.93	3.30	4.32
50	1.65	2.86	3.77
100	1.53	2.68	3.54
200	1.45	2.57	3.40
500	1.39	2.48	3.28
∞	1.28	2.33	3.09

Sources: Values in [Odeh 77] p. 25 and
[MILHDBK 94] pp. 9.220–9.224.

The function $\exp[y]$ denotes e^y, where $e = 2.718\ldots$, and the formulas are noted to be accurate only for $n \geq 16$. Also, a procedure for calculating any desired $k_{R,C}$ is given in the handbook by Natrella (1966).

Example B.3

Repeat Ex. B.2, but now include the uncertainty associated with the finite sample size to estimate the yield strength for a 99% reliability with 95% confidence.

Solution   From Eq. B.7(b), the one-sided tolerance limit factor is obtained by substituting the sample size of $n = 121$ observations, which gives $k_{99.95} = 2.65$. The limit from Eq. B.6 is thus

$$x_{99.95} = \bar{x} - 2.65s_x = 794 - 2.65 \times 38.6 = 692\,\text{MPa} \qquad \textbf{Ans.}$$

This limit is seen to be lower than the previous value of 704 MPa.

B.6   DISCUSSION

Materials properties are sometimes listed in handbooks and supplier information as *typical* values, which should be interpreted as mean values. In other cases, the properties are characterized as *minimum* values. These are generally not derived from statistical analysis, but instead are obtained by examining a set of data and by selecting, as a matter of judgment, a value that is expected to be exceeded in most cases. Such minimum values are typically two or three standard deviations below the mean. Occasionally, limits are given that are based on statistical analysis. Where this is done, one possibility is a *three-sigma limit*, meaning a value $x = \bar{x} - 3s_x$. Another possibility is a *one-sided tolerance limit*, $x_{R,C}$, as discussed in the previous section. Such tolerance limits are given for tensile properties of metals in MMPDS-05, where an adjustment has also been made for possible minor asymmetry (skewness) in the normal distribution.

A three-sigma limit is sometimes used to establish a safety factor in stress for *S-N* curves. (See Section 9.2.4.) For a typical δ_x of 10% on fatigue strength from Table B.4, this corresponds to lowering the *S-N* curve by 31% in stress.

Books on probability and statistics describe other probability density functions besides the normal one. Of these, the *Weibull* distribution is also widely used to analyze materials data, especially where the data do not scatter symmetrically about the mean—that is, for *skewed* data. In addition, quantities related to time to failure, such as creep rupture life or cycles to failure in fatigue, often have a markedly skewed distribution that is sometimes represented by the *lognormal* distribution. This distribution consists simply of a normal distribution in the new variable $y = \log x$, where x is the original variable, such as time or cycles to failure.

REFERENCES

HAUGEN, E. B. 1980. *Probabilistic Mechanical Design*, John Wiley, New York.

JOHNSON, R. A. 2011. *Miller and Freund's Probability and Statistics for Engineers*, 8th ed., Pearson Prentice Hall, Upper Saddle River, NJ.

MMPDS. 2010. *Metallic Materials Properties Development and Standardization Handbook*, MMPDS-05, U.S. Federal Aviation Administration; distributed by Battelle Memorial Institute, Columbus, OH. (See *http://projects.battelle.org/mmpds*; replaces MIL-HDBK-5.)

NATRELLA, M. G. 1966. *Experimental Statistics*, National Bureau of Standards Handbook 91, U.S. Dept. of Commerce, U.S. Government Printing Office, Washington, DC.

Answers for Selected Problems and Questions

This section of the book gives the answers for approximately half of the Problems and Questions where a numerical value or the development of a new equation is requested. Where a series of values needs to be calculated, a typical set of these is given.

CHAPTER 1

1.7 $X_1 = 1.43$

CHAPTER 3

3.15 **(a)** pine = 1, CFRP = 2; **(b)** pine = 1, 1020 steel = 2; **(c)** pine or 7075 Al

3.17 **(a)** mass: pine = 1, CFRP = 2; **(b)** cost: pine = 1, 1020 steel = 2

3.19 Ti-6-4, GFRP, and CFRP also pass requirements. Ti-6-4 and CFRP are extremely costly. GFRP costs 1.8 times the 4340 steel, but weighs 54% as much.

CHAPTER 4

4.5 **(a)** $E = 207.3$ GPa, **(b)** $L_A = 100.493$ mm, $L_0 = 100.00$ mm, **(c)** $\varepsilon_p = 0.01581$, **(d)** $L_B = 101.581$ mm, $L_0 = 101.58$ mm

4.6 $E = 72.4$ GPa, $\sigma_o = 302$ MPa, $\sigma_u = 323$ MPa, $100\varepsilon_f = 14.6\%$, $100\varepsilon_{pf} = 14.28\%$, $\%RA = 28.7\%$

4.7 $E = 97.7$ GPa, $\sigma_o = 180$ MPa, $\sigma_u = 240$ MPa, $100\varepsilon_f = 1.17\%$, $100\varepsilon_{pf} = 0.93\%$, $\%RA = 9.75\%$

4.10 $E = 68.9$ GPa, $\sigma_o = 528$ MPa, $\sigma_u = 597$ MPa, $100\varepsilon_f = 15.3\%$, $100\varepsilon_{pf} = 14.5\%$, $\%RA = 36\%$

4.13 $E = 2530\,\text{MPa}$, $\sigma_{ou} = 63.3\,\text{MPa}$, $\sigma_u = 63.3\,\text{MPa}$, $100\varepsilon_f = 3.19\%$, $100\varepsilon_{pf} = 80.0\%$, $\%RA = 46.5\%$

4.14 $E = 3730\,\text{MPa}$, $\sigma_{0.2\%} = 38\,\text{MPa}$, $\sigma_u = 66.3\,\text{MPa}$, $100\varepsilon_f = 3.19\%$, $100\varepsilon_{pf} = 1.41\%$, $\%RA$ small

4.21 (a) For $\sigma = 587\,\text{MPa}$: $\tilde{\sigma} = 622\,\text{MPa}$, $\tilde{\varepsilon} = 0.0581$, $\tilde{\varepsilon}_p = 0.0490$; (b) $H = 749\,\text{MPa}$, $n = 0.0597$

4.22 (a) $E = 211.9\,\text{GPa}$, $\sigma_o = 317\,\text{MPa}$, $\sigma_u = 576\,\text{MPa}$, $\%RA = 69.3\%$; (b) For $\sigma = 558\,\text{MPa}$: $\tilde{\varepsilon} = 0.341$, $\tilde{\sigma}_B = 725\,\text{MPa}$, $\tilde{\varepsilon}_p = 0.337$; (c) $H = 915\,\text{MPa}$, $n = 0.191$

4.24 (c) $\sigma_u = Hn^n/e^n$

4.27 (a) $E = 100.7\,\text{GPa}$, $\sigma_{oc} = 394\,\text{MPa}$, $\sigma_{uc} = 804\,\text{MPa}$, length change $= -12.9\%$, area change $= -32.6\%$

4.36 $\sigma_{fb} = \dfrac{3L_1}{4tc^2}P_f$, $E = \dfrac{L_1(3L^2 - 4L_1^2)}{32tc^3}\left(\dfrac{dP}{dv}\right)$;   **4.37** $\sigma_{fb} = 317\,\text{MPa}$, $E = 336\,\text{GPa}$

CHAPTER 5

5.4 $\varepsilon_e = 0.0058$, $\varepsilon_p = 0.0194$

5.7 $(\varepsilon, \sigma) = (0.0250, 50\,\text{MPa})$ at $t = 0\,\text{s}$; $(\varepsilon, \sigma) = (0.0230, 40\,\text{MPa})$ at $t = 86{,}400\,\text{s}$

5.9 $t_{50\%} = 19.7$ months

5.11 (a) 254.7 MPa, (b) 0.002523, (c) -0.000883, (d) 200.5 mm, (e) 49.956 mm

5.13 (b) $\sigma_x = \dfrac{E}{1 - \nu^2}(\varepsilon_x + \nu\varepsilon_y)$, $\sigma_y = \dfrac{E}{1 - \nu^2}(\varepsilon_y + \nu\varepsilon_x)$; (c) $\varepsilon_z = -\dfrac{\nu}{1 - \nu}(\varepsilon_x + \varepsilon_y)$

5.15 $\sigma_x = 44.87$, $\sigma_y = -20.87$, $\tau_{xy} = 8.352\,\text{MPa}$, $\varepsilon_z = 3800 \times 10^{-6}$

5.17 $\sigma_x = -5.847\,\text{MPa}$, $\sigma_y = -201.2\,\text{MPa}$, $\tau_{xy} = 32.56\,\text{MPa}$, $\varepsilon_z = 285.9 \times 10^{-6}$

5.18 $\sigma_x = 460.82$, $\sigma_y = 179.56$, $\tau_{xy} = 28.665\,\text{MPa}$, $\varepsilon_z = -1926.48 \times 10^{-6}$

5.20 $\Delta r = \dfrac{pr^2(1 - \nu)}{2tE}$, $\Delta t = -\dfrac{\nu pr}{E}$;   **5.21** $\dfrac{dV_e}{V_e} = \dfrac{pD(5 - 4\nu)}{4tE}$;   **5.23** (a) $E' = \dfrac{E}{1 - \nu\lambda}$

5.25 (a) $\sigma_z = \nu\sigma_x(1 + \lambda)$, (b) $E' = \dfrac{E}{1 - \nu\lambda - \nu^2(1 + \lambda)}$;   **5.27** $\sigma_z = -406.78\,\text{MPa}$

5.29 (a) $\sigma_z = -103.5\,\text{MPa}$, $\varepsilon_x = \varepsilon_y = -889.6 \times 10^{-6}$, $\varepsilon_v = 1779.2 \times 10^{-6}$; (b) $E' = 168.6\,\text{GPa}$

5.30 (a) For MgO: $\Delta T = -30°\text{C}$ (down shock), $\Delta T = 182°\text{C}$ (up shock)

5.33 (b) $\Delta T = -11.99°\text{C}$

5.35 $E_X = 216.6$, $E_Y = 158.72$, $G_{XY} = 59.2\,\text{GPa}$, $\nu_{XY} = 0.31165$, $\nu_{YX} = 0.228$

5.37 $E_X = 44.8$, $E_Y = 8.16$, $G_{XY} = 3.08\,\text{GPa}$, $\nu_{XY} = 0.264$, $\nu_{YX} = 0.0481$

5.38 $E_X = 75.8$, $E_Y = 8.39$, $G_{XY} = 3.15\,\text{GPa}$, $\nu_{XY} = 0.342$, $\nu_{YX} = 0.0379$

5.43 $\sigma_X = 131.2$, $\sigma_Y = -15.25$, $\tau_{XY} = 11.00\,\text{MPa}$

5.45 (a) $E_X = 131.8\,\text{GPa}$, $\nu_{XY} = 0.327$, $E_Y = 9.61\,\text{GPa}$, $\nu_{YX} = 0.0189$, and a better value is 0.0238; (b) $E_r = 201\,\text{GPa}$

5.46 (a) $V_r = 0.651$; (b) $E_X = 48.0$, $E_Y = 6.48$, $G_{XY} = 2.41\,\text{GPa}$, $\nu_{XY} = 0.265$, $\nu_{YX} = 0.0358$

5.48 (a) $V_r = 0.454$; (b) $E_X = 225$, $E_Y = 112.7$, $G_{XY} = 42.2\,\text{GPa}$, $\nu_{XY} = 0.315$, $\nu_{YX} = 0.1581$

5.50 (a) $E_X = 170\,\text{GPa}$ requires $E_r = 254\,\text{GPa}$ min, and $E_Y = 85\,\text{GPa}$ requires $E_r = 213\,\text{GPa}$ min; (b) SiC, Al_2O_3, or tungsten

CHAPTER 6

(Note: For tubes and spherical shells, thin-wall approximations are used where possible.)

Prob.	σ_1	σ_2	τ_3	θ_n	σ_{max}	τ_{max}
6.1	8	4	2	45° CW	8	−5
6.2	7.1	−7.1	7.1	22.5° (CCW)	7.1	3.6
6.3	40	−18	29	21.8° (CW)	40	20
6.5	37.9	18.1	9.9	22.5° (CCW)	37.9	19
6.7	129.3	−84.3	106.8	8.2° (CCW)	129.3	64.7

Note: All values except θ_n are stresses in MPa units.

Prob.	σ_1	σ_2	σ_3	τ_1	τ_2	τ_3	σ_{max}	τ_{max}	θ_n
6.10	4.4	−5.4	−3	1.2	3.7	4.9	4.4	4	45° CW
6.11	14	−56	70	63	28	35	70	63	0
6.12	241	−41	250	146	5	141	250	146	22.5° (CCW)

Notes: All values except θ_n are stresses in MPa units. Rotation θ_n in x-y plane gives 1- and 2-axes; z-axis is 3-axis.

6.15 (a) $\sigma_{1,2,3} = 200, 100, 0$; $\tau_{max} = 100$ MPa; **6.17** $\sigma_{max} = 535$, $\tau_{max} = 268$ MPa

6.19 $\sigma_{max} = 304$, $\tau_{max} = 157.1$ MPa; **6.20** $\sigma_{max} = 306$, $\tau_{max} = 164.0$ MPa

6.22 $\sigma_{max} = 281$, $\tau_{max} = 159.1$ MPa; **6.25** $\sigma_{max} = 130.5$, $\tau_{max} = 79.6$ MPa

6.26 (a) $\tau_{max} = \dfrac{2}{\pi d^2}\sqrt{P^2 + \left(\dfrac{8T}{d}\right)^2}$, (b) $d = 45.8$ mm

6.28 (a) $\tau_{max} = \dfrac{3pr_1^3 r_2^3}{4R^3(r_2^3 - r_1^3)}$; (b) $\sigma_{1,2,3} = 339, 339, -300$; $\tau_{1,2,3} = 320, 320, 0$ MPa

6.30 $\tau_{max} = 151.1$ MPa

6.32 (a) For $R = 160$ mm: $\sigma_r = 81.1$, $\sigma_t = 206$ MPa; (b) $\sigma_{max} = 338$, $\tau_{max} = 168.9$ MPa

Prob.	σ_1	σ_2	σ_3	τ_1	τ_2	τ_3	σ_{max}	τ_{max}
6.34	140.0	10.0	200	95.0	30.0	65.0	200	95.0
6.36	117.5	28.7	−56.2	42.4	86.8	44.4	117.5	86.8
6.38	450	0	−400	200	425	225	450	425
6.41	88.1	−62.5	−125.6	31.6	106.9	75.3	88.1	106.9
6.43	48.7	3.22	−31.9	17.57	40.3	22.7	48.7	40.3

Note: All values are stresses in MPa units.

Prob.	l_1	m_1	n_1	l_2	m_2	n_2	l_3	m_3	n_3
6.34	0.555	0.832	0	−0.832	0.555	0	0	0	1.000
6.36	−0.300	0.945	0.1296	0.0803	−0.1103	0.991	0.951	0.308	−0.0428
6.38	0.485	0.485	0.728	0.707	−0.707	0	0.514	0.514	−0.686
6.41	0.928	0.1337	0.348	0.325	0.1695	−0.930	−0.1835	0.976	0.1138
6.43	0.657	−0.612	−0.440	0.449	0.787	−0.423	0.605	0.0807	0.792

6.46 $\sigma_h = 138,\ \tau_h = 178.2\,\text{MPa}$

6.47 $\sigma_{\max} = \dfrac{1}{2}\left(\sigma_x + \sqrt{\sigma_x^2 + 4\tau_{xy}^2}\right),\ \tau_{\max} = \dfrac{1}{2}\sqrt{\sigma_x^2 + 4\tau_{xy}^2},\ \tau_h = \dfrac{\sqrt{2}}{3}\sqrt{\sigma_x^2 + 3\tau_{xy}^2}$

6.50 $\tau_h = \sqrt{\dfrac{2}{3}}\ \dfrac{pr_1^2 r_2^2}{R^2(r_2^2 - r_1^2)}$

6.53 $\varepsilon_{1,2,3} = 213 \times 10^{-6},\ -783 \times 10^{-6},\ 236 \times 10^{-6};$
$\gamma_{1,2,3} = 1019 \times 10^{-6},\ 23.1 \times 10^{-6},\ 996 \times 10^{-6}$

6.55 $\varepsilon_{1,2,3} = 2439 \times 10^{-6},\ 711 \times 10^{-6},\ -1659 \times 10^{-6};$
$\gamma_{1,2,3} = 2370 \times 10^{-6},\ 4098 \times 10^{-6},\ 1728 \times 10^{-6}$

6.57 $\varepsilon_y = \dfrac{1}{3}(2\varepsilon_{60} + 2\varepsilon_{120} - \varepsilon_x),\ \gamma_{xy} = \dfrac{2}{\sqrt{3}}(\varepsilon_{60} - \varepsilon_{120})$

CHAPTER 7

(Note: For tubes and spherical shells, thin-wall approximations are used where possible.)

7.1 $X_{NT} = 4.08;$ **7.3** $X_{NT} = 2.25;$ **7.5** (a) $X_S = 2.91,$ (b) $X_H = 3.29$

7.7 (a) $X_S = 1.59$ (b) $X_H = 1.84$; **7.9** (a) $\sigma_{oS} = 252,$ (b) $\sigma_{oH} = 218.6\,\text{MPa}$

7.11 $X_S = 1.60,$ or $X_H = 1.82;$ **7.13** $X_S = 1.42,$ or $X_H = 1.46$

7.14 (a) $d_S = \left(\dfrac{32\,T X}{\pi \sigma_o}\right)^{1/3}$, (b) $d_H = \left(\dfrac{16\sqrt{3}\,T X}{\pi \sigma_o}\right)^{1/3}$; **7.16** $X_S = 1.637,$ or $X_H = 1.692$

7.18 $X_H = 4.93;$ **7.20** $X_S = 2.04,$ or $X_H = 2.15$

7.21 (a) $X_S = 1.215,$ or $X_H = 1.340,$ (b) $d_S = 88.5,$ or $d_H = 84.5\,\text{mm}$

7.23 (a) $d_S = \left(\dfrac{32X}{\pi \sigma_o}\sqrt{M^2 + T^2}\right)^{1/3}$, (b) $d_H = \left(\dfrac{16X}{\pi \sigma_o}\sqrt{4M^2 + 3T^2}\right)^{1/3}$

7.24 (a) $X_S = 0.855,$ or $X_H = 0.983,$ (b) AISI 4142 steel (450°C): $X_S = 1.627,$ or $X_H = 1.873$

7.26 (a) $\sigma_z = \dfrac{\sigma_o(1 - v)}{1 - 2v}$, (b) same, (c) $\sigma_{zH} = -1817\,\text{MPa}$

7.28 $\tau_{xy} = 108.3\,\text{MPa};$ **7.30** $X_S = 2.56,$ or $X_H = 2.93$

7.33 (a) $r_{2S} = r_1\left(\dfrac{\sigma_o}{\sigma_o - 2pX}\right)^{1/2}$, or $r_{2H} = r_1\left(\dfrac{\sigma_o}{\sigma_o - \sqrt{3}pX}\right)^{1/2}$,
(b) $r_{2S} = 53.8,$ or $r_{2H} = 51.1\,\text{mm}$

7.35 **(a)** $d_S = 52.1$ mm, $m_S = 16.76$ kg, or $d_H = 50.5$ mm, $m_H = 15.74$ kg

7.37 **(a)** $d_S = \left(\dfrac{32}{\pi \sigma_o} \sqrt{(Y_M M)^2 + (Y_T T)^2} \right)^{1/3}$, **(b)** $d_H = \left(\dfrac{16}{\pi \sigma_o} \sqrt{4(Y_M M)^2 + 3(Y_T T)^2} \right)^{1/3}$

7.39 **(a)** $\sigma_z = -89.7$ MPa; **7.42** **(a)** $\tau_i = 34.6$ MPa, $\mu = 1.477$

7.43 **(a)** $m = 0.794$, $\tau_i = 33.4$ MPa, $\mu = 1.307$, $\phi = 52.6°$, $\theta_c = 18.71°$,
   (c) $\sigma'_{uc} = -197.3$, $\sigma'_{ut} = 22.6$ MPa

7.45 **(a)** $m = 0.631$, $\tau_i = 11.54$ MPa, $\mu = 0.814$, $\phi = 39.1°$, $\theta_c = 25.4°$,
   (c) $\sigma'_{uc} = -48.5$, $\sigma'_{ut} = 10.97$ MPa

7.49 $\sigma_3 = -73.2$ MPa; **7.50** **(a)** $X_{MM} = 2.38$, **(b)** $\sigma_x = \sigma_y = -5.37$ MPa

7.52 **(a)** $X_{MM} = 1.880$, **(b)** $p = 33.4$ MPa; **7.54** $T = 2.22$ kN·m

7.56 **(a)** $X_{MM} = 5.04$, **(b)** $X_{MM} = 3.80$

CHAPTER 8

(Note: Small-crack approximate F values are used where possible.)

8.2 **(c)** $a_t = 2.36$ mm, $a_t = 20.87$ mm, respectively

8.4 **(a)** For AISI 4130 steel, $a_t = 3.24$ mm; for SiC, $a_t = 0.106$ mm

8.6 At $\alpha = 0.8$, $F_a = 1.808$, $F_b = 1.8$, $F_c = 1.565$; **8.7** **(a)** $X_K = 3.47$, **(b)** $X'_o = 3.76$, **(c)** $X'_o = 3.01$

8.10 **(a)** $P = 11.28$ kN, **(b)** $a = 5.09$ mm

8.11 **(a)** $a = 0.719$ mm, **(b)** $a = 11.5$ mm

8.13 **(a)** $K_{Ic} = 20.80$ MPa$\sqrt{m}$, **(b)** $\sigma_o = 46.9$ MPa

8.16 **(a)** $X_K = 1.72$, $X'_o = 2.19$, **(b)** $b = 20.26$ mm

8.17 Using $\alpha = a/b$: **(a)** $P_o = \pi b^2 \sigma_o (1 - \alpha)^2$, **(b)** $M_o = \dfrac{4}{3} b^3 \sigma_o (1 - \alpha)^3$

8.19 $X_K = 0.584$, $X_o = 1.85$; **8.20** **(a)** $M = 146.4$ kN·m

8.22 **(a)** $X_K = 3.05$, $X'_o = 5.22$ (ignoring crack); **8.25** **(a)** $t = 12.30$ mm

8.27 **(a)** $d_o = 55.28$ mm, **(b)** $d_c = 63.28$ mm, **(c)** $d = 63.28$ mm

8.28 **(a)** $X_K = 5.25$, **(b)** $X_K = 3.62$ (exact F)

8.31 $p = 1.236$ MPa; **8.33** $X_K = 2.91$, $X'_o = 3.16$

8.34 **(a)** $X_o = 6.27$, $X_a = 2.99$; **(b)** $X_o = 2.74$, $X_a = 24.7$; **(c)** $K_{Ic} = 112.8$ MPa$\sqrt{m}$,
   (d) $X_K = 3.00$

8.36 $X_K = 3.14$, $X_o = 4.15$; **8.38** **(a)** $M_o = 6.40$ kN·m, **(b)** $M_c = 1.721$ kN·m

8.39 **(a)** $S_{gc} = 46.6$ MPa, **(b)** $S_{go} = 82.8$ MPa

8.41 **(a)** For S-L glass: $\Delta T = -23.7°$C, **(b)** $f_2 = \dfrac{K_{Ic}(1 - \nu)}{E\alpha}$

8.42 **(a)** $d_o = 45.9$ mm, $d_c = 29.4$ mm; **(b)** $d = 45.9$ mm; **(c)** $d = 38.7$ mm, $\sigma_o = 1340$ MPa; **(d)** for
   $a = 0.50$ mm: $d = 37.9$ mm, $\sigma_o = 1420$ MPa; for $a = 2.0$ mm: $d = 39.3$ mm, $\sigma_o = 1275$ MPa

8.46 $X_K = 3.10$; **8.48** **(a)** $K_Q = 37.5$ MPa$\sqrt{m}$; **(b)** not plane strain, LEFM not applicable

8.49 **(a, b)** $K_Q = K_{Ic} = 49.7$ MPa$\sqrt{m}$, **(c)** $2r_{o\varepsilon} = 0.1378$ mm

8.52 For $a_c = 3.00$ mm: **(a)** $S_{gK} = 680$ MPa, **(b)** $S_{gKe} = 498$ MPa

CHAPTER 9

9.3 (a) $D = \dfrac{\sigma_1 - \sigma_2}{\log N_1 - \log N_2}$, $C = \sigma_1 - D \log N_1$, (b) $D = -170.0$ MPa, $C = 1450$ MPa

9.5 (b) $\sigma_f' = 2569.3674$ MPa, $b = -0.1954$; **9.6** (b) $\sigma_f' = 1106.47$ MPa, $b = -0.0759$

9.8 (b) $\sigma_f' = 2025.59$ MPa, $b = -0.185$

9.10 (a) $X_S = 1.2$, $X_N = 5.91$; (b) $\hat{N} = 28,507$ cycles

Prob.	N_f, cycles		
	(a)	**(b)**	**(c)**
9.21	6.7×10^4	3.7×10^4	1.16×10^5
9.23	6.7×10^4	3.51×10^4	1.788×10^5
9.25	3.003×10^4	6.89×10^3	2.39×10^5
9.27	1.422×10^5	1.798×10^4	7.84×10^5

9.29 For σ_a in MPa: (a) $\sigma_a = 738(2N_f)^{-0.0648}$, (b) $\sigma_a = 938(2N_f)^{-0.0648}$, (c) $\sigma_a = 1138(2N_f)^{-0.0648}$

9.31 (a) For $\sigma_a = 379$, $\sigma_m = 621$ MPa: $\sigma_{ar} = 550$ MPa, $\sigma_a/\sigma_{ar} = 0.690$

9.32 For $\sigma_a = 379$, $\sigma_m = 621$: (a) $\sigma_{ar} = 616$, (b) $\sigma_{ar} = 532$ MPa

9.35 For $\sigma_{\max} = 469$ MPa, $R = 0.60$: (a) $\sigma_{ar} = 383$, (b) $\sigma_{ar} = 257$, (c) $\sigma_{ar} = 119.4$, (d) $\sigma_{ar} = 210$ MPa

9.37 $X_S = 1.271$, $X_N = 10.49$ by Morrow; $X_S = 1.173$, $X_N = 4.785$ by SWT

9.39 By SWT: (a) $X_N = 104.02$; (b) $Y_m = 1.62$; by Morrow: (a) $X_N = 337$; (b) $Y_m = 1.69$

9.41 For SWT and $\bar{\sigma}_H$: (a) $p = 15.65$ MPa, (b) $X_H = 1.71$

9.42 (a) $N_f = 284,000$ cycles, (b) $X_o = 1.122$, (c) $d = 52.5$ mm, (d, e) $d = 55.1$ mm

9.45 $B_f = 49.8$ reps by Morrow, or 375 reps by SWT

9.46 $B_f = 21,200$ reps by Morrow, or 3,520 reps by SWT

9.48 $B_f = 101,100$ reps by Morrow, or 53,300 reps by SWT

9.50 $B_f = 4110$ reps by Morrow, or 2770 reps by SWT

9.52 $B_f = 3260$ reps by SWT; **9.53** $X_S = 1.215$, $X_N = 6.52$

9.54 By SWT: (a) $B_f = 1.538 \times 10^9$ revs, 128,200 hrs, (b) $Y = 1.541$ for 2000 hrs; by Morrow: (a) $B_f = 5.96 \times 10^9$ revs, 497,000 hrs, (b) $Y = 1.725$ for 2000 hrs

CHAPTER 10

(Note: For determining k_f, the Peterson equation is used unless Neuber is indicated.)

10.2 $k_t = 3.10$, $k_f = 2.4$; or $k_f = 2.5$ by Neuber

10.4 $k_t = 3.40$, $k_f = 3.2$, $S_{er} = 123$ MPa; or $k_f = 3.00$, $S_{er} = 131$ MPa by Neuber

10.5 $k_t = 1.85$, $k_f = 1.83$, $\sigma_{ar} = 426$ MPa

10.6 $k_t = 2.7$, $k_f = 2.04$, $M_a = 14.38$ N·m

10.10 $M_a = 2.55$ kN·m; **10.12** $T_a = 140.5$ N·m by Juvinall

10.14 (a) $S_a = 1013 - 156.7 \log N_f$ MPa; (b) $N_f = 23,100$ cycles by Eq. 10.21, or 22,500 cycles by Eq. 10.28

10.15 (a) $S_{max} = 356\,\text{MPa}$, (b) $S_{max} = 325\,\text{MPa}$; **10.17** (a) $P_m = 33.9\,\text{kN}$, (b) $P_m = 10.26\,\text{kN}$

10.18 $X_S = 0.727$, $X_N = 26$

10.20 (a) $X_S = 1.43$, (b) $\rho = 1.65\,\text{mm}$ by Eq. 10.28

10.21 For $S_{max} = 207$, $S_m = 69\,\text{MPa}$: (a) $S_{ar} = 159.9\,\text{MPa}$, (b) $S_{ar} = 169.0\,\text{MPa}$, (c) $k_f = 1.92$ by Neuber, $k_{fm} = 1.55$, $S_{ar} = 175.3\,\text{MPa}$

10.23 $A = 1312\,\text{MPa}$, $B = -0.208$, $\gamma = 0.775$; **10.25** $A = 799\,\text{MPa}$, $B = -0.1996$, $\gamma = 0.479$

10.26 $A = 1811\,\text{MPa}$, $B = -0.1074$, $\gamma = 0.652$

10.30 (a) $\sigma_{ar} = 1515\,N_f^{-0.1271}\,\text{MPa}$ $(10^3 \leq N_f \leq 10^6)$, (b) $N_f = 10{,}790$ cycles

10.33 (a) $S_{ar} = 417\,N_f^{-0.0739}$, (b) $S_{ar} = 536\,N_f^{-0.0962}\,\text{MPa}$ $(10^3 \leq N_f \leq 10^6)$

10.35 $S_{ar} = 353\,N_f^{-0.0873}\,\text{MPa}$ $(10^3 \leq N_f \leq 10^6)$, by Neuber

10.37 (a) $B_f = 10.88$ reps for $S_{max} = 240\,\text{MPa}$, $B_f = 19.05$ reps for $S_{max} = 209\,\text{MPa}$

10.40 (a) $B_f = 8.19$ reps; **10.41** (a) $B_f = 7.45$ reps

10.43 (a) $B_f = 203$ years; (b) $X_N = 2.71$, $X_S = 1.393$

CHAPTER 11

(Notes: For Eq. 11.32, F is approximated as F_i. And F is varied to find a_f where possible.)

Prob.	m	C, $\dfrac{\text{mm/cycle}}{(\text{MPa}\sqrt{\text{m}})^m}$	Prob.	m	C, $\dfrac{\text{mm / cycle}}{(\text{MPa}\sqrt{\text{m}})^m}$
11.1	3.16	2.12×10^{-9}	**11.7 (b)**	3.01	9.38×10^{-8}
11.3	24.0	3.84×10^{-19}	**11.9**	4.33	1.296×10^{-8}
11.5 (b)	2.90	5.18×10^{-8}	**11.11**	3.53	4.59×10^{-9}

11.14 $C_{0.5} = 6.80 \times 10^{-8}\,\text{mm/cycle}\big/(\text{MPa}\sqrt{\text{m}})^m$; **11.15** $p = m\gamma$, $q = m(1 - \gamma)$

11.17 (a) $m = 2.46$, $\gamma = 0.762$, $C_0 = 2.57 \times 10^{-8}\,\text{mm/cycle}\big/(\text{MPa}\sqrt{\text{m}})^m$

11.19 (b) $m = 2.96$, $\gamma = 0.553$, $C_0 = 4.08 \times 10^{-8}\,\text{mm/cycle}\big/(\text{MPa}\sqrt{\text{m}})^m$

11.22 $\overline{\Delta K}_{th} = 7.11\,\text{MPa}\sqrt{\text{m}}$, $\gamma_{th} = 0.218$

11.26 $N_{if} = \dfrac{\ln\,(a_f/a_i)}{\pi\,C(F\,\Delta S)^2}$; **11.28** $N_{if} = \dfrac{a_f - a_i}{C}\left(\dfrac{t\sqrt{b}}{0.89\,\Delta P}\right)^m$

11.30 (a) $N_{if} = \dfrac{1}{\pi C\,\Delta S^2}\left(\ln\sin\dfrac{\pi a_f}{2b} - \ln\sin\dfrac{\pi a_i}{2b}\right)$; **11.31** $N_{if} = 46{,}600$ cycles

11.33 $N_{if} = 16{,}730$ cycles; **11.35** $N_{if} = 38{,}900$ cycles; **11.37** $a_i = 0.473\,\text{mm}$

11.39 (a) $a_i = 0.883\,\text{mm}$, (b) for $X_N = 5.0$, $N_p = 20{,}000$ cycles

11.42 $N_{if} = 1{,}346{,}000$ cycles; **11.43** (a) $a_f = 28.8\,\text{mm}$, (b) $N_{if} = 739{,}000$ cycles

11.44 $N_{if} = 45{,}400$ cycles; **11.46** $N_{if} = 2{,}615{,}000$ cycles

11.48 (a) $N_{if} = 425{,}000$ cycles, (b) $X_K = 2.97$

11.50 $B_{if} = 3760$ reps; **11.53** $B_{if} = 1700$ reps; **11.54** $B_{if} = 1509$ reps

11.56 (a) $N_{if} = 56{,}800$ cycles, (b) $X_N = 0.946$, (c) $a_d = 0.268\,\text{mm}$, (d) $N_p = 18{,}930$ cycles, (e) $S_{new}\,/\,S_{old} = 0.720$

11.58 Soda: $n = 20.3$, $A = 1.67 \text{ m/s}/(\text{MPa}\sqrt{\text{m}})^n$;
Ultra: $n = 36.5$, $A = 2.05 \times 10^7 \text{ m/s}/(\text{MPa}\sqrt{\text{m}})^n$

11.59 $t_{if} = (C_2/S)^{20.3}$ for t_{if} in seconds, S in MPa; $C_2 = 166.1, 121.5, 88.9$ for $a_i = 5, 10, 20\,\mu\text{m}$

CHAPTER 12

12.1 $E = 52{,}200\,\text{MPa}$, $\sigma_o = 783\,\text{MPa}$, $\delta = 0.13$

12.3 Eq. 12.1: $E = 206{,}200\,\text{MPa}$, $\sigma_o = 830\,\text{MPa}$

12.4 Eq. 12.8: $E = 201{,}300\,\text{MPa}$, $H_1 = 1759\,\text{MPa}$, $n_1 = 0.0468$

12.7 Eq. 12.12: $E = 198{,}400\,\text{MPa}$, $H = 3020\,\text{MPa}$, $n = 0.1093$

12.9 Parabola: $\sigma = -53{,}800\varepsilon^2 + 3790\varepsilon$ MPa; **12.12** $\dfrac{dV_e}{V_e} = \dfrac{(5-4v)\,pr}{2tE} + \sqrt{3}\left(\dfrac{\sqrt{3}\,pr}{2tH}\right)^{1/n}$

12.14 $\varepsilon_2 = (\lambda - v)\dfrac{\sigma_1}{E} + (\lambda - 0.5)\left(1 - \lambda + \lambda^2\right)^{(1-n)/(2n)}\left(\dfrac{\sigma_1}{H}\right)^{1/n}$;

$\varepsilon_3 = -v(1+\lambda)\dfrac{\sigma_1}{E} - 0.5(1+\lambda)\left(1 - \lambda + \lambda^2\right)^{(1-n)/(2n)}\left(\dfrac{\sigma_1}{H}\right)^{1/n}$

12.16 $\gamma = \dfrac{\tau}{G}$ $(\tau \le \tau_o)$; $\gamma = \dfrac{\tau_o}{G} + (2v - 1 + 3/\delta)\dfrac{\tau - \tau_o}{2G(1+v)}$ $(\tau \ge \tau_o)$

12.18 **(a)** $\sigma_2 = \tilde{v}\sigma_1$, $\sigma_1 = \dfrac{\bar{\sigma}}{\sqrt{1 - \tilde{v} + \tilde{v}^2}}$, $\varepsilon_1 = \dfrac{\bar{\varepsilon}\,(1 - \tilde{v}^2)}{\sqrt{1 - \tilde{v} + \tilde{v}^2}}$

12.20 **(a, c)** $\sigma_{\max} = 600$, $\sigma_{\min} = -600\,\text{MPa}$; **(b)** $\sigma_{\max} = 600$, $\sigma_{\min} = -240\,\text{MPa}$

12.21 **(a)** $\sigma_{\max} = 570$, $\sigma_{\min} = -570\,\text{MPa}$; **(b)** $\sigma = 690, -350, 750\,\text{MPa}$

12.24 $\sigma_{\max} = 1400$, $\sigma_{\min} = -800\,\text{MPa}$; **12.26** $\sigma_{\max} = 478$, $\sigma_{\min} = -311\,\text{MPa}$

12.27 $\sigma_{\min} = -478$, $\sigma_{\max} = 311\,\text{MPa}$; **12.32** **(a)** $H' = 770\,\text{MPa}$, $n' = 0.106$

12.35 **(a)** $H'_\tau = 594\,\text{MPa}$, $n' = 0.212$; **(b)** $G = 79{,}100\,\text{MPa}$, $H'_\tau = 648\,\text{MPa}$, $n' = 0.208$

12.36 **(a)** $\sigma_{\max} = 577$, $\sigma_{\min} = -191.1\,\text{MPa}$; **(b)** $\sigma_{mi} = 193.0$, $\sigma_{m50{,}000} = 38.0\,\text{MPa}$

12.38 $\sigma_{A,B,C} = -478, 278, 354\,\text{MPa}$; **12.40** $\sigma_{A,B,C} = 770\,\text{MPa}, -240\,\text{MPa}, 912\,\text{MPa}$

12.41 $\sigma_{A,B,C} = 1513\,\text{MPa}, -1927\,\text{MPa}, 1660\,\text{MPa}$

CHAPTER 13

13.1 $M = 2bc^2 H_2\varepsilon_c^{n_2}\left(\dfrac{1}{(n_2+2)(n_2+3)}\right)$

13.2 **(a)** $M = \dfrac{2c_2^2 H_2\varepsilon_{c2}^{n_2}}{n_2+2}\left((t_1 - t_2)\left(\dfrac{c_1}{c_2}\right)^{n_2+2} + t_2\right)$; **(b)** $M = \dfrac{h_2^2 H_2\varepsilon_{h2}^{n_2}}{2(n_2+2)}\left(b_2 - b_1\left(\dfrac{h_1}{h_2}\right)^{n_2+2}\right)$

13.7 **(a)** $M = \dfrac{2\sqrt{\pi}\,c^3 H_2\varepsilon_c^{n_2}}{n_2+3}\dfrac{\Gamma(1 + n_2/2)}{\Gamma(1.5 + n_2/2)}$;

(b) $M = \dfrac{2\sqrt{\pi}\,c_2^3 H_2\varepsilon_{c2}^{n_2}}{n_2+3}\dfrac{\Gamma(1 + n_2/2)}{\Gamma(1.5 + n_2/2)}\left(1 - \left(\dfrac{c_1}{c_2}\right)^{n_2+3}\right)$

13.8 (a) 1st: $M = 13.80$ kN·m, $\sigma_{rc} = -166$ MPa, $\varepsilon_{rc} = 0.00044$; 2nd: $M' = 15.60$ kN·m, $\sigma_{rc} = -266$ MPa, $\varepsilon_{rc} = 0.00311$; 3rd: $M = 15.933$ kN·m, $\sigma_{rc} = -285$ MPa, $\varepsilon_{rc} = 0.00604$

13.12 $T = \dfrac{2\pi c_2^3 H_3 \gamma_{c_2}^{n_3}}{n_3 + 3} \left(1 - \left(\dfrac{c_1}{c_2} \right)^{n_3+3} \right)$

13.16 Typical values: (1) $\gamma_c = 0.00500$, $T = 117.78$ kN·m; (2) $\gamma_c = 0.01$, $T = 46.125$ kN·m

13.18 (a) $\sigma^1 = 462.85$ MPa, $\varepsilon^1 = 0.00385$; (b) $\sigma^1 = 630$ MPa, $\varepsilon^1 = 0.00525$;
(c) $\sigma^1 = 822.85$ MPa, $\varepsilon^1 = 0.00685$

13.21 (a) For $k_t S \geq \sigma_o$: $\varepsilon = \dfrac{\sigma_o}{2\delta E} \left(\delta - 1 + \sqrt{(1 - \delta)^2 + 4\delta(k_t S/\sigma_o)^2} \right)$,

$\sigma = \dfrac{\sigma_o}{2} \left(1 - \delta + \sqrt{(1 - \delta)^2 + 4\delta(k_t S/\sigma_o)^2} \right)$; (c) $\sigma = 716.8$ MPa, $\varepsilon = 0.00196$, $k_\sigma = 2.867$,
$k_\varepsilon = 3.136$

13.23 Typical values: $\sigma_y = 485$ MPa, $\varepsilon_y = 0.0214$, $P = 128.7$ kN

13.25 (a) For $k_t S \geq \sigma_o$: $\varepsilon = \dfrac{\sigma_o}{2E} + \dfrac{(k_t S)^2}{2E\sigma_o}$, (b) $S = \dfrac{1}{k_t} \sqrt{\sigma^2 + \dfrac{2E\sigma}{n + 1} \left(\dfrac{\sigma}{H} \right)^{1/n}}$,
(c) Typical values: $\sigma_y = 485$ MPa, $\varepsilon_y = 0.0214$, $P = 164.0$ kN

13.26 (a) $\sigma_r = -490.57$ MPa, $\varepsilon_r = 0.0155$; (b) $\sigma_r = 0$ MPa, $\varepsilon_r = 0$

13.28 (a) $\sigma_r = 0$ MPa, $\varepsilon_r = 0$; (b) $\sigma_r = -396.75$ MPa, $\varepsilon_r = 0.011$

13.30 (a) $\sigma_{\max} = 300$ MPa, $\varepsilon_{\max} = 0.001500$, $\sigma_{\min} = -60.0$ MPa, $\varepsilon_{\min} = -0.000300$;
(b, c, d) $\sigma_{\max} = 400$ MPa, $\varepsilon_{\max} = 0.00450$; (b) $\sigma_{\min} = -320$ MPa, $\varepsilon_{\min} = 0.000900$;
(c) $\sigma_{\min} = -400$ MPa, $\varepsilon_{\min} = -0.000563$; (d) $\sigma_{\min} = -400$ MPa, $\varepsilon_{\min} = -0.00450$

13.31 $\sigma_{\max} = 1070$ MPa, $\varepsilon_{\max} = 0.01432$, $\sigma_{\min} = -999$ MPa, $\varepsilon_{\min} = -0.00967$

13.32 $\sigma_{\max} = 214.314$ MPa, $\varepsilon_{\max} = 0.00422$, $\sigma_{\min} = -115.446$ MPa, $\varepsilon_{\min} = -0.00116$

13.35 $\sigma_{\min} = -540$ MPa, $\varepsilon_{\min} = -0.00610$, $\sigma_{\max} = 280$ MPa, $\varepsilon_{\max} = -0.001673$

13.38 (a) Typical values: (1) $\sigma_a = 500$ MPa, $\varepsilon_a = 0.00242$, $P_a = 5.69$ kN; (2) $\sigma_a = 1000$ MPa,
$\varepsilon_a = 0.01987$, $M_a = 23.1$ kN

13.39 $\sigma_{\max} = 769$ MPa, $\varepsilon_{\max} = 0.00659$, $\sigma_{\min} = -233$ MPa, $\varepsilon_{\min} = 0.001531$

13.40 $\sigma_{A,B,C,D} = 1072, -588, 411, -734$ MPa;
$\varepsilon_{A,B,C,D} = 0.01793, 0.00217, 0.01072, -0.000989$

13.43 $\sigma_{A,B,C,D,E,F} = 585, -500, 509, -420, 345, -541$ MPa;
$\varepsilon_{A,B,C,D,E,F} = 0.01112, -0.001438, 0.00681, 0.000877, 0.00485, -0.00526$

CHAPTER 14

Prob.	σ'_f, MPa	b	ε'_f	c
14.4	939	−0.0916	0.272	−0.449
14.6	3149	−0.1014	0.251	−0.891

14.8 Shaft: $m_s = 0.77$, $m_d = 0.817$, $\sigma'_{fd} = 775$ MPa, $b_s = -0.1100$, $\varepsilon'_{fd} = 0.213$, $c = -0.445$

Prob.	N_f, cycles			
	(a) Morrow	(b) mod Mor	(c) SWT	(d) Walker
14.11	41 990	42 170	30 595	27 931
14.12	86 920	86 310	138 308	155 247
14.14	24 562	17 676	83 556	160 838

14.18 $N_f = 41,207$ cycles by Morrow, or 21,729 by SWT

14.20 For modified Morrow approach, $N_f = 50,670$ cycles and for Walker approach, $N_f = 73,918$ cycles

14.24 For $\sigma_a = 1379$, $\sigma_m = -345$ MPa: **(a)** $\varepsilon_a = 0.00676$, $N_{mi}^* = 1345$ cycles; **(b)** $\sigma_{max}\varepsilon_a = 6.99$ MPa

14.25 **(a)** For $\sigma_a = 517$, $\sigma_m = 414$ MPa: $\varepsilon_a = 0.00264$, $N_w^* = 210,400$ cycles

14.26 For $N_f = 10,000$ cycles: **(a)** $\gamma_a = 0.00827$, **(b)** $\gamma_a = 0.01376$

14.28 $\varepsilon_{1a} = \dfrac{1 - 2\nu\beta}{1 - \beta} \dfrac{\sigma_f'}{E} (2N_f)^b + \varepsilon_f' (2N_f)^c$

14.30 $N_f = 904$ cycles by Morrow (not recommended), or 878 by SWT

14.33 $N_f = 1,344,000$ cycles by Morrow, or 2,089,000 by SWT

14.34 $N_f = 34,280$ cycles by Morrow, or 32,880 by SWT

14.35 For $S_{max} = S_a = 110$ MPa: $\varepsilon_{ca} = 0.00640$, $N_f = 5030$ cycles

14.37 **(b)** For $\sigma_a = 850$ MPa: $\varepsilon_a = 0.00751$, $P_a = 13.09$ kN, $N_f = 1113$ cycles

14.39 **(a)** $B_f = 95,570$ reps by Morrow, or 3236 by SWT; **(b)** $B_f = 4670$ reps by Morrow, or 668 by SWT

14.41 $B_f = 36.5$ reps by Morrow (not recommended), or 43.4 by SWT

14.42 $B_f = 564$ reps by Morrow (not recommended), or 450 by SWT

14.44 $B_f = 402$ reps by Morrow, or 555 by SWT

14.47 $B_f = 303$ reps by Morrow, or 347 by SWT;   **14.49** $B_f = 118.5$ reps by SWT

14.50 **(a)** $B_f = 10.24$ reps by SWT, **(b)** $B_{if} = 1.76$ reps for crack growth, 12.0 total

14.52 $M_a = 1.399$ kN·m by Morrow

14.53 By Morrow: **(a)** $N_f = 245,400$ cycles, **(b)** $N_f = 9,417,000$ cycles, **(b)** using monotonic yield to A: $N_f = 6,422,000$ cycles

CHAPTER 15

15.1 **(b)** $B = 1.596 \times 10^{-5} \dfrac{1/\text{min}}{\text{MPa}^m}$, $m = 2.14$

15.6 $\dot{\varepsilon} = B\sigma^m$; for $T = 900, 1200, 1450$ K: $B = 6.74 \times 10^{-24}, 2.43 \times 10^{-19}$, $1.112 \times 10^{-16} \dfrac{1/\text{s}}{\text{MPa}^m}$

15.8 **(a)** $\varepsilon = 0.00297$, **(b)** $\sigma = 37.9$ MPa, **(c)** $T = 931$ K

15.11 $A_3 = 2640 \dfrac{\text{K/s}}{\text{MPa}^m}$, $m = 1.495$, $Q = 39,600$ J/mol

15.13 (a) $\dot{\varepsilon} = 5.8 \times 10^{-3}$ 1/s, (b) $\dot{\varepsilon} = 5.8 \times 10^{-9}$ 1/s, (c) Mar-M200, $d = 1.0$ mm

15.15 (a) $\hat{T} = 832.8°C$, (b) $X_t = 1.52$;   **15.17** (a) $\hat{t} = 5.45$ hours, (b) $X_\sigma = 2.704$

15.19 (a) $t_r = 3090$ h, (b) $X_\sigma = 1.09$

15.21 (a) $\hat{T} = 211°C$, (b) $X_t = 1.52$, (c) $\Delta T_f = 333$ k

15.23 (a) $t_r = 21,100$ h, (b) $X_\sigma = 1.379$, (c) $\Delta T_f = 25.0°C$

15.25 (a) $b_{0,1,2,3} = 128,210, -141,530, 64,375, -9,960$; (b) $a_{0,1,2,3} = 135.45, -216.1, 99.30, -15.424$

15.27 $Q = 84,490$ cal/mole, $a_{0,1,2,3} = -11.902, 3.962, -2.094, -0.15378$

15.28 (a) $C = 14.569$, $b_{0,1,2,3} = -38,400, 114,200, -62,300, 10,382$; (b) $Q = 107,640$ cal/mole, $a_{0,1,2,3} = -40.12, 47.92, -25.49, 3.989$

15.30 (a) $\sigma = 7.3$ MPa, (b) $\gamma = 0.66$ mm, (c) $\gamma = 12.67$ mm

15.32 (a) $\sigma_c = 138.14$ MPa, (b) $\varepsilon_c = 0.075$, (c) $t_f = 263$ MPa

15.34 $D = 8.27 \times 10^{-5} \dfrac{1}{\text{MPa}^\delta \text{s}^\phi}$, $\delta = 1.742$, $\phi = 0.206$

15.36 $\sigma = \dfrac{\sigma_i}{\left(E D_3 t^\phi (\delta - 1)\sigma_i^{\delta-1} + 1 \right)^{1/(\delta-1)}}$, $\sigma_i = E\varepsilon'$

15.37 (a) $t_{0.5} = 652$ h, (b) $d = 119$ μm, (c) $T = 467°C$;   **15.39** (b) For $t = 5.0$ h: $\sigma = 22.3$ MPa

15.41 (a) $\dot{\varepsilon} = 5.54 \times 10^{-9}$ 1/s, (b) $\Delta d = 3.59$ mm, using $\sigma_z = -p/2$

15.43 $\gamma = \dfrac{\tau}{G} + 3^{(\delta+1)/2} D_3 \tau^\delta t^\phi$

15.45 (a) $\bar{\dot{\varepsilon}} = 8.88 \times 10^{-11}$ 1/s, (b) $100\,\Delta d/d = 1.912\%$, $100\,\Delta L/L = 0.819\%$, using $\sigma_z = -p/2$

15.46 (a) $\sigma = 5.00$ MPa, (b) $v_e = 0.2085$ mm, (c) $v = 0.712$ mm

15.49 (a) For $R = 70$ mm: $\sigma_r = 2.93$, $\sigma_t = 7.68$ MPa; (b) $\Delta r_1 = 3.01$ μm/day, 1.101 mm/year; (c) $\Delta r_2 = 2.95$ μm/day, 1.076 mm/year

15.51 (a) $\gamma_c = 3^{(m+1)/2} B t \left(\dfrac{T(1 + 3m)}{2\pi m c^3} \right)^m$, (b) $\gamma_c = 3^{(\delta+1)/2} D_3 t^\phi \left(\dfrac{T(1 + 3\delta)}{2\pi \delta c^3} \right)^\delta$

15.53 (a) $\varepsilon_c = 0.00740$, (b) $\varepsilon_c = 0.01366$;   **15.55** (a) $b = c = 53.2$ mm, (b) $b = c = 53.6$ mm

15.58 (a) $\Delta U = \dfrac{2JLbc\sigma_{ca}^2}{3}$, (b) $Q_v^{-1} = \dfrac{JE}{\pi}$, (c) $\Delta U = \dfrac{2JLbc\sigma_{cLa}^2}{9}$

15.60 (a) $\Delta u = 4\sigma_o \left(\varepsilon_a - \dfrac{\sigma_o}{E} \right)$, (b) $\Delta U = \dfrac{4Lbc\sigma_o}{\varepsilon_{ca}} \left(\varepsilon_{ca} - \dfrac{\sigma_o}{E} \right)^2$

15.61 $\Delta U = \dfrac{8\pi L c^2 \tau_{ca}^{1+1/n'}}{(H_\tau')^{1/n'}} \left(\dfrac{1 - n'}{1 + n'} \right) \left(\dfrac{\frac{n'}{3n'+1} + \frac{\beta}{2} + \frac{\beta^2}{3+n'}}{(1 + \beta)^2} \right)$, $\beta = \dfrac{\gamma_{pca}}{\tau_{ca}/G}$

Bibliography

[Andrade 10]	E. M. da C. ANDRADE. 1910. "On the Viscous Flow in Metals and Allied Phenomena," *Proc. Royal Soc., Series A*, London, vol. 84, pp. 1–12.
[Andrade 14]	E. M. da C. ANDRADE. 1914. "The Flow in Metals under Large Constant Stresses," *Proc. Royal Soc., Series A*, London, vol. 90, pp. 329–342.
[Antunes 78]	V. T. A. ANTUNES and P. HANCOCK. 1978. "Strainrange Partitioning of MAR-M002 over the Temperature Range 750°C–1040°C," *Characterization of Low Cycle High Temperature Fatigue by the Strainrange Partitioning Method*, AGARD-CP-243, North Atlantic Treaty Organization, Advisory Group for Aerospace Research and Development, Neuilly-sur-Seine, France, pp. 5-1 to 5-9.
[Arthur 10]	K. M. ARTHUR, A. C. MARIN, and K. XIAO. 2010. "Time-Dependent Behavior – Creep," Project report for a graduate course on Mechanics of Deformation and Fracture, Virginia Tech, Blacksburg, VA.
[Ashby 77]	M. F. ASHBY. 1977. "Progress in the Development of Fracture-Mechanism Maps," D. M. R. Taplin, ed., *Fracture 1977: Proc. of the 4th Int. Conf. on Fracture*, Univ. of Waterloo Press, Waterloo, Ontario, Canada, vol. 1, pp. 1–14.
[Ashby 06]	M. F. ASHBY and D. R. H. JONES. 2006. *Engineering Materials 2: An Introduction to Microstructures, Processing and Design*, 3rd ed., Butterworth-Heinemann (Elsevier) Oxford, UK.
[ASM 87]	ASM. 1987. *Engineered Materials Handbook, Vol. 1: Composites*, ASM International, Materials Park, OH.
[ASM 88]	ASM. 1988. *Engineered Materials Handbook, Vol. 2: Engineering Plastics*, ASM International, Materials Park, OH.
[ASTM 97]	ASTM. 1997. *Annual Book of ASTM Standards*, Am. Soc. for Testing and Materials, West Conshohocken, PA.
[AWS 96]	AWS. 1996. *Structural Welding Code: Steel*, 15th ed., ANSI/AWS D1.1-96, American Welding Society, Miami, FL.
[Barsom 71]	J. M. BARSOM. 1971. "Fatigue-Crack Propagation in Steels of Various Yield Strengths," *Jnl. of Engineering for Industry, Trans. ASME, Series B*, vol. 93, no. 4, Nov. 1971, pp. 1190–1196.
[Barsom 75]	J. M. BARSOM. 1975. "Development of the AASHTO Fracture-Toughness Requirements for Bridge Steels," *Engineering Fracture Mechanics*, vol. 7, no. 3, Sept. 1975, pp. 605–618.
[Barsom 87]	J. M. BARSOM and S. T. ROLFE. 1987. *Fracture and Fatigue Control in Structures*, 2d ed., Prentice-Hall, Englewood Cliffs, NJ.

[Bates 69]   R. C. BATES and W. G. CLARK, JR. 1969. "Fractography and Fracture Mechanics," *Trans. of the Am. Soc. for Metals*, vol. 62, pp. 380–389.

[Baumel 90]   A. BAUMEL and T. SEEGER. 1990. *Materials Data for Cyclic Loading, Supplement 1.* Elsevier Science Pubs., Amsterdam.

[Beardmore 75]   P. BEARDMORE and S. RABINOWITZ. 1975. "Fatigue Deformation of Polymers," *Treatise on Materials Science and Technology, Vol. 6: Plastic Deformation of Materials*, R. J. Arsenault, ed., Academic Press, New York, pp. 267–331.

[Berns 91]   H. D. BERNS. 1991. *Minutes of the April 1991 Meeting of the Task Group on Composite Materials Fatigue*, Fatigue Design and Evaluation Committee, Society of Automotive Engineering, Warrendale, PA.

[Boswell 59]   C. C. BOSWELL, JR., and R. A. WAGNER. 1959. "Fatigue in Rotary-Wing Aircraft," *Metal Fatigue*, G. Sines and J. L. Waisman, eds., McGraw-Hill, New York, pp. 355–375.

[Boyer 85]   H. E. BOYER and T. L. GALL, eds. 1985. *Metals Handbook: Desk Edition*, ASM International, Materials Park, OH.

[Bridgman 44]   P. W. BRIDGMAN. 1944. "The Stress Distribution at the Neck of a Tension Specimen," *Trans. of ASM International*, vol. 32, pp. 553–574.

[Bridgman 52]   P. W. BRIDGMAN. 1952. *Studies in Large Plastic Flow and Fracture*, McGraw-Hill, New York.

[Brockenbrough 81] R. L. BROCKENBROUGH and B. G. JOHNSTON. 1981. *USS Steel Design Manual*, ADUSS 27-3400-04, United States Steel Corp., Monroeville, PA.

[Broek 86]   D. BROEK. 1986. *Elementary Engineering Fracture Mechanics*, 4th ed., Kluwer Academic Pubs., Dordrecht, The Netherlands.

[Brose 74]   W. R. BROSE, N. E. DOWLING, and J. MORROW. 1974. "Effect of Periodic Large Strain Cycles on the Fatigue Behavior of Steels," Paper No. 740221, Society of Automotive Engineers, Automotive Engineering Congress, Detroit, MI, Feb. 1974.

[Budinski 96]   K. G. BUDINSKI. 1996. *Engineering Materials: Properties and Selection*, 5th ed., Prentice Hall, Upper Saddle River, NJ.

[Bush 74]   S. H. BUSH. 1974. "Structural Materials for Nuclear Power Plants," *Jnl. of Testing and Evaluation*, ASTM, vol. 2, no. 6, Nov. 1974, pp. 435–462.

[Buxbaum 73]   O. BUXBAUM. 1973. "Methods of Stress Measurement Analysis for Fatigue Life Evaluation," *Fatigue Life Prediction for Aircraft Structures and Materials*, AGARD-LS-62, North Atlantic Treaty Organization, Advisory Group for Aerospace Research and Development, Neuilly-sur-Seine, France, pp. 2-1 to 2-19.

[Campbell 62]   D. CAMPBELL-ALLEN. 1962. "Strength of Concrete Under Combined Stresses," *Constructional Review*, vol. 35, no. 4, pp. 29–37.

[Campbell 82]   J. E. CAMPBELL, W. W. GERBERICH, and J. H. UNDERWOOD, eds. 1982. *Application of Fracture Mechanics for Selection of Metallic Structural Materials*, ASM International, Materials Park, OH.

[Carlson 59]   R. G. CARLSON. 1959. *Fatigue Studies of Inconel*, BMI-1335, UC-25 Metallurgy and Ceramics, Battelle Memorial Institute, Columbus, OH, June 26, 1959.

[Chang 78]   J. B. CHANG et al. 1978. "Improved Methods for Predicting Spectrum Loading Effects: Phase 1 Report, Vol. 1," AFFDL-TR-79-3036, Air Force Flight Dynamics Laboratory, Wright-Patterson AFB, OH.

[Chinn 65]   J. CHINN and R. M. ZIMMERMAN. 1965. "Behavior of Plain Concrete Under Various High Triaxial Compression Loading Conditions," WL TR 64-163, Air Force Weapons Laboratory, Kirtland AFB, NM.

[Chu 70]   S. C. CHU and O. M. SIDEBOTTOM. 1970. "Creep of Metal Torsion-Tension Members Subjected to Nonproportionate Load Changes," *Experimental Mechanics*, June 1970.

[Clark 70]   W. G. CLARK, JR., and E. T. WESSEL. 1970. "Application of Fracture Mechanics Technology to Medium Strength Steels," *Review of Developments in Plane Strain Fracture Toughness Testing*, W. F. Brown, Jr., ed., ASTM STP 463, Am. Soc. for Testing and Materials, West Conshohocken, PA, pp. 160–190.

[Clark 71]   W. G. CLARK, JR. 1971. "Fracture Mechanics in Fatigue," *Experimental Mechanics*, vol. 11, no. 9, Sept. 1971, pp. 421–428.

[Clark 76]   W. G. CLARK, JR., and J. D. LANDES. 1976. "An Evaluation of Rising Load K_{Iscc} Testing," *Stress Corrosion—New Approaches*, ASTM STP 610, Am. Soc. for Testing and Materials, West Conshohocken, PA, pp. 108–127.

[Coffin 50] L. F. COFFIN. 1950. "The Flow and Fracture of a Brittle Material," *Jnl. of Applied Mechanics*, vol. 17 (*Trans. ASME*, vol. 72), Sept. 1950, pp. 233–248.

[Collins 93] J. A. COLLINS. 1993. *Failure of Materials in Mechanical Design*, 2d ed., John Wiley, New York.

[Conle 84]   F. A. CONLE, R. W. LANDGRAF, and F. D. RICHARDS. 1984. *Materials Data Book: Monotonic and Cyclic Properties of Engineering Materials*, Ford Motor Co., Scientific Research Staff, Dearborn, MI.

[Conway 69] J. B. CONWAY. 1969. *Stress-Rupture Parameters: Origin, Calculation, and Use*, Gordon and Breach, New York.

[Coors 89]   COORS. 1989. *Material Properties Standard 990*, Coors Ceramic Co., Golden, CO. (Folding chart of data tables.)

[Cottell 56] G. A. COTTELL. 1956. "Lessons to be Learnt from Failures in Service," *Proc. of the Int. Conf. on Fatigue of Metals*, London, Sept. 1956, and New York, Nov. 1956, The Institution of Mechanical Engineers, London, pp. 563–569.

[Creyke 82] W. E. C. CREYKE, I. E. J. SAINSBURY, and R. MORRELL. 1982. *Design with Non-Ductile Materials*, Applied Science, London.

[Crooker 75] T. W. CROOKER, D. F. HASSON, and G. R. YODER. 1975. "A Fracture Mechanics and Fractographic Study of Fatigue Crack Propagation Resistance in 17-4 PH Stainless Steels," NRL Report 7910, Naval Research Laboratory, Washington, DC.

[Dauskardt 90] R. H. DAUSKARDT, D. B. MARSHALL, and R. O. RITCHIE. 1990. "Cyclic Fatigue Crack Propagation in Magnesia-Partially-Stabilized Zirconia," *Jnl. of the Am. Ceramic Society*, vol. 73, no. 4, pp. 893–903.

[Davis 37]   R. E. DAVIS, H. E. DAVIS, and E. H. BROWN. 1937. "Plastic Flow and Volume Changes in Concrete," *Proc. of the Am. Soc. for Testing and Materials*, vol. 37, part II, pp. 317–331.

[Davis 43]   E. A. DAVIS. 1943. "Increase of Stress with Permanent Strain and Stress–Strain Relations in the Plastic State for Copper under Combined Stresses," *Jnl. of Applied Mechanics, Trans. ASME*, vol. 65, Dec. 1943, pp. A187–A196.

[Davis 45]   E. A. DAVIS. 1945. "Yielding and Fracture of Medium-Carbon Steels under Combined Stresses," *Jnl. Applied Mechanics, Trans. ASME*, vol. 67, Mar. 1945, pp. A13–A24.

[Davis 98]   J. R. DAVIS, ed. 1998. *Metals Handbook: Desk Edition*, 2d ed., ASM International, Materials Park, OH.

[Dennis 86] K. R. DENNIS. 1986. "Fatigue Crack Growth of Gun Tube Steel under Spectrum Loading," MS Thesis, Engineering Science and Mechanics Dept., Virginia Polytechnic Institute and State University, Blacksburg, VA, May 1986.

[Douglass 62]   R. W. DOUGLASS and R. I. JAFFE. 1962. "Elevated-Temperature Properties of Rhodium, Iridium, and Ruthenium," *Proc. of the Am. Soc. for Testing and Materials*, vol. 62, pp. 627–637.

[Dowling 72]   N. E. DOWLING. 1972. "Fatigue Failure Predictions for Complicated Stress–Strain Histories," *Jnl. of Materials*, ASTM, vol. 7, no. 1, Mar. 1972, pp. 71–87.

[Dowling 73]   N. E. DOWLING. 1973. "Fatigue Life and Inelastic Strain Response under Complex Histories for an Alloy Steel," *Journal of Testing and Evaluation*, ASTM, vol. 1, no. 4, Jul. 1973, pp. 271–287.

[Dowling 77]   N. E. DOWLING. 1977. "Fatigue-Crack Growth Rate Testing at High Stress Intensities," *Flaw Growth and Fracture*, ASTM STP 631, Am. Soc. for Testing and Materials, West Conshohocken, PA, pp. 139–158.

[Dowling 78]   N. E. DOWLING. 1978. "Stress-Strain Analysis of Cyclic Plastic Bending and Torsion," *Jnl. of Engineering Materials and Technology*, ASME, vol. 100, Apr. 1978, pp. 157–163.

[Dowling 79a]   N. E. DOWLING. 1979. "Notched Member Fatigue Life Predictions Combining Crack Initiation and Propagation," *Fatigue of Engineering Materials and Structures*, vol. 2, no. 2, pp. 129–138.

[Dowling 79b]   N. E. DOWLING and W. K. WILSON. 1979. "Analysis of Notch Strain for Cyclic Loading," *Fifth Int. Conf. on Structural Mechanics in Reactor Technology*, vol. L, Paper L13/4, North-Holland Pub. Co., Amsterdam.

[Dowling 79c]   N. E. DOWLING and H. WALKER. 1979. "Fatigue Crack Growth Rate Testing of Two Structural Steels," Paper No. 790459, Society of Automotive Engineers, SAE Congress and Exposition, Detroit, MI, Feb. 1979.

[Dowling 82]   N. E. DOWLING. 1982. "Fatigue Failure Predictions for Complex Load Versus Time Histories," Section 7.4 of *Pressure Vessels and Piping: Design Technology—1982—A Decade of Progress*, S. Y. Zamrik and D. Dietrich, eds., Book No. G00213, Am. Soc. of Mechanical Engineers, New York. Also pub. in *Journal of Engineering Materials and Technology*, ASME, vol. 105, Jul. 1983, pp. 206–214, with Erratum, Oct. 1983, p. 321.

[Dowling 83]   N. E. DOWLING. 1983. "Growth of Short Fatigue Cracks in an Alloy Steel," Paper No. 83-PVP-94, ASME 4th National Congress on Pressure Vessel and Piping Technology, June 19–24, 1983, Portland, OR.

[Dowling 87]   N. E. DOWLING. 1987. "A Review of Fatigue Life Prediction Methods," *Durability by Design*, SAE Pub. No. SP-730, Soc. of Automotive Engineers, Warrendale, PA, Paper No. 871966.

[Dowling 89]   N. E. DOWLING and A. K. KHOSROVANEH. 1989. "Simplified Analysis of Helicopter Fatigue Loading Spectra," J. M. Potter and R. T. Watanabe, eds., *Development of Fatigue Loading Spectra*, ASTM STP 1006, Am. Soc. for Testing and Materials, West Conshohocken, PA, pp. 150–171.

[Endo 69]   T. ENDO and J. MORROW. 1969. "Cyclic Stress-Strain and Fatigue Behavior of Representative Aircraft Metals," *Journal of Materials*, ASTM, vol. 4, no. 1, Mar. 1969, pp. 159–175.

[EVC 89]   EVC. 1989. "Engineering Design with Unplasticized Polyvinyl Chloride," European Vinyls Corp. (UK) Ltd., Cheshire, UK.

[Farag 89]   M. M. FARAG. 1989. *Selection of Materials and Manufacturing Processes for Engineering Design*, Prentice Hall International (UK) Ltd., Hertfordshire, UK.

[Felbeck 96]   D. K. FELBECK and A. G. ATKINS. 1996. *Strength and Fracture of Engineering Solids*, 2d ed., Prentice Hall, Upper Saddle River, NJ.

[Floreen 79]	S. FLOREEN and R. H. KANE. 1979. "Effects of Environment on High-Temperature Fatigue Crack Growth in a Superalloy," *Metallurgical Transactions*, vol. 10A, Nov. 1979, pp. 1745–1751.
[Forrest 62]	P. G. FORREST. 1962. *Fatigue of Metals*, Pergamon Press, Oxford, UK, and Addison-Wesley, Reading, MA.
[French 50]	R. S. FRENCH and W. R. HIBBARD. 1950. "Effect of Solute Atoms on Tensile Deformation of Copper," *Jnl. of Metals; Trans. AIME*, vol. 188, pp. 53–58.
[French 56]	H. J. FRENCH. 1956. "Some Aspects of Hardenable Alloy Steels," *Jnl. of Metals; Trans. AIME*, vol. 206, pp. 770–782.
[Frost 59]	N. E. FROST. 1959. "A Relation Between the Critical Alternating Propagation Stress and Crack Length for Mild Steel," *Proc. of the Institution of Mechanical Engineers*, London, vol. 173, no. 35, pp. 811–827.
[Frost 82]	H. J. FROST and M. F. ASHBY. 1982. *Deformation Mechanism Maps: The Plasticity and Creep of Metals and Ceramics*, Pergamon Press, Oxford, UK.
[Gauthier 95]	M. M. GAUTHIER, vol. chair. 1995. *Engineered Materials Handbook, Desk Edition*, ASM International, Materials Park, OH.
[Geil 65]	P. H. GEIL. 1965. "Polymer Morphology," *Chemical and Engineering News*, vol. 43, no. 33, Aug. 16, 1965, pp. 72–84.
[Gerberich 79]	W. W. GERBERICH and N. R. MOODY. 1979. "A Review of Fatigue Fracture Topology Effects on Threshold and Growth Mechanisms," *Fatigue Mechanisms*, J. T. Fong, ed., ASTM STP 675, Am. Soc. for Testing and Materials, West Conshohocken, PA, pp. 292–341.
[Gohn 64]	G. R. GOHN. 1964. "Fatigue in Electronic and Magnetic Materials," *Fatigue—An Interdisciplinary Approach*, J. J. Burke et al., eds., *Proc. of the 10th Sagamore Army Materials Research Conf.*, Syracuse University Press, Syracuse, NY, pp. 287–315.
[Goldhoff 59a]	R. M. GOLDHOFF. 1959. "Which Method for Extrapolating Stress-Rupture Data?" *Materials in Design Engineering*, vol. 49, no. 4, pp. 93–97.
[Goldhoff 59b]	R. M. GOLDHOFF. 1959. "Comparison of Parameter Methods for Extrapolating High Temperature Data," *Trans. of the Am. Soc. of Mechanical Engineers*, vol. 81, pp. 629–644.
[Grant 50]	N. J. GRANT and A. G. BUCKLIN. 1950. "On the Extrapolation of Short-Time Stress-Rupture Data," *Trans. of the Am. Soc. for Metals*, vol. 42, pp. 720–751.
[Grassi 49]	R. C. GRASSI and I. CORNET. 1949. "Fracture of Gray Cast Iron Tubes under Biaxial Stresses," *Jnl. of Applied Mechanics*, vol. 16 (*Trans. ASME*, vol. 71), June 1949, pp. 178–182.
[Griggs 36]	D. T. GRIGGS. 1936. "Deformation of Rocks Under High Confining Pressures," *Jnl. of Geology*, vol. 44, pp. 541–577.
[Grover 51a]	H. J. GROVER, S. M. BISHOP, and L. R. JACKSON. 1951. "Fatigue Strengths of Aircraft Materials: Axial-Load Fatigue Tests on Unnotched Sheet Specimens of 24S-T3 and 75S-T6 Aluminum Alloys and of SAE 4130 Steel," NACA TN 2324, National Advisory Committee for Aeronautics, Washington, DC.
[Grover 51b]	H. J. GROVER, S. M. BISHOP, and L. R. JACKSON. 1951. "Fatigue Strengths of Aircraft Materials: Axial-Load Fatigue Tests on Notched Sheet Specimens of 24S-T3 and 75S-T6 Aluminum Alloys and of SAE 4130 Steel with Stress-Concentration Factors of 2.0 and 4.0," NACA TN 2389, National Advisory Committee for Aeronautics, Washington, DC.
[Grover 66]	H. J. GROVER. 1966. *Fatigue of Aircraft Structures*, NAVAIR 01-1A-13, Naval Air Systems Command, Department of the Navy, Washington, DC.

[Hartmann 59]   E. C. HARTMANN and F. M. HOWELL. 1959. "Laboratory Fatigue Testing of Materials," *Metal Fatigue*, G. Sines and J. L. Waisman, eds., McGraw-Hill, New York, pp. 89–111.

[Haugen 80]   E. B. HAUGEN. 1980. *Probabilistic Mechanical Design*, John Wiley, New York.

[Hayden 65]   H. W. HAYDEN, W. G. MOFFATT, and J. WULFF. 1965. *The Structure and Properties of Materials, Vol. III: Mechanical Behavior*, John Wiley, New York.

[Hertzberg 75]   R. W. HERTZBERG, J. A. MANSON, and M. SKIBO. 1975. "Frequency Sensitivity of Fatigue Processes in Polymeric Solids," *Polymer Engineering and Science*, vol. 15, no. 4, Apr. 1975, pp. 252–260.

[Heywood 62]   R. B. HEYWOOD. 1962. *Designing Against Fatigue of Metals*, Reinhold, New York.

[Herring 89]   S. D. HERRING. 1989. *From the Titanic to the Challenger: An Annotated Bibliography on Technological Failures of the Twentieth Century*, Garland Publishing, Inc., New York.

[Hilsdorf 73]   H. K. HILSDORF, W. R. LORMAN, and G. E. MONFORE. 1973. "Triaxial Testing of Nonreinforced Concrete Specimens," *Journal of Testing and Evaluation*, vol. 1, no. 4, pp. 330–335.

[Hirthe 63]   W. M. HIRTHE and J. O. BRITTAIN. 1963. "High Temperature Steady-State Creep in Rutile," *Jnl. of the Am. Ceramic Soc.*, vol. 46, no. 9, pp. 411–417.

[Hobbs 71]   D. W. HOBBS. 1971. "Strength of Concrete Under Combined Stress," *Cement and Concrete Research*, vol. 1, no. 1, pp. 41–56.

[Hock 26]   L. HOCK and S. BOSTROM. 1926. "Beitrage zur Thermodynamic des Joule-Effektes am Rohkautschuk," *Kautschuk*, June 1926, pp. 130–136.

[Howell 55]   F. M. HOWELL and J. L. MILLER. 1955. "Axial Stress Fatigue Strengths of Several Structural Aluminum Alloys," *Proc. of the Am. Soc. for Testing and Materials*, vol. 55, pp. 955–968.

[Hudson 69]   C. M. HUDSON. 1969. "Effect of Stress Ratio on Fatigue Crack Growth in 7075-T6 and 2024-T3 Aluminum Alloy Specimens," NASA TN D-5390, National Aeronautics and Space Administration, Langley Research Center, Hampton, VA.

[Hunter 54]   M. S. HUNTER and W. G. FRICKE, JR. 1954. "Metallographic Aspects of Fatigue Behavior of Aluminum," *Proc. of the Am. Soc. for Testing and Materials*, vol. 54, pp. 717–732.

[Hunter 56]   M. S. HUNTER and W. G. FRICKE, JR. 1956. "Fatigue Crack Propagation in Aluminum Alloys," *Proc. of the Am. Soc. for Testing and Materials*, vol. 56, pp. 1038–1046.

[Illg 56]   W. ILLG. 1956. "Fatigue Tests on Notched and Unnotched Sheet Specimens of 2024-T3 and 7075-T6 Aluminum Alloys and of SAE 4130 Steel with Special Consideration of the Life Range from 2 to 10,000 Cycles," NACA TN 3866, National Advisory Committee for Aeronautics, Washington, DC.

[Imhof 73]   E. J. IMHOF and J. M. BARSOM. 1973. "Fatigue and Corrosion-Fatigue Crack Growth of 4340 Steel at Various Yield Strengths," *Progress in Flaw Growth and Fracture Toughness Testing*, ASTM STP 536, Am. Soc. for Testing and Materials, West Conshohocken, PA, pp. 182–205.

[Jaeger 69]   J. C. JAEGER. 1969. *Elasticity, Fracture, and Flow with Engineering and Geological Applications*, 3d ed., Methuen, London.

[Jenney 01]   C. L. JENNEY and A. O'BRIEN, eds. 2001. *Welding Handbook, 9th Edition, Vol. 1, Welding Science and Technology*, American Welding Society, Miami, FL.

[Juvinall 67]   R. C. JUVINALL. 1967. *Stress, Strain, and Strength*, McGraw-Hill, New York.

[Kampe 94]   S. L. KAMPE et al. 1994. "Room-Temperature Strength and Deformation of TiB_2-Reinforced Near-γ Titanium Aluminides," *Metallurgical and Materials Transactions A*, vol. 25A, pp. 2181–2197.

[Kaplan 95]   W. A. KAPLAN et al., eds. 1995. *Modern Plastics Encyclopedia*, Published annually by McGraw-Hill, New York.

[Karfakis 90]   M. G. KARFAKIS and M. AKRAM. 1990. "Rock Fracture Toughness in Zero Point of Charge Environment," E. Topuz and J. R. Lucas, eds., *Proc. of the 8th Annual Workshop, Generic Mineral Technology Center, Mine Systems Design and Ground Control*, pp. 35–47. Pub. by Dept. of Mining and Minerals Engineering, Virginia Tech, Blacksburg, VA. See also M. G. Karfakis and M. Akram, "Effects of Chemical Solutions on Rock Fracturing," *Int. Jnl. of Rock Mechanics and Mining Sciences and Geomechanics Abstracts*, Pergamon Press, vol. 30, no. 7, 1993, pp. 1253–1259.

[Karfakis 03]   M. G. KARFAKIS. 2003. Data courtesy of the Mining and Minerals Engineering Department, Virginia Tech, Blacksburg, VA.

[Kelly 86]   A. KELLY and N. H. MACMILLAN. 1986. *Strong Solids*, 3d ed., Clarendon Press, Oxford, UK.

[Kelly 94]   A. KELLY, ed. 1994. *Concise Encyclopedia of Composite Materials*, 2d ed., Pergamon Press, Oxford, UK.

[Keshavan 67]   S. KESHAVAN. 1967. "Some Studies on the Deformation and Fracture of Normalized Mild Steel Under Cyclic Conditions," PhD thesis, University of Waterloo, Waterloo, Ontario, Canada.

[Kim 81]   K. KIM and A. MUBEEN. 1981. "Relationship Between Differential Stress Intensity Factor and Crack Growth Rate in Cyclic Tension in Westerly Granite," *Fracture Mechanics Methods for Ceramics, Rocks, and Concrete*, ASTM STP 745, Am. Soc. for Testing and Materials, West Conshohocken, PA, pp. 157–168.

[Klesnil 80]   M. KLESNIL and P. LUKAS. 1980. *Fatigue of Materials*, Czechoslovak Academy of Sciences, Prague, and Elsevier Scientific, Amsterdam.

[Knott 79]   J. F. KNOTT. 1979. "An Introduction to Fracture Mechanics, Part III," *The Welder*, vol. 41, no. 202, pp. 6–9.

[Kuhn 52]   P. KUHN and H. F. HARDRATH. 1952. "An Engineering Method for Estimating Notch Size Effect in Fatigue Tests on Steel," NACA TN 2805, National Advisory Committee for Aeronautics, Washington, DC.

[Kuhn 62]   P. KUHN and I. E. FIGGE. 1962. "Unified Notch-Strength Analysis for Wrought Aluminum Alloys," NASA TN D-1259, National Aeronautics and Space Administration, Washington, DC.

[Kulak 72]   G. L. KULAK. 1972. "Statistical Aspects of Strength of Connections," *Safety and Reliability of Metal Structures*, Specialty Conference, Am. Soc. of Civil Engineers, New York.

[Landgraf 66]   R. W. LANDGRAF. 1966. "Effect of Mean Stress on the Fatigue Behavior of a Hard Steel," Report No. 662, Dept. of Theoretical and Applied Mechanics, University of Illinois, Urbana, IL.

[Landgraf 68]   R. W. LANDGRAF. 1968. "Cyclic Deformation and Fatigue Behavior of Hardened Steels," T & AM Report No. 320, Dept. of Theoretical and Applied Mechanics, University of Illinois, Urbana, IL.

[Landgraf 69]   R. W. LANDGRAF, J. MORROW, and T. ENDO. 1969. "Determination of the Cyclic Stress-Strain Curve," *Journal of Materials*, ASTM, vol. 4, no. 1, Mar. 1969, pp. 176–188.

[Landgraf 70]   R. W. LANDGRAF. 1970. "The Resistance of Metals to Cyclic Deformation," *Achievement of High Fatigue Resistance in Metals and Alloys*, ASTM STP 467, Am. Soc. for Testing and Materials, West Conshohocken, PA, pp. 3–36.

[Landgraf 80]   R. W. LANDGRAF and F. A. CONLE. 1980. "The Development and Use of Mechanical Properties in Industry," *Use of Computers in Managing Material Property*

Data, MPC-14, J. A. Graham, ed., Am. Soc. of Mechanical Engineers, ·New York, pp. 1–12.

[Landgraf 88]   R. W. LANDGRAF and R. A. CHERNENKOFF. 1988. "Residual Stress Effects on Fatigue of Surface Processed Steels," *Analytical and Experimental Methods for Residual Stress Effects in Fatigue*, ASTM STP 1004, R. L. Champoux et al., eds., Am. Soc. for Testing and Materials, West Conshohocken, PA, pp. 1–12.

[Larson 52]   F. R. LARSON and J. MILLER. 1952. "A Time-Temperature Relationship for Rupture and Creep Stresses," *Trans. of the Am. Soc. of Mechanical Engineers*, vol. 74, pp. 765–771.

[Lazan 52]   B. J. LAZAN and A. A. BLATHERWICK. 1952. "Fatigue Properties of Aluminum Alloys at Various Direct Stress Ratios: Part 1, Rolled Alloys," WADC TR 52-307, Part 1, Wright Air Development Center, Wright-Patterson AFB, OH.

[Lazan 68]   B. J. LAZAN. 1968. *Damping of Materials and Members in Structural Mechanics*, Pergamon Press, Oxford, UK.

[Leese 85]   G. E. LEESE and J. MORROW. 1985. "Low Cycle Fatigue Properties of a 1045 Steel in Torsion," *Multiaxial Fatigue*, K. J. Miller and M. W. Brown, eds., ASTM STP 853, Am. Soc. for Testing and Materials, West Conshohocken, PA, pp. 482–496.

[Lessells 40]   J. M. LESSELLS and C. W. MACGREGOR. 1940. "Combined Stress Experiments on a Nickel-Chrome-Molybdenum Steel," *Jnl. of the Franklin Institute*, vol. 230, Aug. 1940, pp. 163–181.

[Logsdon 76]   W. A. LOGSDON. 1976. "Elastic Plastic (J_{Ic}) Fracture Toughness Values: Their Experimental Determination and Comparison with Conventional Linear Elastic (K_{Ic}) Fracture Toughness Values for Five Materials," *Mechanics of Crack Growth*, ASTM STP 590, Am. Soc. for Testing and Materials, West Conshohocken, PA, pp. 43–60.

[Lubahn 61]   J. D. LUBAHN and R. P. FELGAR. 1961. *Plasticity and Creep of Metals*, John Wiley, New York.

[Luken 87]   R. C. LUKEN, JR. 1987. "Fracture Behavior of CPM 10V," MS thesis, Dept. of Materials Engineering, Virginia Polytechnic Institute and State University, Blacksburg, VA.

[Lyle 74]   A. K. LYLE. 1974. "Glass Composition Design and Development," *Handbook of Glass Manufacture*, vol. 1, F. V. Tooley, ed., Books for Industry, Inc., New York, pp. 3–17.

[MacGregor 52]   C. W. MACGREGOR and N. GROSSMAN. 1952. "Effects of Cyclic Loading on Mechanical Behavior of 24S-T4 and 75S-T6 Aluminum Alloys and SAE 4130 Steel," NACA TN 2812, National Advisory Committee for Aeronautics, Washington, DC.

[Madeyski 78]   A. MADEYSKI and L. ALBERTIN. 1978. "Fractographic Methods of Evaluation of the Cyclic Stress Amplitude in Fatigue Failure Analysis," *Fractography in Failure Analysis*, B. M. Strauss and W. H. Cullen, Jr., eds., ASTM STP 645, Am. Soc. for Testing and Materials, West Conshohocken, PA, pp. 73–83.

[Marandet 77]   B. MARANDET and G. SANZ. 1977. "Evaluation of the Toughness of Thick Medium-Strength Steels..." *Flaw Growth and Fracture*, ASTM STP 631, Am. Soc. for Testing and Materials, West Conshohocken, PA, pp. 72–95.

[Marin 40]   J. MARIN and R. L. STANLEY. 1940. "Failure of Aluminum Subjected to Combined Stresses," *Welding Journal; Welding Research Supplement*, Feb. 1940, pp. 74s–80s.

[Mattson 59]   R. L. MATTSON and J. G. ROBERTS. 1959. "Effect of Residual Stresses Induced by Strain Peening upon Fatigue Strength," G. M. Rassweiler and W. L. Grube, eds., *Internal Stresses and Fatigue in Metals*, Elsevier, Amsterdam, pp. 337–360.

[MILHDBK 94]   MILHDBK. 1994. *Military Handbook: Metallic Materials and Elements for Aerospace Vehicle Structures*, MIL-HDBK-5G, 2 vols., U.S. Dept. of Defense, MIL-HDBK-5 Coordination Activity, Wright-Patterson AFB, OH.

[Morrell 85]	R. MORRELL. 1985. *Handbook of Properties of Technical and Engineering Ceramics: Part 1, An Introduction for the Engineer and Designer; Part 2, Data Reviews*, Her Majesty's Stationery Office, London, 1985 and 1987.
[Munz 81]	D. MUNZ, G. HIMSOLT, and J. ESCHWEILER. 1981. "Effect of Stable Crack Growth on Fracture Toughness Determination for Hot-Pressed Silicon Nitride at Elevated Temperatures," *Fracture Mechanics for Ceramics, Rocks, and Concrete*, S. W. Freiman and E. R. Fuller, Jr., eds., ASTM STP 745, Am. Soc. for Testing and Materials, West Conshohocken, PA, pp. 69–84.
[Musikant 90]	S. MUSIKANT. 1990. *What Every Engineer Should Know About Ceramics*, Marcel Dekker, New York.
[Nadai 41]	A. NADAI and M. J. MANJOINE. 1941. "High-Speed Tension Tests at Elevated Temperatures," *Jnl. of Applied Mechanics, Trans. ASME*, vol. 8, no. 2, June 1941, pp. A-77 to A-91.
[Naghdi 58]	P. M. NAGHDI, F. ESSENBURG, and W. KOFF. 1958. "An Experimental Study of Initial and Subsequent Yield Surfaces in Plasticity," *Jnl. of Applied Mechanics*, ASME, vol. 25, June 1958, pp. 201–213.
[Naumann 59]	E. C. NAUMANN, H. F. HARDRATH, and D. E. GUTHRIE. 1959. "Axial Load Fatigue Tests of 2024-T3 and 7075-T6 Aluminum Alloy Sheet Specimens Under Constant and Variable Amplitude Loads," NASA TN D-212, National Aeronautics and Space Administration, Washington, DC.
[Naumann 62]	E. C. NAUMANN and R. L. SCHOTT. 1962. "Axial Load Fatigue Tests Using Loading Schedules Based on Maneuver Load Statistics," NASA TN D-1253, National Aeronautics and Space Administration, Washington, DC.
[Newman 86]	J. C. NEWMAN and I. S. RAJU. 1986. "Stress-Intensity Factor Equations for Cracks in Three-Dimensional Finite Bodies Subjected to Tension and Bending Loads," *Computational Methods in the Mechanics of Fracture*, S. N. Atluri, ed., Elsevier North Holland, New York.
[Nisitani 81]	H. NISITANI and K. TAKAO. 1981. "Significance of Initiation, Propagation, and Closure of Microcracks in High Cycle Fatigue of Ductile Metals," *Engineering Fracture Mechanics*, vol. 15, nos. 3–4, pp. 445–456.
[Nisitani 84]	H. NISITANI and N. NODA. 1984. "Stress Concentration of a Cylindrical Bar with a V-Shaped Circumferential Groove under Torsion, Tension, or Bending," *Engineering Fracture Mechanics*, vol. 20, nos. 5–6, pp. 743–766.
[Nisitani 85]	H. NISITANI and H. HYAKUTAKE. 1985. "Condition for Determining the Static Yield and Fracture of a Polycarbonate Plate Specimen with Notches," *Engineering Fracture Mechanics*, vol. 22, no. 3, pp. 359–368.
[Novak 69]	S. R. NOVAK and S. T. ROLFE. 1969. "Modified WOL Specimen for K_{Iscc} Environmental Testing," *Journal of Materials*, ASTM, vol. 4, no. 3, Sept. 1969, pp. 701–728.
[NTSB 89]	NTSB. 1989. "Aircraft Accident Report—Aloha Airlines Flight 243, Boeing 737-200, N73711, Near Maui, Hawaii, April 28, 1988," Report No. NTSB/AAR-89/03, National Transportation Safety Board, Washington, DC.
[Odeh 77]	R. E. ODEH et al. 1977. *Pocket Book of Statistical Tables*, Marcel Dekker, New York.
[Orange 67]	T. W. ORANGE. 1967. "Fracture Toughness of Wide 2014-T6 Aluminum Sheet at −320°F," NASA TN D-4017, National Aeronautics and Space Administration, Washington, DC.
[Orr 54]	R. L. ORR, O. D. SHERBY, and J. E. DORN. 1954. "Correlations of Rupture Data for Metals at Elevated Temperature," *Trans. of the Am. Soc. for Metals*, vol. 46, pp. 113–128.

[Paris 64]   P. C. PARIS. 1964. "The Fracture Mechanics Approach to Fatigue," *Fatigue—An Interdisciplinary Approach*, J. J. BURKE et al., eds., Proc. of the 10th Sagamore Army Materials Research Conf., Syracuse University Press, Syracuse, NY, pp. 107–127.

[Paris 72]   P. C. PARIS et al. 1972. "Extensive Study of Low Fatigue Crack Growth Rates in A533 and A508 Steels," *Stress Analysis and Growth of Cracks, Proceedings of the 1971 National Symposium on Fracture Mechanics, Part I*, ASTM STP 513, Am. Soc. for Testing and Materials, West Conshohocken, PA, pp. 141–176.

[PDL 91]   PDL. 1991. *The Effect of Creep and Other Time Related Factors on Plastics*, Plastics Design Library, Norwich, NY.

[Pearson 86] H. S. PEARSON and R. G. DOOMAN. 1986. "Fracture Analysis of Propane Tank Explosion," *Case Histories Involving Fatigue and Fracture Mechanics*, C. M. Hudson and T. P. Rich, eds., ASTM STP 918, Am. Soc. for Testing and Materials, West Conshohocken, PA, pp. 65–77.

[Peterson 59] R. E. PETERSON. 1959. "Analytic Approach to Stress Concentration Effect in Fatigue of Aircraft Materials," *Proc. of the Symp. on Fatigue of Aircraft Structures*, WADC TR-59-507, Wright Air Development Ctr., OH, pp. 273–299.

[Peterson 74] R. E. PETERSON. 1974. *Stress Concentration Factors*, John Wiley, New York.

[Placek 84]   R. J. PLACEK et al. 1984. "Determination of Torsional Fatigue Life of Large Turbine Generator Shafts," Report No. EL-3083, Project 1531-1, Electric Power Research Institute, Palo Alto, CA.

[Raghava 72] R. S. RAGHAVA. 1972. "Macroscopic Yielding Behavior of Polymeric Materials," PhD Dissertation, Mechanical Engineering Dept., The University of Michigan, Ann Arbor, MI.

[Rahka 86]   K. RAHKA. 1986. "Use of Material Characterization to Complement Fracture Mechanics in the Analysis of Two Pressure Vessels for Further Service in a Hydrogenating High-Temperature Process," *Case Histories Involving Fatigue and Fracture Mechanics*, C. M. Hudson and T. P. Rich, eds., ASTM STP 918, Am. Soc. for Testing and Materials, West Conshohocken, PA, pp. 3–30.

[Raju 86]   I. S. RAJU and J. C. NEWMAN, JR. 1986. "Stress-Intensity Factors for Circumferential Surface Cracks in Pipes and Rods Under Tension and Bending Loads," *Fracture Mechanics, Seventeenth Volume*, J. H. Underwood et al., eds., ASTM STP 905, American Society for Testing and Materials, West Conshohocken, PA.

[Randall 57]   P. N. RANDALL. 1957. "Constant-Stress Creep Rupture Tests of a Killed Carbon Steel," *Proc. of the Am. Soc. for Testing and Materials*, vol. 57, pp. 854–876.

[Raske 72]   D. T. RASKE. 1972. "Section and Notch Size Effects in Fatigue," PhD thesis, Dept. of Theoretical and Applied Mechanics, University of Illinois, Urbana, IL.

[Richards 61] C. W. RICHARDS. 1961. *Engineering Materials Science*, Wadsworth, Belmont, CA.

[Richards 70] F. D. RICHARDS and R. M. WETZEL. 1970. "Mechanical Testing of Materials Using an Analog Computer," Tech. Report No. SR 70-126, Scientific Research Staff, Ford Motor Co., Dearborn, MI, Sept. 1970. See also *Materials Research and Standards*, ASTM, vol. 11, no. 2, pp. 19–22, 51.

[Riddell 74]   M. N. RIDDELL. 1974. "A Guide to Better Testing of Plastics," *Plastics Engineering*, vol. 30, no. 4, Apr. 1974, pp. 71–78.

[Ritchie 77]   R. O. RITCHIE. 1977. "Near-Threshold Fatigue Crack Propagation in Ultra-High Strength Steel," *Jnl. of Engineering Materials and Technology*, ASME, vol. 99, Jul. 1977, pp. 195–204.

[Rusch 60]   H. RUSCH. 1960. "Researches Toward a General Flexural Theory for Structural Concrete," *Proc. of the Am. Concrete Institute*, vol. 57, pp. 1–26.

[Ruschau 78]   J. J. RUSCHAU. 1978. "Complete Fatigue Crack Growth Rate Curves for Aluminum Alloy 2124-T851 Including Typical Crack Growth Models," Report No. AFML-TR-78-155, Air Force Materials Laboratory, Wright-Patterson AFB, OH.

[SAE 89]   SAE. 1989. "Technical Report on Low Cycle Fatigue Properties of Wrought Materials," SAE J1099, Information Report, Soc. of Automotive Engineers, Warrendale, PA. See also L. E. Tucker, R. W. Landgraf, and W. R. Brose, "Proposed Technical Report on Fatigue Properties for the SAE Handbook," SAE Paper No. 740279, Automotive Engineering Congress, Detroit, MI, 1974.

[Sakai 00]   T. SAKAI, et al. 2000. "Experimental Reconfirmation of Characteristic *S-N* Property for High Carbon Chromium Bearing Steel in Wide Life Region in Rotating Bending," *Jnl. of the Soc. of Materials Science, Japan*, vol. 49, no. 7, pp. 779–785.

[Schijve 62]   J. SCHIJVE and D. BROEK. 1962. "Crack Propagation Tests Based on a Gust Spectrum With Variable Amplitude Loading," *Aircraft Engineering*, vol. 34, pp. 314–316.

[Schwartz 92]   M. M. SCHWARTZ. 1992. *Composite Materials Handbook*, 2d ed., McGraw-Hill, New York.

[Shah 95]   S. P. SHAH, S. E. SWARTZ, and C. OUYANG. 1995. *Fracture Mechanics of Concrete: Applications of Fracture Mechanics to Concrete, Rock, and Other Quasi-Brittle Materials*, John Wiley, New York.

[Sheffler 72]   K. D. SHEFFLER and G. S. DOBLE. 1972. "Influence of Creep Damage on the Low Cycle Thermal-Mechanical Fatigue Behavior of Two Tantalum-Base Alloys," Report No. NASA CR 121001, TRW ER-7592, National Aeronautics and Space Administration, Lewis Research Ctr., Cleveland, OH.

[Sherby 57]   O. D. SHERBY, J. L. LYTTON, and J. E. DORN. 1957. "Activation Energies for Creep of High-Purity Aluminum," *Acta Metallurgica*, vol. 5, pp. 219–227.

[Sims 78]   C. T. SIMS. 1978. "High-Temperature Alloys in High-Technology Systems," *High Temperature Alloys for Gas Turbines*, C. Coutsouradis et al., eds., Applied Science Pubs., London, pp. 13–65.

[Sinclair 52]   G. M. SINCLAIR and W. J. CRAIG. 1952. "Influence of Grain Size on Work Hardening and Fatigue Characteristics of Alpha Brass," *Trans. of the Am. Soc. for Metals*, vol. 44, pp. 929–948.

[Sinclair 53]   G. M. SINCLAIR and T. J. DOLAN. 1953. "Effect of Stress Amplitude on Statistical Variability in Fatigue Life of 75S-T6 Aluminum Alloy," *Trans. of the Am. Soc. of Mechanical Engineers*, Jul. 1953, pp. 867–872.

[Sines 59]   G. SINES. 1959. "Behavior of Metals under Complex Static and Alternating Stresses," *Metal Fatigue*, G. Sines and J. L. Waisman, eds., McGraw-Hill, New York, pp. 145–169.

[Sines 75]   G. SINES and M. ADAMS. 1975. "The Use of Brittle Materials as Compressive Structural Elements," Paper No. 75-DE-23, *Am. Soc. of Mechanical Engineers*.

[Smith 70]   K. N. SMITH, P. WATSON, and T. H. TOPPER. 1970. "A Stress-Strain Function for the Fatigue of Metals," *Journal of Materials*, ASTM, vol. 5, no. 4, pp. 767–778.

[Smith 82]   S. H. SMITH et al. 1982. "Fracture Tolerance Analysis of the Solid Rocket Booster Servo-Actuator for the Space Shuttle," P. R. Abelkis and C. M. Hudson, eds., *Design of Fatigue and Fracture Resistant Structures*, ASTM STP 761, Am. Soc. for Testing and Materials, West Conshohocken, PA, pp. 445–474.

[Socie 87]   D. SOCIE. 1987. "Multiaxial Fatigue Damage Models," *Jnl. of Engineering Materials and Technology*, ASME, vol. 109, Oct. 1987, pp. 293–298.

[Srawley 76]   J. E. SRAWLEY. 1976. "Wide Range Stress Intensity Factor Expressions for ASTM E399 Standard Fracture Toughness Specimens," *Int. Jnl. of Fracture Mechanics*, vol. 12, Jun. 1976, pp. 475–476.

[Stadnick 72]		S. J. STADNICK and J. MORROW. 1972. "Techniques for Smooth Specimen Simulation of the Fatigue Behavior of Notched Members," *Testing for Prediction of Material Performance in Structures and Components*, ASTM STP 515, Am. Soc. for Testing and Materials, West Conshohocken, PA, pp. 229–252.

[Steigerwald 70]		E. A. STEIGERWALD. 1970. "Crack Toughness Measurements of High-Strength Steels," *Review of Developments in Plane Strain Fracture Toughness Testing*, W. F. Brown, Jr., ed., ASTM STP 463, Am. Soc. for Testing and Materials, West Conshohocken, PA, pp. 102–123.

[Stonesifer 76]		F. R. STONESIFER. 1976. "Effects of Grain Size and Temperature on Sub-Critical Crack Growth in A533 Steel," NRL Memorandum Report 3400, Naval Research Laboratory, Washington, DC.

[Stubbington 61]		C. A. STUBBINGTON and P. J. E. FORSYTH. 1961. "Some Corrosion-Fatigue Observations on a High-Purity Aluminum-Zinc-Magnesium Alloy and Commercial D. T. D. 683 Alloy," *Jnl. of the Inst. of Metals*, London, vol. 90, 1961–62, pp. 347–354.

[Swift 71]		T. SWIFT. 1971. "Development of the Fail-safe Design Features of the DC-10," *Damage Tolerance in Aircraft Structures*, ASTM STP 486, Am. Soc. for Testing and Materials, West Conshohocken, PA, pp. 164–214.

[Tada 85]		H. TADA, P. C. PARIS, and G. R. IRWIN. 1985. *The Stress Analysis of Cracks Handbook*, 2d ed., Paris Productions Inc., St. Louis, MO.

[Taylor 85]		D. TAYLOR. 1985. *A Compendium of Fatigue Thresholds and Crack Growth Rates*, Engineering Materials Advisory Services Ltd., Cradley Heath, Warley, West Midlands, UK. (See also *Computer Database on Fatigue Thresholds and Crack Growth Rates*, same publisher.)

[Thomas 87]		D. W. THOMAS. 1987. "Vehicle Modeling and Service Loads Analysis," *Durability by Design*, SAE Pub. No. SP-730, Soc. of Automotive Engineers, Warrendale, PA, Paper No. 871940.

[Timoshenko 83]		S. P. TIMOSHENKO. 1983. *History of Strength of Materials*, McGraw-Hill, New York.

[Tipton 92]		S. M. TIPTON and G. J. SHOUP. 1992. "The Effect of Proof Loading on the Fatigue Behavior of Open Link Chain," *Jnl. of Engineering Materials and Technology, Trans. of ASME*, vol. 114, pp. 27–33.

[Tobler 78]		R. L. TOBLER and R. P. REED. 1978. "Fatigue Crack Growth Resistance of Structural Alloys at Cryogenic Temperatures," K. D. Timmerhaus et al., eds., *Advances in Cryogenic Engineering*, vol. 24, Plenum Press, New York, pp. 82–90.

[Tobolsky 65]		A. V. TOBOLSKY. 1965. "Some Viewpoints on Polymer Physics," *Structure and Properties of Polymers, Jnl. of Polymers Sciences*, part C, Polymer Symposia, no. 9, John Wiley, New York, pp. 157–191.

[Topper 70]		T. H. TOPPER and B. I. SANDOR. 1970. "Effects of Mean Stress and Prestrain on Fatigue Damage Summation," *Effects of Environment and Complex Load History on Fatigue Life*, ASTM STP 462, Am. Soc. for Testing and Materials, West Conshohocken, PA, pp. 93–104.

[van Echo 58]		J. A. VAN ECHO. 1958. "Short-Time Creep of Structural Sheet Metals," *Short-Time High Temperature Testing*, A. H. Levy, ed., ASM International, Materials Park, OH, pp. 58–91.

[van Echo 67]		J. A. VAN ECHO, D. B. ROACH, and A. M. HALL. 1967. "Short-Time Tensile and Long-Time Creep-Rupture Properties of the HK-40 Alloy and Type 310 Stainless Steel at Temperatures to 2000 F," *Jnl. of Basic Engineering, Trans. of the ASME*, Sept. 1967, pp. 465–479.

[Van Vlack 89]   L. H. VAN VLACK. 1989. *Elements of Materials Science and Engineering*, 6th ed., Addison-Wesley, Reading, MA, Fig. 8-3.4, "Slip by Dislocations," p. 265.

[Venkateswaran 88]   A. VENKATESWARAN, K. Y. DONALDSON, and D. P. H. HASSELMAN. 1988. "Role of Intergranular Damage-Induced Decrease in Young's Modulus in the Nonlinear Deformation and Fracture of an Alumina at Elevated Temperatures," *Jnl. of the Am. Ceramic Society*, vol. 71, no. 7, Jul. 1988, pp. 565–576.

[Voss 88]   H. VOSS and J. KARGER-KOCSIS. 1988. "Fatigue Crack Propagation in Glass-Fibre and Glass-Sphere Filled PBT Composites," *Int. Jnl. of Fatigue*, vol. 10, no. 1, Jan. 1988, pp. 3–11.

[Waisman 59]   J. L. WAISMAN. 1959. "Factors Affecting Fatigue Strength," *Metal Fatigue*, G. Sines and J. L. Waisman, eds., McGraw-Hill, New York, pp. 7–35.

[Warren 38]   B. E. WARREN and J. BISCOE. 1938. "Fourier Analysis of X-ray Patterns of Soda-silica Glass," *Jnl. of the Am. Ceramic Soc.*, vol. 21, pp. 259–265.

[Webber 70]   D. WEBBER. 1970. "Constant Amplitude and Cumulative Damage Fatigue Tests on Bailey Bridges," *Effects of Environment and Complex Load History on Fatigue Life*, ASTM STP 462, Am. Soc. for Testing and Materials, West Conshohocken, PA, pp. 15–39.

[Wei 65]   R. P. WEI. 1965. "Fracture Toughness Testing in Alloy Development," *Fracture Toughness Testing and its Applications*, ASTM STP 381, Am. Soc. for Testing and Materials, West Conshohocken, PA, pp. 279–289.

[Welker 10]   J. R. WELKER, L. N. AZADANI, and B. P. GLAESEMANN. 2010. "Creep of Polycarbonate at Room Temperature," Project report for a graduate course on Mechanics of Deformation and Fracture, Virginia Tech, Blacksburg, VA.

[Wetzel 68]   R. M. WETZEL. 1968. "Smooth Specimen Simulation of Fatigue Behavior of Notches," *Journal of Materials*, ASTM, vol. 3, no. 3, Sept. 1968, pp. 646–657.

[Wetzel 77]   R. M. WETZEL, ed. 1977. *Fatigue Under Complex Loading: Analyses and Experiments*, SAE Pub. No. AE-6, Soc. of Automotive Engineers, Warrendale, PA.

[Whitman 60]   J. G. WHITMAN and J. F. ALDER. 1960. "Programmed Fatigue Testing of Full Size Welded Structures," *British Welding Journal*, vol. 7, no. 4, pp. 272–280.

[Whyte 75]   R. R. WHYTE, ed. 1975. *Engineering Progress Through Trouble*, The Institution of Mechanical Engineers, London.

[Wiederhorn 77]   S. M. WIEDERHORN. 1977. "Dependence of Lifetime Predictions on the Form of the Crack Propagation Equation," *Fracture 1977, Vol. 3; Proc. of the 4th Int. Conf. on Fracture*, D. M. R. Taplin, ed., University of Waterloo Press, Waterloo, Ontario, Canada, pp. 893–901.

[Williams 87]   J. G. WILLIAMS. 1987. "Fracture Mechanics of Polymers and Adhesives," *Fracture of Non-Metallic Materials*, K. P. Herrmann and L. H. Larsson, eds., Kluwer Academic Pubs., Dordrecht, The Netherlands.

[Wirsching 96]   P. H. WIRSCHING and K. ORTIZ. 1996. *Reliability Methods in Mechanical and Structural Design*, notes for the 18th annual seminar and workshop (short course), University of Arizona, Aerospace and Mechanical Engineering Dept., Tucson, AZ.

[Wood 70]   H. A. WOOD et al., eds. 1970. "Proceedings of the Air Force Conference on Fatigue and Fracture of Aircraft Structures and Materials," AFFDL TR 70-144, Air Force Flight Dynamics Laboratory, Wright-Patterson AFB, OH.

[Zachariasen 32]   W. H. ZACHARIASEN. 1932. "The Atomic Arrangement in Glass," *Jnl. of the Am. Chemical Soc.*, vol. 54, pp. 3841–3851.

[Zwikker 54]   C. ZWIKKER. 1954. *Physical Properties of Solid Materials*, Pergamon Press, London.

Index

A

A286 (superalloy), 83, 827
Absolute modulus, 858
Abusive grinding, 540
Accidental loads, 429
Acrylic (PMMA), 21, 139, 140, 202, 341
Activation energies, 811–812
   defined, 809
   evaluation of, 816–817
Adiabatic modulus, 860
AFGROW, 602
Aging. *See* Precipitation hardening
Albert, W. A. J., 417
Allowable stress design, 31–32, 296, 321
Alloy steels. *See* Low-alloy steels
Alloying, 66, 92, 111
Alloying and processing of metals, 66–72
   annealing, 68–69
   cold work, 68–69
   grain refinement, 69
   multiple phase effects, 70–72
   precipitation hardening, 70–72
   solid solution strengthening, 69–70
   strengthening methods, 68
Alloys, 40–41, 43
Alpha iron, 47

Alternating stress, 419
Alumina (Al_2O_3), 41, 55, 96, 97, 161, 202, 341
Aluminum and alloys, 41, 66–67, 80–82, 101, 106,
   111, 138, 152, 202, 296, 340, 343, 578, 582,
   672, 751, 906
Aluminum bronze, 83
American Association of State Highway and
   Transportation Officials (AASHTO), 30, 534
   bridge design code, 534–535
American Institute of Steel Construction, allowable
   stress design code of, 31–32
American Iron and Steel Institute (AISI), steel
   nomenclature, 73–75
   AISI 304, 587
   AISI 310, 73, 827
   AISI 316, 78
   AISI 403, 73, 78
   AISI 1020, 73, 106, 109, 124, 133, 134–137, 138,
     148, 150, 152
   AISI 1040, 78
   AISI 1045, 73, 77, 342–343, 751
   AISI 1195, 73
   AISI 1340, 74
   AISI 4142, 138, 152, 751
   AISI 4340, 73, 77–79, 106, 374–375, 578, 585,
     589, 618, 620, 751
   AISI T1, 73

FREQUENTLY USED SYMBOLS

Roman Letters

a	Crack length		J	Polar moment of inertia; J-integral; damping coefficient
A	Cross-sectional area; creep coefficients; stress–life coefficient		k	Stress concentration factor; spring constant
b	Maximum possible crack length; stress–life exponent; thickness where t is time		K	Stress intensity factor of fracture mechanics
			L	Length
B	Bulk modulus; Bridgman correction factor; stress–life exponent		m	Fatigue limit reduction factor; fatigue crack growth exponent; creep exponent
B_f	Number of repetitions to failure		M	Bending moment
			n	Strain hardening exponent
c	Half-depth of beam; radius of shaft; plastic strain versus life exponent; dashpot constant		N	Number of cycles
			p	Pressure
			P	Force (load)
			q	Notch sensitivity
C	Fatigue crack growth coefficient		Q	Activation energy
			Q^{-1}	Loss coefficient in damping
d	Diameter; damping exponent		r	Radius
e	Base of natural logarithms ($e = 2.718\ldots$)		R	Stress ratio for cyclic loading (minimum $\div$ maximum); universal gas constant
E	Modulus of elasticity			
F	Finite width factor of fracture mechanics		S	Nominal (average) stress
			t	Time; thickness
G	Shear modulus; strain energy release rate		T	Temperature; torque
			u	Energy per unit volume
h	Height; half-height of cracked bodies		U	Energy
			v	Displacement
H	Strength coefficient for stress–strain curves		V	Volume
			w	Width
I	Area moment of inertia about an in-plane axis		x, y, z	Spatial coordinates
			X	Safety factor
			Y	Load factor

Greek Letters

α	Coefficient of thermal expansion; angle; relative crack length ($\alpha = a/b$); Peterson constant		γ	Shear strain; Walker exponent
			δ	Slope reduction factor; crack-tip opening displacement; phase angle
β	Neuber constant			

ε	Normal strain	ρ	Notch-tip radius
η	Tensile viscosity	σ	Normal stress at a point, or in a
θ	Angle		uniformly stressed member
λ	Stress biaxiality ratio σ_2/σ_1	τ	Shear stress
ν	Poisson's ratio	ω	Angular velocity

Subscripts: Meaning (Example)

a	Amplitude (σ_a)	min	Minimum (σ_{min})
ar	Completely reversed	n	Net section (S_n)
	amplitude (σ_{ar})	o	Yield (σ_o); fully-plastic value
c	Creep (ε_c); critical (K_c);		(M_o)
	value at $y = c$ location	p	Plastic (ε_p); proportional
	(σ_c)		limit (σ_p); periodic
e	Elastic (ε_e); fatigue limit (σ_e)		inspection interval (N_p)
f	Final (A_f); failure (N_f)	q	Equivalent constant
g	Gross section (S_g)		amplitude value
h	Value for octahedral planes		(σ_{aq}, ΔS_q)
	(τ_h)	r	Residual (σ_r); rupture (t_r)
i	Initial (A_i); initial yield value	sc	Steady-state creep (ε_{sc})
	(M_i); summation index	tc	Transient creep (ε_{tc})
j	Summation index where i	u	Ultimate (σ_u)
	means *initial*	x, y, z	Direction (σ_x); axis (I_z)
m	Mean (σ_m)	xy, yz, zx	Plane (τ_{xy})
max	Maximum (σ_{max})	1, 2, 3	Principal direction (σ_1)

Modifiers: Meaning (Example)

Δ	Range in cyclic loading ($\Delta\sigma$)	*dot*	Time rate ($\dot{\varepsilon}$)
tilde	True ($\tilde{\sigma}$)	*prime*	Value for cyclic loading (n');
bar	Effective ($\bar{\sigma}$); equivalent		other special values
hat	Actual service value ($\hat{S}$)		

Pocket Guide to

Horses

Pocket Guide to

Horses

ANDERSON
MERCHANDISERS

A QUANTUM BOOK

Published by Anderson Merchandisers
P.O. Box 32270 79120
421 S.E. 34th Avenue
Amarillo, TX 79103
www.amerch.com

ISBN: 978-1-59027-132-2

This book was produced by
Quantum Publishing Ltd
6 Blundell Street
London N7 9BH

QUMPGTH

Printed in Singapore by
Star Standard Industries (Pte) Ltd

PICTURE CREDITS

CONTENTS

EVOLUTION OF THE HORSE

Throughout history, we have long taken our partnership with the horse for granted. Both loyal friend and trusted servant, the horse has been used for everything from heavy agricultural work to sack races in the local gymkhana. Little wonder, you might think, that it has taken about 54 million years for the horse to develop from a small bear-like creature to the enormous diversity of breed and type that makes up the modern species.

It was only in the last million years that Equus caballus, the forerunner of the modern horse, emerged—and developed into the animal we know today.

Eohippus, the first known ancestor of the horse, stood only three hands high, and it ate succulent leaves as it browsed through the swamp-like forests. Instead of hooves which we would recognize today, these creatures had four, weight-bearing pads, each with three hooved-toes. By 35 million years ago, this primitive animal had doubled in size to six hands and became known

as Mesohippus. It had also lost one of the weight-bearing toes and became faster.

Over the next ten million years, more changes took place. By 25 million years ago, Merychippus had evolved—now ten hands high and running on central weight-bearing hooves with a reduced toe on each side of the cannon bones.

At the same time, the jaw and teeth were changing. A definite gap was developing between the molars and tushes and Merychippus had teeth suitable for eating grass.

By ten million years ago, Pliohippus had appeared—characterized by single central hooves and no sign of the toes. The jaw line was longer, the teeth larger, and the animal was around 12 hands high.

BELOW Early art such as this petroglyph, a carving into rock, found in Libya showing an early horse and rider have helped to build a picture of how our ancestors lived. This one may be using a bow to hunt for food.

Early domestic horse

Over the last one million years, dramatic changes have taken place. Equus caballus emerged and grew to a size that made domestication worthwhile. Horses appear to have been domesticated about 6,000 years ago, in Europe and Asia, although they are found in cave paintings from around 15000 B.C. Records exist that show man was riding the horse in 2637 B.C. Gradually, the horse's real worth started to be realized as the animal began to replace the ass for hauling loads and carriages, for entertainment, for war, and as a means of transportation.

BELOW Przewalski's horses are thought to be the ancestors of the modern horse. The massive head and spiky mane are typical of the breed. The pale muzzle, and area around the eyes are also distinguish features of other ,ancient breeds such as the Exmoor and Celtic. pony.

By 1500 B.C., the Hittites (members of a great empire in North Syria and Asia Minor) had worked out how to deal with general horsemanship. The horse's presence spread throughout Assyria and Egypt, India and China, and its progress thereafter is well documented.

Direct ancestors of the "Modern" horse

Early evidence of Equus caballus appears to be confined to Asia and Africa where six distant species of wild Equidae still exist today or at least have been known in modern times. It is interesting to note that most equine fossil evidence exists in the United States, yet when the European colonists first reached the "New World" in the 15th century there were no live species to be found.

The main species of wild horse are:

Przewalski's Horse. This species roamed most of Asia. It still exists today.

The Wild Ass. Originally from North Africa, the wild ass incorporates two subspecies—the Nubian Ass and the Somali Ass. It probably spread to Asia but did not reach Europe until the Middle Ages.

The Asiatic Wild Ass. Also known as a hemionid, it is a mixture between the horse and ass. Perhaps the best known is the onager of Persia, which was domesticated by the ancient Sumerians of Mesopotamia ,long before the arrival of the domesticated horse. Onagers are shown drawing chariots in carvings at The Royal Cemetry of Ur of Chaldees 2500 B.C.

Common or Plains Zebra. Found in Kenya and the Cape of Africa, this zebra has about five or six stripes on the flanks.

BELOW The Common or Plains Zebra with their spectacular markings roam in huge herds in parts of Africa. They have dark muzzles and a tufted end to their tails and spiky black and white manes similar to Przewalski's horse in texture.

Mountain Zebra. Now confined to southwest Africa, this was the first zebra to be encountered by European settlers in Africa and is distinguishable by the "gridiron" striping over the base of the tail and about 12 stripes on the flanks.

The Quaggo. This animal once roamed Cape of Africa in huge herds but was completely exterminated by early settlers in the last century. It had no striping on the hindquarters.

Przewalski's Horses are the most likely ancestors of the modern strain of Equus caballus. In the early 1880s a group of hunters killed an unusual looking horse in the Gobi Desert, west of Mongolia. The skin and skull of this animal were sent to the Russian explorer, Nikolai M.. Przewalski. After the specimens were examined, a new species was declared, named after Przewalski.

HOW THE EQUUS HOOF EVOLVED

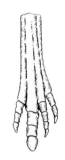

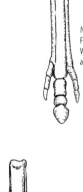

MESOHIPPUS
FORE AND HIND FEET
Weight-bearing central hoof
and 2 hooved toes.

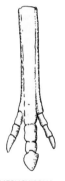

HYRACOTHERIUM OR
EOHIPPUS
FORE AND HIND FEET Weight-bearing pad and 3 hooved toes.

MERYCHIPPUS
FORE AND HIND FEET
Weight-bearing central hooved
toe. Two reduced side toes.

PLIOHIPPUS
FORE AND HIND FEET Weight-bearing central hooved toe. No recognizable side-toe.

EQUUS CABALLUS
FORE AND HIND FEET
The final form of the hoof. The cannon bone is at its longest and no side-bone is apparent.

HORSE TYPES

There is considerable difference of opinion on the recent development of the horse. The most common view is that at the end of the last Ice Age, roughly 10,000 years ago, there were three main types of horse and pony.

Primitive horse types

1. Forest Horse. Probably the ancestor of all modern heavy horses. It was slow moving and heavily built with broad heavy feet adapted for its marshy European habitat.

2. Asiatic Horse. Still exists today and is also known as Przewalski's Horse after the Polish explorer who discovered it in 1879.

3. Tarpan. Originating from Eastern Europe and the Southern Steppes of Russia. Its light build and speed suggest that many of our pony and light horse breeds descend from the Tarpan.

Four direct descendants

Around 5,000 to 6,000 years ago the three primitive types had produced four variants — two northern pony types and two southern horse types.

Pony Type 1. Lived in North West Europe and was small, chunky, tough and resistant to cold, wet windy weather. Today, the Exmoor Pony and Icelandic are similar types.

Pony Type 2. Living in Northern Europe this type was very resistant to sub-zero temperatures. Its closest modern-day relative is believed to be the Norwegian Fjord.

Pony type 1

Pony type 2

Horse Type 3. The tall desert steppe horse of Central Asia had a great resistance to drought and heat. Its closest ancestor today is the Akhal-Teké.

Horse Type 3

Horse Type 4. This was a smaller desert horse from Western Asia. The modern Caspian could be a direct descendant of this horse.

Horse Type 4

Hot, warm and coldblood

Whether a horse breed is hot, warm or cold blooded is decided by its physical characteristics.

Cold blood

Cold blood. Suited to cold climates and built to retain body heat with rounder bodies and thicker coats of hair.

Warm blood

Warm blood. Horses such as the Hanoverian and the Selle Français are crosses between hot blooded and cold blooded horses.

Hot blood

Hot blood. Horses and ponies from hot climates have finer hair, longer legs and carry their tails away from the body to facilitate heat loss.

THE HORSE TODAY

Since it was domesticated, the horse has been used for all types of work. Even today, every horse is, in practice, working for its living, whether it is a child's pony, a racehorse, show jumper or brewery dray.

ABOVE A team of English brewery drays.

The working horse

In the Western world, some breweries use heavy horses for short-haul deliveries and publicity purposes. Some farms still use heavy breeds and horses are an essential asset to the police in many countries.

However, throughout Eastern Europe, South America, Asia and Africa, working horses (including donkeys and burros) are still in widespread use for transportation and agriculture.

The sporting horse

The main role of the horse in the West today is in pleasure and sport. Equestrian sports go from strength to strength, and are increasingly popular with both riders and spectators.

Hunting and polo are both ancient sports, while horse racing has been popular around the world since the early 18th century.

Many forms of equine competition involve large sums of money, both paid for and won by horses as well as sponsorship deals.

However, the main attraction for the public lies in watching the superb achievements and courageous performances of the horse which have made it the object of man's admiration and affection over the centuries.

ABOVE The modern horse excels at show-jumping

KNOWING AND CARING FOR YOUR HORSE

Horses and ponies are sophisticated and intelligent animals. Their anatomy has evolved to make them efficient grazers, and to provide them with speed and quick reactions, to escape from the danger which their acute senses are ideally designed to detect. Looking after horses involves not only supplying their physical needs, but also being aware of their mental well-being and appreciating their senses. Knowing what a horse can see and hear enables you to approach it without causing alarm. Getting to know your horse, its character and idiosyncrasies, should help handling, schooling, and riding — and is one of the main attractions of owning a horse.

POINTS OF THE HORSE

To be able to understand how to identify different part of the horse, it is important to know the names of what are collectively described as the points of the horse. A horse that is described as having black points indicates it has dark or black legs, mane, and tail like those seen in horses of bay or brown. Some have white markings on their faces and on their lower legs, referred to as socks or stockings.

Certain breeds have their own definite distinguishing features which make for easy identification, such as the Arab's dished face, the Exmoor's toad eyes, and the Norwegian Fjord's striking black and white mane. Some heavier breeds have excess hair on their lower legs, referred to as feather. This feather can be very fine and silky on some breeds, or profuse on others, such as on the Clydesdale and the Shire.

Some plain-colored horses with no obvious markings are identified by small twirls in their coats often found around the head, neck or chest areas. These are known Point of shoulder as whorls.

FIELD OF VISION

The horse's field of vision is relatively good. It can see in front of it very well and judges distance from ground level, which is important when it tries to assess heights of fences.

MEASURING

The horse is measured in "hands", one hand is equal to the width of an average hand of 4 in (10 cm). A measuring stick is placed beside the horse next to its forelegs with the measure taken horizontally across the highest point of the withers. (See also pg.42-43.) Generally, horses measure from over 15hh (152 cm), while ponies are those measuring under this height (typically at or under 14.2 hands in the USA).

A horse is considered to have stopped growing and to be mature at six years of age.

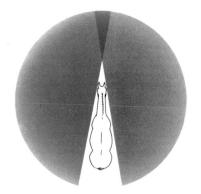

FOOT AND HOOF

The foot is the most important part of the horse, and it is vital to keep it well trimmed and regularly shod if the horse is to remain sound (see pg.76-79). Get to know the parts of the foot both on the outside and the underside so that you are able to identify the area should problems occur. The outside wall is made of very hard horn and cannot expand should there be any inside inflammation caused by an abscess. The veterinarian will cut a small hole in the sole to release the pressure in some cases.

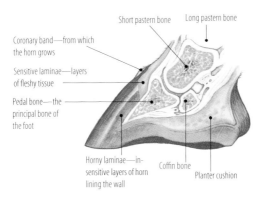

Short pastern bone Long pastern bone

Coronary band—from which the horn grows

Sensitive laminae—layers of fleshy tissue

Pedal bone—the principal bone of the foot

Horny laminae—in-sensitive layers of horn lining the wall

Coffin bone

Planter cushion

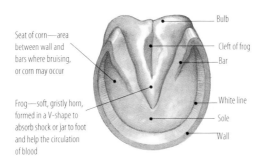

Seat of corn—area between wall and bars where bruising, or corn may occur

Frog—soft, gristly horn, formed in a V-shape to absorb shock or jar to foot and help the circulation of blood

Bulb

Cleft of frog

Bar

White line

Sole

Wall

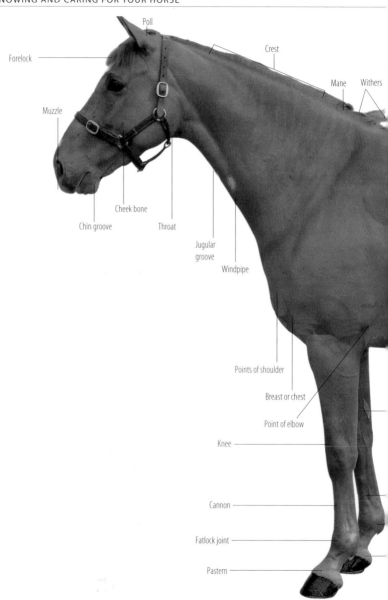

Poll

Crest

Forelock

Mane   Withers

Muzzle

Cheek bone

Chin groove   Throat

Jugular
groove

Windpipe

Points of shoulder

Breast or chest

Point of elbow

Knee

Cannon

Fatlock joint

Pastern

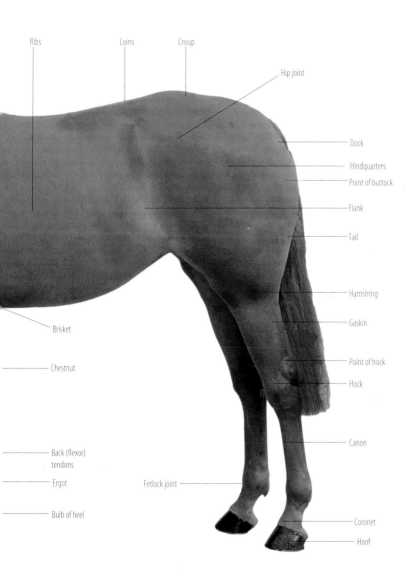

Ribs

Loins

Croup

Hip joint

Dock

Hindquarters

Point of buttock

Flank

Tail

Hamstring

Gaskin

Brisket

Point of hock

Chestnut

Hock

Canon

Back (flexor) tendons

Ergot

Fetlock joint

Coronet

Bulb of heel

Hoof

BREEDING

If you have a healthy mare, plenty of room, good facilities, and sufficient funds, breeding is a fun and rewarding pastime. But too often animals are bred for all the wrong reasons. Sadly, little thought has been given to the end product and the resulting offspring may not be suitable for the role envisioned. If all is carefully thought through, however, there is nothing nicer than to watch your foal grow up into something special.

To be successful, there are many considerations to take into account when deciding whether to breed your mare:

- What you hope to produce.
- The temperament and soundness of the mare.
- The facilities available to keep a mare and foal.
- The time and expense involved.
- Choosing a suitable stallion.

What do you hope to product?

Although a foal may not necessarily conform to your ideal when it arrives, in most cases you can plan to produce something near to what you have in mind by careful choice of a stallion. Think of size, type, and what you have in mind, and remember that breeding is a long-term commitment. It will be if months before the foal arrives. After two years, you can begin to break it to ride, but then it will be another four or five years before you can think of it working seriously in a worthwhile career.

The Mare

The temperament of your mare (also called a dam) will have a major bearing on your choice of stallion. You must choose your stallion to balance out any unfortunate traits. If the mare is naturally calm and easy in every way, then you will have few worries. If, however, she is quick and flighty, you would be wise to put her to a docile stallion whose offspring are known to have inherited his calm disposition.

Soundness is another important consideration.

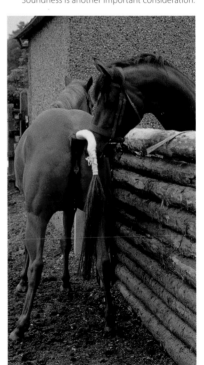

RIGHT When the mare is "in season",w she may lean toward the stallion (seen here on the opposite side of the teasing board). If a mare does not appreciate a stallion's advances she will kick out and squeal, so the teasing board acts as protection for both animals.

Is your mare tough enough to stand up to the work you ask of her? If she has always had lameness problems, you should think twice about whether to breed from her as her foal might inherit the same characteristics. All the best breeds have been developed by breeding only those horses tough enough to do the job expected. Breeding your mare because she is lame is the worst possible reason, unless her condition has been caused by accidental injury.

ABOVE The covering of a mare at a stud is always supervised.

Facilities

You must decide how and where you are going to keep and produce your foal. Do you have a large enough stable for a mother and foal if the weather is bad? If the climate is mild, the mare and foal can live out as nature intended—especially if they are a tough breed. Do you have enough land for this? An absolute minimum of two acres (0.8 hectare) would be necessary if you use excellent paddock management and have an open shed to shelter them in as well. The paddock fencing must be completely safe and secure, and clean, fresh drinking water must be freely available. See pg. 46-57 and 88-95 for more information.

BELOW In some cases, the mare can be inseminated artificially—distance, injury, and transportation expense being some reasons for this choice. Here the semen is being collected from the stallion using a dummy mare. This will be stored and then inseminated into the mare when she is in season.

Expense

Breeding can be a costly affair. First, think of the top range of stud fees, the price you pay for the services of the stallion. If everything goes well, you get your foal at the end as hoped. Sometimes, however, problems occur and your mare does not hold the foal. The whole process then starts all over again. The mare may be difficult to get in foal, so more veterinary fees will be added to your account. In all cases, there will be veterinary fees, as well, for swabs that are taken for culture examinations, pregnancy scans, and routine prenatal care.

The charges for the keep of your mare while at stud can mount up. Think about the timing of when you want a foal and when to take the mare to stud. Taking the mare to stud between five and ten days before she is due to come in season is ideal as this will give her a chance to settle into her new environment. Generally, mares come into season every three weeks for about six to eight months a year.

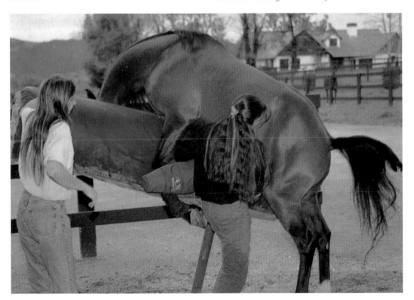

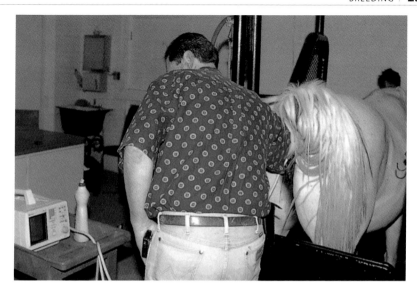

Chossing a stallion

Choosing a suitable mate for your mare can be a fun process. The stallion (also called a stud or entire) must complement the mare's attributes and make up for failings on her side. If she is rather long in the back (mares often are because they need room to hold a foal) and has poor hocks, it is best to choose a more compact stallion with good strong hocks. If she is a mediocre mover choose a stallion with good action.

Temperament is important. Choose a kind, mannerly stallion and ask what his offspring are like. Talk to people who have bred from him recently and find out about his offsprings' temperaments and saleability; go and see the offspring in person, if possible.

Ask about the stallion's fertility too. It's a great waste of time and money if you hear later that your chosen stallion is not very fertile and gets few mares in foal.

Where is the stallion? Be sure that he is within a

ABOVE The veterinarian is inserting a scanning probe into the rectum to ascertain if a fertilized egg is in the uterine horn and if the mare is in foal—usually possible after 16 days from the date of service. It is advisable to repeat this procedure a month later if all is well as pregnancies can sometimes be aborted in the early stages.

distance that you can cope with or arrange easily for your mare's transportation.

Are you satisfied with the way the stud is managed and confident that your mare will be handled properly? Is the facility well run and organized? Do the horses look contented and happy? Ask to see the stallion out of his stable, walked and trotted in hand so that you can assess his conformation, movements, and temperament. Stallions are usually a bit playful and should have plenty of presence—or star quality—but they should not look vicious or mean, or be dangerous.

The stud fee is likely to be a major deciding factor. Investigate this before you even go to see the stallion, and make sure you are clear about the terms.

THE NEW FOAL

After if months of preparing for the big day, your foal could be born into the world at any time. Keep everything as natural as possible for your mare—you are much more likely to be stressed about the event than she is, but keep an eye on her to ensure all is well.

In the majority of cases the mare copes admirably on her I own, especially with the hardy and long established breeds. Still, you should keep a close eye on her and watch for any changes. If you are not experienced, it is wise to have a knowledgeable person on hand, preferably a veterinarian, to assist or advise in the latter stages of delivery.

BELOW The "in-foal" mare will need a little extra care during the last two to three months before foaling unless she is on really good pasture. Extra feed will be required if the pasture is poor, as this is the time when the foal inside really starts to grow. Lack of food at this stage may affect the unborn foal's chances of reaching its full height later on.

Preparation for the foal's arrival

In preparation for the event, the mare should be up-to-date with her routine health maintenance (worming, vaccines and farrier care) the month before she is due. If she will be foaling inside, have a large stall with plenty of clean straw kept ready. Although indoor foaling is preferable, in good weather, and if alone, the mare can foal outside perfectly happily if the paddock is safe and not too big. Remove any other horses, who may become too inquisitive and harm the foal.

The mare's udder (teats, also known as the milk bar) may begin to enlarge any time from six weeks to just a few hours before foaling. Usually

ABOVE The birth is a very emotional and exciting moment. Here the mare looks around at her newborn offspring foaled in a stable. The head is out but the rest of the foal is still covered in the protective amniotic covering within which it has been living inside the womb. The mare will usually lick the foal dry and pull off any excess covering. Should it be necessary you can remove excess covering—especially if still over the foal's mouth or nostrils—by hand.

about 24 hours before the birth, she will "wax up" (show a little pale, waxy substance of colostrum on the teats). She may become a bit restless, and the muscles around the anus and vagina will slacken to allow an easier passage for the foal.

Delivery

Most mares lie down for the actual birth. They may also lie down for the breaking of the waters and then get up once or twice before the birth itself. First to be "born" are the foal's forelegs, which should appear with one slightly behind the other so that the shoulders can get through the pelvic arch. The head should be pointed forward, resting along the forelegs. The hind legs are tucked underneath the belly, and appear last in a normal delivery.

The whole event usually takes from 20 minutes to an hour before the birth is complete. Left alone without too much interference (as long as the foal's mouth and nose are free of the amniotic covering [sometimes called the birth sack]), it is best to allow both to rest for 20 minutes or so. The mare needs time to recover as her womb begins contracting back to shape and she expels the afterbirth. In most cases, this should be expelled within the next hour or so.

Caring for a weaned foal
I have found a friend's foal to go with mine. How should I look after them once my foal has been weaned?

The youngsters should have had a chance to get used to hard feed while still with their mothers. Continue to give two feeds a day and either keep them out or bring them in at night if the weather is bad. Youngsters should be wormed every six to eight weeks (see pg.114-117) and have their feet trimmed as necessary (see pg.76-79). Lead them around once or twice a week and practice picking their feet periodically (or daily if inside). Basically all youngsters .need plenty of fresh air, good food, and exercise to grow to into strong healthy animals.

Thereafter the weaned foal should continue on the mix through the winter months. It is important to reduce this before the foal/yearling is turned out on lush new pasture in the following spring.

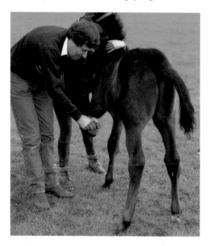

ABOVE It is important to get the foal used to being handled from an early age. This one seems unperturbed about having its feet picked out—a good sign to the farrier who will soon trim its feet.

Weaning

There are two ways of separating mares from their foals, both of which are easier in a group as the companionship of others helps to minimize the inevitable stress caused.

If the horses have been coming in at night and going out during the day, it is best to take the mares out in the morning and remove them far enough away from the foals so that neither can hear each other. This may require arrangements to be made with neighbors or friends. Keep the foals in until they have settled. It may be best to leave them quietly for 24 hours and then turn them out together. The mares will need time for their milk to dry up, so they should be kept on a restricted diet for a few days.

The other method of weaning is to keep the mares and foals in a field together with a suitable old retired mare as a nurse. Take the mares away and leave the foals with the nurse. Large stud operations take two mares away at a time, every few days.

Weaning is a stressful time for both sides. The foals inevitably lose weight at this time but quickly readjust, especially if they are with other horses. If you cannot find other foals to share weaning, find a sensible nurse as a companion.

Growing up

Full of boisterous fun, your youngster will spend its first few years enjoying a life of careless "freedom." Sensitive handling now will pay off when more starts to be expected of your rebellious "teenager" later on.

Once weaned, the foal adapts to its independent life, and with correct feeding (never overfeed) and regular worming it should continue to mature. As a yearling, it may lose its looks a little. Horses tend to grow by fits and starts, often looking a little higher behind and becoming angular as height takes over from roundness. All the temporary teeth will have been in place since the age of nine months (see pg.112-113) for more information on aging by teeth development), and the tail will still look foal-like.

At the age of two years, the animal grows into a more rounded and mature horse. The first permanent teeth, the central incisors, appear at two and a half years, as do two permanent molars on the top and bottom jaws. The mane grows long and the tail loses its foal appearance.

By three years of age, there is a look of maturity and the mane and tail are filled out. The teeth become more mature, with permanent incisors and four permanent molars in place. Only one temporary molar of the original six remains in each jaw. At the age of three, most horses and ponies should not be asked to do anything too strenuous. Not until they reach the age of four will they be ready for more arduous work.

From weaning onward, it is important that youngsters are well handled and accustomed to the general day-to-day chores. They should be used to a halter and lead rope. They should be groomed (see pg.58-65) and have their feet picked out regularly so that they are accustomed to this sort of attention

ABOVE Leading out in hand in quiet surroundings gives a very good grounding for when the time comes for breaking in and hacking out. This youngster led in a bridle for a stroll on a quiet lane looks quiet and happy.

when the farrier comes. They should be led in and out of paddocks and handled calmly yet firmly to get used to human contact at least once a month, even if out at pasture throughout the summer. Confident, quiet but firm handling is essential if youngsters are to become well-adjusted adults.

ABOVE These four handsome yearlings look happy and interested in what is going on. Being herd animals, they will thrive much better in groups than on their own.

BREAKING IN

The special bond you have built with your youngster should make it a willing partner in the first hesitant steps toward its career. How you have done your early work will prove invaluable during this next important stage. If the horse is obedient and understands words of command early in life and has been regularly handled, then the next stage should be most rewarding.

ABOVE This horse has been lunged for some weeks off long reins (two reins used instead of one). This enables the handler to have a little more control and the horse to get used to reins around its legs.

Breaking in becomes the next important milestone in the young horse's career. The trust and confidence built up between horse and humans during the first few years should pay off now with few problems, so long as the horse is given time to understand the role it is expected to play—that of being ridden.

Lunge work

Lunge work, or lunging, involves the horse moving around the trainer on an outside circle attached to a lunge line. The trainer must stay in the center and encourage the horse forward with a lunge whip. This must not be used to frighten the animal, but only to encourage it forward. A triangle is formed between the trainer, the horse, and the whip.

First use of a bit

The first stage, if you have not done so already, is to get the horse used to a bit. Start with a mild rubber or snaffle bit, which can be put into the horse's mouth for 20 minutes each day. Then a stable roller and large comfortable pad can be introduced at the same time (as a forerunner to a saddle), and the horse led about until it is confident. The saddle can then be introduced. Prevent the horse from becoming frightened by securing the stirrups so they do not flap against its sides.

Voice commands

The horse must learn to obey the voice so that you will be able to talk to it when it is ridden. Keep commands simple, such as "walk on", "teerot" for trot, and "whoa" for halt. Animate your voice when you want the horse to move faster, slow your commands when you want to reduce the pace. Horses learn by repetition, so practice each day until the horse begins to understand. Reward the animal when it does well.

Some people prefer not to lunge young horses, fearing that the small circles can strain immature muscles. You can still teach the horse to obey the voice by walking it up and down tracks in hand or long-reining with two lunge lines, one on either side. When long-reining, it is important to have a helper for the first few sessions. That way, the other person can hold the horse's head until it becomes accustomed to the reins and you can maintain control from behind at a safe distance. The horse can be "driven" like this all over the place if it is safe to do so, which will help it to get used to all the different sights and sounds in its environment.

Horse whispering

Horse whispering is a modern term for communicating with horses using skills and techniques which have gone on for centuries but until recently have never been understood or documented. Now this system has been made world-famous by Monty Roberts from California. Monty, a part Cherokee, used his Native American background to show to the world that it is possible to bond or "join-up" with horses by emulating equine body language.

At his ranch in California, Monty runs courses to train people to become "whisperers" and has given spectacular displays of how it is possible to communicate with horses and dispel any fears they may have by empathizing with the horse's mind. Some horses respond quicker than others, but once the "whisperer" has been accepted, they usually respond quietly and willingly.

There are several people who have worked on difficult horses with kindness and understanding and have had equally good results. Either way, the secret is to gain the animal's confidence. If this has already been lost, the need to establish a bond becomes even more important. As with any training, patience and time are vital to success, and this is one of the keys to "whispering."

ABOVE This horse is ready to be backed, and has been taken quietly through the lungeing stage and driven around in long reins while showing no fear or worry. Note the neckstrap around the neck for the rider's use in case the horse moves quickly.

The first rider/"backing the horse"

Ideally, you need three helpers to mount a horse for the first time, but it is quite possible with one. Your horse should still be on a lunge rein. When the horse is relaxed and quiet, bring it into an enclosed area that is familiar—a small paddock, for instance. The rider must wear a helmet and be calm and confident. With two helpers, one can hold the horse, talking to it quietly, and the second can give the rider a leg up across the saddle. Take plenty of time and be patient to ensure that the horse does not become worried at any time. When there is only one helper, that person must hold the horse's head and give the rider a leg up at the same time—making sure that the horse looks completely calm before starting.

Once the horse has felt the weight, it can be moved a step or two and then stopped and rewarded. Let the horse tell you when it is ready to progress. Some will be totally unconcerned, others may need a day or two just doing this before they can progress further. For the next step, lead the horse a few steps and then mount the horse without banging a foot on its rump. Talk all the time in reassuring tones and then progress to walking around the area, doing a little more each day. Allow between one and three weeks to break a horse. Each horse will vary, but with confident and sympathetic handling there is rarely a problem.

Lead the horse out and about and show it the sights, all the time teaching it to obey commands.

The rider must talk to the horse and ask it to walk, halt, and trot as and when required. Once obedient, it can come off the lunge rein and start out on its own. Riding out with another quiet horse will help to improve the young animal's confidence. Most people break horses and ride them for a few weeks, then give them a rest before starting serious work.

ABOVE The rider has been lifted up onto the horse two or three times to ensure the animal is unconcerned. The horse is now being led forward for a few steps to get used to the weight of the rider.

The mature horse

From four years on the horse is usually ready to do a variety of work, and by six years it is considered to be mentally and physically mature. Some, however, especially large horses, may take a year or so longer to mature—some less.

Generally horses are at their best from 6-12 years, but there are star Olympic horses who are 12-16 years old. Thereafter, they need treating very much as individuals. With proper care and individual attention, they may continue to work happily until they are around 18, but some age earlier than others.

Keeping control
What should I do when my horse won't move away from my friend's horse when we are out riding together?

It is very important that you make your horse go where you want by effective use of your legs and short enough reins to keep it under control. (See Control and the Aids pg.172-183 for more information.) A stick correctly used behind your leg once or twice and maybe some sharp words from

---

DAY IN THE LIFE OF A TRAINER

Up early this morning to travel 140 miles (224 km) to run a clinic at a barn in Pennsylvania. On arrival the riders are introduced—six in all for the morning session. Some of the group were novices but some had ridden a little before. I decide to have them two at a time for one hour each. We work on the paces and transitions creating a better understanding of the methods used to obtain smooth obedient changes within the gaits. I found the riders respond well to the use of poles to supple their horses first. One or two needed help with their position on the lunge. After a great barbecue we did the jumping part. Worked on their position over fences and made different distances at combinations for them to practice. Although this job is hard work I get a real sense of achievement when my students have practiced a skill over and over again and then get it right.

ABOVE The horse is being led around with the rider on top, who must sit relaxed and calm to give the horse confidence. An assistant is walking beside the horse to give it some words of encouragement.

you should do the trick. The horse must respect your wishes and you must persevere every time it argues if you want to come out on top.

RIGHT The horse must learn to go out on its own and be quiet in traffic. If it has been taken slowly and not rushed in its training, it will be confident and willing to do everything expected of it.

BELOW Riding the horse out first in company helps to build up confidence. These two are enjoying a splash in the river which will prove invaluable if they later jump cross country.

UNDERSTANDING YOUR HORSE

In the wild, horses use body language to communicate with the rest of the herd. If you take the time to study their behavior and try to understand what they need, it won't be long before you'll be convinced your horse is "talking" to you!

The longer you own your horse or pony, the more you will get to know its likes and dislikes. This is important, as you will be able to recognize if it begins to act out of character (there is usually an underlying reason). Horses may not be able to talk to us literally, but you can tell a lot from their expression and body language. Eyes, ears, and position of the body are the main ways we have of knowing what our horses are thinking.

Ears forward or relaxed denotes a happy or contented horse. Flicking back and forth could indicate nervousness or worry and uncertainty. Ears back usually means anger, pricked very far forward can indicate interest, surprise, or expectation. The eyes in conjunction with the ears give a good indication as well, and often will tell you what mood the horse is in!

The stance of the horse will also be informative. A stubborn animal will dig its toes in just like an obstinate child! It may hold a leg up in pain or point out a front one to relieve pressure. Many rest a hind leg, but this does not necessarily mean they are feeling uncomfortable.

ABOVE The horse may indicate it is unhappy by frequently flattening its ears back and possibly wrinkling its nose. Try to vary its day with a spell in the paddock or some sort of change in routine.

RIGHT The tired horse will generally look rather listless and sleepy, and its eyes wilt periodically close. It may hang its head or even lie down if excessively tired.

BELOW A horse may show the white of its eye and tense its muscles away from sights and sounds that scare it. Reassuring talk and a pat on the neck will often calm a nervous or frightened animal. Be positive in your approach when your horse encounters frightening objects.

REACTING TO A THREAT

The horse will react by raising its head to look and listen intently. It may back off in a nervous way and start pawing the ground while still trying to figure out what is going on. It may also snort, raise its tail, and prance about, then either wheel around on its hind legs and gallop away or stand and face the threat. If the "threat" is another horse, it may kick out viciously if it dislikes what it sees—or do a few playful bucks and kicks and invite the other horse to join in and play!

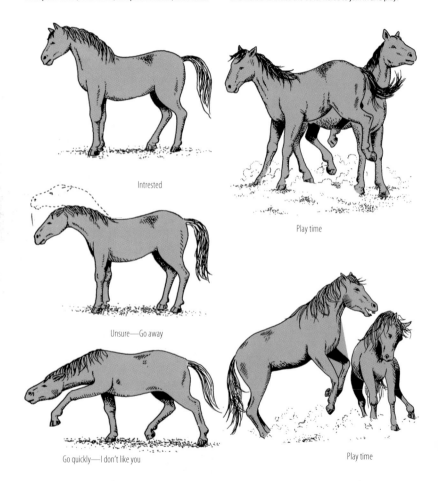

Intrested

Play time

Unsure—Go away

Go quickly—I don't like you

Play time

ABOVE The angry horse may flatten its ears back in a menacing attitude. If it is angry enough to attack it will open its eyes wide and bare its teeth. Some will threaten to turn their quarters toward you and even kick out.

BELOW Suspicious horses will usually back away from anything they are unsure of while flicking their ears back and forth. They may also show a bit of white of the eye and be rather tense near any frightening object.

ABOVE The questioning look which may follow something strange that has caught the horse's eye. Its head is raised and alert, and its ear flicks suspiciously.

Behavior

Because the horse is a herd animal, it will often behave in a different way on its own than when in company. The motivation of the other horses will often encourage a nervous or easily intimidated horse to do things that it would be too timid to do on its own.

Other horses might become a little hyperactive in company, which makes it difficult to control, and therefore more suited to working alone. So much of how a horse reacts, however, will depend on its early handling as a foal and the confidence it has built up from an early age with human beings. The method of backing the horse during the breaking-in period is another time in the horse's life when knowledge and understanding of what the horse is feeling and thinking may well affect its future progress.

Temperament

The temperament of the horse is genetically controlled. It is up to us to handle each type with the same care that we would when dealing with humans of different temperaments.

It makes sense to try to seek a suitable "match" between the temperaments of the horse and its rider. A very nervous rider requires a straightforward confident horse that will take things as they come. An experienced confident rider with a no-nonsense attitude will help a timid horse by instilling boldness.

LEFT The horse is never happier than when running loose in a paddock—preferably with company. This fine Thoroughbred is enjoying a relaxing play in its field.

ABOVE Shying or spooking away from something frightening is an understandable reaction in a young horse. It needs a reassuring pat and time for the horse to overcome its fear.

An inexperienced, reckless rider on a very overconfident horse is a recipe for disaster as they encourage each other to go dangerously fast.

Kicking out
When I come and see my pony, it sometimes turns its behind toward me and tries to kick me. It never used to do this!

Maybe you have spoiled it with too many tidbits which is the ruination of so many nice animals. The occasional treat is fine, but once horses start to "expect" a goodie, they will feel let down like children if it's not there and respond in such a way as to show their displeasure. Walk slowly toward your pony without a tidbit and wait for it to come to you, then pat it and talk to him. A sharp "No" and standing still is the best way to stop its bad behavior. You could give it a break—it may be fed up with humans and enjoy a spell on its own for a while.

ABOVE Rearing is often an expression of freedom and well-being for a horse.

However, such a horse in the right controlling hands could be a champion.

Intelligence

The horse has a small brain in relation to its size, and to humans, its intelligence appears to vary tremendously. Some horses appear remarkably clever, others much less so. All, however, have a special animal cunning which can easily outwit a human in certain situations unless you learn early on to stay "one jump ahead" of your equine friend.

Many horses will find ingenious methods of opening their stable doors or gates. Others will soon learn the quickest route home, and it is up to the rider to ensure the horse goes where directed and is never allowed to take over. Some unfortunately realize that after three jump refusals, they must retire from a competition. A great way of getting out of doing something! When taken back for "a school" to cure this habit, they pop over the jump first time!

Many times after a fall, however, it is the pony who finds its way home to alert others that help is required. For that the animal can be forgiven a lot of their less endearing traits!

Rearing

I went to see a horse to buy and viewed it in its large paddock. It seemed very high-spirited—running around the enclosure and rearing up. I'm worried about the horse rearing. Will it do this when I'm riding it?

There are many reasons why horses rear—it may be startled, displaying its dominant qualities, playing or simply excited and full-of-life. Stallions are particularly fond of showing off in this way!

ABOVE The horse is a herd animal and as such learns much better in company. If loose, most horses tend to follow one another, which is worth remembering when catching. Lead another in and its difficult friend will usually follow!

Rearing while turned out is not necessarily a sign that the horse has developed the vice of rearing while being ridden. But, to be on the safe side if you are thinking of buying any horse or pony you should see the horse being ridden by the vendor to check that it is well-behaved and manageable for you to ride.

CHOOSING AND BUYING A HORSE

Before considering buying a horse or pony, it is essential to think everything through to ensure that you really can cope with owning one. Horses are both time-consuming and expensive, but, if you are prepared to put in the necessary hard work, they make wonderful companions and are a joy to own.

The first question you must ask yourself is whether you can afford a horse. Horses and ponies are fairly expensive to buy, but the cost of upkeep can be enormous also. Year-round feed, stabling, shoeing, veterinary care—such as worming, vaccinations, and dental care—schooling costs, tack and equipment, your own riding gear, transportation, and insurance—all of these add up to substantial expenses.

Do you have the facilities? Do you have a suitable paddock and stabling, or will you have to pay to stable your horse? If you can't afford to pay for full-time care, do you have the time to spare to look after the horse? How often will you be able to ride it?

Who is going to help you if you are a beginner? It's unlikely that basic riding lessons from a local barn or stable will be enough to prepare you to own your own horse. However, if you have also helped to care for horses on weekends or over vacations, then you are probably experienced enough to deal with one at home.

What to look for

Choose a horse that is suitable in temperament, height, and type for you and what you plan to do with it. If you are not an experienced rider, you will need a horse that is quiet and sensible to give you

BELOW Always get your horse vetted to ensure that what you are buying is basically sound in eye, wind, heart, and limb. Consider your veterinarian's findings if there are any problems and be realistic about how you would cope.

the most pleasure. Go for a calm, well-schooled animal that is confident and happy in its work, and easily controlled. Depending on what it is you want to do, choose a horse aged somewhere between five and ten years. If you want an experienced, sensible horse that will get you going and give you confidence, go for something around eight or older. Choose a breed that is suitable for the tasks you require of your horse; such as for endurance or trail riding you need a strong, tough breed such as the Arab. Some breeds are particularly capable at specific roles.

Of all the different factors governing your choice of horse, temperament is the most important of all. Only choose a horse or pony that fits in well with the job you have in mind. And never overwhelm yourself with a flashy animal you simply cannot control.

SUGGESTED SIZE GUIDE

LEFT If you are choosing a horse that needs to be a specific height for a certain activity, have it measured or see its height certificate before deciding to buy.

The height of the horse or pony is important, as nothing is worse than being over-horsed. If buying for children, choose one that is small enough to be handled well, and check that it is not too big or too wide. If your teenager is outgrowing a much-loved pony make sure he or she intends to continue riding before you commit to the expense of buying a horse. Remember that size and shape—of people and horses—will play a key role. Heavy people, for example, require strong horses, such as those of a hunter or cob type. Below is a general guide but much depends on skill and experience.

12.2hh (127 cm) pony—suitable for average size children of 12 or under

13.2-14.2hh (137-147 cm) pony—suitable for average size children of 14 to 16 years

14.2-15.2hh (147-157 cm) horse—suitable for average size children of 14 to 18 years or adults

15.2hh (157 cm) horse and over—suitable for competent riders of all ages

WHERE TO FIND YOUR HORSE/PONY

ABOVE Buying at auction is best left to the professionals.

When you decide to have your own pony or horse and have weighed all the factors involved—where and how to keep it, whether it is affordable—you will need to ensure you have a knowledgeable person to help you choose the right animal for you.

• Reputable dealers may be able to find the perfect animal but you must first tell them what you want, what you hope to do with the animal, and how experienced you are. Your size, weight and age, and your price range will also be needed to assess your requirements accurately.

• Asking friends may be another method, especially if it is a pony you are looking for, as friends may well know of one that is outgrown or no longer required. Check carefully what work the pony has done before.

• Looking at the "For Sale" pages in horsey magazines and local papers will usually provide a mass of possibilities.

• Auction sales are not generally recommended for the first-time buyer because of the difficulty in trying out

horses and ponies properly before the hammer falls and you are committed to buying subject to vetting. If you do go, know what you are looking for and do not get carried away by the occasion or your emotions. Take a knowledgeable person with you and find out all you can. Try to see photographs and ask everything possible about any animal that catches your eye. If it is possible, try to see the horse ridden or at least a photograph of it in action.

If you buy at a sale, you will be expected to produce appropriate funds or banking arrangements on the day and to arrange transportation from the sale. Go prepared for this in case you find what you want right away.

It is essential to know the pitfalls when buying or looking for a horse or pony, as sadly, not everyone is as honest or fair as he or she should be. Make sure you ask plenty of questions and never get drawn into something you do not feel confident about. Take a number and call back later to give yourself time to think before making a final decision.

AVOIDING PROBLEMS

• Make a list of questions to ask regarding the horse's size, color, sex, and whether it is quiet to ride and able to perform those aspects of riding you are interested in.
• Ask the owners if the horse or pony is quiet in traffic, with children, with dogs, other animals, and so on.
• Why are they selling? Do their reasons seem genuine to you?
• Will there be someone there to ride it for you? This is very important: You must ensure the animal is quiet to ride before you get on. Many an accident has occurred by failing to see what type of animal you are about to ride.
• Always check the price they are asking and if not in your range, thank them and cross the horse off your list.

BELOW See the horse ridden first before you try it yourself, and take a knowledgeable person with you to see if he or she thinks it is the right horse for you.

GENERAL CARE

Your horse or pony relies on you to take care of its everyday needs. Whether a top eventer or a favorite family pet, all deserve the best attention you can give to ensure their health and well-being. Food, shelter, and exercise are vital to all horses, and, while geographical locations will inevitably dictate different ways of doing certain things, the basics remain the same worldwide.

Horses thrive on routine, so try to plan a schedule of care FT that is realistic on a daily basis. How you can achieve this all depends on the type of arrangement you have for stabling and/or where the animal is kept. If you have your own stable and land, obviously you can work out a routine that suits your own lifestyle or you may keep your horse at a boarding stable, in which case you will be paying someone else to look after it full time. The horse will even be exercised and turned out into a paddock area for you by the staff during the week and those times when you are unable to do so yourself. The expense varies according to the individual arrangement you have with the owners of the facility.

Do-it-yourself arrangements also exist, where you literally pay for the rental of a box stall and perhaps the use of a paddock and look after it yourself. It's worth bearing in mind that if your horse is likely to be fed by other people, you should display its feed chart prominently. Keep it up to date with any changes, and let everyone know if your horse is on medication (and whether any side effects are likely).

If the animal is kept out at grass, or even just turned out every day, you must make sure there is adequate fodder and fresh water. Pastures must be safe and securely fenced, and free from poisonous plants and trees. Check for potential hazards such as deep holes and broken wire. The emphasis on safety cannot be overemphasized.

RIGHT Some horses and ponies are difficult to catch unless you take some food with you. Be careful doing this if the horse shares the field with others as they may crowd around you. Keep a handful for your horse or pony and tip the rest along the ground. As your horse goes to eat with the others, approach it and offer the separate food. (Left) Gently put on the halter and lead rope (see p.148-149) and lead your horse away. (Right) Keep the bucket in your spare hand—away from your horse or pony.

Safety precautions

Fire can be one of the main hazards at a stable and every effort should be made to ensure that safety precautions are taken. These should include a strict "No Smoking" policy and regular checking of all electrical appliances and wiring (which mice can be especially fond of!). The barn and grounds should be kept free of junk, cans, and bottles, which can ignite (especially in the summer months) and there should be fire extinguishers readily available.

Security precautions

Security is another priority. All fencing should be regularly checked to ensure it is safe and stock-proof, and gates onto'roads

should be padlocked. If the facility is not guarded 24 hours a day—the ideal—security will need special consideration. All stable doors should have extra bottom kickover locks or other horse-proof fixtures, as some animals can become expert escape artists. Consider the various means of horse identification available, just in case of theft. As well as freeze branding, there are other precautions such as microchip implants, lip marking, and hoofbrands (these grow out eventually). Take photographs of your horse or pony, clearly showing both sides, and keep these in a file along with the horse's vaccination card, registration papers, and health records.

Security lighting may be a sensible precaution, and regular checks on the yard cannot be overemphasized. All tack rooms need to be very secure and the contents realistically insured and cataloged.

Stable fittings
What type of electrical fixtures should I use in my horse's stable?

Ideally there should be no electrical fixtures inside the stable, except for lighting. All wires should be encased in piping, and the switch should be outside the stall and out of the horse's reach. The switches should be encased or incapable of causing shocks on touch. There are many safety fixtures available. (See pg.50-53 for more on stable features).

Yard surfacing
My pony is frightened of slipping on the concrete at our barn. What can we do?

Some concrete can become slippery, especially if it has been around for a long time. It may be possible to groove lines or squares into it. Rubber matting can be sealed on top of concrete along the route out of the yard. Alternatively, some non-slip materials, such as rubberized coating or gravel can be poured over existing areas of worn concrete to give greater grip. Never hurry horses on slippery surfaces, especially on turns. Allow them to adjust pace to the new footing.

LEFT A well maintained barn or yard will ensure that all safety features such as fire hoses and extinguishers are in place and that any electrical fixtures are protected and safe. Door fastenings and gates must be secure.

SAFETY KNOT

When tying up your horse, always use a safety knot which consists of a special quick release knot tied as shown. Some horses tend to pull back when tied up. This can cause an accident if the ground is slippery and the horse falls while still tied. To avoid this, it is safest to tie your lead rope with a piece of string to the tie ring, which will then break if the horse starts to struggle.

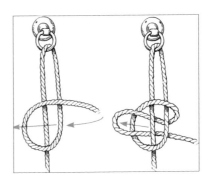

ABOVE Make a loop and pull a loop of rope up through this, but not too tightly.

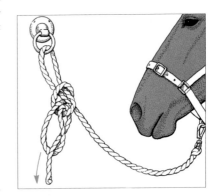

ABOVE The end can be looped back through the loop, but must be pulled out before the loop can be released.

STABLING AND BEDDING

The stable needs to be safe, sheltered and well sited to make it as easy to manage as possible. Running water and storage space for feed and bedding are just the basics, as is an area set out for the muck heap. This needs to be far away enough to reduce the smell and flies, without becoming a major trek every time you clean out the stall or stable.

In Britain, the most typical arrangement in a stable yard consists of a single row of buildings incorporating loose boxes (stables), tack room, and feed room side by side. In the United States, however, you're likely to find everything under one large roof. In this "barn" system, box stalls face each other across a central walkway and all elements of the traditional stable yard (except the muck heap!) are enclosed against the extremes of weather. This all works extremely well, as long as adequate ventilation has been planned into the construction. Similar systems are in operation at the big stud farms in Europe, and are starting to be incorporated into existing agricultural buildings in Britain.

Ideal stable requirements/ fixtures
Stable size

The size of the stall is important to the horse—the bigger the better, to allow more room for movement. The minimum recommended size for box stalls is 10 ft (3 m) square for a pony and about 12 ft (3.7 m) square for a horse. Height, of course, is another consideration. To allow enough head room, ceilings need to be 7 ft (2.1 m) high. Doorways need to be at least 6 ft (1.8 m) high and 4 ft (1.2 m) wide to get the animal in and out safely. Ideally, the roof should overhang the front by about 3 ft (0.9 m) to protect the horse and bedding in bad weather.

Generally, these stalls are constructed of wood, concrete, or brick, or a combination of all three. Many consist of wooden brick, or a combination of all three. Many consist of wooden partitions built on top of a brick or cinder block floor surround to eliminate the problem of wood rotting. Some are made entirely of concrete blocks or brick with just a wooden door. Whatever the construction, allowance should be made for ventilation to ensure a free flow of air without drafts. Any windows should open outward for safety.

Just as important is a good floor base with adequate drainage. Many have slightly sloped concrete floors running into a gully outside the stalls, which then leads into a drain outside the stable area.

RIGHT There are two main types of stabling: those that look out with an overhanging roof to protect horses and helpers from the elements (top); and the internal or "barn" system which tends to have the horses inside under one roof (bottom). This latter system is popular in America and Europe.

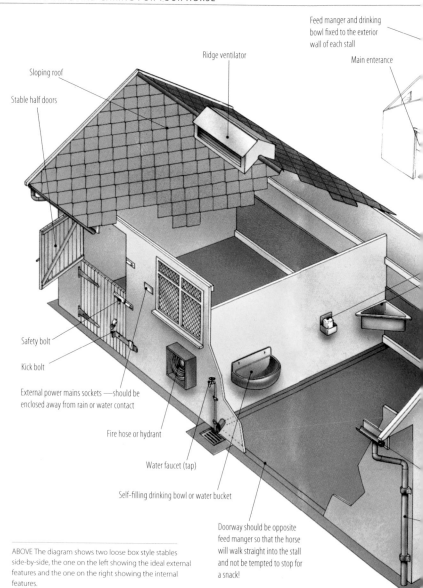

Feed manger and drinking bowl fixed to the exterior wall of each stall

Main enterance

Ridge ventilator

Sloping roof

Stable half doors

Safety bolt

Kick bolt

External power mains sockets —should be enclosed away from rain or water contact

Fire hose or hydrant

Water faucet (tap)

Self-filling drinking bowl or water bucket

Doorway should be opposite feed manger so that the horse will walk straight into the stall and not be tempted to stop for a snack!

ABOVE The diagram shows two loose box style stables side-by-side, the one on the left showing the ideal external features and the one on the right showing the internal features.

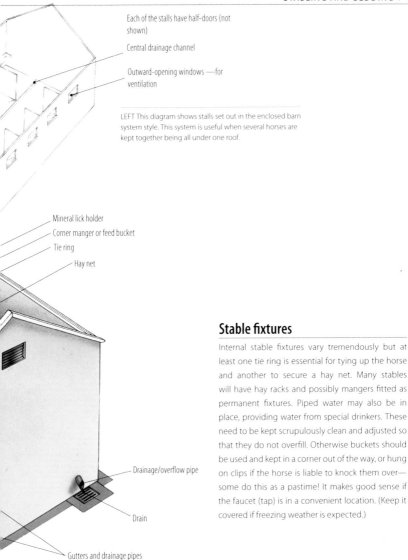

Each of the stalls have half-doors (not shown)

Central drainage channel

Outward-opening windows —for ventilation

LEFT This diagram shows stalls set out in the enclosed barn system style. This system is useful when several horses are kept together being all under one roof.

Mineral lick holder

Corner manger or feed bucket

Tie ring

Hay net

Drainage/overflow pipe

Drain

Gutters and drainage pipes

Stable fixtures

Internal stable fixtures vary tremendously but at least one tie ring is essential for tying up the horse and another to secure a hay net. Many stables will have hay racks and possibly mangers fitted as permanent fixtures. Piped water may also be in place, providing water from special drinkers. These need to be kept scrupulously clean and adjusted so that they do not overfill. Otherwise buckets should be used and kept in a corner out of the way, or hung on clips if the horse is liable to knock them over— some do this as a pastime! It makes good sense if the faucet (tap) is in a convenient location. (Keep it covered if freezing weather is expected.)

ABOVE A well-kept tackroom is a pleasure to use.

Tack rooms

Tack rooms should be easily accessible to the stall or stable area and big enough to accommodate all the necessary bits of equipment. Bridle hooks and saddle racks need to be high enough to ensure that the tack is kept off the ground, and no more than two saddles should ever be placed on top of one another. Western saddles require a rack of their own. A centrally hanging hook is useful for tack cleaning—many are adjustable to different heights. A tack "horse" is a good investment too. It helps to keep the saddle properly supported while it's being cleaned.

ABOVE Keep all tack in good condition by cleaning regularly and storing on appropriate bridle hooks and saddle racks.

Food storage

Storage of food, hay, straw, and other bedding needs careful thought. They have to be as close as possible to the stable area but with consideration to the fact that they pose a fire risk. Hay is normally kept with the bedding, in a barn perhaps, and the feed room itself contains just the grains, concentrates, any supplements and vitamins, and feed buckets. Feed buckets should be dry, and always kept extremely clean. Any storage bins must be vermin-proof.

Fussy feeder
My horse is a very timid feeder. What should I do?

Always ensure the feed bin in the stable is scrupulously Pit clean and well drained and dry before use. Only give small feeds so as not to overwhelm the horse. Experiment with different types of feed and see what it likes or dislikes. Add any succulents such as carrots and apples to its feed as a "tempter." Feed little and often.

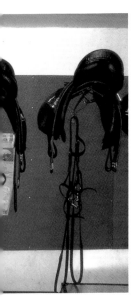

ABOVE If you do not have a hay rack in the stall or loose box (stable) then you can tie a hay net up on a tie ring—ensure that it is kept at the horse's head height. Fix the net securely in place with a safety knot.

Bedding and cleaning out

Cleanliness is an absolute essential throughout the yard, but nowhere more so than in the stall or stable itself. Some types of bedding make this easier to achieve than others, but it's often a matter of personal preference or even a case of what is readily available in your area. Straw, wood shavings, and rubber sheeting are the main types used, although paper and peat are possible alternatives.

Straw The most commonly used bedding, straw comes in three types—wheat, barley, and oat. Wheat is the most resilient and springy; barley is a little softer; oat straw is softer still, but some horses like to eat it. The main drawback to straw is that it can exacerbate respiratory difficulties.

Wood shavings This popular bedding is light and easy to work with, and useful for horses that eat straw or have allergies. If plastic wrapped, it has the advantage of being able to be stored outside. The only disadvantage is that it can be difficult to dispose of because it takes a long time to rot down.

Rubber sheeting This is becoming increasingly popular as an alternative to the above. It can be labor-saving but opinions are divided on whether it

ABOVE A bedding of straw.

is comfortable enough to be used without a light covering of conventional bedding. If bedding, such as wood shavings, is not used, the horse's droppings must be removed frequently to prevent the animal from becoming very soiled when lying down. Without other bedding rubber sheeting can be hosed down daily. It is expensive in the short term but because it is hard wearing works out well over a year or so.

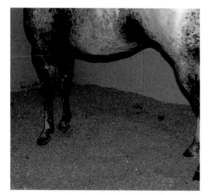

LEFT A bedding of wood shavings.

SHOW DAY — A BUSY TIME FOR A GROOM

When the alarm goes at around 3AM, I often wonder why I chose this job! A quick cup of coffee and out into the gloom of the emerging dawn to get everything ready, muck out and get Weasel ready for the show. We are leaving at 4.30AM!

Weasel looks out with a surprised expression as I bring him his early breakfast and rush off to put all the tack into the trailer. I've made a list and check it off, then quickly braid (plait) Weasel's mane and tail—his mane is a bit difficult to see in the glare of the overhead light. I then put on his travel gear—protective boots, bandage on the braided tail, and blanket (rug) (see pg.100 and 104-105). Another groom, Susie, starts up the truck's engine after making all the safety checks (see p.100) and we are all set to go the 100 miles (160km) 2½ hour trip. Crazy!

The show was great—Weasel was 3rd in one class and got a lovely yellow rosette. I was proud of his gleaming coat and polished tack.

At the end, we packed everything up and set off on what always seems like a long trip home because everyone is so tired. During the trip Weasel was munching his hay from the net I tied in the box, and Susie and I had our sandwiches. Home at last and a flurry of activity to unpack, clean out the trailer, unhitch the truck, and feed Weasel who was feeling very pleased with himself.

Finally a bit of supper and the longed for shower —then bed. I was too tired to even dream of the next show!

GROOMING

Grooming is one of the most rewarding chores. Not only does it help to clean the animal but it also stimulates the circulation of the horse or pony. It is the perfect time to really get to know your horse, as a good grooming session will take up to three-quarters of an hour.

Grooming should be done on a daily basis with the stabled horse. Grass-kept horses and ponies should not be over-groomed, however, as this will remove the natural oils that are keeping them warm. It should be enough just to pick out their feet and remove any mud and stains before tacking up.

The basic grooming kit

1. Hoof pick This is used from heel to toe for picking out dirt from hooves.

2. Hard brush (Dandy brush) This stiff brush is for initial cleaning of mud or dirt from unclipped horses. Do not use on clipped or sensitive-skinned horses or on the tail where it will pull and tear the hairs. Use with short, sharp strokes.

3. Soft brush (Body brush) This is used for removing grease and dust from the coats of fine-skinned or clipped horses, and for cleaning the head and the insides of the legs. Care must be taken in these areas not to knock the prominent bones around the eye, the knees, and hocks—which are extremely sensitive. The soft brush is used in conjunction with a metal curry comb (a cleaning device for the brush). The sequence is, one brush of the horse, one scrape across the metal curry comb with the soft brush to remove dirt, one brush, one scrape, and so on.

4. Metal curry comb Actually a cleaning device, this is used for removing grease from the soft brush only and never used on the horse. Grease can be tapped out of the curry on the floor as necessary. It is held in the opposite hand to the soft brush.

5. Stable rubber This acts like a dust cloth and is used all over the horse to give a final shine to the coat.

6. Water brush Used wet, this helps to lay the mane and tail at the end of the grooming session. A separate water brush is useful for washing the feet.

7. Sponge A most important part of the kit, the sponge is used for wiping the horse's eyes, nostrils, and under the dock. Always keep a separate sponge for the horse's face and for the dock or tail area.

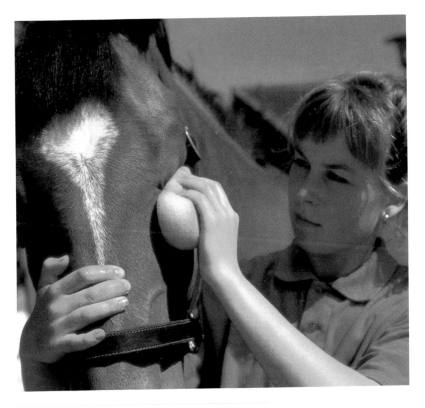

ABOVE You should ensure that you use clean cloths or sponges when wiping your horse's eyes and muzzle as infections spread to these areas can be irritating to the animal and troublesome for you to clear-up.

6. Water brush

5. Stable rubber

9. Rubber curry comb

RIGHT A basic grooming kit with items most commonly found. It should be kept clean and washed approximately once a week.

10. Mane and tail comb

2. Hard (Dandy) brush

1. Hoof pick

Other useful grooming aids

8. Plastic curry comb This makes a useful substitute for the metal curry comb, especially for children to use. This one can be used on the horse for removing mud and loose hair and tidying manes and tails.

3. Soft (Body) brush

8. Plastic curry comb

4. Metal curry comb

7. Sponge

grease to the surface.

10. Mane and tail combs Such combs are useful for removing minor tangles and for "pulling" the mane and tail (which are usually tidied up during grooming sessions).

Grooming mitt Rubber or cactus and rubber mittens can be used to remove grease, sweat, and mud from the coat. The mitten is rubbed in a circular fashion all over the coat.

Cactus cloth Similar to a grooming mitt, this cloth is used damp and will help to promote shine to the coat.

Trimming scissors Large scissors can be used to tidy the horse's heels, in conjunction with a mane comb, or to trim a small area of mane behind the ears as a "bridleway" for the bridle to rest comfortably.

Grooming machines These labor-saving devices are to be found in some of the larger stables and can be hand-held or strapped to the waist. They act like a mini vacuum cleaner, loosening dust and grease. They are best used on the horse once or twice a week with manual grooming in-between.

Electric clippers Used for trimming excess hair on the horse's head, feet, or, at the end of winter, its entire body. Great patience—as well as positive reinforcement—must be used to accustom most horses to the sound and feel of the clippers.

Sweat scraper Used for removing excess water after the horse has been washed down after riding.

9. Rubber curry comb This is a softer curry, designed for allover use on the horse. Applied in a circular motion all over the coat, it will help bring the

TIPS FOR GROOMING

• Always tie up your horse or pony before grooming and ensure that it is dry before you start. If the coat is damp you will not be able to groom properly so it is best to wait until the coat has dried.
• Position yourself safely at all times, never directly in front of or behind the animal. Even the quietest horse or pony can react to an irritating fly or a sudden noise.
• Make sure your grooming kit is washed regularly—once a week is usual to keep it clean and fresh.
• Always be vigilant if you see any unusual skin problems

or scaly round areas that could indicate ringworm (see p.128-129) which would be contagious. Grooming kits can spread infections from one horse to another very quickly, so if in any doubt wash the entire kit in disinfectant. Keep one brush or kit for the suspect horse until the situation has been clarified.
• Grooming time gives you a good chance to check the horse's feet thoroughly so that you may notice any foot problems developing (see pg.118-125) and whether shoes are coming loose.

Oiling hooves
When should I oil my horse's feet and what does it do apart from improving their appearance?

Oiling the feet has little effect on the actual hoof but helps to keep the surface moist. In dry weather, hooves tend to become brittle. If there is serious hoof brittleness, it is best to discuss this with your farrier who will recommend a specific supplement to correct the condition.

BELOW You should make sure your horse or pony gets used to you picking up its feet so that you can oil the hooves and pick out dirt. To pick up the foot of the horse, slide your hand down the leg and, if necessary, gently tap the side until it is raised.

Grooming routine

Grooming is one of the most rewarding moments of horse care and gives you the best chance of getting to know your horse and all its little eccentricities which make your animal so special to you. Some will be very ticklish in a certain spot while others are headshy or hate their ears being touched. It is the perfect opportunity to really study your horse or pony.

ABOVE Picking out feet should be done daily before and after exercise. Oil the feet two to four times a week with a small brush in order to keep them moist and in good condition.

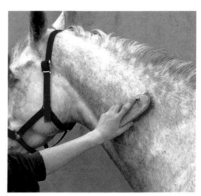

ABOVE The dandy brush should only be used to remove dirt from long coats. It is too tough to use on fine skinned animals except with very gentle strokes.

ABOVE The body brush is used with a sharp scrape through the curry comb to clean it of dust after each stroke or after every two or three strokes.

ABOVE Great care must be taken not to pull out tail hairs when brushing. Hairs are best separated gently by hand. Only brush the tail once a week.

ABOVE Two sponges are needed—one to wipe around eyes and nostrils, the other to sponge under the tail and dock area. This is most refreshing for the horse and should be done daily.

ABOVE The mane (if not too long), is best tidied with a plastic curry comb or a body brush, but this will have little effect unless the mane is kept short and neat.

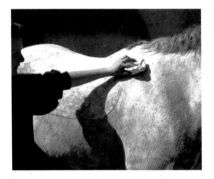

ABOVE The stable rubber removes any excess grease or dust on top of the coat for a final shine. Dampened with hot water, it is excellent for cleaning a recently clipped horse.

Sensitive underbelly
My horse kicks out and tries to lie down whenever I touch his underbelly. How should I handle him?

It would probably be best to give him a fresh hay net to occupy his mind before starting. Ensure he is a bit hungry first! Maybe you're being a bit too vigorous with your grooming, especially if he is a thin-skinned horse, so make your grooming strokes softer and slower. Be firm with your voice. The horse may understand a sharp "No." Reward him with praise when he's good.

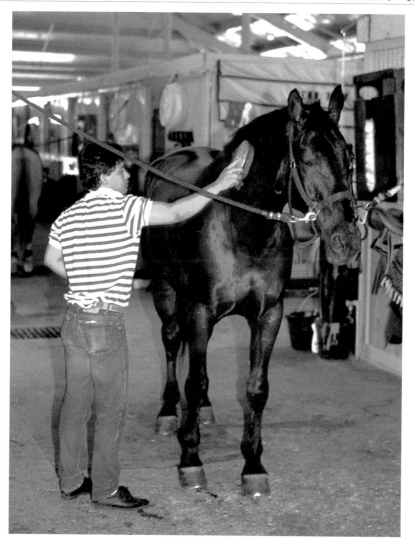

ABOVE The use of "rack chains" allows the handler to keep the horse straight and work on both sides. They are attached to either side of the halter. Never attach to a bit. Quick-release chains age recommended in case the horse panics.

BLANKETS

Stabled horses need some form of blanket (rug) to keep warm, depending on the weather conditions, the breed, and whether or not they have been clipped (see pg.72-75). Keeping your horse warm will help the animal keep in good condition as the horse will not be using its energy stores just to keep warm.

These days, there are numerous types of horse blankets (rugs) available, catering to all horses and ponies. Most are designed so that they stay in place through careful shaping and are "self-righting" if the horse rolls. A variety of fastenings and/or leg straps assist in this. Choose a blanket that is suitable, easy to put on and adjust, and not too heavy.

Types of blanket

There are several different designs to use for different situations.

Stable blanket This is a warm blanket, usually made of cozy quilted material of different weights, for use in the stable. Often there are special fittings to keep them in place, or they can be used with a "roller" (a special strap to stop slippage). Under blanket This is a generally shaped basic blanket without the durable outer layer. It is designed to go under the stable blanket for extra warmth. It may require a roller to keep in place. Always ensure the skin is wrinkle-free under the roller to prevent chafing.

Sheets Usually made of cotton or a cotton mix, sheets are light and suitable for summer wear. They are also used under other, heavier blankets to keep them clean. Cooler This is a large, very light sheet that covers the horse from its ears to its tail. Always light in color, they deflect the sun's rays and protect the horse from flies. They also keep the horse dust-free.

Anti-sweat sheets These meshed sheets are designed to allow the horse to cool down without catching a chill or to prevent sweating. Made of various types of loose cotton-based mesh materials, they are especially useful for travel and after exercise. They are extremely effective at keeping warmth close to the horse when used with other blankets placed on top.

Heavy winter blanket (sometimes called a New Zealand blanket) Horses kept outside in inclement weather usually need to wear a New Zealand blanket. They are designed to be weatherproof and non-slip, and have a variety of harness leg straps to ensure they remain in place. It is important to ensure that the leg straps are kept soft and supple to prevent chafing and soreness and to monitor carefully the horse wearing it to prevent any blanket-related accidents.

Blanket problems
My pony gets very sore on her shoulders when she wears her heavy, winter blanket. What can I do about it?

The continual motion of your pony moving around her paddock is causing friction rubs. These can be prevented by getting the pony a specially designed shoulder vest or bib, or by attaching some thick plastic to the inside shoulder area of her blanket. Always check that the blanket is the right size for the pony. Some designs are better suited to certain shapes than others.

ABOVE Quilted stable blankets are light and easy to use as well as being warm. This one has fastenings and is well fitted.

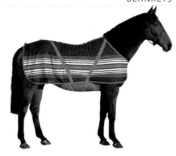

ABOVE This lightweight cotton sheet is secured with criss-cross straps to hold it in place.

ABOVE This smart day blanket has a hooped anti-cast roller which is designed to prevent the horse rolling right over and getting cast (stuck) against a wall.

ABOVE The all weather New Zealand blanket gives the horse great protection against bad weather. It has special leg fastenings.

FITTING BLANKETS

ABOVE The top diagrams show how to fold a woolen Witney blanket, which has a day or night blanket (rug) placed on top and is then folded back and kept in place with a roller.

You must ensure that whatever blanket (rug) you choose to use is fitted properly and has all the buckles or ties fastened securely. An ill-fitting blanket or loose strap could cause the horse or pony to get tangled up and fall badly.

RIGHT Leg straps on New Zealand blankets must be crossed over between the hind legs to prevent any chafing.

BRAIDING

A braided (plaited) mane and tail show off your horse to its best advantage and are regarded as part of a neat turn-out. Although you will not need to braid every day it is a good idea to get your horse used to it by practicing regularly. It is usual to braid your horse for the show ring, when entering large competitions, and for hunting.

It takes a lot of practice to achieve perfect-looking braids, so don't be disheartened if your first attempts are a disaster! The starting point is a well-pulled mane—if it's too thick, it will not braid well. Similarly, the tail needs to be full and not rubbed. Do not shampoo the mane and tail beforehand—it will make the hair too slippery and flyaway.

Manes

Study your horse's neck to see how to present the mane at its best. A thick cresty neck will look finer with neat braids pulled down into the crest. A rather weak neck will be enhanced with larger braids placed on top. There is no limit to how many braids you can do in the mane, as long as they are evenly spaced. You can finish off with the English method, which is a "button" effect, or the continental style of a long fold of braid usually taped in white. The forelock is done separately in the same style as the mane. The braids can be secured with thread, which should match the color of the mane, or rubber bands.

Braiding problems
When I braid my horse's mane it seems to fall apart very quickly. Where am I going wrong?

Always dampen the mane first, then take three even sections of hair and braid together tightly before securing the end with thread or rubber bands. It will remain tight for you to either roll or loop the braid into the form you require. No mane will braid well unless it has been pulled to the same thickness and length down the full length of the neck.

LEFT This running or Arabian braid is also known as a Gypsy braid and is used on horses with unusually long flowing manes.

How to braid the mane

Braiding is an art that needs plenty of practice to achieve really good results. The secret is to separate the sections of mane to be braided into even sections, dampen these well, and make each braid firm and secure. In the English method, the braid is folded once or twice, depending on the length of the mane, and secured with thread, which looks best, or tightly-twisted rubber bands.

ABOVE Start by separating a section of mane and braiding it firmly down to the end. It is best to start at the top.

ABOVE After securing the end with thread or rubber bands, fold up once or twice and secure with the same method on top of the neck.

ABOVE After completing all the braids down the neck, finish off by braiding the forelock, taking care to keep it straight.

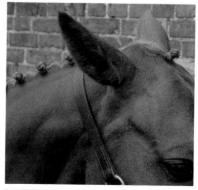

ABOVE If there are any wisps of hair left they can be gently plucked out to leave a neat and tidy head and neck

Braiding tails

To achieve the best results you need a full, untrimmed tail with plenty of length to the hairs at the top of the tail. The secret of success is to keep the hairs evenly spaced. Try to include an even amount of hair from each side, all the way down the length of the dock. The braid formed down the center of the tail must be kept straight and tidy for maximum effect.

How to braid the mane: Continental style

Continental braids can look very effective if done well with small, even braids secured with white tape down the neck (as shown). They are quite eye-catching when used with the white numnahs seen on dressage horses in particular. Continental braids can be difficult to get right but with a little patience you will achieve a good result.

LEFT The finished tail looks neat and tidy with the actual braid kept centrally spaced down the tail.

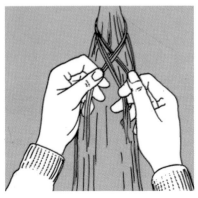

ABOVE Take sections from both sides.

ABOVE Braid down center for two thirds of dock.

ABOVE The start is exactly the same with the mane divided into even sections. Braid tightly and loop the mane up once.

ABOVE Leave approximately 1-1¼ in (2-3 cm) of mane as a loop and secure with thread or rubber bands.

ABOVE Take white tape and wind around the braid, leaving a neat bud of mane showing at the end.

ABOVE Keep the white tape at the same width up the neck to give a really good, even effect.

Problems "Pulling" tail
My horse clamps its tail down and kicks out whenever I try to "pull" his tail. Should I leave it?

A full tail looks nice on many horses and can always be braided if it is suitable. Twitching the horse (see glossary) will usually work to ensure that he does not kick but do watch out for unpredictable behavior. Gently pat him on the rump several times and try to reassure him by pulling just a few hairs at a time from his tail.

CLIPPING

Nature provides the horse with a new summer and winter coat according to the season, but that does not necessarily suit an animal that's working all year round. To ensure your horse or pony stays in top condition you should choose a clip that suits its lifestyle.

You can't expect a horse to be ridden, driven, or compete with a thick winter coat, especially if it's being stabled the rest of the time. Removing the coat has many advantages for the well-being of the horse.

•It enables the animal to work hard without undue stress (and so loss of condition) from sweating caused by a heavy coat.

•It prevents chills. Horses with a thick coat tend to dry slowly, particularly in cold weather.

•You are able to assess the horse's condition much quicker with a clipped coat. You can see at a glance if there are any medical problems.

•It is easier to keep clean and looking attractive.

The coat is removed with a set of clippers, and these come in various designs. Most common are electric clippers, which usually consist of a hand-held motor with blades attached. Always clean the blades after use and keep them well-oiled and in good order for the next time. Sharp blades are a must for a clean, neat cut. It is best to have two sets so that if one is blunt and requires sharpening you have a spare set on hand.

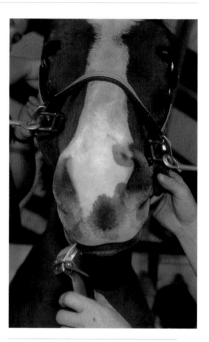

ABOVE Trimming whiskers may prove a ticklish job. The careful use of scissors or a razor may be an alternative.

Preparing to clip

Choose a safe area with good light and a non-slip floor. Give your horse a thorough grooming and ensure that it is dry before you start—clipper blades will not run through a dirty or wet coat. Ideally, the horse should have been stabled and groomed for a few days beforehand. If the horse has never been clipped before, it is a good idea to let it see another horse being done. Let it see, hear, and smell the clippers, and feel them against its coat several times.

Always have an assistant hold a young or nervous horse until it is settled and accustomed to the procedure. Patience will really pay off with the first clip. Some horses may require twitching—usually just for the head area—but avoid doing this if at all possible. Often patience is all that is required—or a handful of food to occupy the mind. Have a blanket on hand to place over the clipped area to prevent the animal from getting cold. Wear overalls and head gear to prevent the hairs from sticking to your clothes.

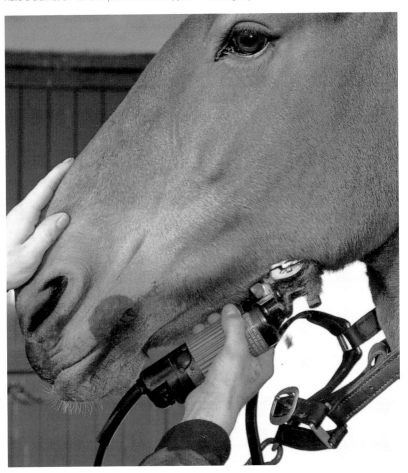

ABOVE The head and face are the most difficult parts to clip. Make sure the horse is kept calm and its head is held still while clipping this area.

Start at the front—the lower neck is usually a good starting point. Allow the horse to settle, then work your way back in sections. Go over any areas that need it two or three times until all is smooth.

Always clip against the lie of the coat and use long sweeping strokes whenever possible. Do one area at a time, keeping the blades close and flat to the skin so as not to produce "lines" in the coat from uneven pressure. Keep the blades well-oiled during the clip. This stops them from getting too hot and burning the horse's skin. If they do become overheated, turn them off until they cool down. Only do sensitive areas such as the head, under the belly, and inside of the legs when the blades are very cool.

Clip the main body of the horse first and, if cold, cover with a blanket before starting on the more sensitive, difficult areas (where you will need to gently stretch the skin to give a flat surface to clip). The front legs will need to be lifted and pulled forward to enable a successful clip around the chest and girth areas. Avoid nicking the skin.

When you have finished, quickly brush the horse all over (rubbing the coat with a hot, damp towel will remove surface grease). Then, blanket the horse immediately. If the horse seems a bit unsettled, take it for a nibble of grass or a short walk before putting it in the stall. Check that the horse is warm enough, especially if a very thick coat has been removed.

Types of clip

The various clips are designed to suit different horses and the kind of work they are expected to do.

Full clip All the hair is removed with a full clip. It is used for fit, stabled horses in hard work.

Hunter clip The legs and saddle patch are left on but the rest of the hair is removed with a hunter clip. Used for hunters and many competition horses because the leg hairs give extra protection, it is suitable for all horses in work.

Blanket clip This leaves hair on a blanket-shaped area on the back and the legs. It is suitable for stabled horses that feel the cold or those in medium work.

Trace clip Hair is removed below a horizontal line running from the buttock through to the shoulder and up the lower neck with a trace clip. The legs are left on. This is popular for working horses and ponies ridden occasionally during winter months.

There are many other variations on these clips, depending on owners' preferences or on how much and where the horse tends to sweat. Some people leave half the head unclipped, following a vertical line down the cheek piece of the bridle. Some horses hate their ears being touched, and leaving these will help to keep it warm. There is no point in upsetting the horse unnecessarily so long as the finished effect is neat and tidy. In exceptionally difficult cases your veterinarian may recommend a tranquilizer, but this is rarely necessary if you take the time to gain the horse's confidence.

Hunter clip

Blanket clip

Trace clip

SHOEING

There's a lot of truth in the old saying, "No foot, no horse". Healthy feet are essential to a horse's well-being. They have to be trimmed at the right angle to keep them balanced and in good condition, and shod correctly for shape and the type of work expected of the horse.

In general, shoeing needs to be done every four to six l weeks, but even a horse that goes without shoes still needs the regular attention of a farrier. Many ponies and horses in light work may not require shoes, particularly if they have tough hardy feet. In this case, feet need to be kept trimmed and shaped correctly every four to eight weeks, depending on the climate and their rate of growth. If the shoe is kept on too long the feet will overgrow and cause pressure which will probably lead to lameness.

Shoes may be fitted through hot or cold shoeing. With hot shoeing, it is possible for the farrier to change the shape of the shoe to properly fit the foot. With cold shoeing, the shoe is pre-cast in different sizes designed to fit most feet.

Types of shoe: For work and correction

There are many different types of shoe, and it is best to discuss your horse's requirements with your farrier. Horses in heavy work may need strong, thick shoes, whereas a racehorse galloping on soft ground is usually shod with light aluminum plates or even plastic shoes for extra speed. Gaited horses and driving horses need special shoes, and this varies according to what is required of them. Even conformational problems can be minimized by special shoeing, as can faulty actions such as swinging a leg. Injuries or disease, such as laminitis (see p.120), can also be helped with remedial shoeing, and close cooperation between veterinarian and farrier is essential in such situations.

Worldwide, most horses are shod with iron or steel metal shoes, either fullered (grooved) or plain. Fullered shoes are lighter and give better grip. A single central toe clip is usual on a front shoe, but this is not used on light racing plates. For hind shoes, there is usually a clip on either side of the toe to hold the shoe in position.

For competitive work, it's a good idea to use studs for extra grip. You can screw these in yourself

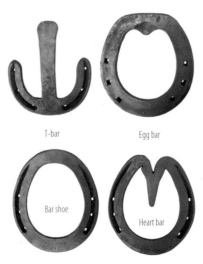

T-bar

Egg bar

Bar shoe

Heart bar

with a spanner into pre-drilled holes in the heel of the shoe. The size and shape of the studs depend very much on ground conditions and personal preference. Never leave them in for long periods of time, and never use them on roads. They could start problems by causing unaccustomed positioning of the foot, especially if the animal is on hard ground or left in the trailer.

ABOVE & LEFT Four different shoes. Top left is a typical aluminum racing plate. Bottom left is a wide web shoe giving a larger weight-bearing surface. Top right is a general purpose front shoe. Bottom right is a general purpose hind shoe. Pictured far right are remedial shoes. (Left) Selection of shoe studs.

HOT SHOEING

1. The old shoe is removed, if necessary, and any reshaping or trimming carried out.

2. The hot shoe that has been shaped to the correct size in the furnace is fitted to the foot. The charring indicates any adjustments required to be made to either the foot or the shoe.

3. The shoe is cooled in water, then fitted and nailed in place with correctly angled nails (studs).

4. The nail ends are twisted off and bent downward to form the clenches, which effectively keep the shoe in place.

5. The foot is finished off with rasping around the clench lines to ensure there are no rough edges.

BELOW If the farrier trims the feet at the correct angle each time it will limit the chances of your horse needing remedial work.

Trimming

My mare will not be ridden for three months; do I need to do anything about her feet?

Yes. She will need her feet trimmed every six to eight weeks. If she has shoes on, these can either be taken off altogether or just the hind ones may be removed. Talk to your farrier about how she would be best protected. If she is out with company, it is usually safest to keep her hind shoes off to reduce the likelihood of kicking injuries. Front feet are more flared and, being weight-bearing, tend to crack more easily than the hind ones. Keeping the front shoes on will help to protect them.

BELOW A paring knife is used to scrape away any excess horn on the sole of the foot before the shoe is put on. It is also used to tidy the frog.

Supplements

Some horses suffer from brittle or dry hooves, particularly in hot weather, and this can lead to foot problems. It may be necessary to feed a supplement containing amino acids to help promote healthy horn—discuss this with your veterinarian or farrier. Although you can oil the hooves (see Grooming pg.101-102), generally topical applications rarely do much for the foot itself, but they do help the appearance.

HOW A SHOE IS REMOVED

1. The clenches (or old nails) are loosened with the use of a hammer and a tool called a buffer.

2. Using pincers, the old shoe is levered off.

3. Hoof cutters are used to trim the excess horn.

4. A rasp is used to level and tidy the foot, now ready for re-shoeing or to be left unshod.

EXERCISE

In the wild, a horse roams at will and so is always in a permanent state of fitness. This is not the case with a stabled horse, however, because it is prevented from moving around for long periods of time. Exercise is vital to good health, so it is important to ensure that this element of your horse's well-being is given serious thought.

The type of work expected from your horse will be the deciding factor. If it is doing strenuous work daily on a farm or ranch, it will be fit. If it is only ridden on weekends, it will need some form of exercise during the rest of the week. A horse that is competing regularly, in whatever sporting discipline, will require fitness work on a daily basis (see pg.84-87).

Most horses that are kept for pleasure do not need to be ridden every day, but they do need to let off steam, have a buck or roll, or at least have the opportunity to spend an hour or two out in the paddock eating grass as nature intended.

BELOW Riding one horse and leading another can be a useful method of getting two horses exercised at one time. Keep the led horse on the inside, away from traffic.

ABOVE Lungeing loose allows the horse to have a buck and a kick. If the horse gets too exuberant or needs serious work, put a roller and side reins on for better control.

Types of Exercise

Exercise can be carried out in several different ways, depending on your lifestyle and what is expected from the horse:

• Turning out—this will exercise the horse but it won't keep it fit.

• Riding daily—this will ensure that the horse gets the exercise it needs for fitness. It will also keep the horse under control, which can mean less chance of accidents.

• Lungeing—this gives relatively controlled exercise. The method of lungeing will determine the degree of the workout.

• Leading from another horse (ponying)—this enables the busy rider to exercise two horses at once.

• Hot walkers (Horse walker)—this is a useful aid for giving exercise to large numbers of horses in a busy stable.

• Hand walking—a satisfying form of exercise for those who have the time, this helps the handler to keep fit as well as the horse or pony!

Change in temperament
My mare has become stubborn and sluggish out on our daily rides, yet she used to be so cheerful and alert. How can I regain her interest?

There are a number of possibilities for this change in behavior. First, is she getting enough food? If you are going out for long rides, it could be that you need to increase the amount of food to give her the necessary energy. Second, how does she look? Is she ill or suffering from a virus? Consult your veterinarian if there has been a recent change in her condition. Third, it could be that you are following the same routine too often and that your mare is suffering from a simple case of boredom. Ride her in company and vary your work.

Warning: overfresh horse!

Whatever type of exercise is chosen, safety must be the top priority. A stabled horse that is not given adequate exercise can become out of control and dangerous, if allowed. Regulate the amount of food according to the ratio of exercise or work. If the horse starts to become overfresh, it is not having enough exercise to burn off the built-up energy. Some horses require much more exercise than others, depending on their breed and temperament. Sometimes, a spell of a few weeks, or even days, out in a paddock will relax a horse that has become overfresh after being stabled for a long time.

Overfresh pony

The pony my child rides has had to be kept in with a heel infection but now looks very overfresh. I do not want to turn him out in the mud. What should I do?

It is better to be safe than sorry, and if the pony cannot be lunged or ridden by an adult first, it would be best to turn him out for a gallop to let off steam before allowing your child to ride him, or ride him yourself. Safety comes first and the sore heel can be cleaned up properly afterwards.

LEFT Nothing is more enjoyable or relaxing than a quiet trail ride out in the country with friends. Horses enjoy the company of others—especially when they are being exercised by riding.

FITNESS

Like an athlete, a horse needs to be fit if it is going to perform to its best ability—particularly in competitive sports of any kind. And, like an athlete, a horse cannot be expected to go from a life of leisure to one where it has to perform a specific role. A horse has to be prepared in a logical way to bring it up to a fit condition. Only then will it be equipped to cope with the demands being made on it with the minimum degree of stress.

Presuming that all health care needs are attended to—such as worming and vaccinations—basic fitness training is much the same for all horses. Start slowly, and build up the fitness work gradually. When a horse returns to work after a lay-off period, the first month is spent conditioning the horse's muscles, tendons, and ligaments in preparation for the more serious work to come (see "progressive work"). During this time, the horse must be ridden forward well to encourage it to use its muscles and not be allowed to dawdle. Keep to good, consistent ground on roads or tracks, or whatever is available. Only walk and slow-trot on the roads so that your horse is not jarred by the concussion effect. Slippery or deep ground will increase the chance of slides and strains.

RIGHT Controlled galloping up gradual or gentle slopes on good ground is on of the most popular forms of fitness work—the horses really enjoy it.

Progressive work

Once the initial slow fitness work is completed, more specific work relevant to what your horse is expected to do can commence, such as arena schooling for dressage, jumping, or pony club events. Again, ensure that any changes are introduced gradually, and that distances, for example, are increased bit by bit. It's important to adjust your horse's feeding routine to reflect the change in the work, bearing in mind the animal's age, type, temperament, and the amount of physical activity.

Traning plan

As the training for specific roles is established, this must be interspersed with the continuance of fitness work. Generally, most competition trainers alternate three days of fitness work with three days of specific training a week until the horse reaches the required condition. Maintaining this then requires careful balance so that the horse does not become stale from being "overtrained". Generally, this can be prevented by giving the horse a few easy days every now and then, either by turning out or just hacking quietly instead of schooling and working. Remember to adjust the horse's food accordingly during such times.

Fitness aids

Many competition trainers use mechanical aids such as hot walkers, treadmills, and swimming pools to help with their fitness programs. These aids can be enormously beneficial if used sensibly. If you have the opportunity to gain access to such aids, give your horse time to adjust to the unfamiliar. Only if the horse is relaxed mentally and physically will it get the full benefit from them.

BELOW: SWIMMING POOL Swimming is excellent to help clear the wind, giving the legs rest from jarring. Once again, it is vital to adjust the horse gradually to this form of exercise. Swimming is strenuous and must never be overdone.

LEFT: TREADMILL Another useful fitness aid, treadmills take up little space. Horses must be warmed up gradually on a treadmill before attempting anything too strenuous at speed or on a slope. They do need to have already done some fitness work before using a treadmill for the first time.

RIGHT: HOT WALKER These are excellent for warming horses up before serious work, for cooling them down afterward, and for maintaining fitness. Many professional trainers like their horses out of their stables at least twice a day, with fitness and schooling done in the morning and exercise on the walker later in the day.

FEEDING

Feeding horses to enable them to perform at their best, and to maintain condition regardless of the environment, requires a careful balance of the right foods. The horse is a herbivore and as such is never happier than when eating grass, which should be its main source of food whenever possible.

Correct feeding generally requires the advice of an experienced professional. However, there are certain rules relative to feeding, which every caring horse person should know. Observation of these will help to minimize any problems.

Overfeeding

It is important not to overfeed your horse or pony. Apart from becoming too fat, the animal may become over-fresh and rank, and start to suffer from health problems because of the nutritional imbalance. Obesity is a prime cause of laminitis, a disease of the foot that causes intense pain. Observe your horse and note whether it is putting on or losing weight, and act to keep it healthy for the type of work it is doing. Remember that while the weight of the horse is the basic determining factor in the quantities of feed required, breeding, temperament, condition, and type of work are important considerations as well.

Little and often

Horses have very small stomachs. In the wild, they would have spent around 18 hours a day picking and grazing at will, which enabled the food to "trickle" through the gut. If the stomach is overloaded, the food is pushed through too fast to be digested properly, and this can lead to health problems, such as colic (stomach ache), swollen legs, and skin rashes.

Turning out

Being a herbivore, the horse's most natural feed is grass. If the horse is not out to pasture, it should be fed hay. The more roughage the horse has the happier it will be. It is this fiber that stimulates the gut to work efficiently.

Grass contains not only roughage but also essential moisture (70-80 percent water). Turn your horse out daily if you can. If you can't, feed succulents such as carrots to make up for it.

If your horse cannot be kept out to pasture you will need to work out how much feed it will need, such as hay and concentrates (which are pure oats, barley, or maize), see the charts on p.104 for general advice.

RIGHT It is important that the horse is fed according to the work it is doing and treated as an individual. Feed buckets must be kept scrupulously clean. The food used must be of good quality. (Always check that each bag used is within the recommended date of consumption).

ABOVE Horses out at grass must have adequate fodder and be allowed plenty of space. Always check that the paddock has freely available fresh water. In poor weather, the grass-kept horse may require extra food such as hay or a daily bucket of feed to supplement the grazing.

Routine

Horses are creatures of habit, so work out a routine for feeding at the same time every day. If you are in a stable with others, arrange a time that suits everyone. For horses or ponies out in the field together, take care that you do not get kicked when feeding. Horses can become aggressive at mealtimes, so put some food down quickly in one place then distribute the remainder nearby.

Feeding a greedy horse
My horse keeps knocking his feed out of his manger.

Many horses do this, especially greedy ones. Try a feed Pi manger with bars so that he cannot swing his head so much. Add more roughage, including chop, to his feed so that he cannot eat it so quickly.

Fresh water

Without water, no animal can survive. Always check that fresh, clean water is freely available. In cold weather it may be necessary to break up ice to ensure that the horse can drink, or you may need to take containers to the paddock. Always clean buckets daily before refilling. If the horse drinks from streams, ensure that the area is safe and the water clean and easy to get to (and not liable to dry up in the summer months).

Exercise

After feeding, allow at least an hour, preferably two, before you exercise. A full stomach will result in pressure on the lungs, which will interfere with the horse's respiratory system. Food that has not been properly digested will be forced into the intestines early and could cause colic.

Making changes

Never change your horse's food suddenly. The digestive system is quite sensitive and bacteria in the gut need time to adapt, as do the enzymes in the digestive juices that help to break down the food. Any dietary changes should be introduced gradually, along with the existing feed, over a period of a week to ten days. Alter the diet only if absolutely necessary. Take care to ensure you always have adequate feed on hand so that sudden not needed.

BELOW Water must be freely available to all horses. A water trough such as this one would be better sited under the fence to prevent the horse from knocking itself.

GENERAL GUIDE TO FEEDING

Below are suggestions for feeding depending on type of horse and work required.

	TYPE OF WORK	MORNING	EVENING	RATIO HAY TO CONCENTRATES
PONY CLUB PONY/ LIGHT RIDING HORSE	Rest	None	None	100% hay/grass
	Light work	1.1 lb (0.5 kg) 8% mix	1.1 lb (0.5 kg) pastur nuts	85% hay 15% concentrates
	Medium work	1.1 lb (0.5 kg) mix + 1.1 lb (0.5 kg) chaff	1.1 lb (0.5 kg) mix + 1.1 lb (0.5 kg) chaff	80% hay 20% concentrates
	Hard work	1.65 lb (0.75 kg) mix + 1.1 lb (0.5 kg) chaff	2.2 lb (1 kg) mix + 1.1 lb (0.5 kg) chaff	75% hay 25% concentrates
RIDING HORSE/ COMPETITION PONY	Rest	None	None	100% hay/grass
	Light work	2.2 lb (1 kg) 10-12% mix	2.2 lb (1 kg) mix + 1.1 1b (0.5 kg) chaff	85% hay 15% concentrates
	Medium work	2.74 lb (1.25 kg) mix	2.74 lb (1.25 kg) mix + 1.1 lb (0.5 kg) chaff	75% hay 25% concentrates
	Hard work	3.85 lb (1.25 kg) mix	3.85 lb (1.75 kg) mix + 1.1 lb (0.5 kg) chaff	65% hay 35% concentrates
COMPETITION HORSE	Rest	None	2.2 lb (1 kg) 12% protein mix	100% hay/grass
	Light work	2.2 lb (1 kg) 14% protein mix	2.2 lb (1 kg) mix + 1.1 lb (0.5 kg) chaff	85% hay 15% concentrates
	Medium work	3.3 lb (1.5 kg) mix	3.3 lb (1.5 kg) mix + 1.1 lb (0.5 kg) chaff	75% hay 25% concentrates
	Hard work	3.85 lb (1.75 kg) mix	3.85 lb (1.75 kg) mix + 1.1 lb (0.5 kg) chaff	65% hay 35% concentrates

FEED BY WEIGHT

It is important to establish a system of feeding by weight and not volume to ensure that your horse is getting the correct amount of food for its size and build. It is worth noting what your food actually weighs per scoop by measuring each type in a plastic bag. The following is a rough estimate:

One scoop of chaff/chop = 1 lb (450 g)

One scoop of mix = 2 lb (900 g)

One scoop of oats = 2 lb (approx. 900 g)

One scoop of pellets/nuts = 3 lb (1.3 kg)

Vitamins

This diagram shows which vitamins are beneficial for particular parts of the horse. Vitamins A, B1, B2, B6, D, and E are all essential. If the horse looks out of condition, consult the veterinarian. A vitamin deficiency can be remedied by supplementing the diet with extra vitamins. Most feed mixes will have added vitamins and minerals in the correct amount and balance, they will include most of those listed here and should be adequate to keep your animal in peak condition. It should not be necessary to feed supplements.

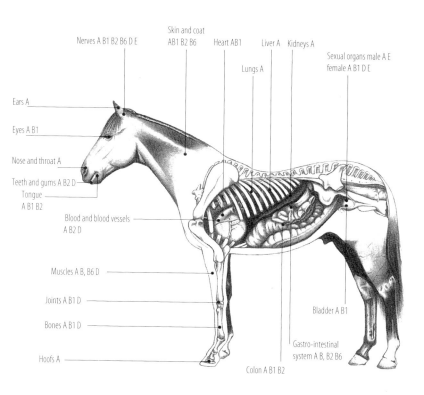

Nerves A B1 B2 B6 D E

Skin and coat AB1 B2 B6

Heart AB1

Lungs A

Liver A

Kidneys A

Sexual organs male A E female A B1 D E

Ears A

Eyes A B1

Nose and throat A

Teeth and gums A B2 D

Tongue A B1 B2

Blood and blood vessels A B2 D

Muscles A B, B6 D

Joints A B1 D

Bones A B1 D

Bladder A B1

Hoofs A

Gastro-intestinal system A B, B2 B6

Colon A B1 B2

Types of feed

Fiber feeds

Grass This is the natural feed for horses—good young pasture may contain all the required nutrients. Grass contains carbohydrates, proteins, vitamins, and water.

Hay This is dried grass, cut when it is mature. Its feeding value will depend on the area and state of the land from which it is cut. It should be only 15-20 percent moisture.

Haylage This is a form of vacuum-packed grass, dried to about 50 percent moisture. This means that it still retains most of its nutritional value. It must be fed within four days of being opened. It is dust-free and so ideal for horses with a dust allergy.

Chop or chaff A short, chopped mixture of hay, straw (usually barley or oat), and/or alfalfa, this is useful as a hay replacement and to extend other feeds. It is often produced with added herbs, molasses, and extra vitamins and minerals.

Straw As an alternative to poor quality hay, straw is a useful source of fiber (especially for ponies with laminitis, see pg.120). Oat or barley straw is best Wheat straw should not be used as it is not easily digested. In some countries, including the United States, straw is usually only used for bedding.

Alfalfa This is a high protein and fiber feed. It can be fed whole, or in chop or in pellet (cube) form. It is relatively dust-free and so useful for horses with respiratory problems. It is low in energy and so also useful for laminitic ponies.

Grain (cereal) feeds

The energy providers, grains consist of carbohydrate concentrates such as oats, barley, and corn (maize). They are fed whole, rolled, micronized, or extruded. They also appear in proprietary mixes sold as complete feeds, which can be loose or in pellet form. The most commonly used cereals are: Oats Popular worldwide, oats are high in fiber but low in energy. They are also low in calcium, which can cause a deficiency, but this is generally corrected by feeding alfalfa, sugar beet, or a vitamin/mineral supplement. Oats can be fed whole or bruised. Naked oats are higher in energy and oil. *Barley* This grain is higher in energy but lower in fiber than oats. It has a hard outer coat, so cannot be fed whole without either soaking or boiling in water for an hour. Generally, it is fed micronized, rolled, or extruded.

Bran The outer coat of the wheat husk, bran is high in phosphorus and fiber. Bran mashes are

LEFT Mineral feed blocks are very popular and give vital mineral and vitamin supplements.

made by pouring boiling water over the bran and leaving it to soak for half an hour. A good laxative, it also makes an excellent poultice for wounds and swellings. Bran can cause an imbalance in calcium absorption if overused.

Corn Often fed with alfalfa, corn (or maize) is particularly popular in the United States. It is higher in energy than barley and oats but low in protein. It is particularly useful for shy eaters because of the ratio of energy gained to amount fed.

Other feeds and supplements

Sugar beet This is a root from which the sugar is removed and the pulp dried into either pellets or shreds. It is a good source of calcium and fiber. Sugar beet must be soaked in water for 12 hours before being eaten. Dried sugar beet expands when in contact with moisture (to twice its size) and can cause fatal colic attacks if eaten unsoaked. Always mark containers of sugar beet and ensure that everyone knows the dangers.

Oil One of the most effective sources of energy, oil contains no starch or protein and is slow releasing. Most pellets and proprietary mixes contain oils but if feeding straights you can add 4 tablespoons (6oml) of vegetable oil a day to increase energy and add an extra bloom to the coat.

Succulents Carrots, apples, and root vegetables are always appreciated and should be given whenever possible to add interest. Carrots especially should be cut lengthways, as round pieces can become lodged in the throat.

Barley

Bran

Oats

Coarse mix

DAILY ROUTINE

Horses are to creatures of habit They like to know when they are to be fed, when they will be going out, and when it's time for bed—and they like it to happen in the same order every day. Whether you keep just one horse or twenty the principle is the same.

Routine is extremely important to a horse's well-being if it is to thrive. Once a routine has been worked out to suit the stable and its particular inhabitants, it is best to stick to it if at all possible. Most barns (yards) run a similar routine of feed and muck out before breakfast, then ride and exercise in the morning, and then tack cleaning. The horses are then groomed in the afternoon, followed by a final check and, if necessary, a feed last thing.

Of course, for any kind of routine, much will depend on the time available to the owner, and the individual circumstances under which the horse is kept. If a horse is kept stabled at a full service barn (yard), it is likely that there will be someone around to attend to its needs all day. If the horse is kept on a Do-It-Yourself basis, the owner may be able to visit the stables only twice a day. Then, it may be that the horse is turned out all day to minimize the amount of work required during the week. Only on weekends may it get the full, undivided attention of its owner.

However your horse is kept, try to maintain a regular schedule on which it can rely. Some periods are bound to be busier than others, according to the season. At the same time, you will have to try to work out when you can fit in some of the other necessary stable chores within your schedule. Tack rooms and feed rooms should both be thoroughly cleaned once a week, for example, and every so often the horse's bed should be completely removed and the stable scoured (scrubbed clean) and disinfected before starting afresh with a new one. Looking after horses is hard work but very rewarding. They are very affectionate creatures, and most respond to

ABOVE Horses thrive on plenty of roughage to keep the gut functioning effectively. This is best given in the form of hay for the stabled horse. Always ensure that you tie the knot high enough so the horse cannot catch its foot in the net as it empties.

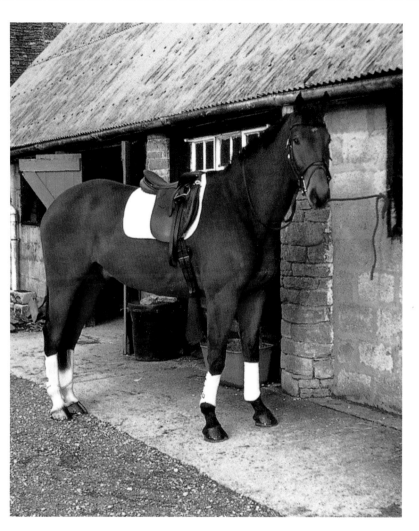

all your care and attention with a warm nuzzle and affectionate whinnies. Caring for your own horse and pony every day gives you a chance to really get to know the character that makes it very special.

ABOVE Exercise time—this horse is waiting for its rider to take it out for its daily schooling session.

TYPICAL DAILY DIARY

7am Feed horse (see pp. 88-95) and check over blankets (rugs), or hay up and feed later.

7:30am Muck out, hay up, and refill water buckets. 8AM Feed (if not done first thing).

9:30am Tack up (see pp. 152-157) and exercise. Turn out afterwards if possible.

11:30am Clean tack and/or groom horse (see pp. 58-65). Sweep out stable.

12:30pm Feed and water.

3:30pm Groom horse. Sweep up and prepare bed for night. Hay up and water.

4-5pm Put on extra blankets if necessary and feed.

8-9pm Last check-over and late feed, if given. Check all is safe and secure. Put on security lights, lock tack room, and shut gates as necessary.

BELOW Picking up droppings and putting them into a receptacle throughout the day will help to keep the stall clean.

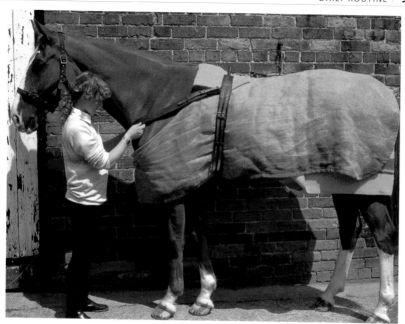

ABOVE Keeping the horse cozy is very important to a horse's welfare, otherwise it uses up vital energy just to keep itself warm. This horse is wearing a blanket and jute rug with a roller to keep it in place. The breastplate helps to prevent everything slipping back (See pg. 66-67).

TRANSPORTATION AND LOADING

The transportation of horses and ponies requires a little forethought and planning before setting off on a journey, however short or long. Careful and calm loading and unloading procedures are essential to ensure that the horse or pony is confident and unstressed by being moved.

If the horse or pony is an experienced traveler, there should be little travel trouble as long as the vehicle is driven sensibly. Generally, problems arise only if the horse is swung too fast around corners and finds difficulty in maintaining its balance, or if the brakes are applied too violently. This is why it is so important for first-time travelers to have an easy, happy experience so that confidence is built up from the start. The sooner foals and youngsters get used to traveling, the easier it will be for all concerned. Foals usually travel alongside their mothers and this is the ideal time to start.

BELOW Protection on the journey will minimize any abrasions, sores, or damage to the legs brought about by braking suddenly or swerving.

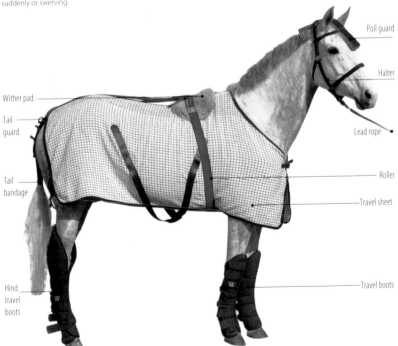

Poll guard

Halter

Wither pad

Tail guard

Lead rope

Tail bandage

Roller

Travel sheet

Hind travel boots

Travel boots

Vehicle preparation

Whether a horse van (horse box) or trailer, the vehicle must be in a safe, roadworthy condition—especially with correctly pressured tires for the load. The ramp must be secure and all fixtures—such as restraint bars and tie rings—must be in good working order so that the animal is properly contained. Water buckets and a hay net are a good idea, as is an emergency first-aid kit (see pg. 136-139). Also, the driver must be someone who is sympathetic to the needs of horses and be a careful driver.

ABOVE Different styles of horse trailer are found across the world. Compare this large goose necked trailer (above right), popular in the United States, with the two-horse trailer (right) which is also popular in Europe.

Loading pointers

Some horses may be frightened of entering a trailer or horse van (horse box) for the first time. To build up confidence, try a few sessions with another horse as a companion or encourage it with food, once inside. A little patience and lots of practice is the key to success.

Be purposeful when loading. If necessary, have some food in your hand and a helper ready both to encourage the horse from behind and to close the door or partition or put restraining straps across once the horse is in. Do not tie the horse up until it is restrained from behind, in case it pulls back or becomes frightened. With a nervous animal, it is helpful to let another horse go in first to give it confidence. Open everything up widely so that it can see where it's to go.

With a horse you know may be difficult to load, it is sensible to take a couple of lunge reins with you as well as some food. The reins will help to keep the horse straight, but you will require two or three people, one to hold and lead the horse, the other two to cope with the reins. Have the food ready to reward the horse once it is loaded.

It is important that your horse has plenty of room to spread his legs so that he can balance. Drive carefully, ensuring a smooth journey and avoiding sudden changes of speed or direction. For nervous horses who haven't traveled before it is a good idea to start with short journeys to begin with.

You can ensure your horse associates the trailer with a positive experience by feeding him in it while it is stationary. This simple technique can yield remarkable results.

Reward your horse for positive steps forward and ensure that you keep stress to a minimum by taking your time with him.

Unloading pointers

When unloading, untie the horse before opening the partition or breaching strap unless you are bringing the horse out forward. Encourage the horse to move out of the trailer slowly and let it have a look around before getting out. If reversing out, try to keep the horse straight and give it time to adjust to the surroundings. Keep it going straight down the ramp without stepping off sideways, and always maintain control. Don't let the horse drag you out.

SAFETY TIP

Never ride a horse or pony into or out of a horse van (horse box) or trailer! The horse could panic and rear in the confined space and you could be seriously hurt by hitting the ceiling or sides.

ABOVE Always be confident and walk forward toward the trailer or horse van (horse box) in a positive attitude. Keep the horse straight and allow it time to adjust to walking up the ramp.

ABOVE Make sure you give the horse or pony enough room to turn into its compartment once you reach the top of the ramp. You may need to go on ahead to stand aside to allow it to turn.

ABOVE Do not hurry the horse down the ramp. It may need a few minutes to adjust to the light and its new surroundings once the ramp has been lowered.

ABOVE Allow the horse or pony to take one step at a time and come down steadily. The animal may slip or stumble if you rush or do not keep it under control in a calm way.

During transportation

Protection when traveling is vital—the most vulnerable areas are the poll, legs, hips, and tail. All should be sensibly protected to ensure that there is minimal damage. In general, horses travel facing backward, forward or on the diagonal (herringbone). They must have sufficient width to brace themselves but not so much that they are swung about. Some horses require more space than others and it is important that this flexibility is available in the partitioning. Some animals become nervous in the dark or when they see the flashing lights of cars and streetlights. This is best overcome by leaving the light on or blacking out any windows.

Travel protection
Legs

1. Place a bandage over leg wraps or other suitable padding.

2. Continue bandaging down over the fetlock joints or use traveling boots which are specifically designed for this purpose.

3. Secure the end of the bandage with a knot or velcro.

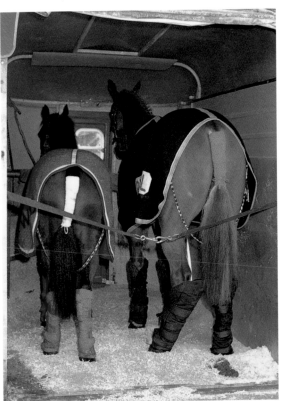

LEFT The horses are generally partitioned for safety in case of accidents when one horse might squash against the other, but sometimes the partition is removed for standing in when stationary or for short journeys. The restraining strap at the back is important to prevent the horses from trying to come out backward. Never undo this strap until they have been untied from in front.

Tail

1. Gently lift the tail while quietly talking to the horse and fold a bandage around under the tail from left to right.

2. Starting at the top and working down in firm folds.

3. Carry on to the end of the dock, then back up. Secure with the tapes or velcro on the bandage.

4. Bend the dock gently into shape if necessary as shown.

Bandages should not be used, however, on journeys of over four hours as it could cause circulation problems.

LEGS

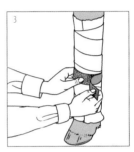

TAIL

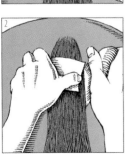
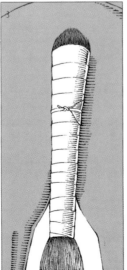
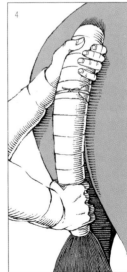

Difficult loaders

Some horses will not load because they are frightened or unsure—in some cases it's plain stubbornness. Each one will need special treatment, depending on the cause of its reluctance, and all will require a degree of patience. Difficult loaders are usually best handled with a bridle and lunge line to ensure they are controllable. If food does not work, a lunge line held by two assistants, just above the hocks, may encourage a reluctant horse. Lifting each foot in turn and placing it further forward also helps. The secret is to keep the horse going forward straight. Occasionally, a sharp tap with a whip just below the hocks or buttocks works. Remember that loading a horse can be dangerous. Wear suitable gloves, footwear, and a riding helmet in case of injury.

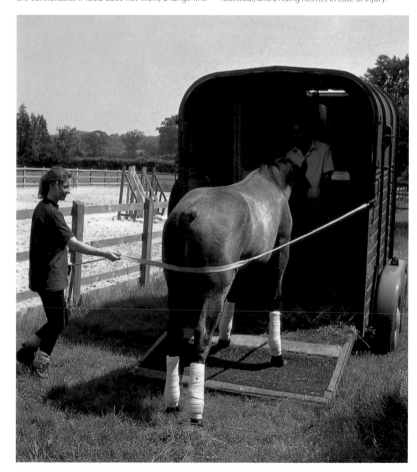

ABOVE The relatively low height of trailers is clearly seen as this horse panics on loading. A bowl of food presented to the horse at ground level may help to keep the head low.

LEFT You can encourage a horse into a trailer or box by securing a lunge rein on one side of the trailer and quietly walking the rein around the back of the horse, thus creating a barrier as shown. Maintain a steady pull but release as a reward for every forward step taken. This is best done with two people

Loading problem
My horse keeps throwing his head up when we try to load him. Why?

Some horses will throw their heads up if too great a pull is exerted on the lead rope because they dislike excessive pressure on the poll (see pg. 18-19). Encourage them to go forward with some food held low and out in front, and keep the rope fairly slack. Protect the poll with a poll guard.

THE HEALTHY HORSE

Owning a horse or pony is a big responsibility. The well-being of your animal is in your hands; you must feed it correctly, ensure the horse is properly exercised, and that it has suitable stabling. The welfare of your animal should be your first thought each day. After all, it is not wild and cannot fend for itself.

A HEALTHY HORSE

The bright eye and shiny coat indicate good health.

The stage of fitness is gauged on the type of work given.

The horse in good health is a pleasure to look at. It should be bright-eyed and alert, well covered but not too fat (see opposite), eating and drinking normally, and should show no signs of lameness.

Furthermore there should be no signs of discharge from the nose or eyes, and the skin should be loose and supple. The droppings should break evenly when they hit the ground, and the urine should be pale yellow. The temperature, respiration, and pulse rates should be within normal levels (all taken when the horse is quiet and resting).

The normal temperature is 100-101 °F (38 °C).
The normal respiration rate is 8-12 breaths per minute.
The normal pulse rate is between 35-45 beats per minute.

This book is intended to give you some of the basic information about caring for a horse or pony which should allow you to make common sense arrangements for the welfare of your animal. One of the most vital skills required of a horse-owner is to know when your animal is healthy and content or is unwell and needs medical treatment.

A SICK HORSE

A sick horse or pony may show any or several of the following symptoms:

1. Listless and unresponsive, with head held low.

2. Not eating or drinking.

3. Skin appears tight. If you pick a fold of skin on the neck and release it, the skin does not readily go back into place.

4. Coat is dull.

5. The temperature is higher or lower than normal.

6. The pulse rate is raised, lowered, or irregular.

7. Breathing is shallow and rapid.

8. Colic signs—such as restlessness, kicking at the belly, pawing at the ground, getting up and down.

9. Obvious cuts or swellings to the legs.

10. Droppings may be very loose, very hard, or absent.

11. Urine may be redlbrown or black (coffee ground) color.

12. Too thin, with hip and backbones sticking out.

13. Excessively overweight.

It is important to know what is normal for your horse or pony. Many have little peculiarities which are normal for them, but may seem odd to someone who does not know the horse.

When to call the veterinarian

The veterinarian should be called at any time when you suspect that there is something seriously amiss with your horse. As a guide, you should call out a veterinarian in any of these cases:

• There are serious wounds, especially if they include arterial bleeding (blood spurting out) or if they require stitching (See pg. 136-139).

• Any signs of colic (see pg. 135) which do not settle after a half hour, or if the horse shows violent signs—flinging itself to the ground and rolling in obvious pain.

• The temperature is high and the horse looks unwell. (Bear in mind that the temperature will always go up after exercise.)

• The horse is lame.

Taking a horse's temperature

To take a horse's temperature, first shake down the mercury in the thermometer or zero rate a digital model. Grease the bulb end with lubricating jelly, and, with an assistant holding the horse's head (if alone, tie the horse up), gently insert this into the horse's rectum. Keep hold of the thermometer so that it does not get drawn into the rectum. Take care to stand to one side when doing this. Remove after one minute, wipe clean, and read.

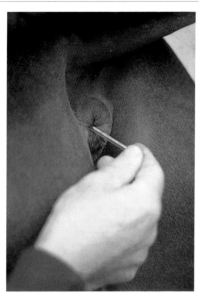

RIGHT Before inserting the thermometer, always check it is shaken down and grease the end. Stand to the side, raise the tail gently, and talk to the horse.

BELOW It will take a little practice to take a pulse rate correctly. Don't rush if you lose the pulse just find the groove in the jaw bone and press the artery again.

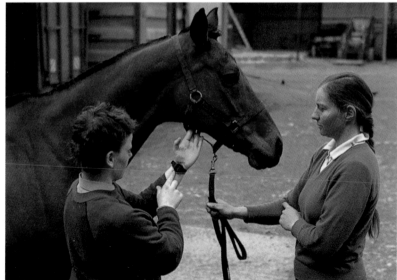

The older horse or pony

Once the horse or pony shows signs of age and stiffness, it should not be expected to work as hard. Discuss the horse's future care with your trainer or veterinarian. Some older horses may enjoy the change of lifestyle; others need further care especially during the winter months when they may need extra feeding and stabling, and perhaps extra blanketing (rugging up) as older horses do not carry so much fat to keep warm. An older horse's teeth need regular rasping to keep them in good shape. Use your regular grooming sessions to check on the overall condition of the animal. When the time comes that modern medicines no longer give the horse relief from old age or lameness, and if the horse is no longer enjoying life, it is your responsibility to have it humanely euthanized—the least you can do for a faithful friend. It is quick and painless and a kindness to an old, or sick horse.

Taking a horse's pulse

To take a horse's pulse, press the facial artery located on the lower jaw against the jaw bone, or the brachial artery located just in front of the elbow (see pg. 18-19). You will feel the pumping sensation. Count the beats for one minute (or 30 seconds and double it). Do not use your thumb as this has a powerful pulse and will confuse any results.

Taking a horse's respiration

For recording the respiration rate, watch the flanks (see pg. 18-19) and count the inhalation and expiration movement as one breath. You may be able to see this from watching the nostrils if the breathing is fast. Also it is sometimes possible to feel the respiration against the top of your hand if you place this close to the horse's nose.

1. Normal

2. Fat

3. Poor condition—thin

ABOVE The condition of the horse or pony can often be determined by the degree of fat and muscle shown over the hindquarters when viewed from behind. This will be affected by feeding, age, kind of work, and general care. **1.** Nicely rounded on both sides of backbone. **2.** Grossly fat, showing excess fat on either side of the backbone. **3.** Poor condition—the muscle is sunken on either side of the backbone and the hip bones are protruding.

Teeth

Dental care is as important for horses as it is for people. A horse that develops problems with its teeth or mouth will not be able to chew and digest its food properly. A bridle and bit may cause extra discomfort, and this will prevent the horse from going forward happily.

The horse's jaw is wider on the top than the bottom. This means that as the horse masticates it tends to wear the teeth down unevenly, causing uncomfortable sharp edges on both the top and bottom molars. These sharp edges can cut the cheeks, and some food, especially grass and hay, may be spat out only half chewed because of the discomfort. You need to ensure that old horses or ponies especially have maximum chewing ability.

A veterinarian or horse dentist should visit twice a year to rasp (float) off any sharp edges, and check that teeth are in good condition and that there are no infections or irritations present. Good horse dentists will use a "gag" to do this effectively. This holds the jaws apart to enable them to work thoroughly without the danger of being nipped. Like a lot of people, some horses don't like the dentist!

Ageing by teeth

The horse can be aged by its teeth fairly accurately up to the age of eight, but thereafter it becomes less easy. However a rough estimate can be made with the shape, degree of wear, and angle of the front teeth, giving the best indication. The horse has replaced its initial milk teeth by the age of five in most cases. In the older horse, the increased angle and more triangular shape give an indication of age. Teeth may be lost around fifteen years onward, or at any time accidentally of course.

Checking for damage

Always check your horse's mouth regularly to see for yourself that there are no obvious injuries. It is quite common for the ridden horse to get sores or bruising from the bit or cracked corners to its lips, which will cause discomfort and affect its response to your instructions.

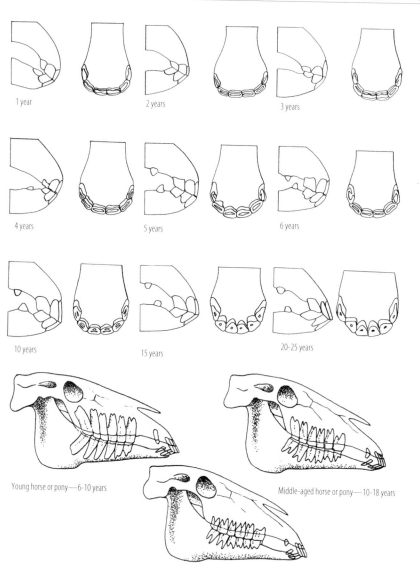

1 year

2 years

3 years

4 years

5 years

6 years

10 years

15 years

20-25 years

Young horse or pony—6-10 years

Middle-aged horse or pony—10-18 years

Old horse or pony—18-25 years

WORMING AND VACCINATION

It is essential for good horse care practice to ensure that your horse or pony is maintained on a regular worming program, and on courses of vaccinations against standard diseases and ailments, such as equine influenza (flu) and tetanus, see pg. 126-135. Failure to carry out such programs and vaccination courses will eventually, and inevitably, lead to your horse or pony becoming susceptible to potentially serious ailments.

Worms are a fact of life for most grazing animals, but especially domesticated horses—which are restricted to feeding repeatedly on the same pasture. All horses carry a certain amount of worms. It is when they become excessive that they cause damage to the digestive system and internal organs. If untreated, the horse could seriously lose condition and even die.

The only way to keep the horse healthy is to maintain a regular worming program. This is best discussed with a veterinarian, as different areas and climates will dictate the frequency required. Most recommend worming every six to ten weeks. A dung sample can be taken to evaluate how serious the problem is if you are unsure of your animal's condition.

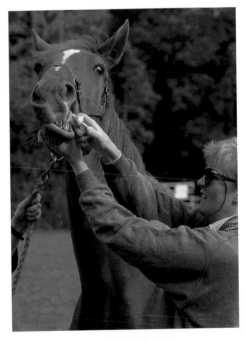

LEFT Wormers can be easily put in the horse's mouth by means of special paste syringes, as shown.

Dealing with worms

There are three main worming drugs on the market: benzimidazole, pyrantel, and ivermectin. They are sold under different brand names but all are effective against most of the species of worms that affect horses. They come in powder, granules, liquid, or in paste form—the latter being the most effective to administer because there is little waste.

The main species that invade the horse's system are the small redworm (*Trichonema*) and large redworm (*Strongylus*), roundworm (*Ascaris*), pinworm or seatworm (*Oxyuris*), lungworm (*Dictyocaulus*), bot (*Gasterophilus*), and tapeworm (*Anoplocephala*).

Redworms are the greatest danger, especially the small redworm which can seriously damage the gut. The worms are passed out in the dung and hatch to produce larvae. If the conditions are right—warm and moist—they develop within a week. The horses in the paddock ingest these larvae, which burrow into the gut lining. They emerge six weeks later as egg-laying adults, completing the cycle and ready to continue to do damage. Some can remain in the gut and become fourth stage larvae, against which not all wormers are effective. These emerge later en masse, causing general malaise, colic, and weight loss. A course of benzimidazole should be effective.

BELOW The diagram shows how the horse picks up the larvae from the grass and the larvae's route through the digestive tract.

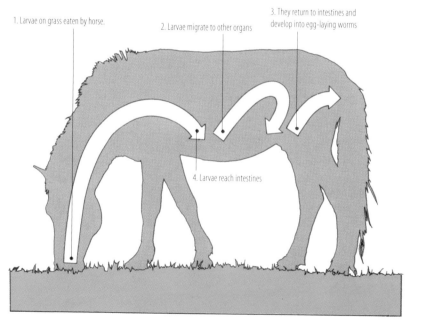

1. Larvae on grass eaten by horse.

2. Larvae migrate to other organs

3. They return to intestines and develop into egg-laying worms

4. Larvae reach intestines

THE LIFECYCLE OF WORMS

Important worms infecting foals and horses

Parasitic worms are a menace to the health and well-being of horses and ponies. Wherever your animals are at grass they are exposed to a wide range of infectious parasites. Some types are so small that they can only be seen under a microscope, while others, like the large roundworm, are up to 20 inches (50cm) long. Some species are very damaging, while others are more of a nuisance. it is essential to understand the basic lifecycles to understand how best to control the worms.

THREADWORMS (*Strongyloides weseri*)	*8-14 days*
LARGE ROUNDWORMS (*Parascaris equorum*)	*10-12 weeks*
SMALL REDWORM (*Cyathostome spp.*)	*5-18 weeks*
LARGE REDWORM (*Strongylus spp.*)	*6-11 weeks*
PINWORM or SEATWORM (*Oxyuris equi*)	*4-5 months*
LUNGWORM (*Dictyocaulus arnfieldi*)	*2-4 months*
STOMACH REDWORM (*Trichostrongylus axel*)	*3 weeks*
LARGE-MOUTHED STOMACH WORM (*Habronema muscae*)	*2 weeks*

Bots are the larvae of gadflies, which worry horses during the hot weather. Gadflies "cement" their eggs onto the horse's coat, often on the legs, which are then licked up. The larvae burrow their way into the mucous membranes of the mouth and tongue, and eventually migrate to the stomach where they attach themselves to the stomach wall until they emerge in the dung to become adult flies.

Vaccinations

Most vaccinations are given by intramuscular (into the muscle) or intradermally (into the skin) injections. Usually these should be administered by a veterinarian and a detailed record of what has been given and when a booster will be necessary should be logged into a diary.

Tetanus inoculation

All horses and ponies worldwide have to be vaccinated against tetanus. This killer disease is picked up from the soil, and can easily invade open wounds. Foals should be vaccinated at around

LEFT Vaccination certificates will vary according to the country, but all should consist of the written and diagrammatic identification of the horse or pony. Most vaccinations will require annual boosters, so it is important to keep a record and to arrange for these to be given by your veterinarian at the appropriate time.

three months in two doses four to six months apart, followed by a booker one year later. From that time on, horses have boosters every two years.

Traveling horse vaccinations

Other vaccinations that should be given depend on the country any current outbreaks of disease in the local area. You should always check on current requirements before you travel. Identity or competition passports or vaccination certificates recording the veterinarian's signature, stamp, and date of vaccination have to be carried with the horse—especially when it is competing internationally or being transported abroad.

Competition horses in most disciplines are required to have equine influenza (flu) vaccinations, and these must be given according to the regulations laid down. Currently this requires two primary vaccinations, followed by a six-month booster and then annually thereafter.

Rhinopneumonitis and equine viral arteritis (E.V.A.) vaccinations are given by your veterinarian. It is your responsibility to ensure that your horse is adequately protected according to local recommendations. Both are serious diseases that affect the horse's respiratory and reproductive systems and can cause abortion in breeding stock. The symptoms of a running nose may pass unnoticed, so it is vital that horses are vaccinated.

LEG AND FOOT CARE

Care of the legs and feet is vital if your horse or pony is to stay sound throughout its career. Ignoring what seems like a minor ailment today, could cause greater problems in the future.

There are many factors which contribute toward keeping your horse fit for work. You should always keep your horse shod regularly, and have its feet correctly balanced. Build up fitness work only gradually so that the horse is never put under strain until it is fit to cope with the demand. Never overwork your horse. Overly tired horses are more likely to injure themselves, due to a lack of oxygen reaching the muscles and tendons.

Always heed any warning signs, such as inflammation or heat, and act immediately to ensure they do not become worse. Similarly, treat any cuts or bruises straight away. Call the veterinarian if you are worried or the horse is badly lame.

BELOW First get an overall impression of the whole leg by feeling down from the top. Look at it from the front and back as well as from the side.

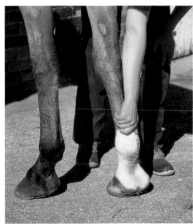

ABOVE When detecting lameness, the veterinarian will see the horse led in hand after feeling for any heat and swelling on the lame leg. It is important to do both these checks to get a true picture.

Detecting lameness

There are numerous reasons why a horse may go lame, so always check the obvious possibilities first. Sudden lameness may well be caused by a stone lodged in the foot. Check this immediately and remove if necessary. Bruising to the foot is probably the most common cause of all other types of lameness, other than obvious injury.

If further tests are needed to find out the cause of lameness the veterinarian may use hoof pincers to apply pressure to the sole of the suspect foot to test for problems. After lifting the limb to look for possible stiffness or inflammation in the joints the veterinarian may back the horse, or turn it in a tight circle, to check for possible hip or back problems. If the problem is still not apparent then X-ray examinations may be required.

Front leg lameness

Obvious lameness in front is not usually hard to detect. The horse will be reluctant to put weight on the affected leg, and also raises its head up as it goes to touch the ground. To alleviate the pain, it puts extra weight on to the good leg—and lowers its head as it does this.

To check for lameness, get someone to trot the horse, in hand, up and down on a level surface. Keep a loose rein to allow free head movement. If the horse's head stays level, it is sound. If it is lame, its head will nod down with the good front leg, and up as the lame one is put down. How much of a nod will depend on the degree of lameness.

How to check feet for problems

BELOW If the problem is in the foot, the hoof may feel warm and a pulse may be felt in the heel by compressing the main foot artery as shown.

BELOW Lift the foot up and ensure there is nothing stuck in the foot such as a stone, nail or other sharp object.

Hind leg lameness

Hind leg lameness is more difficult to detect, especially if only slight. You will need to watch the quarters. The horse will drop on to one side and raise the other, but which one is significant depends on the cause and where the problem is. This is best left to the veterinarian, so long as you have checked for obvious signs such as cracked heels or a stone in the foot. Some older horses will come out stiff behind if they have been cooped up in a stable for 24 hours, but should be fine after five minutes walking.

Laminitis
My horse is standing as if he wants to get the weight off his front feet and is reluctant to move. Why is this?

This sounds like the classic symptoms of laminitis, a severe condition causing inflammation of the feet. Because the horse's hoof is hard and cannot expand, the pain caused by the swelling is excruciatingly bad and causes severe distress. The veterinarian should be called. The cause is thought to be dietary and may follow a sudden change in diet or overly rich grass or food. A laxative diet and cooling of the feet by hosing or standing in the river may ease discomfort. Pain killers will be required in severe cases. Fat ponies are particularly prone and should in any case be kept on restricted grazing when the spring grass is at its richest. It is now known, however, that there are several different reasons why horses develop the disease but as yet the causes are not clearly understood.

BELOW This horse is clearly in pain and leaning back to ease the weight off its front feet.

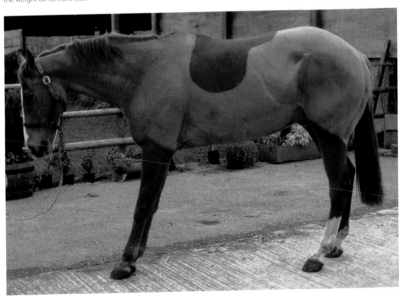

Checking hooves

My horse has been lame and when I told the farrier, he took the shoe off as he suspected corns. What are these and what can I do to prevent them?

Corns are caused by pressure creating bruising under the shoe. The most common area is the heel which may be caused by the shoe being a bit short for the foot, thus putting more pressure in one particular area. It is important that any bruising is cut out so that it does not build up. Some corns go septic, requiring a poultice (see pg.125) to draw out the inflammation before the shoe can be replaced. Sometimes special protective pads or hoof cushions can be used to prevent bruising, or if the horse has very sensitive soles.

LEFT The sole of the foot is particularly vulnerable, especially if the ground has been wet for some time as it tends to soften the feet and make them more prone to bruising and injury. Keeping the feet well trimmed and regularly shod will help toward preventing other injuries.

Bumps and bruises

Sometimes a horse will over reach and give itself a nasty bruise, or sometimes a deep cut on the bulb, of its front heel. This is caused by the back foot over-extending and clipping the front one, and is particularly common when jumping, on deep ground, or when galloping. Some people put on over reach bell boots to protect the heels.

Any bumps or bruises from everyday work are best treated with cold hosing to the area for ten minutes, two or three times a day, to relieve inflammation. After 48 hours of cold treatment, hot poultices or warm dry bandaging are generally the way to create extra circulation to the area to disperse the bruising. The more the animal can move about, the better it will be.

Treating swollen legs

Some horses are prone to filled, swollen legs because of over-feeding and under-exercising. It is usually noticeable in the hind legs first, then all four. Check your food/work program and try cutting down the

food a little, especially if the horse is in good condition. A bran mash, made with a scoop of bran, a handful of Epsom salts, and boiling water to a tacky consistency (allow it to cool), may help to clear out any excess proteins that have built up in the animal's system. The filling will usually disappear when the horse is exercised. If you are in doubt, consult the veterinarian.

Sore legs
I went on a fun ride yesterday and this morning my horse has four filled legs. Is this normal?

The horse will not usually suffer from this if it has been prepared correctly with a gradual build up to condition its legs and body for the work expected (see Exercise and Fitness on pg. 80-87).

You may find that the problem has occurred because you have done more galloping on hard ground than usual which caused some jarring of the legs and this resulted in some filling. Some cold hosing (see pg.138-139) and quiet walking should help.

BELOW Injuries to the legs are common, especially over-reaching (left) and knocking (right). Remedial shoeing is possible for some problems.

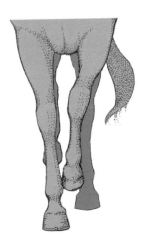

ABOVE The use of protective boots on the legs will help to minimize knocks to the legs. Bell boots will prevent the risk to the heels from over-reaching.

ABOVE Splints may respond to a little ultra-sound treatment to reduce inflammation while forming.

BELOW Cracked heels are difficult to keep clean and free of infection, so special care and attention is needed. Regular cleaning care and use of special creams specifically for the condition will help to ensure healing takes place.

Treating splints

Horses that are worked on hard ground may develop a condition known as splints. These splints can also be caused by a direct blow, or by too much work with a young horse. They are actually a form of new bone growth, generally located on the inside or outside of the cannon bones, just below the knee or hock. This develops into a small, hard lump, sometimes with heat in that area, and the horse may go lame.

Treatment consists of rest and cold hosing to reduce the inflammation. Rest may be necessary for anything up to six weeks, with anti-inflammatory drugs and DMSO applied to the site. Once the splint has formed and hardened, it rarely causes too much trouble.

Treating cracked heels and mud fever

Cracked heels and mud fever are sores that develop in the back of the pastern and heel areas, or anywhere up the legs. They are often caused by damp or muddy conditions, which make the skin soft and sore. Any cracks that develop can quickly become infected if not treated, causing lameness or soreness and swelling.

It is important to clip away excess hair, which tends to hold the moisture and aggravate the problem. A kaolin poultice is effective at cleaning up the area, which can then be treated with an antibiotic or barrier cream to clear up the condition. Keep the area dry and free of dirt. Some animals are more prone than others, especially those with white legs, but early application of barrier creams can help to prevent it.

ABOVE Thrush can be treated with antibiotic spray to dry and harden the area. Ask your farrier to trim any excess frog area.

Treating foot thrush

Horses that are kept in poor conditions can develop thrush, an infection of the foot. It is easy enough to detect because the frog of the foot becomes foul-smelling and appears moist. Treatment consists of thorough cleaning of the frog area and spraying with an antibiotic spray to harden it, twice a day. Some horses are more susceptible to the condition than others, but their beds should always be kept as clean and dry as possible.

Poultices
How do I apply a kaolin poultice to the bruising on my pony's leg and should it be hot or cold?

Kaolin, a type of clay, has been used for centuries for bruising and is generally marketed today as a thick paste. The easiest method of application is to spread a thin layer on some brown paper cut to the required size. This can either be applied direct to the leg cold for recent bruising or at blood temperature for treating older bruises or swellings. Cover the poultice with light plastic and padding and bandage for 24 hours. Renew daily until the problem improves (use from two to five days).

COMMON AILMENTS

Your horse relies on you to recognize when it is sick. Illness can happen at any time, and you need to have at least a basic knowledge of the more obvious symptoms. Knowing what to do will help to ensure that the appropriate action is taken. Always call a veterinarian if you have any doubts.

Most everyday problems are fairly minor and can be treated with normal commonsense. The odd little cut or bruise requires much the same treatment of normal hygiene and cooling down (see cold hosing p. 138-139) that would be needed for any playground tumble. Remember that any treatment given may result in the horse reacting by lifting the injured leg suddenly in such a way that we might say "ouch" to a pin prick or little cut. Have someone hold the horse while treating any wound, or tie it loosely if by yourself so that should it pull back, it can be quickly released.

THE SPORTING HORSE

You should be able to recognize what is wrong with your horse, so that a veterinarian can give the correct treatment without delay. This diagram indicates some typical problems:

1. Poll evil; **2.** Fistulous withers; **3.** Sore back (saddle pinch); **4.** Sore back (saddle rub); **5.** Hip lameness; **6.** Whistling; **7.** Shoulder lameness; **8.** Broken knees; **9.** Sore shins; **10.** Low ring bone; **11.** Girth galls; **12.** Capped elbow; **13.** Elbow lameness; **14.** Brushing injury; **15.** Check for ligament strain; **16.** Suspensory ligament—check for strain; **17.** Side bones; **18.** Overreach injury; **19.** Hind leg locking; **20.** Bone spavin; **21.** Bowed tendon; **22.** Sesamolditis; **23.** Sand-crack; **24.** Capped hock; **25.** Curb; **26.** WIndgalls; **27.** Osselet; **28.** Contracted heels.

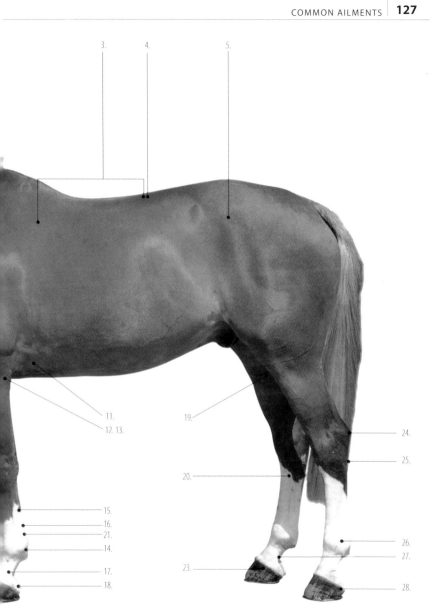

Back problems
My horse feels uneven in his gaits. He sinks down when I first get on him and he keeps jumping to the left. He never used to do this, so what is the cause?

First, look at your saddle (see p. 142-143). If it is pinching him on his withers, the tree may be too narrow. Is the tree broken? Get a knowledgeable person or the saddler to have a look. A pad may temporarily help if the saddle is too low, but you will have to get it re-stuffed to fit correctly.

Some horses may pull a muscle landing awkwardly over a fence or even put their back or pelvis slightly out of line. These can be dealt with by a horse back specialist.

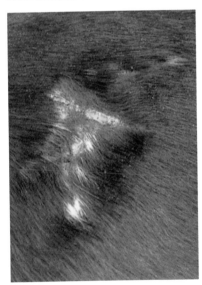

ABOVE Pressure or friction from badly fitting tack causes saddle sores.

Young horses may develop minor strains which a week or two in the paddock will cure. Occasionally, it may be that a problem elsewhere, such as in a hock or foot, is causing the horse to move awkwardly and resulting in strain or pressure to certain areas of the back. Gentle pressure from two or three fingers worked systematically down the backbone on either side of the spine for a reaction to pressure may indicate where the problem is.

Skin problems
A variety of skin problems can arise, and may be the result of a reaction to feed or change of diet, irritation by mites, sensitivity to the sun, or a contagious disease. It is always best to treat any suspicious skin rashes or patches with caution, in case they can be transferred from horse to horse or to humans.

Ringworm
Ringworm is a highly contagious fungal disease. It is easily transmitted by direct contact with an infected horse, infected stables, or equipment, and must be treated with a course of anti-bacterial drugs and creams. Isolation is essential. Isolate the horse, its tack, rugs, and grooming kit from contact with others until the problem is confirmed.

Diet related problems
Most skin reactions to feed or change of diet will settle within 24 hours, although severe cases may need an anti-histamine from the veterinarian.

Sometimes, a bran mash made with Epsom salts can help. It has a laxative effect, and will help to clear out any excesses from the stomach. Take note of what the horse has eaten. It may be that a 'change in diet was introduced too suddenly or that the horse had too much protein. Alternatively, the horse could be reacting to a fly bite. Some animals are sun sensitive and may need to be kept in during the day and turned out only at night.

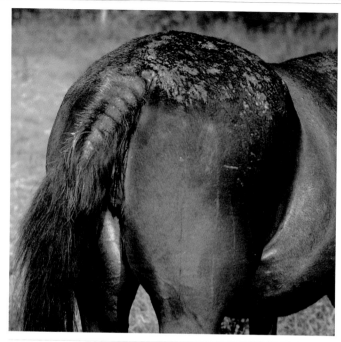

LEFT Here can be seen the typically rubbed tail and other areas so commonly found with sweet itch: some veterinarians believe tiny mites may be a cause by burrowing under the skin and causing severe irritation.

Sweet itch

Sweet itch is a condition that occurs only in the summer, and is believed to be caused by an allergic reaction to midges. It causes acute irritation of the mane and tail, leading the animal to rub itself until it produces sores. Apart from proprietary creams, the best remedy is to keep the horse out of the sun and protect the mane and tail as much as possible by ensuring that there is little for the horse to rub itself on. Tail bandages may minimize the damage. Using fly sprays and impregnated tags can help horses that react to fly bites. Sun-block creams can be effective for those sensitive to the sun, particularly on areas of pink skin, such as the nose and white legs.

Girth galls

Sores found behind the elbow on the girth area are caused by rubbing from the girth (see pp. 142-149) on sensitive skin. These girth galls are particularly common on horses that have just come back to work after a rest, when the skin is soft and the hair often long and dirty. Hard or uncleaned girths can also be a cause. Treat with careful fomentations (topical poultices) and do not ride until the condition has settled. Clean the girth area well before riding and harden the skin with salt water or surgical spirit if the skin is not broken. A girth sleeve and soft well-oiled girths will help to prevent a recurrence.

Fly strike
My horse goes absolutely mad when bitten by flies. What can I do about it?

Flies are a major worry to horses, particularly in hot weather, and some varieties are much more vicious than others. The common horse fly attaches itself to suck blood, and there are others that look rather crablike that drive many horses so crazy they injure themselves.

Fly sprays and impregnated tags that can be attached to the mane will all help. Fringes, for the face, and light fly sheets, which must be adequately secured, are both helpful. Many owners turn their horses out at night and stand them in during the day when the flies are at their worst.

BELOW This horse is very well protected against flies, but may still require fly spray around the legs.

Equine influenza

Caused by a virus, equine influenza (flu) is a highly infectious disease and results in a high temperature, cough, and discharge from the nose. The horse may also go off its feed.

The animal must be isolated from other horses and rested. Leading out in hand to graze (so long as this will not increase the risk to others) will help to maintain circulation and prevent the legs from filling. Cut down the energy food intake (grain) but keep up the roughage, such as hay, and make sure there is plenty of fresh water available. Normally, it will take up to two or three weeks for the horse to recover, when a gradual return to work can commence. Regular vaccinations will help to prevent severe cases, even if they do not cover all strains of the virus.

Tying up

Also known as azoturia, this condition makes the horse's muscles—particularly along the back and quarters—go into spasm. It may start as stiffness behind, then the horse will suddenly slow up as the muscles spasm, start to sweat, and become distressed.

Often, tying up occurs during the breaks at Eventing and Endurance competitions, but it is also common after a day off. It is thought that it may be due to a build-up of protein in the horse's system, making it important to cut down on protein intakes during a day off and to ensure the horse gets some exercise. Electrolytes (salts) may help in hot climates, where dehydration is thought to be a contributing factor.

In severe cases the cramps cause the release of myoglobin into the blood, which results in dark-colored (coffee ground) urine. Watch out for this when the horse passes water. Cease exercise immediately when the condition becomes apparent and keep the horse warm. Take off the saddle or just loosen the girth, if the animal is cold. Arrange transportation home if the horse is very still, as further exercise can do more damage. Once home, rest the horse and give a laxative diet with Epsom salts. Get a veterinarian to take a blood sample, this will determine the severity of the attack by the concentration of muscle enzymes. The test results will then establish the time factor in the horse's return to work, which must be gradual. Discuss a regime of work/food ratio with the veterinarian in order to prevent further attacks.

Chronic obstructive pulmonary disease (COPD)

Chronic obstructive pulmonary disease (COPD) is a chronic respiratory illness particularly common among stabled horses, where sensitivity to dust and spores develops into a cough with thick mucus. Left untreated, the horse will gradually deteriorate as the tiny alveoli in the lungs become more damaged.

To treat the condition, provide as much fresh air as possible. Bed the horse on paper or shavings, and soak its hay or feed haylage. Keep the horse out in a paddock as much as you can, and talk to your veterinarian about whether any drugs are necessary. Bronco dilators and expectorants can help to alleviate symptoms in the more serious cases.

Tetanus

Usually fatal, tetanus is caused by the toxin Clostridium tetani present in soil. Puncture wounds are the most likely site for the bacteria to enter the horse's system.

The initial symptoms of the disease are muscle stiffness. Then, the third eyelid can be seen across the eye, jaw movements become restricted, and spasms and paralysis gradually set in. Few recover, which is why vaccination of all horses and ponies is vital. The sick animal should be isolated in a darkened, quiet area and given large doses of penicillin to prevent further absorption of any toxins. A veterinarian may also administer tranquilizers, muscle relaxants, and sedatives.

ABOVE If your veterinarian suspects a viral infection of some kind it may be necessary to take a blood sample to test in order to administer the precise vaccination or course of antibiotics required.

Arthritis
My horse is now about twenty and getting rather stiff and has enlarged areas around some of his joints. Why is this?

As the horse gets older, it may well develop arthritis in the same way as humans. Talk to your veterinarian, who will probably prescribe some anti-inflammatory drug to relieve any pain or stiffness. You should remember that the condition is there, however, and not over exert your horse, though gentle exercise may help to prevent the condition worsening. The cold weather will often aggravate this, so keep the horse warm and if necessary bandage his legs in very cold weather. There may come a time when pain and discomfort becomes too severe and you need to think seriously whether it would be kinder to put your horse down. Your veterinarian will help to advise you in such cases.

Strangles

Strangles is a severe and highly infectious bacterial disease of the upper respiratory tract that mainly affects the throat area. It causes the formation of large abscesses, which can burst internally or externally and so affect breathing or swallowing. The horse may have a very high temperature, be extremely miserable, and have a thick nasal discharge.

Strict isolation procedures must be implemented immediately. High standards of hygiene are essential if the disease is not to spread. All affected bedding will have to be burned and the whole area thoroughly disinfected. All equipment and clothing will have to be disinfected, as will the hands and feet of any person in contact with the sick animal. Any kit used must be kept only for the affected horse.

Treatment usually takes the form of antibiotics, after the abscesses have burst. A veterinarian will

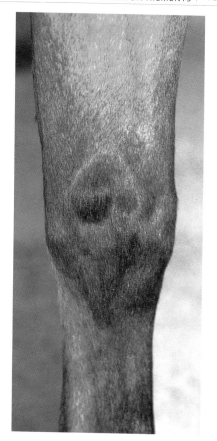

ABOVE Bony enlargements are typical signs of arthritic changes taking place and causing pain and stiffness.

also need to take blood tests and throat swabs to determine when the horse is free of infection. While it is sick, feeding the horse on the floor will make it easier for it to eat. Apply hot fomentations to the throat area regularly and bathe the eyes and nostrils as often as necessary. Birds are known to be a major cause of the disease spreading.

Recognizing problems

As you get to know your horse you will be able to distinguish the difference between simply an off day or the start of an ailment or disease. You may start to worry about your horse getting a patchy coat, or if it starts rolling on the ground sometimes. As explained here, you may be worrying needlessly, but you should ensure you check on your horse regularly in case a symptom shows something serious, such as colic (see right). If you are in any doubt at all, call in a veterinarian.

BELOW Rolling: a great luxury for the horse who may use it to stretch, scratch, and play all in one, then very often getting up and galloping off with huge leaps and bucks afterward!

Rolling on ground

I know rolling can be a sign of well-being and pleasure and nature's way of helping to shift the horse's coat. However, as it may also indicate serious pain and colic if associated with sweating, anxious behavior or general discomfort, how will I know when to call the veterinarian?

If you know your horse or pony, it will be easy to see when it is enjoying itself and when it is ill, but if in any doubt, call your veterinarian for advice and he or she will tell you what to look out for and assess whether a visit is necessary. It is always better to be

ABOVE This horse looks well enough in itself, but is at the stage when the winter coat is still half in place, thus giving a rather moth-eaten look. A few more weeks and a glossy summer coat will be in place.

safe than sorry. Some horses and ponies love to roll and it is very important to get to know when they like to do this – such as after exercise. If so, be sure to take the saddle off immediately or they will go down with that on too if you leave them unattended even for a few seconds!

Patchy coat
It is the end of the winter and my horse is losing its coat. It looks very patchy and comes out in great tufts in places. Is this normal?

The horse changes its coat twice a year and during the winter generally grows a much thicker coat, although some breeds are much more dense than others. This starts to fall out as the warmer weather comes. Regular use of rubber curry combs (see pp. 86-89) in a circular movement will help to shift the coat during this stage.

Occasionally there are problems with lice (tiny mites that enjoy the thick coats and also suck blood causing general debilitation, itching, and rubbing of the coat). If this develops, seek veterinary advice and get a preparatory powder to sprinkle on the coat for a few days or treat as suggested by your veterinarian. If horses are in a group, it is likely they will all be suffering from this and will all need treating. Wear protective clothing when treating. Weather scald caused by prolonged wet weather on the back may cause loss of hair which will grow over with the summer coat. New Zealand blankets (rugs) in wet weather may avoid this.

Colic

This term is used to describe a pain in the abdomen. There are several reasons why it might happen, such as a blockage in the digestive system caused by a change in the diet, dehydration, worm infestation, over feeding or kidney problems. It is potentially very serious, and can lead to death.

With colic, the horse will become very restless, often looking around at its tummy and kicking at it. It may start to sweat, and its breathing and pulse rate will increase. If this does not settle after 20 minutes, or if the horse becomes violent or is in obvious pain, call the veterinarian immediately. Discourage the horse from rolling. A short walk may help to prevent further problems developing. Listen for any tummy sounds or noises or if the horse passes any wind. Take note of any urine passed, and check for recent droppings. You will need to pass this information on to the veterinarian.

FIRST-AID FOR HORSES

Accidents always happen when you least expect them but, if you are prepared, you can minimize the damage caused by an everyday minor injury. In the case of major incidents, such as a road traffic accident, you may also be able to prevent the situation worsening until professional help arrives.

ABOVE If your veterinarian suspects a viral infection of some kind it may be necessary to take a blood sample to test in order to administer the precise vaccination or course of antibiotics required.

HORSE FIRST-AID KIT

- Cotton (cotton wool).
- Container for bathing wounds.
- Kaolin.
- Poultices (see p. 125).
- Scissors for cutting dressings.
- Sterile non-stick dressings.
- Salt or antiseptic solution.
- Bandages or leg wraps to hold dressings in place and for dry bandaging.
- Instant "cold" packs for reducing inflammation.
- Antiseptic wound spray and powder.
- Thermometer.
- Any personal preferences, such as Arnica pills and ointments for relieving bruising.

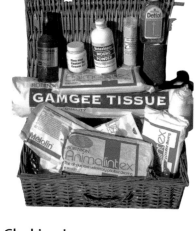

Absolutely essential in any stable is a well-stocked, easily accessible horse first-aid kit. This should contain all the basic ingredients to help you treat a small wound or attend to a bruise or swelling. Use commonsense, stay calm, and assess every situation carefully before attempting first-aid. Then, if you are at all concerned, always contact a veterinarian.

Minor wounds

Minor wounds can be cleaned with a saline solution of one teaspoon of salt to 1 pint (½ liter) of boiling water, which has been allowed to cool to comfortably warm, or a mild antiseptic. Check that the wound is really clean, removing all bits of mud, sand, or debris with a cotton pad. Dry the area and apply wound spray or powder. Take particular care to see that there are no hidden puncture wounds, which will need antibiotics and veterinary assessment. If there are foreign bodies stuck in a wound, do not move until professional help is at hand in case of serious hemorrhage.

Choking horse

My horse is very greedy and grabs at his feed, sometimes choking and coughing which is quite alarming. Is their anything I can do?

Horses that are very greedy will try to bolt down their AMA food. This can be solved by giving them plenty of chaff or chop mixed with their feed thereby making it more difficult to chew quickly.

If possible, small feeds given more often may be better for this type of animal. Feed them on the floor in a feed bucket so that any choking will be done in the most natural position and the hastily eaten feed will be likely to be coughed out.

Emergency

Whenever a problem or accident happens, remember to think clearly and not to panic! First things first!

- Is it life threatening? Deal accordingly by calling an ambulance or veterinarian as appropriate.
- Prevent further injury to either humans or horses.

For example, make sure any unhurt horse or person is moved away from the scene of the accident.

Bruise or minor swelling

A blow to a limb, such as when hitting a jump pole hard, is one of the most common causes of bruises. They may blow up quite quickly or come up gradually. The sooner you can apply ice or a cold pack to the area the better—a packet of frozen peas makes an easy substitute!

You can make an ice pack by crushing ice inside a plastic bag using a hammer or a heavy object. Bandage it lightly over some gauze or toweling to prevent skin scalding. Replace hourly, for two to four hours, then hose with cold water two or three times daily if the bruise is minor. If the bruise is large, increase the number of times you cold hose. Generally, it is the first 24 hours that are most important to reduce swelling and to prevent any further hemorrhage from taking place. Cold hosing can be done for so to 20 minutes every two hours, or whenever possible.

Cuts or tears

With serious cuts or tears, lightly hose the wound or leave it and cover it with a non-stick dressing. Usually the flow of blood will help clean the wound, but bleeding must be stopped if it does not do so by itself after a few minutes. Either a dressing or a clean handkerchief should be placed over the wound and pressure applied. Once bleeding has stopped, another clean dressing can be placed over the wound and a bandage applied until the veterinarian arrives.

BELOW Cold hosing is excellent for bruising and swelling and for helping to clean minor wounds. Keep the flow gentle.

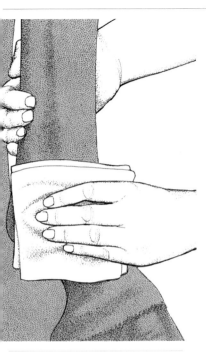

ABOVE Keep a clean pad of material pressed firmly onto a serious cut. Remember that even a docile horse may become agitated while being treated because of the pain. You should have the horse tied up.

Serious cuts or artery damage

Cut arteries are life-threatening, although rare. Call a veterinarian immediately. Apply a firm pad and a bandage, and put another on top if bleeding persists. You will know if it is a cut artery because blood spurts out (veins bleed in a continuous stream). Keep the horse still and quiet. A tourniquet should be applied only if the arterial cut is life-threatening. It should be applied only over the wound or just above, between the heart and the wound. Tourniquets must be loosened every 10 to 15 minutes in case they cause circulation problems.

Swollen knees
My horse hit its knee, which blew up like a football within minutes. How should I treat it?

Ice to the spot or cold water immediately has an amazing effect on reducing swelling in most cases. Continue to reapply every hour for the first three or four hours, then four or five times a day until the swelling has subsided. The first six hours are the most important and most will have reduced dramatically after twenty-four hours.

Puncture wounds
My horse spiked itself on a metal bar. It's only a little hole, but it must be quite deep. Should I call the veterinarian?

Yes! Small puncture wounds can be quite dangerous and it is much safer to get the veterinarian to ensure the wound is thoroughly cleaned inside. Antibiotics may be prescribed and your veterinarian will want to be satisfied that your horse is covered against tetanus (see p. 117 and 132), so keep your vaccination records up to date.

EQUIPMENT
& RIDING
TECHNIQUES

Before you can begin learning to ride, it is essential that you provide your horse with appropriate, good-quality tack and equipment. This chapter shows you all the essential equipment you will need to ensure the safety of you and your horse and to get the most out of riding.

Nothing can beat the buzz you get from riding. From leisurely trots in the country to competing in dressage or show-jumping, the thrill and enjoyment is unsurpassed. This chapter describes all the techniques you will need to be able to ride, from mounting your horse to preparing to jump.

TACK AND HORSE EQUIPMENT

Good quality tack and equipment are essential for the safety of you and your horse or pony—always buy the best that you can afford. Treat your tack well and it will repay you with years of faithful service.

Well-maintained, clean and correctly fitting tack will add to the overall appearance of your horse or pony whether you are riding out or in competition, so it is always worth acquiring items that look good and enhance the overall picture of the "horse and rider."

The saddle

A correctly fitted saddle is an absolute essential—get professional advice before making a purchase. An ill-fitting saddle will not only be painful for a horse, but it can also lead to permanent damage. It should also be comfortable for the rider, and suitable for its intended use. A general-purpose saddle is best for everyday riding, whereas dressage and jumping saddles are designed to meet specific requirements.

For children, there are different variations of felt or part-felt saddles. These are ideal for beginners because they are flat and not slippery.

The girth is attached to the saddle to keep it in position, and generally is made of leather webbing or string. The stirrup irons and leathers are attached to the saddle via the stirrup bar. The irons must be the right size for the foot, neither too narrow nor too wide (no more than ½ in/130mm gap). The various styles available include a safety iron for children, which has a detachable rubber band on the outside. Rubber treads can be used in the base to prevent the boot from slipping through the iron. The leathers should be a suitable size for the rider and adjustable in length, with enough holes to allow flexibility for the long - and short-limbed rider.

RIGHT The saddle, more than any other part of the tack, becomes a very personal item as, after time, it tends to mold to the rider's shape and therefore becomes very comfortable for that rider.

You should always ensure that the saddle you intend to buy is the correct size for you and is the correct type for the sort of work you intend to use it for, that is general riding, dressage, or show jumping, for example. A reputable saddler will give you advice on what you require—and how to look after this vital piece of equipment.

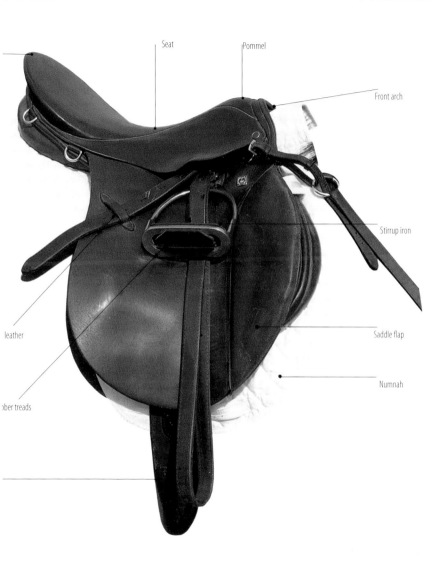

Seat

Pommel

Front arch

Stirrup iron

Saddle flap

Numnah

leather

ober treads

ABOVE Dressage saddle

ABOVE General purpose riding saddle

BELOW Jumping saddle

ABOVE Safety stirrup

ABOVE Stirrup with rubber tread

ABOVE Stirrup without tread

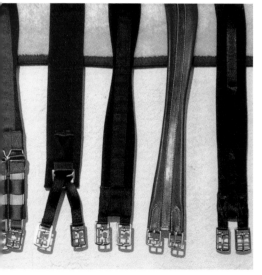

ABOVE FAR LEFT Rubber treads help to prevent the foot slipping through the stirrup and are highly recommended.

ABOVE CENTER In the event of a fall the rubber band or strip on a safety stirrup will pull off so that the foot does not get caught and the rider dragged along the ground. This is an ideal type for children.

ABOVE RIGHT The gap in the foot rest of this stirrup without a tread allows the tread on the rider's boot to push through it and keep the foot in place.

LEFT A variety of girths, some with elasticated inserts for extra "give." The two short girths on the left are used with the long girth straps used on some dressage saddles.

The bridle

Make sure that you have the right size bridle for your horse. It should be a comfortable fit without being too snug. The basic arrangement consists of a headpiece and throatlatch (throatlash), browband, noseband, two cheekpieces (which are adjustable to fit the length of the head), and reins. The two cheekpieces are attached to the bit as are the reins.

The noseband lies under the headpiece, and is fastened at the back underneath the head, according to the particular bridle type. The most common nosebands in use are the cavesson, drop, flash, and grakle.

Bits come in all kinds of designs, but are basically variations on two main categories. Most common is the snaffle, the eggbutt being one of the simplest (and one of the kindest) bits available. Other variations include the loose-ring snaffle, the Fulmer snaffle, and the Dr. Bristol (which has an angled rectangular plate in the middle, and is severe). The other main category is the curb bit or pelham (with double reins), which

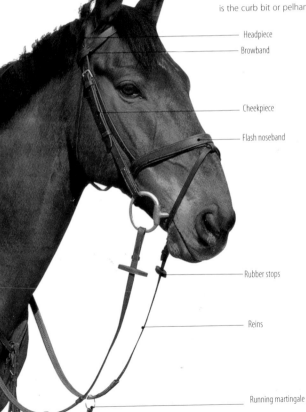

Headpiece

Browband

Cheekpiece

Flash noseband

Rubber stops

Reins

Running martingale

is severe in rough or inexperienced hands. Curb bits have a chain attached which is fastened around the chin groove and gives extra control. Variations include the Kimblewick and the Mullen-mouth pelham. Irrespective of the type of bit used, it should always be the correct width for the horse's mouth.

Variations on the bridle itself include the double bridle, which has two sets of reins attached to two bits in the horse's mouth. One bit is a type of small snaffle known as a bridoon, and the other is a curb. A hackamore, on the other hand, is a completely bitless bridle. This relies on pressure on or round the horse's sensitive nose for control, and can be useful if a horse has a sore mouth.

What bit to use
What is the best bridle to use if you are not very experienced about bits?

The snaffle bridle is always best but be sure it is the right width for your horse's mouth. A loose ring or eggbutt are the simplest. Remember that a softer bit, such as a rubber or plastic bit, is sometimes more effective than a more severe bit. If the bit hurts your horse's mouth it may not be keen to follow your directions through the rein and will become difficult to control. If in doubt, ask a more knowledgeable person, such as a saddler or your veterinarian, for advice about specific problems. (See pp. 154-155 also.)

ABOVE RIGHT The hackamore is a bitless bridle suitable for horses or ponies with difficult or injured mouths.
RIGHT The double-bridle has two bits for extra sensitive riding and is used by experienced riders for lightness of touch and control.

The halter (headcollar)

Halters are used for tying up or leading, and are a basic form of restraint. Normally made from leather or webbing, they should be comfortable without being too tight (or so loose that the horse escapes!) The noseband should rest about halfway down the head. A halter is a simple device, and can be adjusted to fit just about any sized head.

ABOVE A flash noseband with bottom strap fastened below the bit to help prevent the opening of its mouth.

ABOVE A grakle—a cross-over noseband to prevent the horse from crossing its jaw.

ABOVE A plain cavesson is most common. It sits just below the cheek bones on the side of jaw.

ABOVE A drop noseband must be kept high on the nose, but fastened below the bit.

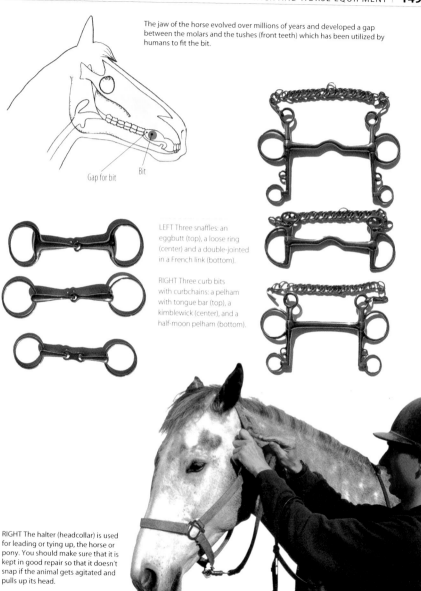

The jaw of the horse evolved over millions of years and developed a gap between the molars and the tushes (front teeth) which has been utilized by humans to fit the bit.

Gap for bit

Bit

LEFT Three snaffles: an eggbutt (top), a loose ring (center) and a double-jointed in a French link (bottom).

RIGHT Three curb bits with curbchains: a pelham with tongue bar (top), a kimblewick (center), and a half-moon pelham (bottom).

RIGHT The halter (headcollar) is used for leading or tying up, the horse or pony. You should make sure that it is kept in good repair so that it doesn't snap if the animal gets agitated and pulls up its head.

ABOVE The running martingale helps with control and steering of the horse. There must always be "stops" fitted as shown.

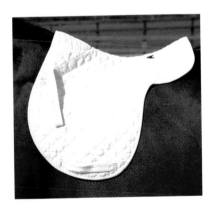

Other equipment

Numnah This is a type of pad used under the saddle to soften the contact between saddle and horse, and to protect the leather from the horse's sweat. It is usually made of fleece, cotton, toweling, felt, or synthetic rubber material, and is secured by tapes to the girth straps. Loose pads and sheepskins are also used.

LEFT The numnah or saddlepad is used under the saddle for extra comfort. It should be washed regularly to prevent rashes.

Neckstrap This useful strap is placed around the horse's neck for beginners, to give added security and to prevent the rider from pulling on the animal's mouth. Often it is also used on youngsters, or whenever the rider requires something secure to hold on to.

Martingale This device is used to prevent the horse from putting its head up too high and out of the angle of control. It gives greater control and steerage. There are two main types: the "standing" martingale, which is attached only to the cavesson or flash noseband and the "running" martingale, through which the reins run. It is essential to have "stops" with a running martingale to prevent the rings from catching on the billets of the reins.

Breastplate Also known as a breastgirth, a breastplate is designed to prevent the saddle from sliding back—perhaps because the horse is lean and fit, or just because of its conformation. Generally, it is used in racing or competition work.

ABOVE The leather breastplate or breastgirth prevents the saddle from slipping back.

Crupper Usually a leather loop, a crupper is used to prevent the saddle from sliding forward, particularly with small, fat ponies who often have insufficient withers to keep it in position. It is attached under the pony's tail to the back of the saddle, to which it is necessary to have a "D" ring added.

RIGHT The crupper does not cause the horse or pony any discomfort but is sometimes necessary to secure the saddle. The red bow denotes that the horse or pony is liable to kick out, so keep other animals and people away.

TACKING UP

Fitting your horse or pony in the equipment required for a ride or a particular job, such as a dressage event, soon becomes second nature, but fitting the equipment correctly is essential for your safety and the animal's comfort and so must always be a task carried out with care and attention.

It is worth going to a professional barn or yard to see what tack and equipment is really necessary before investing in too many gimmicks. Watch the people working there as they "tack-up" to learn how to use all tack correctly.

Prepare to tack up by tying up the horse and, if necessary, brush off any mud before you start. Prepare the saddle with the girths attached on the offside, and the stirrups run up, as shown below, so that they do not bang on the horse's sides.

The saddle

From the near left side, place the saddle over the horse's withers and gently slide it back into position just behind the shoulder blades. Never pull the saddle forward as this will ruffle the coat underneath and could cause saddle rubs. If a numnah is being used, generally this is secured to the saddle first. Loose pads or sheepskins are placed in position on the horse's back and the saddle fitted on top. Always pull numnahs and pads up into the front arch of the

ABOVE This rider is using a saddle pad which is placed on the horse with the saddle centrally fitted on top.

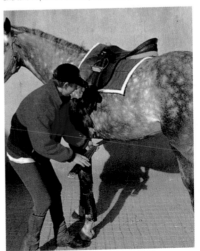

ABOVE The girths are slipped over the far side of the horse and taken up under the belly for fastening on the near side.

saddle before tightening the girths, to ensure there is no pressure on the withers. There should be a clear channel between the saddle and the horse's back and at least two fingers depth between the front arch of the saddle and the withers.

Drop the girth gently down the far right side and ensure it is hanging straight before bending down and taking it up to the girth straps on the nearside. Do not tighten too much at this stage to allow the horse time to get used to the feel. Check both sides to ensure that all is secure.

RIGHT With some horses, the skin may be pinched a little. In this case both front legs (fie legs) can be gently pulled forward as shown to. release any loose folds of skin.

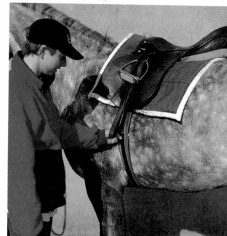

BELOW LEFT Make sure the skin is smooth and not puckered up between the girth and saddle flap when tightening.

BELOW RIGHT Check that all is secure by looking at tack on both sides of the horse.

ABOVE The reins are placed over the horse's head and the bridle raised up over the front of the head.

ABOVE Once the bit is level with the horse's mouth, ease a finger into the side to open.

ABOVE Slip the head piece over each ear individually and straighten the headpiece.

ABOVE Fasten the throat latch (throatlash), ensuring there is room for the width of one hand between this and the jawbone.

The bridle

Take the bridle—which should have the throat latch and noseband undone—in the left hand and go to the near left side of the horse. Place the reins over the horse's head and, facing toward it, unfasten the halter, keeping hold of the horse by the reins. With the right hand holding the bridle, slip the bit toward its mouth. With the left hand, slip your fingers gently between the lips at the side, where there is a gap between its teeth, to ask it to open its mouth. Slide the bridle up and slip one ear at a time through the headpiece. Straighten the browband. Then, fasten the throat latch (throatlash)—it should be loose enough to allow you to slip four fingers underneath it. Secure the noseband, allowing at least a finger's breadth for freedom of the jaw. Check that the bridle is correctly positioned between the cheekbones and lips so as not to cause soreness. Check that your girth is tight enough before setting off for your ride.

Secondhand equipment
Should I use or buy secondhand equipment? The local saddlers have a big secondhand department.

The use of secondhand equipment or saddlery will always depend on the quality and state of the items. Have everything carefully checked by the saddler or a professional. If a saddle is involved, be sure the tree is not broken. If tack has been well cared for, it should last for many more years. However, check all buckles and fastenings for excessive wear and tear. You may be lucky in many cases, but care is recommended nevertheless when purchasing secondhand equipment.

RIGHT The noseband is then fastened, allowing room for freedom of the jaw. Take care it does not press against the cheekbone.

ABOVE You should be able to fit two fingers underneath the noseband

ABOVE The hand is placed where shown when checking the throatlatch (throatlash).

Choosing a bridle

When choosing a bridle for your horse or pony try to choose one that complements the look and lifestyle of your animal. A big, strong hunter type requires a tough looking bridle with wide leather straps. A rather petite, fine looking horse would look best in a more refined type of bridle with narrow leathers. Always check that there is room for adjustment, both upward and downward, so that if you use a different bit with bigger or smaller rings it is possible to alter the bridle appropriately.

The bit too high
My horse looks as if he's smiling when his bridle is on but someone told me the bit is too high. How do you tell when it's too high?

The bit should rest comfortably in the horse's mouth allowing for just one crease at the corners of the mouth. It is very important that the bit is the right width for the horse's mouth. Too narrow and it will pinch the corners—too wide and it will not hang comfortably and may encourage the horse to put his tongue over, which can be very un-comfortable.

Every horse will be a little different and you may need to experiment with bits and the height at which they will feel most comfortable for the horse.

The bit too low
My horse keeps tossing his head and lolls his tongue out at the side and sometimes won't go forward like this. What should I do?

This may be caused by the bit being too low on the mouth and is a typical reaction to the discomfort when the horse puts his tongue over the bit. Ask a professional to advise you on the correct height and whether your horse is using a suitable bit for what you require of him.

ABOVE Always be sure to lift the saddle high enough to clear the back once the girths are undone.

ABOVE Slide the saddle toward you quickly and place it over your arm ready for carrying.

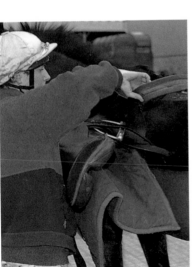

ABOVE Take the girth and place it over the center of the saddle before taking the saddle to the tack room or place it safely over the door.

Untacking

Of course, the same sort of care should be taken in untacking as in tacking up. Both you and your horse will soon become familiar with these daily routine tasks. Make sure you are able to keep the horse controlled by having the halter at hand unless untacking inside the stall or paddock.

Restless horse when untacking

My horse keeps moving round when I try to untack her. How should I control her?

Some horses are excitable after a ride—or over eager for their next meal and can't wait to be untacked. If this is the case, it is best to untack in the stable or after securing the horse with the halter. If you can't do either of these then try to hold her straight up against a wall or fence and then untack.

The saddle

Before you do anything, take the reins over the horse's head and slip them through your left hand so that you have proper control of the animal. Then, run the stirrup irons up the leathers. Undo the girth without letting it bang onto the horse's legs. Lift the front of the saddle at the pommel and slide it toward you, catching the girth with your right hand and placing it over the seat.

The bridle

With the reins still over the horse's head, undo the noseband, throatlatch (throatlash), and curb chain (if used). With your left hand on and just above the nose, ease the bridle off over one ear, then the other, keeping hold of the headpiece. Gently lower the bridle so that the bit can slip out of the horse's mouth easily. Never rush this or the bit may catch the horse's teeth and cause discomfort. If the horse is to be tied up instead of released, place a halter (headcollar) around the neck before taking the bridle off. Then, this can be put straight on without risking losing the horse.

ABOVE Check that everything necessary has been undone before easing it off over one ear at a time.

ABOVE With some horses it is best to keep your hand above their nose to help prevent them throwing their head up as the bit is released from the mouth.

THE RIDER'S EQUIPMENT

Safety is the all-important factor when deciding on what equipment to acquire. Prioritize what you absolutely need and what you can afford, particularly if taking up riding for the first time. Fashionable jodhpurs won't make you a better rider, but a safety helmet could save your life.

ABOVE This rider is wearing a traditional hunt cap instead of the correct helmet with safety harness (see opposite).

Although it is always nice to be well turned out, riding clothes and equipment can be expensive. Some saddlery stores sell good secondhand clothing but the one thing never to buy secondhand is a riding helmet (hat).

Headwear

The head is the most vulnerable part of the body, and everyone should wear a safety helmet (hat) when riding. This should be light and conform to current safety standards, and the chin strap must be secured at all times when mounted. Countless lives have been saved by the safety helmet.

Footwear

Another consideration is the type of footwear. Some form of heel (about 2 in [5 cm]) is essential to prevent the foot slipping through the stirrup iron. The jodhpur boot is ideal, as it is comfortable, practical, and safe. Long leather riding boots are expensive and need to be looked after properly but do give protection against chafing. A cheaper alternative is rubber riding boots.

Legwear

A safety helmet and boots will suffice to start with, along with jeans or pants until you get more ambitious. Some people can get rubbed on the insides of the legs because of chafing against the stirrup leathers. If this is the case, use pantihose (tights) or equi pants, or invest in some jodhpurs especially designed with extra padding. Leather chaps also prevent this problem. You can get them full length or just half chaps, which protect the upper leg only. Usually, Western riders have a wonderfully exotic choice.

Specialist clothing

The more serious rider will need to acquire extra bits of equipment, depending on where their interests lie (see Competitions and Riding Sports). Breeches and hunting boots are required for competition work, for example. The traditional long black boots are used for dressage, show jumping, eventing, and showing. Some sports have a slightly different shaped boot. In polo, players wear a special, more protective boot, which is usually tan-colored.

Endurance riders need footwear they can run and ride in, and many prefer some form of trainer with good cushioning for this work. Comfort is vital, and careful consideration needs to be given to every aspect of the clothing, from the socks up.

Vaulters need pantihose (tights) and/or leggings and leotards or pantsuits. For racing, lightweight breeches, boots, and silks are worn. Each specialist sport has its own specific requirements, with particular regard to safety aspects. Once you are serious enough to need specialist equipment, get an experienced friend to accompany you to a good riding wear store to obtain your outfit. To look professional, always go for quieter colors such as brown, blue, or black. Bright colors are generally only used for special occasions such as parades.

Protective wear
Should I use a back protector when riding in competition?

A back protector is an excellent safety precaution in case of a fall, and in many cases are compulsory for the jumping phases for such activities as eventing, pony club and racing. They are generally styled like a padded waistcoat with extra protection round the shoulders and down the spine. They are hot and can cause dehydration so only wear when necessary in hot weather and be sure to drink plenty of water.

MOUNTING AND DISMOUNTING

For the beginner, the first important achievement is getting on and off the horse correctly. It may seem like a difficult and daunting task at the start but a d a it is not difficult once, with practice, the technique has been mastered. The aim is to mount and dismount in a fluid movement that does not pull at the horse's back or alarm the horse in any way.

Mounting: there are two main methods of getting on—one from the ground and the other via a mounting block of some sort, which involves less pulling on the horse's back. Alternatively, you can also get a leg-up from a helper or, if you are experienced and athletic, you can vault onto the horse, cowboy style!

Before mounting, always check that your girth is tight and that your stirrups have been pulled down on both sides. Choose a suitable area to mount and ensure the reins are in place over the horse's neck. Always mount from the nearside (left side) of the horse.

Mounting: From the ground

Whatever form of mounting you decide on it is essential that you feel confident that you can do it unaided before you start to ride alone. Keep practicing from the ground and from a mounting block so that both methods have been mastered and that you are proficient enough to manage alone.

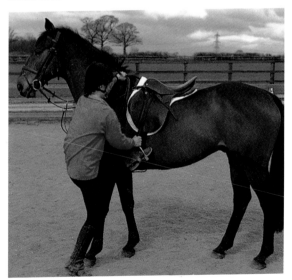

LEFT Take up the reins and hold them at a suitable length to keep the horse controlled without forcing it backward. Face to the rear and take hold of the outside of the stirrup, raise the left foot, and put it into the iron.

RIGHT With your right hand now resting on the seat of the saddle, swivel toward the horse and push your weight down into the stirrup.

ABOVE Jump upward until you are standing with your weight in the left stirrup.

ABOVE Swing your right leg over the quarters and ease yourself into the saddle gently.

ABOVE Place your right foot into the stirrup and adjust yourself centrally in the saddle.

Getting a "leg up"

One of the easiest ways of mounting a horse is by being given a "leg up" from a helper. This, however, requires a certain degree of athleticism from the rider who must spring upward when the helper indicates into the saddle. Mounting this way, as with a mounting block, helps to prevent pulling on the horse's back.

Easy mounts
Are some horses easier than others to get on?

The most important aspect is that the horse stands still during this crucial stage. The height of the horse can make a big difference as well as your own ability to stretch up to reach the stirrup if mounting from

HOW NOT TO MOUNT FROM THE GROUND

It is easy to see how athletic the rider has to be to mount from the ground. This rider is making it very difficult by trying to face toward the horse instead of away from it.

ABOVE Having a leg up is a most effective way of mounting if there are enough people to do this.

ABOVE It should not be necessary to have someone at the head if the rider takes up the reins to control the horse first.

the ground. If possible, use a mounting block of some description to make the process easier if the horse is rather large. If the horse moves a lot you will need a helper until you and your horse have come to an arrangement! Practice making the animal stand to command until it learns to respond.

Mounting from the ground
It worries me that I may damage the horse's back when I try to mount from the ground. Is it a problem?

If you find mounting from the ground very difficult and have to pull and heave at the saddle, you could cause a strain to the horse's back and a twist to the saddle tree in some cases. Again, a mounting block is much the best answer, however these are not always going to be available so it is essential that you do master this important technique.

Girth checks before mounting
My horse humps her back when I first get on and does not like her girth tightened. How should I deal with this?

This is a sign that your horse is filling her lungs with air to make her rib cage bigger so that the girth will be loose when she breathes out again. One of the best ways to deal with this is to tack the horse up early to allow her time to grow accustomed to-saddle. Tighten the girth in hole at a time until the saddle

Mounting: using a mounting block

The mounting block is an invaluable aid for all riders but a necessity for those who have trouble raising their leg high enough to put a foot in a stirrup from the ground. Blocks enable the rider to mount with relative comfort without having the difficulty of pulling and heaving up from the ground into the saddle. Mounting blocks consist of some form of solid platform of around 18-24 in (45-60 cm) high alongside which it is possible for a horse to stand. The closer the horse can stand to this the easier and safer it will be to mount.

RIGHT Take the horse alongside the mounting block. Step onto the block and take up the reins. Place your left foot into the stirrup.

LEFT Swing the right leg over the horse's back and ease down into the saddle.

RIGHT Once settled, move the horse straight forward until clear of the block before turning.

Vaulting on

I've seen children who have been riding a long time vaulting onto their ponies. How do they do it?

You need to be very athletic to do this and the horse or pony needs to be used to the movement. Grab a bit of mane or the front of the saddle and do a double jump on your feet before swinging up into the saddle. A vaulting mount is ideal for the young but a bit of a struggle for the older rider.

Dismounting

Like all basic movements it is most important to practice to get the hang of this vital part of riding. Once you are used to what is required, it will soon become easy as you become accustomed to the distance to the ground and how to keep your balance and flex your knees.

Dismounting a large horse
I find it difficult to keep my balance on landing when getting off my rather large horse. How can correct my dismount?

The important thing to remember when getting off is to bend the knees when you land. This helps you to stay forward close to your horse as you slide down off the saddle. Keep your hand on the saddle when dismounting so that you have a bit more security. If you have a suitable mounting block, you can train your horse to stand beside this and dismount onto this which stops you having to drop too far to the ground off a tall horse.

Falling off
What happens when you fall off—are there any precautions to take that can make it less painful?

The secret when falling is to try to stay relaxed and roll away from the horse as quickly as possible. Whether this is always an option entirely depends on the circumstances. Tuck your head in before you hit the ground and always ensure your safety harness is properly fastened whenever you are mounted. Back protectors obviously decrease the risk of back injuries and serious bruises. There is an old saying that "you can't ride until you've fallen 100 times!"

Restless horse when dismounting
My horse keeps moving around when I try to dismount which is rather frightening. How do I make sure she keeps still for me?

You must teach the horse to stand still to command by practicing each day. Walk your horse forward, halt her then relax, making her stand for a few minutes using your voice command only. Like humans, some horses are a little impatient—so pat her to reassure her you do want her to stay still. When you want to dismount, be sure you are not pulling the horse round with too tight a rein. Remember to take both feet out of the stirrups and prepare to dismount as instructed on this page. Ensure that you are on a non-slippery surface so that the horse feels secure. It is also a good idea to dismount in an enclosed area rather than a wide open field as this gives the horse less incentive to want to move around.

ABOVE First, come to a halt and take the reins into your left hand. Take both feet out of the stirrups and swing forward.

ABOVE Put your right hand onto either the knee roll or the saddle. Swing your right leg over.

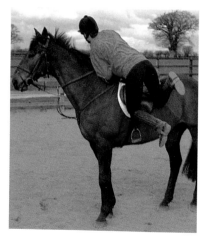

ABOVE Make sure you clear the horse's rump as a bang with your foot may make the horse take a jump forward.

ABOVE Land on both feet on the ground facing the horse. Remember to land with flexed knees to prevent jarring. Take the reins over the horse's head and run up the stirrup irons on both sides.

RIDER POSITION

Once mounted, it is important to find the right position in the saddle and one that is comfortable for you. The rider's position is called the "seat." This will not only affect your balance and comfort, but also that of the horse or pony.

To a certain extent, your position will be determined by the saddle and whether it is a suitable size and shape for you. Your own physique will also make some difference—a short person in a large jumping saddle will find it as awkward as a large person placed on a small-sized dressage saddle. Generally, a medium-sized, general purpose saddle is best for the beginner.

A good "seat"

The overall aim must be to sit as still as possible on the horse and, to achieve this, the rider has to be in good balance at all times. This is called "having a good or independent seat." The rider should be relaxed yet able to stay with the horse's movement. The shoulder, hip, and heel should remain on a perpendicular line, with the weight evenly distributed between the rider's two seat bones.

Head position

The head must remain looking upright and straight ahead. If it tips forward, the balance will shift with it. The shoulders must be relaxed but upright and the back straight, but not stiff.

Leg and foot position

The upper legs must be flat against the saddle with relaxed knees, the lower legs gently resting against the horse's sides. The hip, knee, and ankle joints must be relaxed to allow the rider to sit down well into the saddle.

The balls of the feet should rest lightly in the stirrup irons, with the weight going into the heels. This will keep the heels lower than the toes, which should face forward and upward.

RIGHT The two riders are showing a good basic position sideways and front facing. The body must be straight and relaxed, head up, arms relaxed and close to sides. Heels down, hands soft..

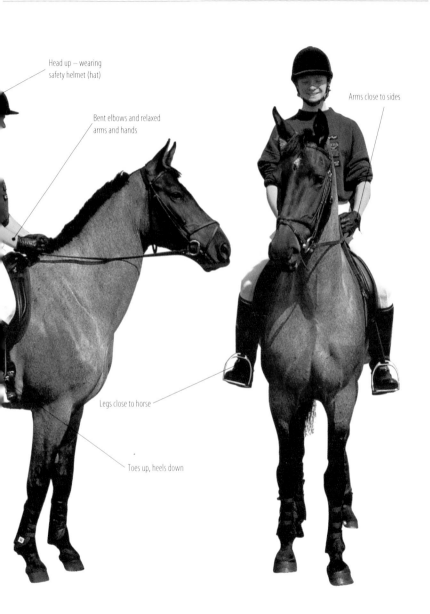

Head up – wearing safety helmet (hat)

Bent elbows and relaxed arms and hands

Arms close to sides

Legs close to horse

Toes up, heels down

Correct heel position
I feel I need to cling on with my heels but I'm supposed to keep my toes up—how do I do both?

It is important to push all the weight down into your heel to enable you to give effective leg aids. Raising the heel tends to make you rise up out of the saddle.

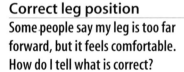

Correct leg position
Some people say my leg is too far forward, but it feels comfortable. How do I tell what is correct?

The leg will be less effective if it is too far forward and the straight vertical line from shoulder through hip to heel is lost. This means you slip to the back of the saddle putting all your weight too far back for the horse to be able to balance itself. A straighter cut saddle may help this problem.

ARM AND HAND POSITIONS

How you hold your arms and hands and, therefore, how you hold the reins is very important. The reins, via the bit, are the principal means of controlling the horse, apart from the leg and seat movements and the horse will be sensitive to every move of the arms or hands.

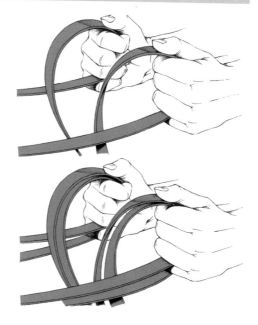

RIGHT The hands hold the reins between the fourth and little fingers, allowing the reins to come up through the palms between the thumbs and first fingers. The contact should be light and relaxed. A well-schooled horse or pony will respond to the movements of the fingers and wrist. The top diagram shows how to hold single reins, the bottom one illustrates how to hold double reins.

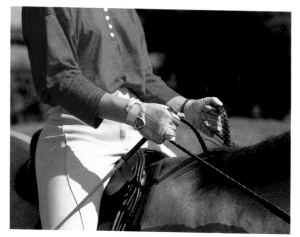

LEFT The arms should hang down in a relaxed attitude, softly bent at the elbows with the hands resting just above the withers. The fingers should remain loosely rounded inward with the thumbs uppermost.

CONTROL AND THE AIDS

To be able to control and influence the horse's direction and speed, it is important for the rider to understand the accepted way of making this possible—by using control methods and the aids that have evolved over the centuries. To ride well you must ensure you are giving the instructions clearly, simply, and in time, so that your horse or pony feels confident too.

The "aids" are the means by which the rider tells the horse what to do. They consist of the effective use of the rider's hands, legs, and seat—known as the natural aids. The voice can also be added to this. The whip and spurs are known as artificial aids.

Natural aids

The hands The rider's hands are not only used for controlling and turning the horse but also to create balance. At all times the rider needs to be aware that

USING THE CONTROLS

This photograph shows how to make use of the hands, legs and seat.

The back is straight and the head up helping with good balance.

A firm deep seat in the saddle.

A strong leg with low heel.

The hands are loose, relaxed, and independent creating good balance.

The horse is accepting the rider's hand instructions through the reins and is responding by being on the bit.

the horse has a metal bar through its mouth, and that the mouth is extremely sensitive. The lightest touch will produce a response from a well-schooled horse and the rider should relax the rein a little before asking for another response, when necessary. An inexperienced rider will tend to use the hands to balance with at first, which is a disaster for the poor horse. The legs and seat are responsible for the rider's balance.

The rider must be sympathetic and gentle to the horse or pony. Try to keep an even feel on the reins, using the fingers and wrists and lightly to help keep the balance, control, and relaxation of the horse's jaw so that it responds willingly. Rarely should the rider need to use the arms to pull the horse back. The hands should remain fairly passive and quiet, being used only to give and to feel what is happening, and to influence the degree of control required.

To turn the horse, a little more contact is exerted on the side you wish to turn toward and the opposite leg is used to control the body of the horse as it changes direction. The outside rein is used to support the horse and maintain the balance while the inside one establishes the bend.

The legs The rider's legs help to create forward movement, to guide, and to control the balance of the horse. Used gently in nudges or little vibratory kicks, the horse will respond by going forward, reining backward, or by going sideways in response to leg pressure. A constant kick will either result in a "dead-sided" animal, immune to the stimuli caused by excessive use of the aid, or one that is so over-responsive it will take off and become out of control.

The legs are applied just behind the girth and must hang loosely at the horse's sides. The rider must not be tempted to tighten upward, which has the effect of drawing the weight up out of the saddle and may cause tension in both rider and horse. The legs are used evenly on both sides for general forward movement.

On turns and circles, the inside leg pressure prevents the horse from falling in on the circle while the outside one maintains the bend and forward movement. The leg can be used to push the horse away from the way of going, such as in lateral work. In the half pass, for instance, the left leg can push the horse across to the right. This can be useful when you are opening a gate and you do not want to dismount.

To create speed, the legs are used strongly (depending on the horse's response). In reining back the use of the leg and a restraining hand cause the animal to step backward.

For balance and to create extra impulsion, the legs are used in conjunction with the seat and hand. In top-level dressage movements, such as passage and piaffe, the balance is created through an effective leg. The better schooled the horse, the more responsive it will be, but this will only come

about if the rider's instructions are subtle, direct, and not overdone.

The seat Once the basics of balance and position have been mastered, the seat is the most influential aid. Straightness in the saddle is essential and it is important to be aware of feeling yourself sitting straight with your weight evenly distributed on both seat bones. It is possible to create extra energy by sitting heavier in the saddle. Then, the seat influences the balance of the horse through

greater or less impulsion caused by the horse's hind quarters coming more underneath it. However, this can have the effect of "hollowing" the horse if the rider is not skilled enough to keep a relaxed back (to absorb the extra energy created) and apply the correct leg aids. To start with, it is better to work on straightness in the saddle and maintaining balance rather than become over-absorbed in how much weight to keep in your seat. It all falls into place with experience and time.

The development of your horse will also have a bearing on weight distribution. A young horse not yet fully matured or strong in its back will not be able to cope physically with a rider with too deep a seat.

The voice This can be a useful extra natural aid, especially for horses that respond well to the voice. It is fun to teach horses to answer simple commands such as whoa, trot, canter, and halt, and often takes only a week or two of patient training (using repetition and reward).

Starting correctly

To ride forward Nudge or gently kick the horse, at the same time softening the hands. This will allow the horse the freedom to move forward. You should then follow the horse's movement with your own body.

WALK At walk allow yourself to lean slightly forward as the horse moves and relax your back to his movement.

LEFT Here the horse is on its forehand and the rider is leaning too far back in an effort to keep the horse's head up. Correcting the leg position would help to create better balance.

TROT In a trot you will need to rise up and down in time to the horse's movement taking the weight through your heel.

CANTER In canter, go forward with the horse and keep your hands low and still. Circle round gradually if it feels a bit fast.

ABOVE The rider sits up and prepares to slow down using a deep seat and use of the legs to create a good balance. The hands on the reins register a slight pull which will restrict forward movement from the horse.

Stopping correctly

To stop or reduce your speed Give a gentle pull on the reins, say "whoa" or "ho," then release the pressure. Keep doing this until you stop. As your skill improves, you can start to use your seat and legs to gain a much more subtle reduction in speed. By then you will start to have a slightly more refined use of the hands rather than pulling back.

ABOVE The horse shortens its stride in response to the previous instructions. As shown here, the horse should come to a smooth, relaxed stationary position (a halt) because the rider's movements are smooth and relaxed.

ABOVE Once stationary, the rider relaxes the hands to enable the horse to relax in a halt. The horse should be allowed to remain still for a few seconds before moving forward to perform the next movement.

LEFT: HOW NOT TO STOP
This rider is hauling at the horse's mouth with the hands and using no leg pressure—a disastrous method of trying to stop.

Turning technique

To turn the horse, the rider must take a more positive feel on the rein on the side to which the horse is to turn. Then a slight pull to the inside rein indicates direction and a strong pressure from the outside leg prevents the horse's quarters swinging outward. Both legs should keep the horse moving forward, maintaining the rhythm.

RIGHT This rider is turning, the horse's head off the forward track by turning the horse's right shoulder in toward the direction of the turn. Pressure is also applied by the legs to control the horse's turn.

ABOVE Here, the rider is applying the leg and has lightened the seat before beginning to restrict the forward movement by applying gentle pressure on the rein.

ABOVE It is important to ask for only one or two steps to begin with, then reward the horse with a pat on the neck or an encouraging word and then move forward.

Reining back

Reining back is a training exercise to help improve balance and coordination for both rider and horse. Before asking your mount to perform a reining back motion, bring it to a halt first. Ask for the rein back by restricting the forward movement with the gentle but firm use of the hands on the reins and use of the leg. Once the horse realizes it cannot go forward it will start to step back. Keep all the instructions through the natural aids slow and quiet.

Changing diagonals

When the rider is in a rising trot, he or she is thrown upward by the movement of the horse's left leg or right leg as it moves forward in each stride. The rider sits for one stride—up again, then sits. This is known as riding on the left or right diagonal. To ensure the horse is not strained by always pushing the rider's weight upward with the same diagonal pair of legs (see diagram on right), it is important to change diagonals whenever there is a change in direction.

When changing to the right diagonal, watch the horse's right shoulder go forward as you rise out of the saddle. If you are sitting at this point, miss one stride by sitting and then rise again with the horse's right shoulder moving forward. When going to the left diagonal, rise upward as the horse's left shoulder moves forward.

LEFT In trot, the off fore and near hind legs move together first (left) and then the near fore and off hind leg move together (right). This is called "moving alternate diagonals."

BELOW Lungeing the horse on the circle is a good way to see which diagonal the rider is rising to. Then you can instruct the rider when to change diagonal.

Artificial aids

The artificial aids are extremely useful if used properly. They come in several different sizes and shapes and are designed for different uses.

The whip This is used to reinforce the leg aids and to increase responsiveness. The long schooling or dressage whip is used by bringing the hand away a little from the neck and just tapping the horse behind the rider's leg or, to create extra activity, down the animal's hind leg. The crop is useful for tapping down the shoulder to keep the horse straight. The rider can also take the hand off the rein and use the whip behind the saddle to create more forward movement. Never keep your hand on the rein while using the whip behind the saddle, as this has the effect of catching the horse in the mouth at the same time. On the occasion when a horse needs a reprimand for deliberate disobedience, this needs to be done immediately after the incident has occurred. Even half a minute later the horse will be unable to understand why it is being punished. With inexperienced riders, it is usually the horse's inability to understand muddled instructions that cause the problem. Therefore the rider must try again to

LEFT Whips are generally held close to the top end. In competition, the jumping whip should not be longer than 30 in (75 cm). Note the correct angle to hold this type of whip is shown in the photograph.

indicate his or her wishes to the horse. Never ever use the whip in anger on a horse.

To change a short whip from one hand to the other, first take both reins and whip in one hand. Pull the whip upward through the palm with the other hand until free. For a long whip, this is quietly swung in a 180° arc in front of the rider's face with a turn of the wrist. The opposite hand then takes the whip and brings it back into position.

BELOW There are two main types of riding whip. The short jumping or cutting whip (top) and the long dressage whip (bottom).

LEFT The dressage whip is very flexible because of its length and needs very sensitive handling. It should be used to accentuate the rider's leg aids. Dressage whips come in various lengths depending on the requirements.

ABOVE It is usual to ride with a whip on the nearside (left side), held in a light grip and only touching the horse when you are asking for a particular action or requiring more forward movement.

ABOVE To change the whip hand, take the top with the opposite hand and draw it through the hand holding the whip, as shown, in a smooth action.

ABOVE Ensure that you don't let the whip tap your horse while you transfer it into your other hand as this may frighten the animal.

Changing whip

Horses may need encouragement to move forward by feeling a light touch of the whip. For Instance, if it were shying to the left away from a spook fence then you would tap the right side.

While riding, you will need to change your whip from hand to hand occasionally. It takes some practice to make the change smoothly and you must remember to talk to your horse and reassure it when you perform this movement.

Rowelled or sharp spurs

SPURS

These increase the horse's feel and responsiveness to the leg. They should only be used by experienced riders who have acquired an independent seat and are capable of full control of the leg.

Usually, spurs are placed along the back seam of a boot with the curved shank pointing upward and downward. The buckle must be fastened on the outside so as not to chafe the horse's sides. To use, the rider's toe is turned out slightly to bring the spur in contact with the horse's side, then released again. It should not be used incessantly, just brought into action when a little more response is required.

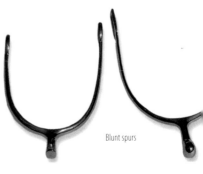

Blunt spurs

The use of spurs
When should I start to use spurs and what are their uses?

Spurs are an artificial aid which have been used for centuries to improve the effect of the rider's legs. When used sensibly, they increase the forward impulsion of the horse. Assist with the bend in the body, especially in lateral work and with the general overall balance. Once the rider has an independent seat and is proficient in all school movements, they can be used periodically for greater effect. They should never be used on a very sensitive horse or by a rough or inexperienced rider.

ABOVE This horse is resisting away from where the rider wishes to go. Strong legs with spurs may help if this is a persistent problem but it should never be necessary to "dig in hard" with spurs.

THE PACES

The horse has four basic paces or gaits: walk, trot, canter, and gallop—the latter being an extended canter. There are variations within these paces, depending on the degree of training, which demonstrate collection or extension. Some horses have unusual gaits, such as pacing, the running walk, the "amble," and the "rack," but in most cases these are specific to the breed.

The schooling of the horse or pony and its responsiveness to the rider's aids will make all the difference to how it is able to perform paces. For the rider, the comfort of the gait is important. In competition work, the quality of the pace will determine the horse's degree of success, to a certain extent.

The walk

The walk, the slowest gait, is a four-time walk with the animal picking up each leg independently of the other. It should be a forward marching movement in which the horse is allowed the necessary amount of hand freedom to be able to move its head and neck slightly as each leg is used to propel it forward. The four beats should be even and regular at all times and there should be no stiffness. In dressage work, there are four different walks recognized: the collected, medium, extended, and free walk.

The rider must sit still and square on the horse, allowing the movement underneath to express itself. The rider's body must follow forward with the movement and the hands should be able to move with the horse's head. When riding on a loose rein, such as when trail riding or out hacking, sit upright

LEFT It is possible to see how the legs move forward in the walk in the following four movement sequence of this gait: off hind, off fore, near hind, near fore.

RIGHT The trot is a two sequence gait where the rider is thrown upwards as the horse transfers its weight from one diagonal pair of legs to the other—the off fore and near hind point forward.

and keep the reins from slipping down the neck. Left to its own devices, the horse is extremely adept at picking its way through the roughest terrain and will often foresee boggy conditions undetectable to the human eye.

The trot

The trot is a two-time gait on alternate diagonal legs (near hind and off fore and vice versa) with a moment of suspension in between. It should be free and active with regular steps. The quality of the trot depends on the horse's natural movement, but with correct schooling even a moderate animal can be made to improve dramatically. There are four trots recognized in dressage: collected, working, medium, and extended.

The rider can rise or post (sit) to the trot. Most riders prefer the sitting trot once the up-down rhythm has been mastered, but young horses may find it hard on their backs if a rider sits for a long time. In the rising trot, the rider rises out of the saddle as the horse goes from one diagonal pair of legs and sits as it changes to the other, in an up-down, up-down rhythm. The weight must be pushed down into the stirrups. You have to adjust your balance a little as you maintain the forward momentum on the upward rise and must not get left behind the movement as you sink back down. To start with, it is easier to find your balance by tending to go too far forward than too far back.

ABOVE The horse will stretch its neck slightly as each stride is taken and the rider's hand should move with this so that there is no restriction.

ABOVE Some horses will glide across the ground, while others will appear rather stilted; it all depends on whether they have a short or long stride.

LEFT By this stage, it is easy to see the horse is now stretching forward the opposite front leg to the one it started with and has completed the sequence.

ABOVE In this picture, the rider is out of the saddle in rising trot and the horse is brining up the front leg towards its highest point.

ABOVE Now both opposite front and back legs are at maximum height and are about to shift the weight onto the opposite diagonal pair. The rider is right up out of the saddle.

LEFT The sequence completed and it is possible to see the horse now has its near fore and off hind pointing forward. The rider is sitting in readiness for the next stride.

The canter

The canter is a three-time gait. The foot falls follow one another in this sequence: left hind, left fore leg and right hind together, then right fore leg. This is followed by a moment of suspension, with all four feet in the air, before the next stride begins.

The canter can be an extremely comfortable pace, whether just loping along or performing in a dressage arena. It is the most important pace to perfect for jumping, as the quality of the strides determines the way the horse will be able to approach the fence. From a controlled, even canter, the horse is able to jump out of its stride. If this is erratic or there is a change in tempo or speed, this will seriously affect the animal's ability to approach the fence in the good, even rhythm so essential in the jumping horse.

Generally, the child's pony, western, and trail animals are expected to do any cantering on a fairly loose rein with little guidance from the rider. These horses may need to adjust their balance without obvious interference from the rider or, in some cases, because of interference from the rider—such as when an inexperienced child loses its balance and nearly falls off.

LEFT The three sequence gait of the canter is demonstrated here where only the off hind is on the ground taking the entire weight of the horse..

LEFT The gallop is a speeded-up version of the canter. This makes the four movement sequence much more difficult to see when all the weight is on the off foreleg.

The gallop

The fourth pace, the gallop, is an extended canter. The speed very much depends on what the horse is doing. The racehorse in a sprint race is traveling at around 25 mph (38 kph), whereas it may only be going 15 mph (22 kph) in a four-mile (8 km) chase.

For endurance work the horse may be traveling slowly at a steady 6-8 miles (9-13 km) an hour, or, in certain races much more over shorter distances at the gallop. Galloping around steeplechase or cross-country courses is particularly exciting and in the Maryland Hunt Cup in the United States, the solid timber fences provide an even more thrilling occasion.

The balance of the rider at speed is helped by use of a shorter stirrup, hence the reason jockeys ride so short. This provides them with extra leverage to be able to hold a pulling horse at speed. They can brace their legs forward, in most cases providing an effective means of staying under control.

In the gallop, the horse really lengthens and lowers its frame, reaching forward in ground vouring strides. Some horses have a lovely fluid way of galloping which takes far less out of them than those with a short, choppy, jarring stride. The reins should be short and the rider must maintain an even feel on the reins. Any pulling or shifting of weight could seriously unbalance the horse. It is important to ensure you have a suitable bit to enable you to maintain control when galloping.

ABOVE The balance has gone forward and the two hind legs and near fore are taking the weight at this stage. The off fore is now free of the ground.

ABOVE The weight is now on the near fore as the other three legs are lifted forward to come into position for the next stride to take place.

LEFT The stride completed, the horse is now back in the same position as it was at the start. The rider's hands have eased forward slightly with each stride taken.

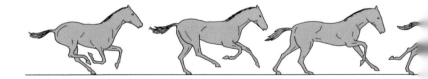

ABOVE The moment of suspension when all four legs are just off the ground. You can just see the legs prepare for the landing onto three legs.

ABOVE At this stage, the horse is on three legs, stretching forward again ready to propel itself into taking the next stride. The rider is leaning forward over the horse's front legs.

LEFT The horse is back into the next stride and in the same position as in the first picture for the sequence to start all over again.

PREPARING TO JUMP

The horse has four basic paces or gaits: walk, trot, canter, and gallop—the latter being an extended canter. There are variations within these paces, depending on the degree of training, which demonstrate collection or extension. Some horses have unusual gaits, such as pacing, the running walk, the "amble," and the "rack," but in most cases these are specific to the breed.

Preparing to jump

The horse is a natural jumper. In the wild it can be seen leaping over bushes, ditches, and puddles, and careering down drops or scrambling up mountain trails with great ease. When ridden, it has to adjust its balance to cope with the weight of the rider.

The way your horse is introduced to jumping may influence its attitude for life. The young horse needs to be physically fit and mature enough before being asked to do anything strenuous too soon. The rider needs to be confident and sufficiently experienced to cope with what is required, and to have a basic knowledge of how the horse jumps and how to respond. Both horse and rider out trail riding or hacking will have encountered small jumps of a natural type and jumped them unwittingly. This is the ideal way to learn gradually, making a conscious effort to observe any small obstacle worth jumping and go for it.

The canter is the most important gait for jumping and practice at riding in the forward jumping seat is vital so that the change in balance can be mastered. The horse must go forward willingly with rhythm and balance. This energy is created by the rider's legs pushing the horse into the hands, which control the speed and power necessary for the horse to make a good, "round" jump.

With a forward going horse, it is easy to achieve a good canter. The lazy horse has to be stoked up and asked to go faster than necessary to create a sufficiently forward approach for it to remain in canter until over the fence.

Pole work

A useful start to jumping is by the use of poles. These can be placed on the ground at random distances and the horse first trotted and then cantered over them. Practice your approach by coming in toward them absolutely straight. Later, practice approaching off a turn for example, or on a large circle. Change the direction of the pole, all the time aiming for a steady rhythm. A series of three or four poles placed approximately 3 yards (3 meters) apart for horses (2½ yards [2.5 meters] for ponies) will help to create the "jump" feeling, as the horse should make the effort to jump over each pole in the canter if they are evenly spaced. That way, the rider will be able to recognize the feeling of what it is like to "go with the movement of the horse." The rider must swing slightly forward as the horse lifts off over the pole and then sit up as it lands, following the animal's movement.

ABOVE Polework in training will teach the horse to look where it is going and to think what it is doing.

ABOVE It will also teach it to adjust its stride and get used to colored poles which it will soon have to jump. Once happy, move on to single small fences.

ABOVE The small single fence in the background is the next stage. A low double of two fences with one or two strides in between can then be introduced.

ABOVE Polework in training will teach the horse to look where it is going and to think what it is doing.

ABOVE It will also teach it to adjust its stride and get used to colored poles which it will soon have to jump. Once happy, move on to single small fences.

ABOVE The small single fence in the background is the next stage. A low double of two fences with one or two strides in between can then be introduced.

The flying lead change

One of the most useful exercises, the flying lead change, can be practiced at the same time as pole work. This is the method of changing from one leading leg in the canter to the other. Once mastered, it becomes easy to do it with a half halt or rebalancing of the horse, and then shifting the weight and rein contact to the opposite side during the moment of suspension when all four feet are off the ground. Often this is taught over a pole initially. liming is paramount as the horse can only change when its front legs are off the ground and the hind leg of the side you are changing onto is coming forward.

Canter on a circle on the inside lead and diagonally "jump" across the pole, changing your hand aid to the opposite side as you are in the air. Shift your weight toward the leading leg as you go onto a circle in the opposite direction, making a figure eight. Use of your outside leg will help to put the horse onto the lead.

BELOW One method of teaching flying changes is to change direction during the moment the horse is in the air over a pole. Keep practicing until you feel confident about the technique.

PHASES OF A JUMP

There are four basic phases to how the horse jumps the fence. The approach must be balanced with the horse maintaining a good consistent pace into the fence.

The take off requires the horse to bring its hocks well up underneath if it is to spring upward over a fence of any height. The rider can ensure that the horse arrives at the right spot by regulating the stride into the fence.

The moment of suspension over the fence requires absolute freedom from the rider to enable the horse to round its back over the top of the fence and prepare for the landing without interference.

The landing is a time during which the horse requires the rider to be in a good upright position and balanced so that he or she does not lean too far forwards and thereby push the horse onto its forehand. He or she must sit up and settle the horse into a steady rhythm before the next fence.

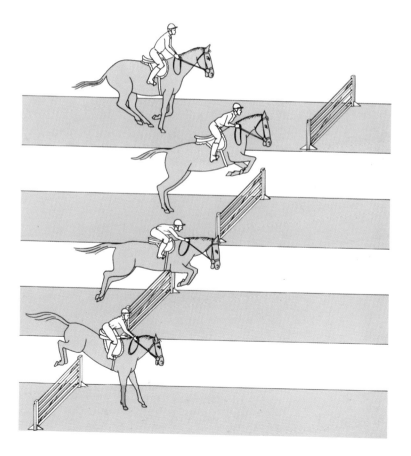

JUMPING

Only by hours of training will it be possible to build up the rapport between horse and rider that is so essential for that all important clear round at a competition. Jumping should be practiced two or three times a week, with different exercises to ensure horse and rider are fully prepared for all eventualities.

LEFT The earlier you can start to ride and jump, the quicker you will be able to master the art! Most children are totally fearless and love the sensation of jumping.

Single fences are easy to jump. Always use a straight approach and ride at the middle of the fence. Ride away straight afterward so that you are teaching yourself and the horse to be prepared to jump another. If you are in a class with other horses and riders, never jump a fence and let the horse run back to the group, as this will let the horse develop bad follow through on the jump and encourage the horse to disobey commands.

Grids

An excellent training exercise is to set up a series of poles and fences in a sequence or grid. The distances between them must be suitable for the size and standard of the individual horse. It is unwise to have a horse and pony using the same grid, as the pony will have a much shorter stride. Build up the number of poles and fences gradually, as it can be confusing to see a line of poles if you are unprepared. Leave the horse to do the jumping, and think of approaching with enough impulsion to maintain the rhythm necessary. Sit up over the poles to help balance the horse and go with the horse over the fences. Cross poles, verticals, bounces, and spreads can be used in grids, in between poles on the ground.

GRID WORK

ABOVE The young horse may benefit from having done some grid work on the lunge or been ridden at an early stage in its career.

ABOVE Grids consist of jumps and poles at varying distances. Make sure you start gradually as it may prove very intimidating for the horse to see too many poles at one time.

LEFT Try to vary the exercises so that your horse becomes adept at doing several different types of strides on the lunge or ridden.

DIRECTORY OF HORSE BREEDS

The directory includes over 90 of the world's most fascinating horse breeds. Some are particularly pure while others have been adapted by selective breeding over the yeas to meet with modern requirements. Information of origin, height, color, physique, character, and principal uses is provided for each of the featured breeds, alongside locater maps and height diagrams.

COLORS AND MARKINGS

The horse's coat insulates the body against extremes of temperature and the effects of the elements. It is water resistant and varies in texture according to the horse's genes and habitat.

COAT COLORS

Breeds which evolved in cold regions for example, often have virtually waterproof coats with a soft underlay-er for extra insulation. Within color categories there are different shades and varieties. Some of the most common are shown on the facing page.

HEIGHT BOXES

Throughout the book, height boxes are used to display the height range for each particular breed in hands.

FACIAL MARKINGS

Facial markings are an important means of identification. Some of the common ones are shown below.

MAPS

The country of origin of each horse is shown on the small map in each entry.

White face   **Snip**   **Blaze**   **Star**   **Stripe**

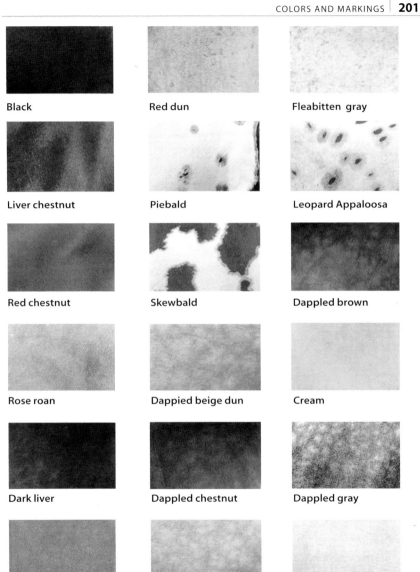

Black

Red dun

Fleabitten gray

Liver chestnut

Piebald

Leopard Appaloosa

Red chestnut

Skewbald

Dappled brown

Rose roan

Dappied beige dun

Cream

Dark liver

Dappled chestnut

Dappled gray

Bay

Palomino

Gray

HORSE BREEDS

QUARTER HORSE

Named after the quarter-mile race in 17th century Virginia and the Carolinas. It is noted for its extremely fast starts and great speed over short distances. It is an ideal ranch horse. They are the most numerous breed in the USA.

Origin USA.
Height 15-16hh.
Color Solid colors.
Physique Large build, muscular.
Character Intelligent, sensible, nimble, active.
Principal uses Riding, ranchwork, rodeos and in racing.

SADDLEBRED

Developed as an enduring working horse, they are one of the most glamorous and loving horses in the world. The breed's gait distinguishes it from others, "slow gait", "rack", "three-gaited" and "five-gaited", were developed for long hours under saddle.

Origin USA.
Height 15-16hh.
Color Solid colors, including Palomino.
Physique Long legs, high neck and nicked and set tail.
Character Fiery, spirited, gentle.
Principal uses Show horse, jumper.

APPALOOSA

Bred by the American Indian tribe, the Nez Percé, from stock brought by the conquistadores. They have a patterned coat with six variations of mottling and spotting. They are used as competition, working, parade and display horses.

Origin USA.
Height 14-15hh.
Color White with spots of chestnut, brown, black.
Physique Compact, strong legs.
Character Docile, enthusiastic.
Principal uses Riding, dressage, cross-country, show jumping

TENNESSEE WALKING HORSE

Developed by plantation owners for long hours in the saddle. They are all round riding and harness horses. They owe their existence to one stallion which was discarded because of his strange walk and founded a new breed.

Origin USA.
Height Not less than 15hh.
Color Chestnut, brown, black with white markings.
Physique Compact, well-muscled, strong legs and feet.
Character Docile, alert.
Principal uses Show ring, general riding and harness horse.

PONY OF THE AMERICAS

Bred from the Scottish Shetland Pony from Britain and the Iberian-based American Appaloosa. They have the Appaloosa coloring and patterns and the conformation of a miniature Arab/Quarter Horse cross.

Origin USA.
Height 11-13hh.
Color White pattern with spots of chestnut, brown, black.
Physique Arab-type head, strong hindquarters, clean legs.
Character Versatile, willing, gentle.
Principal uses Children's riding pony.

11-13hh

STANDARDBRED

The fastest trotting and pacing racer in the world. Bred for one purpose only, to trot or pace harnessed to an ultralight, two-wheeled racing sulky for one mile (1.6km) to a minimum standard time.

Origin USA.
Height 14-16hh.
Color Brown, black, bay with black tail and a chestnut mane.
Physique Muscular, short legs, powerful shoulders.
Character Docile, easy to handle, energetic and extremely competitive.
Principal uses Trotting and pacing races.

14-16hh

MISSOURI FOX TROTTER

Developed by settlers who wanted a comfortable, speedy enduring horse able to cross all terrains. They have been raced but are now more of a utility, all purpose horse. They have a distinctive fox trotting gait.

Origin USA.
Height 14-16hh.
Color Chestnut, brown, pinto.
Physique Substantial, stylish horse, fine legs, strong feet.
Character Hardiness, willing to work, versatile, great stamina.
Principal uses Leisure riding, showing and endurance riding.

AMERICAN SHETLAND

The breed was started from Shetland Ponies imported into America. The American Shetland retains the thick Shetland mane and tail hair, but has a definite horse character and longer body and legs.

Origin USA.
Height Up to 11hh.
Color Solid colors, roan, cream and dun.
Physique Rugged, long legs, long feet.
Character Intelligent, easy to keep.
Principal uses Harness classes: sulky racing, four-wheeled buggy, driving, children's shows.

MORGAN

The most versatile of the American breeds, an all-round riding and light harness horse. It was the official mount of the US Cavalry until mechanisation, and has been instrumental in founding several other American breeds.

Origin USA.
Height 14-15hh.
Color Hay, brown, black.
Physique Broad back, muscular hindquarters, legs set square.
Character Spirit, stamina, speed.
Principal uses All-rounder, ideal family horse.

CRIOLLO

The breed's ancestors, Iberian, Barb and Arab horses, arrived in America 300 years ago. Adaptable to the extremes of climate, breeding stock undergo selection tests where the horses are marched for 470 miles (750km) carrying 238lb (108kg).

Origin USA.
Height 14-15hh.
Color Primitive dun or brown.
Physique Stocky, strong shoulders and legs, small feet.
Character Hardy, independent.
Principal uses Cattle horse, endurance riding.

FALABELLA

Claimed to be the smallest horse in the world, the breed was founded by crossing Shetland and Thoroughbred blood. Continual breeding for smaller size has resulted in inherited and congenital weaknesses which breeders are trying to overcome.

Origin USA.
Height Not exceeding 30 in (75 cm).
Color Appaloosa type coloring.
Physique Horse-like proportions, not strong, small feet.
Character Quiet, friendly.
Principal uses Pets, shown in hand, pulling small vehicles.

MANGALARGA

They are descended from an Altér Real stallion and South American Criollo mares. The Mangalarga has a fifth gait called the marcha, which is a fast, rolling gait halfway between the trot and canter, making the breed useful for stock work.

Origin Brazil.
Height 15hh.
Color Bay, gray, chestnut, roan.
Physique Long head, powerful hindquarters, long legs.
Character Tough, hardy, cooperative.
Principal uses Stock work on ranches of Brazil.

AZTECA

The Azteca replaces the Mexican strain of Criollo. Andalusian stallions were crossed with South American Criollo and Quarter Horse mares to produce a horse for leisure riding and competition. They have the qualities of speed, agility of the Quarter Horse, and toughness of the Criollo.

Origin Mexico.
Height 14-15hh.
Color All colors.
Physique Elegant, compact, agile.
Character Tough, hardy, stamina.
Principal uses Leisure riding and competition.

GALICENO

Descended from the Spanish pony, they are a popular pony for older children and adaptable for showing and competing. They have great stamina and a natural fast running walk, which is comfortable over long distances.

Origin Mexico.
Height 12-13hh.
Color All colors.
Physique Intelligent head, short back, fine legs, small feet.
Character Tough, hardy, intelligent, lovely and friendly temperament.
Principal uses Ranch work and light harness work.

PERUVIAN STEPPING HORSE

The blood brother of the Paso Fino, the Peruvian Stepping Horse has developed a large heart and lungs to enable it to work in an atmosphere of very low oxygen. They instinctively work on rocky ground, sliding shale, deep water and steep inclines without fear or panic.

Origin Peru.
Height 14-15hh.
Color All colors, bay or chestnut.
Physique Sure footed, strong legs.
Character Calm, enduring, willing.
Principal uses Ranching, travel, parade work, showing.

PASO FINO

The Paso Fino comes from Puerto Rico and is the best-looking of the Paso types. It is famous for its refined gaits the paso fino, the paso corto or fino fino and the paso largo. It is also a working horse and is used for trans¬portation on coffee plantations.

Origin Puerto Rico.
Height 14-15hh.
Color All colors.
Physique Refined gaits, Arab-type head, Andalusian body.
Character Gentle temperament, easy to handle, intelligent.
Principal uses Riding, showing, display work, ransportation.

POLO PONY

The Polo Pony is a type of pony, not a breed. They need to be tough, agile, and fast over short distances. The best polo ponies are usually regarded as the Argentinian ones; although most countries where polo is played, breed some of their own ponies.

Origin Argentina.
Height 15hh.
Color All colors.
Physique Fit, strong, natural balance, with powerful hindquarters.
Character Determined, obedient.
Principal uses Polo games.

PALOMINO

The Palomino is not strictly a breed but a color. There is no actual Palomino stud book and as they cannot be made to breed to color. The exception to this is in America where there is a register of color-breeds with strict requirements.

Origin USA.
Height Over 14hh.
Color Gold, light mane and tail.
Physique Riding horse type.
Character Intelligent.
Principal uses Riding, rodeos, trekking, ranchwork.

PINTO

The term means horses with large patches of white and one other color on their bodies. Only in the USA is the Pinto regarded as a true breed. The Native American tribes loved these horses as their broken outline provided camouflage.

Origin USA.
Height Variable.
Color Black patches with white, white with any color except black.
Physique Depends on type.
Character Intelligent, enduring.
Principal uses Showing, ranchwork, riding.

MUSTANG

The Mustang is the feral horse of the North Americas and was used by Indian tribes. The Mustang developed toughness to cope with living wild, but few run free today. Most are enclosed on ranches, or used to breed riding and ranch horses.

Origin Western USA/ Mexico.
Height 14-15hh.
Color All colors.
Physique Lightweight, sturdy build, tough legs and feet.
Character Independent, intractable.
Principal uses Endurance riding, stockwork, and general riding.

CLYDESDALE HORSE

Originated in the Clyde Valley when Flemish stallions were mated with native mares. They were developed for carrying coal and although their use as a haulage and farm horse has decreased, their popularity as dray horses is increasing.

Origin Great Britain.
Height 16-17hh.
Color Roan, bay, brown, chestnut.
Physique Heavy build, strong, large feet, short back.
Character Calm temperament.
Principal uses Haulage, showing, competitive ploughing.

DALES PONY

The breed originates from the north of England. At one time, they and the Fell pony were collectively called Pennine Ponies. They are superb trotting ponies, and were used for transporting ammunition in wartime, and surface work in the mining industry.

Origin Great Britain.
Height Up to 14hh.
Color Black, brown, bays, grays.
Physique Powerful body, short legs, neat head.
Character Quiet, intelligent.
Principal uses Trekking, competition driving.

DARTMOOR PONY

The Dartmoor is a superb example of a riding pony. The habitat of the Dartmoor Pony is wild and harsh, supporting poor vegetation and scrub. The pony is tough and hardy but needs hay to survive over the winter.

Origin Great Britain.
Height Up to 12hh.
Color Bay, brown.
Physique Sturdy, strong hindquarters, slim hard legs.
Character Quiet, sensible, kind.
Principal uses Ideal children's riding pony and competitive driving.

EXMOOR PONY

One of the purest pony breeds in the world still run free on Exmoor, although most are owned by local farmers and wardens. The breed is a neighbor of the Dartmoor and is just as wild.

Origin Great Britain.
Height Up to 12hh.
Color Bay, brown, or dun.
Physique Sturdy, thickset, strong legs.
Character Willing, hard working.
Principal uses Trekking, competition driving, endurance riding.

SHETLAND PONY

Named after the islands in the far north of Scotland, the Shetland has developed due to the extreme climate. They are small, tough ponies adept at reducing heat loss but lose type when exported to breed elsewhere in the world.

Origin Great Britain.
Height 40 in (100 cm).
Color All colors
Physique Small head, deep thick-set body, short legs small open feet.
Character Headstrong.
Principal uses Children's riding pony, harness and driving events.

FELL PONY

Related to the Dales Pony, the Fell is smaller and purer blood. They are true mountain and moorland ponies, still bred and running free on the hills. They were used for sheep herding, trotting-racing and as pack ponies.

Origin Great Britain.
Height Up to 14hh.
Color Black, brown, bay, gray.
Physique Long neck, muscular body, strong legs.
Character Friendly, willing, determined nature.
Principal uses Children's riding pony, harness, herding, trekking.

SHIRE HORSE

The Shires are the tallest horses in the world. They were developed in the 19th century to meet the demand for a stronger animal to pull the heavier farm machinery and transportation vehicles.

Origin Great Britain.
Height 17-18hh.
Color Bay with dapples, brown, black with white on face and legs.
Physique Dense muscular body, long legs, wide chest.
Character Docile, patient, gentle.
Principal uses Dray, working, ploughing matches, pulling contests.

HACKNEY HORSE

Used in the Middle Ages, they were developed as a fast means of transport on the expanding road network. They can be traced back to the Yorkshire and Norfolk trotters and may descend from Danish horses.

Origin Great Britain.
Height Up to 12-15hh.
Color Bay, brown, black.
Physique Small head, compact body, short legs, high set tail.
Character Fiery, fast, alert.
Principal uses Show ring, carriage driving and show jumping.

HIGHLAND PONY

This native Scottish pony has a good temperament having lived in close contact with people for hundreds of years. There have been two strains: the smaller Western Isles type, and the Garron from the mainland. Cross breeding has now more or less eliminated these distinctions.

Origin Great Britain.
Height 14hh.
Color Range of shades of dun.
Physique Deep body, short legs.
Character Trusting, cooperative.
Principal uses Crofting, forestry, deer ponies, trekking, pets.

THOROUGHBRED

Although bred purely for racing by British royalty, the popularity of the sport has led to the spread of Thoroughbred racing and breeding worldwide. Imported Arab stallions in England were mixed with more Oriental blood to produce a larger, faster, horse with longer stride.

Origin Great Britain.
Height 15-16hh.
Color Solid colors.
Physique Elegant, refined, quality.
Character Fast, highly strung.
Principal uses Racing, hurdles, steeplechase, showing, competition.

NEW FOREST PONY

The largest and least hardy of Britain's ponies, they have traditionally grazed on open scrubland and been used for farming and transport. When the New Forest is crossed with Thoroughbred or Arab stallions, they produce good performance horses.

Origin Great Britain.
Height 12-14hh.
Color Any colors.
Physique Short back with deep girth, nimble footed, strong.
Character Calm, intelligent.
Principal uses Riding, trekking, forest rides.

SUFFOLK PUNCH

A small and heavy horse, the Suffolk was developed by crossing Flanders horses with heavy mares from East Anglia. They met a need for smaller, agile, heavy horses required around towns and cities. The Suffolk is renowned for working long hours, needing little rest.

Origin Great Britain.
Height 15-16hh.
Color Shades of chestnut.
Physique Large head, massive shoulders, lean legs.
Character Willing workers, gentle.
Principal uses Showing, dray work.

WELSH COB

The Welsh Cobs have been in use for centuries for farming, herding sheep under saddle, and taking the family to chapel in a cart. Welsh Cob stallions are renowned for their fire and personality, unique to their breed.

Origin Great Britain.
Height 15hh.
Color All colors.
Physique Compact, good head, strong shoulders, deep back.
Character Stylish, gentle.
Principal uses Competitive driving, jumping, cross-country, show jumping.

ANGLO-ARAB

A combination of two breeds, the Arab and an English breed of Thoroughbred. It is common to mate an Arab stallion with a Thoroughbred mare, but the reverse may also occur. They make superb riding horses.

Origin Great Britain.
Height Height 14-16hh.
Color Any parent color.
Physique Deep chest, short back, well-proportioned hindquarters.
Character Spirited, 'thinkers', affectionate, courageous.
Principal uses Competitions, dressage, eventing, show jumping.

IRISH DRAUGHT

The breed was developed by farmers as a working horse and for hunting and riding. Irish Draught crossed with a suitable Thoroughbred produce superb horses capable of jumping and crossing any country when hunting or in competition.

Origin Ireland.
Height 15-17hh.
Color Solid colors, black is rare.
Physique Long powerful body, strong legs, large round feet.
Character Spirited, amenable.
Principal uses Riding horse, hunter, breeding stock.

15-17hh

CONNEMARA

The Connemara is a native breed, descended from the Irish Hobbye which had great speed, stamina, agility and reliability. They are a good cross with Thoroughbreds producing performance horses for riding and jumping.

Origin Ireland.
Height 13-14hh.
Color Mainly gray, solid colors.
Physique Deep compact body on short legs, intelligent looking.
Character Tough, hardy docile.
Principal uses Riding pony, hunter, hack, trekking mount.

13-14hh

COB

The term cob refers to a distinct type of strong, stocky horse. Only the Welsh Cob is classified as a breed. They are ideal for elderly and nervous riders and are also immensely strong and can carry a heavy rider all day.

Origin Great Britain.
Height 15hh.
Color All colors.
Physique Stocky, compact, short back, short strong legs.
Character Intelligent, obedient, placid.
Principal uses Riding, hunting.

HUNTER

The term hunter refers to a horse that is suited to carrying a rider behind foxhounds safely, sensibly, for a season's hunting. They provide a mount with a calm temperament, surefootedness, lots of stamina and a good instinct for self preservation.

Origin Great Britain.
Height Height 14-16hh.
Color Solid colors with white.
Physique Strong back, powerful hindquarters, long hard legs.
Character Obedient, controllable.
Principal uses Showing, hunting.

HACK

The term hack comes from the word hackney which in medieval times referred to a hired horse of poor quality. The modern hack however, is based on the Thoroughbred and is known for its conformation, presence, good manners and quality of ride.

Origin Great Britain.
Height 14-15hh.
Color Solid colors with white.
Physique Thoroughbred type with attractive head.
Character Obedient, responsive, comfortable.
Principal uses Riding, showing.

RIDING PONY

The riding pony type, has been developed to provide a mount that is particularly suitable for children. Thoroughbred blood has been infused, to produce ponies that are athletic, elegant and gentle in addition to their traditional sturdiness.

Origin Great Britain.
Height Under 14.2hh.
Color All colors.
Physique Broad body, sturdy.
Character Intelligent, good natured.
Principal uses Children's riding, show jumping.

SELLE FRANÇAIS

The Selle Français exhibits considerable variety of type within its breed. They resemble a middleweight Thoroughbred of good conformation and are excellent performance horses.

Origin France.
Height 15-16hh.
Color Chestnut, bay, gray.
Physique Short back, powerful hindquarters, well-set head.
Character Variable, common sense.
Principal uses Competitions, leisure/riding horse, show jumping.

FRENCH TROTTER

The sport of trotting is popular in France, both in harness and under saddle and the French Trotters have been bred for speed. Horses which do not prove themselves at racing do well at jumping and riding.

Origin France.
Height 16hh.
Color Chestnut, bay, brown.
Physique Strong, straight shoulders, short back, well-muscled hindquarters, long hard legs.
Character Good temperament.
Principal uses Trotting, racing in saddle and under harness.

CAMARGUE PONY

These horses graze on coastal grass up to their knees in salt water. They are annually rounded up to select riding horses, the sub-standard colts and stallions are culled to improve the breed.

Origin France.
Height 13-14hh.
Color White-gray, bay and brown.
Physique Oriental head, short back, fine legs, large feet.
Character Once broken in, docile, willing and high spirited.
Principal uses Herding black bulls, trekking mounts.

FRENCH ANGLO-ARAB

One of the best riding horses in the world. They are bred from Anglo-Arab, Thoroughbred and Arab blood. The horses must have at least 25 percent Arab blood and the absence of any other than Arab and Thoroughbred blood for at least six years.

Origin France.
Height 15-16hh.
Color Chestnut, all colors.
Physique Deep chest, well-proportioned hindquarters, long legs.
Character Intelligent, good natured.
Principal uses Show jumping, dressage, endurance riding.

FRIESIAN

One of the oldest European horse breeds, the Friesian comes from Holland where it is used as a working horse. It has been used in the formation of Britain's Fell and Dales Ponies and influenced trotting breeds throughout the world.

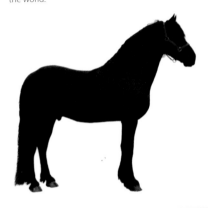

Origin Holland.
Height 15hh.
Color Black.
Physique Long head, strong compact body, short legs.
Character Quiet, hard working.
Principal uses Driving, riding, all-round workhorse.

GELDERLANDER

Created by farmers who wanted to produce horses for their own use as well as to sell. They are now a recognizable, top class light carriage and saddle horse and have been used by several royal houses of Europe.

Origin Holland.
Height 15-16hh.
Color Solid colors, chestnut.
Physique Plain head, deep shoulders, compact body, powerful hindquarters, short legs.
Character Quiet, good natured.
Principal uses Riding, driving, carriage horse.

DUTCH DRAUGHT

These are the heaviest draught horses for their height and are probably descended from medieval knight's horses crossed with Brabant and the Belgian Ardennais. Despite their massive size, they are docile and active.

Origin Holland.
Height 17hh.
Color Chestnut, bay, gray, black.
Physique Heavy and massive, very strong, pillar like legs.
Character Docile, willing, intelligent.
Principal uses Farm work, heavy draught work, pulling brewer's drays.

DUTCH WARMBLOOD

A new breed, the Dutch Warmblood is one of the most successful, popular, and sought-after competition and riding horses in the world. A product of the 20th century, its foundation is the Gelderlander and the Groningen as well as other European blood.

Origin Holland.
Height 16hh.
Color Bay, brown, chestnut.
Physique Long, flowing gaits.
Character Quiet, willing, intelligent, spirited.
Principal uses Showing, dressage, general riding horse, carriage driving.

PERCHERON

The most famous of the French draught horses they were bred to carry armoured knights into battle. They are heavier and 'chunkier' than the Clydesdale, but just as elegant and active. They are resistant to most types of weather conditions and are adaptable to new climates.

Origin France.
Height 15-17hh.
Color Gray or black.
Physique Elegant head, short legs.
Character Intelligent, good natured.
Principal uses Draught, agriculture, logging and breeding.

BRABANT

Also known as the Belgian Heavy Draught, the Brabant has influenced almost every other breed in the world. It is one of the strongest of the heavy breeds and has been used to improve other breeds of heavy horse.

Origin Belgium.
Height 14hh.
Color Red roan, bay, brown, dun.
Physique Square head, compact body, massive hindquarters.
Character Docile, hard working, good natured and active.
Principal uses Draught and farm work.

SALERNO

Developed from the Neapolitan, the Salerno was favored by royalty. They later became cavalry mounts and with the introduction of Thoroughbred and Arab blood, they are excellent carriage horses and show jumpers.

Origin Italy.
Height 16hh.
Color Any solid color.
Physique Refined head, prominent withers, strong sloping hindquarters.
Character Intelligent, responsive.

ITALIAN HEAVY DRAUGHT

Bred from several different blood lines, the Italian Heavy Draught is a distinctive breed. The Italians did not want to breed massive horses, eventually settling for a cross with the Postier-Breton for a smaller, lighter, more active horse.

Origin Italy.
Height 14-16hh.
Color Chestnut, flaxen mane, forelock and tail.
Physique Powerful shoulders, robust body, muscular legs.
Character Friendly, calm, energetic.
Principal uses Farm work.

HAFLINGER

Modern Haflingers descend from an Arab stallion introduced in 1868 to upgrade the coarse stock. Regarded as an Austrian breed, it has an Italian counterpart, the Avelignese which is slightly bigger. They are popular European ponies.

Origin Austria.
Height 14hh.
Color Chestnut, flaxen mane/tail.
Physique Long back, well-muscled hindquarters, short legs.
Character Docile, hard working.
Principal uses Mountain pony, driving packhorse, riding.

NORIKER

An ancient breed, the Noriker is founded on various heavy breeds, introduced by the Romans. They have been developed to suit agricultural and forestry work in the harsh climates of mountainous terrain.

Origin Austria.
Height 15-16hh.
Color Bay, chestnut, roan, spotted.
Physique Well-muscled shoulders, sturdy legs, sure-footed.
Character Strong, calm, quiet.
Principal uses Farming, forestry, transportation.

LIPPIZANER

One of the world's most famous breeds, from the Spanish Riding School of Vienna renowned for their displays of high-school dressage. They are used as carriage horses in Hungary and circuses around the world.

Origin Austria.
Height 15-16hh.
Color Gray.
Physique Compact body, powerful hindquarters, clean legs, agile.
Character Obedient, intelligent, proud.
Principal uses Haute Ecole.

KLADRUBER

The Kladruber comes from the world's oldest operational stud in Kladruby. They were originally bred as ceremonial coach horses for Emperor Maximillian II in 1597. Today's smaller animals are excellent riding and draught horses.

Origin Czech Republic.
Height 16-17hh.
Color Gray or black.
Physique Andalusian type, long body and rounded hindquarters.
Character Proud, obedient, intelligent, good natured.
Principal uses Driving, riding.

WIELKOPOLSKI

The Wielkopolski is descended from the remaining stock at the Trakehnen stud at the end of World War II. They became the foundation stock for the Masuren and the Poznan which were then combined to form the Wielkopolski.

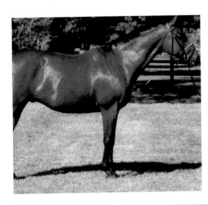

Origin Poland.
Height 16hh.
Color All solid colors.
Physique Small head, deep girth, fine legs, medium length back.
Character Gentle, intelligent.
Principal uses Riding, light draught work.

EAST FRIESIAN

The East Friesian has developed alongside its blood brother, the Oldenburg, and been bred with Arabs and Hanoverians to produce a lighter, more compact horse, suited to competitions.

Origin Germany.
Height 16-17hh.
Color Any solid color.
Physique Muscular chest and body, strong hindquarters, short legs.
Character Bold, sensible.
Principal uses Riding, competition, driving.

SHAGYA ARAB

Named after the gray Arab which sired the breed, the Shagya was developed by crossing Arabs and native stock to produce a robust cavalry mount and light carriage horse. They are of the highest quality but not well-known outside their home country.

Origin Hungary.
Height 14-15hh.
Color Satiny, gray coat.
Physique Arab-type, but robust.
Character Intelligent, hardy.
Principal uses Riding, cavalry, driving.

TRAKEHNER

The Trakehnen stud developed the Trakehner using local Schwieken horses. At the end of World War II, 700 Trakehners trekked west with refugees and these horses were used to re-establish the breed in Germany.

Origin Poland/Germany.
Height 16hh.
Color Any solid color, usually dark.
Physique Elegant head, deep chest, strong back, slender legs.
Character Spirited, courageous, versatile, tractable.
Principal uses Riding, competition.

HANOVERIAN

The breed has altered from its origins to suit different requirements. The farm horse was adapted to the needs of the army and further developed for farming and riding. After World War II, breeders have been aiming at world-class competition horses.

Origin Germany.
Height 15-17hh.
Color All solid colors.
Physique Variable, but a compact, powerful body on short strong legs.
Character Intelligent, sensible, bold.
Principal uses Riding, competition.

SCHLESWIG HEAVY DRAUGHT

The Schleswig was developed during the 19th century specifically to meet the demand for horses capable of heavy agricultural work. It has the blood of other heavy horses including the Jutland, a Danish war-horse.

Origin Germany.
Height 15-16hh.
Color Usually chestnut with flaxen mane and tail.
Physique Large head, deep girth, long body on short muscular legs.
Character Kind and willing.
Principal uses Draught.

HOLSTEIN

The Holstein is known to have lived in the marshlands of Schleswig-Holstein in the 14th century, and was originally a heavy, powerful horse. Since the 19th century, it has been successively bred with lighter, more refined breeds.

Origin Germany.
Height 16-17hh.
Color Most solid colors.
Physique Elegant head, strong hindquarters, short legs.
Character Intelligent, versatile.
Principal uses Riding, competition.

OLDENBURG

The Oldenburg was ousted as a working horse after World War II, so breeders lightened their horse for riding. Further Thoroughbred blood was introduced, and they are now used for carriage work and competitive riding.

Origin Germany.
Height 16-17hh.
Color Black, brown, bay.
Physique Muscular chest and body, strong hindquarters, short legs.
Character Bold, sensible.
Principal uses Riding, competition, driving.

FURIOSO

One of Hungary's high-quality half-breeds, they excel as a harness horse and are in demand all over the world for competition driving. A Furioso/ North Star cross, the Mozohegyes, is fast becoming Hungary's top sports horse.

Origin Hungary.
Height 16hh.
Color Dark, with white markings.
Physique Powerful shoulders, strong back, powerful hindquarters.
Character Tractable, intelligent.
Principal uses Riding, competition, steeple-chasing, driving.

ANDALUSIAN

This elegant horse has been used in the founding of other breeds including the Lippizaner, Peruvian Stepping Horse and the Paso Fino. They are much sought after and excel at high-school work.

Origin Spain.
Height 15-16hh.
Color Usually gray.
Physique Deep short body, powerful round hindquarters, strong legs.
Character Docile, willing, proud, affectionate.
Principal uses High-school dressage, parades, bull-fighting.

ALTER REAL

The national horse of Portugal is closely related to its neighbor, the Andalusian, and was bred from them during the 18th century when the fashion was for high-school dressage competitions.

Origin Portugal.
Height 15-16hh.
Color Bay, brown, gray.
Physique Strong shoulders, short body, powerful hindquarters, hard legs.
Character Intelligent, highly strung.
Principal uses Riding, high-school dressage.

LUSITANO

Once primarily a cavalry horse, the Lusitano was used by farmers for their strength. Best known as the mounts of bull-fighters, they are renowned for their agility, speed, obedience and training.

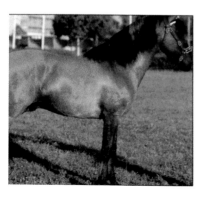

Origin Portugal.
Height 15-16hh.
Color Usually gray.
Physique Small head, compact body, powerful hindquarters, long fine legs, abundant mane and tail.
Character Intelligent, responsive, brave.
Principal uses Riding, bull-fighting.

ORLOV TROTTER

The best known of the Russian horse breeds, the Orlov was developed in the 18th century when trotting races were very popular. They have been recently crossed with the Standardbred to produce the Russian Trotter.

Origin Russia.
Height 15-17hh.
Color Gray or black.
Physique Powerful shoulders, strong back, powerful hindquarters.
Character Broad chest, long back, powerful loins, fine hard legs.
Principal uses Trotting, driving, riding.

DON

The Don's toughness, stamina and ability to cope with vicious weather, led it to be used as the Cossack's mount. Persian Arab and other Oriental blood has been introduced to heighten, refine and correct the Don's physique.

Origin Russian steppes.
Height 15-16hh.
Color Chestnut, bay, gray.
Physique Long neck, long back, strong hindquarters, long hard legs.
Character Calm, reliable, independent.
Principal uses Riding, long-distance riding, racing, breeding.

BUDYONNY

Created after the Russian Revolution, the Budyonny was bred to produce a perfect cavalry horse for the military. Thoroughbred stallions on Don mares proved successful. Large herds still run free.

Origin Russia.
Height 15-16hh.
Color Chestnut, bay with a sheen.
Physique Small head, strong compact body, fine hard legs.
Character Spirited, patient, kind, courageous.
Principal uses Flat-racing, competition, steeple-chase.

15-16hh

KABARDIN

An adaptable animal, the Kabardin can live at sea-level or in the mountains. It is a descendant of the Tarpan and remained unchanged until the Russian Revolution, when Oriental blood was introduced to improve its height and riding work.

Origin Russia.
Height 14-15hh.
Color Bay, brown, black.
Physique Long head, long ears, long back.
Character Intelligent, sensible.
Principal uses Transportation, sports, breeding.

14-15hh

TERSKY

There are three types of Tersky and all are excellent performance horses. They were bred for steeple-chasing but are usually raced on the flat against other Arabs. They are popular in dressage and the circus ring.

Origin Russia.
Height 15hh.
Color Usually gray.
Physique Deep chest, muscular hindquarters, fine hard legs.
Character Gentle, intelligent.
Principal uses Flat-racing, competition, circus.

KARABAKH

The Karabakh look like Arabs as both come from the same genetic type. They have existed since the 4th century and remain a popular riding mount. As it has been mixed with Persian, Turkmene and Arab blood, it is said that there are no pure Karabakh left.

Origin Azerbaijan.
Height 14hh.
Color Dun, bay or chestnut.
Physique Strong compact body, fine legs, powerful hindquarters.
Character Quick-witted, calm, robust.
Principal uses Riding, racing.

UKRAINIAN RIDING HORSE

Founded by crossing several large breeds with native mares, to produce a good sporting horse for high-class riding and competitions. They have been bred for temperament and are quality warmbloods.

Origin Ukraine.
Height 16hh.
Color Chestnut, bay, black.
Physique Elegant, refined.
Character Obliging, willing, kind-natured.
Principal uses High-class competition, riding, light harness.

LATVIAN

There are three types of Latvian; the heavy, Latvian Draught; the standard, Latvian Harness Horse; the lighter, Latvian Riding Horse. Scandinavian blood was introduced to increase substance and strength.

Origin Latvia.
Height 16hh.
Color Black, brown, bay, chestnut.
Physique Strong, great stamina.
Character Relaxed, quiet.
Principal uses Heavy farm work or competitive riding purposes.

SWEDISH WARMBLOOD

Developed as a cavalry horse, the Swedish Warmblood is in demand for show-jumping, eventing and dressage. They are one of the most successful competition horses in the world and their quality is rigorously monitored at all times.

Origin Sweden.
Height 16-17hh.
Color Solid colors.
Physique Elegant, deep body, fine legs, rounded hindquarters.
Character Sensible, intelligent.
Principal uses Riding, driving, competition.

GOTLAND

A descendant of the Tarpan, the Gotland pony has run wild on the Swedish island it is named after since pre-historic times. They were used for farming and transportation but their popularity abroad led to their depletion in numbers.

Origin Sweden.
Height 12-13hh.
Color Black, bay.
Physique Well muscled, fine legs.
Character Independent, tractable, willing.
Principal uses Trotting races, general riding and light harness.

NORTHLANDS

Little known outside Norway, the Northlands closely resembles the Scottish Shetland Pony. They were used and bred by farmers with little selection policy. Numbers declined in the 1920s but one fine stallion brought them back from certain extinction.

Origin Norway.
Height 13-14hh.
Color Chestnut, gray, bay, brown.
Physique Strong legs, large head, small and tough feet.
Character Quiet natured, energetic.
Principal uses Children's riding pony, farm work.

DØLE-GUDBRANDSDAL

The Døle and the Gudbrandsdal were originally separate breeds which have amalgamated. They account for almost two thirds of Norway's horse population. They have had Thoroughbred and Arab blood introduced, to produce an offshoot, the Døle Trotter (pictured).

Origin Norway.
Height 13-14hh.
Color Black, brown.
Physique Powerful body, short legs.
Character Kind, patient.
Principal uses Farm work, forestry, trotting races.

FJORD

The Fjord's color, marking and ancient mane trimming are unique in the equine world. The Fjord has been bred into the Highland Pony and the Icelandic Pony.

Origin Norway.
Height 13-14hh.
Color Distinctive yellow or dun.
Physique Powerful body, short legs, coarse mane in three layers.
Character Strong willed, tractable.
Principal uses Farm work, driving, mountain work, packhorse.

FREDRIKSBORG

One of the original Haute Ecole horses, the Fredriksborg was bred for speed and stamina. They were used as an officer's charger and as carriage horses for state occasions. Few of the old types of Fredriksborg remain and new blood has been introduced to breed up the numbers.

Origin Denmark.
Height 15-16hh.
Color Chestnut.
Physique Deep chest, long body, strong legs.
Character Good tempered, tractable.
Principal uses Riding, driving.

KNABSTRUP

The Knabstrup was a victim of breeding almost entirely for color and the breed deteriorated. The introduction of Thoroughbred blood has resulted in a much improved animal, distinctive for its spotted coat.

Origin Denmark.
Height 15hh.
Color Spotted; Appaloosa patterns.
Physique Varies, similar to Fredriksborg but somewhat lighter.
Character Intelligent, tractable.
Principal uses Riding, circus.

ICELANDIC

There are several variations of Icelandic but all share great stamina, strength and sure-footedness. Their unusual gaits are the amble, a running walk and a rapid amble. The Icelandic lives in a half wild state, surviving the harsh winters by foraging.

Origin Iceland.
Height 12-13hh.
Color Most colors.
Physique Large head, compact body, strong legs, large feet.
Character Intelligent, tractable.
Principal uses Riding, circus.

ARAB

The Arab has greatly influenced the breeding of horses and ponies throughout the world, more than any other, as it breeds true to type. They are famous for their stamina and are in much demand as competition endurance horses.

Origin Arabia.
Height 14hh.
Color Chestnut, bay, gray.
Physique Small head, stronghindquarters, hard clean legs.
Character Brave, fiery, intelligent, enduring.
Principal uses Riding, breeding.

CASPIAN

Believed to be extinct, a herd of 40 Caspian horses was discovered on the shores of the Caspian Sea, in 1965, and were brought to Britain. These small horses are now increasing in numbers at studs throughout the world.

Origin Iran.
Height 10-12hh.
Color Chestnut, bay, gray.
Physique Arab-type head, narrow body, short back, fine legs.
Character Gentle, quick witted, tractable.
Principal uses Riding, driving.

AKHAL-TEKÉ

The descendant of the Turkmene, the Akhal-Teke has evolved to be one of the most hardy and enduring horses. They are desert horses and still run in managed herds, but need heavy covers to protect their fine skin from the desert sun and bitter nights.

Origin Turkmenistan.
Height 14-15hh.
Color Chestnut, bay.
Physique Small head, long back, shallow body, long legs.
Character Obstinate, difficult to handle.
Principal uses Riding, competition.

PRZEWALSKI'E HORSE

Discovered by a Polish explorer, the Przewalski had been hunted almost to extinction. There have been no wild horses seen since 1970 and animals are now being bred from captive stock, in order to reintroduce the breed.

Origin Mongolia.
Height 12-14hh.
Color Yellow dun.
Physique Stocky, long back, fine legs, tough feet.
Character Ferocious temperament, untamed, known for its courage.
Principal uses Breeding.

BARB

An old Oriental-type breed, the Barb has helped to found other breeds. They are tough, enduring, fast and responsive and are the mount of the Bedouin people. Few pure-bred Barbs are left as Arab blood has been introduced to make them easier to train.

Origin North Africa.
Height 14-15hh.
Color Bay, chestnut, black, gray.
Physique Large head, long back, long fine legs.
Character Quick tempered, courageous.
Principal uses Riding, cross-breeding.

JAVA PONY

The Java Pony has had the benefit of Arab blood which makes it bigger and stronger than other ponies in Indonesia. It is a widespread "taxi" pony on Java and is also used for riding and other light draught work.

Origin Indonesia.
Height 12hh.
Color Most colors.
Physique Slightly built, strong.
Character Willing.
Principal uses Driving, all-round work pony.

AUSTRALIAN STOCK HORSE

Known until 1971 as the Waler, this hardy, agile horse was worked on cattle stations. Numbers declined after World War II and new blood was indiscriminately introduced. Arab and Thoroughbred blood has now been added to improve the horse.

Origin Australia.
Height 16hh.
Color All colors.
Physique Thoroughbred type, with a strong back and hindquarters.
Character Versatile, reliable worker.
Principal uses Herding, rodeos, riding, competition.

AUSTRALIAN PONY

Founded by crossing Arab with Welsh Mountain Pony, the Australian Pony is an excellent riding pony, refined yet not too light. They have a good temperament and are easy for children to ride and care for.

Origin Australia.
Height 12-14hh.
Color All colors.
Physique Arab-like head, short back, short legs with hard feet.
Character Lively, intelligent.
Principal uses Children's riding pony.

GLOSSARY

Against the clock In show jumping—a competition or jump off decided by time, the winner being the competitor with the least number of faults in the fastest time.

Aid Signals used by a rider to give instructions to the horse, through his seat, legs, and hands.

Airs Movements, usually found in formal dressage, which are other than the normal walk, trot, and canter.

All-rounder A horse or pony which is very good at everything.

Amble A slow gait in two time in which the horse's hind and foreleg on the same side are moved forward together.

Arena The area in which a horse show or show jumping competition is held.

Artificial aids Items such as whips, spurs, and martingales which are used by the rider to help convey instructions to the horse.

Backing the horse To mount a horse for the first time.

Bit A device, normally made from metal or rubber, attached to the bridle and placed in the horse's mouth to help control its pace and direction.

Bloodline The sequence of direct ancestors, especially in a pedigree.

Bloodstock Thoroughbred horses that are bred for racing.

Blue feet Horn that is dense and blue-black in color.

Bosal A simple, bitless noseband made from rawhide.

Breastplate A device, normally made from leather, attached to the saddle to prevent it from slipping back on the horse.

Bridle A part of the horse's saddlery or harness which is placed about the head.

Cannons The lower part of the horse's legs between the fetlocks and the knees or hocks.

Cantle The upward projecting rear part of the saddle.

Carriage horse An elegant horse used for carriage-driving, usually with Thoroughbred in its ancestry.

Chaff Meadow hay or green oat straw cut into short lengths for use as a foodstuff.

Cheekpiece (a) The leather part of the bridle to which the bit is attached at one end and the headpiece at the other. (b) Side pieces of a bit to which the reins are attached.

Chestnuts (a) Small piece of horn on the inside of the horse's legs. (b) Bright brown coat color.

Chukka A period of play in polo lasting seven and a half or eight minutes, depending on which country the game is being played in.

Cinch (girth) (a) The circumference of the horse or pony, from behind the withers around the deepest part of the body. (b) A band made from leather, nylon, or webbing, passed under the belly of the horse to hold the saddle in place.

Cob A type rather than a breed. A short legged animal with a maximum height of 15hh (150 cm) with the bone

and substance of a heavyweight hunter and capable of carrying a substantial weight.

Coldblood A horse, not a pony, of heavy, common or "cart" blood.

Colic Sharp abdominal pains, often with the symptom of flatulence; an obstruction created by a mass of hard food, or feces in the bowel, which can lead to a twisted gut.

Collection Shortening the pace by a light contact from the rider's hands and a steady pressure with the legs to make the horse flex its neck, relax its jaw, and bring its hocks well under so that it is properly balanced.

Colt An ungelded male horse less than four years old.

Colostrum The first milk that the foal drinks from the dam, rich in vital antibodies.

Condition The state of physical fitness and health of the horse or pony.

Conformation A horse's make-up and shape. The basic requirement is symmetry—the horse should look balanced.

Corn Bruising of the sole in the angle between the wall of the hoof and the heel.

Cow horse The horse which a cowboy rides while working cattle.

Crupper A leather loop which passes under the horse's tail and is buckled to the saddle.

Curb bit A type of bit used in conjunction with a snaffle bit in a double bridle with a curb chain.

Curb chain A metal chain which is fitted to the hook of a curb or pelham bit and lies in the curb groove of the horse's jaw.

Cutting horse A horse especially trained for separating selected cattle from a herd.

Dam The female parent of a foal.

Deep seat A good seated position on the saddle, but sitting slightly heavier with an independent seat.

Dirt track A racetrack, the surface of which is a combination of sand and soil—common in the USA.

Dished face A profile which appears slightly concave between the eyes and nostrils. Highly regarded in Arabs.

DMSO (Dimethyl sulfoxide) A substance used as medication to treat bruises and strains.

Dorsal eel stripe Found usually in dun-colored animals, this is a continuous strip of black, brown, or dun hair, running from the neck to the tail.

Double bridle A bridle consisting of two bits, a curb and a snaffle, which are attached by means of two cheekpieces and may be used independently.

Doubles In show jumping, a combination of obstacles consisting of two separate jumps.

Draft (draught) Refers to a horse drawing any type of vehicle.

Dressage The art of training horses to perform movements in a balanced, supple, obedient, and enthusiastic manner.

Driving Refers to the horse being hitched to a carriage, with the driver sitting on the carriage and controlling the horse by the means of long reins.

Equine (a) Of, or pertaining to, the horse. (b) The term used for the horse.

Extension The leg positions and gait of the horse.

Farrier A person who make horseshoes and shoes horses—often called a blacksmith.

Feather Copious hair around the fetlocks or entire lower legs.

Fender (Stirrup leather) The adjustable strap by which the stirrup iron is attached to the saddle.

Filly A female horse less than four years old.

Flexion The yielding of the lower jaw to the pressure of the bit; at the same time the neck is high and arched, and bent at the poll.

Foal A young horse up to the age of twelve months.

Forehand The part of the horse which is in front of the rider, that is, the head, neck, shoulders, withers, and forelegs.

Fox trot A gait in which the horse walks with the front feet and trots with the hind, the hind legs stepping into the foreprints and sliding forwards.

Frog The rubbery pad of horn on the underside of the hoof which acts as a shock absorber.

Gait The horse's basic movements in action. Natural gaits are walk, trot, canter, and gallop; artificial ones are the running walk, fox trot, amble, and broken amble.

Gaited horse An American term for a saddle or riding horse which can perform artificial as well as natural gaits. A three-gaited horse must show walk, trot, and canter. A five-gaited horse must also show a slow gait and a fast rack.

Gelding A male horse which has been castrated.

Groom (a) Any person who is responsible for looking after a horse. (b) To clean the coat and feet of a horse.

Gymkhana Mounted games, most frequently for children under sixteen.

Half halt The rider prepares to halt by sitting up and using the reins, but pushes the horse forward again just before stopping.

Half pass A dressage movement where the horse travels both forward and sideways in the direction of travel.

Halter (Headcollar) A hemp rope headpiece with lead rope attached, used for leading a horse when not wearing a bridle, or for tying up in the stable.

Hand A linear measurement equaling 4 in (10 cm) used in giving the height of a horse.

Handicap (a) The weight allocated to a horse in a race. (b) A race in which the weights to be carried by the horse are estimated so as to give each horse an equal chance of winning.

Harness The equipment of a draft (draught) animal.

Harness horse A horse used for driving in harness rather than under saddle.

Haute Ecole/High School The so-called classical method of riding, practiced in many countries, said to descend from the simple, natural principles evolved particularly by the ancient Greeks. Refined and developed in the 17th and 18th centuries, Haute Ecole is today perpetuated most famously by the Spanish Riding School in Vienna, Austria, and the Cadre Noir at Saumur, France.

Haylage Stored forage.

Headpiece Any equipment—headstall, headcollar—worn on a horse's head.

Headstall Part of the bridle that encircles the horse's head.

Heavy horse A horse of muscular build, often tall and very strong, and best suited to heavy transportation, forestry, or agricultural work.

Hocks The region in the hind leg which corresponds to the ankle of humans, but which in the horse is elevated and bent backwards.

Hotblood Horses of desert or steppe ancestry. Normally taken as being the pure Thoroughbred or Arab breed.

Hunter A horse bred and trained to be ridden for hunting.

Hunt The sport of following different types of hound in pursuit of fox, stag, hare, or an artificial scent.

Hunting The sport of following different types of hound, either mounted or on foot in pursuit of the fox, the stag, or the hare or an artificially laid drag line if drag hunting.

Independent seat The ability to maintain a firm, balanced position on a horse's back without relying on the hands for security.

In-hand Any of various show classes in which the animals are led, usually in a show bridle or headcollar, but otherwise without saddlery (except for draft [draught] horses which are often shown in their harness) and are judged chiefly for conformation and/or condition.

In season The state of sexual readiness during which the mare is ready to conceive.

Jog A short-paced trot.

Knee roll Any bandages applied to the horse's legs.

Lateral work Dressage movements such as the half halt, counter canter and flying lead.

Lead rope A rope attached to a halter for leading a horse.

Leathers (a) Pieces of leather attached to the stirrup. (b) Slang for leather shoes worn to protect a horse's hooves while healing.

Leg yielding One of the first dressage movements to be learned whereby the horse moves forward and sideways away from the rider's leg.

Leg up A helping hand or boost into the saddle.

Livery stable An establishment where privately owned horses are kept, exercised, and generally looked after, for an agreed fee. Called Livery in the USA.

Loins The kidney are just behind the saddle.

Long in the back Excessive length of a horse's back, desirable in some breeds, undesirable in others.

INDEX